MARSHALL'S
PHYSIOLOGY OF
REPRODUCTION

EDITED BY

A. S. PARKES, M.A., D.Sc., Sc.D., F.R.S.
National Institute for Medical Research, London

VOLUME I : PART ONE

1724

LONGMANS, GREEN AND CO
LONDON ◆ NEW YORK ◆ TORONTO

LONGMANS, GREEN AND CO LTD
6 & 7 CLIFFORD STREET LONDON W 1
BOSTON HOUSE STRAND STREET CAPE TOWN
531 LITTLE COLLINS STREET MELBOURNE

LONGMANS, GREEN AND CO INC
55 FIFTH AVENUE NEW YORK 3

LONGMANS, GREEN AND CO
20 CRANFIELD ROAD TORONTO 16

ORIENT LONGMANS LTD
CALCUTTA BOMBAY MADRAS
DELHI VIJAYAWADA DACCA

First Edition, 1910

Second and Revised Edition, 1922

Third Edition, 1956

PRINTED IN GREAT BRITAIN BY
SPOTTISWOODE, BALLANTYNE AND CO. LIMITED
LONDON AND COLCHESTER

EDITOR'S PREFACE

TO THE THIRD EDITION

THE appearance of *The Physiology of Reproduction* in 1910 was an event in the history of biological literature. Here, for the first time, was a book containing virtually everything known about the physiological processes involved in reproduction, a book which mapped the present and pointed the way to the future. The work was immediately acclaimed as a masterpiece and placed Marshall in the front rank of British biologists. After the first war a new edition was called for, and appeared in 1922. This edition missed the very rapid expansion of the subject, especially on the endocrinological side, which took place during the 1920's, and by 1935 it was clear that a third edition should be prepared as soon as possible. Marshall realised, however, that the increase of knowledge had placed beyond the powers of a single writer a book of the scope achieved in 1910 and maintained in 1922, and he felt that a number of British workers must be asked to contribute. Arrangements were therefore made for the book to be revised by some fourteen different contributors under my editorship, and to appear in two volumes. By 1939 the preparation of the manuscript was far advanced, but on the outbreak of war it was decided to postpone further work. This decision, for which I was largely responsible, was perhaps a wrong one, but the delays and frustrations of post-war publication could hardly have been foreseen. In 1945 the project was taken up again and the task of revising existing manuscripts and preparing new material was begun. Several new contributors were called upon and estimates of the ultimate size of the book had again to be increased.

The scope of the work is not fundamentally different from that of the 1922 edition, but several new chapters have been required (mainly in Volume I) to accommodate certain aspects of the subject which have grown almost beyond recognition since the book first appeared. Similarly, the general sequence of the book, based so far as possible on the order of physiological events, has been retained, and it has been possible to make the division between the two volumes at what is functionally a convenient point. Volume I, generally speaking, deals with events up to and including fertilisation ; Volume II deals with embryonic and foetal development and physiology, lactation, and certain general problems. Unfortunately, it has been necessary to omit much of the older material. In relation to the present literature, the scope of the first edition was enormous and now defies the bibliographic completeness which was Marshall's original aim. In these circumstances, contributors were asked for a workmanlike exposition of the main relevant facts and principles. Moreover, some parts of the subject which once appeared distinct and fell naturally into separate chapters have now tended to run together, and problems of co-ordination between contributors have arisen. A liberal line has been taken in this matter. A particular group of facts may be an integral part of the build-up of more than one chapter, and it would have been impossible, even had it been desirable, to insist upon exclusiveness. It is to be hoped that the greater value of individual chapters due to their greater completeness will more than offset the disadvantages of some overlap. The reader must judge for himself to what extent these policies have been successful and whether the third edition is a worthy successor to its predecessors.

In existing conditions it seemed likely that there would be difficulty in getting both volumes ready at the same time, and it was decided to treat the two volumes as separate publications, prefaced, paged, indexed, published, and sold separately. In the end, Volume II was completed first and got so far ahead in the press that its publication before Volume I became inevitable. This sequence, though perhaps not unknown in scientific works, is to be regretted, and it is hoped that the value of the book will not thereby be impaired. In other ways, too, the logistics of this edition have not been easy. It is often said that the difficulty of getting anything done increases as the square of the number of people involved ; there are 18 contributors to the book, as well as the editor, printers and publishers. My apologies are due to Longmans, Green & Co. for the erratic way in which manuscript has come to hand, and to those contributors who, having written their chapters promptly, have been called upon to revise and revise again because of the delays of others. I realise, however, that contributors' delays have been occasioned mainly by striving for perfection, and I am sure that Marshall would have wished to express his appreciative thanks, as I do mine, to all the contributors, who have worked on the book with a care and enthusiasm which it is not always easy to bring to a co-operative work.

A book of this size, published under present conditions, cannot be completely up to date. The material for Volume II was received over a period of three years, and publication will not take place for more than three years after the last manuscript was sent in. In these circumstances, unless page proofs are to be regarded merely as a working draft, very recent material cannot be included. This fact, however, should be judged in proper perspective. The work as a whole embraces the accumulated knowledge of some 2,000 years ; the present edition bridges a gap of nearly 30 years since the previous edition, and will, we hope, be the standard work for a decade or more. Moreover, the value and relevance of biological observations are rarely certain immediately, and a book of this kind should, in our opinion, deal with established and orientated matter. As Marshall himself said, the book cannot be up to date, but it should never be out of date. In these circumstances, no attempt has been made to include stop press news, and the reader who wishes to explore the shifting sands of contemporary effort should consult current reviews rather than this book.

It is sad to record that several contributors or prospective contributors died during the course of preparation of the book. Dr. Batty Griffiths was killed in the North African Campaign in 1943, after having accumulated much material for the chapter on embryology. Sir Joseph Barcroft died in 1947, shortly after completing Chapter 17, and Professor W. H. Newton died in 1949 before receiving page proofs of Chapter 18. Dr. Marshall himself died in February 1949, after having taken a most active and urgent interest in the preparation of the new edition, which occupied a major place in his thoughts during the last few years of his life. It was a tragedy that he did not live to see its publication and that the third edition must be his monument. At the time of Marshall's death there was in press a biographical note for inclusion in Volume 6 of the *Journal of*

Endocrinology which was to be dedicated in honour of his 70th birthday. This biography unhappily became an obituary notice, and is reprinted, together with a photograph and a bibliography of his writings, as part of the introduction to this edition.

A. S. PARKES,
National Institute for Medical Research,
London, N.W. 7.

September 1950.

EDITOR'S NOTE TO VOLUME I, PART ONE

VOLUME I has become much larger, and has taken much longer to complete than was anticipated when Volume II was published. It will therefore be published in two parts. Part One contains Chapters 1 to 6, and deals with the breeding season, the morphology of the reproductive organs, and cyclic changes in the female. Part Two will deal with events in the male, fertilisation, biochemical matters, and the endocrine regulation of the reproductive processes.

Chapter 1 was written by Dr. Marshall before his death in 1949 and no attempt has been made to revise his text.

F. H. A. MARSHALL, C.B.E., M.A., Sc.D., F.R.S.

(*J. Russell & Sons*)

F. H. A. MARSHALL

IT was intended to recognise the 70th birthday of one of our most distinguished biologists, Dr. F. H. A. Marshall, by dedicating Volume 6 of the *Journal of Endocrinology* in his honour. Unfortunately, this plan to mark a happy occasion was forestalled by his death, which occurred suddenly on 5 February, 1949.

Recent developments, by their nearness, have tended to overshadow the pioneer work in which Marshall played so important a part, and it is with appreciation that the writer recalls, for a new generation of biologists, the achievements of his friend and one-time tutor.

Marshall's name is associated, mainly or even exclusively, with the study of the physiology of reproduction in its many branches. He was preceded in this field by another pioneer, Walter Heape, who was completing his classic studies of the primate uterus and collecting material for his analysis of the oestrous cycle at the time when Marshall was an undergraduate in Cambridge. The two men did not meet until later, but they corresponded freely, and Heape's morphological studies and extensive knowledge of living animals were of great value to Marshall in his early days. Heape, however, was not a physiologist—he seems, for instance, to have regarded the ovary merely as a producer of eggs—and it is to Marshall that we owe the foundations of our present knowledge of the role of internal secretions in the reproductive processes.

Marshall's debut was characteristic of an age in which research was a calling rather than a profession ; a precarious calling to which young men were drawn by interest, not by ambition. In 1900, the late Lord Carmichael gave £200 to Prof. Cossar Ewart, Professor of Natural History in the University of Edinburgh, to enable a Research Student to assist with his long-term experiments on telegony, and to undertake work on reproduction in farm animals. Cossar Ewart's inquiries resulted in Marshall accepting an invitation to go to Edinburgh. The work on telegony, which involved a detailed study of the hair of the Equidae, was uninteresting and unproductive, and Marshall turned his attention to research on the sexual cycle in the sheep, for which he was to make use of Ewart's farm at Penicuik. This work was the subject of his first important scientific publication, which appeared in the *Transactions of the Royal Society* in 1903. Similar studies followed with Schäfer on the oestrous cycle in the ferret (1904), and with Jolly on the oestrous cycle in the dog (1905).   A communication on the ovary as an organ of internal secretion, written in collaboration with Jolly and published in the *Transactions of the Royal Society* in 1905, constituted the first serious attempt to correlate the changes in the uterus during the reproductive cycle with the cyclic production of different internal secretions by the ovary.

Marshall returned to Cambridge in 1908, and continued his work on the physiology of reproduction.   During the war, 1914–18, he studied, on behalf of the Ministries of Food and Agriculture, such problems as the most economic age and condition at which to slaughter cattle.   Subsequently, Marshall's researches have dealt mainly with the influence of exteroceptive factors—light, climate, etc.— on the reproductive processes, and in 1936 he made this the subject of his Croonian Lecture.   He was also intensely interested in the courtship and breeding behaviour of birds, on which he was a considerable authority.

Marshall spent a great deal of time preparing the first edition of *The Physiology of Reproduction* in which he gathered together all relevant knowledge concerning the breeding season, cyclic changes in the reproductive organs, fertilisation, fertility, lactation, and so on.   The book was published by Longmans, Green & Co. in 1910, and immediately achieved success.   A second edition was called for after the 1914–18 war.   This second edition, published in 1922, was necessarily much larger than the first, for since 1910 knowledge of the reproductive processes in mammals and lower vertebrates had increased considerably.   A third edition, largely rewritten by Marshall's pupils and colleagues, and again much enlarged, is now in the course of publication.

Marshall's main contribution to biology has been twofold.   In the first place, the stimulating synthesis of existing knowledge embodied in the first edition of *The Physiology of Reproduction* gave impetus and balance to a branch of biology sadly lacking in both.   The fact that between the wars the physiology of reproduction became a subject of intensive study by scientists in all countries was due in no small measure to the stimulus given by Marshall's writings.   In the second place, Marshall's remarkable prescience in deducing correctly the existence and respective roles of follicular and luteal hormones long before either was isolated, or even obtained in active extracts, had a profound influence on the development of the subject.   During the early years of the century Ludwig Fraenkel in Breslau and P. Bouin in Strasbourg, working on the rabbit, concentrated attention on the corpus luteum ; in the 1920's intensive study of the follicular hormone by Edgar Allen and his colleagues in the U.S.A. swung attention to the follicular apparatus. It fell to the English school of workers, under Marshall's influence, to hold the balance until the final demonstration and isolation of the corpus luteum hormone in G. W. Corner's Rochester laboratory completed the working out of his early predictions.

Scientists are of many kinds, but inspiration flows most fruitfully from those who are able, by some gift withheld from lesser men, to divine the richness of uncharted country and sense the vital landmarks.   Thus do they avoid the barren places and the morasses of unimportant detail which engulf so many.   To these, discovery is an art rather than a science, a matter of instinct rather than of intellectual machinery.   Such was Marshall.

A. S. P.

20 *October*, 1948.
Revised 10 *February*, 1949.

CURRICULUM VITAE

FRANCIS HUGH ADAM MARSHALL was the younger son of the late Thomas Marshall, J.P., and was born at High Wycombe on 11 July, 1878. He was educated at St. Mark's School, Windsor, and privately. After a short time at University College, London, he went to Christ's College, Cambridge, in 1896, and took the Natural Science Tripos in 1899. During the latter part of the time in Edinburgh Marshall became Carnegie Fellow and Lecturer on the physiology of reproduction. After his return to Cambridge he was Lecturer and then Reader in Physiology, in the School of Agriculture, for more than 35 years, until 1943. For a short period, Marshall followed the late Prof. T. B. Wood in directing the Institute of Animal Nutrition. He became in succession, Fellow, Tutor, Dean, and finally, in 1940, Vice-Master of Christ's College. He was a Proctor in 1911–12 and afterwards served on the Council of the Senate. Marshall was an original member of the Council of Management of the *Journal of Endocrinology* and was one of the four honorary members of the Society for Endocrinology. For many years he was an editor of the *Journal of Agricultural Science*, and finally became principal editor. Marshall's scientific distinctions included D.Sc. (Edin.), Sc.D. (Cantab.), D.Sc. (Hon. Manch.), LL.D. (Hon. Edin.), F.R.S. (1920), C.B.E. (1933), Council of the Royal Society (1933–5), Baly Medal of the Royal College of Physicians (1935), Croonian Lecturer (Royal Society) 1936, and Royal Medal (Royal Society) 1940.

REPRINTED FROM *THE JOURNAL OF ENDOCRINOLOGY*

EXCERPTS FROM THE INTRODUCTION
TO THE FIRST EDITION

SINCE the time when physiology first became an organised science many volumes have been written on the digestive, excretory, nervous, and other systems of the body, but no attempt has yet been made to supply those interested in the reproductive processes with a comprehensive treatise dealing with this branch of knowledge. Indeed, in most text-books on physiology now commonly in use either the section devoted to the reproductive organs is restricted to a few final pages seldom free from error, or else the subject is entirely omitted. Yet generative physiology forms the basis of gynaecological science, and must ever bear a close relation to the study of animal breeding. In writing the present volume, therefore, I have been actuated by the desire to supply what appears to me to be a real deficiency ; and in doing so I have attempted, however inadequately, to co-ordinate or give a connected account of various groups of ascertained facts which hitherto have not been brought into relation. For this purpose I have had occasion to refer to many books and memoirs dealing with subjects that at first sight might have been supposed to differ considerably. Thus, works on zoology and anatomy, obstetrics and gynaecology, physiology and agriculture, anthropology and statistics, have been consulted for such observations and records as seemed to have a bearing on the problems of reproduction.

The present volume is addressed primarily to the trained biologist, but it is hoped that it may be of interest also to medical men engaged in gynaecological practice, as well as to veterinarians and breeders of animals. As a general rule, I have confined myself to the physiology of generation among the higher forms, and more particularly the Mammalia, but I have not hesitated to discuss the reproductive processes in the Invertebrata on cases where they seemed likely to elucidate the more complex phenomena displayed by the higher animals. The all-important questions of heredity and variation, although intimately connected with the study of reproduction, are not here touched upon, excepting for the merest reference, since these subjects have been dealt with in various recent works, and any attempt to include them would have involved the writing of a far larger book. Similarly, the subject matter of cytology, as treated in such works as Professor Wilson's volume on the cell, is also for the most part excluded.

It may be objected that, for a book on physiology, too much space is devoted to the morphological side of the subject. This has been done purposely, since it seemed impossible to deal adequately with the physiological significance of the various sexual processes without describing the anatomical changes which these processes involve.

LIST OF CONTRIBUTORS

TO THE THIRD EDITION, VOLUME I, PART ONE

F. W. Rogers Brambell, D.SC., F.R.S., *University College of North Wales, Bangor.*

P. Eckstein, M.A., M.D., *The Medical School, Birmingham.*

The late Dr. F. H. A. Marshall, C.B.E., F.R.S., *Cambridge.*

L. Harrison Matthews, M.A., SC.D., F.R.S., *Zoological Society of London.*

S. Zuckerman, C.B., M.A., M.D., D.SC., F.R.S., *The Medical School, Birmingham.*

ACKNOWLEDGMENTS

CONTRIBUTORS have been much assisted in the preparation of their chapters by permission to reproduce illustrations from a great variety of original papers and other works. The source of such illustrations is indicated in each case, and the contributors wish to offer their acknowledgments and thanks to the respective authors, especially to those who have provided new prints of photographs, and to the Editors of Journals.

Contributors wish to make personal acknowledgments to the following :

Chapter 1   Michael S. Pease, M.A., for writing the section on " The egg-cycle of the fowl " (p. 28).

Chapters 2, 4 *and* 6.   Mr. W. J. Pardoe, for artist's work.

Chapter 5.   The late Professor J. P. Hill, F.R.S., and Dr. A. Subba Rau, for making material available for study.
Dr. Elizabeth A. Frazer, for personal communications.

The Editor again offers his best thanks to Miss S. Carswell, B.Sc., National Institute for Medical Research, for her most valuable assistance.

The Index is the work of Mr. W. J. Bishop, to whom the Editor is indebted for this and other work in connection with the preparation of this volume.

CONTENTS

CHAPTER 6

BY P. ECKSTEIN AND S. ZUCKERMAN

CHAPTER 1

THE BREEDING SEASON

By F. H. A. Marshall

" It is well known that almost all animals, except man, have a stated season for the propagation of their species. Thus the female cat receives the male in September, January and May. The she-wolf and fox in January ; the doe in September and October. The spring and summer are the seasons appointed for the amours of birds, and many species of fishes. The immense tribe of insects have likewise a determinate time for perpetuating their kind ; this is the fine part of the year, and particularly in autumn and spring. The last-mentioned class of beings is subject to a variation that is not observed in the others. Unusual warmth or cold does not retard or forward the conjunction of birds or quadrupeds ; but a late spring delays the amours of insects, and an early one forwards them. Thus it is observed that, in the same country, the insects on the mountains are later than in the plains."

The foregoing quotation from Spallanzani's *Dissertations* (1784), although not strictly accurate in all its statements, contains a clear recognition of two fundamental facts which, indeed, have been realised from the earliest times ; first, that the periods of reproductive activity among the great majority of animals (not to mention plants) occur rhythmically, the rhythm usually having a connection with the changes of the seasons ; and secondly, that the reproductive rhythm is liable, to a greater or less extent, to be disturbed or altered by climatic or other environmental influences. And while there may be a basis of truth for the statement that the periodicity of the breeding season in the higher animals is less liable to modification than is the case with certain of the lower forms of life, there is abundant evidence that among the former no less than among insects the sexual functions are affected by external conditions and food supply.

Darwin remarks that any sort of change in the habits of life of an animal, provided it be great enough, tends in some way to affect the powers of reproduction.

" The result depends more on the constitution of the species than on the nature of the change ; for certain whole groups are affected more than others ; but exceptions always occur, for some species in the most fertile groups refuse to breed, and some in the most sterile groups breed freely." " Sufficient evidence has now been advanced to prove that animals when first confined are eminently liable to suffer in their reproductive systems. We feel at first naturally inclined to attribute the result to loss of health, or at least to loss of vigour ; but this view can hardly be admitted when we reflect how healthy, long-lived, and vigorous many animals are under captivity, such as parrots and hawks when used for hunting, chetahs when used for hunting, and elephants. The reproductive organs themselves are not diseased ; and the diseases, from which animals in menageries usually perish, are not those which in any way affect their fertility." (Darwin, 1868.)

It would seem probable that failure to breed among animals in a strange environment is due not, as has been suggested, to any toxic influence on the organs of generation, but to the same causes as those which restrict breeding in a state of nature to certain particular seasons, and that the sexual instinct can only be called into play in response to definite stimuli, the existence of which depends to a large extent upon appropriate seasonal and climatic changes.[1]

The manner in which these stimuli probably act and the parts played by the internal organs upon which they act are dealt with in later chapters treating of the exteroceptive factors generally and the gonads and anterior pituitary glands as organs of internal secretion. It should, however, be at once pointed out that apart from external influences there is in a very large number of animals as well as in plants an inherent tendency towards a reproductive rhythm as shown especially in those species which discharge their generative products in bulk (e.g. fishes and many invertebrates), this process involving a natural alternation between periods of activity when the sexual cells or gametes ripen and are released, and periods of quiescence when the essential reproductive organs or gonads undergo a process of recovery preparatory to their renewed growth before the next sexual season.

There are at present no sufficient data for anything like a complete comparative account of the physiology of breeding among the lower animals ; and in the present chapter, which is preliminary in character, I shall chiefly confine myself to stating a few general facts about the breeding season, giving illustrations, taken from various groups of invertebrates and vertebrates, of its seasonal recurrence, and the manner in which this varies under altered conditions of life.

I. Protozoa

Among the Protozoa the organisms pass through successive phases of vitality, which have been compared with the different age-periods of the Metazoa. In such simple forms of life, fission or division into two parts is the usual method of reproduction,[2] and the frequency of its occurrence has been thought to depend more upon the phase which has been reached in the life-cycle, than upon the influence of the environment. Thus, experiments seemed to show that there was a period of extreme vigour in cell-multiplication, corresponding to the youth of a metazoön ; and secondly, a period of maturity, characterised by changes in the chemical and physical properties of the cell, and leading to the formation of conjugating individuals ; and finally, in forms which do not conjugate, a period of senescence which ended in death. It is interesting to note, however, that the rapidity of fission is affected by the temperature and the food ; for example, an individual of the ciliate infusorian, *Stylonychia pustulata*, if well supplied with food, divides once in twenty-four hours in a temperature of from 5° to 10° C., and once in twelve hours in a temperature of from 10° to 15° C. (Sedgwick, 1898).

[1] Cf. page 20, where Bles's observations on the breeding habits of Amphibia are referred to, and Chapter 13, below.

[2] In this process no material is lost, and two simple nucleated organisms result. During the period of maturity referred to in the text, multiplication is often preceded by union (either temporary or complete) of two individuals, and this process is called conjugation.

In *Paramoecium aurelia*, too, it has been found that the rate of reproduction is influenced by temperature after the manner of a chemical reaction (Woodruff and Britsell, 1911). Again, flagellate Infusoria of different kinds have been induced to conjugate by changing the temperature or increasing the density in the surrounding medium. Calkins (1906) points out that the same experiment is performed by mosquitoes and other insects on certain parasitic Protozoa, as when a parasite is withdrawn from the hot environment of the mammalian blood into the comparatively cold region of the mosquito's alimentary tract (cf. next paragraph). Furthermore, the life-cycle of *Paramoecium* may be renewed without the occurrence of conjugation ; that is to say, fission can be made to continue and senescence can be avoided by introducing a change in the composition of the medium surrounding the culture.

Whereas some species of Protozoa are monomorphic or only vary slightly, there are others that present different phases in which the form may vary widely, the succession of phases being determined largely if not entirely by the conditions of the environment. The life-cycle of *Arcella vulgaris* is a case of this kind. The adult *Arcella* reproduces itself by several methods which, however, belong to two different types, binary fission and gemmation ; in the latter of these, small amoeba-like organisms (amoebulae) are formed and these are either gametic individuals which conjugate or agametic which grow up without conjugating. The ordinary binary fission takes place in the summer when the animal is actively feeding and growing. The adult *Arcella* is, however, of only one type which produces both gametes and agametes. On the other hand, there are many kinds of Protozoa such as *Trichosphoerium* in which there are two distinct forms of adult organisms, one giving rise to gametic and the other to non-conjugating individuals. In this way an alternation of generations is brought about in the life-cycle. In free living forms such as the one mentioned this alternation of generations is related to external conditions of the environment, the sexual generation appearing only in the autumn (Minchin, 1912). In parasitic species such as the *Haemosporidia*, or malaria parasite, the alternation of generations is related to an alternation of hosts, the gametes being formed in the invertebrate host, while in the blood of the vertebrate successive generations of individuals may be produced by fission without conjugation occurring.

Moreover, there is evidence that in the case of the free living ciliate *Colpoda steini* and some other forms, the occurrence of conjugation is determined entirely by the conditions of the surrounding medium.

With the majority of the Metazoa, as already indicated, there is a more or less definitely restricted season to which the occurrence of the chief reproductive processes is confined.

II. Porifera

In sponges belonging to the genera *Sycon*, *Grantia* and *Leucosolenia* breeding is reported to occur periodically (Flattely and Walton, 1922). According to Orton (1914) *Grantia compressa* has two breeding seasons at Plymouth, one in summer and the second in autumn. The same individuals may breed twice. Temperature is believed to be the main external factor in reproduction.

III. COELENTERATA

In the common hydra of Bengal (*Hydra orientalis*, Annandale), which, like most other coelenterates, reproduces by budding as well as by the sexual method,[1] the former process occurs chiefly during winter, the buds developing into new individuals.   Towards the beginning of the hot weather budding becomes less active, and in some individuals ceases altogether, while the same thing happens during periods of temporary warmth in winter.   A rise in temperature induces a proportion of the individuals present in the aquarium or pond to develop testes or male reproductive glands ; if the rise is considerable it may cause a few of the remaining individuals to produce ova.   On the other hand, no individual living in its natural environment has been known to exhibit any sign of sex after the rise in temperature has become steady.   The conditions most favourable to the production of ova appear to be a period of comparatively low temperature and abundant nutrition followed by a sudden but not excessive rise of temperature (Annandale, 1906).   In *Hydra viridis*, according to Whitney (1907), an abundance of food following a low temperature causes a suppression of the formation of testes and ova.

Certain hydroids (*Pennaria*, *Corydendrium*) shed their polyps and enter into a state of latent life when the autumn storms come on, and develop fresh polyps in the following spring (Flattely and Walton, 1922).   This has been interpreted teleologically as a protection against wave action.   Issel (1918) has suggested various ecological factors such as temperature, density and food supplies as being the cause.   This, however, is a matter of temporary cessation of asexual reproduction though sexual reproduction must be also affected.

Some of the marine hydroids show an alternation of generations which does not appear at first sight to be in any way related to change in the environment. In such cases the fertilised ovum develops into a polyp which gives rise to a colony of polyps by a process of sexual reproduction.   After the colony has reached a certain size, a new kind of bud is formed, and this becomes a jelly-fish. The latter after leading an independent existence, produces eggs, and these in turn become fertilised, giving rise to a new generation of polyps.   Morgan (1907) points out that as the polyp colony goes on increasing in size, its relation to its surroundings must undergo change, and that, very possibly, it is this change which determines the development of jelly-fish in place of polyps.   If this interpretation is correct the breeding season among marine hydroids is controlled by environmental conditions, just as it is among most other animals.[2]

---

[1] Asexual reproduction is of very common occurrence among the majority of the lower animals and plants.   It may take the form of simple binary fission (in unicellular organisms), of spore formation, or of gemmation or budding.   Sexual reproduction consists essentially of the union of two cells and their subsequent division to give rise to the new individual. In the multicellular organisms (Metazoa and Metaphyta) there are two kinds of conjugating cells, or gametes, which are specialised for the purpose.   These are produced in the gonads of animals by the male and female respectively, and are known as spermatozoa and ova.   Thus, sexual reproduction in the Metazoa is a modification of conjugation in the Protozoa.

[2] Morgan shows that the same point is illustrated by certain experiments of Klebs on flowering plants.   These at first produce only leaves and branches.   When they reach a certain size they produce flowers.   Klebs regards the development of the flowers as being

Panikkar and Aiyar (1939) record that with *Campanulina* in the brackish water of Madras sexual reproduction of the medusae goes on from June to February, but is especially intense from July to September, and that asexual reproduction of the hydroids is particularly well marked from June to August.

Some interesting observations have been recorded by Ashworth and Annandale (1904) about the breeding habits of sea-anemones. The species *Sagartia troglodytes* and *Actinia mesembryanthemum*, which are very prolific in captivity, have been noticed to breed regularly in the early spring. *Actinia* commences to produce young in the beginning of February, and *Sagartia* about a month later. As a rule the young are extruded in the early morning, and one individual may repeat the process every morning for a number of weeks, when the breeding season comes to an end. In one season, when the aquaria were somewhat neglected, the specimens of *Sagartia* produced fewer young than usual, and these were not extruded until the beginning of April. Specimens of *Actinia* living in the same aquaria were more prolific, but their breeding season was also somewhat retarded. In the month of August two anemones of the species *Sagartia troglodytes* were brought from Thorshavn in the Faroes, and placed in the aquaria. In the following October both of these produced several young ; while in April of the next year one of them again gave birth, but only to a single anemone. It seems probable that in this case the change of temperature or environment had induced the anemones to breed at an unusual season ; for it is unlikely that October is the normal period for reproduction in the Faroes, as by this time the sea has already begun to run high, and there would be a great risk of the young anemones becoming destroyed, being unable to attach themselves.

Flattely and Walton (1922) state that the gonads of British species of anemones usually ripen in spring or summer but that specimens in aquaria, if fed regularly will breed at any time of the year. (Cf. Panikkar and Aiyar, 1939, for brackish-water anemones of Madras, which breed all the year.)

Ashworth (1899) has pointed out that in the coral, *Xenia hicksoni*, which lives in the tropics, there is every evidence that spermatozoa are discharged over a very considerable period, if not practically throughout the whole year, whereas in the related form *Alcyonium digitatum*, of northern Europe, the period during which the spermatozoa are discharged is limited to about a month in the winter. Ashworth remarks that the difference is probably due to the fact that *Xenia*, living on reefs in the shallow waters of tropical seas, is not subject to great variations in temperature and food supply, while with *Alcyonium* such variations are no doubt considerable. In a similar way Pratt (1905) who has studied the process of oögenesis in *Sarcophytum*, *Holophytum*, and *Sclerophytum*, concludes that the sexually mature condition in these tropical genera extends over a considerably longer period than in the case of corals inhabiting temperate waters. In some genera, on the other hand, the breeding season is said to be very restricted. Thus, the coral, *Pocillopora bulbosa*, at the Great Barrier Reef, has two breeding

---

due to a relation that becomes established between the plant (when it has reached a certain stage of growth) and the environment. He shows also that by altering the environment a shoot may be induced to go on growing vegetatively, when it would ordinarily develop into a flowering branch. The flowering of the plant, therefore, is not merely the culmination of its form, as most botanists regard it. For much valuable and suggestive information on the factors which control breeding in plants Klebs' work (1903) should be consulted.

seasons in the year, one at the full moon and the other at the new moon (Marshall and Stephenson, 1933).   The spawning seasons of many other Coelenterata in different parts of the world are recorded by Hickson (1906).

It may also be noted that, whereas in the Ctenophora of the Mediterranean the breeding season extends through the year, in members of the same class in northern seas it only lasts through the summer (Bourne, 1900).

IV. Nemertea

The breeding season and its relation to the environment have formed the subject of a careful investigation by Child (1901) in the case of a small nemertean, *Stychostemma asensoriatum*, which is found very abundantly in one of the park lagoons of Chicago.   The season extends from May to November or December, according to the temperature of the water.   Egg-laying can occur freely in the laboratory, the eggs being deposited always during the night, or in darkness, when the animals move about freely.   Although breeding in the natural state is restricted to the warmer part of the year, eggs can be obtained in the laboratory at practically any time, by simply regulating the temperature.   Thus egg-laying can be induced in the winter at ordinary room-temperature, even though the worms are kept without food.   " In animals which contained only a few small oöcytes when taken, and which are kept in clean water without food, the growth of the oöcytes will continue, and, within a week or two, eggs may be laid."   " The body of the animal may even decrease somewhat in size during the growth of the oöcytes."   It is clear, therefore that in *Stychostemma* the limits of the breeding season are determined chiefly by the temperature of the water, and that the quantity or quality of the food is a factor of secondary importance.

V. Platyhelminthes

In the parasitic trematode, *Diplozoön paradoxum*, which ordinarily produces eggs only in the summer, it has been found that the formation of eggs could be artificially prolonged throughout the winter if the fishes on whose gills the animal lives are kept in an aquarium at summer heat (Semper, 1881).   The case is therefore comparable to that of the nemertean described above.

On the other hand, in the freshwater planarian (*Planaria alpina*) it has been shown by Beauchamp (1933) that sexual development is associated with low temperatures and that individuals with developed reproductive organs are rarely found at temperatures above 10° C.   Thus in cold springs there is no fundamental seasonal rhythm in the reproduction of this species.   In winter, however, the temperature of the whole stream in which these animals live is lowered and consequently sexual development becomes possible in the entire planarian population. In correlation with the growth of the gonads the planarian acquires a positive rheotaxis and swims upstream.   Owing to the large number of planarians that thus migrate there is a shortage of food for this species at the head of the stream and many individuals die.   The survivors, however, complete their sexual cycle by laying cocoons.   They then become negatively rheotactic and swim downstream again to the place where they started.   In *Planaria alpina*, therefore, the sexual migration is regulated by temperature, but food is an important factor since partially starved individuals also tend to become negatively rheotactic without forming cocoons, while on acquiring a sufficiency of nourishment their generative organs undergo renewed development and the animals again swim upstream. Beauchamp (1935) has shown further that the receptor sense organs which on being stimulated regulate the movements are placed on the extreme anterior end of the head. Moreover, the nature of the rheotactic response depends on the excitatory state of the central nervous system (Beauchamp, 1937) and this is presumably correlated with the sexual periodicity.

Flattely and Walton (1922) remark that tidal rhythm sometimes has a profound effect in timing the life-cycle. This is illustrated by the small planarian worm *Convoluta roscoffensis* which living symbiotically with green algae has to come periodically to the surface of the sand in which it lives in order to provide the algae with light. On the other hand, it is necessary for the worms to burrow into the sand before the incoming tide in order to prevent them from being washed away, and the process of burrowing is believed to be a nervous reaction to wave-shock. At Roscoff, however, when the sand is uncovered at night time the planarians do not come up to the surface, there being no light to attract them. It follows that they remain for 18 hours of the 24 in the sand, and it is at this period that egg-laying reaches its maximum (Keeble, 1910).

VI. ROTIFERA

In rotifers generally reproduction occurs parthenogenetically from unfertilised eggs throughout the summer, but when the environmental temperature falls with the advent of winter gametogensis takes place, the so-called " winter eggs " requiring to be fertilised before they can develop. Gametic reproduction thus occurs cyclically, the sexual periodicity being seasonal. According to Wesenberg-Lund (1930) and Berg (1934) the transition from parthenogenesis to gameto-genesis is probably due to " depression " in the animals. The depression in Berg's view is determined by various adverse environmental factors. Sexuality is thought to occur in the animal's life-cycle when its strength is spent (Wesenberg-Lund, 1930). The chief result of the sexual period is the so-called winter or resting egg from which the colony starts a new life with larger and more fully developed individuals. The period of degeneration which precedes sexuality does not occur in the colony every year, but may be only every second or every third year ; it often, however, takes place only at a certain season. It appears to be still an open question as to whether there is any really inherent periodicity in the life of the colony, and the facts seem rather to point to sexual reproduction taking place as a result of environmental stimuli which are generally seasonal (cf. the Cladocera).

VII. ANNELIDA

Certain species of polychaete annelids, known as the palolo worms, exhibit a quite remarkable regularity in the periodicity of their breeding habits. During their immaturity all the palolos live in burrows at the bottom of the water. With the attainment of sexual maturity, and under certain peculiar conditions, they swarm out for purposes of breeding. In the Atlantic palolo (*Eunice fucata*) and the South Pacific palolo (*Eunice viridis*) the process invariably takes place twice, upon or near the day of the last quarter of the moon and with the first rays of the sun ; but with the former species it occurs in June and July, and with the latter in October and November. The general conditions of existence for these worms would appear to be remarkably uniform, the temperature variation being from 24° to 30° C. only. There are other species of *Eunice* which behave in a similar manner (Heape, 1931). In the Japanese palolo (*Ceratocephale osawai*) the swarming takes place on nights closely following the new and full moons (i.e. when the spring tides occur) in October and November, the worms swimming out regularly four times a year. Each swarming-period lasts from one to four days. It has been noted further that the swarm is greater after the new moon (when the spring tide is highest) than after the full moon (when the tide is not so high), that each swarming takes place invariably just after the flood in the evening, that it continues for from one to two hours, and is generally larger on warm, cloudy nights than on clear, chilly nights. It would appear also that no individual worm takes part in more than one swarming in the year (Izuka, 1903). This worm is a phyllodocid and is not a true palolo. Other swarming polychaetes are *Platynereis dumerilii*, which swarms occasionally ; *Nereis limbata*, in which each sex secretes a substance which activates the other, the males swarming first and being followed by the females ; and *Odontosyllis enopla* (a Bermudan syllid), in which the female is phosphorescent intermittently at the hind end of the body, her appearance being followed by the male, the phosphorescence of the female ceasing after spawning is over. (I am indebted to Dr. C. F. A. Pantin for this information.)

The swarming habits and lunar periodicity of *Platynereis* in Madras Harbour are fully described by Aiyar and Panikkar (1937) who also record similar phenomena in about a dozen other polychaetes and give a complete account of the literature.

Besides polychaet worms there are other animals which have spawning periods in association with lunar phases (Pearse, 1939), and many further instances are given below in this chapter. The direct correlation may be with the tides rather than with the moon, e.g. *Amphitre ornata* (Scott, 1909).

Saville-Kent (1893) has briefly described the swarming of nereids in the Pacific off many of the islands in October. The ova were emitted in large quantities so that the surface of the sea became milky over a wide area. According to Hemplemann (1911) the swarming of *Nereis* (*Platynereis*) is regulated by the cycle of spring and neap tides.

Fage and Legendre (1925) have described the swarming of the mud-burrowing worm (*Scalibregma inflatum*). It takes place in the bay of Concordeau in the autumn and is associated with breeding (Heape, 1931). The lug-worm (*Arenicola*) on the other hand appears to spawn in the spring (Flattely and Walton, 1922).

VIII. ARTHROPODA

Innumerable instances of the periodicity of breeding and its relation to seasonal and environmental changes might be adduced from the great group of arthropods, but the reasons for the variations which occur are not usually very apparent.

In the Cape species of *Peripatus* (*P. capensis*) birth takes place in a fixed season (during April and May), whereas in the South American species births are said to occur probably throughout the entire year (Sedgwick, 1901). In the common crayfish (*Astacus fluviatilis*), in France the males are said to approach the females in November, December and January, whereas in England they begin to breed as early as the commencement of October, if not earlier (Huxley, 1880). Of other species of crayfish it is said that warm water ones mate in the autumn and spawn in the spring, but that cold water ones breed more or less all the year round (Pearse, 1939). In New Zealand, crustaceans of the same or allied genera breed at the reverse (or Southern hemisphere) times to what they do in Europe. Thus *Chiton* has been observed spawning in March and April (Benham, 1933, 1934).

Panikkar and Aiyar (1939) in dealing with the brackish water Crustacea of Madras record that for many species vigorous females are only found in the months from October to January. Some, however (e.g. hermit crabs), are perennial breeders, but reproduction with these is apt to be more intense when the harbour bar is open and the salinity of the water higher.

It is known that various species of crabs undertake periodic migrations for the purpose of breeding. According to Heape (1931) the northerly movement of the edible crab (*Cancer pagurus*) along the east coast of Britain to the Moray Firth in the winter is of this character. There is a return journey in the spring. Flattely and Walton (1922) state that the crabs migrate from the shore to deep water, starting in September, spawning in December, January and February, and afterwards migrating back again, the hatching season being in summer. They probably spawn in deep water because the temperature is more stable there. The West Indian land crab (*Gecarcinus*) makes lengthy spring migrations from sheltered situations inland to breed and spawn in the sea and then returns inland (Calman, 1911). Another land crab, *Gecarcoidea*, behaves similarly on Christmas Island, migrating during the rainy season in enormous numbers. The robber crab (*Birgus latro*) also has a breeding migration to the sea (Willey, 1900).[1]

Wheeler and Brown (1936) have described a periodic swarming in the prawn (*Anchistioides antiquensis*) at Bermuda. The periodicity coincides with the two weeks of the lunar cycle when the moon changes from the last quarter to the first quarter. It consists of two maximal appearances separated by an interval of some days. Wheeler thinks, however, that the swarming probably depends on the periodic activity of the worms that form the food and is not a reproductive swarming like that of the palolo Polychaeta.

Emrys Watkin (1941) found that in the amphipod *Corophium volutata* the mature forms breed in February and gradually disappear in March and April. Immature forms reached maturity in March or July, producing successive broods, some of which reached maturity in July. In August the new broods were in active reproduction and breeding ceased in October. The breeding cycle recommenced the next year.

Insects also furnish numerous instances of periodic breeding migrations and a summarised account of these has been given by Heape (1931). Among butter-

---

[1] Benham (1934) states that the common crab of New Zealand (*Cancer novae-zelandiae*) has been taken with full batches of eggs in both April and October.

B*

flies the monarch (*Anosia (Danaida) plexippus*) undertakes this kind of movement, and Williams (1930) describes it as follows :

" *D. plexippus* collects in bands in the northern states of the U.S.A. and in southern Canada in the autumn and these bands fly southwards, with the approach of winter, to the southern States. The butterflies stay in the south during the winter in a state of semi-hibernation ; usually resting in masses on certain special trees. In the following spring the hibernating bands break up and the individuals go north again, apparently laying eggs as they go."

The males may contain spermatozoa in the seminal vesicle and ducts in the autumn, but the eggs of the female are not ripe until March or April. Breeding migrations appear to occur in a number of other kinds of butterflies, and the known facts and conclusions drawn from them are summarised by Williams, Cockbill, Gibbs and Downes (1942).

In the case of the hemipterous insect known as the plant-louse (*Aphis*), we have evidence that the mode of reproduction is dependent upon temperature. In a favourable summer the females of this animal may produce as many as fourteen consecutive generations of young by parthenogenesis, the ova undergoing development without being fertilised by the male. At the beginning of the winter, male plant-lice make their appearance and fertilise the eggs, which develop in the succeeding spring. Réaumur, however, by artificially maintaining a constant summer temperature, succeeded in producing more than fifty parthenogenetic generations of plant-lice, all descended from a single mother (Semper, 1881).

Morgan (1907), however, describes some observations which seem to indicate that the change is not merely due to temperature. He shows, for example, that the sexual forms of *Aphis* may appear in the autumn before the onset of the cold weather, and conversely that many individuals may continue to reproduce parthenogenetically, until finally they perish from the cold. Morgan suggests that the alternation in the mode of reproduction may depend upon changes which take place in the food-plant in the autumn, instead of being solely a temperature effect. He shows also that there is evidence for the conclusion that in the genus *Chermes*, in which the alternation of generations occurs between the fir-tree and the larch, the conditions existing on the larch are those that call forth the sexual forms. Further information about the breeding and other migrations of various species of Aphidae as well as of locusts is given by Heape (1931) and Imms (1931). The latter author gives an account of the " phase theory " of locust migration.

That gametogenesis may be initiated by environmental stimuli in otherwise parthenogenetic forms has been shown very clearly also in the Cladocera, a group of crustaceans. Concerning these animals Weismann (1876–79) had supposed that the life-cycle was subject to definite rules, the animals passing through a certain number of parthenogenetic generations which were then followed by gametogenetic generations producing fertilised eggs, and that this occurred independently of the environment. The rhythm was regarded as being inherent in any given form and adapted through selection to the habitat. Berg (1934, 1936) and Mortimer (1936), on the other hand, have shown that under controlled optimum conditions, in *Daphnia* and other Cladocera, parthenogenetic reproduction may be maintained indefinitely, but that gametogenesis and sexual reproduction can be induced at any time by adverse circumstances. Berg and Mortimer differ, however, in that the former considers gametogenesis to result from a general " depression " (cf. rotifers), while the latter author, as a result of a series of further experimental observations, ascribes the change in the mode of reproduction to definite specific factors (e.g. food shortage, crowding of the medium, variations in temperature, etc.) from which a loss of weight or other indications of " depression " may also result.

It has been supposed in the aphids that change in the environment is also responsible for determining the sexes. Stevens (1906), however, has shown that what appears to be a change in sex should rather be regarded as a change from the parthenogenetic to the sexual mode of reproduction, and there can be no doubt that the Rotifera and Cladocera are similar. According to this view the sex of each individual is determined by the character of the gamete or gametes from which it is developed.

The supposed influence of food and external conditions upon sex-determination in various kinds of insects, and other animals, is discussed in Chapter 22.

Semper remarked long ago that the occurrence of reproduction (or of the particular mode of reproduction), with insects as with other animals, depends among other things, upon the nature of the diet, upon the chemical conditions of the surrounding medium, upon the moisture of the air, or upon other circumstances which are often unknown. Thus, failure to breed in a new environment is experienced by many Lepidoptera. For example, Death's-Head hawk moths, which are commonly blown over to this country from the Continent, but do not breed here continuously, deposit their eggs on young potato plants, and these develop into moths which emerge in the autumn. These moths, however, are quite infertile, so that, as a result, the Death's-Head has never established a permanent footing in Britain, though stray specimens are often captured (Anonymous, 1906). In the case of other insects, such as the mosquito (*Anopheles*), there is direct evidence that food is an important factor in egg-formation (Ross, 1909a). Thus it was found that mosquitoes fed on bananas refused to breed, but when fed on human blood they invariably laid eggs after two or three days. Moreover, it is stated that females of *Culex* and *Stegomya* apparently only desire to suck blood after fertilisation (Ross, 1909b). It is interesting to note also that in the mosquitoes and other Culicidae, the males are generally unable to suck blood, this habit being apparently correlated with the function of oviposition. Among the Empidae, which are carnivorous, the females, during the nuptial flights, are always fed by the males on small insects, and they seem incapable of discharging their sexual functions unless they are fed in this way (Howlett, 1907). The Hon. Charles Rothschild, however, has suggested another explanation of this phenomenon, namely, that the females would eat the males were they not supplied with a specific pabulum to divert their attention. Richards (1927), on the other hand, states that the acceptance of the prey by the female facilitates the male in taking up the correct attitude for coition. In some forms, according to Huxley (1938) the offering is made more conspicuous by being embedded in a large glistening object made of bubbles secreted by the male. The " box " presented may contain a flower-petal or it may be empty. The female sometimes goes through the routine of eating though there is nothing to eat, and Richards suggests that this is a case of " chain-reflex " which normally leads to coition. Howlett (1912) has shown that with the fruit-fly of Pusa (*Dacus*) sexual attraction is brought about by an odour emitted by the female and that this can be imitated artificially by oil of citronella.

Hora (1927) has adduced evidence that some species of mayflies (*Ephemeridae*) tend to emerge and make their nuptial flights at definite phases of the moon, and Williams (1936) has cited observations on other groups of insects which may point to similar conclusions.

The periodicity of reproduction has been the subject of investigation in a series of memoirs by Barnes (1930, 1932, 1934, 1935a and b), who has made intensive studies of the fluctuations in numbers displayed by various kinds of gall midges (*Cecidomyidae*) and the possible factors involved in causing these fluctuations. In the case of the leaf-curling pear midge (*Dasyneura pyri*) he shows that though minor variations are produced by weather conditions, in general there are four flights in the year, the first brood emerging in late April or May, the second in June, the third about August, and the fourth in late August or early September. Barnes lays stress on the adjustment between the plants to be attacked by the midges and the insects, pointing out that the optimum time of emergence must be when the plant has reached the stage of growth necessary for successful oviposition. " In another country, e.g. New Zealand, the climate may be such as to allow growth of the trees to be prolonged and so extra broods of the midge could occur, as they do." Barnes states further that the percentage of males both in *Dasyneura pyri* and in *D. arabis* decreases with successive broods and suggests that temperature may control the rate of segmentation of the egg and so determine the extent of development of the egg at the time of entry of the sperm, the higher number of males resulting from the more advanced development of the egg at fertilisation.

In some insects oviposition takes place long after the death of the males. Thus Lefroy and Howlett (1909) state that in the mango weevil (*Cryptorhynchus gravis*) the males die in August while the females live until the following March to lay eggs.[1]

IX. MOLLUSCA

Among the marine Mollusca as with many kinds of fish, in contrast to other forms of life, winter is the usual time for the deposition of the eggs (Lo Bianco, 1888, 1899).[2] On our own coasts nudibranchs come to shore to lay their eggs from January to April. *Patella* spawns from October until the end of the year. *Purpura lapillus* is said to be most active during the same season, but it breeds to some

[1] Wigglesworth (1942) has given an excellent summary of what is known concerning the phenomenon attending breeding, including the periodicity of breeding in the different groups of insects.

[2] Much valuable information concerning the breeding habits of Mollusca and other animals, inhabiting the Bay of Naples, is given in the papers by Lo Bianco (1888–1911). *See also* Issel (1918). Lo Bianco records that species which live exposed to wave shock generally spawn in the seasons of calm or during the warmer months and consequently the larvae survive. This applies to all kinds of animals. Exceptional animals which

extent throughout the year. *Buccinum undatum* breeds from October until May, whereas *Littorina* breeds all the year round (Cook, 1895). In New Zealand the large whelk (*Argobuccinum australasiae*) has been seen spawning on July 1 and *Chiton* in March (Benham, 1933).

According to Amirthalingam (1928) spawning with the scallop (*Pecten opercularis* — *Chlamys opercularis*), near Plymouth is at a maximum at full moon and at a minimum at new moon. The pearl oyster on the Great Barrier Reef is said to breed in May and November and each time at the full moon (Stephenson, 1933).

There are other factors which stimulate spawning. Thus, with *Ostrea virginica*, whereas a rise of temperature is a factor in spawning, the males and females are respectively stimulated by the presence of eggs or sperm in the water. There is, however, no specificity, for eggs of other molluscs or of echinoderms stimulate spawning, as well as green algae which contain sugar and starches and other chemical substances (Galtsoff, 1938a and b; 1940).

Among the land Mollusca there is, generally speaking, a more marked periodicity in the breeding season than among the marine forms. In temperate climates breeding is restricted to the summer. In the tropics the occurrence of the breeding season is generally determined by the alternations of wet and dry seasons. In other cases, where there are no great seasonal changes, the land Mollusca may breed all the year round. The snails of the Mediterranean area, according to Semper (1881), arrive at sexual maturity when they are six months old, and before they are fully grown. Those individuals which reach this age in the spring deposit eggs a second time after the heat of the summer is over, and so experience two breeding seasons in the year, with an interval of a few months between them during the hot weather. Semper shows, further, that individuals of the same genera, or perhaps even of the very same species, in the damper and colder climates of the north, do not lay eggs till development is complete ; while in the dry, warm region of the Mediterranean, they have produced two lots of eggs before they are fully grown. This is because completion of growth and sexual maturity do not necessarily coincide. In a similar way, in the pond-snail (*Limnaea*) the minimum of temperature which admits of the assimilation of food, and so of growth, is much above the winter temperature of egg-deposition.

In tropical climates, where the variation in temperature throughout the year is reduced to a minimum, the periodicity in the breeding habits of animals is to a considerable extent obliterated, at least in so far as it is dependent upon temperature (cf. Panikkar and Aiyar, 1939). Semper (1881) says that few things impressed him more in the Philippine Islands than the absence of all true periodicity in the breeding habits not only of the land-molluscs, but also of the insects and other land-animals.

" I could at all times find eggs, larvae, and propagating individuals, in winter as well as in summer. It is true that drought occasions a certain periodicity, which is chiefly perceptible by the reduced number of individuals in the dry months, and the greater

spawn in winter and spring attach their eggs to rocks and protect them by capsules (*Murex, Asteima, Blennius*). Species which inhabit shallow and stagnant harbours that are subject to great heat and putrefaction in summer usually breed in winter and spring. Commensal and parasitic species whose medium is approximately constant may breed at any time of the year (Flattely and Walton, 1922).

number in the wet ones ; it would seem that a much smaller number of eggs are hatched under great drought than when the air is very moist. Even in January, the coldest and driest month, I found land-snails which require much moisture, and at every stage of their development, but only in shady spots, in woods, or by the banks of streams. But what was far more striking in these islands was the total absence of all periodicity in the life of the sea-animals, particularly the Invertebrata ; and among these I could not detect a single species of which I could not at all seasons find fully grown specimens, young ones, and freshly deposited eggs."

Semper goes on to remark that even in some cold seas periodicity is far more often eliminated than is commonly supposed, and mentions that the eggs of the sea-mollusc, *Tergipes*, have been found at all seasons, like those of *Littorina* on our own coasts.

X. ECHINODERMATA

Sea-urchins and starfish, and other Echinodermata, appear generally to have a regularly recurrent breeding season, at which the genital organs swell up to an enormous size. In the sea-urchin, *Echinus esculentus*, these organs grow into huge tree-like structures with branched tubes, lined by the sexual cells. These are sold for food by the fishermen in Naples, who call them " frutta di mare." It is said that a single female *E. esculentus* will produce as many as 20,000,000 eggs in a breeding season. At other times of the year the generative organs are so reduced as to be scarcely recognisable. *E. esculentus* at Port Erin, in the Isle of Man, spawns in June (Chadwick, 1900). At Dunbar, in Scotland, it has been observed to spawn at the same time. The sea-urchins in Naples spawn at the end of the year (*E. acutus* being mature in November and December, and *E. micro-tuberculatus* from September onwards (Lo Bianco, 1888–1911). The spawning times of most of the Naples echinoderms are given in these memoirs. The common starfish (*Asterias rubens*) spawns in November at St. Andrews (M'Intosh, 1875). In New Zealand one of the common sea-urchins was seen to spawn in January (that is, in summer) (Benham, 1934). Professor H. Munro Fox, to whom I am indebted, has written as follows concerning the Mediterranean and Red Sea species :

" The sea-urchins at Suez, *Centrechinus* (*Diadema*) *serosum*, breed from the spring until September. During the season the genital products are developed in cycles correlated with the lunar periods. Spermatozoa and eggs are discharged into the sea between the first and third quarters of each moon, the majority of individuals spawning about the time of full moon. The greater number of specimens examined between the first quarter and full moon have the gonads swollen and filled with spermatozoa or eggs in a state ready for discharge into the sea, while a smaller number show that the genital products have lately been shed. As the third quarter of the moon approaches, whereas some individuals still have testes or ovaries full of spermatozoa or eggs, most have already spawned. After the third quarter all have extruded their genital products, and the gonads, now smaller in size, contain numerous spermatocytes or oöcytes in the process of development into spermatozoa or eggs, to be shed into the sea round about the next full moon. From the new moon until the first quarter following it the gonads are filled with spermatocytes or oöcytes in a more advanced stage of development, and, in addition, there are present in some individuals spermatozoa and unripe or ripe eggs. After this the same cycle is repeated."

The gonads of the sea-urchins are eaten in different parts of the world, and their variation in size has often been thought to correspond with the phases of the moon, as in the fish markets of the Mediterranean and elsewhere. This supposed fact is referred to by Aristotle [1] and other classical writers, both Greek and Roman. Fox (1923), however, has shown that while partly true for the sea-urchins in the Red Sea it is false for other parts, and he concludes that the belief originated in the east and afterwards spread westward and has since persisted.

Elmhirst (1922) states that with *Echinus esculentus* a shoreward migration sets in about February or March and may continue until June when spawning occurs. Similar breeding migrations are said to occur with *Solaster papposus*, *S. eudeca*, *Henricia sanguinolenta*, *Archidoris tuberculata*, *Leander squilla*, and many other species (Heape, 1931).

XI. CEPHALOCHORDATA

In the lancelet (*Amphioxus lanceolatus*) of the Mediterranean the breeding season extends from spring until autumn, the glands becoming so large by the ripening of ova and spermatozoa that the atrium is used up to its utmost capacity. Spawning, when it occurs, invariably takes place about sun-down (i.e. between 5 and 7 P.M.) and never, so far as known, at any other times (Willey, 1894).

XII. CYCLOSTOMATA

Knowles (1939) has described the circumstances attending the breeding of the river lamprey. It spawns in April. Shortly before spawning the cloacal labia enlarge through vasodilation. In the male the urogenital papilla erects. The sperms are shed to the exterior. In the female the cloacal region also swells. These changes occur only a few days before spawning. However, a month before spawning the dorsal and caudal fins of the male enlarge and unite by a thickening at the base. A small ventral fin develops behind the cloaca of the female, but not in the male.

XIII. PISCES

Among fishes the duration of the breeding season varies considerably according to the group to which they belong. The ova of the elasmobranchs (sharks, etc.) are deposited singly or in pairs at varying intervals throughout a great part of the year, but some species appear to have regular recurrent breeding seasons (Couch, 1862). According to Metten (1939) the common dogfish about our coasts has no breeding season but is always sexually active though slightly more prolific in the spring. The comparatively small number of eggs in elasmobranchs is correlated with the fact that in most members of this group the young are hatched within the body (but not in the dogfish and rays). The eggs may be shed from the ovary on successive days or there may be intervals of several days or a week between the periods of ovulation. In such a genus as the picked dog-fish (*Spinax*) it is stated that the eggs descend in successive pairs into the two horns or branches of the uterine receptacle or their descent may be by twos or threes on either side. In those genera which do not produce their young alive the eggs are deposited in purses as with *Scyllium* and the rays.

[1] *See* D'Arcy Thompson's translation (1910) and footnote by the translator.

In the sturgeon the roe consists of small grains as in the teleostean or bony fishes. Moreover, in these, the breeding season is limited as a rule to the spring and summer in temperate climates. In a single individual spawning may last no longer than a few weeks or even days (Bridge, 1905). The enormous number of eggs produced by most teleosts must be connected with the absence of internal fertilisation, involving a large wastage of ova which never come in contact with male cells or spermatozoa. In the ling it has been found that the ovaries contained from 14 to 60 millions of eggs (and in a large specimen as many as 160 million eggs), in the cod and the conger 8 to 10 millions, while in the sun-fish there might be as many as 160 millions (Kyle, 1926).

The cod, off our own coasts, has a spawning season extending from January to June, but the majority of individuals spawn in March. It has been found, however, that in some parts of the North Sea the cod may spawn in the autumn. In the whiting the spawning period lasts from early March until the third week in August (Masterman, 1900). The investigations of the Marine Biological Association have shown that in the plaice of the South Devon bays the maximum spawning period is between the third week of January and the second week of February. This period in the North Sea and Irish Sea would appear to be slightly later. Herdman (1904) [1] records that, in the year 1904, the plaice in the open-air ponds at the Port Erin Biological Station started spawning on March 3, and those at the Peel (Lancashire) Sea Fish Hatchery (under cover) on March 1.

The majority of sea-water teleosts likewise spawn mostly in early spring and the same is true of freshwater species.[2] The Salmonidae, however, mostly spawn in or about December. Menzies (1925) says that broadly speaking the more northerly the river the earlier will the salmon spawn. The grayling, however, spawns in the spring. The introduced Salmonidae in New Zealand spawn in the cold season. Thus with the brown trout (*Salmo fario*) spawning takes place in July; with the steel-head trout (*Salmo gairdneri*) it occurs from July to September; and with the American brook-char (*Salvelinus fontinalis*) spawning takes place " during the early spring months " (Phillips and Hodgkinson, 1922; Calderwood, 1927). Thus fish introduced from England breed at the reverse times, complying with the southern hemisphere seasons. The freshwater minnow is similar.

In the holostean fish, *Lepidosteus*, which lives in the fresh waters of North America, the breeding season recurs with a wonderful regularity about May. At this time the fish resort in large numbers to shallower water, where the temperature is higher. Here the ova and spermatozoa are emitted during recurrent periods of sexual excitement (Agassiz, 1878). The related fish, *Amia*, of Central and southern North America, spawns usually in May, the exact season depending somewhat upon the temperature of the water. The fish make their way from deep

[1] *See also* Wallace, W. (1904). For further information concerning the spawning seasons of different species of fish, *The Journal of the Marine Biological Association*, the publications of the English and Scottish Fishery Boards, the New Zealand (Marine Department) *Reports on Fisheries*, and the reports of the International Council for Fishery Investigation, should be consulted. These reports show that the migratory and reproductive periods of fishes are affected by the temperature, salinity, etc., of the sea. *See also* Kyle (1926) and Heape (1931).

[2] This is true also of American fish, e.g. the striped bass (*Roccus saxatilis*) spawns in spring or early summer (Pearson, 1938).

water to the shallow spawning place, which is generally at the end of a swampy lake (Bashford Dean, 1895).

In the crossopterygian fish, *Polypterus bichir*, the ova ripen in the summer months from June to September, the breeding season depending upon the period of inundation, as in most of the Nile fishes (Harrington, 1899). The other species of *Polypterus* (*P. senegalis* and *P. lapradii*), which inhabit the river-basins of tropical Africa, spawn also in the wet season in July and August (Budgett, 1901).

In the dipnoan, *Ceratodus*, of Australia the principal time for spawning is September and October, at the end of the dry season (Semon, 1899). In the other two dipnoans, *Lepidosiren* of South America and *Protopterus* of Africa, spawning occurs shortly after the emergence of the fish from their summer sleep. Kerr, writing of the former, says that the exact time for breeding varies greatly from year to year in correlation with the extreme variability of the climate, the swamps, which the mud-fish inhabit, sometimes remaining dry for prolonged periods (Kerr, 1900).

Some fish, of which the viviparous cyprinodont *Xiphophorus helleri* is an example, appear to breed continuously. The females are said to give birth to young at intervals all the year round like some mammals (Moore, 1932). Such a condition, is, however, exceptional, for most fishes like the great majority of other vertebrates, exhibit a well-marked sexual periodicity. (For observations on the breeding etc. of the viviparous fish, *Heterandria formosa*, *see* Fraser and Renton, 1940.)

Most fishes migrate, before the commencement of the breeding season, to localities suitable for the deposition of their eggs. Thus, certain marine fishes like the salmon, the shad, and the sturgeon ascend rivers for long distances before spawning (anadromous fishes) ; others merely migrate to shallower water nearer shore. The eel, on the other hand, is a freshwater fish which migrates to the sea for breeding (catadromous fish), and deposits its eggs in deep water (in spring and early summer) after travelling an immense distance (Schmidt, 1922).

Jacobi (1880) stated that the migration of the eel is not determined by the growth of the genital organs, for these do not begin to develop until the fish have reached the sea. He concluded, therefore, that eels need salt water before the genital organs can develop. On the other hand, Miss Lowe at Windermere, informed me that the " yellow eels " which become " silver eels " when they are about to migrate to the sea, appear to undergo this change when there is a certain definite proportion reached between the weight of the ovary and that of the body as a whole (cf. Lowe, 1948).

Miss Frost (1945) states that female eels may spend from nine to nineteen years in fresh water, and at this time range from 47 cm. to 95 cm. in length, and that male eels spend from seven to twelve years in fresh water and are only about 39 cm. The gonads are presumably undeveloped until they are about to migrate to the sea.

Noel Paton (1898) stated that salmon, with their genitalia in all stages of development, are ascending the rivers throughout the whole year. Miescher (1897) has shown that salmon go practically without food so long as they are in fresh water, being nourished by the large store of material which they accumulated while they were in the sea. This observation has been confirmed by Noel Paton. Miescher and Paton have shown, further, that the gain in solid material (proteins, etc.) by the genitalia, due largely to the formation of comparatively simple proteins (protamines, histones, etc. *see* Vol. I, Part 2) as the fish pass up the rivers, is met by a loss in solid material in the muscles.   This transference is not brought about by anything of the nature of a degeneration taking place in the muscles, but the latter appear simply to excrete or give out the material which has been accumulated in them.   It should be noted, however,

" that the gain of solids by the genitalia is small as compared with the loss of solids by the muscle ; that, in fact, the greater part of the solids lost from the muscles is used up for some other purpose than the building up of the genitalia." (Paton, 1898.)

Paton concludes that the state of nutrition is the main factor determining migration towards the river, and that, when the salmon has accumulated a sufficiently large store of material, it returns to the rivers which were its original habitat.   It does not seem possible, however, to maintain that nutrition is a determining influence in the growth of the genital glands, since these are undeveloped when the fish begin to migrate and enter upon their period of starvation.   Greene (1926) and Needham (1931) give further details and references.   Orton, Jones and King (1938) have shown that a great many of the two- and three-year-old salmon " parr " become sexually mature in October in the rivers in which they were reared before migrating to the sea.   They found that the spermatozoa of these parr may be mature and can fertilise ova, thus confirming the work of Shaw (1840) who suggested that this probably occurred also in a state of nature.

More details are given by King, Jones and Orton (1939), and Jones and Orton (1940).   After spawning a high proportion of the male parr migrate to the sea as smolts, along with immature males and females.

Milroy (1908) has shown that similar changes take place in the herring, in which, however, the starvation period is briefer.

The breeding migrations of freshwater fishes are for the most part closely comparable to those of sea fishes for they tend to seek shallower water, whether in lakes or upstream in rivers, for purposes of spawning.   Miss Frost (1943) in an investigation on the minnow (*Phoxinus phoxinus*) of Lake Windermere and the River Brathay, found that the fish are active from April to October and migrate into deeper water where they are relatively passive and hidden under stones from November to March.   The breeding season extends from May to July and is experienced by all fish above their second year as well as by most of those in their second year and a few at the end of their first year.   Nesting fishes are as a rule inshore breeding migrants, and Craig-Bennett (1931) has shown that the three-spined stickleback (*Gasterosteus aculeatus*) has a well-marked spawning migration from the river to the shallow streams.

" Thus it would appear that a breeding migration is almost universal amongst fishes . . . and that the length of [some of] the breeding migrations is equalled by only a very few birds and is far beyond the capacity of any other animals except whales.   Further, in fishes the rule is accentuated that growth and reproduction are alternative activities. Feeding and growth stop before the gonads begin to develop, and as a rule the fish are in poor condition when spawning takes place because the reproductive cells have matured at the expense of the nutriment already stored in the tissues and organs of the parent. It is also seen that in the case of some fish which spend long months in a state of aestivation or hibernation, the reproductive cells are matured during that period, and spawning takes place after freedom is gained and before feeding and growth have begun again." (Heape, 1931.)

The reproductive cycle of the three-spined stickleback has been investigated in detail by Craig-Bennett (1931). The generative organs as well as the secondary sexual characters undergo an annual cycle of development and regression. In different habitats (a river, a pond and a canal) at the same latitude in England the beginning of the breeding season occurs at about the same date —in April or May. The development of the secondary sexual characters coincides with the acquisition of the sexual instincts. At this time a red colour appears on the throat and ventral surface of the body, the iris and the back of the body appear blue, and many of the tubules of the kidney become modified in correlation with the mucous secretion which is used in building the nests (*see* below, p. 172). The muscles of the pectoral fins also hypertrophy so that they can " fan " the water over the nests. It is shown also that the periodic acquirement of those characters is brought about by two factors, an internal factor which is the secretion of the interstitial cells of the testis (*see* below, pp. 171 and 172), and an external one which is increase of temperature. Variations of food and light apparently had no direct effect on the sexual cycle.[1] (But cf. Chapter 13.) Panikkar and Aiyar (1939) deal with the breeding of Madras fishes.

XIV. AMPHIBIA

The intimate connection between sexual periodicity and climatic variation exhibited by many Amphibia and Reptilia, especially in temperate climates, was commented on by Spallanzani (1784). This close dependence upon environmental conditions is evidently due largely to the habits of life of these animals, many of which hibernate or show great sluggishness in cold weather; while among Amphibia it must be associated with the further fact that, whereas most members of the group live to a great extent upon land, it is necessary for them to deposit their eggs in water. Spallanzani concluded that the reason why Amphibia are subject to a variation which is not observable in birds and mammals is because the former, like insects, are cold-blooded, and have a comparatively small supply of internal heat to animate them when it is cold.

" As therefore the exercise of their functions depends on the heat of the atmosphere, their amours will also depend upon this cause, and will, of course, be later in cold than in hot climates, and in both will vary with the season."

Spallanzani illustrated the truth of this fact by pointing out that various species of frogs and toads begin to propagate earlier in Italy than in Germany

---

[1] Wiltshire states that in some fishes, at the period of oviposition, the lips of the genital orifice swell and become congested. This condition he regards as comparable to that which occurs during the " heat " period of a mammal. Further references to cyclical changes in the generative organs of fish, courtship phenomena, migrations, etc., are made by Craig-Bennett (1931), Moore (1932) and Norman (1936). The factors which control the cycle and determine the times of spawning are well discussed by Craig-Bennett who quotes numerous references to the observers. Among many facts bearing on this subject he records that according to Cahn (1927) the spawning of *Labisdesthes sicculus* coincides very accurately with a high temperature (20° C.), whereas *Leucichthys artedi* in the same region spawns at 3.5° C. Many other fish show an extreme sensitivity to changes of temperature and only spawn when it is at a certain definite level.

or Switzerland.[1]   On the other hand, he records the observation that the tree-frog and the fetid terrestrial toad were copulating in the ponds and reservoirs of Geneva in March, at a time when in Lombardy they had not yet quitted their subterranean abodes.   In view, however, of recent researches, it would seem probable that once the amphibians have emerged from their winter retreats light may also be a factor in the growth and activity of the generative organs (cf. March, 1937 ; *see* below, p. 22).

It is interesting to note that in the frog and many other Amphibia the ova are produced during the winter hibernation when the animals eat little or nothing, just as the genital organs of the salmon develop during the period of migration, when the fish have practically ceased to feed.   The testes of the males, like the ovaries of the females, also increase enormously in size with the approach of the annual breeding season.

Of the group as a whole, Moore (1932) writes as follows :

" In the main the Amphibia present the common feature of an annual seasonal spermatogenetic and breeding cycle ; the periods of the year at which a given stage is reached, however, are so different that no feature common to the group is evident to suggest the controlling influences that are operating.   Spermatogenesis may be completed rapidly during mid-summer ; it may be more or less continuous throughout the year ; or it may occur slowly during summer and winter."

(*See* below, Chapter 3, p. 185.   For an account of the seasonal change in the ovaries in *Xenopus laevis*, the South African clawed toad, see Shapiro and Shapiro, 1934.)

With some species (e.g. *Bombinator*) spawning may take place several times during the spring and summer.   With *Discoglossus* in Algeria the pairing season is said to last from January to October (Gadow, 1901).   Moreover, in *Bufo melanostictus*, a tropical species living in Siam, the breeding season extends through all months of the year except perhaps in October, but a larger number of breeding females are to be found from November to January than at other times. In the males there appear to be individual sex cycles, uncorrelated with the seasons.

Bles (1905) has discussed at some length the conditions under which it is possible to induce various species of Amphibia to breed in captivity.   He states that the most necessary condition is that the animals should be allowed to hibernate at the proper season, and in order to accomplish this they must be in thoroughly good health when the winter sets in, having passed the summer in the best circumstances in regard to light, heat and supply of food.   Bles's observations relate more especially to the African frog, *Xenopus laevis*, but he believes his conclusions to apply in a large degree to many other species of Amphibia.

The frogs in question were kept in a " tropical aquarium " (that it to say, an aquarium which could be kept at a tropical temperature by regulating a heating apparatus).   In the summer the temperature was maintained at about 25° C. ;

[1] In the common frog (*Rana temporaria*) the usual time for spawning in middle Europe is March, earlier in warm, later in cold seasons ; in southern countries, January or February, but in Norway not until May.   *See* Gadow (1901) whose book contains a quantity of valuable information concerning the breeding habits of many amphibians and reptiles.

in December it was allowed to drop to 15°–16° C. during the day, and 5°–8° C. during the night. The bottom of the aquarium was covered with earth and stones, on which the weed *Vallisneria* thrived. The water in the aquarium was never changed. The frogs were fed daily upon small worms, or strips of liver, until they would eat no more. During winter they became lethargic, taking very little food. When the temperature rose in the spring and the days became brighter, the frogs became more active, especially the males. At this time breeding could be induced by a certain method of procedure which Bles describes as follows :

" First, the temperature of the aquarium is raised to 22° C. ; and secondly, when it has become constant, a certain amount of water, say two gallons, is drawn off morning and evening, allowed to cool for twelve hours, and then run in slowly in the following manner, in order to simulate the fall of rain. The cooling vessel is raised above the level of the aquarium, and a syphon is used to run off the water. The lower end of the syphon is drawn out to a fine point, and turned up in such a way that the water rises up like from a fountain, and falls as spray into the aquarium. . . . By carrying out such measures I obtained from one female, between April and July 1903, more than fifteen thousand eggs."

The abdomen of the female *Xenopus* is stated to become very much distended during the winter by the enormously enlarged ovaries. " The three flaps surrounding the cloacal aperture are flaccid until the spring, when they become swollen and turgid, and more highly vascularised." (Cf. the changes in the female genital organs of mammals during the " heat " periods, described in subsequent chapters.) The male *Xenopus* is said to assume its nuptial characters two days after the temperature is raised to 22° C., and a very little later to become vocal, the voice strengthening from day to day. Copulation takes place only at night, and spawning may commence an hour afterwards ; but this does not occur unless the water is changed in the manner above described.

According to Leslie (1890) it would appear that *Xenopus*, in its native country, breeds only in August, i.e. in the South African spring. Bles, however, is disposed to think that *Xenopus*, like *Discoglossus* in the wild state, may sometimes breed several times during the spring and summer, since the frogs in confinement in some years spawned three times, and this has been confirmed by later observers.

Semper (1878, 1881) has shown that if axolotls are kept crowded together in small aquaria, without plants or seed, individuals which are sexually mature will not deposit ova even though the water be changed and abundant food supplied. But if they be suddenly transferred to aquaria stocked with plants, and with stones and sand on the bottom and running water, they can be induced to spawn within a few days, and may do so as often as three or four times a year. Bles states that he is able to confirm Semper's observations upon axolotls, and that he obtained similar results by treating individuals of *Triton waltlii* and of *Discoglossus* in the same way.

Annandale (1903) states that in the Malay Peninsula *Rhacophorus leucomystax* and *Rana limnocharis* appear to breed only after a heavy fall of rain, and he concludes that the stimulus set up by falling water is necessary before the sexual impulse can be induced.

An investigation by Savage (1935) on *Rana* also emphasises the importance of rainfall in the period preceding actual mating, and a similar point has been stressed by Berk (1938) in relation to *Xenopus* in South Africa.   The latter author after discussing the factors responsible for the anoestrum or period of rest (from September to February), for the pro-oestrum or period of generative development (from February to July), and for oestrus or the period of actual breeding (usually from July to September), states that " the sharp rise in temperature and the high rainfall (at the last period) correspond closely in point of time with the onset of pairing in the pools."

The sexual cycle in the frog and various other Amphibia has also been the subject of investigations by March (1937a and b) who, after describing among many other matters the great increase that occurs normally in the ovaries and other organs in spring prior to breeding, shows that light may play an important part in regulating the cycle, seeing that experimental irradiation stimulates sexual activity not only in spring but also in autumn.

Thus there appears to be abundant evidence that breeding in mature amphibians does not occur cyclically merely, but takes place only in response to certain definite external stimuli which are of different kinds, and in a state of nature occur naturally in a regular order.   Bles remarks that if this view is correct, and assuming it to apply to other groups besides the Amphibia, it helps to explain why many animals fail to breed in captivity ; and also how it is that others, e.g. insects, in a state of nature, appear in large numbers in one year and are much less numerous in another.

It is interesting to note that among frogs and other cold-blooded vertebrates, there is a periodicity in the occurrence of their reflex responses.[1]   It has been shown that if the region of the shoulder-girdle bearing the forelimbs, together with the connected skin and muscles, and the three upper segments of the spinal cord, are cut out from the male frog during the breeding season (but not at other times), the irritation of the skin will cause a reflex clasping movement, similar to that characteristic of the normal male at this period.   In spring and early summer, after reviving from their winter sleep, frogs tend to be irregular in certain other reflex responses.   MacLean (1908) has shown that in the heart of the frog, newt and salamander, and also the eel, vagus inhibition is absent or markedly diminished at certain periods corresponding roughly to the seasons of sexual activity, but the significance of the changes is not very apparent.

An example of an amphibian sexual character which develops cyclically is seen in the thickened pad of skin on the first digit of the frog's forelimb at the time of breeding.   Associated with it is an increased musculature in the forearm preparatory to the act of embracing the female during copulation.

The remarkable nuptial dress of some Amphibia, e.g. the vividly coloured crests and frills of the newts and salamanders, which develop in correlation with breeding activity, are a striking feature of the group at this season.

As is well known, in association with the amphibian habit, newts and frogs migrate to water for purposes of breeding, but according to Heape (1931) these are not true migratory movements since they occur within the territory normally inhabited.

---

[1] The sexual posture of frogs in the act of copulation is maintained as a spinal reflex. The tortoise is similar.   The reflex is inhibited by excitation of the optical lobes (Spallanzani, 1784 ; Tarchanoff, 1887 ; Albertoni, 1888).

XV. REPTILIA

Reptiles which hibernate usually begin to breed shortly after the commencement of the warm weather which terminates the hibernating period, just as in the case of amphibians.[1] Other reptiles, which live in warm or tropical climates, also have regularly recurrent breeding seasons, in some cases extending over many months, generally in the spring and summer (Gadow, 1901). Thus, Mahendra (1936), writing of the Indian house gecko (*Hemidactylus flaviviridis*) states that with this lizard the breeding season extends from the end of February or beginning of March to late September or even October, but much depends on climatic conditions. Moreover, Weekes (1935) referring more particularly to Australian lizards, says that the viviparous species have one breeding season each year, its commencement varying within the same species according to whether the region they inhabit has an early or a late spring. The oviparous *Amphibolarus musicatus* was found to have at least two breeding seasons in the warmer part of the year, and the eggs maturate two weeks earlier than those of other lizards in the same locality. It would seem that in reptiles, as with amphibians, breeding only occurs in response to certain external stimuli, but that temperature is the main factor, as supposed by Spallanzani. Nevertheless, there are generic differences, and it is stated that of the two species of caiman inhabiting the Amazon, *C. niger* breeds in October and November and *C. scheropis* in May and June (Pearse, 1939).

The breeding cycles of various kinds of reptiles are referred to more fully in the third chapter (pp. 189–204) where the changes in the internal organs are described. It is to be noted that in all the species recorded therein, breeding occurs in the spring, but that in the Saharan lizard (*Acanthodactylus*) testicular activity may extend over a great part of the year.

In certain species of reptiles the young are produced considerably later in the year than the mating season when copulation takes place. This is due to the fact that the fertilised eggs may undergo development (and for varying degrees of time) in the oviduct of the female. Thus in the common viviparous lizard (*Lacerta vivipara*) copulation occurs in the spring but the young are born sufficiently mature to feed and look after themselves in the late summer. The egg-membrane in which the young develop, ruptures at or just before parturition. The other English species, the sand lizard (*Lacerta agilis*) copulates in May or June and the eggs are deposited about four weeks later, usually in July. The eggs are then left to hatch out by the aid of external warmth. The green lizard (*L. viridis*) of the continent of Europe and the Channel Islands, is also oviparous, the eggs developing for about four weeks within the mother and for another four weeks externally before being hatched (Leighton, 1903).

The slow-worm (*Anguis fragilis*) is viviparous ; it breeds in spring but the young are not born until August or September. They are carried to full term within an egg-membrane. The dwarf chameleon (*Chamaeleon pumilus*) is similarly

[1] The common Mediterranean tortoise, *Testudo graeca*, is especially active in May, often traversing long distances. This occurs when the gonads are presumably most developed but the animal never actually breeds in England. That its habits are regulated by the seasons is obvious ; nevertheless, it must have an internal rhythm, for an individual in my possession will bury itself in preparation for hibernation regularly on or about October 7, even though the environmental temperature may be higher than it was some weeks previously, or higher than when the tortoise emerged in the spring.

viviparous. There are other viviparous species in which the young are born fully formed and without egg-membranes after a gestation of approximately three months (Weekes, 1934; this paper contains further references). It would appear that there are all gradations in lizards between oviparity and viviparity and that the seasons of parturition vary accordingly. Furthermore, among the Ophidia, the adder (*Vipera berus*) has a spring breeding season but carries its young until August or September. Most of the Viperidae and some other ophidians are similar. The other two species of British snakes, the ring-snake (*Tropidonotus natrix*) and the smooth-snake (*Coronella laevis*) are oviparous like most ophidians, depositing their eggs in the spring or summer (*see* below, Chapter 3, p. 198). The same is true of the majority of reptiles. The eggs usually take several months to hatch and in the tortoise (*Emys orbicularis*) the hatching is postponed until the next spring (Gadow, 1901).

Weekes (1935) suggests that the habit of viviparity among reptiles has been evolved in cases where owing either to cold or desiccation resulting from extreme heat, development cannot readily occur outside the body. Thus, it is usual in lizards at high altitudes (above 4,000 feet) and in the hot inland plains of Australia.

Some reptiles undertake periodic breeding migrations and the evidence on this subject has been summarised by Heape (1931). Thus, the hawkbill turtle in the Island of Ascension may migrate 800 miles. The leathery turtle also migrates every year in the spring for purposes of breeding.

XVI. Aves

It would appear almost superfluous to cite examples of sexual periodicity among birds. That spring and summer are the seasons when most birds pair, build their nests, and incubate their eggs, and that these processes are wont to vary slightly with the characters of the season, are facts that are familiar to all.[1] Bird-fanciers know also that the capacity of certain birds for egg-laying may be influenced by diet, and that this capacity can sometimes be increased, e.g. in the common fowl, by the supply of suitable food (Wright, 1902). However, in the domestic fowl the production of eggs is largely influenced by the season of the year, the maximum production taking place in the months of March and April and the minimum in October and November. Whetham (1933) has brought forward statistical evidence that light is an important factor (*see* Chapter 13). In very high producing strains Pearl and Surface (1911) found that there is an additional egg-laying season in the autumn months. Buckley (1917) found in the south of England that maximum production occurred in March and April, whereas in places where the spring is later the maximum is not attained so soon.

---

[1] Baker (1938a) has published tables of the egg-seasons of all the principal old-world birds, together with their respective latitudes and the countries inhabited by them. In an earlier paper, Baker and Baker (1931) have recorded that the blackbird breeds earlier in the south of England (March) than in the north of Scotland (mid-April). They conclude that the effect of light on the reproductive processes (*see* below) must have existed before the equinox when the days were longer in the south. For an account of the breeding seasons of southern hemisphere birds in the northern hemisphere *see* Baker and Ranson (1938) who show that whereas most species adapt themselves and change their rhythm after importation, a few appear to maintain their original rhythm (*see* below, Chapter 13). These papers give very full references.

Moreover, it is well known that the time of greatest production is earlier if the birds are given shelter (Simpson, 1912). Those and similar facts have long been recognised, but it is only comparatively lately that an attempt has been made to put the subject on a proper scientific basis.

The factors controlling breeding periodicity in birds generally and the important part played by light in regulating the cycle will be discussed at some length in a later chapter (Chapter 13). It may be said at once, however, that there is a great species variation, and that in addition to light, ecological factors such as rain, droughts, temperature, suitable food, the existence of an appropriate nesting site, etc., may play very important or essential parts with wild birds as well as domestic ones. In some species where there is no appreciable variation in light, breeding phenomena still show an apparently " inherent " rhythm which is, nevertheless, usually brought into relation with seasonal environmental change. The whole subject is discussed by Baker (1938b) who gives numerous instances of the different kinds of stimuli to which birds and other animals of different kinds respond in the course of their sexual cycles. Baker remarks further that some birds will not breed at all in the absence of the appropriate factor ; thus, the cockatoo may miss a season altogether if it is dry. Conversely, many African birds breed whenever the rains start, and the same is true of some species of birds in other parts of the world (e.g. Indian ducks, rails, egrets, etc.).

Archer also remarks that the breeding season of birds in tropical Africa is normally governed by the rains (Archer and Godman, 1937). In British Somaliland, a semi-arid region,

" there are in fact two well-defined breeding seasons—the one beginning . . . in April and May and continuing until June and even early July, and the other beginning directly after the fall of the small rains, called the *dair*, in October. Even in the interim period of late July birds are apt to breed sporadically, and the sea-birds breed from July to September in the Gulf of Aden. Thus, it comes about that I have found eggs in British Somaliland in every month of the year."

The vultures and great birds of prey nest after the *dair* rains throughout the cold weather months, and October may be regarded as the opening of the oölogical year. Size would seem to predispose to early breeding. The bateleur and martial eagles are the first, and then follow the three great vultures, the African white-backed, the Nubian and the white-headed vultures. The common vulture, the Abyssinian tawny eagle and Verreaux's eagle-owl come next, and by December which is the height of the cold weather season, the serpent eagle, Verreaux's eagle, the osprey and the goliath heron lay their eggs. The last of the big raptorial birds to lay is the African hawk-eagle and about the same time—in the second half of January—the white Egyptian vulture also breeds. The falcons, buzzards, goshawks and smaller eagle-owls breed during the transition period which succeeds. Thus the chanting goshawk, the Somali buzzard, and the Abyssinian spotted eagle-owl lay their eggs in the second half of March, the Gabar goshawk, the Eritrean shikra and the lanner in April, and the kestrels in May and June. However, by mid-April the main breeding season of the year has begun and from this time onwards to June some 150 species are in full sexual activity (Archer and Godman, 1937). These remarks further illustrate the general truth that with birds generally spring is the main breeding season, but that the different species respond to special local or ecological stimuli, each according to its kind, so that although all the birds of the area show a definite cyclical periodicity, nevertheless, in Somaliland as in many other regions, especially in the sub-tropics and tropics, there is no time of the year when eggs of some birds may not be found. (*See also* Chapter 13, where the subject is further elaborated.[1])

The evidence relating to the general question as to the relation between latitude and breeding seasons in birds has been recently summarised by Baker (1938c), whose paper contains diagrammatic figures illustrating the seasonal changes of various groups with much valuable information. His general conclusions are quoted at length in a later chapter (Chapter 13).

With the approach of the breeding season the genital organs grow enormously until the whole oviduct reaches a state of hypertrophic turgescence. Gadow (1893–96) states that in the common fowl the oviduct at the period of rest is only six or seven inches long and scarcely a line wide, but that at the time of egg-laying it becomes more than two feet in length and nearly half an inch in width, thus increasing the volume about fifty times. This remarkable growth occurs annually. Gadow remarks also that the testes of the house sparrow increase from the size of mustard seeds to that of small cherries, and in so doing temporarily displace the usual arrangement of the viscera in the body cavity. Disselhorst (1908), too, has called attention to the enormous increase in size and weight of the testicles and ovaries in many birds (and also in some mammals) in the breeding season. Thus, in *Fringilla*, the testicles may increase three-hundredfold. Watson (1919) states that in the greenfinch the testes are largest and most active in May, and that after the breeding season they diminish.[2] Bissonnette (1930a and b) made similar observations on the starling. The testes were found to be smallest in November and December and largest in the second half of April.

The ovary undergoes comparable seasonal changes in size and condition, growth taking place from December to the end of April when ovulation may occur (Bissonnette and Zujko, 1936). It is thus seen that there is a well marked gonadal cycle in birds and that this, at any rate in most species, is correlated with the changes of the seasons. For brief accounts of the histological changes in the gonads *see* Chapter 3, p. 204, and for further details as to the phases of the sexual cycle in birds *see* Chapter 13.

A very large number of birds seasonally migrate, and this habit, as in the case of the migratory fish already referred to, is closely associated with the function of breeding. For much of the information given here regarding migration, I am indebted to the late Dr. Eagle Clarke. Jenner (1824) showed long ago that migration was invariably associated with an increase in size of the ovaries and testes, and that when these begin to shrink, after discharging their functions, the birds take their departure. *See also* John Hunter (1786). Thus the ovaries of the cuckoo are stated to be almost atrophied in July. It would seem probable that the annual development of the sexual organs is the immediate stimulus which, in the individual,

---

[1] Moreau (1936) states that in the evergreen forest of East Africa the birds nest between the beginning of October and the end of February and then moult.

[2] Baumgartner (1938) found that in the American tree sparrow (*Spizella arbreca*) the maximal development of the male gonad was in April and that of the female gonad was in June ; regression in both set in in July.

fixes the time for the spring migration, for it is known that in birds passing north-ward the ovaries and testes are well developed. (But cf. fishes, p. 15.) Thus wading birds, such as the sanderling shot by Dr. Eagle Clarke at Spurn Head, in May, were found by him to have their sexual organs in a very advanced state of growth. These birds were probably on their way to Greenland or Siberia. (Cf. Chapman, 1894, and Eagle Clarke, 1912.) Moreover, experiments by Rowan (1926, 1930), to be described later, in which he subjected migratory finches (juncos) to ad-ditional illumination in winter and found that the resulting growth of the gonads was associated with a migratory tendency supply evidence of a functional correlation such as that postulated. The evidence, however, is not quite clear, for some birds, but not all, which migrate north over the equator, have been thought to start their journey with the gonads still undeveloped. The subject is referred to again when the exteroceptive stimuli concerned in periodic breeding are more fully discussed (Chapter 13).

Schäfer (1907) already had suggested that the migratory impulse is determined by the relation of daylight to darkness, having been brought into being through the agency of natural selection, in consequence of the necessity to most birds of daylight for the procuring of food. This hypothesis explains both the northerly migration in spring and the southerly migration in autumn, since at both times the birds are travelling in the direction of increased light (or, if they start before the equinox, towards regions where they will enjoy longer daylight later in the season). The conception that the time of the spring migration is determined in each individual by a stimulus set up by the growing genital organs (or at any rate by the cyclical changes in them) is in no way opposed to Schäfer's theory, which provides an explanation of the general fact of migration.

It has been noted that the northerly spring migration is far more hurried than the somewhat leisurely autumn migration in the reverse direction. Further-more, although the north-south migratory movements are as a rule extraordinarily regular, it has been observed that the birds do not all set out together, and that the times of departure and arrival for each species may vary in any one year by several weeks. Moreover, golden plovers are found migrating across Britain on their way northward (perhaps to Iceland) at a time when other individuals of the same species are rearing young in Britain. (The breeding season in Iceland is about a month or six weeks later than in Britain.) In view of these facts it is evident that the occurrence of the migratory movement is dependent not merely upon external or environmental influences, but also upon internal or individual ones, and, as already stated, it is not improbable that one of the factors involved is the state of development of the organs of generation or the stage of the sexual cycle.

Many birds are double-brooded, having young ones not only in spring, but also in autumn before the close of the mild weather (in temperate climates). Swifts are stated sometimes to have a second brood in southern Europe after leaving Britain in August, and the same is said to be the case with nightingales. Wiltshire (1883) mentions that a pair of swifts that stayed behind the others, had a brood in September, which migrated with the parent birds in October. Whether birds are single- or double-brooded probably depends to a large extent upon the duration of the period of incubation. This period in wading birds and sea-birds is approximately double that of passerine birds ; but, within the limits of the group to which they belong, it is closely related to the size of the birds, the size of the egg, and the temperature of the bird (Bergtold, 1917). Thus the incubation period of the stormy petrel is thirty days ; that of the starling is twelve or thirteen days ; while that of the raven (the largest passerine bird) is about twenty days. The starling, is at any rate, very often double-brooded, while the petrel and the raven are single-brooded. For details concerning numbers of broods, incubation periods, numbers of eggs, and breeding seasons of British birds, *see* Jourdain in Witherby's *Handbook* (1938–41). For incubation periods of many different species, *see also* Needham (1931), and for relations between the sizes of the eggs and the incubation periods in many species, *see* Brokeworth (1940). Nethersole-Thompson (1942) shows that in some birds (long-tailed tit, tree creeper, gold-crest, sedge warbler and reed bunting) two eggs may be laid in one day. Ryves (1943) shows that whereas in some birds incubation begins with the laying of the first egg, with others it begins with the last, and there may be a month between the completion of the nest and the laying of the first egg (song thrush, robin). Roberts (1940) states that in Wilson's petrel and other Turbinares the ovary can only produce one egg in a year, so if this is taken it cannot be replaced. For African birds *see* Bannerman (1930–39) and Moreau and Moreau (1940). Other birds, such as the sparrow and chaffinch are often treble-brooded. It is, of course, well known that domestication tends to increase the number of broods which a bird may produce, e.g. in pigeons and poultry. In some cases, however, domestication has had the opposite effect, e.g. those breeds of poultry such ast he non-sitting breeds which produce large numbers of eggs but have lost the power of brooding them. Broodiness in fowls is most frequent in spring and summer, the time of greatest egg production, and is usually associated with warmth.

The egg-cycle of the fowl.—The general habit of *Gallus bankiva* when kept in captivity in this country is to lay a clutch of a dozen or so eggs in late spring or early summer, which she then hatches out. This is the usual habit, too, of the general run of fancy breeds, where there has been no selection for egg production. In some, however, the hens usually do not go broody. Punnett (1923) experimenting with Sebrights and Hamburghs and their crosses did not observe any broodiness even when the hens were kept till they were two or three years old. In these experiments the eggs were removed from the nests every day. But Punnett records the interesting observations that in two cases where the eggs were left in the nests the hens went broody, hatched, and reared chicks. It is not known, however, how far Punnett's case is of general application to non-broody breeds of poultry ; it is, however, in line with what is known to occur in various species of wild birds if treated similarly (*see* Chapter 13).

Harland (1927) has compared the egg records of primitive jungle fowl with those of domesticated poultry under tropical conditions in Trinidad. There, at any rate, most of the native hens gave fairly definite indications of rhythm in egg production ; a clutch of about twelve eggs was laid, after which the bird went broody, the period of the cycle being about one month and the cycle being repeated about eight times in the year. After long pauses two or three clutches were found to follow one another without a broody interval. The domesticated poultry recorded by Harland (1927) at Trinidad showed no sign of the clutch habit.

In temperate zones, season and moulting exercise the predominant control. Chicks normally hatched in late spring and early summer begin to lay in winter and early spring, and continue in lay till the oncome of the moult in the autumn. This seasonal effect is often referred to in American literature as the egg-cycle ; but it should not be confused with the clutch habit discussed above.

This American school (Goodale, 1918a ; Hays and Sanborn, 1927 ; Atwood, 1929) maintain that in ordinary laying hens, the clutch size is a definite trait, giving to egg records a rhythmic character.   The actual records of individual hens show that the good, steady egg-producer tends to lay, throughout the season, on three consecutive days out of four, or on four out of five, and so on ; the bad layer, on the other hand, shows no such regularity.   This makes it doubtful if there is any homology between the clutch habit described by Harland and the clutch size noted by the American worker.   Moreover, Warren (1930) has shown that the actual time between the laying of consecutive eggs by a particular hen is usually more than twenty-four hours.   Thus, on successive days she tends to lay her egg later and later, till finally she skips a whole day, beginning again in the early morning—for the domesticated hen, even to-day, does not lay during the hours when her wild prototype would normally perch in the trees.   Thus, the characteristic clutch size described by the American workers is, in fact, a measure of the time interval between successive eggs rather than any manifestation of alternating activity and pause in the ovaries.   Voitellier (1931) in France, and Dudley (1931) in this country, from a statistical treatment of laying scores, also incline against the view that there is any rhythm in egg production.

Pearl (Goodale, 1918b) pointed out some years ago that the interval between successive eggs was probably characteristic of the functioning ovary, for non-laying hens were often found to visit the nests as regularly as their normal sisters.   In such cases autopsies usually revealed normally functioning ovaries, so that there was generally present some abnormality of the infundibulum, so that the eggs escaped into the body cavity.

Whatever may be the case in wild fowls, there is, therefore, no critical evidence for the existence of an egg-cycle, *sensu strictiori*, in domestic poultry.[1]

XVII. Mammalia

The breeding season in the Mammalia, and the variations in its periodicity, are discussed at some length in the fourth chapter.   Here it will suffice to point out that the occurrence of breeding in any one country or locality is closely connected with the climatic conditions and the periodicity of the seasons in that country, this rule holding for the Mammalia even more closely than for some other groups.   Thus, species which are transferred by the agency of man from one country to a new one or from one hemisphere to the other soon become adjusted to the reversed or altered seasons of the part of the world to which they have been brought.   This phenomenon is well shown by the domestic animals as well as by wild ones as a result of acclimatisation.   Nevertheless, individual animals may tend to keep their internal sexual rhythm for a year or two before becoming adjusted to the conditions of a new country.   In certain cases, however, the stimuli necessary for breeding may not exist and the strain may almost at

[1] *See also* Pearl (1914), Harris and Blakeslee (1918), Dryden (1921) and Lerner and Taylor (1937).   These papers contain numerous further references

once die out. It has been already noted that some mammals refuse to breed in captivity, while in many others the occurrence of breeding can be regulated by such factors as accommodation, lighting, heating and feeding. Also, in certain domestic animals such as the sheep, the condition of " heat " can be induced more readily by the supply of additional or special kinds of food.[1] The part played by external factors in regulating sexual periodicity and their probable modes of action are dealt with below (Chapter 13).

XVIII. Phenomena Associated with Breeding

The approach of the breeding season in many animals, if not in most, is marked by a display of greater vitality, as manifested by an increased activity, which relates not merely to the sexual organs but to the whole metabolism of the body. This enhanced vitality is, as a rule, maintained throughout the breeding season. Thus, male birds at the time of pairing are in a state of the most perfect development, and possess an enormous store of superabundant energy. Under the influence of sexual excitement they perform strange antics or rapid flights which according to Wallace, probably result as much from an internal impulse to exertion as from any desire to please their mates. Such, for example, are the rapid descent of the snipe, the soaring and singing of the lark, the strange love-antics of the albatross, and the dances of the cock-of-the-rock, and of many other birds (Wallace, 1870). The migratory impulse, which, as already mentioned, is closely associated with the periodic growth of the sexual organs, may also very possibly be regarded as affording evidence of increased vitality at the approach of the breeding season. Moreover, many of the secondary sexual characters, both those of the embellishing kind and others as well, are developed during only a part of the year, which is generally the period of breeding. Such characters, however, may possess a special significance. (*See* Chapter 13 and cf. Amphibia, Pycraft, 1913.)

A familiar example of this correspondence between the development of secondary sexual characters and the activity of the reproductive organs is supplied by the growth of the antlers in stags. At the time of rut, which in the red deer (*Cervus elaphus*) begins in September or October, the antlers, or branched outgrowths from the frontal bones, are completely developed, having shed their " velvet " or covering of vascular skin. The animals during this season are in a state of constant sexual excitement, and fight one another with their antlers for the possession of the hinds. The larynx also is said to enlarge at this season, when the stag is wont to utter a loud bellowing noise. By the end of the year the fighting and excitement have ceased and the stags begin once more to herd together peaceably and apart from the females. Shortly afterwards the antlers are shed. In most parts of Britain this occurs about April, but a Highland stag has been known to drop his antlers as soon after the rutting season as December, while, on the other hand, some immature animals in the Lake District are said to carry them until May. After the shedding of the antlers new ones begin to grow from the pedicles, the growth taking place chiefly in July and August. When the new antlers have reached their full development the " velvet " is shed

---

[1] This point is referred to more fully in Chapter 21, where the causes which influence fertility are discussed.

(about the beginning of September). The size of the antlers, and the number of branches or " points," go on increasing every year throughout the reproductive period of the stag's life and until he begins to decline with old age (Cunningham, 1900).

In the American prongbuck (*Antilocapra americana*), which is unique among hollow-horned ruminants in shedding the horns every year, the shedding follows the rutting season more closely than in the stag. The rutting in this species begins in September and lasts about six weeks. In old bucks the horns are shed in October, while the new growth is not completed until July or August in the following year (Cunningham, 1900).

A secondary sexual character comparable to the antlers of deer occurs in the male salmon, in which the tip of the lower jaw, during the breeding season, is turned up and enlarged, as if to protect the fish in fighting when charged by another male (Darwin, 1871).

In *Polypterus* during the breeding season, the anal fin of the male becomes greatly enlarged and thickened, and has its surface thrown into folds between the fin-rays (cf. fin development in the lamprey, p. 15). The object of this modification is not known (Budgett, 1901).

The papillae on the hind limbs of the breeding male *Lepidosiren* are structures which seem to possess a special significance, since Kerr (1900) has shown that they probably serve as accessory organs of respiration. During the greater part of the year they are relatively inconspicuous, but as soon as the animal is set free at the beginning of the wet season, they begin to grow with remarkable rapidity, forming slender filaments two or three inches in length and blood-red in colour from their intense vascularity. After the breeding season is over the filaments commence to atrophy, and eventually shrink to their former size, but still present for some time a distinctive appearance owing to their being crowded with black pigment-cells. Whatever may be the precise purpose of this curious modification it is certain that its development is associated with reproductive activity, and so may be regarded as an expression of the intense vitality which the organism exhibits at this period.

Fishes quite often exhibit in the breeding season a particularly vivid coloration which is absent from them at other times. The case of the male dragonet (*Callionymus lyra*), which becomes a brilliant blue-and-yellow colour, has been discussed at some length by Cunningham (1900) who concludes that the production of the guanin and pigment that give rise to the colour is to be connected with the intense nervous excitement which affects the fish at the time of courtship.

" Physiological processes are known to be governed largely by nervous impulses, and not merely the circulation, but the excretory activity of the skin, are known to be influenced by nervous action. Pigment and guanin are produced in the skin by the secretory or excretory activity of the living cells." (Cunningham, 1900.)

Whatever be the precise explanation of this particular instance of intenser coloration, there is evidence that it is associated with a more active metabolism.

The brilliant colours of the male lump-sucker (*Cyclopterus lumpus*), and of other fish [1] at the time of breeding, are probably due to the same causes as in the

---

[1] Numerous instances are given by Darwin (1871) both for fishes and amphibians. The crests and frills and vivid coloration of breeding newts are familiar examples of this kind of phenomenon (Pycraft, 1913).

dragonet. Nevertheless, as with comparable characters in other animals, they may have a functional significance as stimulating organs acting upon the other sex.

The nuptial changes which occur in fishes are not necessarily in the direction of increased brilliance of coloration. Newbigin (1898) describes these changes in the salmon as follows :

" When the fish comes from the sea the skin is of a bright silvery hue, while the flesh has the familiar strong pink colour. The small ovaries are of a yellow-brown colour. As the reproductive organs develop during the passage up the river, certain definite colour-changes occur. The skin loses its bright silvery colour, and, more especially in the male, becomes a ruddy-brown hue. At the same time the flesh becomes paler and paler, and in the female the rapidly growing ovaries acquire a fine orange-red colour. The testes in the male remain a creamy white. After spawning the skin tends, in both sexes, to lose its ruddy colour and to regain the bright silvery tint ; the flesh, however, remains pale until the kelt has revisited the sea."

Barrett-Hamilton (1900, 1902) draws attention to many such sexual phenomena, and more especially to those occurring in the spawning season in certain salmonoid fishes of the genus *Onchorhynchus*. The fish undergo extraordinary changes in colour and shape, and, since they die when spawning is accomplished, it is argued that the changes cannot have any aesthetic significance, but represent a pathological condition in which the fish become continually more feeble and eventually succumb.

The tail of the lyre-bird, which is shed at the end of the breeding season, not to be renewed again in the same form until the following summer, the brilliant plumage of the breeding drake, the more intense colouring of the phalarope, and many other birds during the season of courtship, are familiar instances of the same kind of phenomena. Beebe (1908) describes an experiment in which certain tanagers and bobolinks, which had been prevented from breeding, were kept throughout the winter in a darkened chamber with a somewhat increased food-supply. As a consequence the nuptial plumage was retained until the spring, when the birds were returned to normal conditions. They shortly afterwards moulted. The breeding plumage was then renewed, so that in this case the dull winter plumage was never acquired. The remarkable plate of horn which is developed in the upper mandible of the pelican in the breeding season, and bodily shed at the end of it, and the " gular pouch " in the throat of the breeding bustard, are examples of a more special kind, the existence of which, however, must be connected, either directly or indirectly, with the contemporaneous increase of sexual activity.

With birds, however, the assumption of the most perfect male plumage is not necessarily synchronous with the period of enhanced vitality. Thus Grinnell (1911) says that in the linnet " the brilliant hue of the nuptial dress " is acquired in August, or several weeks after the season of mating, instead of immediately preceding it, and so is not directly associated with excessive sexual vigour. There is only one moult annually and no pre-nuptial moult, but a progressive increase in coloration up to and beyond the breeding season. The assumption of plumage by birds (ducks, bullfinches, etc.) in the autumn and long before the breeding season may be due to the time of moult. Patten (1911) has shown that in the sanderling there is a pre-nuptial plumage closely resembling the plumage of the sexually mature bird, but preceding the enlargement of the gonads. The usual meaning of adornment and sexual display in birds and other vertebrates is discussed below in Chapter 13.

A species of oriental squirrel (*Sciurus caniceps*) assumes, during the breeding season, a brilliant orange-yellow coat which is in striking contrast to the dull grey coat worn during the rest of the year. This ornamental coat is probably comparable to the bright breeding plumage of birds, but is almost or quite unique among mammals (Flower and Lydekker, 1891).

In some animals certain glandular organs, apart from those concerned in the reproductive processes, show a special activity at the breeding season. For example, in the swiftlets (*Collocalia*) the salivary glands become peculiarly active, and secrete a substance which is allied to mucin, and is employed in building the edible birds' nests of Chinese epicures (Geddes and Thomson, 1901).

A somewhat similar peculiarity exists in the male of the sea-stickleback (*Gasterosteus spinachia*), which binds together the weeds forming its nest by means of a whitish thread, secreted by the kidneys, and produced only during the breeding season (*see* above, p. 172). The male gets rid of the thread-like secretion by rubbing itself against objects, and thus, by an almost mechanical process, the weaving habit is supposed to have become evolved.

During the breeding season the anal scent-glands of snakes are said to be actively functional, but not at other times. A similar fact is stated about the submaxillary glands of crocodiles, and the cloacal glands of tortoises and other reptiles (Laycock, 1840 ; Owen, 1866). The secretions of these glands, like the musk glands of mammals probably serve the purpose of enabling the sexes to detect one another's presence more easily, but they may also serve as excitants in connection with pairing since they are usually only produced during the season of rut (Pycraft, 1913).

XIX. PERIODICITY

The subject of sexual periodicity and the factors which control it are dealt with in greater detail later in this book. Here in this introductory chapter the general principles governing the phenomenon may be briefly enunciated and a few further references to the older authors may be made. That the occurrence of cyclical rhythm is a marked feature of living organisms, and not merely in relation to sexual change, was well appreciated by Semper (1881) whose general study of the subject is still well worthy of attention. This author concluded that the phenomenon in question is dependent on the extremes of summer and winter temperature to which the animals are exposed.

" Every individual requires a certain duration of life to achieve its individual development from the egg to sexual maturity and full growth ; the length of time requisite for this is very various, and, above all, bears no proportion to the size attained. . . . This length of time, which we may generally designate as the period of individual growth, is not alike even for all the individuals of the same species ; on the contrary, it depends on the co-operation of so many different factors that it must necessarily vary considerably. Now, if from any cause the period of individual growth, say of the salmon, become changed in consequence of the slower development of the embryo in the egg or of the young larvae, most of all the young salmon thus affected would die in our climate, because the greater heat of spring is injurious to them at that stage."

In a similar way it may be argued that the periodicity of the breeding season, no less than the rate of growth, is governed by the necessities of the young. No doubt this is largely true, yet it is equally evident, as has been shown above in numerous instances, that this periodicity is greatly affected by climatic and environmental changes, and also by stimuli of a more particular nature (cf. frogs, p. 20). But this power, which all animals in some degree possess, of responding to altered conditions, may none the less have arisen primarily to meet the requirements of the next generation; or, to speak more accurately, that those animals which breed at a certain particular season (or in response to certain conditions which prevail at that season) have the advantage in being able to produce a new generation to which this capacity to respond similarly will be transmitted. In other words, the restriction of the breeding habit to certain seasons may have been brought about under the influence of natural selection to meet the necessities of the offspring. Westermarck (1921) says it is " obvious that the sexual functions are, at least to some extent, affected by different conditions in different species. This is shown by the fact that every month or season of the year is the pairing time of one or another species of mammals." He goes on to cite examples. Moreover, he points out that while the Adélie penguin rears its young in the warmest and lightest months, the giant emperor penguin does this in the dark season, so that the young birds may be fostered by their parents until the warm weather, and have the whole summer in which to change their plumage (Levick, 1914). Westermarck points out also that where the conditions amid which certain animals live are fairly uniform throughout the year there may be no sexual season. He instances the whale, the elephant, and the birds of the Galapagos Islands which are situated very near the equator. Nevertheless, even in tropical regions, as pointed out by Baker (1929), sexual periodicity is far commoner than was formerly suspected. (*See* above, p. 25, and Chapter 13, below.) The teleological problem as to purpose is, however, one matter; the question as to cause in the individual animals is quite another, and the two problems must not be confused.

Heape (1900) objected to the view that the restricted breeding seasons in mammals at any rate have been brought about owing to their increased survival value to the off-spring on the ground that there is a period of gestation of greatly varying length in the different species. If the theory were correct, why, he asks, do some bats experience a breeding season in the autumn, and not produce young until the following June, although only two months are required for the development of the embryo in these animals; why do roe-deer in Germany breed in autumn, while the embryo does not develop beyond the segmentation stage until the following spring; and why does the seal take eleven or twelve months for gestation when a large dog requires only nine weeks? Heape believed that the recurrence of the breeding season is governed directly by climatic, individual, and maternal influences, and that " variation in the rate of development of the embryo, in the length of gestation, and in the powers of nursing, are quite sufficient to provide for the launching of the young at a favourable time of the year." Under the heading of " individual influences " Heape includes special nervous, vascular, and secretory peculiarities of the individual and its habits of life. The length of the gestation and lactation periods he calls " maternal influences."

I cannot altogether concur with Heape's view of this question. For it seems to me that whereas the necessities of the offspring, under changed environmental conditions, may sometimes have been provided for by modifications in the rate of development or length of gestation, yet in other cases a similar result may have been effected by alterations in the season of breeding. The mere fact that breeding in any one species occurs, as a rule, periodically at a time which is on the whole well suited to the requirements of perpetuating the race, is itself presumptive evidence that the periodicity of the breeding season is controlled (through natural selection) by the needs of the next generation. Flattely and Walton (1922) give a number of illustrations of periodicity in generative activity among animals inhabiting the sea-shore, and the tendency to modify chapters of the normal life-history in accordance with special needs, or in response to peculiar environmental conditions. Further, the breeding season having been fixed at one period in the history of the species, the same season would probably be retained (in the absence of disturbing factors) by the descendants of that species under the directive influence of heredity. This view is in no way opposed to the doctrine that the sexual capacity is developed in the individual in response to definite stimuli, which are largely environmental and often seasonal, as in the case of increase of light (*see* Chapter 13).

The occurrence of a succession of " heat " periods within the limits of a single breeding season no doubt arose in consequence of the increased opportunity afforded thereby for successful copulation. The number and frequency of the " heat " periods in these circumstances are affected by the conditions under which an animal lives in just the same kind of way as the periodicity of the breeding season is affected, as will be illustrated in a subsequent chapter on the oestrous cycle in the Mammalia. Concerning the immediate cause of " heat," and the nature of the mechanism by which it is brought about, a good deal will be said later.

The origin of the breeding season is a wider question. For its complete solution, as pointed out by Heape, a comparative study of the sexual phenomena in the lower animals is essential, while, as already remarked, sufficient data for a comprehensive treatment of this subject do not yet exist.

That the breeding season occurs in some animals " as the result of a stimulus which may be effected through the alimentary canal is demonstrated by the effect upon ewes of certain stimulating foods."

" That it is associated with a stimulus which is manifested by exceptional vigour and exceptional bodily ' condition ' is demonstrated by the pugnacity of the males at such times, by the restless activity of the females, by the brilliant colouring of such widely divergent animals as, for instance, annelids, amphibians, birds, and mammals, by the condition of the plumage of birds, and of the pelage or skin of mammals.

" That it is [frequently] associated with nutrition, and that it is a stimulus gradually collected is indicated by the increased frequency of the [breeding] season among domesticated mammals as compared with nearly allied species in the wild state.

" That it is manifested by hypertrophy and by congestion of the mucous tissue of the generative organs, and of various other organs, such as the wattles and combs of birds, the crest of the newt, and by the activity of special glands, the affection of all of which may be exceedingly severe, is true.

" These, and many other similar facts, are well known, but they do not assist in the elucidation of the origin of the function.

" The most they do is to show that the sexual instinct is seasonal, and that nutrition, whether affected by external or internal factors, plays an important part in its manifestation." (Heape, 1900.) [It should be remembered, however, that many animals, such as the salmon, have their breeding season after prolonged fasts.]

The last proposition may be expressed even more generally in the statement, already formulated, that generative activity in animals occurs only as a result of definite stimuli, which are partly external and partly internal, while the precise nature of the necessary stimuli varies considerably in the different kinds of animals according to the species, and still more according to the group to which the species belong.

The quotation cited above is from Walter Heape's paper on the sexual season of mammals published in the year 1900. Since that date an immense amount of work bearing upon the subject has been accomplished, and while there is still much that remains obscure the physiology of the sexual processes has undergone a remarkable development. It is the purpose of the succeeding chapters in this book to give as far as possible a co-ordinated account of what has been ascertained about these processes with a view both to satisfying and stimulating enquiry in this important branch of knowledge.

Bibliography

AGASSIZ, A. (1878). The development of Lepidosteus. *Proc. Amer. Acad. Arts Sci.*, **14**, 65.

AIYAR, R. G., & PANIKKAR, N. K. (1937). Observations on the swarming habits and lunar periodicity of *Platynereis* sp. from the Madras Harbour. *Proc. Ind. Acad. Sci.*, B5, 245.

ALBERTONI, P. (1888). Expériences sur les centres nerveux inhibiteurs du crapaud. *Arch. ital. Biol.*, **9**, 19.

AMIRTHALINGAM, C. (1928). On lunar periodicity in reproduction of *Pecten opercularis* near Plymouth in 1927–28. *J. Mar. biol. Ass., U.K.*, **15**, 605.

ANNANDALE, N. (1903). *Fasciculi Malayenses.* Liverpool.

—— (1906). The common hydra of Bengal : its systematic position and life history. *Mem. Asiat. Soc. Beng.*, **1**, 339.

ANONYMOUS (1906). *Countryside*, Oct. 27.

ARCHER, G. F., & GODMAN, E. M. (1937). *The birds of British Somaliland and the Gulf of Aden ; Their life histories, breeding habits and eggs.* London.

ASHWORTH, J. H. (1899). The structure of *Xenia hicksoni* nov. sp., with some observations on *Heteroxenia Elizabethae Kölliker*. *Quart. J. micr. Sci.*, **42**, 245.

—— & ANNANDALE, N. (1904). Observations on some aged specimens of *Sagartia troglodytes*, and on the duration of life in coelenterates. *Proc. Roy. Soc. Edinb.*, **25**, 295.

ATWOOD, H. (1929). Observations concerning the time factor in egg production. *Poult. Sci.*, **8**, 137.

BAKER, J. R. (1929). *Man and animals in the New Hebrides.* London.

—— (1938a). Latitude and egg-seasons in Old-World birds. *Tabul. biol., Berl.*, **15**, 333.

—— (1938b). The evolution of breeding seasons. *Evolution.* Essays on evolutionary biology—presented to Prof. E. S. Goodrich. Ed. by G. R. de Beer. Oxford.

—— (1938c). The relation between latitude and breeding seasons in birds. *Proc. zool. Soc. Lond.*, **108**, 557.

—— & BAKER, I. (1931). The breeding season of the blackbird (*Turdus merula* Linn.). *Proc. zool. Soc. Lond.*, **101**, 661.

—— & RANSON, R. M. (1938). The breeding seasons of southern hemisphere birds in the northern hemisphere. *Proc. zool. Soc. Lond.*, **108**, 101.

BANNERMAN, D. A. (1930–1939). *The birds of Tropical West Africa.* 5 vols. London.

BARNES, H. F. (1930). On some factors governing the emergence of gall midges. *Proc. zool. Soc. Lond.*, **100**, 381.

—— (1932). Periodic fluctuations in the prevalence of the wheat blossom midges. *J. Anim. Ecol.*, **1**, 191.

—— (1934). Sudden outbreaks of insect pests. *J. S.-E. agric. Coll. Wye*, **34**, 260.

—— (1935a). Studies of fluctuations in insect populations. 5. The leaf-curling pear midge *Dasyneura pyri* (Cecidomyidae). *J. Anim. Ecol.*, **4**, 244.

—— (1935b). Studies of fluctuations in insect populations. 6. Discussion on results. *J. Anim. Ecol.*, **4**, 254.

BARRETT-HAMILTON, G. E. H. (1900). A suggestion as to a possible mode of origin of some of the secondary sexual characters in animals as afforded by observations on certain salmonids. *Proc. Camb. phil. Soc.*, **10**, 279.

—— (1902). Investigations upon the life-history of salmon, and their bearing on the phenomena of nuptial and sexual ornamentation and development in the animal kingdom generally. *Ann. Mag. nat. Hist.*, **9**, 106.

BAUMGARTNER, A. M. (1938). Seasonal variation in the tree sparrow. *Auk*, **55**, 603.

BEAUCHAMP, R. S. A. (1933). Rheotaxis in *Planaria alpina*. *J. exp. Biol.*, **10**, 113.

—— (1935). The rate of movement of *Planaria alpina*. *J. exp. Biol.*, **12**, 271.

—— (1937). Rate of movement and rheotaxis in *Planaria alpina*. *J. exp. Biol.*, **14**, 104.

BEEBE, C. W. (1908). Preliminary report on an investigation of the season changes of colour in birds. *Amer. Nat.*, **42**, 34.

BENHAM, W. B. (1933). Biological notes. *Rep. Fish., N.Z.*

—— (1934). Biological notes. *Rep. Fish., N.Z.*

BERG, K. (1934). Cyclical reproduction, sex determination and depression in the *Cladocera*. *Biol. Rev.*, **9**, 139.

—— (1936). Reproduction and depression in the *Cladocera*. *Arch. hydrobiol. Plankt.*, **30**, 438.

BERGTOLD, W. H. (1917). *A study of the incubation period of birds.* Denver.

BERK, L. (1938). Studies in the reproduction of *Xenopus laevis*. I. The relation of external environmental factors to the sexual cycle. *S. Afr. J. med. Sci.*, **3**, 72.

BISSONNETTE, T. H. (1930a). Studies on the sexual cycle in birds. 2. The normal progressive changes in the testes from November to May in the European starling. *Amer. J. Anat.*, **45**, 307.

—— (1930b). Studies on the sexual cycle in birds. 3. The normal regressive changes in the testes of the European starling (*Sturnus vulgaris*). *Amer. J. Anat.*, **46**, 477.

—— & ZUJKO, A. J. (1936). Normal progressive changes in the ovary of the starling (*Sturnus vulgaris*), from December to April. *Auk*, **53**, 31.

BLES, E. J. (1905). The life history of *Xenopus laevis*. *Trans. Roy. Soc. Edinb.*, **41**, 31, 789.

BOURNE, G. C. (1900). The Ctenophora. *A treatise on zoology*, **2**. London.

BRIDGE, T. W. (1905). Fishes. *Cambridge Natural History*, **7**. London.

BROKEWORTH, C. (1940). Egg volumes and incubation periods. *Auk*, **57**, 44.

BUCKLEY, W. (1917). *Farm records and the production of clean milk at Monadsmere.* London.

BUDGETT, J. S. (1901). On the breeding habits of some West African fishes. *Trans. zool. Soc. Lond.*, **16**, 115.

CAHN, A. R. (1927). An ecological study of Southern Wisconsin fishes. *Illinois Biol. Monogr.*, **11.**

CALDERWOOD, W. L. (1927). Atlantic salmon in New Zealand. *Salm. Trout Mag.*, July.

CALKINS, G. N. (1906). The protozoan life-cycle. *Biol. Bull. Wood's Hole*, **11**, 229.

CALMAN, W. T. (1911). *The life of Crustacea.* London.

CHADWICK, H. C. (1900). Echinus. *Liverpool Marine Biological Committee Memoirs*, **3.**

CHAPMAN, F. M. (1894). Remarks on the origin of bird migration. *Auk*, **11**, 12.

CHILD, C. M. (1901). The habits and natural history of *Stychostemma*. *Amer. Nat.*, **35**, 975.

CLARKE, W. E. (1912). *Studies in bird migration*, **1**. London.

COOK, A. H. (1895). Mollusca. *Cambridge Natural History*, **3**. London.

COUCH, J. (1862). *A history of the fishes of the British Isles*, **1**. London.

CRAIG-BENNETT, A. (1931). The reproductive cycle of the three-spined stickleback. *Philos. Trans.* B, **219**, 197.

CUNNINGHAM, J. T. (1900). *Sexual dimorphism*. London.

DARWIN, C. (1871). *Descent of man and selection in relation to sex*. London.

—— (1905). *Variation of animals and plants*, **2**. London.

DEAN, BASHFORD (1895). The early development of *Amia*. *Quart. J. micr. Sci.*, **38**, 413.

DISSELHORST, R. (1908). Gewichts- und Volumszunahmen der männlichen Keimdrüsen bei Vögeln und Saugern in der Paarungszeit. *Anat. Anz.*, **32**, 113.

DRYDEN, J. (1921). Egg-laying characteristics of the hen. *Bull. Ore. agric. Exp. Sta.*, No. 180.

DUDLEY, F. J. (1931). Short period trapnesting as a means of estimating annual egg production and average annual egg weight. *Harper Adams Util. Poult. J.*, **16**, 557.

ELMHIRST, R. (1922). Habits of *Echinus esculentus*. *Nature, Lond.*, **110**, 667.

FAGE, L., & LEGENDRE, R. (1925). Essaimages de *Scalibregma inflatum Rathke*, observés pendant des pêches à la lumière. *C.R. Acad. Sci., Paris*, **180**, 1373.

FLATTELY, F. W., & WALTON, C. L. (1922). *Biology of the sea shore*. London.

FLOWER, W. H., & LYDEKKER, R. (1891). *Mammals living and extinct*. London.

FOX, H. M. (1923). Lunar periodicity in reproduction. *Proc. Roy. Soc.* B, **95**, 523.

FRASER, E. A., & RENTON, R. M. (1940). Observations on the breeding and development of the viviparous fish *Heterandria formosa*. *Quart. J. micr. Sci.*, **81**, 479.

FROST, W. E. (1943). The natural history of the minnow (*Phoxinus phoxinus*). *J. Anim. Ecol.*, **12**, 139.

—— (1945). The age and growth of eels (*Anguilla anguilla*) from the Windermere Catchment Area. *J. Anim. Ecol.*, **14**, 106.

GADOW, H. (1893–96). Reproductive organs. *Newton's Dictionary of Birds*. London.

—— (1901). Amphibia and reptiles. *Cambridge Natural History*, **8**. London.

GALTSOFF, P. S. (1938a). Physiology of reproduction in *Ostrea virginica*. I. Spawning reactions of the female and male. *Biol. Bull. Wood's Hole*, **74**, 461.

—— (1938b). Physiology of reproduction in *Ostrea virginica*. II. Stimulation of spawning in the female oyster. *Biol. Bull. Wood's Hole*, **75**, 286.

—— (1940). Physiology of reproduction in *Ostrea virginica*. III. Stimulation of spawning in the male oyster. *Biol. Bull. Wood's Hole*, **78**, 117.

GEDDES, P., & THOMSON, J. A. (1901). *Evolution of sex*. (Rev. Edition.) London.

GOODALE, H. D. (1918a). Internal factors influencing egg production in the Rhode Island Red breed of domestic fowl. *Amer. Nat.*, **52**, 209.

—— (1918b). Internal factors influencing egg production in the Rhode Island Red breed of domestic fowl. *Amer. Nat.*, **52**, 228.

GREENE, C. W. (1926). The physiology of spawning migration. *Physiol. Rev.*, **6**, 201.

GRINNELL, J. (1911). Concerning sexual coloration. *Science*, **33**, 38.

HARLAND, S. C. (1927). On the existence of egg-laying cycles in the domestic fowl. *J. Genet.*, **18**, 55.

HARRINGTON, N. R. (1899). The life habits of *Polypterus*. *Amer. Nat.*, **33**, 721.

HARRIS, J. A., & BLAKESLEE, A. F. (1918). Correlation between egg production during various periods of the year in fowls. *Genetics*, **3**, 27.

HAYS, F. A., & SANBORN, R. (1927). Intensity, or rate of laying in relation to fecundity. *Tech. Bull. Mass. agric. Exp. Sta.*, **11**, 183.

HEAPE, W. (1900). The sexual season of mammals. *Quart. J. micr. Sci.*, **44**, 1.

—— (1931). *Emigration, migration and nomadism*. Cambridge.

HEMPLEMANN, F. (1911). *Zur Naturgeschichte von Nereis dumerilii*. Stuttgart.

HERDMAN, W. A. (1904). Spawning of the plaice. *Nature, Lond.*, **69**, 465, 488.

HICKSON, S. J. (1906). Coelenterata and Ctenophera. *Cambridge Natural History*, **2**. London.

HORA, S. L. (1927). Lunar periodicity in the reproduction of insects. *J. Asiat. Soc. Beng.*, **23**, 339.

HOWLETT, F. M. (1907). Note on the coupling of *Empis borealis*. *Ent. Mag.*, **43**, 229.

—— (1912). The effect of oil of citronella on two species of *Dacus*. *Trans. R. ent. Soc. Lond.*, Pt. 2, 412.

HUNTER, J. (1786). *Animal oeconomy*. London.

HUXLEY, J. S. (1938). Darwin's theory of sexual selection and the data subsumed by it, in the light of a recent research. *Amer. Nat.*, **72,** 416.

HUXLEY, T. H. (1880). *The crayfish.* London.

IMMS, A. D. (1931). *Recent advances in entomology.* London.

ISSEL, R. (1918). *Biologia marina.* Milan.

IZUKA, A. (1903). Observations on the Japanese palolo, *Ceratocephale osawai.* *J. Coll Sci. Tokyo,* **17.**

JACOBI, L. (1880). *Die Aalfrage.* Berlin.

JENNER, E. (1824). Some observations on the migration of birds. *Philos. Trans.,* **12.**

JONES, J. W., & ORTON, J. H. (1940). The paedogenetic male cycle in *Salmo salar* L. *Proc. Roy. Soc.* B, **128,** 485.

JOURDAIN, F. C. R., & ALEXANDER, W. B. (1938–41). *The handbook of British birds.* (5 vols.) Ed. by H. F. Witherby. London.

KEEBLE, F. (1910). *Plant animals. A study in symbiosis.* Cambridge.

KERR, J. G. (1900). The external features in the development of *Lepidosiren paradoxa,* Fitz. *Philos. Trans.* B, **192,** 299.

KING, G. M., JONES, J. W., & ORTON, J. H. (1939). Behaviour of mature male salmon parr. *Nature, Lond.,* **143,** 162.

KLEBS, G. (1903). *Willkürliche Entwickelungsanderungen bei Pflanzen.* Jena.

KNOWLES, F. G. W. (1939). The influence of anterior pituitary and testicular hormones on the sexual maturation of lampreys. *J. exp. Biol.,* **16,** 535.

KYLE, H. M. (1926). *The biology of fishes.* London.

LAYCOCK, T. (1840). *A treatise on the nervous diseases of women.* London.

LEFROY, H. M., & HOWLETT, F. M. (1909). *Indian insect life.* Calcutta.

LEIGHTON, G. (1903). *The life-history of British reptiles.* Edinburgh & London.

LERNER, I. M., & TAYLOR, L. W. (1937). Interrelationships of egg production factors as determined for White Leghorn pullets. *J. agric. Res.,* **55,** 703.

LESLIE, J. M. (1890). Notes on the habits and oviposition of *Xenopus laevis. Proc. zool. Soc. Lond.,* **69.**

LEVICK, G. M. (1914). *Antarctic penguins.* London.

LIPSCHÜTZ, A. (1924). *The internal secretion of the sex glands.* Cambridge and Baltimore.

LO BIANCO, S. (1888). Notizie biologiche riguardanti specialmente il periodo di maturità sessuale degli animali del golfo di Napoli. *Mitt. zool. Sta. Neapel.,* **8,** 385.

—— (1899). Notizie biologiche riguardanti specialmente il periodo di maturità sessuale degli animali del golfo di Napoli. *Mitt. zool. Sta. Neapel.,* **13,** 448.

—— (1906). Azione della pioggia di cenere, caduta durante l'eruzione del Vesuvio dell' Aprile 1906, sugli animali marini. *Mitt. zool. Sta. Neapel.,* **18,** 73.

—— (1909). Notizie biologiche riguardanti specialmente il periodo di maturità sessuale degli animali del golfo di Napoli. *Mitt. zool. Sta. Neapel.,* **19,** 513.

—— (1911a). L'influence dell' ambiente sul periodo riproduttivo degli animali marini. *Mitt. zool. Sta. Neapel.,* **20,** 129.

—— (1911b). Su alcuni stadii postlarvali appartenenti a Gadidi rari del golfo di Napoli. *Mitt. zool. Sta. Neapel.,* **20,** 170.

LOWE, M. (1948). Unpublished work.

MACLEAN, H. (1908). The action of muscarin and pilocarpin on the hearts of certain vertebrates, with observations on sexual changes. *Biochem. J.,* **3,** 1.

MAHENDRA, B. C. (1936). Contributions to the bionomics, anatomy, and reproduction of the Indian house gecko. *Proc. Ind. Acad. Sci.,* **4,** 250.

MARCH, F. (1937a). Relative growth in amphibia. *Proc. zool. Soc. Lond.,* **107,** 415.

—— (1937b). Some hormone effects in amphibia. *Proc. zool. Soc. Lond.,* **107,** 603.

MARSHALL, S. M., & STEPHENSON, T. A. (1933). Great Barrier Reef Expedition. *Sci. Rep. Gr. Barrier Reef Exped.,* **3,** 219.

MASTERMAN, A. T. (1900). A contribution to the life-histories of the cod and whiting. *Trans. Roy. Soc. Edinb.,* **40,** 1.

MENZIES, W. J. M. (1925). *The salmon. its life story.* London

METTEN, H. (1939) Studies on the reproduction of the dogfish. *Philos. Trans.* B, **230,** 217.

MIESCHER, F. (1897). *Histochemische und Physiologische Arbeiten*, **2**. Leipzig.

MILROY, T. H. (1908). Changes in the chemical composition of the herring during the reproductive period. *Biochem. J.*, **3**, 366.

MINCHIN, E. A. (1912). *An introduction to the study of the protozoa.* London.

M'INTOSH, W. C. (1875). *The marine invertebrates and fishes of St. Andrews.* Edinburgh.

MOORE, C. R. (1932). The biology of the testis. In *Sex and internal secretions*. Ed. by E. Allen, London.

MOREAU, R. E. (1936). Breeding seasons of birds in East African evergreen forest. *Proc. zool. Soc. Lond.*, **106**, 631.

—— & MOREAU, W. M. (1940). Incubation and fledging periods of African birds. *Auk*, **57**, 313.

MORGAN, T. H. (1907). *Experimental zoology.* New York.

MORTIMER, C. H. (1936). Experimentelle und cytologische Untersuchungen über den Generationswechsel der Cladoceren. *Zool. Jb.*, **56**, 323.

NEEDHAM, J. (1931). *Chemical embryology.* Cambridge.

NETHERSOLE-THOMPSON, D. (1942). Passerines laying twice on the same day. *Brit. Birds*, **36**, 95.

NEWBIGIN, M. I. (1898). *Report of the Scottish Fishery Board.*

NORMAN, J. R. (1936). *A history of fishes.* London.

ORTON, J. H. (1914). Preliminary account of a contribution to an evaluation of the sea. *J. Mar. biol. Ass. U.K.*, **10**, 312.

—— JONES, J. W., & KING, G. M. (1938). The male sexual stage in salmon parr. *Proc. Roy. Soc.* B, **125**, 103.

OWEN, R. (1866). *Anatomy of vertebrates*, **1**. London.

PANIKKAR, N. K., & AIYAR, R. G. (1939). Observations on breeding in brackish water animals of Madras. *Proc. Ind. Acad. Sci.*, B**9**, 342.

PATON, N. (1898). *Fishery Board Report of investigations on the life history of the salmon.* Glasgow.

PATTEN, C. J. (1911). The vernal plumage changes in the adolescent blackbird and their correlation with sexual maturity. *Rep. Brit. Ass.*, **404**.

PEARL, R. (1914). Studies on the physiology of reproduction in the domestic fowl. VII. Data regarding the brooding instinct in its relation to egg production. *J. Anim. Behav.*, **4**, 266.

—— & SURFACE, F. M. (1911). A biometrical study of egg production in the domestic fowl. *Bull. U.S. Bur. Anim. Ind.* **110**.

PEARSE, A. S. (1939). *Animal ecology.* New York and London.

PEARSON, J. C. (1938). The life-history of the striped bass or rockfish, *Roccus saxatilis* Walbaum. *Bull. U.S. Bur. Fish.*, **49**, 825.

PHILLIPS, W. J., & HODGKINSON, E. R. (1922). Further notes on the edible fishes of New Zealand. *N.Z. J. Sci. Tech.*, **5**, 91.

PRATT, E. M. (1905). On some alcyonidae. *Herdsman's Ceylon Reports*, **3**, 247.

PUNNETT, R. C. (1923). *Heredity in poultry*, 179. London.

PYCRAFT, W. P. (1913). *The courtship of animals.* London.

RICHARDS, O. W. (1927). Sexual selection and allied problems in the insects. *Biol. Rev.*, **2**, 298.

ROBERTS, B. (1940). The life-cycle of Wilson's petrel. *British Graham Land Expedition, British Museum, Natural History*, **1**, 141.

ROSS, E. H. (1909a). Mosquitos and malaria at Port Said. *Nature, Lond.*, **80**, 286.

—— (1909b). Report of Malaria Expedition to Nigeria. Liverpool. *Trop. Med. Memoir*, IV.

ROWAN, W. (1926). On photoperiodism, reproductive periodicity, and the annual migration of birds and certain fishes. *Proc. Boston Soc. nat. Hist.*, **38**, 147.

—— (1930). Experiments on bird migration. 2. Reversed migration. *Proc. nat. Acad. Sci., Wash.*, **16**, 520.

RYVES, B. H. (1943). An examination of incubation in its wider aspects based on observation in North Cornwall. *Brit. Birds*, **37**, 42.

SAVAGE, R. M. (1935). The influence of external factors on the spawning date and migration of the common frog, *Rana temporaria temporaria* Linn. *Proc. zool. Soc. Lond.*, **105**, 49.

SAVILLE-KENT, W. (1893). *The Great Barrier Reef of Australia*. London.

SCHMIDT, J. (1922). The breeding places of the eel. *Philos. Trans.* B, **211**, 179.

SCOTT, W. (1909). An ecological study of the plankton of St. Lawrence Cove. *Biol. Bull. Wood's Hole*, **17**, 386.

SEDGWICK, A. (1898). *Students text-book of zoology*, **1**. London.

—— (1901). *Peripatus. Cambridge Natural History*, **5**. London.

SEMON, R. (1899). *In the Australian Bush and on the coast of the Coral Sea*. London.

SEMPER, C. (1878). Ueber eine Methode Axolotl-Eier jederzeit zu erzeugen. *Zool. Anz.*, **1**, 176.

—— (1881). *Animal life*. London.

SHAPIRO, B. G., & SHAPIRO, H. A. (1934). Histological changes in the ovaries and ovarian blood of *Xenopus laevis* associated with hypophysectomy, captivity and the normal reproductive cycle. *J. exp. Biol.*, **11**, 73.

SHARPEY SCHÄFER, E. (1907). On the incidence of daylight as a determining factor in bird migration. *Nature, Lond.*, **77**, 159.

SHAW, J. (1840). Account of experimental observations on the development and growth of salmon-fry from the exclusion from the ova to the age of 2 years. *Trans. Roy. Soc. Edinb.*, **14**, 547.

SIMPSON, S. (1912). An investigation into the effects of seasonal changes upon body temperature. *Proc. Roy. Soc. Edinb.*, **32**, 110.

SPALLANZANI (1784). *Dissertations relative to the natural history of animals and vegetables*, **2**. Trans. from the Italian. London.

STEPHENSON, T. A. (1933). Breeding of pearl oysters coincident with full moon. *Nature, Lond.*, **131**, 665.

STEVENS, N. M. (1906). Studies on the germ-cells of aphids. *Publ. Carneg. Instn.*, No. 51.

TARCHANOFF, J. R. (1887). Zur Physiologie des Geschlechtsapparatus des Frosches. *Pflüg. Arch. ges. Physiol.*, **40**, 330.

THOMPSON, D'ARCY (1910). *The works of Aristotle*. 4. *Historia animalium*. Oxford. Footnote by translator.

VOITELLIER, CH. (1931). Possibilities with regard to introducing various kinds of periodical testing of egg production in place of permanent testing. *4th World's Poult. Congr.*, **11**.

WALLACE, A. R. (1870). *Darwinism*. London.

WALLACE, W. (1904). Spawning of plaice. *Nature, Lond.*, **69**, 489.

WARREN, D. C. (1930). The effect of disturbance of the rhythm of egg production. *Poult. Sci.*, **9**, 184.

WATKIN, E. E. (1941). The yearly life-cycle of the amphipod *Corophium volutator*. *J. Anim. Ecol.*, **10**, 77.

WATSON, A. (1919). A study of the seasonal changes in avian testes. *J. Physiol.*, **53**, 86

WEEKES, H. C. (1934). The *corpus luteum* in certain oviparous and viviparous reptiles. *Proc. Linn. Soc. N.S.W.*, **59**, 380.

—— (1935). A review of placentation among reptiles. *Proc. zool. Soc. Lond.*, **105**, 625.

WEISMANN, A. (1876–79). *Beiträge zur Naturgeschichte der Daphnoiden*. Leipzig.

WESENBERG-LUND, C. (1930). Contributions to the biology of the Rotifera. 2. The periodicity and sexual periods. *K. danske vidensk. Selsk. Skr.*, **2**, 1.

WESTERMARCK, E. (1921). *The history of human marriage*. 5th Ed. London.

WHEELER, J. F. G., & BROWN, F. A. (1936). The periodic swarming of *Anchistioides antiquensis*. *J. Linn. Soc. (Zool.)*, **39**, 413.

WHETHAM, E. O. (1933). Factors modifying egg production with special reference to seasonal changes. *J. agric. Sci.*, **23**, 383.

WHITNEY, D. D. (1907). The influence of external factors in causing the development of sexual organs in *Hydra viridis*. *Arch. EntwMech. Org.*, **24**, 524.

c*

WIGGLESWORTH, V. B. (1942).   *The principles of insect physiology*.   London.

WILLEY, A. (1894).   *Amphioxus and the ancestry of the vertebrates*.   New York.

—— (1900).   *Zoological results*.   Pt. 5.   Cambridge.

WILLIAMS, C. B. (1930).   *The migration of butterflies*.   Edinburgh.

WILLIAMS, C. B. (1936).   The influence of moonlight on the activity of certain nocturnal insects, particularly of the family Noctuidae, as indicated by light trap.   *Philos. Trans*. B, **226**, 357.

—— COCKBILL, G. F., GIBBS, M. E., & DOWNES, J. A. (1942).   Studies in the migration of Lepidoptera.   *Trans. R. ent. Soc. Lond*., **92**, 101.

WILTSHIRE, A. (1883).   The comparative physiology of menstruation.   *Brit. med. J*., **1**, 395, 446, 500.

WITHERBY, H. F. (1938).   See Jourdain and Alexander.

WOODRUFF, L. L., & BRITSELL, G. A. (1911).   The temperature coefficient of the rate of reproduction of *Paramoecium aurelia*.   *Amer. J. Physiol*., **29**, 147.

WRIGHT, L. (1902).   *The new book of poultry*.   London.

CHAPTER 2

MORPHOLOGY OF THE REPRODUCTIVE TRACT[1]

By P. Eckstein and S. Zuckerman

I—Reproductive Patterns in Vertebrates

The anatomy of the generative organs in different groups of vertebrates varies with their reproductive physiology and behaviour. The basic reproductive process, production and union of male and female sex cells or gametes, is identical and common to all, but the manner of fertilisation and the subsequent fate of the ova vary considerably. Two clearly distinct patterns can be recognised. In most vertebrates the eggs are deposited by the female and develop outside the maternal body (oviparous or ovoviviparous reproduction). Thus embryonic development (and usually fertilisation) is external, and the numerous young receive either little or no parental care and attention. The generative tract of the female as a rule lacks a special brood-chamber, and external copulatory organs are poorly developed or absent.

In the second and smaller group, to which almost all mammals belong, well developed external genitalia are present. Both fertilisation and gestation are internal, and the (few) young are born without any coverings of foetal or shell membranes (viviparous reproduction). They are delivered after spending a variable length of time within a specially modified part of the female genital tract known as the uterus. During this period, they are in close contact with the inner lining membrane of the uterus, called the endometrium. As a result of this contact between foetal and maternal organism, a new structure, the placenta, arises, whereby the exchange of gaseous and nutritive substances between them becomes possible. Different groups of mammals develop very diverse types of placentae, depending on litter size, the internal structure of the uterus, and the degree of fusion between maternal and foetal tissues (Grosser, 1925, 1933 ; Wislocki, 1929 ; de Lange, 1933 ; Mossman, 1937a ; Amoroso, 1952). In those in which fusion is incomplete, the foetal part of the placenta separates easily from the uterus during parturition, leaving the endometrium behind (non-deciduate placenta). In others, the foetal and maternal tissues form an inseparable whole and must be shed together (deciduate placenta). The newborn of placental animals are as a rule very immature, develop slowly and depend on maternal care for considerable periods, during part of which they receive nourishment from the mother's mammary glands.

[1] Except in the section on Primates, where, for convenience, Zuckerman's classification (1933) has been adopted, the taxonomic nomenclature follows Simpson's classification (1945). Anatomical terms conform to the Final Report on Nomenclature of the Anatomical Society of Great Britain and Ireland (1933).

II—GENERAL STRUCTURE OF THE REPRODUCTIVE SYSTEM

Basically, the generative tract in both sexes comprises :

(a) primary sex organs or gonads ;
(b) a series of accessory reproductive organs ;
(c) external genital and copulatory organs.

The gonads are paired organs, but in many vertebrates (e.g. fishes, birds, mono-tremes) the two glands fuse or one of them atrophies during development.   In both sexes they usually lie within the abdominal cavity, but in male mammals the position of the testis is variable, and it may become an extra-abdominal organ.

The accessory reproductive organs are embryologically derived from two specialised tubes known as the mesonephric (Wolffian) and the paramesonephric (Müllerian) duct, respectively.   The former is the excretory channel of the mesonephros, an aggregation of mesodermal nephric tubules which forms the kidney in primitive vertebrates, but which in higher vertebrates acts as an excretory organ only during an early and transitory phase of embryonic life.   In reptiles, birds and mammals the metanephros (which forms the definitive kidney) replaces the mesonephros.   Some of the lower tubules as well as the duct of the meso-nephros persist, however, and eventually form the permanent excretory apparatus of the male gonad.   A dorsal offshoot of the mesonephric duct forms the ureter of the permanent kidney.

In the male the persistent mesonephric tubules link up with the testis and become the efferent ductules, while the mesonephric duct develops into the epi-didymis, vas deferens and its terminal dilatations, the ampulla and seminal vesicle. Both the spermatic and urinary channel open into the urogenital sinus, which is derived from the ventral segment of the primitive cloaca (Fig. 2. 2B).

In the female the Wolffian duct, although present, remains insignificant, and it is the Müllerian duct which provides the foundation of the reproductive tract. It is developmentally connected with the mesonephric duct, but differentiates independently into the oviduct, which consists of the uterine (Fallopian) tube, uterine segment and part of the vagina.   A brood-chamber or uterus is present in some lower vertebrates (e.g. selachians, certain reptiles), as well as in mammals. In birds, this part of the oviduct is made up of various sections provided with com-plex albuminous and shell glands.   These are responsible for the formation of the albumen and outer covering membranes of the eggs.   The lowest parts of the paramesonephric ducts and the adjacent part of the urogenital sinus form a solid epithelial cord from which the single vagina develops.

A. Non-mammalian Vertebrates

A characteristic feature of the genital tract of lower vertebrates is its close association with the urinary system.   This shows itself embryologically in the mode of origin of the two systems, anatomically by their intimate connection in the adult organism, and functionally by the frequent occurrence of a common excretory duct (in the male) which conveys the products of the gonads and kidneys together out of the body.   A similar but less pronounced association of the two systems is observed in higher vertebrates and mammals.

In the most lowly phyla the gonadal tissue is either distributed over various segments of the body (in *Branchiostoma* [*Amphioxus*]) or concentrated as a single organ (e.g. cyclostomes, some teleosts), and the germ cells are shed into the coelomic

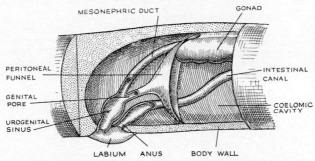

Fig. 2. 1—Diagram of the urogenital system of an adult cyclostome (lamprey). Gametes pass from the gonads into the coelomic cavity and reach the exterior through peritoneal funnels and the urogenital sinus. (Redrawn from Turner, 1948.)

cavity from which they escape to the outside through genital pores opening near the anus or into the urogenital sinus (Fig. 2. 1). In all other vertebrates the gonads are unsegmented organs, and the gametes reach the exterior through conducting tubes derived from the Wolffian and Müllerian ducts. These open

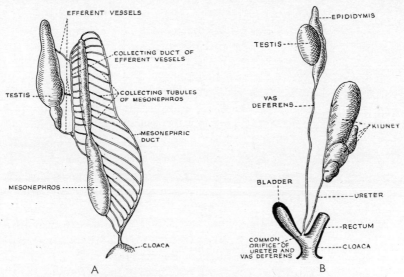

Fig. 2. 2—The male urogenital system in lower vertebrates (schematic).
A, Amphibian (slightly modified from Wiedersheim, 1907).
B, Reptile (modified from Wiedersheim, 1907, and Retief, 1949).

separately from, or jointly with, the ureters into the cloaca, which therefore serves as the outlet of the genital, urinary and intestinal systems.

A joint excretory duct for the kidney and gonad is the rule in male amphibia (Fig. 2. 2A) and most fishes, but in selachians, as well as in reptiles and birds, the urinary and reproductive tracts remain separate in both sexes (Fig. 2. 2B).

In accordance with the macrolecithal nature of their eggs, the ovaries of all lower vertebrates are voluminous, often grape-like structures, in marked contrast to the small size and relatively smooth outline of these organs in mammals. The reptilian ovary is distinguished by the presence of a large central cavity which is surrounded by a follicle-bearing mantle of cortical tissue. As the follicles mature,

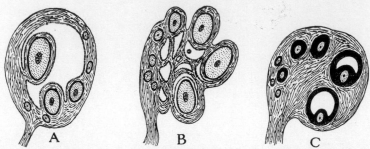

Fig. 2. 3—Schematic diagram of the structure of the ovary in A, reptile; B, monotreme; C, higher mammal. (Slightly modified from Van den Broek, 1933.) Thick black lines: follicular epithelium.

they project into the lumen of this cavity and eventually are attached to the peripheral cortex only by thin pedicles. In birds and monotremes there is an intricate network of small spaces instead of a single large cavity. In all mammals other than monotremes the ovary is a solid organ in which the only spaces found are those which form within the maturing Graafian follicles (Fig. 2. 3). A rudimentary structure known as Bidder's organ is present in the gonads of toads. It can be distinguished from the main functional part by its position, form and colour (Fig. 2. 4). Histologically it resembles an immature ovary and contains small oöcytes which may develop yolk (Brambell, 1929). It usually persists throughout the life of the male toad, but in the female it tends to atrophy gradually or to merge with the true ovary. In both sexes Bidder's organ undergoes hypertrophy after castration and may become transformed into a fully functional ovary. In the castrate male this is accompanied by hypertrophy of the (persisting) paramesonephric ducts (Ponse, 1924).

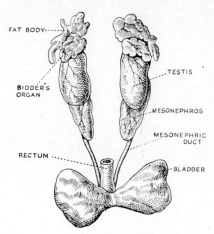

Fig. 2. 4—The urogenital organs of the male toad (*Bufo vulgaris*). (Redrawn from Brambell, 1930.)

Asymmetry of the reproductive organs is frequent in both sexes of the lower vertebrates. Thus in cyclostomes there is only a single right-sided testis, while in selachians the two testes are fused at their caudal extremities (Van den Broek, 1933). Asymmetry is particularly marked in birds in which, as a rule, only the left ovary and oviduct develop, the right gonad and corresponding oviduct remaining rudimentary. Their atrophy begins very early in embryonic development, in the chick and sparrow between the third and fourth day. Up to that stage the germ cells are evenly distributed between the right and left glands (Witschi, 1935), and the Müllerian ducts are equally developed on both sides of the body. Predatory birds differ from other birds in possessing, like reptiles, paired ovaries. Exceptionally, the right oviduct may persist in the chick in spite of an absent ovary on that side (Crew, 1931). In the viviparous lizard *Anniella* both ovaries are present, although the left oviduct is suppressed (Coe and Kunkel, 1906).

With the exception of certain lower forms (e.g. cyclostomes, teleosts), all non-mammalian vertebrates possess a true cloaca.

Copulatory organs are generally poorly developed or absent in lower types of vertebrates. They are usually lacking in cyclostomes, most fishes and amphibians, as well as in the great majority of birds (including the common fowl). In other lower vertebrates a rudimentary penis occurs either as a single intracloacal organ (e.g. in crocodiles, turtles, ducks and ostriches), or as a paired structure placed behind the cloaca (in snakes and lizards ; Gerhardt, 1933). Even in these animals, the persistence of the cloaca precludes the development of a true bladder and anterior urethra, and hence the prostate and bulbo-urethral glands of Cowper are absent (Retief, 1949).

B. Mammals

Man

The lay-out of the human reproductive tract provides a useful basis for considering the anatomy of the tract in other mammals.

The male

The primary sex organs of the male are the two testes which lie in a pendulous scrotal sac below the root of the penis. The germ cells or spermatozoa produced by them pass through a complex system of channels, known as the rete testis, which open into twelve to twenty efferent ductules (or vasa efferentia). These, after passing through the fibrous capsule of the upper pole of the testis, become enlarged and coiled to form the head of a slender crescentic structure called the epididymis. This is applied to the posterior border of the testis, and the twelve to twenty lobules that comprise its head open into a single convoluted canal which forms the body and tail of the organ. The latter is continued as a long sperm-conducting tube, the vas deferens, which passes upwards out of the scrotum through the inguinal canal into the pelvic cavity. Behind the neck of the bladder the two vasa become sacculated and tortuous (the so-called ampullae), and then join the ducts of the seminal vesicles, a pair of lobulated organs some 5 cm. long, to form the (common) ejaculatory ducts. These pierce the postero-superior aspect of the prostate, to open into the first or prostatic part of the urethra. The prostate is a firm glandular body about the size of a chestnut in the normal adult, which completely surrounds the urethra immediately beneath the neck of the bladder.

The ejaculatory ducts measure about 2 cm. in length and open by slit-like orifices on the summit (the colliculus seminalis) of a ridge-like projection on the posterior wall of the urethra, called the urethral crest. Between these openings is a small blind diverticulum which passes up for a variable distance into the substance of the prostate, and which is the homologue of the utero-vaginal canal of the female. It is known as the utriculus prostaticus or utricle. The bulk of the glandular tissue of the prostate is situated behind and on both sides of the urethra, the part of the organ lying in front being almost devoid of glandular elements. The prostatic collecting ducts open into the floor of the urethra on either side of the urethral crest. The glandular tissue which lies between the urethra and the ejaculatory ducts is called the median or prespermatic lobe.

Distal to the prostate the ducts of the paired bulbo-urethral (Cowper's) glands open into the urethra, which terminates externally on the glans penis. The latter is surrounded by a loose sheath of skin known as the prepuce.

The female

With the exception of the mammary glands, the reproductive organs are situated in the pelvis. They consist of the primary sex organs, the ovaries, and the accessory tract, comprising the uterus, uterine tubes and vagina.

The ovaries are flattened oval bodies about 3–4 cm. long, and lie near the side wall of the pelvis. Close to them are the open lateral ends of the coiled uterine tubes, each of which passes medially towards the uterus in a double fold of peritoneum called the broad ligament. The opening or ostium abdominale of the tube is hidden in the centre of a fringe of irregular convoluted projections called fimbriae. The adjacent part of the tube, or infundibulum, is continued into the wide ampulla, which makes up about half of the tube's entire length of 10 to 12 cm. The next segment, or isthmus, of the tube, is much narrower. It opens into the upper part of the uterus, which is a muscular organ, with roughly the shape and size of an inverted pear (7·5 × 5·0 × 2·5 cm.). The upper, movable part of the uterus, which is known as the body, has attached to its sides the two broad ligaments, while its lower segment, or cervix, is fixed to the pelvic floor. Between the body and cervix is a short and narrow section, the isthmus. The part of the uterus which lies above the level of the uterine tubes is known as the fundus.

The inner coat of the uterus consists of a glandular mucosa, the endometrium. The lumen of the uterine cavity tapers from the fundus towards the isthmus, but in the cervix it expands into a spindle-shaped space, the cervical canal. The upper end of this canal, which is characterised by an " arbor vitae " of mucosal folds, is separated from the uterine cavity by the internal os. Below, it opens into the vagina through a small aperture, the external os, which lies between the anterior and posterior lips of the cervix. The lower part of the cervix, or " portio vaginalis," projects into the vault of the vagina, thereby forming two recesses known respectively as the anterior and posterior fornix.

The vagina is a wide canal about 7·5 cm. long, which passes forwards to open on the vulva. Anteriorly the vagina is in contact with the bladder above, and the urethra below. The urethra measures about 3–4 cm. in length and drains into the vestibule, just in front of the vaginal opening. The vulva consists of the mons pubis, two broad outer folds or labia majora, enclosing two delicate inner folds, the labia minora, which unite anteriorly around a small projection called the clitoris. Apart from the vagina and the urethra, the ducts of the greater vestibular (Bartholin's) glands, and the para-urethral tubules of Skene open into the vestibule.

Other Mammals

I. The gonads

In all but a few mammals the gonads are compact, paired organs. The duck-bill (platypus) in which atrophy of the right ovary leads to a condition of ovarian asymmetry, similar to that in birds, is an exception. The reverse state, predominance of the right ovary over the left, is found in certain bats. The size, shape, histological structure and, in the male, position of the gonads, depend largely on their state of physiological activity.

The gonads consist in the female of the follicular apparatus and in the male of the seminiferous tubules, with a supporting stroma of vascular connective tissue. During early development germinal epithelium covers the entire surface of the gonads in both sexes. It persists in the female, but in the male it becomes separated from the surface by a tough outer membrane, the tunica albuginea. The sperm reach the exterior through a complicated system of excretory ducts, whereas in the female the eggs set free from the Graafian follicles pass into the peritoneal cavity before entering the abdominal opening of the oviduct. In some mammals the ovary is enclosed in a more or less complete peritoneal capsule or bursa ovarica (e.g. in bats, rodents, insectivores).

The position of the gonads varies considerably in both sexes. The ovary tends to be relatively fixed, but it may be found anywhere between the lower pole of the kidney (e.g. monotremes) in the lumbar region, and the true pelvis (women). The testes may remain in the abdomen, but more frequently they descend through the inguinal region into the scrotum.

In both sexes the gonads receive their blood supply through branches of the abdominal aorta, an indication of their origin from the lumbar region of the coelomic cavity. A variety of patterns in the course and distribution of the testicular artery to the testis can be recognised in different groups of mammals (Harrison, 1949).

Migration of the testis to an extra-abdominal position occurs only in mammals. The process is subject to much variation. In some species it does not take place at all, and in others the ultimate position assumed by the descended organ may be either inguinal, perineal or scrotal. In a third group of mammals, the testis is abdominal during the greater part of the year, but descends into the scrotum during the breeding or rutting season. This constitutes true periodic descent, and species exhibiting it should be distinguished from others in which the testes, although normally scrotal or perineal, may at moments of fright and excitement be withdrawn, through the action of the cremaster muscle, within the patent processus vaginalis towards the peritoneal cavity.

Table I summarises such information as there is about testicular descent in different species of mammals (modified from Wislocki, 1933a, and Van den Broek, 1933).

In spite of considerable research, the nature of the process by which the testis descends remains obscure (Soulié, 1895 ; Weber, 1904 ; Hart, 1909 ; Van den Broek, 1933 ; Wells, 1943). Among the factors thought to be involved are :

(1) The increase in mobility of the testis (owing to the reduction in size of the mesonephros and persistence of its ligamentous connections).

(2) Abdominal pressure.

(3) Endocrine factors, in particular the gonadotrophic secretions of the adenohypophysis and the androgenic hormones produced by the testis and adrenal cortex.

TABLE I

POSITION OF THE TESTES IN MAMMALS

	Permanently in abdomen	Outside abdominal cavity		
		Subintegumental (Inguinal or Perineal)	Scrotal	
			Periodically	Permanently
Monotremata	Duckbill, spiny anteater	—	—	—
Marsupialia	—	Some (e.g. wombat)	—	Most (e.g. opossum, numbat)
Xenarthra	Sloth, armadillo	—	—	—
Sirenia	Dugong	—	—	—
Proboscidea	Elephant	—	—	—
Hyracoidea	Hyrax	—	—	—
Cetacea	Whale, dolphin	—	—	—
Ungulata	—	Some (e.g. rhinoceros, hippopotamus)	—	Most (e.g. stallion, bull)
Carnivora	—	Some (e.g. hyaena, seal)	—	Most (e.g. dog, lion)
Rodentia	—	Most [1] (e.g. rat, rabbit)	Some (e.g. ground squirrel)	—
Chiroptera	—	—	Most(?all)bats	—
Insectivora	Some (e.g. golden mole, tenrec)	Some [1] (e.g. mole, shrew)	—	—
Tupaiidae	—	—	—	*Tupaia*
Primates	—	—	Some (e.g. loris, potto)	Most [1] (e.g. monkey, man)

[1] Testes can be voluntarily or reflexly withdrawn into abdomen (in primates only during infancy).

Moore (1926) has assembled evidence in support of a view that the germinal elements of the testis function only at a temperature below that of the abdominal cavity, and he ascribes a thermo-regulatory function to the mammalian scrotum.   However, it is difficult to see why the optimum temperature for spermatogenesis should vary in closely-allied species (e.g. among marsupials), or why animals like the whale and armadillo, living under grossly differing external conditions, should both have retained their testes in the abdomen (*see* Wislocki, 1933a).

II. *The accessory reproductive organs*
The male

The accessory reproductive organs of the male consist, in addition to the two vasa deferentia which open into the proximal part of the urethra (*see above*, p. 47), of several associated glandular structures.   These have been classified by Rauther (1903) as follows :

(i) Connected with the vas deferens : ampullary and vesicular glands (including the seminal vesicles).

(ii) Connected with or arising from the urogenital sinus.   This group comprises the prostatic and a variety of urethral glands.   The most important representatives of the latter type are the bulbo-urethral or Cowper's glands.   They vary considerably in number, degree of development and general arrangement.

(iii) Associated with the external genitalia and hence of ectodermal origin. They comprise such structures as the preputial and anal glands.

The following summary is based on the comprehensive accounts of Weber (1904) and Retief (1949).

The lower end of the vas deferens frequently possesses a glandular wall.   This is known as the ampullary gland (" glandula vasis deferentis "), and occurs in bats, certain insectivores and rodents, ruminants, some carnivores and lower primates. A true dilatation of the wall or " ampulla " is present only in man, although the dog and stallion possess it in less well-developed form.

The seminal vesicles are paired glandular organs.   They are absent in many mammals such as monotremes, marsupials, Cetacea (whales) and carnivores (e.g. the dog), and are therefore not thought to be essential for reproduction.   In other species such as boars, hedgehogs, rats and guinea-pigs, they are enormously developed.   When present they do not as a rule communicate with the vas deferens, but open into the pelvic urethra through separate openings.   In primates, however, the terminal parts of the seminal vesicles and the vasa deferentia join to form a common ejaculatory duct.   In most mammals, their anatomical arrangement precludes the seminal vesicles from acting as sperm reservoirs (Knaus, 1933 ; Retief, 1949).   For this reason the term of " vesicular glands " seems preferable to the older one of " seminal vesicles."   The glands appear to be essential for the production of a bulky ejaculate (e.g. in the boar).   In animals in which the vesicular glands are absent (as in the dog), the volume of seminal fluid is very small.

Prostatic glands or their equivalents are found in nearly all mammals, with the exception of the monotremes.   According to Retief (1949), two main varieties of prostate can be recognised. In the first or " disseminate type," the organ is a diffuse collection of urethral glands and does not penetrate the voluntary urethral muscle of Wilson which surrounds the pelvic part of the urethra, and which functions during urination and ejaculation. This kind of prostate occurs in marsupials, sloths and ruminants like the sheep and goat. In most other mammals the prostate penetrates Wilson's muscle and forms definite lobes outside it. As a rule there are two such lobes, but in many rodents, bats and catarrhine monkeys, a third or " cranial " lobe is present, the secretion of which is responsible for the seminal plug (" bouchon vaginal ") deposited by the male during copulation. In animals like the bull and boar the prostate combines the characters of both the lobed and disseminate varieties. Apart from man and the tree-shrew *Ptilocercus*, only the dog possesses a prostate which completely surrounds the urethra, but in man the anterior commissure is normally aglandular.

In the star-nosed mole (*Condylura cristata*) the prostate consists of two large and distinct lobes which drain by single excretory ducts into the urethra (Eadie, 1948).

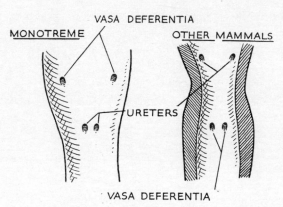

Fig. 2. 5—The relative positions of the openings of the ureters and vasa deferentia in monotremes and other mammals. (After Weber, 1904.)

In some mammals the prostate is the only accessory sex organ (e.g. in whales, dolphins and carnivores like mustelids, the bear and dog). Practically all other mammals have, in addition, at least one pair of bulbo-urethral glands. These are greatly developed in insectivores like moles, and especially in squirrels.

In monotremes the ureters open into the urogenital canal. In all other mammals they open into the bladder. This difference explains why the ejaculatory ducts lie above the internal orifices of the ureters in monotremes, but below them in the rest of the mammals (Weber, 1904 ; *see* Fig. 2. 5).

The female

The uterine tube, uterus and vagina, being basically derived from the Müllerian ducts, are laid down in the embryo as paired and entirely separate structures. They remain so even during adult life in monotremes and marsupials. In the higher mammals, however, they show a marked tendency to fuse in a caudo-cranial direction, and the definite accessory sex tract consists of a single caudal and a paired cranial segment. According to Weber (1904), this process of fusion never extends beyond the point of attachment, in the adult, of the round ligament of the uterus.

As might be expected, every intermediate stage from entire separation to the most complete degree of union of the two Müllerian ducts is found among the different orders of mammals. In both Ornithodelphia and Didelphia the whole reproductive tract is paired from the abdominal ostium of the oviduct to the opening into the urogenital sinus. But whereas in the former there are either no or only very short vaginal segments, in the latter the vaginae are bilateral, exceptionally well-developed and tortuous structures. The great majority of Monodelphia (with the possible exception of certain types of Xenarthra, e.g. the sloths), have only a single vagina, but differ among each other in the degree of development and fusion of the uterine and cervical segments. The most primitive arrangement, two separate uteri and cervical canals, is found in the rabbit and many rodents. Except for the presence of a single vagina, it is comparable to the arrangement which exists in marsupials. A slightly more advanced degree of fusion is represented by the guinea-pig, in which the more caudal parts of the cervical segment are fused to form one lumen. Consequently, in this animal there are two internal uterine orifices but only a single external os. The uterine segments proper remain separate, although superficially they appear to be slightly fused (bicornuate uterus). In other mammals the process of fusion extends even further in a cranial direction, and affects the uterine as well as the cervical elements. This leads to the formation of a common uterine cavity, in addition to a single cervical canal. In ruminants (cow, goat, sheep), in spite of a considerable degree of external fusion, this common uterine cavity is very small, the two uteri remaining separated by a thin midline septum which almost, but not quite, reaches the internal os. In the sow this septum is smaller, thereby increasing the size of the common cavity, while in carnivores (the bitch and cat) only a short septal spur persists. In the mare there is no trace of a median septum, and the size of the internal cavity corresponds to the externally fused part or " body " of the uterus. However, the primitive paired condition is still reflected by the presence of two uterine horns.

In Xenarthra and primates, with a few exceptions, fusion is complete and a unilocular uterus results. Even the uterine horns disappear and are incorporated into a single spacious organ known as the " uterus simplex." Internally and externally hardly any trace of the bilateral origin remains, and only the uterine tubes recall the development of the entire structure from the two Müllerian ducts.

Three different morphological patterns of tubo-uterine junction have been recognised in mammals (Andersen, 1928). The first, which is found only in marsupials, is characterised by a tortuous isthmus with a wide lumen constricted at its uterine end. The second pattern characterises all Monodelphia with bicornuate uteri. In these the isthmic part is either straight or tortuous, and always possesses a thick muscular wall with a narrow lumen. In most species the tube enters the side of the uterus, usually the mesometrial side, near its end, and the opening is guarded by mucosal folds and villi, or by a sphincter mechanism. In the cow and sheep, however, the tube enters the tip of the uterus, and there are no sphincters or mucosal folds present to protect the opening.

The third pattern is found in all mammals which possess a uterus of the " simplex " type. In it, the tube joins the uterine cavity near the fundus after a long interstitial course, and its opening is not protected by villi or mucosal folds.

The urinary tract bears very variable relations to the accessory reproductive organs, whose structure and general configuration it greatly affects.

In monotremes and marsupials the ureters lie medial to the oviducts. This is

of little significance in monotremes, in which the oviducts remain separate throughout life.   But in marsupials they tend to meet each other in the midline and to form
short median vaginae.   Complete caudal fusion, however, is prevented owing to
the origin of the ureters from the medial side of the Wolffian ducts (Buchanan and
Fraser, 1918), a relationship which is retained throughout life.   As a result the
ureters cross over the lateral vaginae in marsupials and then proceed between them
and the median vaginal canals towards the bladder.   On the other hand, in the
Monodelphia the developing ureters shift secondarily from the medial to the lateral
aspect of the Wolffian ducts and from then on remain lateral to them as well as the
Müllerian ducts.   This fundamental difference between Monodelphia and Didelphia has important bearings on the length of gestation, the type of placenta, and

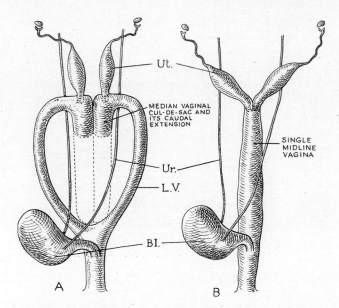

Fig. 2. 6—The relations of the ureters to the vagina or median
vaginal culs-de-sac in *Monodelphia* (A) and *Didelphia* (B).
(Slightly modified from Pearson, 1944.)

Ut., uterus ; Ur., ureter ; L.V., lateral vagina ; Bl., bladder.

particularly upon the processes of parturition which characterise these two mammalian divisions.   Pearson (1944) has pointed out that in spite of this developmental " disability," the marsupials have secondarily evolved a direct median
vaginal passage which connects the uteri during parturition with the urogenital
sinus, and passes medial to the ureters, as does the single vagina of the Monodelphia
(Fig. 2. 6).
    Various glands are associated with the accessory reproductive organs of the
female.   Among them are urethral or vestibular (Bartholin's) and clitoridal glands,
which correspond, respectively, to the bulbo-urethral and preputial glands of
the male. Homologues of the prostatic glands occur in the females of certain
species (e.g. Skene's tubules in women, catarrhine monkeys (Zuckerman, 1938)
and bats (Matthews, 1941a)). Anal glands are also present in many female
mammals.

III. Vestigial structures derived from the mesonephric and paramesonephric ducts

Although the mesonephric duct is primarily associated with the testis and the paramesonephric duct with the ovary, both persist to a varying degree in the opposite sex. Thus, in the male monotreme, the latter duct may persist in its entire length, from close to the upper end of the epididymis to the common orifice in the urogenital sinus. Short segments of the duct can also be recognised in marsupials, but in Monodelphia (Eutheria) it persists only near its cranial end as the hydatid of Morgagni or appendix testis, and at its caudal end as the utriculus prostaticus. In certain species the utricle consists of a small median part which ends in two lateral extension or horns (e.g. in the beaver, certain ungulates, etc.). In others it is absent altogether (e.g. in the mouse, rabbit, hedgehog and mole).

Histologically, the utricle varies considerably, and, according to Hütt (1927), three main types can be recognised. The first, which characterises animals like the fox, cat and rat, consists of a sac covered with a thin, non-glandular epithelium. The second, represented by insectivores and hystricomorphs, is a glandular organ. The third, typical of man, the stallion, boar and ram, is a structure which varies from individual to individual between the two extremes represented by the two other types.

In the female, the mesonephric duct may persist either completely as in monotremes, or in part as in marsupials and in Eutherian mammals. In the latter it is present as a thin-walled tube known as Gartner's duct, which runs close to the side wall of the uterus and vagina. It ends either by opening into the vagina and, as in marsupials, by contributing to its formation, or as a blind cul-de-sac. The duct has been described in a variety of species such as ruminants, ungulates, carnivores and primates. In the latter its upper end may be associated with the epoöphoron which represents a remnant of the mesonephric tubules.

IV. The external genital and copulatory organs

In most lower vertebrates the urogenital and alimentary tracts, as already observed, open jointly into the cloaca. Among mammals this primitive arrangement is found only in monotremes and, in modified form, in marsupials, Xenarthra, and certain rodents like the beaver. In all other types of mammal the urogenital and intestinal canals open on the body surface separately, and by orifices which on occasion may lie far apart (e.g. in ruminants). The fibro-muscular tissue intervening between the two openings forms part of the perineum.

The male

In monotremes the penis forms part of the ventral aspect of the cloaca. The urogenital sinus serves exclusively for the conveyance of spermatic fluid, and the testes remain in the abdomen. In all other mammals the penis is attached to the external surface of the body, the cloaca is closed, and a scrotal sac may be developed. In this way the urogenital sinus becomes a closed canal for the passage of both sperm and urine. The position of the penis appears to be governed by the development of the perineum and only secondarily by the scrotum. Thus in marsupials the scrotum is prepenial, but in most other mammals with permanently descended testes the penis shifts forward along the ventral abdominal wall and so comes to lie in front of the scrotum. However, among gibbons the scrotum may be pre- or parapenial, and in bats it may be pre- or post-anal in position (Fig. *2*. 7).

Both the penis and scrotum may be short and closely attached, or long and more pendulous. A pendulous scrotum is found in most carnivores, Equidae and Artiodactyla, as well as in many primates.

The distal or free part of the penis is usually concealed within an invagination of the skin of the lower abdomen known as the preputial sac, from which it emerges only during erection. In animals like the bull, this sheath is very long and firmly attached to the belly wall, and the penis is completely hidden. In others (e.g. primates) the sheath is shorter and only partly attached, so that the penis is semi-pendulous. In others again most of the free segment of the penis is provided with a tubular and entirely unattached investment of skin which forms only a short and shallow preputial sac around the glans. A truly pendulous penis of this type is found only in man, tree shrews and certain bats.

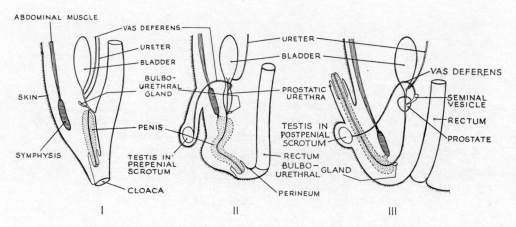

Fig. *2*. 7—Schematic lay-out of the male reproductive tract in I, monotreme ; II, marsupial ; III, higher mammal. (Modified from Weber, 1904.)

The external features of the penis, in particular the shape of the glans, vary considerably among mammals (Pocock, 1925 ; Pohl, 1928 ; Gerhardt, 1933). The glans is split into two halves in some, though not all, marsupials, but remains single in all other mammals. In many ruminants it is drawn out into a long filiform process which contains the urethra (e.g. in the ram). Occasionally it is covered by minute horny spikes or styles (especially in rodents, insectivores, carnivores). In some primates the glans is very rudimentary.

A cartilaginous or bony reinforcement of the penis (the os penis or baculum) is found in many mammalian orders such as carnivores (e.g. bears, dogs and seals), rodents, bats and, to a lesser extent, in insectivores and primates, excluding man. On the other hand, an os penis is absent in monotremes, most marsupials, Xenarthra, whales and ungulates. Accessory erectile bodies (in addition to the corpus spongiosum and corpora cavernosa) occur in many types of bat.

In certain species the length of the penis exceeds that of the preputial sac in which it is contained. The organ is therefore bent upon itself in angular or S-shaped fashion, and must straighten out before full erection is possible (e.g. in marsupials, insectivores and certain rodents such as the guinea-pig).

The female

The definitive appearance of the external genitalia of the female depends on the degree of development of the clitoris, urethra and vaginal vestibule.

In mature female carnivores, insectivores and primates, the clitoris retains its embryonic prominence. In carnivores it may even contain cartilage (e.g. in the cat) or bone (in bears), homologous with the os penis of the male. In the mole the clitoris is present as a pendulous prominence which in the non-breeding condition is almost as long as the penis (Matthews, 1935). In marsupials the glans clitoridis is frequently split into two halves.

In certain mammals the female urethra does not open into the urogenital sinus and acquires a separate distal orifice (e.g. women). It may even become incorporated in and perforate the clitoris in a manner fully resembling the penile urethra of the male (e.g. in insectivores and many rodents). In the females of these orders the anal, genital and urinary canals open separately at the caudal end of the body.

The external orifice or vestibule of the vagina may be enclosed by loose skin folds or labia. These are well developed in carnivores, ungulates and primates, and are usually referred to as labia minora. True labia majora occur only in women, although they may be feebly or temporarily present in certain other primates. Strictly speaking, it is therefore unjustifiable to use the term " labia minora " in connection with non-primate mammals.

In certain species the vagina is not always open to the exterior. For instance, in the mole such an orifice is established only during the breeding season, while in the guinea-pig the vagina opens during oestrus, but is closed during all other phases of the oestrous cycle.

Mammary glands, one of the main defining characters of mammals, are present in both sexes, but ordinarily reach full development only in the female. They are paired and occur in the pectoral (axillary), thoracic or inguinal region, or in all three. For instance, in animals like the cat, bitch and sow which possess several pairs of glands, they are found in a row extending from the lower chest to the groin. In rodents they are usually arranged in two separate groups, a pectoral and an abdomino-inguinal one, but in the mountain viscacha (a hystricoid rodent related to the chinchilla) a single pair of mammary glands is situated on the sides of the thorax (Pearson, 1949). In other species like the cow, goat, sheep and mare the glands of the two sides are partly fused to form an udder in the pubic region.

In a very general way the number of pairs of glands in an animal is related to the number of young it delivers at birth. One pectoral pair is the rule in species with single offspring like bats, the elephant and most primates. However, in prosimians there may be two to three pairs, and in at least one species (*Daubentonia*) the nipples are inguinal in position (Schultz, 1948). Most domestic animals possess multiple glands, corresponding to the number of their offspring. Average figures for the cat are four pairs, for the bitch four to five, and for the sow five to six. But there are great individual and intra-specific variations. Thus, in the domestic pig, the number of glands may be reduced from the average of twelve to eight or increased to eighteen (Bresslau, 1920), while in the closely allied peccary (*Pecari angulatus bangsi*) there are only two (Wislocki, 1931). The number of pairs may also vary in a given mammalian order. For instance, in most rodents five to seven pairs are the rule (e.g. rat, mouse, hamster), but the multimammate mouse (*Mastomys erythroleucus Temm.*) possesses ten pairs (Brambell and Davis, 1941), while in guinea-pigs only a single inguinal pair is present. The site (or number) of the nipples does not always correspond with the number and location of the mammary glands. Thus in the whale, various rodents and the mole, the position of the nipples may bear very little relation to that of the glandular tissue. In addition, supernumerary nipples are common in many mammalian orders (e.g. primates, rodents, ruminants). The largest number of nipples (and presumably mammary glands) appears to be present in *Centetes*, a primitive insectivore with twenty-two to twenty-four nipples and up to twenty-one young at birth (Schultz, 1948).

III—PROTOTHERIA

MONOTREMATA (= Ornithodelphia)
Tachyglossus ; Echidna (Spiny anteater ; Echidna)
Ornithorhynchus (Duckbill ; Platypus)

The male

The outstanding features of the reproductive tract in male monotremes are :

(1) The retention of the gonads in the primitive position high up on the posterior abdominal wall.

(2) The opening of the vasa deferentia into the urogenital canal above, instead of below, the ureters, as in other mammals (*see* Fig. *2. 5*).

(3) The presence of a true cloaca.

The following outline of the arrangement of the genital organs is based on the descriptions given by Disselhorst (1904), Van den Broek (1933) and Gerhardt (1933).

The gonads are characterised by an unusual arrangement of the excretory ducts. A few seminiferous tubules penetrate the tunica albuginea near the upper pole and join a short rete testis which lies in the mesorchium, entirely outside the testis itself. From it ductuli efferentes arise which enter the head of the epididymis, a conspicuous structure of peculiar shape, which may appear almost as a separated part of the testis (as in *Ornithorhynchus*, Disselhorst, 1904). The vas deferens shows no ampullary dilatation, and opens into the urogenital canal just above the orifices of the ureters. The urogenital canal (subsequently referred to as urethra) is about 10 cm. long and opens into the ventral aspect of the cloaca about 2·5 cm. proximal to the anus. It communicates with the penile sperm tube (" Sahmenrohr "). This serves exclusively to convey the seminal fluid, and divides at its lower end into narrow channels which open by means of multiple tiny pores on the free end of the penis. During copulation the swollen root of the penis is believed to obstruct the cloacal opening of the urethra, thereby preventing the sperm from passing anywhere except through the sperm tube.

The penis lies within a preputial pouch located on the ventral cloacal wall just distal to the opening of the urethra (Fig. *2. 8*).

Although the gross structure of the penis is very similar in *Echidna* and *Ornithorhynchus*, the appearance of its free extremity varies considerably in the two species. In the former the entire organ, when erect, measures about 7·5 cm. in length, and the glans is divided into four symmetrical bulbous processes. In platypus the glans is split into two halves each of which carries a group of long epidermal spurs which enclose terminal ramifications of the sperm tube.   In both species the mucous membrane of the urethra contains many tubular glands.   In the duckbill these form glandular agglomerations in the region of the neck of the bladder, but remain deep to the fibro-muscular wall of the urethra (Disselhorst, 1904).

A so-called " femoral spur " is present on the lower limb of *Ornithorhynchus*. This is connected with the excretory duct of the " femoral gland " and constitutes a secondary sex character which is found only in the male.

The female

The oviducts remain separate throughout their entire length.   Their upper ends communicate with the peritoneal cavity through a wide, smoothly lipped ostium and are continued into narrow and convoluted Fallopian tubes which pass gradually into the fusiform uterine segments. These open distally into the urogenital canal, and the latter is continued into the cloaca which has a single external opening.   Thus there is no vagina, and the ureteric orifices lie below as well as behind the openings of the oviducts.

The right ovary and oviduct are generally of little functional significance.   This asymmetry is less marked in *Echidna* than in *Ornithorhynchus*, in which the left (functional) ovary is always much larger than the right. According to Garde (1930), the left ovary of the duckbill measures 1·5 cm. in length and 1 cm. in thickness.   It is oval to triangular on transverse section and is distinguished by the size of the ripe Graafian follicles

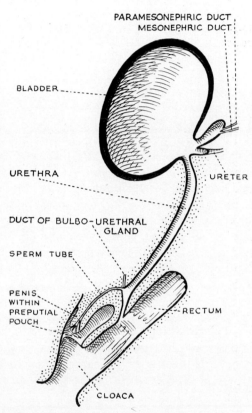

Fig. 2. 8—The reproductive tract of the male echidna. (Modified from Gerhardt, 1933.)

arranged uniformly near the surface of the ovary, and by the presence of many vascular trabeculae and lacunae.   In the non-functional (right) ovary follicles never reach maturity, and the lacunae do not form such a characteristic feature.

The ovum in monotremes is relatively enormous (2·5 mm. in *Ornithorhynchus*, and 3·0 mm. in *Echidna*; Hartman, 1929), and receives a keratin layer as it passes through the oviduct.

In platypus no pouch is present, and the egg is laid and " brooded in a nest-chamber " (Wood Jones, 1943).   In *Echidna*, however, an " incubatorium " or " marsupium " develops from the ventral " pouch area " at breeding time, and the egg hatches there soon after its arrival.

IV—METATHERIA

MARSUPIALIA (= Didelphia)

The male

The reproductive tract of one species, the opossum (*Didelphis*), is described in detail below (*see* p. 63).   The following brief remarks are made about the order as a whole.

The testes of marsupials lie in a pendulous or non-pendulous scrotum in front of the penis, and are permanently descended.   The vas deferens is without a terminal ampulla and remains lateral to the ureter throughout its intra-abdominal course.   Few species have a colliculus seminalis, and the seminal vesicles are uniformly absent.[1]

The pelvic part of the urethra is fusiform and elongated.   In spite of an abundance of diffuse urethral glands which may extend from the neck of the urinary bladder to the bulbo-urethral glands (*see* p. 64), there is no distinct prostate as in higher mammals.

The form of the marsupial penis has been described in detail by Gerhardt (1933).   The proximal part is invariably single, but the distal end may be split into two tips each of which carries a branch of the urethra.   A clearly bifid penile end occurs in *Didelphis philander*, and less markedly in *Dasyurus* and *Phascolomys*, while there is no trace of it in the Macropodidae and in *Tarsipes*.   How far this diversity can be related to the morphology of the female tract in these species is not settled.   The penis is surrounded by a preputial pouch which lies just in front of the anus and opens with the latter into a shallow cloacal depression. No perineum intervenes between the two orifices, and there is only one common sphincter cloacae muscle.

The female

The following brief account of the reproductive organs in female marsupials is based on the descriptions provided by Lister and Fletcher (1881); Hill (1899, 1900) ; Hill and Fraser (1925) ; Wood Jones (1923–24, 1943) and Pearson (1944).

As pointed out before, the outstanding feature of the marsupial reproductive tract is the unusual relation of the ureters to the uterine segments of the oviducts whereby the fusion of the latter and the formation of a single midline uterus is prevented.   Hence the two oviducts remain separate from each other and, after being crossed by the ureters, pursue a tortuous course as the paired " lateral vaginal canals " before joining the single urogenital sinus.

Apart from many minor points of distinction, the reproductive tract of the various types of marsupials differs particularly in the degree of development of the uterine segment of the oviduct near its junction with the lateral vaginal canal. This region has been variously described as the " median cul-de-sac," " median vagina," or " sinus vaginalis."   Much confusion has been caused through these differences in nomenclature, but the term most commonly used to-day seems to be " median cul-de-sac."   The internal structure of this passage and its connection

---

[1] The absence of seminal vesicles and the ampulla of the vas deferens is thought to explain the natural occurrence of spermatorrhoea in marsupials like the bandicoot and common opossum (Bolliger and Carrodus, 1938).

with the urogenital sinus are of such importance for the mechanism of delivery of the young that both will be briefly discussed together.

According to Wood Jones (1943), three main patterns can be distinguished : (a) types in which the two culs-de-sac are normally closed at their caudal ends,

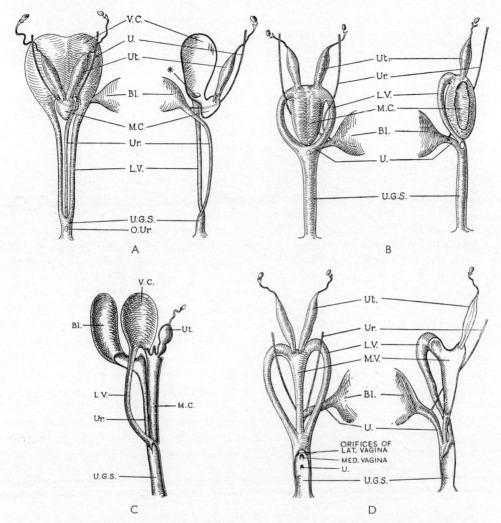

Fig. 2. 9—The reproductive tract of female marsupials (diagrammatic). Dorsal and paramedian views. A, *Perameles* ; B, *Trichosurus* ; C, *Bettongia* ; D, wallaby. (Modified from Wood Jones, 1943 ; and Pearson, 1944.)

Key : Bl., bladder ; L.V., lateral vagina ; M.C., median vaginal cul-de-sac ; M.V., median vagina ; O.Ur., urethral orifice ; U., ureter ; Ur., urethra ; Ut., uterus ; U.G.S., urogenital sinus ; V.C., vaginal caecum.

* Opening of vaginal caecum into lateral vagina.

but communicate with each other and the urogenital sinus during parturition ; (b) types in which there is a fused median vaginal pouch which may communicate with the urogenital sinus after the first act of parturition ; (c) types in which a patent connection is a constant feature even in non-parous animals (Fig. 2. 9).

The common bandicoot (e.g. *Perameles nasuta*) is a representative of the first group. The median uterine segments are relatively small structures, which " tend to sag inwards towards the middle line as simple loops (the two culs-de-sac) " and terminate well in front of the very short urogenital sinus (Hill and Fraser, 1925). During pregnancy their adjacent walls fuse and finally break down to form a " make-shift median uterus." At parturition the tissues intervening between it and the fundus of the urogenital sinus (extending over an area of about 5 cm.) rupture, and the young are born through a long median passage which is described as " a tear through all the maternal tissues that lie in the line of their passage." The rent heals very quickly, however, and on the third day following delivery the pseudo-vaginal canal or cleft is no longer open (in *Dasyurus viverrinus*, Hill and Fraser, 1925). This process is repeated in each supervening pregnancy.

Apart from the length of the gap which separates the median cul-de-sac from the urogenital sinus, *Perameles* is distinguished by the large size of the proximal parts of the lateral vaginae. These form bladder-like expansions or vaginal caeca which lie anterior to the uteri (Fig. *2*. 9A), and are believed to function as seminal receptacles. They are, however, not typical of marsupials in general, and occur in only one other genus (*Bettongia* : *see* Pearson, 1944 ; Fig. *2*. 9C).

The second type is represented by the Phalangeridae. In the virgin Australian opossum (*Trichosurus vulpecula*), the median culs-de-sac, although enlarged and closely approximated, are completely separated from each other by a median partition (Wood Jones, 1943). During pregnancy, however, they are converted into one chamber or median vaginal canal which, once created, seems to persist. This single chamber has a length of about 25 mm. in mature females, and its lower (or posterior) extremity is in close contact with the anterior wall of the urogenital sinus, but does not open into it (Pearson, 1944 ; Fig. *2*. 9B). During parturition a communication is established by a process of rupture similar to that already described, and the young are born through the resulting pseudo-vaginal cleft. The rent usually heals completely, but occasionally it may persist permanently as a very small opening.

The third and most advanced type of specialisation is found in the kangaroos and wallabies (Macropodidae), in which the median culs-de-sac form a true single median vagina. This is not a tissue cleft, but a tube with properly organised muscular walls and a complete epithelial lining. In kangaroos this tube may be about 7 cm. long and over 1 cm. wide. It usually ends blindly close to the wall of the urogenital sinus, from the cavity of which it is separated by a very thin (translucent) septum. This septum breaks down during pregnancy or parturition, and the opening may or may not persist indefinitely afterwards. In wallabies, however, a permanent communication between the two chambers may exist even in the virgin animal (Fig. *2*. 9D).

The lateral vaginal canals usually unite externally and form a short internal common vagina after opening into the dorso-lateral aspect of the urogenital sinus.[1] In the tree-kangaroo, *Dendrolagus*, their fused medial walls form a median septum

---

[1] This condition is not confined to the Macropodidae, for it exists also in *Caluromys philander*, among the Didelphidae (Hill and Fraser, 1925), and in *Caelonestes* (Baxter, 1935). In the latter, the lateral vaginae are characterised by their extensive folding. For instance, in *Orolestes*, " each canal is looped upon itself several times in the cephalic part of its course " (Baxter, 1935).

which reduces the size of this common chamber (Matthews, 1947). The urethral meatus lies below the orifice of the median vagina, in the midline of the urogenital sinus, and may be situated on the summit of two longitudinal ridges which continue almost to the tip of the clitoris (Matthews, 1947). The terminal parts of the lateral vaginal canals show well-marked muscular constrictions and may be narrowed further by small folds of the mucosa, so arranged as to form a valvular barrier to a body passing up the canal (Lister and Fletcher, 1881). Similar constrictions of the lateral vaginae are found in many American marsupials, including the common opossum (*Didelphis virginiana*). Although none of these species reaches the degree of structural perfection of the median vaginal canal attained by the Australian Macropodidae, it seems clear that they follow the same mechanism of delivery of the young.

Reviewing the entire Didelphian order, Hill and Fraser conclude that " This median mode of birth will ultimately be found to hold good for the whole of the Marsupialia." This view is strengthened by recent experimental work on the effect of sex hormones on the structure of the reproductive tract (e.g. Risman, 1947).

One of the few known exceptions is *Potoroüs tridactylus*, in which there appears to be definite evidence that birth of the young takes place through the lateral vaginae (Flynn, 1923 ; Pearson, 1944).

The mammary glands have well-developed nipples which are usually, but not invariably, situated within the pouch or marsupium. As a rule there are four nipples, but this number may be reduced to two (e.g. *Notoryctes*), or increased to over twenty (e.g. *Didelphis henseli* ; Weber, 1904). The typical marsupial location of the nipples is in the lower abdomen, but in *Peramys* and *Marmosa* they may be distributed along the " milk lines " between the axillae and cloaca.

Not all Didelphia develop a proper pouch. For instance, it is absent in the white-banded anteater (*Myrmecobius fasciatus*) and in the American genera *Marmosa* and *Monodelphis*. In pouchless forms (e.g. *Myrmecobius*), the young hang from the nipples and are dragged about by the mother, sometimes for months (Wood Jones, 1923-24). The nipples lack true lactiferous ducts and possess only minute openings for the conveyance of the milk. A compressor mammae muscle is present, and is considered homologous to the cremaster muscle of the male. According to Weber (1904), it serves to inject milk directly into the mouth of the young, a most important function in view of the known immaturity and inability to suck of the newborn. This is, however, disputed by other observers such as Vosseler (1930), who believes that the young obtain milk by active sucking, aided by rhythmic movements of the head and arms.

Didelphis (Opossum)

The male

The reproductive system in the male opossum has been described by Chase (1939). The following summary is based on his detailed account.

The bilobed scrotum is prepenial in position and attached to the body by means of a slender stalk. In the mature male the parietal layer of the tunica vaginalis is heavily pigmented and black (Finkel, 1945). Only a single efferent duct connects the testis with the epididymis, thereby approaching the condition met in rodents.

The urethral tract is relatively larger, and shows a more complex structure than in the Monodelphia. It can be roughly divided into two parts, a conspicuous proximal glandular segment and a short constricted distal portion, the membranous urethra. The glandular part shows marked individual variation in length and diameter. In young specimens it is narrow and straight, but in mature animals it is usually large and tortuous, and may describe a " complete loop " between the bladder and the bulbar urethra (Chase, 1939). Three distinct regions, differing in colour, diameter, and in the character of their glandular elements, can be recognised in its course (Fig. 2. 10). The first one, which Chase calls " Prostate I " is orange to brownish-grey in colour, the second (" Prostate II ") is a light pink and constitutes the widest part of the entire urethral tract. An almost straight line divides it from the third segment (" Prostate III ") which appears dark grey-green in colour and may be " somewhat translucent." This part is longer and narrower than either of the other two. Cross-section of fresh specimens reveals that the pigmentation of all three parts extends half-way towards the lumen. The latter lies nearer the dorsal than the ventral aspect of the urethra and is lined by transitional epithelium in its entire length.

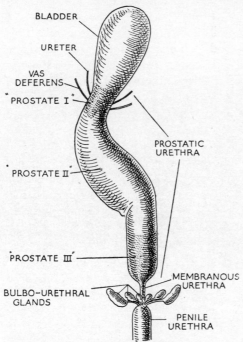

Each of these three regions contains large numbers of glands with slightly variable histological characters. They are radially disposed in the submucosa and do not penetrate the urethral muscle, as in sloths and monotremes. Apart from this they correspond anatomically as well as embryologically to the prostates of higher mammals, with which, in Chase's opinion, they are fully homologous. The presence of true urethral glands in the urethral tract of the opossum provides additional support for this view. They consist of small groups of acinous glands and are distributed throughout the membranous urethra, especially along its dorsal aspect.

Fig. 2. 10—The bladder and urethra of the male opossum. (Slightly modified from Chase, 1939.)

Ampullary glands and seminal vesicles are absent, but the bulbo-urethral glands are well developed and consist of three pairs. The first and largest of these (Cowper's I) are distinct, but the other two (Cowper's II and III) are much smaller and enclosed in a common capsule of striated muscle. The epithelial lining of these glands differs slightly in the three lobes, and varies with the season and the degree of distension (Chase, 1939 ; Rubin, 1944).

The excretory ducts of all three pairs of lobes are unusually large and join to form a series of sinuses before opening into the urethra.

The female

The following account is based on the detailed descriptions of Nelsen and Maxwell (1942) and Morgan (1946).

As in most marsupials the entire reproductive tract, with the exception of the urogenital sinus, is bilaterally symmetrical.

The uterine tubes have thin-walled, fimbriated infundibula and long, narrow and richly-coiled ampullae. Their constricted uterine ends are protected by flap-like projections of the mucosa. Each of the two separate uteri contains a dilated corpus and opens caudally through a constricted cervical segment into the median vaginal cul-de-sac. This is a hollow structure, as a rule internally divided by a thin median septum into two compartments, which projects blindly downwards towards the urogenital sinus. Each of its chambers communicates cranially with the narrow uterine cervix and laterally with the conspicuous lateral vaginal canal. In adult females the midline septum may be deficient or absent. The epithelium of the median culs-de-sac (or " median vaginal apparatus " in Nelsen and Maxwell's terminology) consists of a single layer of columnar secretory cells which change into a stratified squamous type of epithelium at the junction with the lateral vaginae. The proximal two-thirds of the latter are made up of the lateral loops which describe nearly a circle between their origin and termination in the midline of the body, at the level of the neck of the bladder. The distal third of each lateral vaginal canal is straight and lies side by side with its fellow in a fibro-muscular structure known as the urogenital strand or cord, which also contains the urethra. The two vaginae fuse to form a short common chamber before opening into the dorso-lateral aspect of the urogenital sinus, just cranial to the orifice of the ventrally situated urethra. The cord tissue forms a dense, well-vascularised support for the urethra and distal parts of the lateral vaginae, and extends forward as far as the lower extremity of the median cul-de-sac. Following parturition it contains, in addition, the pseudo-vaginal passage, through which the young are believed to make their way to the urogenital sinus. The distance separating the vaginal cul-de-sac from the upper end of the urogenital sinus (and hence the length of the pseudo-vaginal canal) is about 1 to 2 cm., or a little less than the length of the urogenital sinus itself.

In most females the pseudo-vagina forms at the time of birth of the young and disappears shortly afterwards. It can, however, also occur in virgin animals or persist indefinitely after parturition, thereby resembling the normal condition in wallabies (Macropodidae). This was shown by Ratcliffe (1941), who demonstrated the presence of a definite median vagina lined with columnar epithelium in some 10 per cent of a series of normal, non-pregnant females.

The " median mode of birth " appears to be firmly established in the opposum, the lateral vaginae merely serving in fertilisation and the transport of spermatozoa.

The greater vestibular glands are well-developed and vascularised in adult females, especially during the breeding season (Rubin, 1944). At the height of sexual activity they measure about $7 \times 3 \cdot 5$ mm. in size, and consist of closely packed tubules lined with a highly differentiated glandular epithelium and containing colloid-filled lumina.

The clitoris possesses a bifid glans.

V—Eutheria

(= Placentalia ; Monodelphia)

edentata (= *Xenartha*)

Families : *Bradipodidae* (Sloths) ; *Dasypodidae* (Armadillos)

The morphology of the reproductive tract in the two- and three-toed sloths (*Choloepus* and *Bradypus*) has been described by Wislocki (1928).

The male

In mature specimens of *Bradypus* the testes lie in the pelvis between the bladder and rectum, and are attached to the broad urogenital mesentery which extends from the testes to the adrenal gland. They attain their pelvic position presumably because of a partial or rudimentary descent during postnatal development.

The epididymes lie medial to the spherical testes and are united across the midline by a strong band of connective tissue.

In *Bradypus* and *Choloepus* the prostate lies within, not (as is the rule in mammals) outside the urethral musculature. The organ is similar in both species and consists of a glandular swelling around the urethra immediately adjacent to the neck of the bladder. It contains a small utriculus prostaticus. On the other hand, in the armadillo (*Dasypus*) the prostate, a well-developed bilobed structure, lies outside the urethral muscle.

Seminal vesicles are present in these three species, but vary considerably in their degree of development. They are large and well developed in both *Dasypus* and *Choloepus*, where they may attain a length of 10 cm. when straightened out, and a width of 1·5–2·0 cm. In *Bradypus*, by contrast, the seminal vesicles are rudimentary, averaging from 0·5 to 1·0 cm. in length and 2 mm. in diameter. They and the vasa deferentia open into the urogenital sinus by means of independent openings.

The structure of the penis varies considerably among edentates. The organ is exceptionally well developed in the armadillo, but almost rudimentary in the giant anteater (*Myrmecophaga*) and in *Bradypus*, in which there is also some degree of hypospadias (Gerhardt, 1933). The presence of a separate glans penis or prepuce has been variously asserted or denied, but the lack of an os penis in the entire order appears to be fully established.

The female

The ovaries are bilobed or fusiform in shape.[1] In sloths and armadillos, but not in the anteaters, they lie within ovarian bursae which must be opened in order to reveal the organs. The uterine tubes are coiled to either side of the uterus and open by slit-like orifices surrounded by a fimbriated fringe (Wislocki, 1928). The uterus is a slender, pear-shaped organ flattened in an antero-posterior direction, and contains a single narrow lumen (uterus simplex), the lower part of

---

[1] The occurrence of an extra-ovarian mass of sex cords containing oögonia and oöcytes in a single, sexually mature armadillo has been recorded by Hamlett (1935).

which is separated from the vaginal cavity by high mucosal folds. A specialised cervical segment is present in sloths, but not in the armadillo and anteaters.

In sloths the upper two-thirds of the vagina consist of a single tube, while the lower third is double. This caudal duplication is brought about by a wedge of tissue or septum which projects from below into the vaginal cavity, so producing two funnel-shaped canals. In non-pregnant animals the lower vaginal orifices appear to be closed by a special membrane. In the armadillo a true vagina is absent. It is replaced by the urogenital canal which opens to the outside by a long vestibular cleft.

SIRENIA

Dugong (Dugong)

Notes on the dissection of a male and female dugong have been published by Hill (1945).

The male

The testes are generally assumed to be intra-abdominal (Owen, 1838), but Hill did not identify them among the pelvic viscera, and their exact position and character remain uncertain. The vasa deferentia join the ducts of the corresponding seminal vesicles to form common ejaculatory ducts which drain into the bulbar part of the urethra. The seminal vesicles are not unlike the human ones, and measure $26 \cdot 5 \times 11$ mm. in length and width.

The urethral tract presents some very unusual features. The first part is completely surrounded by a prostate-like body which is composed partly of muscle and partly of erectile tissue, but contains no glandular elements. This segment protrudes into the wider bulbar urethra " like a miniature cervix uteri," being guarded distally by an " os " and surrounded by urethral " fornices " (Hill, 1945). A similar but smaller cervix-like structure is found in the female.

Bulbo-urethral glands and a prostatic utricle appear to be absent.

The prepuce opens about half-way between the umbilicus and anus. The glans penis is composed of two lateral lobes and a conical median projection which contains the urinary meatus. An os penis was not seen by Hill.

The female

The ovaries are comparatively large ($66 \times 34 \times 17$ mm.) and lie within pouches which are hidden beneath the peritoneum of the dorsal abdominal wall below the kidneys. The convoluted uterine tubes measure some 4 cm. in length and are directly continued into the uterine horns. The latter run at first straight for about 11 cm., then turn sharply dorsally and cranially to lie parallel to each other and, after a second bend in a caudal direction, unite externally to form the uterine body. Internally, however, they remain separated by a median septum except in the lowest part of their course where the uterus has a single median cavity. In the animal examined, the narrow cervical canal ended blindly below without opening into the vagina. This, Hill believed, may have been due to the specimen's immaturity, since delayed canalisation or temporary occlusion of the uterus and vagina are not unknown among other orders of mammals (e.g.

insectivores, carnivores). On the other hand, in the closely-related manatee (*Trichechus latirostris*) Wislocki (1935) found a massive cervical segment perforated by a transversely-flattened canal. In both species the cervix projects deeply into the wide upper part of the vagina and forms a deep fornix, except ventrally. The lower part of the vagina is constricted, and its walls are composed of heavy, rubbery mucosal folds which converge towards the vaginal outlet.

In the dugong the vagina opens on the cranial aspect of a long and shallow groove which externally simulates a vulval cleft, but which is largely made up of the perineal body. In front of the vagina lie the urethral orifice and the clitoris. The latter possesses a conspicuous rounded glans.

Perissodactyla

Equus (Domestic horse)

The stallion

The short account given here follows Sisson's detailed description (1940).

The testes are ovoid in shape and lie in a globular, somewhat asymmetrical scrotum. They measure about 10–12 cm. × 6–7 cm. × 5 cm., and weigh about 225–300 g. each ; they lack a distinct mediastinum and rete testis. The organs vary considerably in different breeds, and are frequently of unequal size, the left one usually being the larger. The epididymis is closely bound to the testis, the head by the efferent ductules, the tail by a separate ligament, the ligamentum epididymidis.

There is no spermatic cord in the usual sense of the word. Instead, the visceral layer of the tunica vaginalis forms a wide sheet or " mesorchium " which has a free anterior edge and is continuous posteriorly with the parietal layer of the tunica. The spermatic vessels and nerves are contained in the free border (the so-called " vascular part ") of the mesorchium, well in front of the vas deferens, which is suspended in a special fold close to the point of reflection of the visceral layer. The mesorchium also contains bundles of unstriped muscle which represent the internal cremaster muscle. The tunica vaginalis is a flask-like serous sac which extends through the inguinal canal to the base of the scrotum. Its parietal layer is reflected from the posterior wall of the inguinal canal to become the visceral layer. The latter forms the mesorchium and covers the structures of the spermatic cord, the testis and epididymis.

The lower 15–20 cm. of the vas deferens are enlarged to form a conspicuous, highly glandular ampulla. Beyond this point the vas diminishes abruptly in size, and opens either separately from, or jointly with, the duct of the seminal vesicle on the side of the colliculus seminalis. There is no true ejaculatory duct, as in man.

The seminal vesicles consist of two elongated piriform sacs which measure about 15–20 cm. × 5 cm. in the stallion ; they are much smaller in the gelding.

The prostate is a lobulated organ and comprises two lateral parts connected by a thin transverse isthmus. The lateral lobes are somewhat prismatic in form, and their deep surfaces are closely applied to the seminal vesicle. There are 15 to 20 prostatic ducts which perforate the urethra and open on either side of the colliculus seminalis.

In most cases the utriculus prostaticus is minute or lacking. Occasionally, however, it is well developed, and may attain a length of 10 cm. It opens into the urethra on the summit of the colliculus seminalis ; alternatively, it may join a duct of the seminal vesicle or end blindly.

The bulbo-urethral glands of the stallion are ovoid in form and measure about 4 cm. in length and 2·5 cm. in width ; they are considerably smaller in the gelding. Each gland has six to eight excretory ducts which open into the urethra in a series of small papillae behind the prostatic ducts, close to the median plane.

The urethra is divided into pelvic and extra-pelvic parts, while a true membranous portion is missing. In the pelvic part the mucous membrane contains two sets of urethral glands, one close to the median plane and another which extends on either side from a point near the prostatic ducts to the end of the pelvic urethra.

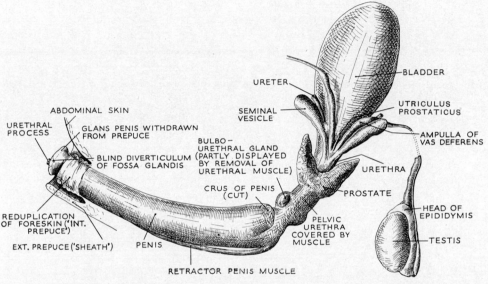

Fig. 2. 11—The reproductive tract of the stallion in lateral view. Bladder and upper urethra twisted to expose posterior aspects (about ⅓ natural size).

The penis is a laterally-compressed cylindrical organ. In the quiescent state it measures about 50 cm. in length, of which 15–20 cm. lie freely in the prepuce. The glans is surrounded by a prominent denticulated corona. Its surface is convex, while its upper part slopes backward and presents a deeply depressed fossa glandis, in which the urethra protrudes for about 2·5 cm. as a free tube, the urethral process (Fig. 2. 11). Thus the urethra is surrounded by a circular fossa which opens superiorly into the skin-covered bilocular diverticulum, the so-called "urethral sinus." The structure of the prepuce or preputium (popularly called the 'sheath,' is described by Sisson (1940) as a "double invagination of the skin which contains and covers the free or pre-scrotal portion of the penis when not erect." It consists of an external and internal part. The external part or sheath extends from the scrotum to within 5–7 cm. of the umbilicus, where the external layer is reflected dorsally and backwards, to form the thick margin of the preputial orifice (ostium preputiale), while dorsally it is directly continuous with the integument of the abdominal wall. The internal layer passes backwards from the preputial orifice for about 15–20 cm., lining the cavity of the external part of the prepuce, and is then reflected forwards until it approaches the orifice, where it is again reflected backward. Thus it forms " within the cavity of the sheath a secondary tubular invagination, the prepuce proper, in which the anterior part of the penis lies." This tubular cavity is closed behind by the reflection of the internal layer on to the penis to form the penile layer of the prepuce.

The skin of the external part resembles that of the scrotum. The internal layers of skin, as far as the preputial ring, are almost hairless, and form irregular folds which contain numerous large preputial glands.

The mare

The reproductive organs of the mare have been described by Hammond and Wodzicki (1941).

The ovary is a bean- or kidney-shaped organ, and larger than in any other domestic animal. At birth it weighs about 10 g. It attains its maximum size during the 3rd to 4th year, when it is approximately 5·5 to 8 cm. long and 2·5 to 4 cm. thick, and weighs from 40 to 70 g. The size of the mature organ is greatly influenced by the growing follicles, and varies considerably during different phases of the oestrous cycle.

In the newborn foal the ovary has a circular outline, and is completely covered by germinal epithelium (Schmaltz, 1921a ; Petten, 1932). Shortly after birth its ventral border becomes concave and the germinal plate begins to sink below the surface, thereby forming a shallow depression subsequently known as the " ovulation fossa " (Fig. 2, 12). This fossa assumes a funnel-shaped appearance between the first and second year, and in sexually mature mares it forms a well-marked narrow depression about 7 mm. deep.

The microscopical structure of the ovary shows some unusual features. The follicles, instead of being arranged in a well-marked cortex, are distributed through-out the interior of the ovary and are surrounded by an almost complete peripheral layer of vascular stroma, while serosa instead of germinal epithelium covers the external surface, except the ovulation fossa. As they mature, the Graafian follicles migrate towards this fossa and eventually rupture into it.[1]

A narrow cleft-like " ovarian bursa " is stated to be present in the mare, but does not enclose the ovary itself.

The uterine tube is 3 to 7 cm. long, and consists of a dilated ampullary part with a diameter of 4 to 8 mm. and a narrower uterine end. The latter is arranged in tight coils and joins the uterine horn slightly eccentrically by means of a small papilla which projects into the lumen of the uterus. The tube as a whole is distinguished by a large number of primary and secondary mucosal folds.

The uterus consists of a long and slender body joined by two comparatively short and straight horns at almost right angles. The body measures about 18-20 cm. and shows no trace of a median septum. Its mucous membrane is characterised by a number of conspicuous longitudinal folds which are continued into the cervix, where they form both the internal and external orifices. The entire cervical segment measures approximately 7·5 cm. in length, and is distinguished by the

---

[1] In young donkeys the rupture of follicles is not necessarily confined to the ovulation fossa (Küpfer, 1928).

presence of conspicuous " plicae palmatae," and by a well-developed muscular layer. The internal os is somewhat indefinite, but the external os opens on the summit of a definite " portio " which projects into the vaginal fornices (Fig. 2. 12). There are no tubular " uterine " glands in the cervix, but the epithelial lining contains numerous mucous cells which act as an important mucous gland during the cycle (Hammond and Wodzicki, 1941).

The vagina is 30 to 32 cm. long and can be divided into a proximal (supra-urethral) segment or vagina proper, and a distal (infra-urethral) or vestibular part,

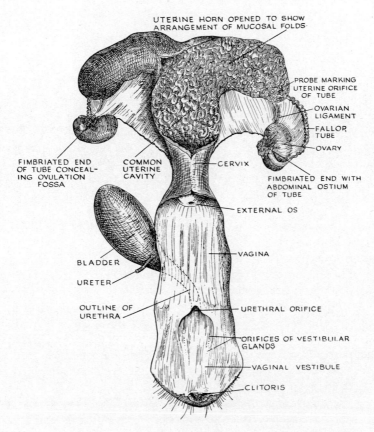

Fig. 2. 12—The reproductive organs of the mare (posterior view). Vagina and right half of uterus opened (about ⅓ natural size).

the former accounting for three-fifths and the latter for two-fifths of the total length of the organ. The vagina proper is covered by a relatively thin epithelium consisting of a few layers of polygonal cells, with round nuclei. The vestibule possesses stratified squamous epithelium which is nearly twice as thick as that of the proximal portion. In virgin mares a hymen is usually present at the boundary zone between the two segments.

The external genitalia consist of a pair of prominent labia and a well-developed clitoris surrounded by a wide clitoridal groove. The greater vestibular glands open into the lateral aspect of the vestibule.

The paired mammary glands lie in the prepubic region, on either side of the

midline.   Each gland " has the form of a very short, flattened cone, much compressed transversely, and having a flat medial surface " (Sisson, 1940).   The teats
are flattened transversely and vary in length from 2·5 to 5 cm.   As a rule two
lactiferous ducts open on the apex of each teat.   The size, shape and relative
amount of glandular parenchyma of the mammary glands depend on the age and
physiological state of the animal concerned and are therefore subject to considerable
variation in different mares.

ARTIODACTYLA

Fam. *Bovidae*
  Bos (Domestic cattle)
  Ovis (Sheep)
  Capra (Goat)

Fam. *Camelidae*
  Lama (Llama)

Fam. *Suidae*
  Sus (Pig)

Family *Bovidae*
Bos

The bull

The reproductive tract of the bull basically resembles that of the stallion, but
differs in certain respects (Fig. *2.* 13).

The scrotum is situated further forward than in the stallion, and consists of a
long and pendulous structure with a well-marked neck.   A large mass of fat may
be present above the neck of the scrotum, and two to four rudimentary teats are
frequently found in front of it.   The testes are relatively larger than in the horse.
In the adult bull their average size is 10–12 cm. in length, and 6–8 cm. in width and
thickness ; each weighs about 300 g.   Unlike the stallion, the bull possesses a
well-developed mediastinum and rete testis.   Both the spermatic cord and tunica
vaginalis are considerably longer than in the horse ; the extra-inguinal part of the
cord measures 20–25 cm. in length.

The vas deferens has a much thinner wall than that of the horse.   Its
lower part is dilated in the form of an ampulla which measures some 10–12 cm. in
length and 1·2–1·5 cm. in width.

The seminal vesicles consist of two elongated, lobulated and slightly yellow
masses.   They measure approximately 7 cm. in length and are rarely symmetrical
in size or shape (Davies, 1949).   Each excretory duct is about 1·5 cm. long, and
forms with the vas deferens of its own side a very short ejaculatory duct which
opens as a slit-like orifice on the colliculus seminalis.

The prostate consists of two parts which are continuous with each other.   The
body (corpus prostatae) is a small mass which stretches behind the dorsal surface of
the neck of the bladder and measures about 3·5–4 cm. across, and 1·0–1·5 cm. in
width and thickness (Sisson, 1940).   The remainder (pars disseminata) surrounds
the pelvic part of the urethra, and is very thin on its ventral aspect, but forms a
dense layer some 10–12 cm. in thickness, dorsally (Fig. *2.* 13, 3.).   The prostatic
ducts open into the urethra along a number of longitudinal rows.

The utriculus prostaticus is either very poorly developed or completely absent. The bulbo-urethral glands are a little smaller than in the stallion, and open into the urethra through single ducts.

The penis is cylindrical and both longer and much thinner than in the horse. Just behind the scrotum it forms an S-shaped curve (the sigmoid flexure), by means of which the total length of the non-erect penis (about 90 cm.) is reduced by about one-third. The asymmetrical glans penis measures about 8 cm. and possesses a pointed and twisted distal end with the external opening of the urethra situated at

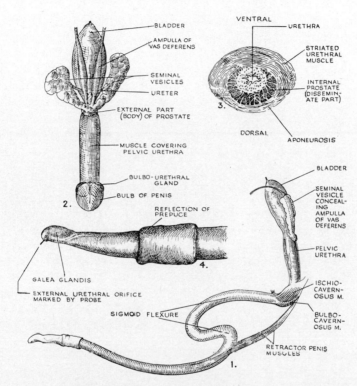

Fig. 2. 13—The reproductive organs of the bull.
1. General view from left side (approx. $\frac{1}{10}$ natural size).
2. Bladder and pelvic urethra (dorsal view). 3. Cross section through the upper part of the pelvic urethra, showing disseminate part of prostate (after Schmaltz, 1921b). 4. Extremity of penis, partly withdrawn from prepuce (approx. $\frac{1}{3}$ natural size).

the end of a groove formed by this twist (Fig. 2. 13, 1.; 4.). The prepuce is long and narrow, and opens about 5 cm. behind the umbilicus, where it is surrounded by long hairs. The preputial cavity is about 35–40 cm. long, and about 3 cm. in diameter. Protrusion and protraction of the prepuce are brought about by means of special muscles.

The cow

The ovaries of the cow are considerably smaller than those of the mare. Age changes in ovarian weight have been described by Hammond (1927), who states that there is little difference between the ovaries of calves and heifers (3–3·5 g.)

In older animals the organ is much heavier (7–10 g., without luteal tissue), and has a very irregular shape owing to the presence of large follicles and vividly-coloured corpora lutea protruding from the surface.

The uterine tube is relatively long, thin-walled and slightly coiled. Its lumen is wider than that in the mare. The tubo-uterine junction lies at the tip of the uterine horn. It is straight and possesses only a poorly-developed sphincter which does not prevent the regurgitation of fluid from the uterus (Andersen, 1928). The bursa ovarica is roomy and shallow, and communicates with the peritoneal cavity.

The uterus consists of a short compact body and two slightly larger horns. Each of the horns describes one complete spiral turn before joining the uterine tube ; in old cows there may be only half a turn.

Internally, the greater part of the " body " is subdivided into two halves by a well-marked median septum which, however, stops short of the most distal segment. Thus the latter, which measures only some 1·5–3 cm. in length, remains undivided and constitutes the true " corpus " of the uterus. The mucous membrane is folded irregularly, and contains numerous " caruncles " or cotyledons which develop into the maternal placenta during pregnancy. They are arranged in a series of rows and extend into the uterine horns. The average weight of the uterus and uterine tubes is 60 g. in calves of 4 months, 330 g. in virgin heifers aged 2 years 3 months, and 714 g. in parous cows of different ages (Hammond, 1927).

The cervix is a firm, thick-walled structure, some 10 cm. long, the lumen of which is spiral owing to the presence of annular ridges or sphincters. These are elaborately folded and account for the extremely complex arborisation (" plica palmata ") of the cervical mucosa. The main folds increase in height in a cranio-caudal direction, and the lowest ones project into the vagina as the " portio " with the external os at its centre (Fig. 2. 14). The lamellated mucosa is lined by a single layer of columnar cells and acts as a mucous gland which forms the copious vaginal secretion characteristic of cattle. According to Hammond the rigidity of the cervix is a normal condition in the cow.

The vagina is a tough and voluminous canal some 22 cm. in length, which frequently fills with air or " balloons " on examination (Asdell, 1947). On anatomical and functional grounds Hammond (1927) distinguishes three separate areas in the vagina and describes them as follows :

" The portion next the os is very like the latter in the character of its epithelium (one or two cells thick) and in appearance, being very wrinkled and thrown up into ridges. The portion between the vulva and the opening of the urethra is covered with stratified epithelium very like the mucous membrane of the mouth. The portion just above the urethra combines the character of these two parts."

The occurrence of post-oestrus vaginal bleeding is observed in many breeds of cows, especially young animals and heifers. In Hammond's opinion most of it is derived from that part of the vagina which is just above the urethra. Some blood, however, appears to be of uterine or cervical origin (see pp. 244 ; 555).

The cow is peculiar in possessing an anterior vaginal sphincter muscle " just back of the external os " in addition to a posterior sphincter which lies at the junction with the vaginal vestibule and is common to other domestic animals

(Asdell, 1947). A true hymen is absent, but occasionally hymenal rudiments may persist into adult life.

The vestibular glands are roughly the size of a walnut and open into the vestibule at about the middle of the lateral wall.

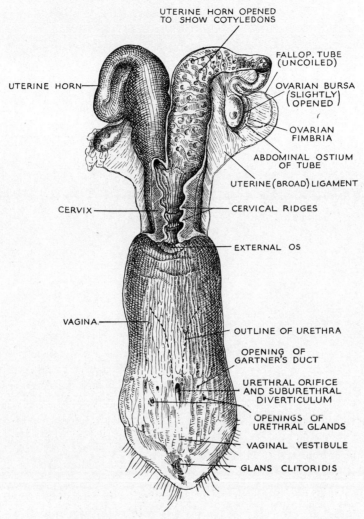

Fig. 2. 14—The reproductive tract of the cow (posterior view). Vagina, cervix and right uterine horn opened and right Fallopian tube traced through broad ligament to show its relation to the ovarian bursa (approx. ⅕ natural size).

The vulva is formed by a pair of loosely wrinkled and hairy labia which enclose a well-developed clitoris.

The mammary glands of the cow (the udder) are very much larger than in the mare. The body of each is ellipsoidal in form and flattened transversely. The base of each gland is firmly attached to the abdominal wall by means of a well-developed suspensory apparatus (Lig. suspensorium mammaricum), which consists of sheets of yellow elastic tissue. There are four teats which average 7–8 cm. in length. Accessory teats frequently occur behind the main ones. They are usually rudimentary and devoid of glandular substance (polythelia), but sometimes they drain a small amount of glandular parenchyma (polymastia). Dairymen frequently consider the udder as consisting of four " quarters." The hind-quarters are usually larger than the fore-quarters. No septum or visible division is present between the two quarters of the same side, but injection experiments show that the cavities drained by the two teats of each gland are not connected with each other. On each teat a single duct opens which communicates with the wide lactiferous sinus (" milk cistern "). The lower part (approximately 1 cm.) of the lactiferous duct is narrow and is closed by an unstriped sphincter muscle. The size and shape of the mammary glands of the cow vary greatly, both in different breeds of dairy cows and in relation to the physiological state of the animal concerned. The average weight of the udder in the calf is about 500 g., that in the two-year-old heifer about 2,000 g., and 5–6,000 g. in adult dry cows (Hammond, 1927).

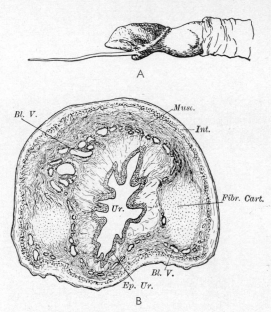

Fig. 2. 15—A, distal end of ram's penis seen from the left, showing glans and filiform appendage. B, transverse section through filiform appendage, near the tip. × 45.

Bl.V., blood vessels ; *Fibr. Cart.*, fibro-cartilage ; *Int.*, skin ; *Ur.*, lumen of urethra ; *Ep. Ur.*, epithelial lining of urethra; *Musc.*, muscular layer. (Reproduced from Marshall, 1922.)

Ovis

The ram

The reproductive organs of the ram resemble those of the bull, except for the relatively larger size of the testes. The dimensions of the latter, in the adult animal, amount to 10 cm. in length by 4–6 cm. in thickness by 5–6 cm. in width (Gutzschebauch, 1935), and they weigh about 250–300 g. each. Cryptorchidism is a frequent occurrence in sheep. The scrotum of the ram lies nearer the umbilicus than in the horse, but it is relatively shorter than in the bull, and has no proper neck. The prostate is " entirely disseminate," and the bulbo-urethral glands are " relatively very large " (Sisson, 1940). The glans penis is drawn out in characteristic fashion to form a filiform appendage which contains the terminal part of the urethra, known as the " processus urethrae." Hence, the latter projects about 3–4 cm. beyond the end of the penis (Fig. 2. 15).

The ewe

Apart from size, the generative organs of the sheep are very similar to those of the cow. Only the more important points of distinction will be briefly referred to.

The ovaries are not so irregular in outline and general appearance, and the corpora lutea are less vividly coloured than in the cow. There is a roomy and widely open ovarian bursa.

The uterine tube is relatively longer than in cattle, and much coiled in its ampullary part. There are no sphincter muscles or villi at its junction with the uterine horn, and fluid passes readily into it from the uterus, as in the cow.

The uterus strongly resembles that of the cow, but its horns are relatively longer and taper more towards the uterine tubes. The true or undivided part of the body is only 0·5–2·5 cm. long. This compares with a length of 4–7 cm. of the paired, though externally fused, part of the body. The caruncles of the sheep are saucer-shaped and more numerous than in the cow. A characteristic feature of the sheep uterus is the presence of black pigment which, as a rule, is found only in a few caruncles, but which may affect also the intercotyledonary areas. It is now thought to be melanoblastic and not haematogenous in origin, as was previously believed (*see* Asdell, 1946).

The cervix is much narrower than both the uterus and vagina. It is closely applied and partly adherent to the ventral wall of the vagina, a fold of which surrounds its lower part in horse-shoe fashion. The wall of the cervical canal itself is characterised by the presence of conical ridges which fit accurately into each other and close off the cervix against the vagina.

The cervical mucous membrane is less richly folded than in either the cow or mare. It is lined by a single-layered high columnar and frequently ciliated epithelium, and contains no glands.

Neither the vagina, which measures 10–12 cm. in length, nor the external genitalia show any remarkable features.

Capra

The reproductive tract of the goat greatly resembles that of the sheep in all its main features, but differs from it in certain minor details.

The uterine horns are more coiled than those of the sheep. The cervical canal is characterised by numerous mucosal folds arranged in a series of horizontal rings—unlike the hard ridges present in the sheep. In the goat the cervical mucosa contains simple tubular glands, unlike that of the ewe (*see* above). Neither the internal nor the external os uteri is well defined, and there is no true vaginal " portio."

The external genitalia show no special features. The greater vestibular glands do not seem to be present.

The ovary of the goat is bean-shaped and measures approximately 2 to 3 cm. in length, 1 to 2 cm. in width, and 0·8 to 1·0 cm. in thickness. Its weight varies from 1·1 to 3·0 g. (Harrison, 1948).

Family *Camelidae*

Lama

A few notes on the structure of the reproductive tract in a female llama have been published by McIntosh (1930).

The ovaries are conspicuous organs attached to the broad ligaments like "tuberculated nodules." In the single specimen examined the left ovary was larger than the right, and contained 8 or 10 corpora lutea of bluish-grey colour.

The uterine tubes join the extremity of the two uterine horns. Their

" pouting " ends lie at the extremity of each cornu.   The uterus is of the bicornuate
kind, while the cervix is marked by rough grooves and striae, and appears darker
in colour than the uterus itself.

Family *Suidae*
Sus

The boar

The scrotum lies a short distance in front of the anus and is less clearly demarcated than in other domestic animals.   The size and weight of the testes vary

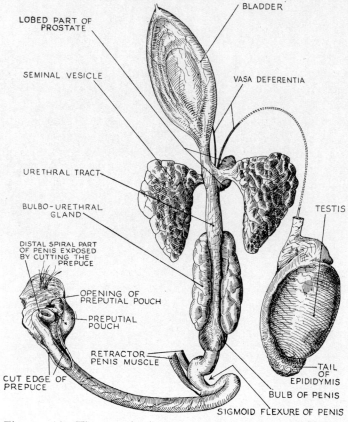

Fig. 2. 16A—The reproductive tract of the boar in anterior view.
Urethra slightly twisted to expose posterior lobed part of prostate
(approx. $\frac{1}{6}$ natural size).

considerably.   Average figures are 6 cm. × 4·5 cm. × 3·8 cm., and 150 g.
(Gutzschebauch, 1935), but a testis weighing 367 g. has been recorded.   Cryptorchidism is fairly common in pigs.   The epididymis is relatively long and the
spermatic cord averages 20 to 25 cm. in medium-sized boars, while the vas
deferens lacks a distinct ampulla.   The seminal vesicles are very large and compact.   In the adult boar they may measure 12 to 15 cm. (length) × 5 to 8 cm.
(width) × 4 to 5 cm. (thickness), and weigh 200 to 250 g. (Sisson, 1940).   They
are pyramidal in shape, distinctly lobulated, and usually extend into the abdominal
cavity.   Their single excretory duct, formed from half a dozen or more large,

thin-walled ducts, passes back laterally to the vas deferens. The two ducts open closely together, but occasionally join to form a short ejaculatory duct which opens near the summit of the small colliculus seminalis.

The prostate can be subdivided into a series of glands which do not penetrate the urethral muscle, and a small upper component of glands that do. This part consists of a small, lobulated whitish body which lies dorsal to the neck of the bladder. Occasionally the prostate in young boars may be contained entirely within the urethral wall. The prostatic ducts are numerous, and open into the

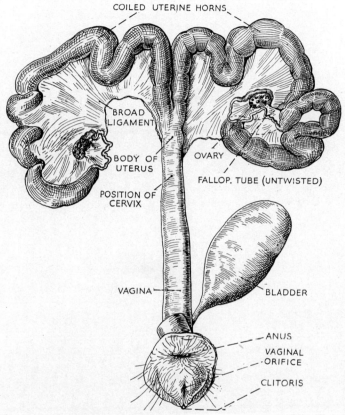

Fig. 2. 16B—The reproductive tract of the sow
in dorsal view (approx. ¼ natural size).

upper part of the urethra, mostly below the openings of the ejaculatory ducts. The internal structure of the prostate shows no unusual features. A utriculus prostaticus is present in the normal adult boar, but is usually very small.

The bulbo-urethral glands of the boar are very large (ca. 12 cm. × 3 cm. in a mature animal), and their long excretory ducts perforate the dorsal wall of the urethra. The glands possess a central cavity.

The general structure of the penis resembles that of the bull (*see* above), but the sigmoid flexure is pre-scrotal in position. In the adult boar the entire organ measures about 45 to 50 cm. in length. Its distal part is spirally twisted, and a proper glans is lacking. The external orifice of the urethra lies to the left of the midline close to the pointed tip (Fig. 2. 16A). The erectile tissue of the penis is highly developed, especially in the region of the bulb, but does not extend as far as the tip. The prepuce has a narrow orifice. A circular opening is present in its dorsal wall which leads into a large cul-de-sac, the so-called preputial diverticulum.

The sow

The ovaries of the sow are very variable in size and shape and often present a clustered or grape-like appearance, owing to the projection of large follicles and corpora lutea beyond the surface. They are largely hidden from view inside the wide ovarian bursae. The uterine tubes are relatively long, not greatly folded, and directly continued into the uterine horns. Their junction with the horns is guarded by large finger-like projections of the mucous membrane, rather than by true sphincters.

The uterus itself is distinguished by the relative length of its coiled horns which considerably exceed the size of the body (Fig. 2. 16B). The uterine cavity is subdivided proximally by a median septum. The development of the latter, and hence the size of the distal undivided segment, varies a good deal in different sows.

The most important features of the cervix are its length, narrow diameter, dense fibrous consistence and non-glandular mucous membrane. Its lower end gradually becomes wider and passes into the vagina without forming either a proper external os or vaginal fornices. Internally, the cervix presents a number of tough projections which are arranged in corkscrew fashion, similar to the spiral twisting of the tip of the penis (*see* above). These ridges are best developed in the middle of the cervical canal, and distally are continuous with two longitudinal folds in the vagina.

Remnants of a hymenal ring may be present in young, but not in old, pigs.

Urethral glands open into the floor of the vaginal vestibule by means of two converging rows of pores.

The clitoris is long and sinuous, and ends in a small point or cone.

PROBOSCIDEA

Elephas (Elephant)

The male

The following account is based on the description given by Schulte (1937).

The testes are intra-abdominal and retro-peritoneal, and lie medial to the lower poles of the kidneys, each being attached there by a tough fold of peritoneum (Fig. 2. 17). The epididymis is between the testis and the kidney. In the single adult specimen described, the two testes weighed 1·8 kg. and 2·2 kg. respectively, and the left one measured 175 mm. × 150 mm. × 115 mm. in length, width and thickness. A well-developed mediastinum testis is present. It is of some interest that bladder urine collected 12 hours after death contained a large number of motile spermatozoa.

The ductuli efferentes arise as 12 groups of coiled tubules, each having a diameter of about ½ mm., and join to form a rather ill-defined head of the epididymis. When uncoiled, this measures about 3 metres, and merges gradually into the vas deferens. The latter dilates to form an ampulla 75 mm. long and 40 mm. wide, which lies between the bladder and seminal vesicles. The terminal portions of the vas deferens and the excretory duct of the seminal vesicles are described by Schulte as follows :

" The two ejaculatory ducts, one from each ampulla, were 30 mm. long and 5 mm. inside diameter and ran in the dorsal wall of the posterior urethra parallel, ventral to the ejaculatory ducts of the seminal vesicles from which they were separated by a fold of mucosa 2 mm. thick containing no muscle fibres. They emptied into the common ejaculatory ducts."

The seminal vesicles are retroperitoneal, freely movable, and lie ventral to the coiled caudal ends of the vasa deferentia. They are fusiform in shape, measure approximately 225 mm. in length and 75 mm. in width, and may contain diverticula. Their excretory ducts measure 35 × 8 mm. before joining the vasa deferentia to form common " ejaculatory ducts "[1] some 15 mm. in length. The colliculus seminalis measures 60 mm. in length × 20 mm. in width × 10 mm. in height, and is formed by a well-arched fold of mucous membrane, but there is no marked crista urethralis. A small pouch, conceivably the utriculus prostaticus, lined with mucosa and measuring 5 × 5 × 5 mm., opens upon its distal end.

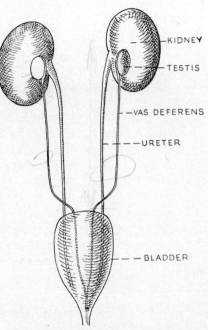

The prostate lies on the dorsal wall of the posterior urethra, and is similar to the human kidney in shape. It is about 40 mm. in length, 50 mm. in width, and 25 mm. in height, and drains by multiple ducts about 80 mm. in length which open on either side of the colliculus seminalis by means of orifices 2 mm. in diameter.

Cowper's glands are a pair of flattened oval organs which measure 125 mm. in length, 65 mm. in width, and 100 mm. in height. They lie adjacent to the bulbar

Fig. 2. 17—The position of the testes in the African elephant (ventral view). (Slightly modified from Weber, 1904.)

urethra, and drain through excretory ducts which are about 19 cm. long and 4 mm. wide.

The length of the penis is about 150 cm., a third of which is formed by the pendulous portion. In adult specimens no glans appears to be present in the non-erect state, and there is no prepuce.[2] The organ consists of two incompletely divided corpora cavernosa, each 13 cm. in length, and a corpus spongiosum, all three being composed of erectile tissue. There are two very powerful levator muscles which arise from the tuberosity of the ischium and measure 63 cm. in length and 28 mm. in width. Each muscle inserts into a single tendon near the

---

[1] From Schulte's description it is not entirely clear whether true (i.e. common) ejaculatory ducts are actually present.

[2] Schneider (1930), however, pictures an elongated glans which bears a certain resemblance to that of the stallion.

penis which join to form a very tough and flexible suspensory ligament on the dorsum of the organ.

Schulte (1937) suggests that the discrepancies concerning the anatomy of the reproductive tract of the male elephant evident in the literature are probably due to differences in the ages of the specimens dissected by different observers.

The female

The following summary is based on Perry's study (1953) of the African elephant, *Loxodonta africana*, and on Paterson and Dun's (1898) account of the Indian elephant.

Like the testes of the male, the ovaries lie relatively far forward, near the kidneys. Each measures about 5 to 7 cm. in length, and is almost completely enclosed in an ovarian bursa formed by an expansion of the infundibulum of the uterine tube and covered on the outside with peritoneum. Strongly developed ligaments connect the ovarian hilus with the uterine horn and the body wall. Each bursa is open on its medial aspect, and is divided by a peritoneal fold into an inner and an outer compartment. The ovary lies within the inner half, while the uterine tube opens into the outer wall of the outer compartment. The tube runs beneath the peritoneum, curving behind the ovarian pouch. It is very long and has a narrow lumen which leads directly into that of the uterine horn.

The uterus can be subdivided into three regions, one in which the two horns are distinct, another in which they fuse externally but retain separate lumina, and a third with a single (unilocular) cavity. The mucosa of the first two segments is glandular, but that of the third, representing the body of the uterus, is not, and histologically resembles the lining of the vagina.

The inner surface of the horns is smooth, and their size increases from about 4 cm. near the insertion of the ovarian ligaments to approximately 14 cm. near their junction. The lumen of each horn, however, does not increase in proportion, owing to the remarkable thickness of the myometrium, and is no more than $1 \cdot 0$ to $1 \cdot 5$ cm. at its widest point.

The external os of the uterus is a thick and rigid muscular ring with a very irregular free margin which projects for some distance into the much thinner and distensible vagina.

The vagina is a simple, capacious tube which measures nearly 50 cm. in length (Paterson and Dun, 1898), and is more or less constricted by a transversely-placed hymen.[1]

Beyond the hymen the vagina is continued into the curved urogenital canal. This measures about 90 cm. and so is approximately as long as the rest of the reproductive tract. The great length of this canal is the most outstanding feature of the female reproductive tract of the elephant, and is responsible for the unusually forward position of the vulva, which is very similar to that of the preputial orifice in the male. The urogenital canal is relatively thin and extensible like the vagina. Near its lower end, the urethra opens into the ventral wall through a round, thick-lipped aperture 2 cm. in diameter.

Greater vestibular glands are present, but are much smaller than their homologues in the male. They may have double excretory ducts, and open into the floor of the urogenital canal, close to the midline.

---

[1] The anatomy of this region is very variable, both as regards the structures entering into its formation and their relative degree of development (*see* Perry, 1953).

The vulva measures about 22 × 15 cm. and lies immediately behind the umbilicus, at a distance of some 60 cm. from the anus, projecting slightly from the body wall (Paterson and Dun). It is formed by two thick, wrinkled labia united anteriorly and meeting behind in a thin, sharp margin which encloses the urogenital orifice with the glans clitoridis in front of it. The clitoris is relatively large (not much smaller than the penis of the male), and both the corpora cavernosa and the corpus spongiosum with their attached powerful muscles extend along the roof of the urogenital canal for nearly half its length. According to Paterson and Dun, the glans measures 7 cm. in both length and width, and has a free extremity, bifurcated for 1·5 cm. in the centre. Its tip is partly covered by a fold of skin, but lacks a true prepuce.

HYRACOIDEA

Procavia (Hyrax ; Dassie)

The male

In the male hyrax the testes do not normally undergo a descent but remain attached to the posterior abdominal wall below the kidneys (Lunn, 1947).

The female

A few notes on the appearance of the ovaries and uterus of the female Dassie have been published by Wislocki (1930a) and Wislocki and Van der Westhuysen (1940).

The uterine tubes are relatively long and end in delicate membranous fimbriae which conceal the ovaries. They help in forming an incomplete ovarian pouch which communicates with the abdominal cavity by means of a slit-like aperture. The ovaries measure about 8 × 4 × 3 mm., and are very irregular in outline owing to the presence of large numbers of Graafian follicles and conspicuous corpora lutea. The latter are nearly spherical and protrude from the surface of the ovary as pedunculated smooth nodules about 3 mm. in diameter. Histologically the ovaries possess a central core of stroma surrounded by a shell of follicle-bearing cortex. The latter is deeply subdivided by indentations, so giving the ovary a " foliate appearance."

The uterus of Procavia is bicornuate, and consists of a body and two horns which together assume the shape and proportions of a letter Y, the body and the horns being about equal in length.

LAGOMORPHA

Oryctolagus (Rabbit)

The male

The testes are elongated or fusiform in shape and measure approximately 3·0 cm. × 0·8 cm. in length and width. They lie in subcutaneous scrotal sacs which communicate freely with the peritoneal cavity, and can be reflexly withdrawn or moved from the inguinal canals into the abdomen.

The head of the slender epididymis is marked by a bulbous swelling.

There is much confusion concerning the morphology and nomenclature of the accessory organs of the male rabbit. The following summary is based on the detailed account of Bern and Krichesky (1943) written with the main object of clarifying the subject and establishing a consistent nomenclature.

The vasa deferentia possess glandular walls and enlarge to form ampullary dilatations before entering the ventral wall of the seminal vesicle to join the ejaculatory duct. The seminal vesicle is a sac-like structure about 2·5 cm. long, bilobed at its anterior end, and lies between the ampullae of the vasa deferentia ventrally and the prostate dorsally. It can be divided into (a) two anterior lobes ; (b) a single body ; and (c) an unpaired ejaculatory portion which empties as a single ejaculatory duct into the urethra.

The seminal vesicle has been frequently mistaken for the (non-existing) utriculus prostaticus (Hütt, 1927 ; Deanesly, 1939). According to Bern and Krichesky (1943) it must be considered a true Wolffian-duct derivative, similar in all essentials to the seminal vesicle of rodents and man.[1]

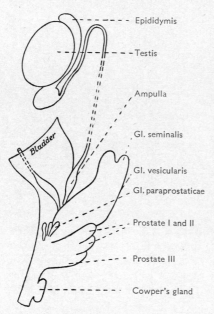

The structures known as the paraprostates consist of a group of small glands histologically very similar to Cowper's glands, which lie lateral to the ampullae, outside the muscularis of the urethra (Fig. 2. 18). The true bulbo-urethral glands present no unusual features.

The penis is comparatively short and points backwards in the non-erect state. Its free extremity lacks an os penis as well as a true glans, and is surrounded by an extensive prepuce which is perforated by the openings of numerous preputial glands. In addition there are paired inguinal and anal glands.

Labels in figure: Epididymis, Testis, Ampulla, Gl. seminalis, Gl. vesicularis, Gl. paraprostaticae, Prostate I and II, Prostate III, Cowper's gland, Bladder

Fig. 2. 18—Reproductive organs of the male rabbit (semi-diagrammatic). (Davies and Mann, 1947.)

The female

The ovary is flattened antero-posteriorly, and measures about 1·5 cm. in length, and 0·5 cm. in breadth. In mature specimens its weight varies between 200 and 400 mg., but may exceed 800 mg. (Emmens, 1939). The uterine tube is about 5–7 cm. in length (Drahn, 1924), and extensively coiled in mature specimens. It describes an almost complete circle around the ovary, so that its infundibular extremity and the abdominal ostium are commonly found on the medial aspect of the gonad. The ovarian bursa communicates freely with the abdominal cavity.

The most important feature of the reproductive tract is the complete duplication of the uterine segments. These remain entirely separate from the tubo-uterine to the cervico-vaginal junction, although they meet and are externally fused in the cervical region (Fig. 2. 19). There are thus two long uterine horns and two fully separate cervical canals, possessing internal and external ora, while a

[1] On functional grounds Davies and Mann (1947) have, however, concluded that the " glandula vesicularis as a whole, rather than the glandula seminalis by itself, should be regarded as homologous to the seminal vesicle in other mammals."

corpus in the usual sense of the word is completely lacking. The length of the horns is about 9 to 12 cm. in average specimens. The endometrium is arranged in numerous transverse and longitudinal folds which are particularly prominent along the mesometrial borders. The cervical canals have a narrower lumen and a more extensively folded mucous membrane than the uterine horns.[1] The mucosa has a high columnar epithelium without any glands, and is continued beyond the external os of each canal into the uppermost part of the vagina. The vaginal portions of the cervical segments are surrounded by a complete ring of fornices.

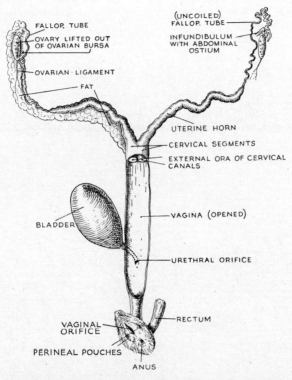

FALLOP. TUBE
OVARY LIFTED OUT OF OVARIAN BURSA
OVARIAN LIGAMENT
FAT
(UNCOILED) FALLOP. TUBE
INFUNDIBULUM WITH ABDOMINAL OSTIUM
UTERINE HORN
CERVICAL SEGMENTS
EXTERNAL ORA OF CERVICAL CANALS
BLADDER
VAGINA (OPENED)
URETHRAL ORIFICE
RECTUM
VAGINAL ORIFICE
PERINEAL POUCHES
ANUS

Fig. 2. 19—The reproductive tract of the female rabbit (dorsal view). Fat body dissected away on right side; perineum twisted to expose vaginal and rectal orifices (about ¾ natural size).

The weight of the entire uterus varies in different breeds of rabbits, but is usually 2 to 4 g. in mature animals, though considerably heavier organs are found occasionally (Emmens, 1939).

The single vagina measures about 7 to 8 cm. in length. Although very distensible, it is comparatively thin-walled and narrow, and may be even smaller than the opening of the short urethra which protrudes into its lumen by a prominent mucosal fold. The greater vestibular glands are thin elongated organs, ca. 1·5 cm. in length. The clitoris is well developed, and resembles the penis

[1] Drahn (1924), however, states that the lower ends of the uterine horns are not differentiated into true cervical segments. According to this author, the rabbit lacks both a uterine " corpus " and " cervix."

both in general structure and consistency.   It may be 2·5 to 3·0 cm. long, and possesses a prominent tip which projects towards the vaginal orifice which latter lies well behind the caudal aspect of the pubic symphisis and immediately in front of the anus.   The perineum is very short (only about 0·3 cm.) and communicates with two small diverticula, the openings of the perineal glands.   A pair of anal glands is also present.

RODENTIA

Fam. *Muridae*
        Mus (Common mouse)
        Rattus (Common rat)

Fam. *Cricetidae*
        Cricetus (Golden hamster)

Fam. *Sciuridae* (Squirrels)

Fam. *Caviidae*
        Cavia (Guinea-pig)

Family *Muridae*

Mus

The male

The following account is based on the description provided by Fekete (1941).

The testis of the mouse is distinguished by the unusual position of the excretory ducts.   The rete testis opens into a single " lacuna " which lies outside the tunica albuginea, and is drained by three to seven efferent ductules.   The latter are placed entirely outside the testis in the mesorchium, where they are surrounded by a collection of adipose tissue, the so-called " fat body " of the testis.   They unite eventually into a single duct which forms the first small segment of the head of the epididymis, and which is continuous with its duct (a similar arrangement is found in the rat, rabbit, and guinea-pig ; Benoit, 1925).

The head of the epididymis is much thicker than the body, while the tail is elaborately coiled in a manner not unlike that in the mole, in which a sperm receptacle is formed.   The vas deferens ends by opening high up into the posterior wall of the urethra close to the neck of the bladder.   Before its termination each vas shows a fusiform dilatation or ampulla which narrows before entering the urethra.   The ampulla is surrounded by lobules of branched ampullary glands.   These lie outside the wall of the vas deferens itself, but open into the lumen of its ampullary part through a common excretory duct (Rauther, 1903).

The seminal vesicles (or vesicular glands) consist of a pair of conspicuous organs which may reach half-way up the ureters.   They are long, narrow and curved at their tips, and enclose an elongated cavity with medial alveolar out-pocketings.

The duct of each vesicle opens on the colliculus seminalis separately from, and immediately behind, the ampulla of the corresponding vas deferens.   Occasionally, however, the two structures unite in their terminal parts, thereby forming a true ejaculatory duct.   There appears to be no utriculus prostaticus.

The prostate is of very complex structure and consists of three pairs of glands. The first of these is attached to the lesser curvatures of the vesicular glands and is generally known as the " coagulating gland " (Walker, 1910). It corresponds to Rauther's prostate I. The two other pairs of glands are located on the dorsal and ventral aspect of the urethra (" dorsal and ventral prostates ") and correspond to Rauther's prostate II and III, respectively. Occasionally the two lobes of the dorsal prostate are connected by a very small median lobe, but more often this lobe is absent (Fekete, 1941).

The mucous membrane of the coagulating glands is arranged in curved folds which project into the lumen. No such folds are found in the dorsal and ventral prostates. The glands drain through excretory ducts (two or three in the case of each coagulating gland) into the dorsal urethra at the level of the openings of the vasa deferentia.

A feature of the urethra is the presence of a diverticulum or " sinus " in the region of the bulb. This is described by Hall (1936) as a " large sac-like glandular diverticulum completely surrounded by and closely attached to, the musculature of the bulb." It may be represented by a narrow, thick-walled cleft or by a large rounded cavity with thin walls, depending on the degree of its distension and the accumulation of secretion in its lumen. The tip of the sinus often bifurcates, though it does so less in the mouse than in other rodents. Its structure is essentially similar to that of the urethra, which is described as glandular as far as the opening of the sinus, and non-glandular beyond.

The bulbo-urethral glands lie outside the musculature of the bulb, within a sheath of fibro-muscular connective tissue. Their ducts pass inwards and run obliquely through the muscle and erectile tissue to open into the sinus very close to its junction with the urethra.

A very similar urethral sinus is present in field mice, voles, rats and musk rats, and in the golden hamster, but not in the guinea-pig (Hall, 1936). A somewhat unusual type of urethral sinus has been described in the red squirrel (Mossman, Lawlah and Bradley, 1932).

Each corpus cavernosum is surrounded by its own tunica albuginea, but in the distal part of the penis this is reduced to a narrow fibrous septum. A small baculum is present in the septum and projects beyond the external urethral orifice. The glans penis lies within the prepuce and appears slightly rough owing to the presence of low epidermal papillae.

A pair of large, flat and leaf-shaped preputial glands is present just proximal and closely adherent to the glans penis. Their long excretory ducts open into the preputial cavity near the extremity of the prepuce. There are also minute anal glands.

A few instances of hermaphroditism in the mouse (as well as in other rodents) have been recorded in the literature (Hooker and Strong, 1944).

The female

Considering the importance and wide use of rats and mice in experimental work, the information on the morphological characters of the female reproductive tract in these two species is far from adequate.

The following account is mainly based on the descriptions given by Allen (1922), Agduhr (1927) and Fekete (1941).

The rounded ovaries measure about 2 mm. in diameter and lie just below the kidneys within the transparent ovarian capsules, from which each of them is separated by the periovarian space. The latter, in addition to receiving the infundibulum of the uterine tube, communicates with the peritoneal cavity by means of a narrow, tunnel-like passage 1 to 1·5 mm. in length, which lies in the region where the fused portions of the mesotubarium and ovarian capsule join the ligamentum ovarii proprium (Wimsatt and Waldo, 1945). Apart from its anatomical interest, this passage (which is also present in the rat) appears to take part in the fluid interchange between the periovarian space and the peritoneal cavity and so may have considerable functional significance (Alden, 1942 ; Wimsatt and Waldo, 1945).

Well-developed muscles are attached to both the uterine horn and ovary. They run from the former to the ovary and kidney and extend as far up as the diaphragm (Agduhr, 1927), supplying muscle fibres to the ovary, the tube and to the wall of the ovarian bursa. In the adult mouse the different tracts of fibres are surrounded, and to some extent split up, by masses of adipose tissue (" corpus adiposum ") which obscure the bursa and part of the oviduct.

In the non-pregnant animal the length of the densely-coiled uterine tube is approximately 1·8 cm. Its fimbriated end is intracapsular and shows no infundibular dilatation. The medial end of the tube joins the uterine horn eccentrically, close to and just behind its tip. Its entrance is marked by folds of the mucosa which form a mound-like protrusion, so that the end of the tube appears to be partly inverted into the lumen of the uterus (Lee, 1928).

The epithelial lining of the tube is ciliated and thrown into high folds in the ampullary part. Elsewhere it is non-ciliated and contains only a few, low folds.

The uterus consists of two straight horns with rounded-off ends measuring about 4 cm. in length, which join to form a short undivided segment or corpus uteri. In the upper part of this segment the two lumina are separated by a wedge-shaped median septum. Their fusion to form a single cavum uteri occurs a few millimetres above the opening of the external os (Allen, 1922). Thus, the uterine horns remain separate in by far the greater part of their extent. The transition of the low cuboidal uterine epithelium into the stratified squamous vaginal type occurs " at the cervix " (Fekete, 1941). The latter is surrounded by deep vaginal fornices.

The vagina of the mouse opens directly on the exterior and is not surrounded by any structures homologous to the labia minora (Allen, 1922). According to Drahn (1924), there is no true clitoris, but in front of the vagina is a small cone-shaped prominence or " clitorium " which is traversed by the urethra and, in addition, contains two large clitoridal glands. These open close to the external urethral orifice on the summit of the " clitorium," and correspond to the preputial glands of the male. Each contains a single hair follicle.

A well-developed perineum measuring about 0·5 cm. in length intervenes between the vagina and anus.

There are five pairs of mammary glands, three of which are thoracic and two abdomino-inguinal in position (Fig. 2. 21).

In old females the glands undergo partial involution so that only the main ducts and a few secondary branches remain (Fekete, 1941).

Rattus

The male

The testes of the mature rat lie in the scrotum. This forms a prominent subcutaneous swelling about 4 cm. in length between the anus and the tip of the penis. There are two entirely separate scrotal sacs, but externally the partition between them is hardly discernible.

Each pouch communicates with the peritoneal cavity through a wide inguinal canal which permits the withdrawal of the gonads into the abdomen throughout

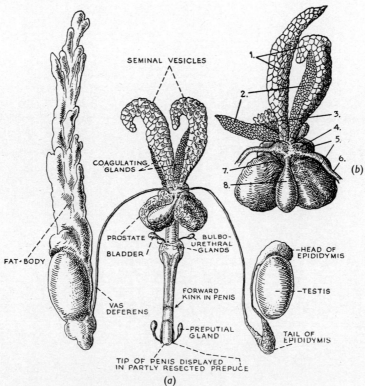

Fig. 2. 20, I—The reproductive organs of the male rat : (*a*) anterior view, fat body removed on left side ; inset (*b*) magnified view of prostatic lobes and seminal vesicles (right lobe of coagulating gland drawn away from seminal vesicle to display posterior lobe of prostate).

1, seminal vesicles ; 2, lobes of coagulating gland ; 3, posterior lobe of prostate ; 4, ampullary gland ; 5, anterior lobe of prostate ; 6, vas deferens ; 7, ureter ; 8, bladder (displaced downwards).

life. The testis is ovoid in shape and about 2 cm. long. It weighs a little over 1 g. without the epididymis. The arrangement of its excretory duct system is essentially the same as that of the mouse.

The elongated epididymis consists of a large head connected by a slender body to a very coiled tail. It surrounds the testis completely, except over part of the anterior border. As in other rodents, the head is embedded in a large fat body, and both the body and tail are lightly attached to the testis by means of connective tissue. On severing this connection the tail is found to reach well below the lower pole of the testis. The structure of the vas deferens, especially in the terminal part of its course, is similar to that of the mouse (*see* above).

The seminal vesicles are conspicuous, deeply lobulated organs and extend as far as the level of the iliac crests. Their superior extremities are sharply bent backwards and caudally (Fig. 2. 20, I).

As in the mouse, the prostate consists of three pairs of glands, the dorsal and ventral lobes and the coagulating glands.[1] The latter, the largest pair, are closely associated with the seminal vesicles and lie along their inner borders and

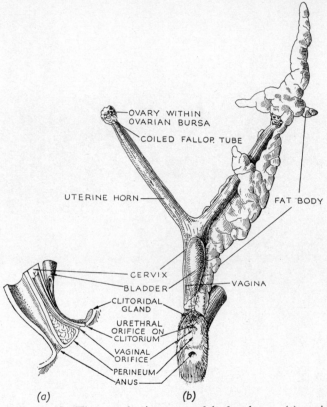

OVARY WITHIN
OVARIAN BURSA

COILED FALLOP. TUBE

UTERINE HORN

FAT BODY

CERVIX

BLADDER

VAGINA

CLITORIDAL
GLAND

URETHRAL
ORIFICE ON
CLITORIUM

VAGINAL
ORIFICE

PERINEUM

ANUS

(a)   (b)

Fig. 2. 20, II—The reproductive organs of the female rat: (*a*) semi-diagrammatic paramedian view; (*b*) anterior view, fat body removed on right side (about natural size).

within the same fascial sheath. They measure about 14–18 mm. in length and 3–6 mm. in breadth (Walker, 1910).

Cowper's glands are about 5 mm. in length, bean-shaped in appearance, and drain into the dorsal aspect of the urethra near its flexure. The latter contains a urethral sinus similar to that of the mouse (*see* p. 87).

The penis is in " the form of a figure seven, with the angle antero-ventral," and possesses one or two small ossa penis (Hunt, 1924). The blunt and slightly

[1] Other classifications such as that by Pallin (1901) have been proposed and have caused considerable confusion. Histologically, the two posterior lobes (i.e. the dorsal prostate and the " coagulating gland ") are not identical. According to Price (1936), the posterior lobe resembles the distended portion of the coagulating gland as regards the shape and folding of the acini, but the epithelium itself differs from that of both other lobes.

rough glans lies within the preputial pouch. The prepuce with the contained preputial glands and the anal glands are as described for the mouse.

The female

The ovaries lie at the level of, and slightly lateral to, the lower poles of the kidneys, and are often embedded in fat. In adult specimens they measure approximately 0·5 cm. in length by 0·3 cm. in width. Their shape, size and weight depend on the number and degree of development of the Graafian follicles and corpora lutea present, and hence on the physiological state of the animal concerned.

Each ovary is attached by a mesovarium some 0·3 to 0·8 cm. in length, and lies within the ovarian bursa. As in the mouse, the periovarian space is not completely shut off from the general peritoneal cavity. The two communicate through a slit-like opening on the anti-mesometrial side of the bursa at about the level of the tip of the uterine horn (Alden, 1942).

The anatomy of the uterine tube has been described in detail by Kellogg (1945). It is completely coiled, between 2·5 to 3·0 cm. long, and lies close to the caudal pole of the ovary and the cephalic end of the uterine horn. Smooth muscle fibres connect the coils with the ovarian ligament, and indirectly both with the hilus of the ovary and the cranial end of the uterine

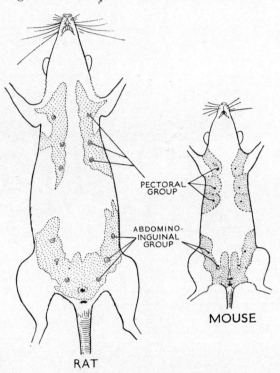

Fig. 2. 21—Location of the nipples and extent of the mammary glands in the lactating rat and mouse (after Greene, 1935 and Cloudman, 1941). The mammary tissue is indicated by stippling.

horn. There is a short segment within the periovarian space which includes the infundibulum, ostium and fimbriae. The remaining part of the tube, consisting of 7 to 10 coils, lies outside the periovarial sac. It can be divided into a short and thin proximal segment with a wide lumen lined by ciliated epithelium, and a much longer distal one with a narrower lumen, thicker wall, and with irregularly or non-ciliated epithelium. The lower end of the tube opens into the posterior wall of the uterus at the apex of a small intrauterine papilla (or colliculus tubarius), which projects freely into the lumen of the horn.

The uterus is of the bicornuate type and consists of two horns (partly embedded in fat) and a short unpaired segment which comprises the corpus and cervix (Fig. 2. 20, II). Each horn is about 4 to 6 cm. long × 2 mm. thick (except during pro-oestrus, when it markedly swells ; see Chapter 4), while the body and cervix measure about 0·3 to 0·5 cm. each in length. In spite of their apparent external fusion the lumina of the two horns remain separate as far as the paired external orifices.   The latter are difficult to detect among the folds of the vaginal part of the cervix (Long and Evans, 1922).   The cervical segment projects only slightly into the vagina, and consequently the fornix is very shallow, unlike that of the mouse.

The vagina is straight and measures about 2·5 cm. in total length and 0·5 cm. in diameter.   The external genitalia closely resemble those of the mouse (*see* p. 88), except for the fact that the ducts of the well-developed clitoridal glands open separately on the " clitorium," and do not join the urethral fossa, as in the mouse.   The perineum, between the vaginal orifice and the anus, is approximately 0·6 to 1·0 cm. long.   Small anal glands are present.

There are twelve mammary glands.   They lie within loose fatty tissue, and are disposed over the lateral aspects of the thorax and inguinal regions (Fig. 2. 21). The cervical (or first thoracic) gland is anterior to the forelimb just under the skin. The second and third thoracic glands extend into the axillae and spread out between thin muscular planes over the sides of the thorax.   The abdominal and the first and second inguinal glands occupy a thick fat pad which extends from above the iliac crest to the ischial tuberosity.   The abdominal glands are usually the largest of the entire series (Astwood, Geschickter and Rausch, 1937).

Family *Cricetidae*

Cricetus

The reproductive organs of the golden hamster are very similar to those of the mouse and rat.

The male

The only remarkable feature is the large size of the testes and accessory organs (Grosz, 1905 ; Parkes, 1931).

The female

The ovary is small and compact, and completely encapsulated.   Histologically it resembles that of the mouse in possessing a variable amount of interstitial tissue, but differs by the absence of any accumulation of corpora lutea.   Normally only one set of corpora lutea or large follicles can be distinguished on the surface of each ovary (Deanesly, 1938).

The uterine tubes and the uterus are similar to those of the mouse.

The cervix is described by Deanesly as follows : " Two cervical canals run separately up about two-thirds of the length of the cervix and then fuse.   The cervix projects some little way into the vagina, so that transverse sections show the vaginal epithelium of the fornices first outside the two cervical canals and further back outside the fused canal."

The vagina departs from the normal rodent pattern in the following respects. Its upper part is lined by a mucified type of epithelium which undergoes cyclic changes.   About 1 cm. above the vulva it changes abruptly to stratified epithelium, so that the vulva and lower vagina form a sharply defined region differing from the rest.   In its lower part the vagina also forms two lateral dilatations, containing large masses of cornified epithelium.   These pouches, Deanesly states, are in a constant state of growth, and it is impossible to trace cyclic vaginal changes, except by smears taken from the upper part of the vagina (*see* Chapter 4).

The vaginal wall contains urethral glands of the female prostate type. The clitoris is large and traversed by the urethra, as in the mouse.

The mammary glands of the hamster are both thoracic and abdominal. Six or seven nipples are present and arranged along the ventral body wall on both sides. The glands themselves lie on the flanks of the animal lateral to the nipples, as in the mole, and do not radiate from the nipples, as they do in the rabbit and ferret.

Family *Sciuridae*

The male

The reproductive organs of the male have been described in detail by Mossman, Lawlah and Bradley (1932), on whose account the following summary is based.

Typically, the sciurid reproductive tract is characterised by the presence of a pair of coiled and relatively little-branched seminal vesicles, a simple compact tubular prostate gland, which opens by a single pair of primary ducts, and by a pair of very large compound bulbo-urethral glands, whose excretory ducts show certain unusual features not met with in other mammals. They consist of wide spiral tubes which are constricted as they enter the bulb. Immediately after entering, they expand and then unite, forming in this region a well-developed gland which Mossman and his associates have called the " bulbar gland " (glandula bulbi). It is lined by a type of epithelium different from that of the true Cowper's gland, and it drains through a single duct (" penile duct ") which runs distally through the corpus spongiosum to join the urethra close to the ventral flexure of the penis (Fig. 2. 22, a, b). There are no ampullary and no para-urethral glands.

This description applies to the following species : grey squirrel (*Sciurus carolinensis* Gmelin) ; fox squirrel (*Sciurus niger* L.) ; chipmunk (*Tamias striatus*) ; ground squirrel (*Citellus franklini*) ; 13-striped gopher or spermophile (*Citellus tridecem-lineatus*) ; woodchuck (*Marmota monax*) ; and flying squirrel (*Glaucomys volans*). On the other hand, the red squirrel (*Tamiasciurus*), although it closely resembles the remainder of the group in its general morphology, differs in some of its reproductive organs. Thus the bulbo-urethral glands are minute structures, entirely enclosed within the sheath of the corpus spongiosum. They open by an extremely short, non-glandular common duct into the ventral side of the urethra at the distal end of the bulb. Unlike other squirrels, *Tamiasciurus* also possesses a large non-glandular urethral sinus (*see* above, p. 87) in the bulb, while it lacks an os penis—generally present in Sciuridae.

In the grey squirrel the testes, which measure 15 × 35 mm. without the epididymis, lie in a semi-pendent scrotum, from which they are readily retracted into the abdomen. In young animals the testis may be located either in the inguinal canal or the scrotum. Once sexual maturity is reached, the organ is never more than temporarily retracted. The vasa efferentia emerge from a minute area of the testes. Compared with other species of squirrel, the seminal vesicles of the grey and fox squirrels are poorly developed, and measure approximately 9 × 5 × 4 mm. in length, breadth and thickness.

The prostate is a large compound, tubular gland which fills most of the true pelvis and projects forward into the abdomen. In sexually mature animals it measures 30 × 15 × 10 mm. Its cranial extremity is notched on either side for the accommodation of the seminal vesicles, but extends between the latter as two asymmetrical processes about 6 mm. long and 3 mm. thick. There is no prostatic tissue ventral to the urethra. The utriculus prostaticus is represented by a small glandular tube about 1 mm. in length lying in the mid-plane of the body. The prostatic ducts drain into two main ducts which receive the common opening of the united vasa deferentia and seminal vesicles, before piercing the prostatic urethra. Thus all three structures open by a single pore into the urethra. A

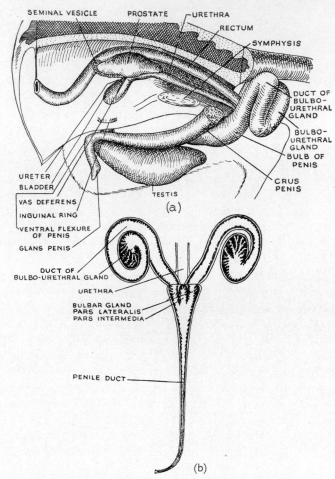

Fig. 2. 22—The reproductive organs of the male grey squirrel. (Slightly modified from Mossman, Lawlah and Bradley, 1932.) (a) Semi-diagrammatic paramedian section through the posterior half of the body. (b) Diagram of the urethral tract to show the relations of the bulbo-urethral glands and their ducts to the bulbar gland and penile duct.

similar arrangement is found in the European grey squirrel (*Sciurus vulgaris*) and in the chipmunk.

The muscular urethra of the grey and fox squirrel (which corresponds to the membranous urethra of man) is about 25 mm. in length and about 2·3 mm. in external diameter. Cowper's glands are very well developed, measuring about 12 mm. × 15 mm. They lie on each side of the anus at the root of the tail and are covered only by thin fascia. The wide cylindrical excretory duct arises from the medial surface and makes a complete circle around the gland, on the medial and cephalic aspect of which it enters the dorsal and caudal part of the bulb. As it enters, its epithelium changes from the relatively smooth lining of the duct to a deeply and complexly-folded glandular type of epithelium. At the same time the duct expands and joins on its medial aspect an unpaired intermediate pouch of similar glandular structure. The " bulbar gland " already referred to is formed in this way (Fig. 2. 22, b).

The penis has a total length of about 75 mm., of which 15 mm. are formed by the glans. Just proximal to the latter the organ shows a strongly marked ventral flexure. This bend characterises all the Sciuridae. An os penis is present, but there are no anal or preputial glands.

The spermophile (*Citellus*) is distinguished from all other Sciuridae by the enormous development of the bulbar gland, by the large size of the seminal vesicles, (which measure $20 \times 7 \times 7$ mm.), and by the fact that all three genital ducts open independently into the prostatic urethra. As in other sciurids, the utriculus prostaticus is either completely absent or very rudimentary (Siddiqi, 1937). The spermophile possesses two preputial and anal glands.

In the red squirrel, *Tamiasciurus*, the vas deferens and seminal vesicles open by a common duct into the urethra, while the prostatic ducts are separate. This constitutes an arrangement intermediate between that found in the grey squirrel and the chipmunk.

The female

The size of the ovaries in the ground squirrel varies with the reproductive activity of the animal. In the hibernating female they weigh only 6 to 8 mg. This increases to 18 to 24 mg. at oestrus (Foster, 1934).

The uterus is of the duplex type, with paired cervices, corpora and cornua uteri (Wells and Overholser, 1940). Each corpus possesses its own separate layer of muscle, but the fibres are securely bound together in the median plane by connective tissue. There appears to be a single " portio " surrounded by deep fornices through which the separate cervical canals open into the vagina. In anoestrous females the mucosa of the corpora and cervices uteri is lined by a low epithelium and lacks endometrial glands. Such glands are present in the uterine horns, but have either small or no lumina. During oestrus the horns possess a glandular endometrium which is covered by tall columnar epithelium. At the junction of the uterine horns with the corpora the epithelium abruptly becomes stratified squamous, and the glands disappear. This type of mucous membrane lines the remainder of the reproductive tract. In spite of this extensive distribution of squamous epithelium cornification occurs only in the vagina. The latter and its external orifice are normally closed and become patent only at oestrus, thereby resembling the condition found in the mole and guinea-pig.

Family *Caviidae*
Cavia

The male

The testes of the guinea-pig are ovoid in shape and lie in separate pouches on either side of the penis, slightly below the level of the anus (Fig. 2. 23, I). Their average weight is about $2 \cdot 5$ to $3 \cdot 0$ g., but in large males they may approach 4 g. (Deanesly and Rowlands, 1936). Their dimensions are approximately 12 to

13 mm. in length, 10 to 12 mm. in width, and about 8 mm. in thickness (Andres, 1927). The upper part of the testis is almost completely surrounded by the " fat body," which is continued to the posterior abdominal wall along the testicular vessels. The vasa efferentia lie outside the testis and unite to form the epididymis in a manner similar to that described for the mouse (p. 86). There is a well-developed cremaster muscle which permits the temporary (physiological) with-drawal of the testes into the abdomen.

The vasa deferentia join the lower dilated ends of the seminal vesicles just cranial to the point at which these structures unite. Hence there are no ejaculatory ducts in the usually accepted sense, and the wide canal created in this way opens on the dorsal aspect of the urethra, on the height of the colliculus seminalis.

The utriculus prostaticus consists of an unpaired lower section with paired upper extremities. It communicates with the united vas deferens and seminal vesicle, and so with the urethra.

The seminal vesicles are remarkably well developed, rather twisted and elongated " worm-like " structures, reminiscent of the uterine horns of the female. They measure about 10 cm. in length and 0·6 cm. in width at their base (Walker, 1910). Their weight is very variable (1 to 10 g. in large pigs ; Deanesly and Rowlands, 1936). The seminal vesicles frequently possess diverticula, especially in immature animals.

The prostate gland, as in other rodents, consists of three separate pairs of lobes. These can be distinguished by their external appearance, position, and histological character, and have been described by Engle (1926) as proximal, intermediate and distal lobes. The proximal lobes lie very close to the base of the seminal vesicles (Walker, 1910). Their ducts open on the apex of the colliculus seminalis sepa-rately from the ducts of the other two lobes, and in close proximity to the common orifice of the vasa deferentia and seminal vesicles.

A single pair of bulbo-urethral glands is present. These open into the cavernous part of the urethra by means of fairly long excretory ducts. Their structure closely resembles that of the small glands which are formed along the entire extent of the urethra.

There are poorly developed preputial glands, while anal glands are altogether absent (Disselhorst, 1904).

The penis of the guinea-pig and that of allied hystricomorph rodents has been described by Dathe (1937). When not erect, the organ shows a marked curvature, the concavity of which looks down and backwards (the guinea-pig is retromingent). Its distal end is completely concealed within the preputial sac, an invagination of the skin of the perineum which opens on the top of a small, almost hairless promin-ence immediately in front of the anus. At rest, the tip of the glans lies some 6 mm. above this orifice. During erection the penis straightens out and points forward. At the same time the preputial sac is everted and forms an outer cover for it. The length of the penis in the adult is approximately 45 to 50 mm., the glans alone accounting for a third of this total. Its greatest diameter is 4 to 5 mm.

While conforming to the basic mammalian pattern, the penis of the guinea-pig shows certain unusual features. Among them are the T-shaped external urinary pore, brought about by a blind dermal pouch or saccule which opens into the urethra just proximal to the external meatus, and the presence of innumerable horny spikes or spurs arranged either singly or in small groups like combs. Apart from a narrow median strip on the ventral surface, these invest the entire circumference of the glans. They tend to be more sparsely arranged proximally near the reflection of the prepuce. Histologically these structures consist of modified dermal papillae with a desquamating surface layer. They are also represented on the internal surface in the form of many tiny spikes and two large spurs or styles (" Hornstifte ") about 3 to 5 mm. in length, which are found at the bottom of the saccule. During erection they are evaginated with the latter, and then protrude conspicuously from the swollen glans.

The significance of all these structures has been variously interpreted, but the most acceptable explanation seems to be that they help to anchor the penis within, while not preventing its movements inside, the vagina. They may also have special sensory stimulating effects.

The female

The ovary is ovoid in shape and measures 0·3 to 0·6 cm. × 0·2 to 0·4 cm. The combined weight of both organs in mature animals varies between 50 and 150 mg. and is not much increased during pregnancy (Deanesly and Rowlands, 1936).[1]

The ovaries lie just cranial to the tips of the uterine horns, and are partly hidden in ovarian bursae, the medial

[1] Stafford, Collins and Mossman (1942) have described the existence of a " thecal gland " in the ovary of the guinea-pig at oestrus similar to that of the pocket gopher (Mossman, 1937b) and other animals (*see* Harrison, 1946).

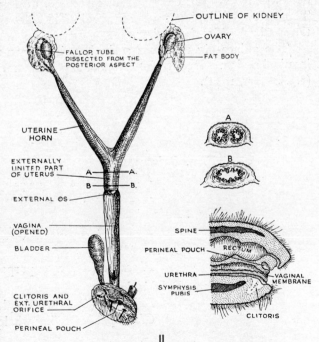

Fig. 2. 23—The reproductive tract of the guinea-pig. I. The organs of the male *in situ* (half schematic) (about ¾ natural size). II. The organs of the female (ventral view). Perineum twisted to show the openings of the urethral, vaginal and anal canals (indicated by probes) (about ⅔ natural size). Upper inset: transverse sections through the cervical segment of the uterus at levels A and B. Lower inset: diagrammatic median section through lower part of the body. Anoestrous condition, vagina closed by epithelial membrane. (After Seiferle, 1933.)

boundary of which is formed by the ovarian ligament. The uterine tubes measure about 5 to 6 cm. in length, and are greatly twisted, becoming wider as they join the straight uterine horns. The latter measure from 3 to 4·6 cm., with an external diameter of 0·2 to 0·4 cm. (Drahn, 1924), and diverge from each other in the form of a widely-open V. They join distally to form what appears externally as a single uterine body (Fig. 2. 23, II). Actually, they are separated by a thin median septum as far as the lower cervical segment, where they fuse with each other. Hence there are two internal cervical openings, but only one common external os, which protrudes from a well-developed " portio " into the vagina (Seiferle, 1933). Very occasionally the uterine canals may remain separate throughout their entire extent.

The distal end of the vagina is continued into a shallow groove, without forming a true vestibule. In addition to the vagina the intestinal and urinary tracts open into this groove which has consequently been described as the " fossa ano-vagino-urethralis." As in the rabbit, there is a small blind diverticulum (the so-called " perineal sac ") between the anal and vaginal openings. This communicates with two modified sebaceous " perineal " glands, and is usually filled with their secretions.

The lower end of the vagina is normally closed by an epithelial membrane but opens periodically at oestrus and, of course, during parturition (Fig. 2. 23, II). There are no labia, but a superficial skin fold hides the well-developed clitoris and the urethral orifice from view.

The guinea-pig possesses a single pair of mammary glands, situated in the inguinal region. Isolated instances of supernumerary nipples have been recorded (e.g. Speert, 1942).

CETACEA

Fam. *Balaenopteridae*
　　Balaenoptera (Blue, Fin whale)
　　Megaptera (Humpback whale)
Fam. *Balaenidae*
　　Balaena ; Eubalaena (Right whale)
Fam. *Phocaenidae*
　　Phocaena (Common porpoise)
Fam. *Delphinidae*
　　Delphinus (Common dolphin)
　　Globicephala (Ca'ing whale ; " Blackfish ")

Families : *Balaenopteridae ; Balaenidae*
Genera : *Balaenoptera ; Megaptera ; Balaena* (= *Eubalaena*)

The reproductive organs of whales have been described in detail by Mackintosh and Wheeler and by Matthews in the " Discovery Reports " (1929, 1937–1938), as well as in other papers (Mackintosh, 1946 ; Matthews, 1948). The following summary is based on these various sources.

The male

   The penis is retractile and is usually withdrawn into a preputial sac situated within a sagittally-disposed genital groove which is separated by a considerable distance from the anus (about 10 per cent of the total length of the animal). In fully-grown blue and fin whales, the penis, when extruded, measures from 2 to 2·5 m. It ends in a terminal cone which is not a reflection of the corpus spongiosum over the corpora cavernosa, and hence does not constitute a true glans penis. In some whales the penis is cylindrical and tapers to a point. In others (e.g. the southern right whale) it ends in a short blunt flagellum. Pigmentation of the penis is frequent in blue and fin whales.

   The testes in the Cetacea are situated at the posterior end of the abdominal cavity. Ommanney (1932) states that the testes of the fin whale (*Balaenoptera physalus*) are always immediately below the kidneys. Engle (1927), on the other hand, in discussing the fin whale (*B. physalus*) and the humpbacked whale (*Megaptera nodosa*), states that the testes do not lie, as is usually maintained, in the abdominal cavity, but that they are found in the pubic region in a pouch which appears to begin at the subcutaneous inguinal ring, and from which they are readily withdrawn into the abdominal cavity.

   The testes are rounded cylindrical organs which, while subject to much individual variation in size, reach prodigious dimensions in mature animals (e.g. over 1 m. in length in the southern right whale). The approximate volume of a mature testis varies between 20 and 50 litres in blue and fin whales, and between 5 and 17 litres in humpbacked whales.

   Except in the fin and humpbacked whales (Engle, 1927 ; Matthews, 1937c), there is little evidence of an annual breeding season in the male. As a rule few spermatozoa are found on histological section, and there is little seasonal variation in testicular size. The slow and steady production of spermatozoa throughout the year in most whales is correlated with the fact that pairing may take place at any time.

   There are no seminal vesicles, and the prostate consists of a diffuse series of urethral glands which lie within a differentiated region of the circular urethral muscle to which the name compressor prostatae is applied (Ommanney, 1932). There was no trace of a utriculus prostaticus in the two specimens of fin whale examined by this worker. This structure has, however, been described as occurring in other whales, and it may be assumed that the degree of its persistence in Cetacea is variable (*see* below).

The female

   In the mature female whale the vulva is a long elliptical groove which lies immediately cranial to the anus. By contrast, the male possesses a well-developed perineum (*see* above), and this feature constitutes the most obvious external difference between the two sexes. The vulva is open in front so that the clitoris is just visible, and the nipples of the mammary glands are situated on either side of it in slits or mammary grooves. When the female is in heat, the vulva is believed to contain more mucus than normal and to be more open and congested. Immediately before parturition the vulval cleft is greatly swollen and stretched open. In some species, such as the sperm and southern right whale, both the anus and vagina open jointly into what is usually referred to as the " cloacal groove." A short fleshy pad separates the two openings within this groove. Structures believed to be homologous with the human labia majora and minora have been identified in whales (Harrison, 1949).

The clitoris is an incurved keeled structure about 8 cm. long. Its apex is trilobed and is directed backwards. Beneath it are the openings of a pair of small glands and behind these the urethra opens. From an attachment immediately behind the urethra, a thick strand of tissue some 7 or 8 cm. long and about 1 cm. in diameter stretches in young animals across the star-shaped entrance of the vagina and joins its posterior margin. This vaginal band is believed by Mackintosh and Wheeler (1929) to represent the hymen. When unbroken, it indicates sexual immaturity. Its remains are usually inconspicuous in mature animals.

The ovaries of whales vary between 20 and 40 cm. in length, and in the humpbacked whale (*Megaptera nodosa*) a single ovary may weigh as much as 1·4 kg. The organs are convoluted, and have a very irregular surface, owing to the prominence of numerous corpora lutea and follicles. The former are conspicuous structures which may measure more than 10 cm. in diameter (Mackintosh, 1946). Up to thirty old corpora lutea may be found in a single pair of whale ovaries. The convolutions on the surface of the ovaries are represented in the foetus by furrows. In humpbacked whales large Graafian follicles (3·5 to 5·0 cm. in diameter) are found only at oestrus (Dempsey and Wislocki, 1941).

The uterus lies close to the ventral abdominal wall, and consists of a relatively short common cavity or body and two long cornua. In the fin whale the diameter of the non-pregnant horns rarely exceeds 25 cm. and averages 10 to 12 cm., but a horn nearly 80 cm. wide has been reported in a blue whale (Matthews, 1948). Involution of the enlarged pregnant uterus occurs rapidly after parturition.

In at least some species of whale the cervical canal and the upper part of the vagina show a very complex arrangement similar to that met in the Delphinidae (*see* below).

The mammary tissue in blue and fin whales is situated almost entirely cranial to the teats. In shape each gland resembles an elongated pear some 2 metres long, the apex of which is farthest removed from the (single) teat. The glands are normally involuted and do not increase in size until late pregnancy. During lactation they may be from 15 to 30 cm. deep (Matthews, 1948).

Families : *Phocaenidae* ; *Delphinidae*

Genera : *Phocaena* ; *Delphinus* ; *Globicephala*

A detailed account of the reproductive organs of the family Delphinidae has been given by Meek (1918). As in whales, the sexes in the dolphins are readily distinguished by the fact that in the female the anal and vulval openings are close together, and sometimes occupy the same groove, while in the male the preputial pouch is situated well in front of the anus. As in whales, too, the teats of the mammary glands are found in slit-like openings on either side of the vulva. The vestigial teats of the male lie on either side of the anus.

The male

The testes of the common porpoise (*Phocaena phocaena*) are intra-abdominal organs and undergo an enormous increase in size during the summer (up to

700 g.). The vasa deferentia open separately on either side of the colliculus seminalis in the floor of the urethra. Between their openings, and somewhat caudal to them, is the single or double opening of the utriculus prostaticus.[1] Seminal vesicles do not occur in the porpoise. The collecting ducts of the prostate are numerous and open on either side of the colliculus caudal to the openings of the vasa deferentia. The prostate is a fairly compact gland situated lateral and dorsal to the upper part of the urethra. There are no bulbo-urethral glands.

The penis is highly developed and its muscles are massive and strong. They are associated mainly with the retraction of the organ into the preputial sheath and with its erection. Only the distal part of the penis enters the vagina during coitus, and it is separated from the rest by a " joint " which allows it a wide range of movement.

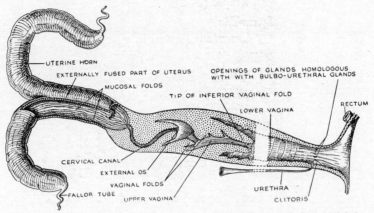

Fig. 2. 24—The reproductive tract of a female Ca'ing whale. (Slightly modified from Harrison, 1949.)

The female

The uterus in the porpoise is typically bicornuate. The uterine tubes are much coiled, and the short body of the uterus descends as a cervix into the vagina, which is greatly modified in its uppermost part. The ventral vaginal wall occupies the same plane as the uterus, but the dorsal wall is distended into a cavity. The vaginal mucosa at the caudal extremity of this cavity is modified to form two strong folds which act as valves and convert the upper dilatation of the vagina into a " spermathecal " recess. There are two main folds, the upper springing from the ventral vaginal wall and the more caudal from the dorsal wall. Caudal to these folds the vaginal mucosa is smooth, although superficially somewhat furrowed. The aperture between the vagina and the vestibule of the vulva is very small, and is controlled by a strong sphincter which under ordinary conditions is presumably contracted. According to Meek the narrow entrance to the vagina is an adaptation for occluding the vaginal cavity from the sea, while the spermathecal recess prevents the semen leaving the vagina on the withdrawal of the penis.

[1] The persistence of fused and blindly-ending Müllerian ducts in addition to a normal utriculus prostaticus in a white-beaked dolphin (*Lagenorhynchus albirostris*) has been reported by Meek (1918).

In the Ca'ing whale (*Globicephala*) the uterine cavity opens through a small aperture into a curved and narrow canal which measures about 8 cm. in the adult and which represents the true cervical canal. Below its projecting lower end are a series of large transverse folds, two of which entirely encircle the vagina, and thus create two chambers (Harrison, 1949). The cervix projects into the upper of these vaginal chambers, while the lower one communicates with the distal part of the vagina. Secondary folds may arise from the main or primary ones just referred to (Fig. 2. 24).

CARNIVORA

Fam. *Canidae*
        Canis (Domestic dog)
        Vulpes (Fox)
Fam. *Hyaenidae*
        Crocuta (Spotted hyaena)
Fam. *Felidae*
        Felis (Cat)
Fam. *Mustelidae*
        Mustela (Ferret, weasel, stoat)

Family *Canidae*
Canis

The male

The scrotum is globular in shape, and is situated between the inguinal region and anus (Sisson, 1940). The testes are comparatively small, round to ovoid in shape, and usually arranged one behind the other in separate scrotal compartments. Their size varies with the breed. Average figures are : 3 to 4 cm. in width by 2 to 2·5 cm. in thickness. The weight is extremely variable, and ranges from 3·25 to 29 g. (Gutzschebauch, 1935). The epididymis is large and closely attached along the dorso-lateral surface of the testis. The vasa deferentia have small and narrow ampullae. As in most carnivores, there are no seminal vesicles.

The relatively large and globular-shaped prostate is divided externally into two lateral lobes by a shallow median furrow. It varies considerably both in size and position, depending on the state of the bladder. It is often enlarged, particularly in old animals, but involution is equally common (Zuckerman and McKeown, 1938). The utriculus prostaticus is a small compressed saccule within the colliculus seminalis, and there are no bulbo-urethral glands.

The penis is distinguished by a long os penis which in large dogs may reach a length of 10 cm. Posteriorly, the two corpora cavernosa are separated by a median septum. The glans is very long and extends over the entire length of the os penis. Its anterior part is cylindrical, and its free end is pointed. Behind this the glans shows a rounded enlargement, the bulbus glandis, also composed of erectile tissue. The prepuce forms a complete sheath around the anterior part of the penis. Its inner or penile layer is closely attached to the anterior prolonged part of the glans, and more loosely to the posterior bulbar part (Fig. 2. 25a).

The bitch

The reproductive tract of the bitch presents a few unusual morphological features.

Each of the flattened ovaries is completely enclosed in a roomy peritoneal pouch, the bursa ovarica. The walls of the latter, as well as the broad uterine ligaments, are loaded with fat so that the ovaries are practically invisible *in situ*. To inspect them they have to be delivered through the slit-like opening of each bursa.

The uterine tube is buried in the fat of the ovarian bursa and describes almost a complete circle around the ovary before it joins the uterine horn, the junction of the two being marked by a small papilla.

The slender uterine horns are long and straight. They are of equal diameter throughout their entire course, but frequently differ in length. They converge upon the body of the uterus in V-shaped fashion (Fig. 2. 25*b*).

The body of the uterus is of the " subseptus " type, i.e. consists of a common cavity which is subdivided only in its most cranial extent by a short midline septum.

The superficial layer of the uterine mucosa may contain dark pigment, especially on old implantation sites.

The cervix is represented by a short and thick-walled segment, about 0·3 to 1 cm. in length, and is distinguished by the remarkable development of

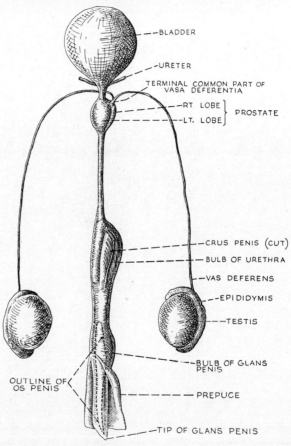

Fig. 2. 25*a*—The reproductive organs of the male dog in ventral view. Urethra and penis shown from side (about ⅓ natural size).

its fibro-muscular elements. There is no well-defined internal os, and glandular uterine epithelium is present in the proximal part of the cervical canal. The junction with the squamous epithelium of the vagina is indistinct, and occurs above the level of the external os. The latter opens on the summit of a short cone-shaped vaginal " portio," which is completely surrounded by the vaginal fornix, except posteriorly.

The upper part of the vagina is wider than the lower. Its length varies from 7 to 15 cm., depending upon size and breed (Asdell, 1947).

The large clitoris consists of tough adipose, non-erectile tissue, but its glans contains a corpus cavernosum. The greater vestibular glands are missing.

The vaginal orifice is concealed by prominent, hairy folds or labia.

There are usually 5 pairs of mammary glands. These are arranged in two series, and extend from the posterior part of the pectoral region to the inguinal

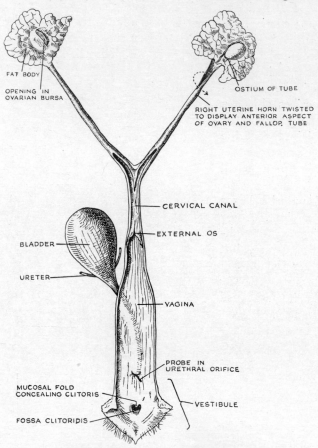

FAT BODY

OPENING IN
OVARIAN BURSA

OSTIUM OF TUBE

RIGHT UTERINE HORN TWISTED
TO DISPLAY ANTERIOR ASPECT
OF OVARY AND FALLOP. TUBE

CERVICAL CANAL

EXTERNAL OS

BLADDER

URETER

VAGINA

PROBE IN
URETHRAL ORIFICE

MUCOSAL FOLD
CONCEALING CLITORIS

VESTIBULE

FOSSA CLITORIDIS

Fig. 2. 25b—The reproductive organs of the bitch in dorsal
view. Right uterine horn and ovary twisted to expose
ventral aspects; uterine (Fallopian) tube traced through fat
body (about ½ natural size).

region (Sisson, 1940). The short teats contain some 6 to 12 excretory ducts which open through small orifices.

Vulpes

The reproductive tract of the fox closely resembles that of the dog.

The male

The testis and epididymis show well-marked seasonal changes in weight. At the peak of the breeding season, the testis weighs approximately 10 g. and the epididymis 2·4 g. The os penis does not appear to show a corresponding change.

The female

Neither the gonads nor the accessory organs present many noteworthy peculiarities. The ovary is distinguished by the prominence of the corpora lutea.

These seem to persist for a long time during pseudopregnancy and after parturition, and in this respect resemble the corpora lutea of the bitch.   During
pseudopregnancy they " dominate the ovaries to the total exclusion of any except
the smallest follicles " (Rowlands and Parkes, 1935).

An unusual feature is the partial or complete occlusion of the uterus and vagina
of the vixen during the progestational phase of the cycle (Rowlands and Parkes,
1935).   The condition in the uterus seems to be unique for the fox,[1] but atrophy
of the mid-vagina in pregnancy and local occlusion of the lumen have also been
observed in the shrew (Brambell, 1935).

Family *Hyaenidae*
Crocuta

This species is of unusual interest owing to the almost complete lack of external
sexual dimorphism.   The following summary is based on Matthews' detailed
account (1941b).

The male

The testes measure about 4 cm. by 2 cm. in length and width.   They are contained in the posterior compartments of two shallow scrotal pouches which lie on
either side of the midline.   Complete descent into the scrotum appears to be the
rule, but occasionally the gonads may lie subcutaneously in the perineum without
revealing themselves by external swellings.   The vasa deferentia unite to form
a minute common duct about 3 mm. in length just before opening into the
urethra, on the summit of a poorly developed colliculus seminalis.

There are no seminal vesicles, and the prostate is very variable in general development and size.   As a rule, it is hardly distinguishable as a separate organ,
being buried in the connective tissue surrounding the urethra.   When it is well
developed, it consists of two lobes, joined medially, that lie dorsal to the urethra,
at the level of the openings of the vasa deferentia (Fig. *2*. 26, II).

The bulbo-urethral glands consist of a pair of well-formed pyriform organs
which measure approximately 3·5 cm. × 2·0 cm. in length and width.   Their
ducts are about 6·5 cm. long.

The anal glands are conspicuous and consist of numerous small lobes which
surround a central cavity.   Their short ducts open into the " anal pouch," a
circular depression surrounding the anus, which lies immediately behind the
scrotal pouches and 5–7 cm. in front of the root of the tail.

The penis varies from 15 to 20 cm. in length from the insertion of the ischio-
cavernosi muscles to the tip of the glans.   Its distal part is free and pendulous and
at the base measures about 5 cm. × 3 cm.

The glans penis is approximately 3 to 4 cm. long and is an elongated ovoid
with a pointed end and its greatest width towards the base.   Its distal part is
smooth, but the proximal part is covered with a large number of small, backwardly-
directed spines.   This spine-covered area extends nearer the tip of the glans on
the ventral than on the dorsal surface, and is sharply marked off from the smooth
area.   It stops abruptly a few millimetres distal to the junction of glans and

[1] Some doubt exists about a similar condition reported in the dugong (Hill, 1945 ; *see*
p. 67, above).

E*

prepuce. The meatus is a longitudinal slit about 2 to 3 mm. in length on the dorsal surface of the tip.

A pair of rudimentary nipples is present on each side of the mid-ventral line, approximately level with the anterior border of the base of the free part of the penis.

The female

The external genitalia of the female, especially the immature female, closely resemble those of the male. The " peniform " clitoris is perforated by the urogenital canal and resembles in shape and position the penis of the male. Scrotal pouches closely simulating those of the male occur in corresponding positions.

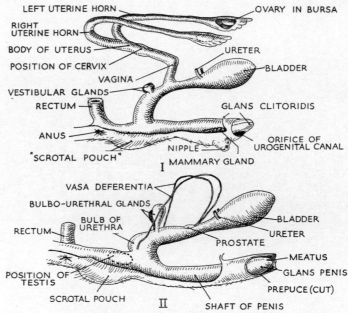

Fig. 2. 26—The urogenital tract of the female (I) and male (II) hyaena.
(Slightly modified from Matthews, 1941b.)

The perineum and anal glands are superficially similar to those of the male (Matthews, 1941b). The glans clitoridis is " strikingly similar," both in shape and in the presence of a proximal spinous area, to the corresponding male organ. It is, however, slightly smaller (Fig. 2. 26, I).

The urogenital canal opens at the tip of the glans of the clitoris. In the prepubertal state the meatus is no larger than that of the male, but during sexual maturation it increases in size and " spreads down the under-surface of the glans, splitting the fraenum preputii, so that a larger orifice is formed, through which copulation and parturition can take place " (Matthews, 1941b). In this way a condition similar to " hypospadias " is produced. At the completion of the process of transformation the meatus " instead of being a longitudinal slit 0·25 cm. long on the dorsal surface of the tip of the glans, is a longitudinal opening 1·5 cm. long." Corresponding growth changes occur in the prepuce.

The nipples of the mammary glands in the non-parous mature female are no bigger than in immature animals. They undergo considerable hypertrophy during pregnancy and lactation, when they grow to about 2·5 cm. in length and

1·0 cm. in diameter, and become surrounded by large conically-raised areolae. Non-functional supernumerary nipples may also be present. After the end of lactation the nipples show little involution. Their large size constitutes a characteristic feature of the parous animal. It is the only character by which the sexes can be readily distinguished, without dissection.

The relations of the urethra and vagina to the urogenital canal are the only other points of interest presented by the female sex tract. This canal, which is formed by the junction of the vagina and urethra, measures about 4 cm. in length to the base of the clitoris. A hymenal fold shuts it off from the vagina just proximal to the junction of the urethra. The fold may act as a valve which prevents the contents of the bladder entering the vagina. There is a pair of well-developed greater vestibular glands which open into the urogenital canal close to the base of the clitoris.

Contrary to long-established belief, there is a true vagina which varies from 6 cm. in length in the pre-pubertal to 13 cm. in the parous animal. Proximally, it is separated from the uterus by a low mucous fold, representing the external os uteri.

The two uterine horns are separated from each other in the greater part of their extent by a longitudinal median septum which, however, does not reach as far as the external os. The most distal part is thus undivided and forms a short " corpus."

The ovaries are ovoid in shape, and in the parous animal measure about 2 cm. in length. They lie within ovarian bursae which communicate with the peritoneal cavity through longitudinal slit-like openings.

Family *Felidae*

Felis

The Domestic Cat

The male

The testes are enclosed in a scrotum which lies ventral to the anus and the distal part of the penis. Neither the epididymis nor the vas deferens show any unusual features. According to Mivart (1881), both the hydatid of Morgagni and the organ of Giraldès may be represented near the head of the epididymis.

A firm, compact prostate is present round the neck of the bladder, but, as usual in Carnivora, there are no seminal vesicles. Cowper's glands are well developed, and each opens into the urethra by a single duct at the root of the penis. Within the prostatic urethra there is a typical colliculus seminalis on which open the utriculus prostaticus (between the openings of the vasa deferentia) and the prostatic ducts. The distal part of the urethra is lined by squamous epithelium.

The penis is conical and is suspended from the abdomen by a fold of skin which envelops the glans penis to form a prepuce (Fig. 2. 27 A). In its sexually inactive condition the penis is bent backwards, so that the cat is retromingent. There is an os penis or baculum, and the surface of the glans is covered by hard papillae whose points are directed towards the corona of the glans.

The female

The ovaries of the cat are ovoid bodies which lie within folds of the peritoneum that form ovarian bursae. The right ovary lies at the lower pole of the corresponding kidney.   The left is somewhat higher and more lateral.   The medial (lower) poles of the ovaries are attached to the uterus by strong ovarian ligaments.

The lateral end of the uterine tube is attached in the region of the hilus of the ovary by one or more fimbriae.   The infundibulum passes over the superior pole of the ovary, parallel to whose long axis the tube runs, to be continued into the uterine horn at about the level of the caudal pole of the ovary.   The mucosa of the ampullary part of the uterine tube is considerably folded, the folds running parallel to the lumen.   The juxta-uterine part has a narrower lumen, and its

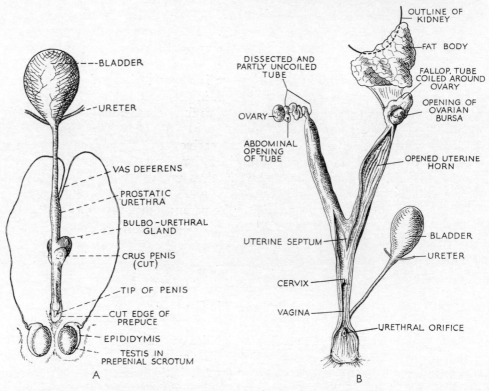

Fig. 2. 27—The reproductive organs of the cat.   A, the male in ventral view; urethra and penis shown from side (about ½ natural size).   B, the female in dorsal view; ovary and tube dissected on left side and twisted on right side to expose ventral aspects (about ⅖ natural size).

mucosa is less folded.   It is furnished with a well-developed circular muscle layer.

The uterine horns are very long and join caudally to form the body of the uterus. As they approach each other they increase in girth.   In the resting phase their mean diameter is 7 mm.   The body of the uterus has a single lumen and its cervical part, which opens into the vagina, is lined by mucosa identical with that of the uterus proper.

The cervix is remarkably short (only about 2 mm.).   It lacks a true internal os, and is directly continuous with the dorsal wall of the vagina.   The external os is usually present as a V-shaped opening.   It is surrounded anteriorly and on both sides (but not dorsally) by vaginal fornices (Fig. 2. 27B).

The junction between the uterine and vaginal epithelium is gradual and distinct and lies in the region of the external os.

The fact that the uterine cornua unite to form a corpus uteri with a single lumen may be related to the finding that fertilised ova may pass down one uterine horn across the body of the uterus into the other uterine horn. This has been shown in experiments, in which one uterine horn has been ligated and divided (a procedure which precludes the passage of fertilised ova along that horn), and in which it has been observed that embryos may attach themselves in the basal part of that horn after the subsequent mating of the animal (Markee and Hinsey, 1933 ; Gros, 1936).

The vaginal mucosa is folded and has a squamous epithelium, and its stroma contains many mucous glands. The vagina is continued into the vestibule of the urogenital canal, the external opening of which lies a little in front of the anus. The urethra also opens into the vestibule and in front of it lies the clitoris flanked on either side and posteriorly by hairy wrinkled labia covering the greater vestibular glands. The clitoris is about 1 cm. long and does not possess a proper glans. In the region of the vestibule the vaginal musculature is arranged to form a sphincter, but there is no bulb.

The mammary glands of the cat extend on either side of the ventral surface from the axilla to the pelvic region. Each gland has a fibrous investment which sends off septa to divide the parenchyma into numerous lobules. The collecting ducts end in conical dilatations or reservoirs from which excretory ducts extend to the nipples. The excretory ducts have a lining of small columnar cells and walls of connective and elastic tissue. There are four nipples on each side. The whole mammary apparatus of the cat does not necessarily function at the same time. For example, the cranial two segments may be involuted when the caudal two are active.

The mammary gland in the male cat is rudimentary, but has the same structure and disposition as in the female.

The Scottish Wild Cat

The reproductive tract in this species differs only in details from that of the domestic cat (Matthews, 1941c).

In the male, the prostate and Cowper's glands are " proportionally smaller," and the prostate causes only a slight swelling of the urethra just distal to the junction of the vasa deferentia. This swelling has to be verified histologically for the presence of glandular tissue.

In the female the ovaries lie within ovarian bursae which communicate with the peritoneal cavity by means of longitudinal slits placed on their internal aspects. The length of the uterine horns depends on the state of reproductive activity of the animal concerned, and varies from 12·0 to 34·0 cm. The cervix projects into the vagina for about 2·0 mm. Its position is indicated externally by a slight swelling at the junction of the corpus uteri and vagina. The vagina measures 2·4 to 3·8 cm., and its lower end is marked off from the vestibule by a distinct hymenal ring.

As in the domestic cat, there are usually four pairs of mammary glands. Of these only the lower two (inguinal and abdominal) are regularly functional during lactation, while the axillary pair is sometimes absent.

Family *Mustelidae*

Mustela

The Ferret

Compared with the wealth of information on the sexual physiology of the ferret, there are astonishingly few accounts of the morphology of the reproductive system.

The male

Most descriptions of the reproductive tract are concerned with the seasonal changes undergone by the testis and epididymis (Allanson, 1931, 1932 ; Allanson, Rowlands and Parkes, 1934).

In the Northern hemisphere the breeding season of the ferret lasts from April to August. Regression of the sexual organs takes place during autumn, and in October the weights of the testis and epididymis reach their lowest levels (0·16 to 0·2 g. and 0·15 g., respectively). At the same time the diameter of the seminiferous tubules averages 75 to 100 μ, and spermatogenesis, except very occasionally, is in abeyance. During November and December the weight of the testes begins to increase, reaching a peak during April and May when the testis has increased to 1·25 to 2·0 g. (a ten-fold increment), and the epididymis to 0·35 g. At this time the seminiferous tubules measure 150 to 190 μ. Corresponding changes take place in the size of the penis, the diameter of the vas deferens and in the volume of the interstitial cells of the testis.

Active spermatogenesis begins in November. Spermatocytes are present in December, spermatids in January and mature spermatozoa early in February. The accessory organs of the ferret are vestigial, and there is no seasonal movement of the testis (Allanson, 1931).

The appearance of the reproductive tract is shown in Fig. 2. 28A.

The female

The reproductive tract of the female is of the usual carnivore type, and was described by Marshall (1904) in the following terms : " The uterus of the ferret is typically bicornuate, each of the uterine horns passing forward into a slender Fallopian tube, which is very much coiled at its anterior end, passing several times round one side of the ovary. The mouth of the Fallopian tube encloses the ovary, so that the ova on being discharged pass into a sac, and consequently are not shed into the body-cavity." The uterine horns fuse externally and internally a short distance from the vagina, thereby forming a short single cavity which is continued into that of the cervix (Fig. 2. 28B). The cervical segment is " multi-diverticular," and invaginated into the upper part of the vagina (Hamilton and Gould, 1940).

The epithelium in the upper part of the fused horns is essentially uterine in character, but in the lower part, where it grades into that of the cervix, it becomes pseudo-stratified and the glands disappear.

The ovaries are irregular ovoids whose cranio-caudal length always exceeds the dorso-ventral and side-to-side dimensions. According to Robinson (1918), the left ovary is usually bigger than the right.

The dimensions of the gonads and accessory organs undergo cyclic changes very similar to those of the male. During the breeding season (April to August),

the ovaries weigh between 100 to 200 mg., and the uterus " up to about 1·0 g."
(Hill and Parkes, 1933).   The remainder of the year is occupied by a period of
anoestrus, during which the ovaries average about 50 mg. (though liable to much
individual variation) and the uterus between 50 and 200 mg.

The number of mammary glands varies greatly in different animals.   The usual
number is four pairs, which are distributed along a slightly curved line between the
umbilicus and the vulva, but there may be as many as seven on one side (Thomson,
personal communication).   The distances between the individual glands on each

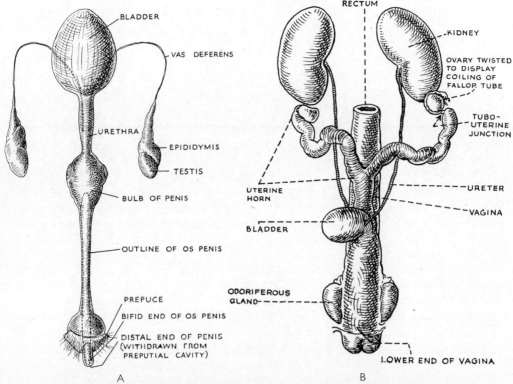

Fig. 2. 28—The reproductive tract of the male (A) and female (B) ferret during the breeding season
(ventral view, semi-diagrammatic ; approx. natural size).

side also vary considerably in different specimens.   The glands undergo well-
marked changes during pregnancy and pseudo-pregnancy (Hammond and Marshall, 1930).   At oestrus duct growth begins round the nipples and, with the
formation of corpora lutea, the gland develops rapidly in a lateral direction,
adjacent glands meeting about the seventeenth day.

The Weasel

The male

The reproductive tract of the male weasel conforms to the general carnivore
pattern and has been briefly described by Hill (1939).

The testes appear to remain scrotal throughout the year, irrespective of the
breeding period.   Seasonal variations in the size of the gonads are not quite as
marked in the weasel as in the ferret.   During the short anoestrus (November to

February) the weight of the aspermatic testis is 25 to 35 mg. It undergoes a six-fold increase during the breeding season, the maximum average weight of about 200 mg. being reached in April or May. Seasonal variations in the size of the epididymis are closely related to those of the testis.

The vas deferens is slightly convoluted close to the tail of the epididymis, where it also reaches its greatest diameter. Beyond that point it continues as a thin, narrowing tube. Its terminal portion is slightly enlarged to form a " rather poorly developed ampulliform " swelling. Immediately behind the openings of the vasa the urethra is slightly thickened. There are no seminal vesicles and no obvious prostate gland.

The female

In the female, the periovarial sac is incomplete (Alden, 1942). The opening connecting it with the peritoneal cavity is inconspicuous but relatively large. It is protected by a greatly expanded infundibulum.

The Stoat

The reproductive organs of the stoat have been described by Deanesly (1935).

The male

In the immature male the testes lie in the inguinal region, from which they descend into scrotal sacs at the onset of the breeding season. The animal possesses an os penis which increases rapidly in weight as sexual maturity approaches. It does not regress during anoestrus.

The female

The reproductive organs of the female, which closely resemble those of the ferret, are described as follows by Deanesly. " The ovaries are flattened bodies enclosed in a capsule ; their surface is smooth and neither follicles nor corpora lutea project conspicuously. The Fallopian tube is not coiled but lies in a ring round the ovary and opens into the uterus just below the extremity. The uterus is small and bicornuate, and the uterine canals run side by side for about 1·5 mm. and then fuse at the top of the cervix. The single cervical canal is lined by uterine endometrium almost up to the vaginal opening. The vagina is thin and terminates in a vulval swelling which enlarges to about 0·5 cm. in diameter just before oestrus ; there are no vaginal glands. A minute knob of cartilage corresponding to the os penis may be found in the vulva."

The mammary glands lie low on the abdomen. The nipples which are often asymmetrical in position or number, vary from four to six pairs and are inconspicuous in the non-parous animal (Deanesly, 1935).

CHIROPTERA

Fam. *Vespertilionidae*
  Pipistrellus (Pipistrelle)
  Myotis (Common bat)
Fam. *Rhinolophidae*
  Rhinolophus (Horse-shoe bat)

Fam. *Nycteridae*

   Nycteris (Hispid bat)

Fam. *Phyllostomatidae*

   Glossophaga (" Vampire " bat)

Matthews (1941a), who has made a detailed study of certain African bats, writes that in *Chiroptera* the morphology of the reproductive tract shows great diversity of detail. Apart from the fairly homogeneous Megachiroptera and Phyllostomatidae, surprisingly wide differences are found in closely-allied species. The following is a brief summary of his findings (1937a, b, 1941a).

The male

The scrotum is never permanent. In many (and possibly all) bats the testes descend seasonally, and are contained in scrotal pouches which are found anywhere between the inguinal ring and the base of the tail. Their position may thus be either pre-anal (e.g. in *Nycteris*) or post-anal (e.g. in Vespertilionidae, in which the gonads lie on each side of the caudal vertebrae between the dorsal and ventral layers of the inter-femoral membrane). The epididymis of all bats is large in proportion to the testis, and its enlarged tail serves as a sperm reservoir. The vasa deferentia usually, but not always, possess large glandular ampullae. The seminal vesicles may be present and well developed (as in *Triaenops afer*), but are more frequently absent. No instance is, however, on record in which both the seminal vesicles and the ampullae were absent in the same species, one structure always substituting for the (missing) other.

The prostate is a large, glandular mass which completely surrounds the urethra in some species, but is incomplete or only represented by the posterior part in others. Occasionally the ampullae of the vasa deferentia are partly embedded in the prostate (e.g. in Vespertilionidae). Contrary to previous reports, a small utriculus prostaticus is present in some bats.

The " urethral gland," which is found only in certain species of bat, appears to be peculiar to the Chiroptera. It lies between the prostate and the openings of Cowper's glands under cover of the urethral muscle and surrounding the urethra, into which its numerous short ducts open. Histologically it resembles the bulbo-urethral glands which occur and are comparatively large in all species of bat.

In rhinolophid bats the penis, which has a relatively large and furrowed glans and a thin and retractile prepuce, appears to be always directed cranially, while in the Vespertilionidae it varies from the cranially directed to the completely pendulous type. In the vespertilionid bats the glans is generally small, with no constricted neck separating it from the shaft of the penis, and is covered by a thick prepuce. Most species possess an os penis of very variable size and shape, but in two vespertilionid bats it is absent (Matthews, 1941a). In many species the corpora cavernosa and the corpus spongiosum are supplemented by a paired structure, called the accessory corpus cavernosum, which may form the greater part of the glans. The meatus is sometimes terminal, sometimes subterminal, and in *Pipistrellus pipistrellus*, instead of opening on the ventral surface, does so on the dorsal surface of the penis.

The female

The structure of the female reproductive organs has also been described by Matthews (1937b, 1941a).

The ovary measures about 1 to 2 mm. in its long axis, and is enclosed in a bursa ovarica which opens into the peritoneal cavity close to the point where the uterine tube joins the uterine horn, after taking a sinuous and circular course within the bursa.

The uterine horns are flattened dorso-ventrally and usually show some degree of asymmetry.   According to Matthews this varies from the asymmetrical functioning of symmetrical structures to definite structural asymmetry, accompanied by unilateral degeneration.   Most bats have bicornuate uteri.   Nevertheless they produce only one young at birth, with a marked tendency for the right horn to be the functional one, and the left horn to be atrophic (the reverse of the condition in birds and monotremes).   In one species not only the left cornu but also the left ovary is degenerate, and apparently never produces mature ova (Matthews, 1937a). On the other hand, in some types of bat (e.g. *Pipistrellus subflavus*) the horns are equal in size, and eggs ripen with equal frequency in the two ovaries (Guthrie, 1933).

The form of the uterus and cervical segment varies greatly.   For instance, in the horse-shoe (rhinolophid) bats the body of the uterus is about the same length as the uterine horns, but is smaller in diameter ; the os uteri is conical and projects into the dorsal surface of the upper vagina.   In *Nycteris*, on the other hand, there is no internal uterine body, and each horn communicates with its own cervical canal which opens separately into the vagina, while in *Taphozous* there is a completely divided septate uterine body communicating with a single cervical canal. In yet another species, *Glossophaga soricina*, the uterus is unilocular and has no cornua.   In this bat the endometrium undergoes cyclical changes which are of particular interest (Hamlett, 1934).

In some bats the round ligament of the uterus appears to be a character of taxonomic significance.   Thus, it is pigmented in *Myotis sodalis* and *grisescens* but not in *M. leucifugus* (Guthrie, 1933).

The large vagina extends ventrally well above the os uteri to form a large pouch which may be regarded as homologous with the human anterior fornix.   Its mucosa is thrown into many longitudinal folds and undergoes marked cornification at oestrus.   The zone of transition between the cylindrical uterine epithelium and the squamous vaginal epithelium is within the cervical canal.   The urethra lies to the right of the midline of the vagina, and opens into the urogenital sinus close to its external orifice, which is transversely disposed.

Some species possess a well-developed " female prostate," consisting of greatly enlarged urethral glands, the homologues of the male prostate.

There is one pair of pectoral mammary glands, each with a single nipple. A pair of false teats is situated on the os pubis (" pubic teats ") on either side of the midline.   The young animal clings upside down to its mother with one of these false teats in its mouth.   Although they do not contain any mammary tissue, it is of interest that these anchoring teats increase greatly in size during the first pregnancy and lactation, after which they do not return to their former condition.   Minute rudimentary pubic teats occur in the males of *Cardioderma* (Matthews, 1941a).

INSECTIVORA

Fam. *Erinaceidae*
        Erinaceus (Hedgehog)
Fam. *Talpidae*
        Talpa (Mole)
Fam. *Soricidae*
        Sorex (Common shrew)
        Blarina (Short-tailed shrew)
Fam. *Macroscelididae*
        Elephantulus (Elephant shrew)

Family *Erinaceidae*
Erinaceus

The male

The testes are intra-abdominal, and lie on each side of the bladder in the inguinal region, a true scrotum being absent. Dorsal to the bladder is a pair of multi-lobulated glands arranged in three fairly distinct main lobes, whose separate ducts ultimately run together and become invested in a common capsule. They enter the urethra immediately caudal to the neck of the bladder.

A pair of somewhat more compact, although also obviously lobulated, glands lie ventral to the bladder, and the common duct of each gland passes into the same region of the urethra as the multiple ducts of the dorsal glands. Outside the pelvis, situated caudal to the ischia and embedded in fascia close to the anus, are two large lobulated glands whose long ducts pass into the urethra. The utriculus prostaticus is well developed.

About fifteen orifices are to be seen on either side of the colliculus seminalis (Disselhorst, 1904). The most cranial pair represents the openings of the glands which lie under the skin near the anus. Immediately below are three or four openings of the ducts of the large glands dorsal to the bladder, and, next to them, those of the vasa deferentia. Still more distally are the openings of the two large glands placed ventral to the bladder. Beneath these lies the horse-shoe-shaped mouth of the bladder.

In addition to the openings referred to above, there are bulbo-urethral glands which do not penetrate the muscle of the bulb, and which open directly into the bulbar part of the urethra. Some of the ducts of these structures, which probably represent Cowper's glands, may open on the lower part of the colliculus.

Apart from these diffuse bulbo-urethral glands, there are thus three distinct pairs of accessory glands connected with the male reproductive tract : the largest and multi-lobed pair lying behind the bladder in the region usually occupied by the seminal vesicles ; a ventral pair, situated in front of the neck of the bladder, in the region generally associated with the prostate ; and a caudal pair which, though situated outside the pelvis, opens into the uppermost part of the urethra (Fig. 2. 29A). The proper designation and homologies of these structures has been the subject of considerable dispute (*see*, for example, Rauther, 1903 ; Disselhorst, 1904 ; Courrier, 1927).

The nomenclature adopted here is, for convenience, based on that accepted by Courrier (1927) in his study of the cyclical changes in the accessory organs of the hedgehog.   Courrier refers to the dorsal vesicular glands as " seminal vesicles," to the ventral vesicular glands as the " internal prostate," and to the external pelvic (para-anal) glands as the " external prostate."   Since the latter pair of glands occupy the site which in many animals is taken up by true Cowper's glands, they have been referred to as such by several writers, e.g. Seubert (1841) and Allanson (1934).   However, Linton (1907) and Courrier (1927) state, on the basis of histological studies, that the external prostate of the hedgehog has a very different structure from that of ordinary Cowper's glands, which, moreover, open into a completely different part of the urethra.

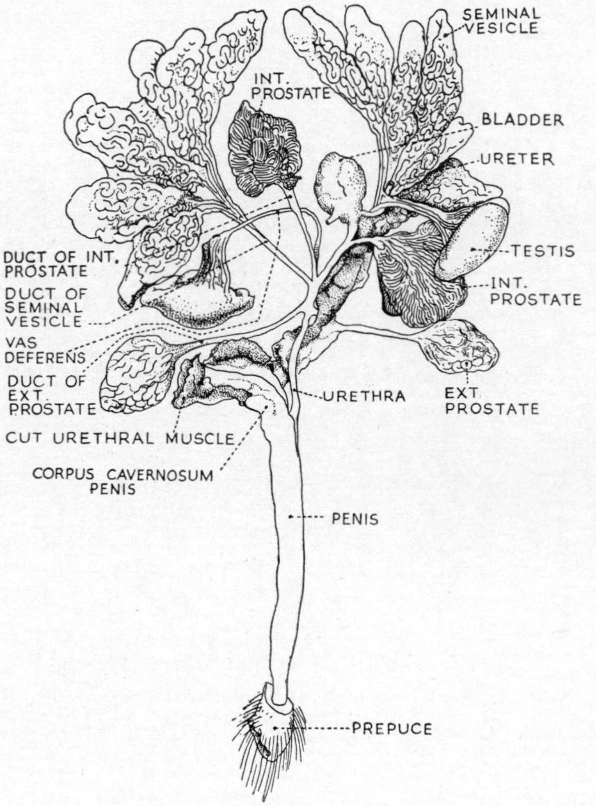

As already noted, the two dorsal structures to which the name seminal vesicles is applied, consist of three main lobes, which have the same internal structure.   Each is made up of a number of smaller lobules consisting of alveoli and ducts, which unite together to form main ducts. In their inactive condition the alveoli are separated by a vascular stroma of fibro-muscular tissue, and they are lined by a cylindrical epithelium which is much folded and which undergoes seasonal changes.

The internal and external prostates are similar in structure.   They are almost purely tubular glands, and differ furthermore from the seminal vesicles in the character of their epithelial lining.

The bulbo-urethral glands penetrate into the urethral muscle and comprise numer-

Fig. 2. 29A—The reproductive organs of the male hedgehog during the breeding season ; urethral muscle removed on one side.   (Redrawn from Allanson, 1934.)

ous lobules with an alveolar structure.   The alveoli are lined by cylindrical epithelium, and open, as noted above, by numerous ducts into the urethra.

At the height of the breeding season the reproductive tract may weigh over 50 g. or nearly 10 per cent of the total body weight (Allanson, 1934).   About four-fifths of the weight is due to the accessory organs.   The testes of mature animals are active from April to the end of August, then retrogress and remain quiescent until the spring.   However, atrophy of the reproductive organs is not as marked as in the ferret, and production of spermatogonia and spermatocytes never ceases entirely.

The penis lacks a baculum, and the glans is very indistinctly developed.   Anal and preputial glands are absent in the hedgehog.

The female

The reproductive organs of the female hedgehog vary in size according to their state of activity, but retain their essential form throughout the year (Deanesly, 1934).

The ovaries are roughly U-shaped and are bent round a thick muscular hilus. They are well vascularised, frequently pigmented, and their surface is always irregular, especially in the breeding season, when corpora lutea and follicles are prominent.

The ovaries are surrounded by peritoneal capsules which support the uterine tubes. The latter are about 50 to 80 mm. in length and are crescentically shaped, lying against the tips of the uterine cornua, into which they plunge after having become slightly narrower in diameter. A conspicuous parovarium is present in the hedgehog. It lies near the ovarian hilus, and consists of tubules of ciliated epithelium which show seasonal changes in size and activity.

The usually-pigmented uterine horns are thick and muscular, and measure from 1·5 to 2 cm. in length and 0·5 cm. in diameter. They lie almost at right angles to the cervix and vagina, and their lumina are continuous across the top of the short muscular cervix. The latter projects into the swollen region

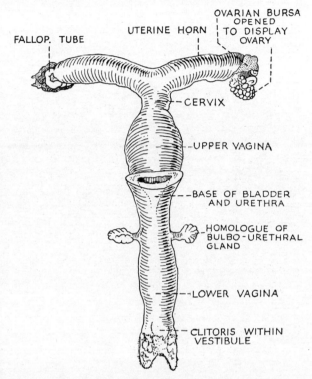

Fig. *2*. 29B—The reproductive organs of the female hedgehog during the breeding season; diagrammatic. (Slightly modified from Deanesly, 1934.)

of the upper vagina, surrounded by well-defined fornices, and the transition from uterine to vaginal epithelium occurs within the single cervical canal.

The vagina of the hedgehog is peculiar and is described by Deanesly as follows. It " is large and muscular, and undergoes seasonal size changes, but remains patent. For descriptive purposes it may be divided into three regions, which show a progressive decrease in the size of the lumen. In the first of these, or upper vagina, extending from behind and round the cervix to the point of junction of the urethra, the lumen is large and the wall relatively thin."

This part of the vagina shows the most marked changes during the reproductive cycle. At the onset of the breeding season it increases in size and becomes much dilated at oestrus. It is collapsed during most of pregnancy and lactation, as well as during anoestrus. In animals coming into heat after pregnancy the vagina is not as dilated as at the first oestrus. During the breeding season the upper vagina is often entirely filled by a thick fluid containing desquamated cornified epithelium mingled with the secretions of the cervical and vaginal glands (Courrier, 1924a, b).

The mid-vagina has a " more muscular wall and a much smaller lumen than the upper vagina " (Deanesly, 1934). The urethra, which runs within the wall of this segment, opens into the lumen some 2 cm. from the vulval orifice.

The lower vagina represents is the urogenital sinus, and has a simple and even narrower lumen. Immediately deep to its epithelium are several large lymph nodes.

The clitoris, which may contain a small cartilage, projects into the urogenital passage. In transverse sections of the clitoris a paired epidermal infolding can be seen, and below this a mass of blood vessels and connective tissue homologous with the corpora cavernosa.

The ducts of several small accessory glands open into the vagina. A pair of these, consisting of branched tubular, mucous glands lie at the level of the base of the bladder beneath the epithelium. Larger paired glands are found in the mid-vagina and extend dorso-laterally on either side of the urethra. Similar but smaller glands are found near the clitoris.

The most conspicuous of the vaginal glands are those lying outside the muscle wall, against the pelvic girdle. These are different in type from the preceding ones, and are probably homologous with the external prostates of the male. When dissected, they appear fan-shaped. They are composed of numerous very irregular tubules, and drain by a single main duct which opens into the vaginal lumen on each side. The tubules and ducts contain nuclear débris, especially during the breeding season, and in this they resemble those of the external and internal prostate. If, as Deanesly suggests, the glands found in the female are truly homologous with the external prostate, the interesting problem arises of the embryological relationship between the part of the vagina into which they open, and the upper urethra in the male (Fig. 2. 29B).

The mammary glands of the hedgehog are large and are situated somewhat laterally ; they ramify in the axillary and inguinal regions. Of the five symmetrical pairs of nipples which are usually present, one is thoracic and four are abdominal.

Family *Talpidae*

Talpa

The male

The anatomy of the reproductive tract of the male mole is not as difficult to interpret as that of the hedgehog, but it is nevertheless somewhat complicated.

The testes are intra-abdominal, and in their descent during the breeding season they migrate into small pouch-like extensions of the peritoneal cavity on either side of the base of the tail. Apart from the seminiferous elements, they contain interstitial cells aggregated in the form of an interstitial gland. This shows its most marked development in the anoestrous period, and begins to regress as spermatogenesis and the breeding season advance (Tandler and Grosz, 1912). A peculiarity of the reproductive tract is the presence of a large sac-like development of the tail of the epididymis to form a sperm reservoir (Fig. 2. 30, II).

The accessory organs consist of the vasa deferentia ; a symmetrically bilobed gland in front of the neck of the bladder which represents the prostate ; a pair of bulbo-urethral glands which are situated outside the pelvis on either side of the anus, and whose long ducts open into the urethra at the site of junction of the two crura penis ; and some simple sac-like urethral glands which do not penetrate the urethral wall.

The prostate consists of two bundles of ramifying tubules bound together with connective tissue. On cross-section the appearance of the organ is somewhat like that of the vesicular glands of higher mammals, for which it has been mistaken in the past. Each main lobe opens into the upper true urethra by one or two ducts opposite the openings of the vasa deferentia. Real seminal vesicles are not present in the mole.

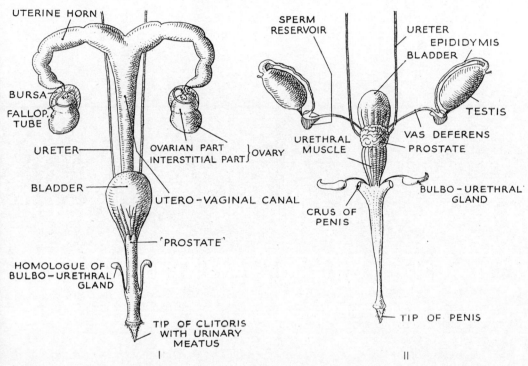

Fig. 2. 30—The reproductive organs of the mole. I, female at oestrus (ventral view). II, male (dorsal view). (Slightly modified from Godet, 1949.)

The upper urethra is similar in structure and arrangement to that of the hedge-hog. Thus in both species a blind extension of the urogenital sinus passes up in front of the upper part of the true urethra, externally similar to the utriculus pro-staticus of other animals, which is, however, said to be missing in the mole.

The female

Except during the breeding season, the female mole is almost indistinguishable from the male of the species. Detailed examination shows, however, that the mean total length of the body, the tail, the hind foot, and the anal papilla of the female are smaller than in the male, and that both the penis and the length of the perineum, i.e. the distance between the base of the clitoris or penis and the base of the anal papilla, are always longer in the male. According to Matthews (1935), " any adult mole, in which the external organ is less than 6 mm. in length, is female, or over 6 mm. in length is male ; while any mole, without an open vaginal orifice, in which the perineal length is less than 4 mm. is a female, or in which it is over 5 mm. is a male. The last two characters, taken together, give a complete diagnosis of the sex of any adult mole."

The similarity of the external genitalia of the male and female mole is reflected in their apparently more or less identical embryonic development. This has been studied by Wood Jones (1914), who found that in both sexes the opening of the urogenital sinus is carried forwards by closure of the inner genital folds, to the tip of the genital tubercle, which then becomes secondarily ensheathed within the overgrowing outer genital folds.

The vaginal orifice lies between the base of the clitoris and the anal papilla, and is frequently darkly pigmented. The pigment, which is occasionally present in prepubertal animals, may extend along the under surface of the clitoris, thereby marking the site of fusion of the labio-scrotal folds. The vaginal area is also often indicated by one or two depressions or, in parous animals, by a scar. At the time it opens it becomes purplish, and when patent, the surrounding tissue becomes oedematous, so that the vaginal orifice is situated on a small mound. This swelling is a sign of oestrus.

Anatomically the position of the vagina is of considerable interest. Wood Jones (1914) has shown that in the embryo of the mole up to about 30 mm. the Müllerian ducts open into the urogenital sinus close to the Wolffian ducts. After the urogenital sinus is carried forwards to the tip of the clitoris by the fusion of the inner genital folds, the connection of the Müllerian ducts with the sinus becomes lost, and the ducts, though fused above to form a common chamber with a wide lumen, pass downwards towards the central region of the perineum as attenuated strands of cells. At the same time the solid cords of ectodermal tissue grow in from the surface to meet the apparently desquamating Müllerian cells. This ingrowth is occasionally unilateral, but is always crescent-shaped in outline. Desquamation of this solid epithelial mass leads to the formation of the vaginal orifice during the breeding season. It is noteworthy that the Müllerian component of the female reproductive tract, which constitutes the uterus and tubes, is completely patent until some distance from the perineal surface, and that it is impossible to tell whether or not the epithelial cord of cells which connects the canalised Müllerian part of the tract with the surface is purely ectodermal in nature or both ectodermal and Müllerian.

At the end of the breeding season the canalised vaginal cord once again becomes solid. According to Matthews, the length of the solid epithelial strand varies from 2 to 5 mm., as compared with about 13 to 36 mm. for the whole utero-vaginal canal, which he took as the distance between the perineal site of the vagina and the junction of the utero-vaginal canal with the uterine cornua.

The reproductive tract of the female mole at the stage when the Müllerian ducts open into the urogenital sinus, which is carried forwards to the tip of the clitoris, bears an interesting resemblance to the permanent condition met with in the hyaena (*Crocuta crocuta*). In the hyaena the utero-vaginal canal undoubtedly opens into the urethra, which thus not only has the function associated with its name, but also serves as a copulatory organ and as a channel for birth (cf. p. 106). A further point of interest is the fact that, like the vagina in the mole, the urethra in the male squirrel is an ectodermal organ (Barnstein and Mossman, 1938). It should also be noted that the so-called utriculus prostaticus in rhesus monkeys, which reacts to oestrogenic stimulation like the definitive vagina in the female, is embryologically a paired and not a single organ.   Occasionally it remains a double structure, and the canalised columns of cells which form it, and which open into the urethra, are also crescentic in outline.

The uterus of the mole is typically bicornuate, the horns being two small tubes which approach the upper end of the utero-vaginal canal at right angles, and join it without forming an os uteri.   Matthews' (1935) description of the utero-vaginal canal is as follows : " In the anoestrous mole, during the last half of the year, the utero-vaginal canal, when viewed from the ventral surface, with the animal lying on its back, is a thin-walled tube running forward a short distance over the rectum.   It is moderately folded on itself, with a slight kink towards the dorsal surface a short distance above the bladder, and a more pronounced one with the convexity directed ventrally about two-thirds of the distance between the perineum and the uterine cornua.   The latter kink may be so pronounced as to take the form of an S-bend.   It is of such prominence that when the internal genitalia are removed from the body, and stretched out with their dorsal surface downwards, a hummock projecting upwards remains at the side of the kink."   Whether or not the S-bend is straightened out during coitus is unknown, although since the length of the penis during the breeding season is some 35 to 40 mm., it is possible that the bend may be obliterated and that the tip of the penis reaches the junction of the uterine cornua.   Schwarz (1928) suggests that the utero-vaginal canal does not assume its definitive form until after the first pregnancy.

The uterine tubes are small, and for most of their course they lie in the wall of the ovarian capsule, which they encircle.   The capsule is closely applied to that part of the ovary which is termed the interstitial gland (see below), but it forms a pouch around the ovarian part of the ovary.   The pouch is completely shut off from the peritoneal cavity, and the uterine tube opens into it (Fig. 2. 30, I).

The ovary is divided into two parts, and the division is visible macroscopically. The ovarian part of the gonad shows the usual structure, but in addition a variable number of interstitial cells is scattered in its stroma.   The interstitial part of the ovary (which is invested by the peritoneal capsule, and not by obvious germinal epithelium) was described in detail by Macleod (1880), and comprises a mass of interstitial cells in which are embedded medullary follicles consisting of cords of cells with deeply staining nuclei.   As will be described in Chapter 4, the two parts of the ovary undergo alternate phases of activity, comparable to those believed to occur in the testis (see above).

Family *Soricidae*
Genera : *Sorex ; Blarina*

The male

Descriptions of the reproductive tract in the common and short-tailed shrews (*Sorex araneus* Linn. and *Blarina brevicauda* Say) have been given by Arnbäck-Christie-Linde (1907), Brambell (1935) and Pearson (1944).

The testes of most immature and many mature animals are located in the abdominal cavity, within which they are firmly attached by a stout ligament.   In animals in which they lie in pouch-like extensions of the posterior end of the abdominal cavity, they can be easily returned to the abdomen by gentle pressure.

The testes of all wild adults remain large and functional during the breeding season, which lasts over spring and summer. They decrease in size, and spermatogenesis ceases, in the autumn. This regression is less marked in captive shrews, and in immature shrews kept in a laboratory the organs may actually increase in size and show active spermatogenesis during the autumn.

In the common shrew the vas deferens is narrow at its origin from the tail of the epididymis. It gradually widens and forms " an upper swelling which is limited distally to a clearly defined structure situated about half-way between the epididymis and the urethra. The distal part of the vas is enormously swollen and forms a conspicuous structure which is rounded proximally and gradually tapers distally to its junction with the urethra."
(Brambell, 1935.) These swellings consist of alveolar pouches opening into the central duct, and they may contain sperm. They are absent in immature animals.

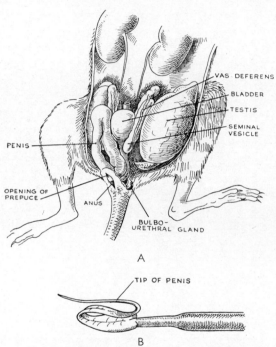

Fig. 2. 31—The reproductive organs of the male *Blarina* (slightly modified from Pearson, 1944). A, the entire tract *in situ*. B, the folded tip of the penis.

As in the mole, there is no pubic symphysis, and the large intestine passes through a ligamentous arch that extends from each pubic bone to the base of the penis. The paired "prostate glands " lie behind the bladder and vasa deferentia. There is, however, some difference of opinion concerning their true nature. Arnbäck-Christie-Linde (1907) called these organs the prostate, but modern investigators consider them to be more like seminal vesicles (Brambell, 1935; Hamilton, 1940; Pearson, 1944). Whether or not there is a true prostate gland appears to be unknown.

Cowper's glands are the only other important accessory organs in the shrew. They lie subcutaneously on either side of the base of the tail and in *Blarina* measure about 3 mm. in length. The preputial glands of the common shrew are diffuse, and, unlike those of many rodents, inconspicuous (Brambell, 1935).

In *Blarina* the non-erect penis lies between the skin and the ventral musculature immediately anterior to the anus, and is therefore not externally visible. The proximal half of the organ extends along the midline in an anterior direction for about 12 mm., then bends sharply down and backwards in the opposite direction for a similar distance. This flexure in the corpus of the penis is eliminated during erection. The glans may occupy 10 to 15 mm. of the total length of approximately 30 mm. It is characterised by a series of horny ridges or rings which are not visible to the naked eye, but which can be easily seen under a dissecting microscope, or felt with a delicate probe (Pearson, 1944). When erect, the glans expands laterally at its base and becomes very curved in a vertical plane. Its tip is long, slender and very flexible (Fig. 2. 31). There is no os penis.

The weight of the entire reproductive tract in the common and lesser shrew may amount to approximately 6 per cent of the total body weight, both the penis and the testis accounting for about 2 per cent each of this total (Brambell and Hall, 1936).

The female

The structure of the female reproductive tract in the common shrew (*Sorex araneus* Linn.) has been described by Brambell (1935).

The ovary is completely shut off from the peritoneal cavity by an ovarian bursa, and, except during the breeding season, is smooth and extremely small. During the breeding season it becomes much larger, and large follicles and corpora lutea projecting from its surface give it a mulberry-like appearance.[1] The ovarian extremity of the uterine tube is bent like the letter S around the ovary, and its opening into the ovarian bursa is funnel-shaped. The distal part of the tube is not convoluted, and is much narrower than the ovarian end. It enters the uterine horn near its tip, on the mesometrial side, by passing diagonally through the muscle, and projects slightly into the lumen.

The uterus is bicornuate, and the horns show a roughly T-shaped lumen on transverse section, the cross of the T being on the mesometrial side. The uterine glands are only present in thickened pads of mucosa along each side of the slit-like anti-mesometrial borders. There is a single short cervical canal which opens into the vagina by means of a deep external os. In the immature animal, or during anoestrus, the uterus is very small and measures only about 0·6 mm. in diameter. It has a diameter of 1 mm. during oestrus.

In mature animals the upper part of the vagina is sharply bent back upon itself ventrally (as it is also in the short-tailed shrew and mole). This flexure is particularly well marked in non-pregnant adult animals, and is brought about by the relative shortness of the broad ligaments and uterus on the one hand, and the length of the vagina on the other. The upper and lower regions of the vagina differ structurally from each other. The junction of the two parts lies opposite the level of the neck of the bladder, where the vaginal lumen is constricted by a circular fold of mucosa which Brambell believes to represent the hymen. In support of this hypothesis he notes that in immature animals the upper part contains a characteristic zone of fibrous connective tissue between the muscularis and mucosa. This zone can be traced down into the vagina only as far as the "hymen." It is entirely absent in parous animals (as well as in parous and non-parous *Blarina brevicauda*; Pearson, 1944).

The distal segment of the vagina, between the opening of the urethra and the vulva, is wider than the proximal part, and has a much thinner wall, owing to a reduction of the muscular and fibrous coats. Its lumen is wide and slit-like laterally, but flattened dorso-ventrally. In immature shrews the region of the vagina between the upper part and the opening of the urethra is closed, the lumen being completely absent and the epithelium being represented by a solid band

[1] "Testis cords" similar to embryonic seminiferous tubules are a common occurrence in the ovaries of parous or pregnant *Sorex vagrans* (Wilcox and Mossman, 1945).

15 to 25 μ in thickness. In mature oestrous females the epithelium of the vagina hypertrophies. The change is much more marked in the upper part, where the mucosa may reach a maximum thickness of 50 to 110 μ.

The vagina passes into the urogenital canal, which is deep and tubular. The urethra opens half-way between the " hymen " and the external vaginal orifice, and the clitoris is inconspicuous.

The mammary glands of the shrew are peculiar. Three pairs of nipples are situated in the inguinal region. The glandular tissue belonging to the cranial pair extends laterally round the lower part of the abdominal wall, and, when fully developed during lactation, almost reaches the midline of the back. The glands of the second pair of nipples are bilobed, the smaller lobe being situated in the groin, and the larger lobe extending forward to the midventral line. The caudal pair of glands extends, when fully developed, from the side of the anus, around the side of the body behind the thigh, to the dorsal part of the root of the tail.

According to Pearson (1944), the reproductive organs of the short-tailed shrew are larger, but otherwise resemble in all essentials those of the common shrew. The ventral flexure of the vagina is characteristic of oestrus, and does not appear to be present in young or anoestrous animals. The vagina decreases considerably in size in parous females, but remains larger than in immature or non-parous individuals.

Family *Macroscelididae*
Elephantulus

The genital tract of the female elephant shrew shows a number of unusual features, and will therefore be described separately. A full account has been given by Van der Horst (1942).

In appearance the whole reproductive tract is Y-shaped. It consists of a median part which lies behind the bladder and symphysis pubis, and two long and fairly straight horns. The ovary is situated far forward in the abdominal cavity, lateral to and only a little behind the kidneys. This arrangement is different from the normal insectivore pattern, in which the uterus is bicornuate and the tract as a whole is T-shaped in appearance (e.g. in the shrew and mole).

There is a well-developed " bursa ovarica," which is formed by the dorsal and ventral mesosalpinx and the ligamentum ovarii and mesovarium, but which, curiously enough, does not contain the ovary itself. This, instead, is surrounded by an enormously enlarged infundibulum, as by a sac, the opening of which is folded up and tightened around the mesovarium.

The uterine tube opens into the caudal half of the periovarial sac. Its ostium is situated at the lateral side of the ovary, away from the uterus. The ampullary part of the tube is arranged in a double S-shaped loop, but the isthmic part is almost straight. After ovulation the ampullary part shows a histological differentiation into a longer ciliated distal and a shorter non-ciliated proximal segment. Fertilisation takes place in the latter, which can therefore be referred to as the " tubal egg chamber." The uterine tube is directly continuous with the uterus. Externally, there is no sign of a separation, but internally the junction is very complicated by the presence of many deep, concentrically arranged pockets around the narrow central lumen, not unlike the arrangement found in the sow.

The uterus consists of two nearly straight horns, about 1·5 cm. in length, which diverge from the median uterus to the ovaries. The upper end of each horn is very thin, " hardly thicker than the oviducts," but the two horns gradually increase in thickness to reach a diameter of about 2 mm. at their junction with the median uterus. The lumen of each horn is slit-like and straight, except for a distance of about 2 mm. near the tip, where " starting from the tubo-uterine junction, the lumen follows a zigzag course, or sometimes it shows the appearance of a cochlea."

The endometrium is of uniform thickness throughout each horn, unlike the condition in the common shrew, in which the uterine glands are concentrated along the antimesometrial border (*see* above). But there is only a small and circumscribed area within each horn in which the mucosa undergoes progestational proliferation, thus allowing implantation of the blastocyst (Van der Horst and Gillman, 1941a). This curious feature is responsible for the fact that in *Elephantulus* only one embryo develops in each horn of the uterus, although as many as sixty ova are regularly discharged from each ovary (Van der Horst and Gillman, 1941b ; *see also* Chapter 4).

The uterine horns communicate with the urogenital canal by means of a median segment about 1·5 cm. in length. In spite of the presence of sparse uterine glands throughout this region, it is thought by Van der Horst to correspond functionally to the vagina, a true vagina lacking in the elephant shrew. There is no information about the responsiveness of this " vaginal " segment to oestrogenic stimulation.

TUPAIIDAE

The tree shrews are no longer classified as Insectivora, and by many authorities they are regarded as having closer affinities with the Lemuroidea, a suborder of the Primates. It is therefore of interest that the reproductive organs of the tree shrews are in several ways not only more primate in character than insectivorous, but that in some respects they have departed less from the arrangement seen in higher primates than have the Lemuroidea.

A detailed account of the anatomy of the generative organs in the tree shrews *Tupaia minor* and *Ptilocercus lowii* is given by Clark (1926, 1934).

The male

In *Tupaia* the testes are permanently scrotal. In *Ptilocercus* the testes descend seasonally, a fact which suggests that this species has a restricted breeding season. The cauda epididymidis is large. The penis in both *Tupaia* and *Ptilocercus* is pendulous and does not possess a baculum, a characteristic in which they differ from all lemurs.

The vas deferens opens into the urethra by a short common duct, which also drains part of the seminal vesicle. The latter is divided into two main lobes, of which one (the vesicular gland) opens directly into the urethra on the margin of the entrance of the utriculus prostaticus, and immediately cranial and lateral to the opening of the (common) ejaculatory duct. The other lobe (the seminal vesicle proper) joins the vas. The vesicular gland is lined by masses of cubical or columnar epithelium which frequently almost occludes the alveoli. The seminal vesicle is lined by a more evenly arranged epithelium, and is similar in structure to the dilated caudal end of the vas.

The prostate is a large compact unilobular organ in *Ptilocercus*, but relatively small in *Tupaia*.   In *Ptilocercus* it forms a ring-like structure which completely encircles the urethra, as does the human gland.   Unlike the latter, however, the collecting ducts open on all sides of the urethra, including the ventral aspect.   One small lobe of prostatic tissue lies outside the main capsule of the prostate, and its close association with, and relations to, the utriculus prostaticus and seminal vesicles suggests that it is homologous with the pre-spermatic or middle lobe of the prostate of higher primates (Clark, 1926).

The utriculus in both *Tupaia* and *Ptilocercus* is a relatively large, simple pyriform sac which extends cranially almost as far as do the seminal vesicles.   It opens into the urethra on the summit of a prominent colliculus seminalis, between the openings of the ejaculatory ducts.   The mucosa of the utriculus is thrown into complicated folds like those of the uterine tube, and its epithelium resembles the typical prostatic epithelium of man and monkeys more closely than does the epithelium of any other part of the reproductive tract (Zuckerman and Parkes, 1935).

The tree shrews possess compact and normally disposed anal and bulbourethral glands.

The female

The external genitalia of the female consist of prominent labia minora which project beyond a pair of poorly defined labia majora, and completely conceal a small clitoris which is grooved on its under-surface.

The uterine tubes are slightly coiled, and the uterus is more primitive in arrangement than in either lemurs or *Tarsius* (*see* below).   It is bicornuate, the horns being relatively long, and the corpus uteri relatively short.

PRIMATES[1]

Suborder LEMUROIDEA

    Fam. *Lemuridae*
        Lemur (Common lemur)

    Fam. *Lorisidae*
        Loris (Slender loris)
        Nycticebus (Slow loris)
        Perodicticus (Potto)

    Fam. *Galagidae*
        Galago (Galago)

Suborder TARSIOIDEA

        Tarsius (Spectral tarsier)

[1] The classification of this order is that followed by Zuckerman (1933), the Tupaiidae being considered separately.

Suborder PITHECOIDEA

The Platyrrhine (New World) Monkeys

Fam. *Cebidae*
    Cebus (Capuchin)
    Saimiri (" Squirrel " monkey)
    Aotes (Douroucouli)
    Ateles (Spider monkey)
    Alouatta (Howling monkey)

Fam. *Hapalidae*
    Hapale ; Callithrix (Marmoset)

The Catarrhine (Old World) Monkeys

Fam. *Cercopithecidae*
    Macaca (Macaques ; rhesus, bonnet monkey, etc.)
    Papio (Baboon)
    Semnopithecus (Langur)

The Anthropoid Apes

Fam. *Hylobatidae*
    Hylobates

Fam. *Pongidae*
    Pan (Chimpanzee)
    Pongo (Orang-utan)
    Gorilla (Gorilla)

The order Primates is divided into three suborders : Lemuroidea, Tarsioidea and Pithecoidea. The first comprises the lemuroid animals of Madagascar, the small lorisiform creatures of Asia and Africa and, in the view of modern taxonomists, the Tupaiidae (*see* above). The suborder Tarsioidea consists to-day of only the single genus, *Tarsius*, which is found in the West Indies. To the Pithecoidea belong all the New World monkeys, which form the division Platyrrhini, and all the Old World monkeys, anthropoid apes and man, who together constitute the division Catarrhini.

Suborder LEMUROIDEA

Families : *Lemuridae ; Lorisidae ; Galagidae*
Genera : *Lemur ; Nycticebus ; Loris ; Perodicticus ; Galago*

The male

In the loris (*Loris tardigradus*) (Rau and Hiriyannaiya, 1930), in the potto (*Perodicticus potto*), and probably in the aye aye (*Daubentonia*) (Nayak), the testes descend seasonally into a scrotum. In other species of lemur it is believed that the testes are permanently scrotal in position—a fact which is somewhat surprising, since all lemurs appear to have a very restricted breeding season (p. 329). Except in the potto, in which the scrotal sacs lie on either side of the penis, the scrotum is retropenial in all the Lemuroidea. In most lemurs the main collecting duct of the seminal vesicles and the vas deferens open separately into the urethra, and so do not form a true ejaculatory duct. *Galago* and *Propithecus*, however, are exceptions. In *Daubentonia* seminal vesicles are completely absent, and in this rare species it also seems that a thickening which is present at the caudal end of the vas deferens does not represent a true glandular ampulla.

The prostate is a compact organ in all the lemurs, and the collecting ducts appear to open only on the dorsal side of the urethra, in relation to the margins of the colliculus seminalis. As far as is known these animals lack a utriculus prostaticus (Zuckerman and Parkes, 1935).

Cowper's glands are large. Anal glands are usually missing in lemurs.

The penis in the Lemuroidea is much more specialised than in other primates (Pocock, 1918 ; Pohl, 1928). With few exceptions, the glans is furnished with small or large recurved spicules which may be arranged in a very complicated fashion. In some species the urinary meatus is encircled by a frill of " grooved, wrinkled epithelium, forming a sort of secondary prepuce, which is attached by a fraenum to the lower lip of the orifice and encloses a glandular space " (Pocock, 1918). In all lemurs the penis appears to be provided with a well-developed baculum, the shape and size of which varies from species to species.

The female

The uterus in the Lemuroidea is always bicornuate, although in the relative size of the corpus uteri these animals appear to be less primitive than the tree shrews.

The external genitalia of female lemurs are usually as specialised as is the penis (Pocock, 1918). In all the Lorisiformes the clitoris, which in one species at least is supported by a baculum, is traversed by the urethra. The clitoris is usually very long in both lorisiform and lemuriform lemurs, and in the latter the urethra usually opens at its base—although in the species *Lemur catta*, the ring-tailed lemur, it is carried forward to near its tip. Pocock describes the presence of a hymen in the genus *Lemur*, a genus which shows pronounced variations and specialisations in the form of the external genitalia. Some of the lemurs appear to possess not only labia minora, but also prominent labia majora.

The number of nipples in prosimians varies greatly both inter- and intra-specifically. According to Schultz (1948), two or even three pairs are more frequent in this group " than the specialised reduction to only 1 pair of nipples." Species in which six nipples have been found include *Lemur*, *Microcebus*, *Nycticebus*, *Perodicticus* and *Galago*.

Suborder TARSIOIDEA

Tarsius

The spectral tarsier (*Tarsius spectrum*) is in many ways one of the most interesting of the primates, and the importance which is attached to its phylogenetic relationship to the higher primates warrants the following description of its reproductive tract, taken from Woollard's detailed account (1925).

The male

The testes are enclosed in a large scrotum which lies behind the penis. The cauda epididymidis is large, as it is also in tree shrews, and the vas deferens joins the excretory duct of the seminal vesicle to form an ejaculatory duct. The lower end of the vas contains no glands. The seminal vesicles are large, simple dilated sacs whose lining is smooth and not thrown into folds. The prostate is peculiar in so far as it lies entirely on the dorsal side of the urethra. It consists in the main of a single lobe, and the muscle fibres which surround and penetrate it are continuous with the circular muscle of the urethra. The ejaculatory ducts enter the urethra almost at the cranial border of the prostate on either side of the summit of the colliculus seminalis. The utriculus prostaticus opens between them as a small blind, flask-like diverticulum lined by transitional epithelium. It possesses no glandular offshoots.

A " pre-spermatic " lobe is present in the upper part of the prostate (Zuckerman and Parkes, 1935). This lobe is formed by bilateral medial extensions of prostatic tissue which all but meet each other in the mid-line, ventral to the lower ends of the seminal vesicles, the vasa deferentia and the ejaculatory ducts.

Prominent bulbo-urethral glands of the tubulo-acinous type are found in the usual position.

The end of the penis is covered by a very long prepuce, and the glans penis is also extremely long and unexpanded. The urinary meatus opens at its tip as a vertical slit between two leaf-like folds. The corpora cavernosa extend to the tip of the glans, as a result of which the corpus cavernosum urethrae becomes relatively reduced.

The female

The short uterine tube is very coiled and ends in a single extended fimbria which overlaps the globular ovary. The uterus is bicornuate, but the lateral horns are short as compared with the corpus uteri—an arrangement which presages the unilocular condition. The mucosa of the lower half of the vagina is thrown into longitudinal folds. The clitoris has a bifid glans, and is concealed by relatively large labia minora. These are surrounded by hairy labia majora.

As a rule there are four mammary glands, one pair of nipples being situated in the axillae and the other above the navel. Occasionally, there may be two pectoral pairs and one abdominal pair (Hill, Porter and Southwick, 1952).

Suborder PITHECOIDEA

In the following paragraph certain essential features are set out which are characteristic of sub-human primates in general, and which serve to distinguish them as a group from man. The morphology of the reproductive tract in the Pithecoidea is dealt with more fully in subsequent sections.

The male

The testes of most platyrrhine and catarrhine monkeys are relatively much larger, and those of the anthropoids (except the chimpanzee) a little smaller, than in man. A membranous fold suspending the epididymis and spermatic cord from the sidewall of the tunica vaginalis (or "mesepididymis ") occurs in many monkeys and at least one anthropoid ape, but not in man. Hydatids of Margagni occur in many catarrhine and some platyrrhine monkeys (*see* Zuckerman and Krohn, 1937). In apes, in which their incidence has not been fully investigated, they appear to be absent or rare.

The processus vaginalis remains continuous with the general peritoneal cavity in most catarrhine and platyrrhine monkeys, but in anthropoids and man it is usually obliterated.

The prostate of monkeys and apes consists of two macroscopically and histologically distinct parts known as the cranial and caudal lobes. They are considered homologous to the isthmus plus middle lobe and to the posterior commissure plus lateral lobes, respectively, of the human gland (Mijsberg, 1923). In addition, the prostate in sub-human primates is deficient on the ventral aspect of the urethra, but in man it forms a complete ring in which normally only the part lying in front of the urethra (the anterior commissure) is devoid of glandular tissue.

The structure and distribution of the utriculus prostaticus varies greatly between and within the different species of primates (*see* Zuckerman and Parkes, 1935). It may be completely absent (e.g. in the lemur); represented by a simple, non-glandular diverticulum (as in macaques and baboons); or by an essentially glandular structure of " uterine " appearance (as in mona and vervet monkeys, the langur and chimpanzee).

A scrotum is usually present in apes and monkeys, but is rarely as well developed as in man. The penis is generally incorporated into the front of the scrotum, and is never completely pendulous. As a rule it contains a baculum or os penis of variable dimensions. In a few platyrrhine species this structure is absent, as it is in man.

The female

In spite of its basic similarity, the generative tract in female primates shows much diversity of anatomical pattern. Thus in the lemurs and *Tarsius* the uterus is of the bicornuate type. It is unilocular in monkeys and apes. Among the latter the size and structure of the ovaries and cervix uteri, the shape of the fundus, and especially the degree of development of the external genitalia, vary considerably both within and between the different groups. Moreover, individual variation is probably as great in primates as in other mammalian orders (Wislocki, 1932). Therefore, the commonly-held view that the female reproductive organs of monkeys, apes and man resemble each other so closely as to be practically alike, is only partly true.

Little more than an outline of the anatomy of the generative tract in monkeys and apes is given in the following sections. Attention is mainly directed to the features of the reproductive organs by which the different species can be distinguished from man and from each other. At the outset two morphological characters need to be referred to, as they are present only in certain primates. These are, respectively, the " sexual skin " and ischial callosities.

Sexual skin. The term " sexual skin " (first introduced by Langley and Sherrington in 1891) refers to a specialised area of skin which is contiguous with the external genitalia, and which undergoes variations in general conformation and colour in relation to the menstrual cycle. Histologically this region is characterised by the thickness of the dermis, marked oedema of the subcutaneous connective tissues and an unusually rich blood supply.

A sexual skin does not occur in platyrrhine monkeys (but *see* p. 134, below). Among anthropoids it is regularly found only in the chimpanzee. Even among catarrhine monkeys it is not always present, and its activity varies from species to species, from individual to individual, and in the same individual from time to time (Zuckerman, 1933). It is particularly well developed in the baboon (*Papio*), mandrill (*Mandrillus*), mangabey (*Cercocebus*), and in many, but by no means all, species of macaque (*Macaca*). Thus sex-skin activity is intense in the pig-tailed monkey (*M. nemestrina*) and in *M. cyclopis*, but very slight in the common macaque (*M. irus* or *fascicularis*) and in the bonnet monkey (*M. radiata* and *sinica*).

The position of the rhesus monkey (*M. mulatta*) is intermediate and somewhat atypical in this respect. In this species the sexual skin area of the adult animal is coloured a vivid red, but is quite smooth. It does not undergo sharp variations in relation to the cycle. However, during limited periods (for instance, during puberty, *see also* below) the skin swells greatly, and the swelling may involve a more extensive area than it does in such forms as the baboon, in which a cyclically-swollen sexual skin is a normal feature of the mature female.

Lastly, in the Colobidae (e.g. the langur), *Erythrocebus* (e.g. the Patas monkey), and in *Cercopithecus* (e.g. the green monkey and guénon) sexual skin changes are completely absent.

Ischial callosities. In all catarrhine monkeys the skin over the ischial tuberosities is greatly thickened to form horny sitting pads or ischial callosities. Among the higher primates these are normally present only in gibbons ; irregularly and in variable form in chimpanzees and gorillas ; very rarely in the orang ; and never in man. They are completely absent in platyrrhine (New World) monkeys.

Their external appearance in catarrhines has been described in detail by Pocock (1925). In both sexes the two callosities are usually separated in the midline. In the males of certain species (e.g. *Macaca maura, Cercocebus, Papio*), however, they are fused and may appear as horse-shoe-shaped prominences which surround the anus ventrally and on both sides. In the female they remain invariably separate, owing to the intervention of the vulva. Structurally, two distinct types of callosities can be recognised (Miller, 1945). In lower catarrhine monkeys and gibbons they are hairless, well-circumscribed areas of thickened skin, which are immovably attached to the ischial tuberosities by means of dense fibrous tissue. For that reason the hamstring muscles attach along the borders and not to the surfaces of the tuberosities.

In the second type, exemplified by the chimpanzee and occasionally by the orang-utan and gorilla, the callosities consist of toughened cushions which are movable over the tuberosities and intervene between the skin and the origins of the hamstring muscles. Histologically, these swellings are composed of loose connective tissue and fat, and represent skin pads rather than true callosities.

The callosities in catarrhine monkeys are known to undergo certain changes during postnatal development. For instance, in the rhesus macaque, their long axes are not parallel but intersect each other at an angle which is acute in young females, and becomes obtuse as age advances (Zuckerman, Van Wagenen and Gardiner, 1938).

The Platyrrhine (New World) Monkeys

Families : *Cebidae ; Hapalidae*

Genera : *Cebus ; Saimiri ; Aotes ; Ateles ; Alouatta ; Hapale ; Oedipomidas*

The male

As a rule the testes of the sexually mature animal are completely descended. There is some doubt, however, about the position in the marmoset (*Hapale jacchus*), in two adult specimens of which Beattie (1927) found incompletely descended testes. The degree of development of the scrotum varies from a shallow puckered pouch (in marmosets) to an extremely flaccid, pendulous scrotum (in the howler monkey ; Wislocki, 1936). In marmosets, capuchins and squirrel monkeys the surface of the scrotum is studded with small nodules similar in structure and distribution to those present in the genital region of females of the same species, and described below (*see* p. 134). In *Oedipomidas* they are found not on the scrotum, but along two ventral extensions of the scrotal area or " pubic ridges."

There is some difference of opinion about the persistence of the processus vaginalis in platyrrhine monkeys. For instance, in *Cebus* (the capuchin), Mijsberg (1923) finds a wide communication with the abdominal cavity, but according to Wislocki (1936) the inguinal ring is closed in this species. On the other hand, there is agreement that an open processus occurs in the squirrel monkey (*Saimiri örstedii*), and that the canal is greatly narrowed or closed in the spider monkey (*Ateles*) and marmoset (*Oedipomidas*).

The weight of the gonads varies both absolutely and relatively in different species of platyrrhines (*see* Schultz, 1938b). In the Douroucouli (*Aotes zonalis*), the combined weight of the two testes amounts to 1·2 g. (or to 0·11 per cent of the total body weight), and in the howler monkey (*Alouatta*) to 25 g. (or 0·34 per cent). Even in the former species the testes are relatively heavier than in man, though considerably lighter than in most catarrhines (*see* below).

In marmosets the epididymis is usually large, and may be nearly half the size of the testis. In *Cebus* and *Chrysothrix sciurea*, but not in *Oedipomidas*, the cranial and medial thirds of the epididymis are suspended by a mesepididymis (*see* p. 129). The vas deferens of platyrrhines has no ampulla. In marmosets it unites with the excretory duct of the minute seminal vesicle to form an ejaculatory duct (Beattie, 1927).

In most platyrrhine monkeys the prostate is divided into a cranial and caudal part, but in the marmoset no such distinction is possible (Mijsberg, 1923).

The form of the penis and its glans is subject to great variation (*see* Pohl, 1928). In species like the marmoset, squirrel monkey and capuchin it is relatively short and protrudes from the anterior part of the scrotum. In *Ateles* it consists of a stout cylindrical organ, some 4 cm. × 1·5 cm. in size, which is remarkable for the presence of numerous small, intensely black barbs of cornified epithelium. They are of particular interest in view of the morphology of the vagina in this species (*see* Wislocki, 1932, 1936 ; and below, p. 134).

A small or minute os penis is present in all platyrrhines, except the spider (*Ateles*) and woolly monkeys (*Lagothrix*).

The female

The ovaries of platyrrhine monkeys are thick and compact (Wislocki, 1932) and, with the exception of the marmoset, much larger than those of the catarrhines. This is mainly due to the presence of large amounts of interstitial lutein tissue. This constitutes a distinctive feature which sets the New World primates apart from the Old World apes and monkeys, with the sole exception of the gibbon (*see* below). A further contributory factor is the large size of the Graafian follicles, which may attain a diameter of 2–4 mm. in spider and howler monkeys (Dempsey, 1939). Approximate figures for the size of the gonads in two platyrrhine species and the rhesus monkey (*M. mulatta*) are shown in Table II.

TABLE II

THE SIZE OF THE OVARIES, IN MILLIMETRES (MODIFIED FROM WISLOCKI, 1932).

$$
\begin{array}{lll}
\textit{Ateles} & \text{R.} & 15 \times 10 \times 10 \\
& \text{L.} & 16 \times 10 \times 9 \\
\textit{Cebus} & \text{R.} & 11 \times 8 \times 7 \\
& \text{L.} & 12 \times 9 \times 8 \\
\textit{Rhesus} & \text{R.} & 10 \times 8 \times 7 \\
& \text{L.} & 8 \times 7 \times 5 \cdot 5 \\
\end{array}
$$

In marmosets, in which twinning is the rule (in 78 per cent of cases ; Schultz, 1948), a follicle ruptures in both of the ovaries at ovulation time, so that two corpora lutea are normally present during the progestational phase of the cycle, one in each gonad (Wislocki, 1939).

The uterine tubes are markedly coiled in most platyrrhines, but in *Saimiri örstedii*, the squirrel monkey, and in the marmoset, they are nearly straight (Beattie, 1927 ; Wislocki, 1932). A superior mesosalpinx (a fold formed by the free border and adjacent parts of the broad ligament) is generally present, and with it an ovarian bursa of variable depth which wholly or partly encloses the ovary.

The size of the uterus varies considerably in different species of platyrrhines (*see* Table III). For instance, in *Ateles* (spider monkeys) it exceeds that of certain anthropoids (*see* below, Table V), but in *Cebus* (capuchins) it is much smaller and does not even reach the dimensions of the organ in the (Old World) rhesus monkey.

TABLE III

THE DIMENSIONS OF THE NON-GRAVID UTERUS, IN MILLIMETRES (SLIGHTLY MODIFIED FROM WISLOCKI, 1932).

Species	Greatest length	Greatest breadth	Greatest ant.-post. diameter
Ateles	47	21	21
Cebus	30	13	13
Rhesus	40	18	14

In general the cervix is absolutely and relatively much more developed in lower monkeys than in anthropoid apes, and the differences indicated in Table III are at least partly due to the variable length of the cervical segment, especially that of the infravaginal part. Thus, in *Ateles* the length of the " portio," which projects far into the vagina, exceeds that in most anthropoids. A similar condition is found in other platyrrhines, but in the Douroucouli (*Aotes zonalis*) the cervix is diminutive and does not protrude into the vagina, thereby resembling the gibbon (*see* below).

The fundus of the uterus in platyrrhine and catarrhine monkeys is globular, and so differs characteristically from the human, which is markedly flattened in an antero-posterior direction. Owing to a thickening of the dorsal wall, the fundus of *Cebus* and *Ateles* appears triangular on cross-section. In the marmoset the uterus possesses two lateral projections of the fundus and a median groove on the ventral surface, which suggest a bicornuate structure. On section, however, the organ is found to be single (Beattie, 1927).

The most distinctive feature of the vagina in platyrrhines is the presence of numerous low mucosal " bosses " which are covered by small papillae (Wislocki, 1932). In the spider monkey, *Ateles*, the thick surface layer of cornified epithelium is thrown into ridges, resulting in the formation of numerous denticles which project into the vaginal lumen.   Extensive vaginal desquamation takes place during midcycle in this species, but in the howler monkey (*Alouatta*) cyclic changes in the vaginal epithelium are inconspicuous (Dempsey, 1939).

In general, the external genital organs of the platyrrhines are much better developed than those of the catarrhines, a fact which has been related to the absence of ischial callosities in the former and their presence in the latter division (Wislocki, 1932).

As a rule the vulval cleft is narrow and flanked by delicate unpigmented labia, which are homologous with the labia minora of man.   The clitoris is minute in most platyrrhine monkeys, and its ventral aspect is grooved, as in all sub-human primates.   In adult capuchins the tip of the clitoris may contain a small baculum. The clitoris in *Ateles* is exceptional in being very large and almost as prominent as the penis of the male.   In spite of its size, however, it contains neither erectile tissue nor a baculum (Gerhardt, 1933).   Structures corresponding to the human labia majora are generally present in platyrrhines, but vary considerably in their extent and degree of development.   For instance, in *Ateles* they are variable and inconspicuous, but in *Alouatta* both the labia majora and minora are greatly developed, and in the adult form " a semi-pendulous labial pad strikingly analogous in form, colour and location to the pendulous scrotum of the male " (Wislocki, 1936).   In marmosets (e.g. *Oedipomidas*) the labia majora are deeply pigmented and extend forward as two conspicuous cushions over the pubes.

In certain species the surfaces of the labia majora (and of the scrotum in the male) are covered with minute whitish nodules, somewhat suggestive of glandular structures.   These are present in marmosets (*Hapale* and *Oedipomidas*), capuchins (*Cebus*), and squirrel monkeys (*Saimiri örstedii*).   Histologically, they consist of complexly-modified, tubular and sebaceous glands, and should be considered as representing a specialised form of scent gland (Wislocki, 1936).

A " sexual skin " is generally lacking in platyrrhines.   Russell and Zuckerman (1935) have, however, observed such a structure in an adult female marmoset believed to be of the " *albicollis* " variety.   It consisted of a turgid circumgenital swelling, and histologically as well as functionally resembled a true sexual skin as it occurs in many catarrhine monkeys and in the chimpanzee.   It appears to be the only instance of a sexual skin in a New World monkey so far recorded.

The Catarrhine (Old World) Monkeys

Family *Cercopithecidae*

Genera : *Macaca* ; *Papio* ; *Semnopithecus*

The male

The rhesus macaque (*M. mulatta*) can be taken as representative of the catarrhine monkeys (Fig. 2. 32, I).

The testes of mature specimens are fully descended into the scrotum, and are remarkably large, relative to the size of the animal.   Their average combined weight (without epididymes) is of the order of 30 to 50 g., but weights of 74 and 78 g., respectively, have been reported in the literature (Schultz, 1938b).   This represents over 0·5 per cent of the total body weight, a ratio which is six to seven times higher than in man.

In fully grown males the scrotum is as a rule semi-pendulous, and vividly red in colour. It shows no trace of a median raphe. It lies relatively far forward over the pubes, and is separated from the anus by a long perineum.

The postnatal changes undergone by the external genitalia and testes have been fully described by Wislocki (1933c, 1936). This author has shown that the newborn rhesus monkey resembles man in possessing a well-developed scrotum and, frequently, scrotal testes, but that it differs in the subsequent retrogression of the scrotum, and the reascent of the gonads to an inguinal position. The testes

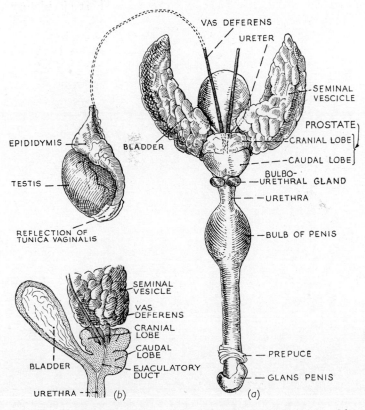

Fig. 2. 32, I—The reproductive organs of the male rhesus monkey (about ⅔ natural size). (a) Entire tract (dorsal view). (b) Prostatic urethra (median view, semi-diagrammatic; after van Wagenen, 1936).

remain extremely mobile, but are rarely found below the level of the base of the penis until the end of the third year. Ultimate, permanent descent and the onset of spermatogenesis take place later still, probably during the fifth to sixth year (*see* Wislocki, 1933, 1936; Eckstein, 1948).

In the rhesus monkey, as in other catarrhine species, the cremaster muscle is well developed. It has a special origin from the pubic bone (Mijsberg, 1923; Wislocki, 1933b). There is an open processus vaginalis which communicates with the peritoneal cavity through a narrow slit at the inguinal ring. The spermatic vessels, the vas deferens, and most of the epididymis are suspended from the parietal wall of the tunica vaginalis by a mesepididymis. The testis itself is completely enclosed by the visceral layer of the tunica vaginalis, but its lower pole adheres frequently to the parietal layer, and may then be a little difficult to free (e.g. during castration).

Hydatids of Morgagni are frequently present in normal rhesus monkeys. They are found attached variously to the head or body of the epididymis ; to the testis itself ; or to the serosal fold between them (Zuckerman and Krohn, 1937). As a rule only one hydatid is present on each testis and epididymis, but occasionally there may be two.

The vas deferens, which has no conspicuous ampulla, unites with the duct of the seminal vesicle within the prostate to form a short ejaculatory duct.   On

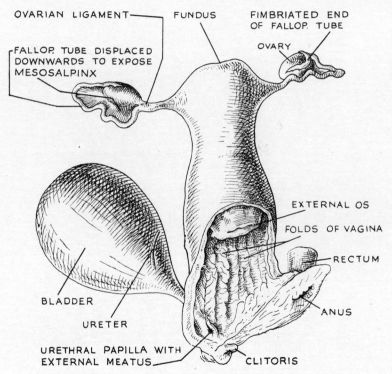

Fig. 2. 32, II—The reproductive organs of the female rhesus monkey in dorso-lateral view (about $\frac{4}{3}$ natural size).

the other hand, in the langur (*Semnopithecus entellus*) the terminal part of the vas is slightly expanded into an ampulla and has a few small diverticula on its lateral aspect (Ayer, 1948).   In this species the seminal vesicles are slender structures, about 5 cm. long.   Each consists of a tube with numerous small diverticula projecting along its entire length.   In this respect the langur resembles man, but differs from the rhesus monkey in which the seminal vesicles are conspicuously large, densely lobulated organs.   Their lower ends and ducts are encircled by the lobed upper part (pre-spermatic or " cranial " lobe) of the prostate, which resembles the seminal vesicles in structure.   The lower part (or " caudal " lobe) of the prostate is much more compact, as well as smoother and darker in colour. By dissection both parts can be separated from each other almost to the urethra.

The lower lobe lies almost entirely below and behind the ejaculatory ducts, while the prespermatic lobe lies in front.   Neither extends to the ventral aspect of the urethra, and the anterior prostatic lobe of man is entirely absent in the monkey. According to van Wagenen (1936), the cranial lobe has a different histological structure from the caudal lobe, and may be functionally compared to the " coagulating gland " of rodents (Fig. 2. 32, I b).

The ejaculatory ducts end on the prominent colliculus seminalis on a level with the coronally-disposed and somewhat semilunar mouth of the utriculus prostaticus (Zuckerman and Parkes, 1935).   The latter is a blind and non-glandular diverticulum lined by a low epithelium, and is T-shaped on cross-section.   Cowper's glands are oval in shape and measure nearly 10 mm. in their longest diameter.

Most of the penis lies within the anterior wall of the scrotum, and the organ is inconspicuous except during erection.   Only its distal extremity is pendulous. It consists of a characteristic cap- or mushroom-shaped glans and a narrower, proximal part or neck which is surrounded by loose folds of the prepuce.   The external meatus of the urethra is formed by a vertical slit on the tip of the glans.   Its lips may be distorted owing to the presence of a well-developed baculum which protrudes more on the left than on the right (Pocock, 1925 ; Wislocki, 1933b).

The female

Compared with that of the platyrrhines, the reproductive tract in catarrhine monkeys shows several distinguishing features.

The ovaries are relatively smaller, and contain less lutein tissue.   Ischial callosities are invariably present, and the external genitalia are generally less well developed.   A large number of species possess conspicuous " sexual skin " areas.

The large number of genera belonging to this family (Cercopithecidae) precludes a description of them all.   Here, only three species, the baboon, langur and macaque, will be reviewed in some detail.   These have been adequately studied, and may be considered as representative of the group as a whole.

For more comprehensive accounts dealing with the morphology of the reproductive tract in catarrhines reference is made to Pocock (1925), Zuckerman (1930), and Wislocki (1932, 1936).

Papio

The internal reproductive organs of the female baboon have been described by Zuckerman and Parkes (1932).

The expanded fimbriated end of the tube surrounds and forms a roof over the bean-shaped ovary.   As a rule the endometrial cavity has a single lumen, but occasionally it may show a central constriction at the fundus, a condition which has also been described in the common macaque (M. irus ; Joachimovits, 1928). Externally, however, the fundus gives no indication of a division into two cornua. On cross-section at the fundus the uterus is oval, but the isthmus is narrow and circular in outline.   The transition from the body to the cervical segment is marked by a slight but abrupt lateral expansion of the central lumen which becomes increasingly wide towards the lower part of the cervix.   The cervical mucosa is arranged in characteristic folds which form an arbor vitae very similar to that in women.   The line of junction between the cervical and vaginal epithelia is clearly demarcated, and can be made out macroscopically some 4 mm. within the lips of the

F*

cervix.   The external os is a coronal slit between a thicker anterior and a thinner posterior lip.   There is a well-marked vaginal fornix of approximately uniform depth.   The urethra opens into the vagina about 3 cm. from the vulva.

The size of the uterus varies considerably in different types of baboon.   In the chacma baboon (average body weight 17·2 kg.) its dimensions are 7·3 cm. long × 2·5 cm. wide × 2·2 cm. antero-posteriorly.   Corresponding figures for the Hamadryas baboon (average body weight 9·3 kg.) are 4·6 × 2·1 × 1·8 cm.

A well-developed sexual skin is present in the mature female baboon.   It can be divided into two parts, a ventral one which roughly comprises the clitoris and its preputial sheath, and a dorsal one composed of the posterior vagina and circumanal region.   The appearance of the external genitalia, including the sexual skin, depends on the stage of the menstrual cycle.   During the follicular phase the prepuce swells into a rounded body which passes forward beyond the symphysis and surrounds the tip of the clitoris.   The posterior swelling is much larger than the anterior one, completely hiding the ischial callosities and encroaching upon the anus, which presents as a transverse groove.   The vaginal orifice lies between both turgid swellings, which appear as shining red or pink masses.   Following its sudden subsidence during mid-cycle, the sexual skin remains collapsed until menstruation, when it begins to swell again (Zuckerman, 1930).   Swelling is associated with the retention of a great deal of water (as much as 25 per cent of the body weight in some females).

Macaca
The Rhesus Monkey

The gross morphological and microscopical features of the reproductive tract in this species have been the subject of many detailed studies.   Reference may be made to the accounts of Collings (1926) ; Hartman (1932) ; Wislocki (1933b, 1936) ; and Zuckerman, van Wagenen and Gardiner (1938).

The ovaries are oval and vary greatly in size and weight.   Average dimensions are about 10 × 7 × 6 mm. (*see* Table II), but the range may extend from 6·5 × 2·8 × 5 mm. to 13 × 11·9 × 10·2 mm., depending on the stage of the reproductive cycle (Hartman, 1932).   The weight of a single ovary is about 200 to 300 mg., but ovaries weighing over 400 mg. are not uncommon.   The structure of the ovary resembles that of the anthropoids (*see* below).   There is no extensive interstitial luteinisation in the way characteristic of platyrrhine monkeys.

The uterine tube is coiled, and it possesses a slit-like abdominal orifice surrounded by an ovarian and a uterine fimbria of about equal length.   There is an inferior as well as a superior mesosalpinx.   The latter consists of a membranous reduplication of the peritoneum which runs along the upper free border of the tube (Wislocki, 1933b).   In this way a deep ovarian bursa is formed which partially encapsulates the ovary.

The uterus is roughly divided into an upper segment consisting of the body and fundus and a lower segment formed by the thick-walled cervix (Fig. 2. 32, II). The fundus is irregularly pear-shaped and frequently shows a shallow depression in the sagittal plane, which may give it a bicornuate appearance, especially in young specimens.   On transverse section the lumen of the uterine cavity at the level of the fundus is distinctly bicornuate.   The uterus lies usually a little to the left of the mid-plane. Its size varies in different individuals and with the stage of the menstrual cycle. Its greatest width is usually 15 to 18 mm. in mature females (*see* Table III) ; it rarely exceeds 21 mm. in the non-gravid state (Hartman, 1932).

The cervical segment is remarkable for its size and complexity, as revealed by section in the mid-sagittal plane. The canal is not straight as in most mammals, but bent upon itself in two almost right-angled turns. The proximal curve is convex towards the ventral aspect and the distal one towards the dorsal aspect of the uterus. This unusual arrangement is due to the presence of two or three cervical " colliculi " which project into the lumen of the cervical canal and cause its distortion (Sandys and Zuckerman, 1938). The main collicle forms a projection of the ventral cervical wall. Opposite the point of junction of its cranial and dorsal surfaces is a cul-de-sac which cuts off part of the dorsal cervical wall, which may thus be considered as a second and smaller colliculus. These two formations are constant, but in about 40 per cent of cases a second, more ventrally situated cul-de-sac is present and demarcates a further (or third) subsidiary colliculus.

The external os is slit-like and lies nearer the anterior than the posterior aspect of the cervix. Because of this, the dorsal lip is thicker than the ventral one, and as a rule the dorsal fornix is deeper than the anterior. The line of transition between the cervical and vaginal epithelia varies considerably, and may lie anywhere between the vaginal surface of the cervix uteri and the apex of the cul-de-sac below the main colliculus.

The vagina is a thick-walled muscular structure, the mucous membrane of which is elaborately folded into longitudinal and transverse ridges. Its lower end widens into a funnel-shaped, relatively deep vestibular recess. The external orifice of the urethra is more concealed than in man, and lies at the junction of the vagina and the vestibule. It is usually marked by a raised papilla (Fig. *2*. 32, II).

The vulval cleft lies between the inner margins of the ischial callosities and is separated from the anus by a short perineum. It is bounded by a pair of low and poorly-developed labia minora. In mature specimens obvious labia majora are absent.

The ventral aspect of the clitoris is slightly grooved, as in other primates. The organ is much more conspicuous in mature or aged than in young animals, and possesses a praeputium, but no distinct fraenulum.

As already noted, the sexual skin of the rhesus monkey shows certain unusual features. In fully mature females the skin of the genital region does not usually swell, and the only external changes present are slight and often irregular variations in coloration, not clearly related to the menstrual cycle (Hartman, 1932 ; Zuckerman 1930, 1937). In the pubertal animal, however, the onset of function in the ovaries is accompanied by a series of conspicuous changes in the circumgenital areas, whereby the latter acquire their adult conformation (Fig. *2*. 33).

Three different stages can be recognised in this maturation process (Zuckerman, van Wagenen and Gardiner, 1938). The first or pubertal phase is characterised mainly by swelling of the central circumgenital region, and by a pink flush of the entire perineum which replaces the pale grey-blue present during infancy. These changes begin at an average age of $2\frac{1}{2}$ years, and usually, but not always, precede the onset of the ménarche (Eckstein, 1948).

During the second or adolescent phase, the swelling disappears from the central area and passes to the periphery, the former then becoming indurated. Up to this stage colour changes are present, but rarely very conspicuous. During the third

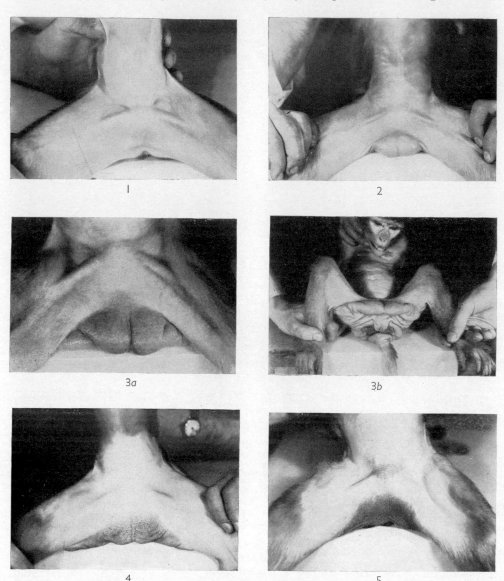

Fig. *2.* 33—The maturation process of the sexual skin in the rhesus monkey (ventral view). 1. Before puberty. 2. Early puberty. 3, *a, b.* At the height of puberty. 4. Adolescence. 5. Maturity.

phase the genital region attains its mature state. The oedema gradually disappears, and the outstanding remaining feature is reddening of the skin. This mainly affects the perineum, buttocks and upper two-thirds of the thighs, but it may extend down the legs, beyond the iliac crests and spread ventrally in triangular fashion from the symphysis to the umbilicus. The reddening, which may persist into old age, is due to vascular engorgement, and not to pigmentation (Collings, 1926). It is of a uniform character, except in the suprapubic region where it presents as "petechiae" or "stippling" (as it does around the nipples, *see* below).

Maturation takes a variable time and lasts on an average one to two years. It is only during this pubertal and early adolescent period that *M. mulatta* may be said to possess a sexual skin comparable with that of adult baboons, mangabeys or chimpanzees. Very exceptionally, skin oedema of the peripheral kind may develop in mature rhesus monkeys (e.g. in lactating animals, after the return of menstrual periodicity ; Zuckerman, van Wagenen and Gardiner, 1938).

As in other subhuman primates, the mammary glands of the rhesus monkey are poorly developed in the non-gravid state. The gland tissue itself is thin and well spread out under the skin, so that is is invisible and barely palpable except in the latter part of pregnancy. A complex duct system is present before the first signs of puberty, but full alveolar development does not become apparent until ovulation and luteinisation has occurred (Folley and Zuckerman, 1938). The nipples lie approximately at the level of the sixth sternocostal junction (Stewart, 1933), and are about 3 to 4 cm. apart from each other. Their length and general development varies greatly in different specimens and depends on the state of the reproductive organs and parity. Average dimensions are 10 mm. in length and 5 to 6 mm. in breadth at the base ; occasionally their size differs on the two sides. In healthy mature females they are usually pink to red in colour, and surrounded by mottled red areolae of very variable extent. During pregnancy this reddened area may reach a diameter of 20 to 30 mm. Supernumerary nipples are occasionally present and lie below the normal pair of nipples. Their incidence is of the order of 1 to 1·5 per cent, as in other primates and women (Speert, 1942 ; Schultz, 1948).

The Common Macaque

Many but not all mature females of this long-tailed species (*Macaca irus*) show skin changes confined to a triangular area on the ventral aspect of the root of the tail. These may be accompanied or replaced by variations in the colour of the perineum. In Spiegel's view (but not according to Zuckerman, 1930), these changes are related to the menstrual cycle (Spiegel, 1931).

The Bonnet Monkey

The only noteworthy feature of the genital tract of the bonnet macaque (*Macaca radiata ; sinica*) is the cervix which is as tortuous as, but much larger and more complexly folded than, that of the rhesus monkey. Its mucosal lining is composed of large glandular cells which also line the glands that dip in all directions. This is responsible for the copious vaginal discharge which characterises this species, and which consists of large, transparent, colourless clots of mucus (Zuckerman, 1930).

Normally the sexual skin is quite inconspicuous both in colour and external configuration. During pregnancy, however, a swelling develops which involves the vulval labia and a triangular area of circumanal skin, the base of which is bounded by the dorsal margin of the sitting pads and the apex of which lies at the root of the tail, 3 or 4 cm. caudal to the anus (Hartman, 1938).

Semnopithecus

The following summary of the langur's reproductive organs is based on Ayer's monograph (1948).

The size of the ovary is 20 × 7 × 3·5 mm. An ovarian bursa is typically present on one side only, where it is formed " by a forward rolling of the ovary and a backward flapping of the superior mesosalpinx." It is open medially between the uterine end of the tube and the ovarian ligament, and laterally near the fimbriated part of the tube. Thus it resembles the peritoneal recess of other catarrhine monkeys, but differs from the complete bursa present in rodents.

The uterine tube does not run along the free border of the broad ligament, but lies within duplications of the peritoneum (the superior mesosalpinx), each of which is attached to the broad ligaments above them.

The uterus in a sub-adult animal measured 3 cm. in length × 2 cm. in width × 4 mm. in thickness. It is a unilocular organ without a trace of a median groove. The cervix constitutes the narrow lower half of the uterus and does not show the elaborate bending of the lumen as in the rhesus monkey. The infravaginal segment forms well-marked vaginal fornices and opens by a transverse external os between a thin anterior and a thicker posterior lip.

The vagina measures 3·5 cm. in length and is only slightly folded. An irregularly-formed annular fold lies between the vagina and vestibule ; it may represent the hymen.

The vestibule of the vagina is about 2 cm. deep and opens into the vulval cleft which is bounded by a pair of labia minora. These are wider behind than in front where they form the prepuce of the clitoris. The latter is a conspicuous organ which projects below the labial level in parous and non-parous animals. Its body measures about 5 mm. in length and the ventrally-grooved glans 4 × 3 mm. The urethra opens on a small urethral papilla in front of the vagina.

According to Ayer (1948), no trace of the mons pubis and labia majora can be made out in the langur.

The Anthropoid Apes [1]

Families : *Hylobatidae ; Pongidae*

Genera : *Hylobates ; Pan ; Pongo ; Gorilla*

The male

The size of the testes varies greatly in the different species of anthropoid ape. According to Schultz's data (1938), they are largest in the chimpanzee, where their average combined weight is about 119 g. (corresponding to 0·27 per cent of the total body weight), and relatively smallest in the orang (0·05 per cent). This compares with a ratio of about 0·08 per cent in man. In the gorilla, the testes are surprisingly small, compared with the size and weight of the animal. Their dimensions in one adult and one sub-adult specimen were 45 × 24 × 17 mm. and 30 × 20 × 18 mm., respectively (Hill and Matthews, 1949).

In mature animals the testes are invariably descended,[2] but their ultimate

---

[1] The human reproductive tract is described on pp. 47–48.

[2] This summary follows Wislocki's detailed account (1936), whose finding of a fully developed scrotum and descended testes in mature anthropoids is at variance with the observations of other workers such as Bolk (1907) and Mijsberg (1923). Additional

location depends on the degree of development of the scrotal sac, and varies accordingly. In the chimpanzee the scrotum is well formed. It is sessile in juvenile, but becomes semi-pendulous in adult specimens (Wislocki, 1936). In the orang it is relatively small, and in the gorilla exceedingly small. In the latter it forms a scrotal area rather than a true scrotum. This comprises a pair of symmetrical sessile pockets separated by a deep median raphe situated close to the body, well behind the base of the penis and partially concealed by long hair (Hill and Matthews, 1949).

The scrotum is postpenial in most anthropoids, but in gibbons (e.g. *Hylobates lar, cinereus*) it may lie to either side of or anterior to the penis (Wislocki, 1936).

With the exception of the orang, in which a free communication is said to persist into adult life, as it normally does in catarrhine monkeys (Mijsberg, 1923), the processus vaginalis appears to be obliterated in anthropoid apes.

An ampulla of the vas deferens occurs in the gibbon, but is lacking in all other apes.

The seminal vesicles are elongated and of moderate size. The prostate is separated into a cranial and a caudal part in all anthropoids, except the orang-utan. In the giant Sumatran type of orang the prostate measures 25 mm. × 15 mm. in size, or a little less than the human prostate (Hill, 1939). Glandular tissue is not plentiful, and is restricted to the deeper parts neighbouring the urethra ; none is present between the ejaculatory ducts and the urethra or in front of the urethra. The prostatic ducts open on the sides of the colliculus seminalis. A shallow utriculus prostaticus is present.

The penis is usually slender and relatively short. In gibbons it may be very small, but considerable variation occurs in this species (Pocock, 1925). Its distal part is often poorly developed, and in the chimpanzee a true glans is thought to be lacking altogether (Pohl, 1928 ; Wislocki, 1936). In the giant orang of Sumatra the body and glans are laterally compressed, and the glans is globular. The urethral meatus is a vertical slit without differentiated lips. Papillary elevations on the skin of the penis similar to those which occur in prosimians and platyrrhine monkeys have been described in the orang (Pohl, 1928), some chimpanzees (Hill, 1946) and gibbons (Matthews, 1946), but not in the gorilla. In the latter species the penis has an external length (*pars libera*) of only 10 to 12 mm. It projects distally forwards and possesses a well differentiated conical glans, a coronal sulcus, and a rudimentary fraenulum praeputii. It is consequently believed to resemble the human penis more than that of any other anthropoid ape (Hill and Matthews, 1949).

An os penis is found in all the anthropoids.

The female

The ovaries resemble the human gonads in shape, but are relatively larger and more slender. Their absolute dimensions are generally smaller, but in the gorilla they are equal to or a little larger than those of the human ovaries.

The approximate size of the ovaries in different species of anthropoid apes and in women is given in Table IV, all figures referring to the non-pregnant state.

observations on the appearance of the external genitalia in anthropoids have been published by Hill (1946) and Hill and Matthews (1949).

TABLE IV

Dimensions of the Ovaries, in Millimetres. (From Wislocki, 1932)

Gorilla	R.	40 × 11 × 9
	L.	43 × 28 × 10
Human	R.	45 × 21 × 8
	L.	43 × 20 × 7
Chimpanzee	R.	19 × 11 × 4
	L.	30 × 13 × 6
Orang	R.	21 × 16 × 10
	L.	20 × 17 × 17
Gibbon	R.	16 × 12 × 7
	L.	16 × 10 × 10

The ovaries of catarrhine monkeys like *M. mulatta* are smaller than, and those of platyrrhines about equal in size to the ovaries of the gibbon (Tables II, IV). This indicates that there is no clear correlation between the size of the ovaries and total body weight of the adult female in primates.

By comparison, the diameter of the ovarian oöcyte varies only within very narrow limits in different primates (approximate range : 119–140 μ ; Hartman, 1929 ; Hill, 1932).

Apart from their large size, the ovaries of the gorilla are distinguished by the presence of small superficial papilliform elevations. These consist of a connective tissue core partly covered by a low columnar epithelium and, therefore, differ in structure from the " decidual " papillae which occur on the surface of the human ovary during pregnancy (Săglik, 1938). Similar patches have been described in the chimpanzee and orang, but not in any other primate.

A noteworthy feature of the ovary of the gibbon is the intensive luteinisation of all follicular elements during the progestational phase of the cycle, pregnancy and lactation. In this respect, the gibbon resembles the platyrrhine monkeys, and differs from man and other catarrhines, in whom thecal luteinisation takes place only during pregnancy (Săglik, 1938 ; Dempsey, 1940).

The uterine tubes are very similar to those in women, but tend to run a straighter course. The fimbriae are generally longer than the human ones, and the uterine and ovarian fimbriae are poorly demarcated. A large amount of fat is usually present in the inferior mesosalpinx, but there is no superior mesosalpinx and no ovarian bursa. In the gorilla the muscular layer of the tube is particularly well developed (Wislocki, 1932).

According to Wislocki the uterus of the gorilla is much larger, and that of the chimpanzee a little smaller than the human uterus, while that of the orang is considerably smaller and very similar in size to the uterus of the gibbon. Approximate measurements of the uterus in these species are given in Table V.

In the chimpanzee, orang, gibbon and man the fundus shows a characteristic dorso-ventral flattening, but in the gorilla this portion is spherical or globular in outline, and thus resembles the type of uterus found in the catarrhine monkeys (Fig. *2*. 34).

The greater length and breadth of the uterus of the gorilla is due to the development of all muscular elements. This is manifest in its thick myometrium and bulky cervix which exceeds that of man in every dimension. In the other

TABLE V

<small>DIMENSIONS OF THE NON-GRAVID UTERUS, IN MILLIMETRES.</small> (From Wislocki, 1932)

	Greatest length	Greatest breadth	Greatest ant.-post. diameter
Gorilla . . .	101	52	46
Human 1 . .	80	52	31
2 . .	62	55	24
Chimpanzee 1 .	51	37	21
2 .	65	41	27
Orang . . .	42	28	18
Gibbon 1 . .	45	25	19
2 . .	44	25	19

anthropoids the cervix is surprisingly small, and is least developed in the gibbon, in which the portio hardly protrudes into the vagina, and the fornices are shallow. In this species the external os is surrounded by delicate folds of epithelium.

In the gorilla the epithelium of the vagina is arranged in low transverse folds, less numerous and conspicuous than the columnae rugarum of the human vagina. Such folds are also found in the gibbon, where their size, texture and degree of cornification varies with the phase of the cycle (Dempsey, 1940). In the chimpanzee and orang they are almost completely absent.

The urethro-vaginal septum is deficient in the gorilla and tapers to a sharp wedge, below which the urethra and vagina open into the vestibule. The urethral opening into the vestibule lacks a papilla and is relatively concealed, owing to the depth and conical outline of the vestibule, and thus the meatus is not externally visible. This arrangement of the urethro-vaginal tract is also found in the chimpanzee and orang and, therefore, differs considerably from that present in man. According to Wislocki (1932), a hymen is " a structure characteristic of the Simiae as a group," but he admits that his opinion is not shared by other authorities. Ashley Montagu could find no evidence of it in a sexually immature gorilla (1937).

The configuration of the external genitalia in the great apes varies in different species and at different stages of postnatal development. The subject is very complex and has been more recently reviewed by Wislocki (1932, 1936) and Ashley Montagu (1937). According to the former, the labia majora are present in foetal and infant anthropoids and consist of " fatty cushions situated on either side of the medial structures and extending from the symphysis to the perineum." However, unlike their homologues in man, they tend to diminish during later postnatal life, when they become relatively inconspicuous, and may disappear almost completely. This ontogenetic reduction of the labia majora is also subject to considerable individual variation. It appears to be most marked in the gorilla, and least so in the gibbon, which in this aspect resembles man more closely than the other anthropoids. In the chimpanzee well-developed labia majora have been identified in an almost mature specimen (Zuckerman and Fulton, 1934), but in an infantile gorilla (estimated at 2½ years) these structures were only represented by two narrow cushions of skin situated immediately lateral to the praeputium clitoridis, and measuring about 25 mm. in length and 5 mm. in breadth (Ashley Montagu, 1937).

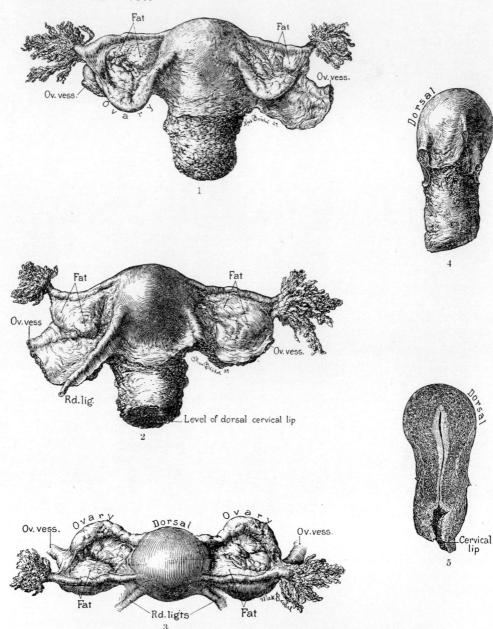

Fig. 2. 34—The reproductive organs of the female gorilla (Wislocki, 1932).
Views : 1. Dorsal.   2. Ventral.   3. Fundus.   4. Right-lateral.   5. Median sagittal.

The labia minora and clitoris are generally well developed in the anthropoid apes, especially the chimpanzee, and in some gibbons (*see* Pocock, 1925).   The clitoris with the associated fraenulum and praeputium are relatively as well as absolutely larger than in man. The former is grooved throughout its length on the ventral aspect. This furrow is very conspicuous when the clitoris is everted and forms an anterior continuation of the vulval cleft.

Among anthropoids a true sexual skin, involving the perineum as well as the perianal tissues and undergoing cyclical changes, is found only in the chimpanzee. However, some degree of activity of the genital skin occurs also in the gorilla and orang. In the former, Noback (1939) has described regular, though slight, changes in the vulval cleft, which are comparable to the more conspicuous changes undergone by the sexual skin in species like the baboon and chimpanzee. In the orang swelling of the sexual skin area has been observed during late pregnancy (Schultz, 1938a). No sexual skin is present either in the gibbon or in man. The lack of cyclical changes in the configuration of the female genitalia in the gibbon is responsible for the difficulty often experienced in distinguishing the two sexes during life (Zuckerman, 1930).

The degree of development of the ischial callosities varies considerably in the different species of anthropoids (*see* above). True callosities are present only in the gibbon. In the chimpanzee they are represented by loose pads of hypertrophied connective and fatty tissue. In the orang and gorilla they are even less developed, and in women they are completely absent.

Bibliography

AGDUHR, E. (1927). Studies on the structure and development of the bursa ovarica and the tuba uterina in the mouse. *Acta zool., Stockh.*, **8**, 1.

ALDEN, R. H. (1942). The periovarial sac in the albino rat. *Anat. Rec.*, **83**, 421

ALLANSON, M. (1931). The reproductive cycle in the male ferret. *J. Physiol.*, **71**, 20P.

—— (1932). The reproductive processes of certain mammals. III. The reproductive cycle of the male ferret. *Proc. Roy. Soc.* B, **110**, 295.

—— (1934). The reproductive processes of certain mammals. VII. Seasonal variation in the reproductive organs of the male hedgehog. *Phil. Trans.* B, **223**, 277.

—— ROWLANDS, I. W. and PARKES, A. S. (1934). Induction of fertility and pregnancy in the anoestrous ferret. *Proc. Roy. Soc.* B, **115**, 410.

ALLEN, E. (1922). The oestrous cycle in the mouse. *Amer. J. Anat.*, **30**, 297.

AMOROSO, E. C. (1952). In *Marshall's physiology of reproduction*, vol. II. 3rd ed. London.

ANDERSEN, D. H. (1928). Comparative anatomy of the tubo-uterine junction. Histology and physiology in the sow. *Amer. J. Anat.*, **42**, 255.

ANDRES, J. (1927). Die Arterien der Keimdrüsen bei männlichen und weiblichen Versuchssäugetieren. (Anatomische Untersuchungen an injizierten Aufhellungspräparaten bei *Lepus cuniculus, Cavia cobaya, Mus rattus* und *Mus musculus*.) *Z. Anat. EntwGesch.*, **84**, 445.

ARNBÄCK-CHRISTIE-LINDE, A. (1907). Der Bau der Soriciden und ihre Beziehungen zu anderen Säugetieren. *Morph. Jb.*, **36**, 463.

ASDELL, S. A. (1946). *Patterns of mammalian reproduction*. New York.

—— (1947). In *The physiology of domestic animals*. Ed. Dukes, H. H. New York.

ASHLEY-MONTAGU, M. F. (1937). Note on the external genitalia in three female Old World primates. *Anat. Rec.*, **69**, 389.

ASTWOOD, E. B., GESCHICKTER, C. F., & RAUSCH, E. O. (1937). Development of the mammary gland of the rat. Study of normal, experimental and pathologic changes and their endocrine relationships. *Amer. J. Anat.*, **61**, 373.

AYER, A. A. (1948). *The anatomy of Semnopithecus entellus*. Madras.

BARNSTEIN, N. J., & MOSSMAN, H. W. (1938). The origin of the penile urethra and bulbourethral glands with particular reference to the red squirrel (*Tamiasciurus hudsonicus*). *Anat. Rec.*, **72**, 67.

BAXTER, J. S. (1935). On the female genital tract in the Caenolestids (Marsupialia). *Proc. zool. Soc. Lond.*, **1935**, 157.

BEATTIE, J. (1927). The anatomy of the common marmoset. *Proc. zool. Soc. Lond.*, **1927**, 593.

BENOIT, J. (1925). Recherches anatomiques, cytologiques et histophysiologiques sur les voies excrétices du testicule chez les mammifères. *Bull. d'histol. appliq. à la physiol.*, **51**, 78. (Quoted by Broek, A. J. P. van den, 1933.)

BERN, H. A., & KRICHESKY, B. (1943). Anatomic and histologic studies of the sex accessories of the male rabbit. *Univ. Calif. Publ. Zool.*, **47**, 175.

BOLLIGER, A., & CARRODUS, A. L. (1938). Spermatorrhoea in *Trichosurus vulpecula* and other marsupials. *Med. J. Aust.*, **2**, 1118.

BOURG, R. (1935). Étude des modifications provoquées par la gravidine au niveau de l'ovaire et du tractus génital chez la chatte. *Arch. Biol., Paris*, **46**, 47.

BRAMBELL, F. W. R. (1929). The application of Goldschmidt's hypothesis to the differentiation of sex in vertebrates. *Sci. Progr. Twent. Cent.*, **24**, 643.

—— (1930). *The development of sex in invertebrates.* London.

—— (1935). Reproduction in the common shrew (*Sorex araneus* Linnaeus). I. The oestrous cycle of the female. *Phil. Trans. B*, **225**, 1.

—— & DAVIS, D. H. S. (1941). Reproduction of the multimammate mouse (*Mastomys erythroleucus* Temm.) of Sierra Leone. *Proc. zool. Soc. Lond. B*, **111**, 1.

—— & HALL, K. (1936). Reproduction in the lesser shrew (*Sorex minutus* Linnaeus). *Proc. zool. Soc. Lond.*, **1936**, 957.

—— & PERRY, J. S. (1946). The development of the embryonic membranes of the shrews, *Sorex araneus* Linn. and *Sorex minutus* Linn. *Proc. zool. Soc. Lond.*, **115**, 251.

—— & ROWLANDS, I. W. (1936). Reproduction of the bank vole (*Evotomys glareolus*, Schreber). I. The oestrous cycle of the female. *Phil. Trans. B*, **226**, 71.

BRESSLAU, E. (1920). *The mammary apparatus of the mammalia in the light of ontogenesis and phylogenesis.* London. (Quoted by Schultz, A. H., 1948.)

BROEK, A. J. P. van den (1933). In *Handbuch der vergleichenden Anatomie der Wirbeltiere.* Ed. Bolk, L., Göppert, E., Kallius, E., and Lubosch, W. 6. Bd. Berlin, Wien.

BUCHANAN, G., & FRASER, E. A. (1918). The development of the urogenital system in the marsupialia, with special reference to *Trichosurus vulpecula. J. Anat., Lond.*, **53**, 35.

CHASE, E. B. (1939). The reproductive system of the male opossum, *Didelphis virginia* Kerr, and its experimental modification. *J. Morph.*, **65**, 215.

CLARK, W. E. LE GROS (1926). On the anatomy of the pen-tailed tree shrew (*Ptilocercus lowii*). *Proc. zool. Soc. Lond.*, **1926**, 1179.

—— (1934). *Early forerunners of man.* London.

CLOUDMAN, A. M. (1941). In *Biology of the laboratory mouse.* Ed. Snell, G. D. Philadelphia.

COE, W. R., & KUNKEL, B. W. (1906). Studies on the California limbless lizard, Anniella. *Trans. Conn. Acad. Arts. Sci.*, **12**, 1. (Quoted by Witschi, E., 1935.)

COLE, H. H., HART, G. H., LYONS, W. R., & CATCHPOLE, H. R. (1933). The development and hormonal content of fetal horse gonads. *Anat. Rec.*, **56**, 275.

COLLINGS, M. R. (1926). A study of the cutaneous reddening and swelling about the genitalia of the monkey, *Macacus rhesus. Anat. Rec.*, **33**, 271.

COURRIER, R. (1924a). Le rhythme vaginal du hérisson ; action de l'injection de liquide folliculaire. *C.R. Soc. Biol., Paris*, **90**, 808.

—— (1924b). Le cycle sexuel chez la femelle des mammifères. *Arch. Biol., Paris*, **34**, 369.

—— (1927). Étude sur le déterminisme des caractères sexuels secondaires chez quelques mammifères à activité testiculaire périodique. *Arch. Biol., Paris*, **37**, 173.

CREW, F. A. E. (1931). Paired oviducts in the fowl. *J. Anat., Lond.*, **66**, 100.

DATHE, H. (1937). Über den Bau des männlichen Kopulationsorganes beim Meerschweinchen und anderen hystriocomorphen Nagetieren. *Morph. Jb.*, **80**, 1.

DAVIES, D. V., & MANN, T. (1947). Functional development of accessory glands and spermatogenesis. *Nature, Lond.*, **160**, 295.

DEANESLY, R. (1934). The reproductive processes of certain mammals. Part VI. The reproductive cycle of the female hedgehog. *Phil. Trans. B*, **223**, 239.

—— (1935). The reproductive processes of certain mammals. Part IX. Growth and reproduction in the stoat (*Mustela erminea*). *Phil. Trans. B*, **225**, 459.

DEANESLY, R. (1938). The reproductive cycle of the golden hamster (*Cricetus auratus*). *Proc. zool. Soc. Lond.* A, **108**, 31.

—— (1939). The uterus masculinus of the rabbit and its reactions to androgens and oestrogens. *J. Endocrinol.*, **1**, 300.

—— & ROWLANDS, I. W. (1936). Growth of the reproductive and endocrine organs of the guinea-pig. *J. Anat., Lond.*, **70**, 331.

DEMPSEY, E. W. (1939). The reproductive cycle of new world monkeys. *Amer. J. Anat.*, **64**, 381.

—— (1940). The structure of the reproductive tract in the female gibbon. *Amer. J. Anat.*, **67**, 229.

—— & WISLOCKI, G. B. (1941). The structure of the ovary of the humpback whale (*Megaptera nodosa*). *Anat. Rec.*, **80**, 243.

DISSELHORST, R. (1904). In *Lehrbuch der vergleichenden mikroskopischen Anatomie der Wirbeltiere*. Ed. Oppel, A. 4. Bd. Jena.

DRAHN, F. (1924). In *Biologie und Pathologie des Weibes*. Ed. Halban, J., and Seitz, L 1. Bd. Berlin.

EADIE, W. R. (1948). The male accessory reproductive glands of *Condylura* with notes on a unique prostatic secretion. *Anat. Rec.*, **101**, 59.

ECKSTEIN, P. (1948). M.D. Thesis, University of Cambridge.

ELLENBERGER, W., & BAUM, II. (1926). *Handbuch der vergleichenden Anatomie der Haustiere*. 16. Aufl. Berlin.

EMMENS, C. W. (1939). Growth of the reproductive and endocrine organs of the female rabbit. *J. Endocrinol.*, **1**, 409.

ENGLE, E. T. (1926). A morphological and experimental study of the proximal lobes of the prostate of the guinea-pig. *Anat. Rec.*, **34**, 75.

—— (1927). Notes on the sexual cycle of the Pacific cetacea of the genera *Megaptera* and *Balaenoptera*. *J. Mammal.*, **8**, 48.

FEKETE, E. (1938). A comparative morphological study of the mammary gland in a high and low tumour strain of mice. *Amer. J. Path.*, **14**, 557.

—— (1941). In *Biology of the laboratory mouse*. Ed. Snell, G. D. Philadelphia.

FINKEL, M. P. (1945). The relation of sex hormones to pigmentation and to testis descent in the opossum and ground squirrel. *Amer. J. Anat.*, **76**, 93.

FLYNN, T. T. (1923). Remarks on the method of parturition in *Potoroüs tridactylus*. *Proc. Linn. Soc., N.S.W.*, **47**, 28.

FOLLEY, S. J., & ZUCKERMAN, S. (1938). Development of the mammary gland in the rhesus monkey. *J. Anat., Lond.*, **72**, 613.

FORBES, W. A. (1881). On some points in the anatomy of the koala (*Phascolarctos cinereus*). *Proc. zool. Soc. Lond.*, 180.

FORDHAM, M. G. C. (1928). The anatomy of the urinogenital organs of the male *Myrmecobius fasciatus*. *J. Morph.*, **46**, 563.

FOSTER, M. A. (1934). The reproductive cycle in the female ground squirrel, *Citellus tridecemlineatus* (Mitchill). *Amer. J. Anat.*, **54**, 487.

FOX, H. (1929). The birth of two anthropoid apes. *J. Mammal.*, **10**, 37.

GARDE, M. L. (1930). The ovary of *Ornithorhynchus*, with special reference to follicular atresia. *J. Anat., Lond.*, **64**, 422.

GERHARDT, U. (1909). *Das Kaninchen, zugleich eine Einführung in die Organisation der Säugetiere*. Leipzig.

—— (1933). In *Handbuch der vergleichenden Anatomie der Wirbeltiere*. Ed. Bolk, L., Göppert, E., Kallius, E., & Lubosch, W. 6. Bd. Berlin, Wien.

GREENE, E. C. (1935). Anatomy of the rat. *Trans. Amer. phil. Soc.*, No. 27.

—— (1942). In *The rat in laboratory investigation*. Ed. Farris, E. J., & Griffith, J. Q. Philadelphia.

GROS, G. (1936). Contribution à l'endocrinologie sexuelle. Le cycle génital de la chatte. *Thèse, Université d'Alger.* No. 21.

GROSSER, O. (1933). Human and comparative placentation. Part I. (General principles of placentation.) Parts II and III. (The early stages of human development; human placentation and its meaning.) *Lancet*, **224**, 999; 1053.

GROSZ, S. (1905). Beiträge zur Anatomie der accessorischen Geschlechtsdrüsen der Insektivoren und Nager. *Arch. mikr. Anat.*, **66**, 567.

GUTHRIE, M. J. (1933). The reproductive cycles of some cave bats. *J. Mammal.*, **14**, 199.

GUTZSCHEBAUCH, A. (1935). Der Hoden der Haussäugetiere und seine Hüllen in biologischer und artdiagnostischer Hinsicht. *Z. Anat. EntwGesch.*, **105**, 433.

HALL, K. (1936). The structure and development of the urethral sinus in the male white mouse with notes on its occurrence in other rodents. *J. Anat., Lond.*, **70**, 413.

HAMILTON, W. J., Jr. (1940). The biology of the smoky shrew (*Sorex fumeus fumeus* Miller). *Zoologica, N.Y.*, **25**, 433. (Quoted by Pearson, O. P., 1944.)

HAMILTON, W. J., & GOULD, J. H. (1939–40). Normal oestrous cycle in the ferret. *Trans. Roy. Soc. Edinb.*, **60**, 87.

HAMLETT, G. W. D. (1934). Uterine bleeding in a bat, *Glossophaga soricina*. *Anat. Rec.*, **60**, 9.

—— (1935). Extra-ovarial sex cords in an armadillo ovary. *Anat. Rec.*, **62**, 195.

HAMMOND, J. (1927). *The physiology of reproduction in the cow.* Cambridge.

—— & MARSHALL, F. H. A. (1930). Oestrus and pseudopregnancy in the ferret. *Proc. Roy. Soc. B*, **105**, 607.

—— & WODZICKI, K. (1941). Anatomical and histological changes during the oestrous cycle in the mare. *Proc. Roy. Soc. B*, **130**, 1.

HARRISON, R. G. (1949). The comparative anatomy of the blood supply of the mammalian testis. *Proc. zool. Soc. Lond.*, **119**, 325.

HARRISON, R. J. (1946). The early development of the corpus luteum in the mare. *J. Anat., Lond.*, **80**, 160.

—— (1948). The changes occurring in the ovary of the goat during the oestrous cycle and in early pregnancy. *J. Anat., Lond.*, **82**, 21.

—— (1949). Observations on the female reproductive organs of the Ca'ing whale, *Globiocephala melaena* Traill. *J. Anat., Lond.*, **83**, 238.

HART, D. B. (1909). The nature and cause of the physiological descent of the testes. *Trans. Edinb. Obstet. Soc.*, **34**, 101.

HARTMAN, C. G. (1929). How large is the mammalian egg? *Quart. Rev. Biol.*, **4**, 373.

—— (1932). Studies in the reproduction of the monkey *Macacus* (*Pithecus*) *rhesus*, with special reference to menstruation and pregnancy. *Contr. Embryol. Carneg. Instn.*, **23**, 1.

—— (1938). Some observations on the bonnet macaque. *J. Mammal.*, **19**, 468.

HILL, J. P. (1899–1901). Contributions to the morphology and development of the female urogenital organs in the marsupialia. Part I. *Proc. Linn. Soc., N.S.W.*, **24**, 42 ; **25**, 519.

—— (1932). The developmental history of the primates. *Phil. Trans. B*, **221**, 45.

—— & FRASER, E. A. (1925). Some observations on the female urogenital organs of the Didelphyidae. *Proc. zool. Soc. Lond.*, **1925**, 189.

HILL, M. (1939). The reproductive cycle of the male weasel (*Mustela nivalis*). *Proc. zool. Soc. Lond. B*, **109**, 481.

—— & PARKES, A. S. (1933). Studies of the hypophysectomised ferret. IV. Comparison of the reproductive organs during anoestrus and after hypophysectomy. *Proc. Roy. Soc. B*, **113**, 530.

HILL, W. C. O. (1939). Observations on a giant Sumatran orang. *Amer. J. phys. Anthrop.*, **24**, 449.

—— (1945). Notes on the dissection of two dugongs. *J. Mammal.*, **26**, 153.

—— (1946). Note on the male external genitalia of the chimpanzee. *Proc. zool. Soc. Lond.*, **116**, 129.

—— & MATTHEWS, L. H. (1949). The male external genitalia of the gorilla with remarks on the os penis of other hominoidea. *Proc. zool. Soc. Lond.*, **119**, 363.

—— PORTER, A., & SOUTHWICK, M. D. (1952). The natural history, endoparasites and pseudoparasites of the tarsiers (*Tarsius carbonarius*) recently living in the Society's gardens. *Proc. zool. Soc. Lond.*, **122**, 79.

HOOKER, C. W., & STRONG, L. C. (1944). Hermaphroditism in rodents, with a description of a case in the mouse. *Yale J. Biol. Med.*, **16**, 341.

HORST, C. J. VAN DER, (1942). Some observations on the structure of the genital tract of *Elephantulus*. *J. Morph.*, **70**, 403.

HORST, C. J. VAN DER, & GILLMAN, J. (1941a). The menstrual cycle in *Elephantulus*. *S. Afr. J. med. Sci.*, **6**, 27.

—— (1941b). The number of eggs and surviving embryos in *Elephantulus*. *Anat. Rec.*, **80**, 443.

HUNT, H. R. (1924). *A laboratory manual of the anatomy of the rat*. New York.

HÜTT, A. (1926–7). Recherches anatomiques et histophysiologiques sur l'utricule prostatique. *Arch. Anat., Strasbourg*, **6**, 361.

JOACHIMOVITS, R. (1928). Studien zu Menstruation, Ovulation, Aufbau und Pathologie des weiblichen Genitales bei Mensch und Affe (*Pithecus fascicularis mordax*). *Biol. Gen., Vienna*, **4**, 447.

KELLOGG, M. (1945). The postnatal development of the oviduct of the rat. *Anat. Rec.*, **93**, 377.

KNAUS, H. (1933). Zur Physiologie der Samenblase. *Klin. Wschr.*, **12**, 1606.

KÜPFER, M. (1928). The sexual cycle of female domesticated mammals. The ovarian changes and the periodicity of oestrum in cattle, sheep, goats, pigs, donkeys, and horses. *Rep. vet. Res. S. Afr.*, 13 & 14, Part 2, 1209.

LANGE, D. DE (1933). In *Handbuch der vergleichenden Anatomie der Wirbeltiere*. Ed. Bolk, L., Göppert, E., Kallius, E., and Lubosch, W. 6. Bd. Berlin, Wien.

LEE, F. C. (1928). The tubo-uterine junction in various animals. *Johns Hopk. Hosp. Bull.*, **42**, 335.

LINTON, R. G. (1907). A contribution to the histology of the so-called Cowper's gland of the hedgehog (*Erinaceus europaeus*). *Anat. Anz.*, **31**, 61.

LISTER, J. J., & FLETCHER, J. J. (1881). On the condition of the median portion of the vaginal apparatus in the Macropodidae. *Proc. zool. Soc. Lond.*, 976.

LONG, J. A., & EVANS, H. M. (1922). The oestrous cycle in the rat and its associated phenomena. *Mem. Univ. Calif.*, **6**, 6.

LUNN, H. F. (1947). *J. Anat., Lond.*, **81**, 384.

MACKINTOSH, N. A. (1946). The natural history of whalebone whales. *Biol. Rev.*, **21**, 60.

—— & WHEELER, J. F. G. (1929). Southern blue and fin whales. "*Discovery*" *Rep.*, **1**, 257.

MACLEOD, J. (1880). Contribution à l'étude de la structure de l'ovaire des mammifères. *Arch. Biol., Paris*, **1**, 241.

MARKEE, J. E., & HINSEY, J. C. (1933). Internal migration of ova in cat. *Proc. Soc. exp. Biol., N.Y.*, **31**, 267.

MARSHALL, F. H. A. (1904). The oestrous cycle in the common ferret. *Quart. J. micr. Sci.*, **48**, 323.

—— (1922). *The physiology of reproduction*. 2nd ed. London.

MATTHEWS, L. H. (1935). The oestrous cycle and intersexuality in the female mole (*Talpa europaea* Linn.). *Proc. zool. Soc. Lond.*, **1935**, 347.

—— (1937a). The form of the penis in the British rhinolophid bats, compared with that in some of the vespertilionid bats. *Trans. zool. Soc. Lond.*, **23**, 213.

—— (1937b). The female sexual cycle in the British horse-shoe bats, *Rhinolophus ferrumequinum insulanus* Barrett-Hamilton and *R. hipposideros minutus* Montagu. *Trans. zool. Soc. Lond.*, **23**, 224.

—— (1937c). The humpback whale, *Megaptera nodosa*. "*Discovery*" *Rep.*, **17**, 7.

—— (1938a). Notes on the southern right whale (*Eubalaena australis*). "*Discovery*" *Rep.*, **17**, 169.

—— (1938b). The sei whale, *Balaenoptera borealis*. "*Discovery*" *Rep.*, **17**, 183.

—— (1938c). The sperm whale, *Physeter catodon*. "*Discovery*" *Rep.*, **17**, 93.

—— (1941a). Notes on the genitalia and reproduction of some African bats. *Proc. zool. Soc. Lond. B*, **111**, 289.

—— (1941b). Reproduction in the spotted hyaena, *Crocuta crocuta* (Erxleben). *Phil. Trans. B*, **230**, 1.

—— (1941c). Reproduction in the Scottish wild cat, *Felis silvestris grampia* Miller. *Proc. zool. Soc. Lond. B*, **111**, 59.

—— (1946). Notes on the genital anatomy and physiology of the gibbon (*Hylobates*). *Proc. zool. Soc. Lond.*, **116**, 339.

—— (1947). A note on the female reproductive tract in the tree kangeroos (*Dendrolagus*). *Proc. zool. Soc. Lond.*, **117**, 313.

MATTHEWS, L. H. (1948). Cyclic changes in the uterine mucosa of balaenopterid whales. *J. Anat., Lond.*, **82**, 207.

McINTOSH, W. C. (1930). Notes on a female llama. *J. Anat., Lond.*, **64**, 353.

MEEK, A. (1918). The reproductive organs of *Cetacea*. *J. Anat., Lond.*, **52**, 186.

MIJSBERG, W. A. (1923). Über den Bau des Urogenitalapparates bei den männlichen Primaten. *Verh. Akad. Wet., Amst.*, **23**, 1.

MILLER, R. A. (1945). The ischial callosities of primates. *Amer. J. Anat.*, **76**, 67.

MIVART, ST. G. (1881). *The cat.* London.

MOORE, C. R. (1926). The biology of the mammalian testis and scrotum. *Quart. Rev. Biol.*, **1**, 4.

MORGAN, C. F. (1946). Sexual rhythms in the reproductive tract of the adult female opossum and effects of hormonal treatments. *Amer. J. Anat.*, **78**, 411.

MOSSMAN, H. W. (1937a). Comparative morphogenesis of the fetal membranes and accessory uterine structures. *Contr. Embryol. Carneg. Instn.*, **26**, 129.

—— (1937b). The thecal gland and its relation to the reproductive cycle. A study of the cyclic changes in the ovary of the pocket gopher, *Geomys bursarius* (Shaw). *Amer. J. Anat.*, **61**, 289.

—— LAWLAH, J. W., & BRADLEY, J. A. (1932). The male reproductive tract of the *Sciuridae*. *Amer. J. Anat.*, **51**, 89.

NAYAK, U. V. *A comparative study of the Lorisinae and the Galaginae.* Unpublished thesis. (Quoted by Clark, W. E. Le Gros, 1934.)

NELSEN, O. E., & MAXWELL, N. (1942). The structure and function of the urogenital region in the female opossum, compared with the same region in other marsupials. *J. Morph.*, **71**, 463.

NOBACK, C. R. (1939). The changes in the vaginal smears and associated cyclic phenomena in the lowland gorilla (*Gorilla gorilla*). *Anat. Rec.*, **73**, 209.

OMMANNEY, F. D. (1932). The urogenital system of the fin whale (*Balaenoptera physalus*). " Discovery " Rep., **5**, 363.

OWEN, Sir R. (1838). On the anatomy of the Dugong. *Proc. zool. Soc. Lond.*, 28.

—— (1868). *On the anatomy of vertebrates.* Vol. III. London.

PALLIN, G. (1901). Beiträge zur Anatomie und Embryologie der Prostata und der Samenblasen. *Arch. Anat. Physiol., Lpz.*, 135.

PARKES, A. S. (1931). The reproductive processes of certain mammals. Part I. The oestrous cycle of the Chinese hamster (*Cricetulus griseus*). *Proc. Roy. Soc.* B, **108**, 138.

PATERSON, H. M., & DUN, R. C. (1898). The genito-urinary organs of the female Indian elephant. *J. Anat., Lond.*, **32**, 582.

PEARSON, J. (1944). The female urogenital system of the Marsupialia with special reference to the vaginal complex. *Pap. roy. Soc. Tasm.*, 71.

PEARSON, O. P. (1944). Reproduction in the shrew (*Blarina brevicauda* Say). *Amer. J. Anat.*, **75**, 39.

—— (1949). Reproduction of a South American rodent, the mountain viscacha. *Amer. J. Anat.*, **84**, 143.

PERRY, J. S. (1953). The reproduction of the African elephant, *Loxodonta Africana*. *Phil. Trans.* B, **237**, 93.

PETTEN, J. L. (1932). Beitrag zur Entwicklung des Pferdeovariums. *Z. ges. Anat.*, **99**, 338.

POCOCK, R. I. (1918). On the external characters of the lemurs and of *Tarsius*. *Proc. zool. Soc. Lond.*, **1918**, 19.

—— (1925). The external characters of the catarrhine monkeys and apes. *Proc. zool. Soc. Lond.*, **1925**, 1479.

POHL, L. (1928). Zur Morphologie der männlichen Kopulationsorgane der Säugetiere, insbesondere der Versuch einer vergleichend anatomischen Studie über den Penis der Primaten, einschliesslich des Menschen. *Z. Anat. EntwGesch.*, **86**, 71.

PONSE, K. (1924). L'organe de Bidder et le déterminisme des caractères sexuels secondaires du crapaud (*Bufo vulgaris* L.) *Rev. Suisse Zool.*, **31**, 177.

PRICE, D. (1936). Normal development of the prostate and seminal vesicles of the rat with a study of experimental post-natal modifications. *Amer. J. Anat.*, **60**, 79.

RATCLIFFE, H. L. (1941). A median vaginal canal and other anomalies of the genital tract of the opossum, *Didelphis virginiana*. *Anat. Rec.*, **80**, 203.

RAU, A. S., & HIRIYANNAIYA, S. (1930). The urino-genital system of *Loris lydek-kerianus. J. Mysore Univ.*, **4**, 149. (Quoted by Ayer, A. A., 1948.)

RAUTHER, M. (1903). Über den Genitalapparat einiger Nager und Insektivoren. *Jena. Z. Naturw.*, **37**, 377. (Quoted by Disselhorst, R., 1904.)

RETIEF, P. J. M. (1949). The accessory glands of reproduction in the male. *Clin. Proc., Cape Town*, **8**, 31.

RISMAN, G. C. (1947). The effects of oestradiol and progesterone on the reproductive tract of the opossum, and their possible relation to parturition. *J. Morph.*, **81**, 343.

ROBINSON, A. (1918). The formation, rupture and closure of ovarian follicles in ferrets and ferret polecate hybrids, and some associated phenomena. *Trans. Roy. Soc. Edinb.*, **52**, 303.

ROWLANDS, I. W. (1936). Reproduction of the bank vole (*Evotomys glareolus* Schreber). II. Seasonal changes in the reproductive organs of the male. *Phil. Trans. B*, **226**, 99.

—— & PARKES, A. S. (1935). The reproductive processes of certain mammals.—VIII. Reproduction in foxes (*Vulpes spp.*) *Proc. zool. Soc. Lond.*, **1935**, 823.

RUBIN, D. (1944). The relation of hormones to the development of Cowper's and Bartholin's glands in the opossum (*Didelphis virginiana*). *J. Morph.*, **74**, 213.

RUSSELL, A. E., & ZUCKERMAN, S. (1935). A " sexual skin " in a marmoset. *J. Anat., Lond.*, **69**, 356.

SÄGLIK, S. (1938). Ovaries of gorilla, chimpanzee, orang-utan and gibbon. *Contr. Embryol. Carneg. Instn.*, **27**, 179.

SANDYS, O. C., & ZUCKERMAN, S. (1938). Observations on the cervix uteri and the urethra of monkeys. *J. Anat., Lond.*, **72**, 352.

SCHMALTZ, R. (1921a). *Das Geschlechtsleben der Haussäugetiere.* Berlin.

—— (1921b). In *Handbuch der vergleichenden mikroskopischen Anatomie der Haustiere.* Ed. Ellenberger, W. 2. Bd. Berlin.

SCHNEIDER, K. M. (1930). Einige Beobachtungen über des Geschlechtsleben des indischen Elefanten. *Zool. Gart., Frankfurt*, **3**, 305.

SCHULTE, T. L. (1937). The genito-urinary system of the *Elephas indicus* male. *Amer. J. Anat.*, **61**, 131.

SCHULTZ, A. H. (1938a). Genital swelling in the female orang-utan. *J. Mammal.*, **19**, 363.

—— (1938b). The relative weight of the testes in primates. *Anat. Rec.*, **72**, 387.

—— (1948). The number of young at a birth and the number of nipples in primates. *Amer. J. phys. Anthrop.*, **6**, 1.

SCHWARZ, F. (1928). Die Harnkeim (Urogenital) gegend der Nabeltiere (Amniota). I. Die Entwicklung des Harnkeimwerkes (Urogenitalia) beim Maulwurf (*Talpa europaea*). *Z. Anat. EntwGesch.*, **88**, 181.

SEIFERLE, E. (1933). Über Art-und Altersmerkmale der weiblichen Geschlechtsorgane unserer Haussäugetiere. *Z. Anat. EntwGesch.*, **101**, 1.

SEUBERT, M. (1841). *Inaug. Diss., Bonn.* (Quoted by Disselhorst, R., 1904.)

SIDDIQI, M. A. H. (1937). The development of the penile urethra and the homology of Cowper's gland of male spermophile (*Citellus tridecemlineatus*) with a note on the prostatic utricle. *J. Anat., Lond.*, **72**, 109.

SIMPSON, G. G. (1945). The principles of classification and a classification of mammals. *Bull. Amer. Mus. Nat. Hist.*, **85**.

SISSON, S. (1940). *The anatomy of the domestic animals.* 2nd ed. Philadelphia; London.

SNELL, G. D. (1941). *Biology of the laboratory mouse.* Philadelphia.

SOULIÉ, A. H. (1895). *Recherches sur la migration des testicules.* Toulouse.

SPEERT, H. (1942a). Bilateral hyperthelia in a guinea-pig. *Anat. Rec.*, **83**, 317.

—— (1942b). Supernumerary mammae, with special reference to the rhesus monkey. *Quart. Rev. Biol.*, **17**, 59.

SPIEGEL, A. (1931). Untersuchungen über die Fortpflanzung bei Javanakaken. *Zbl. Gynäk.*, **55**, 1762.

STAFFORD, W. T., COLLINS, R. F., & MOSSMAN, H. W. (1942). The thecal gland in the guinea-pig ovary. *Anat. Rec.*, **83**, 193.

STEWART, T. D. (1933). In *The anatomy of the rhesus monkey*. Ed. Hartman, C. G., Straus, W. L., Jr. Baltimore.

TANDLER, J., & GROSZ, S. (1912). Über den Saison-dimorphismus des Maulwurfhodens. *Arch. EntwMeck. Org.*, **33**, 297.

TINKLEPAUGH, O. L. (1933). Sex cycles and other cyclic phenomena in a chimpanzee during adolescence, maturity and pregnancy. *J. Morph.*, **54**, 521.

TRAUTMAN, A., & FIEBIGER, J. (1931). *Histologie und vergleichend-mikroskopische Anatomie der Haussäugetiere*. Berlin.

TURNER. C. D. (1948). *General endocrinology*. Philadelphia; London.

VOSSELER, J. (1930). Zur Fortpflanzung des Känguruhs. *Zool. Gart., Frankfurt*, **3**, 1.

WAGENEN. G. VAN (1936). The coagulating function of the cranial lobe of the prostate gland in the monkey. *Anat. Rec.*, **66**, 411.

WALKER, G. (1910). A special function discovered in a glandular structure hitherto supposed to form a part of the prostate gland in rats and guinea-pigs. *Johns Hopk. Hosp. Bull.*, **21**, 182.

WEBER, M. (1904). *Die Säugetiere*. Jena.

WELLS, L. J. (1943). Descent of the testis : anatomical and hormonal considerations. *Surgery*, **14**, 436.

—— & OVERHOLSER, M. D. (1940). Effects of oestrogen on the genital tract and urethra of anoestrous female ground squirrels. *Anat. Rec.*, **78**, 43.

WIEDERSHEIM, R. (1907). *Einführung in die vergleichende Anatomie der Wirbeltiere*. Jena.

WILCOX, D. E., & MOSSMAN, H. W. (1945). The common occurrence of " testis " cords in the ovaries of a shrew (*Sorex vagrans*, Baird). *Anat. Rec.*, **92**, 183.

WIMSATT, W. A., & WALDO, C. M. (1945). The normal occurrence of a peritoneal opening in the bursa ovarii of the mouse. *Anat. Rec.*, **93**, 47.

WISLOCKI, G. B. (1928). Observations on the gross and microscopic anatomy of the sloths (*Bradypus griseus griseus* Gray and *Choloepus hoffmanni* Peters). *J. Morph.*, **46**, 317.

—— (1929). On the placentation of primates, with a consideration of the phylogeny of the placenta. *Contr. Embryol. Carneg. Instn.*, **20**, 51.

—— (1930a). An unusual placental form in the hyracoidea : its bearing on the theory of the phylogeny of the placenta. *Contr. Embryol. Carneg. Instn.*, **21**, 83.

—— (1930b). On a series of placental stages of a platyrrhine monkey (*Ateles geoffroyi*) with some remarks upon age, sex and breeding period in platyrrhines. *Contr. Embryol. Carneg. Instn.*, **22**, 173.

—— (1931). Notes on the female reproductive tract (ovaries, uterus and placenta) of the collared peccari (*Peccari angulatus* Bangsi Goldman). *J. Mammal.*, **12**, 143.

—— (1932). On the female reproductive tract of the gorilla with a comparison of that of other primates. *Contr. Embryol. Carneg. Instn.*, **23**, 163.

—— (1933a). Location of the testes and body temperature in mammals. *Quart. Rev. Biol.*, **8**, 385.

—— (1933b). In *The anatomy of the rhesus monkey*. Ed. Hartman, C. G., Straus, W. L., Jr. Baltimore.

—— (1933c). Observations on the descent of the testes in the macaque and in the chimpanzee. *Anat. Rec.*, **57**, 133.

—— (1935). The placentation of the manatee. *Mem. Harv. Mus. comp. Zool.*, **54**, 159.

—— (1936). The external genitalia of the simian primates. *Hum. Biol.*, **8**, 309.

—— (1939). Observations on twinning in marmosets. *Amer. J. Anat.*, **64**, 445.

—— & WESTHUYSEN, O. P. VAN DER (1940). The placentation of *Procavia capensis* with a discussion of the placental affinities of the hyracoidea. *Contr. Embryol. Carneg. Instn.*, **28**, 65.

WITSCHI, E. (1935). Origin of asymmetry in the reproductive system of birds. *Amer. J. Anat.*, **56**, 119.

WOOLLARD, H. H. (1925). The anatomy of *Tarsius spectrum*. *Proc. zool. Soc. Lond.*, **1925**, 1071.

WOOD JONES, F. (1914). Some phases in the reproductive history of the female mole (*Talpa europea*). *Proc. zool. Soc. Lond.*, **1914**, 191.

—— (1917). The genitalia of the Cheiroptera. *J. Anat., Lond.*, **51**, 36.

WOOD JONES, F. (1923–4).   *The mammals of South Australia.*   Parts I, II.   Adelaide.

—— (1943).   *Habit and heritage.*   London.

ZUCKERMAN, S. (1930).   The menstrual cycle of the primates.   Part I.   General nature and homology.   *Proc. zool. Soc. Lond.*, **1930**, 691.

—— (1933).   *Functional affinities of man, monkeys and apes.*   London.

—— (1937).   The duration and phases of the menstrual cycle in primates.   *Proc. zool. Soc. Lond.* A, **1937**, 315.

—— (1938).   The female prostate in the green monkey, *Cercopithecus aethiops sabaeus.*   *J. Anat., Lond.*, **72**, 472.

—— & FULTON, J. F. (1934).   The menstrual cycle of the primates.   Part VII.   The sexual skin of the chimpanzee.   *J. Anat., Lond.*, **69**, 38.

—— & KROHN, P. L. (1937).   The hydatids of Morgagni under normal and experimental conditions.   *Phil. Trans.* B, **228**, 147.

—— & McKEOWN, T. (1938).   The canine prostate in relation to normal and abnormal testicular changes.   *J. Path. Bact.*, **46**, 7.

—— & PARKES, A. S. (1932).   The menstrual cycle of the primates.   Part V.   The cycle of the baboon.   *Proc. zool. Soc. Lond.*, **1932**, 139.

—— —— (1935).   Observations on the structure of the uterus masculinus in various primates.   *J. Anat., Lond.*, **69**, 484.

—— WAGENEN, G. VAN, & GARDINER, R. H. (1938).   The sexual skin of the rhesus monkey.   *Proc. zool. Soc. Lond.*, **108**, 385.

CHAPTER 3

CYCLICAL CHANGES IN THE REPRODUCTIVE ORGANS OF THE LOWER VERTEBRATES

By L. Harrison Matthews and F. H. A. Marshall

In the first chapter instances are given of breeding periodicity in all the great groups of the animal kingdom including the four classes of the lower vertebrates, namely, fishes, amphibians, reptiles and birds, and brief accounts are included of the sexual cycle in various members of these classes with descriptions of some of the phenomena attending sexual activity. In the present chapter an attempt will be made to give short comparative descriptions of the cyclical changes shown by the generative organs in the different species of lower vertebrates so far as these changes are known.[1]

I. Pisces

Elasmobranchii

It has already been mentioned (p. 15, Chapter 1) that the eggs of the elasmo-branch fishes are usually deposited singly or in pairs at varying intervals throughout most of the year and that the intervals between the ovulation periods may be so short as to suggest a condition comparable to the polyoestrous habit of many of the Mammalia (*see* below, Chapter 4). This condition is in striking contrast to that of most teleosts which usually spawn many thousands or even millions of eggs in bulk at comparatively restricted seasons.

In *Scylliorhinus canicula*, Metten (1939) finds that there is no breeding season, but that the fish are always sexually active, though slightly more prolific in the spring. The ova pass from the ovary to the coelomic opening of the oviduct by ciliary action, for the abdominal cavity of the adult female is abundantly ciliated, though no cilia are present in the male or immature female. The oviducal gland serves as a receptaculum seminis, as well as secreting albumen and the egg case, and active sperm are found there all the year round in all adult females. Ferti-lisation takes place in the oviducal gland, and not in the upper oviduct as formerly supposed. In resting glands sperm are found in the shell-secreting tubules, and in actively secreting glands some spermatozoa are emitted with the shell material. In a later study Metten (1944) shows that the spermatozoa penetrate the oviducal wall in the region of the " uterus " and a small part of the oviduct anterior to it, but the cloacal epithelium is not invaded. More or less complete digestion of the spermatozoa takes place in vacuoles formed in the epithelial cells ; but, where

---

[1] For detailed accounts of the processes of oögenesis and spermatogenesis as they occur in vertebrates, but more particularly in mammals, *see* Chapters 5 and 7.

the cells are columnar, vacuoles are not produced, and the spermatozoa pass right through into the superficial connective tissue, where, presumably, they are phago-cytosed. The proportion of spermatozoa destroyed in the lower oviduct is not sufficient to prevent them ascending in large numbers to the upper part. It is suggested that the epithelium may produce a nutritive secretion capable of diffusion into the lumen of the oviduct, and a hostile secretion incapable of such diffusion. A high concentration of the nutritive secretion in the cells would explain the invasion by spermatozoa, and the killing of them by the hostile secretion would serve as a protection for the oviducal wall.

In *Mustelus canis*, Hisaw and Abramowitz (1938) find that there is a yearly cycle. Parturition occurs in late May and early June, the litter consisting of some sixteen young about 35 cm. in length. The females grow 20 to 30 cm. a year, and become sexually mature at the end of their third or fourth year. All females below 95 to 100 cm., and all males below 70 to 80 cm. in length, are sexually immature. In the females about 90 cm. long the ovary contains numerous small follicles, and the distal part of the Müllerian duct is transformed into a small uterus. In the spring of the following year these females, now 95 to 100 cm. long, become fully mature : the ovary contains sixteen to twenty large yellow ova, and the uterus and oviducal gland are fully developed. In late June and early July ovulation and fertilisation take place, and, usually, each uterine horn contains about eight embryos. The oviducal gland atrophies after ovulation, and the embryos grow very rapidly from July to September. By the latter month growth has gone on at such a pace that all the yolk has disappeared and the placenta is formed. Pregnancy lasts ten months, until the following spring, when parturition occurs. Meanwhile another wave of oögenesis has taken place during autumn and winter so that sixteen to twenty more mature ova are present when the dogfish migrate inshore in spring. Ovulation, fertilisation and pregnancy recur, and the cycle is repeated. In a later communication Hisaw and Abramowitz (1939) add that ovulation does not take place completely without copulation. In *Squalus acanthias* they find that gestation lasts about twenty-two months, so that in this species the cycle must occupy at least two years.

The epithelial cells of the ovarian follicles in some elasmobranchs have been described as undergoing hypertrophy, after the eggs have been discharged, in a similar manner to that of the luteal cells of the ruptured follicles of mammals. This process has been found to occur in *Myliobatis*, *Rhinobatis* and *Spinax*. Giocomini (1896) first reported that in *Myliobatis bovina* the follicle, after ovulation, is transformed into a glandular organ. Samuel (1943) has investigated the formation and structure of this gland in another batoid, *Rhinobatis granulatus*, more fully and by more modern methods. After the discharge of the ovum the gland, or corpus luteum, is formed in a manner homologous with that of mammals. The luteal cells are derived from the follicular epithelium and invading cells of the theca interna. Intrusions of the theca externa, accompanied by blood vessels, without either the hypertrophy or luteinisation of its cells, provide a supporting framework.

As pointed out by Cunningham (1931), and Cunningham and Smart (1934), it seems reasonable to suppose that the formation of bodies resembling corpora lutea in these fish is associated with the internal development of the fertilised ova in the same kind of way as occurs in mammals, and this conclusion is supported by the existence of a like correlation in viviparous reptiles, though similar structures also occur in some reptiles which are not viviparous (cf. p. 196). But, Samuel (1943) notes that though the fully formed corpus luteum of *Rhinobatis* resembles that of a mammal, it also has its own distinctive characteristics. In the mammal the corpus luteum is associated with the maintenance of pregnancy and its presence in an active state appears to suppress ovulation. Each ovary in *Rhinobatis*, however, may contain twenty corpora lutea in all stages of development, from the newly formed to fully active glands, and also maturing follicles.

In the Basking Shark (*Cetorhinus maximus*) Matthews (1950) found that the testes are embedded in the anterior ends of the epigonal organs which form an investing cortex round them. The testes are divided into lobes, and these into lobules which contain many ampullae. Testis tubules lead the spermatozoa from the ampullae to the vasa efferentia, whence they pass through the ductuli and ductus epididymidis to the enormous ampulla ductus deferentis, where they are incorporated in spermatophores.

The ampulla ductus deferentis contains numerous transverse septa, each with an eccentric perforation ; successive perforations form the lumen of the organ as a whole. Spermatic fluid enters the ampulla ductus deferentis and becomes broken up into small aggregations which pass into the pockets between the septa. Here they are rotated by ciliary action while the secretion from the deeper epithelial cells is laid down round them in concentric layers. The spermatophores are up to 2·0 to 3·0 cm. or more in diameter and consist of a translucent hyaline cortex surrounding an opaque core of spermatozoa. Several gallons of spermatophores are present in each ampulla.

The skeleton of the clasper is comparatively simple in structure, the cartilages being few in number and forming a scroll proximally and a groove distally. There is a movable style towards the distal end, armed with a sharp claw. The musculature of the clasper is reduced, the dilatator muscle being the largest. The inner surface of the clasper groove within the scroll is covered with a thick layer of glandular tissue whose secretion is produced by the swelling, degeneration and detachment of the superficial cells.

The siphons are long and wide sacs lying between the skin and the body wall on the ventro-lateral surface of the abdomen. They are connected by the siphon tubes with the bases of the clasper grooves and are invested by a thin sheet of muscle, part of the compressor muscle, derived from the pelvic fin. The siphon is probably used in some way not understood for introducing the spermatophores into the female by way of the clasper groove, but the spermatophores do not enter the siphon sacs.

The ovary of the right side alone is developed ; it is large and enclosed in a fibrous tunica. It consists mainly of a mass of small follicles loosely held together by a small amount of connective tissue, and is penetrated everywhere by the ramifications of a sytem of branching tubes which derive ultimately from a pocket on the right side of the outer surface of the ovary. The ova are discharged from the follicles when they are not more than 5·0 mm. in diameter and pass through the ramifying tubes to reach the exterior through the pocket. The epithelium of the discharged follicle proliferates to form a corpus luteum, the cells of which contain large quantities of lipoid material. Most of the ova, however, are not discharged but degenerate within the follicles, forming atretic corpora lutea. Great numbers of corpora lutea atretica are present in the ovary. In an average ovary there are at least six million ova 0·5 mm. or more in diameter, a size at which there is a considerable amount of yolk already present. The ovary is thus unlike that of other elasmobranchs in which there are usually a few large ova, and in general appearance is more like that of an oviparous teleost. This is remarkable in view of the fact that *Cetorhinus* is almost certainly viviparous.

The unpaired infundibular part of the oviducts opens at the ostium abdominale and lies shallowly embedded in the liver adjacent to the attachment of the falciform ligament. It follows a course such that the ostium abdominale is brought directly opposite, and into contact with, the pocket on the right side of the ovary. Ova thus pass from the ovary at once into the oviduct and do not wander in the peritoneal cavity. The paired oviducts are applied to the posterior surface of the septum transversum and pass to the parietal wall of the abdomen where they join the nidamentary glands. Their lumina are very narrow, not more than 2·0 to 3·0 mm. in diameter, and their walls are thick and inelastic so that it is impossible for an object larger than an ovum about 5·0 mm. in diameter to pass through them, and even an ovum of this size must undergo considerable distortion.

The nidamentary gland is comparatively small and shows no subdivision into albumen and shell-secreting parts ; no stored spermatozoa were found in it. An elongated narrow isthmus leads from the nidamentary gland to the enormous uterus. The greater part of the uterus is lined by innumerable villus-like trophonemata. These are based upon low longitudinal ridges and may be regarded as strap-like prolongations of their free edges. Each trophonema is supported by a central core of connective tissue and is richly vascularised ; no separate glands are present upon it but the epithelial cells increase greatly in number, and become swollen with secretion, perhaps trophic in function, which they release by becoming detached and disintegrating. In many places the proliferation of epithelial cells is so great that a solid mass of swollen cells, in which the trophonemata are partly or wholly buried, results. Numerous vesicles up to 4·0 or 5·0 mm. in diameter and containing a clear fluid may be present in the solid cell-mass. It is possible that their secretion may have a solvent action on the cortex of the spermatophores.

The lateral walls of the common vagina bear thick pads of dense fibrous tissue ; in adult fish these pads bear scars or lacerations caused by the claw on the clasper of the male. The incidence of the lacerations shows that one clasper only is inserted at a time. A small but distinct hymen marks the lower limit of the common vagina.

The majority of the sharks seen basking at the surface of the inshore waters of the west coasts are non-pregnant females, and pairing certainly takes place during the late spring and early summer ; it may possibly also take place at other times of the year. The basking habit, however, is possibly in some way connected with the sexual behaviour-pattern, as is the annual appearance of the fish near the coast. *Cetorhinus* shows the paradox of having an ovary containing a vast number of small ova and a large uterus thickly lined with trophonemata, the first suggesting that reproduction is by spawning as in teleost fish but the second showing that it is undoubtedly viviparous. There is no record of a female fish containing recognisable embryos ever having been examined in modern times. It is evident therefore, that the female fish, after being inseminated and before any embryo is recognisable, must refrain from basking, and either swim nearer the bottom or leave inshore waters, or both.

Teleostomi

Chondrostei

In *Acipenser ruthenus*, the sterlet of the Volga and other rivers flowing into the Caspian and Black Seas, Loukine (1941a) reports that there is an annual spawning season, but that the fish take some years to reach maturity. The youngest sexually mature females that he examined were seven years old, and he found that many had not yet spawned even at ten years of age. Some males are sexually mature at three years, but the average is six or seven. He found all stages of maturity present together, so that the spawning shoals are not composed only of mature fish. In a previous paper, Loukine (1941b) had recognised a number of stages in the ovarian cycle and Moltchanova (1941) gives some particulars of their histology. In stage 1 the ovaries are yellow or white, several millimetres wide, with no eggs visible to the naked eye. The cells are of irregular angular shape with central nuclei, and occur in groups : smaller oögonia and larger oöcytes, with scattered connective tissue cells among them. In stage 2 the ovaries are yellow, and, in addition to cells as in stage 1, there are other larger white oöcytes, visible to the naked eye. The oöcytes as in stage 1 are at the margins, but the larger ones are in the middle of ovarian plaques which carry the eggs. The oöcytes are invested by their own and the follicular membranes, the former very fine and homogeneous, the latter a thicker single layer of cells. In stage 3 the ovaries are yellow, and large white eggs are clearly distinguishable. These are 383 to 667 micra in diameter and show the first appearance of yolk granules. At the same time the zona radiata appears, and outside it the follicular envelope consists of an alveolar layer surrounded by a single layer of cells. The yolk granules of different sizes are arranged in zones. In stage 4 oögonia and oöcytes as in stage 1 are still present, but the large eggs are now pigmented, and measure 1022 to 1647 micra in diameter. The zona radiata is in two layers, of similar structure, separated by a very fine membrane. Outside this lie the alveolar layer, and the follicular envelope of very flattened cells in a single layer ; an envelope of connective tissue encloses the whole. The membrane separating the last two has now completely disappeared. The yolk granules are arranged in four zones. In stage 5 the eggs are mature and running from the fish, but no histological details are available. In stage 6 the ovary is collapsed, and oöcytes of the next generation, in stage 2, are visible to the naked eye, while the remains of old ones appear as black spots of pigment. The cavity of the ovary is full of oöcytes in stages 1 and 2, and also fragments of ripe eggs and many empty follicles. The layers of connective tissue are much more prominently developed than in stage 2. After spawning there is a complete resorption of the empty follicles and remains of ripe eggs, and the ovary passes back to stage 2. Thus fish with ovaries in stage 1 have not yet spawned for the first time. Whether all the fish have an annual sexual cycle is not clear, though Loukine states that at least some of them spawn each year once they have become mature. There is no information about the cycle in the male beyond the observation that in fish less mature than the females in stage 1 the gonad in both sexes is a narrow semi-transparent band. There are some indications that there may be separate winter- and spring-spawning races of the sterlet in the Volga.

Teleostei

Although the vast majority of the teleosts are oviparous, a minority of them are viviparous or ovo-viviparous. The latter unusual conditions are of such interest that a number of workers have investigated the breeding habits of the fishes in which they occur. In the viviparous blenny, *Zoarces viviparus*, the young undergo development within the body in a uterine receptacle (*see* above, p. 15, Chapter 1). Furthermore, when the ova are released the epithelial cells of the follicles hypertrophy in a manner similar to those of some elasmobranchs, so that bodies resembling the corpora lutea of mammals are formed. As mentioned above, these bodies may be concerned with the maintenance of pregnancy during the internal development of the fertilised ova.

The condition found in such viviparous fishes as *Xiphophorus helleri* is not comparable. Here the ovum is fertilised within the ovarian follicle, the spermatozoon having access through a minute pore in the epithelium. Later, this aperture enlarges to form the birth-pore through which the developed young escape, first into the central cavity of the ovary and then through a single median oviduct communicating with the urogenital sinus (Bailey, 1933; this paper contains references to the older literature on viviparous teleosts). The ruptured follicle hypertrophies after the embryo has been released but the enlarged follicular cells cannot be comparable to luteal cells since the process of hypertrophy is most marked after parturition. Moreover, Bailey says that the enlarged follicular cells do not resemble luteal cells but are more like endometrial cells. He adds that they may serve an endocrine function of some kind or even activate the spermatozoa which are stored in the cells of the oviduct, presumably in readiness for subsequent fertilisation. The cavity of the spent follicle contains a bulky secretion at this stage, but this again cannot have a nutritive function for the embryos have already been delivered. Eventually the hypertrophied follicle is sloughed away.

In the cyprinodont teleost fishes there are four or five families which are ovoviviparous or viviparous. The Poeciliidae are ovo-viviparous, e.g. *Xiphophorus*; that is to say, the ova are fertilised within the ovarian follicle where the embryos are retained until birth, when they are erupted into the ovarian cavity and evacuated through the vent as described above. In *Lebistes reticulatus* the anatomy of the gonopodium, or copulatory organ, of the male is such that the female orientates herself tipped up at an angle of 30° to 70° to the horizontal for copulation. She also takes up this attitude when at rest, and not swimming about, during oestrus. Using this posture as a criterion, Jaski (1939) found that there is a four to six-day oestrous cycle. A more intense and frequent recurrence of oestrus is imposed on this rhythm by the presence of males, or by putting the females into filtered water in which males have swum. The gonopodium is a secondary sexual character developed when the male fish reach maturity. In *Molliensia latipinna*, Cummings (1943) finds that the juvenile anal fins in male and female are identical at birth. During the juvenile stage segments are added to the rays of this fin, ankylosis progresses along the basal segments, and bifurcation of certain rays takes place. At puberty the female fin continues to follow essentially the same pattern of growth as the juvenile fin, but the male fin undergoes a rapid transformation, differentiating into a copulatory organ.

Many of these ovo-viviparous fish, such as *Lebistes*, give birth to a large number of young at one time. *Heterandria formosa*, on the other hand, according to Fraser and Renton (1940), though much less prolific, breeds fairly continuously from February to September or October, with intervals between the births, but produces on an average only one to three at a time. The numbers tend to decrease towards the end of summer, when a resting period sets in until the following February. The ovary is a single oval structure much distended when full of young in various stages of development. It is covered by a thin peritoneal epithelium, immediately within which is a very sparse coat of connective tissue ; the ovarian cavity is lined with a single layer of cubical cells. In the young fish a canal extends ventrally from this cavity along the entire length of the ovary, and from it narrow passages run out towards the ova. Later, with the development of the embryos and consequent enlargement of the whole ovary, this ventral extension becomes irregular and branching. In all young females, whether virgin or not, but more extensively in those which have had no contact with the male, ripe and unripe ova are continually degenerating. During this process the nucleus becomes unrecognisable, and the follicular cells multiply and begin to penetrate the egg, the zona thinning out at the places where this occurs. As degeneration proceeds the follicle cells entirely lose their epithelial character, the whole becoming transformed into a mass of cells in many of which vacuoles appear. The lining of the central lumen of the ovary breaks away and the disintegrated cells and solid clumps of tissue stream into the ovarian cavity and down into the oviduct. Posterior to the ovary the lining of the oviduct is produced into a number of well-marked villi, usually containing blood vessels. As the detritus passes into this part of the oviduct the villi lose their epithelial character, and solid particles of the debris, together with entangled spermatozoa, are ingested. Degeneration of the ova in large females containing many embryos is probably due to lack of space, and to pressure from the growing young surrounding them.

In *Gambusia affinis*, too, Self (1940) finds that there is a breeding season among wild fishes, although aquarium fish produce young during the winter as well as the summer. In Oklahoma, *Gambusia* breeds from March to late September, when there is a lull in reproductive activity, followed by another breeding period in November. Oögenesis begins early in March, but was never found in wild fish from December to February. Development of the male germ-cells takes place during the late spring and summer months. During August the testes contained nothing but spermatogonial prophases, showing that breeding was not occurring then. During September testicular cysts containing mature sperm were present, but in October the males examined had already bred and the testes were without sperm. During December the testes had only inactive spermatogonia and mature sperm ; no cell divisions were found and the spermatogonial cells were considerably enlarged. The testicular canals were enlarged by the presence of sperm balls, and the testes were also distended by the large inactive spermatogonia. Spermatozoa remain in the testicular canals through the winter and are released in spring. The greatest amount of copulation occurs in the spring, the sperm having been produced during the previous year. Some copulation must take place, however, in the autumn to produce the autumn crop of young.

In contrast to *Gambusia* there is no seasonal variation in the attaining of maturity in the males of *Brachyraphis episcopi* at Barro Colorado, Panama, where environmental conditions are very constant throughout the year (Turner, 1938a). In females reproduction occurs in the short cycles characteristic of poeciliid fishes, but the cycles are continuous and not seasonal.

A number of studies on the breeding cycle in the poeciliid fishes has been made by Turner (1937a, 1940a, 1942), who points out that many viviparous fishes, particularly those which inhabit the tropics, have short breeding cycles in which young are produced every two or three months, and that a still shorter cycle of about one month exists in the typical poeciliids. This contrasts with the viviparity found in some fishes in which there is a seasonal periodicity and an annual reproductive cycle. There is a close resemblance between the reproductive behaviour of the latter fishes and that of many marine and freshwater oviparous fishes which have an annual reproductive cycle. During the investigation of the relation of oöcyte development in gravid ovaries to stages of embryos in the same ovaries, Turner (1937a) discovered that different relationships exist in different groups of poeciliids. At the height of the breeding season broods are produced at regular intervals varying from about forty-five days in some species to five or six days in others. In *Molliensia*, *Gambusia* and some other species, the oöcytes of the oldest group remaining in the ovary just after a brood has been extruded are very small. Growth is rapid and the ova are ready for fertilisation about eight days after the voiding of the last group of embryos. In *Xiphophorus*, *Lebistes* and other species with similar reproductive cycles, the oöcytes of the oldest group remaining in the ovary just after a brood has been voided are much larger than in *Gambusia*, and fertilisation occurs a few days earlier than in that species. In *Quintana atrizona* the oöcytes have grown to full size and are ready for fertilisation immediately after the evacuation of a brood. Superfoetation occurs in *Poecilistes pleurospilus*, *Poeciliopsis infans* and several other species. Fertilisation of the oldest group of ova takes place before the birth of the brood already in the ovary, and two broods at different levels of development are found in the same ovary. In *Heterandria formosa*, and possibly other species, there is a great development of superfoetation with six or, in extreme examples, as many as nine small broods, at different stages of development, occurring in the ovary at one time at the height of the breeding season. Older groups of ova, and embryos retained in the ovary, retard the development of younger groups of cells and a balance is maintained between this retarding influence and the agent, assumed to be a follicle-stimulating hormone from the pituitary, which causes the maturation of the oöcytes. Gestation is practically continuous with this high degree of superfoetation, in which a new group of ova is fertilised by sperm either stored in the ovary or acquired by new copulation. The conditions described above occur in laboratory-reared specimens at the height of the breeding season. In such specimens, and in those breeding in temperate zones, the shortest interval between broods is in spring and early summer, and the longest interval during autumn and winter. When reproduction is at a low ebb the oöcytes grow slowly, and are relatively much smaller at the time of the birth of the embryos, than they are when reproduction is at its height. Turner (1940a) adds that the most important factor favouring superfoetation in the ovo-viviparous cyprinodonts is the short, frequently repeated reproductive cycle, in which the differentiation of oöcytes and the maturation of ova occur in an ovary that is already gravid.   The fertilisation of the ova within the ovarian follicles makes it unnecessary for ovulation to intervene, and the reproductive behaviour of the female provides for receptivity to the male while she is still gravid.   The male is ready to copulate at any time, for there is an almost continuous production of sperm in the testis ; and, further, the ovary is able to store viable sperm over long periods of time.

The Anablepidae, e.g. *Anableps*, are very similar to the Poeciliidae, the embryos being retained in follicular sacs within the ovary until a late stage of development is reached, probably up to the time of birth.   In the Jenynseidae and Goodeidae, e.g. *Lermichthys*, the eggs are also fertilised in the ovarian follicles, but are erupted at an early stage into an ovarian cavity where they are retained throughout development.   These fishes are therefore truly viviparous.   The epithelium and stroma of the ovary undergo an extensive development during the period of pregnancy (Turner, 1938b).   Moreover the embryos, of at any rate many species, have large rectal processes called trophotaeniae, which serve as absorptive organs by which the developing young absorb nutritive substances dissolved in the ovarian fluid (Turner, 1937b).

In *Neotoca bilineata*, one of the Goodeidae, Mendoza (1940) finds that the most conspicuous changes in the ovary during gestation are an increase in size, a swelling of the ovigerous folds, and a marked secretory activity of the internal epithelium. There is also an increase in the number of certain wandering cells of a secretory nature, and an increase in the vascularity of the ovary.   In a later paper (Mendoza, 1941) this author points out that *Neotoca* differs from the poeciliids, in which groups of oöcytes mature in waves, in that the oöcytes show a continuous gradation in size throughout gestation, and there are no waves or groups of embryos or oöcytes.   Unlike the *Gambusia* type, the growth of oöcytes is not inhibited completely, merely somewhat retarded ; and throughout gestation there is present a variable number of eggs of maximal size.   Because of this, there is no necessity for a period of marked growth in the interval between the birth of young and the following fertilisation period ; the different sizes of oöcyte merely continue their growth over the non-gestation period.   There is, however, a general activation of oöcytes of all sizes in the resting interval, because there is a doubling or tripling in the number of cells in all stages of growth before the following fertilisation period.   Mendoza (1943) also gives some details of the changes in the ovary during gestation.   The germ-cells are borne by two ovigerous folds, one on each side of the median sagittal septum of the ovary, and oöcytes normally occur in clusters at the surface of the ovigerous folds.   Follicular pores not only facilitate the access of the spermatozoa to the ovum, but also provide a passage for the escape of the fertilised egg.   The growing oöcyte is characterised by the absence of large masses of yolk, and by the presence of numerous oil droplets.   The follicle changes during growth from a tenuous layer of scattered squamous cells to a thick, simple layer of columnar cells.   Fertilisation, the completion of the meiotic divisions, and the escape of the egg occur simultaneously or in extremely rapid succession.   Mendoza believes that normally evacuated follicles cannot be compared in any way with the mammalian corpus luteum.   In atresia of the follicles he finds that there is some fatty degeneration, some liquefaction or vacuolation of cells and some infiltration by lymphocytes.   In addition to phagocytosis, there is some absorbtion by surrounding cells.   Mendoza (1939) agrees with other investigators (Kunz, 1913 ; Turner, 1937a) that the recurrent broods of *Neotoca* during the season are comparable to several annual broods rather than to one extended annual brood, because in this fish there is a definite and complete activation of the ovary, including separate copulation and fertilisation, for every brood.

The development of placental structures in the cyprinodont fishes is discussed in a series of papers by Turner (1940b, c, d), who writes that the yolk supply of the oviparous cyprinodonts is sufficient for the embryo up to the time of hatching, when feeding by the mouth starts. But in the poeciliids the yolk sac is small and in *Heterendria formosa* it is greatly reduced in correlation with a number of compensating mechanisms. Discussing the different species as a progressive series he points out that the maternal blood begins to furnish materials through the blood stream of the ovarian follicles, and the embryonic portal network formerly concerned with respiration and the transport of absorbed yolk, now takes up nutritive materials from the blood vessels of the follicles. The efficiency of the absorption from the follicular blood supply is increased by the development of devices for increasing the surface of the follicle, and for changing the character of the absorbed materials by secretion. These changes in the follicle are accompanied by an increase in the expansion of the external portal system of the embryo upon the expanded belly sac. This development of a follicular pseudo-placenta and the larger external portal system enable the embryos to remain within the follicles for a longer period of gestation. With highly developed devices for interchange between the embryo and follicle, the yolk sac becomes less important as a nutritional supply and may be practically vestigial, as in *Heterandria formosa*. In the embryo of the oviparous cyprinodonts, respiratory exchange occurs between the blood of the embryo and the surrounding water. The vascular network upon the yolk sac is extended to the outer walls of the pericardial sac. In the typical poeciliid the respiratory surface is increased by an extension of the yolk sac over the posterior part of the head in the form of a neck strap. Exchange now takes place between the embryonic and maternal blood by absorption through the thin intervening tissue. With the reduction of the yolk sac the portal network shifts more and more to the outer walls of the expanding pericardial sac and coelom. In the extreme case of *Heterandria formosa* the somato-pleural walls of the pericardial sac are folded dorsally so as to enclose the head. The inner pseudo-amnion thus formed is not vascular, but the outer pseudo-chorion is very vascular and important in increasing the respiratory surface. In some simpler species there is a hood-like extension of the pericardial walls which partly encloses the head of the embryo and increases the respiratory surface. The increase of the internal surface of the surrounding follicle by means of villi also facilitates respiratory exchange. In the Anablepidae a follicular pseudo-placenta, more complicated than any similar structure in the Poeciliidae, is composed of a vascular follicle wall provided with villi, and the vascular belly wall of the embryo. This pseudo-placenta is a temporary respiratory organ and probably plays some part in the transfer of nutritional materials to the embryo. The pseudo-amnion and pseudo-chorion of the Poeciliidae have no parallels in the Anablepidae.

In the Goodeidae and Jenynsiidae, in which the embryos develop in the ovarian cavity instead of the ovarian follicles, devices other than the follicular pseudo-placenta are developed in compensation for the early decrease of the yolk sac. In these families, too, superfoetation does not occur as in the poeciliids, where each embryo is walled off from the rest of the ovary within a modified follicle, and each embryo with its surrounding follicle becomes a separate physiological unit.   On the contrary, all the embryos are expelled into the ovarian cavity, so that no such isolation occurs, and the entire brood together with the ovary becomes the physiological unit, and a new brood of embryos has little chance of survival.   In the Jenynsiidae a close relationship is developed between flaps of ovarian tissue and the mouth and pharyngeal cavities of the embryo, and this probably has a respiratory function, while materials for growth are obtained by imbibing fluid secreted by the ovary.   An early disappearance of the yolk and shrinkage of the extra-embryonic pericardial sac also occurs in the embryos of the Goodeidae.   In this family, respiration, and probably to some extent the absorption of food materials, occurs through the trophotaeniae.   Nutrition also takes place by the absorption in the gut of imbibed ovarian fluid, and there may be some respiratory exchange as the fluid passes through the pharynx and over the gills of the embryo.   The conditions in these families are thus in contrast with those in the poeciliid and anablepid fishes where the yolk is absorbed completely in early stages and the extra-embryonic pericardial sac is retained in a highly differentiated state.   The latter forms, with the modified walls of the follicle, a pseudo-placenta through which nutriment is absorbed and, probably, metabolic wastes are discarded.   In all families of cyprinodont fishes where they occur the changes in the structure of the embryo, associated with greater or less degrees of viviparity, are extensions or reductions of structures already represented to some extent in the embryos of oviparous members of the order.   The only changes in the basic pattern of the embryonic vascular system are thus quantitative. New developments in the ovarian follicle do not affect the pattern of the maternal blood supply to the capsule and epithelium except in small details.

In another family, the Embiotocidae, viviparity is even more highly developed. Thus in *Cymatogaster aggregatus* the cycle of changes is as follows.   The females are born in June and July and are inseminated soon after by males which are already sexually mature at birth.   The spermatozoa enter the ovarian cavities of the females and remain there until December when they fertilise the ova.   The embryos are retained in the ovarian cavity until the following spring when they are born.   The epithelial cells lining the ovarian cavity form internal fluid reservoirs which reach their maximal size in early gestation, and there is a considerable sloughing off of epithelial cells.   Later in gestation the epithelium becomes restored to its original state and the cells subsequently undergo multiplication. The ovarian stroma becomes swollen and contains a quantity of fluid in early gestation, but it undergoes a shrinkage as the embryos develop.   A number of ova degenerate, failing to acquire maturity at the time of fertilisation.   Some of the immature ova also degenerate during gestation but others survive and reach maturity in the next season.   Shoals of the females of this marine fish come into shallow water in May and June to give birth to broods of large, well-developed embryos.   Males migrate shorewards shortly after the females and copulation takes place in June and July.   All then return to deeper waters where they remain until the breeding season of the following year.   The cyclical changes which occur in the ovaries of the Goodeidae and the Jenynseidae in which, as already mentioned, viviparity is highly developed are parallel and closely similar to those of the Embiotocidae.   It is to be noted that with most oviparous fishes there is a large yolk sac and abundance of yolk, but that with increasing degrees of viviparity the yolk sac diminishes and in Cymatogaster the eggs are exceptionally small and poor in yolk (Turner, 1938c).

The complete cycle of changes in the internal generative organs has been investigated in only a few species of oviparous fishes and the fullest accounts are those which have been given of *Fundulus, Cottus, Perca, Gasterosteus* and *Phoxinus*.

The cycle in *Fundulus heteroclitus*, an oviparous cyprinodont, has been studied by Matthews (1938) who examined specimens from New Jersey. He records that in the male during late May, June and July the medulla of the testis is swollen and the ducts are filled with sperm. Nearly all the cysts in the lobules of the cortex of the testis are also filled with sperm, but round the periphery there is a narrow zone composed mainly of primary spermatogonia. These cells are dividing rapidly, producing small cysts of secondary spermatogonia. Thus before the matured sperm of one generation of sex cells is completely expelled the beginnings of the next generation are apparent. Ordinarily the sperm are shed during June and July. In some cases, however, the sperm are not expelled until the end of August. Complete expulsion of the sperm is rare. Small clusters of sperm which are apparently left from the previous period of sexual activity can be found in nearly every testis examined regardless of the time of year. After the spawning season, there is a striking reduction in the amount of cortical tissue relative to the diameter of the testis, even though the preliminary stages in the production of the next generation of sperm have already produced small cysts. Cells within these cysts continue to divide slowly, the cysts gradually enlarge, and the cortex of the entire testis increases in thickness. In September a few spermatids appear. Throughout the period from October to the latter part of February there is a gradual increase in the number of spermatogonia, spermatocytes and spermatids, and the cysts become larger. In March the cells within the cysts begin to divide more rapidly, as evidenced by the number of mitotic figures and the rapid increase in size of the cysts during this period, and spermatids become increasingly more numerous in proportion to other cells. In late April and May spermatozoa appear in increasingly large numbers. During this process the testis changes markedly in colour and size. The active testis during May, June and the early part of July is milky white and enlarged. The exhausted testis in late July and August is colourless for the most part, more or less transparent, and much reduced in size. The testis forms the greatest percentage of the total body weight during the period from late in March to the latter part of June. The greatest weight of the testis corresponds to the period in the seasonal cycle following the start of rapid division of spermatogenic cells and the consequent enlargement of the cysts. This occurs from March up to the time when most of the sperm is expelled, usually in June or July.

In the female at the end of the spawning season, late in July, Matthews finds that all ripe eggs have been expelled. The ovary then contains corpora lutea and atretic follicles, as well as all stages in the development of oöcytes from the initial stage up to and including the late development of vesicular yolk. After the egg is discharged from the follicle the follicular epithelium undergoes marked hypertrophy, the cells developing large amounts of some substance which is dissolved out during the preparation of sections, leaving large vacuoles whose contents may have been fat. Mitotic figures have not been found in these follicular cells during the formation of this structure. This " corpus luteum," which is actually yellow in colour in the fresh condition and can be seen on the surface of the ovary as a yellow spot, gradually shrinks and disappears, though traces of it may be found as late as December or January. The smallest recognisable stage of the developing oöcyte can be found just within the epithelium lining the ovigerous lamellae at any time throughout the year, so that it is conceivable that they begin maturation at different times. Hence it is not clear whether the larger oöcytes found at the end of the spawning period belong to the same generation of cells as those which matured completely and were shed, or whether they are maturing oöcytes which began development somewhat later.

Changes in the gross appearance and weight of ovary are more striking than similar changes in the testis. The ripe ovary is recognisable at a glance by the presence of numerous ripe eggs, which appear as large, pale, semi-transparent spheres that cause the wall of the ovary to bulge at numerous points. The exhausted ovary, on the other hand, is very reduced in size and the largest oöcytes which it contains are much smaller than ripe eggs and are yellowish and opaque. Just after the spawning period the ovary forms the smallest percentage of the total body weight. From this point on there is a gradual increase from month to month in the weight of the ovary, paralleled by an increase in the size of the follicles, and their contained oöcytes, and in the number of yolk vesicles. The chorionic membrane appears as early as October in a few oöcytes, the number of chorionic membranes and the amount of yolk increasing during subsequent months. Droplets of intra-vesicular yolk may appear as early as March or even February, but rapid development of this secondary yolk takes place late in April, increasing greatly in amount from then up to the time of spawning. The ovary forms the maximum percentage of the body weight in June, at the beginning of the spawning period. From this high point the weight of the ovary falls off rapidly as the eggs are shed, to reach its lowest value in July at the end of spawning ; it then gradually increases again to its maximum weight at the beginning of the next spawning period.

In another oviparous cyprinodont, *Oryzias latipes*, Robinson and Rugh (1943) describe the ovary as an unpaired hollow organ consisting of a thin but strong wall, lined with developing follicles on all sides except the dorsal. The development of the oöcytes is similar to that in *Fundulus heteroclitus*. The oviduct is a short, muscular tube with no function except that of egg transport.

The ovulation process is not cataclysmic, but takes on an average about thirty minutes. Twenty to thirty relatively large eggs must be matured, ovulated and laid, in the space of 24 hours, the bulk of this time being used in the maturation process. Contraction of the ovary as a whole is not necessary, although this does not preclude the possibility of action by smooth muscle in the walls of the follicles themselves. The force causing the initial rupture of the follicle is not known.

The eggs are laid almost immediately after ovulation during a definite series of actions undertaken by both fishes, when the sperm and eggs are shed simultaneously.

The fishes normally ovulate just before dawn, and inverting the periods of light and darkness causes ovulation to be shifted from the time of the natural dawn to that of the artificial one. It is suggested that light governs the time of ovulation by regulating the general metabolic activity of the female. The eggs are matured during a period of quiescence and are released at the beginning of the period of activity. In the normal daily cycle light is probably the most important environmental factor, acting as a stimulant to general activity and hence to ovulation and oviposition.

Hann (1927) has described the history of the male and female germ cells in *Cottus bairdei*, a freshwater teleost found in Michigan. He states that oögonia or egg-mother cells are present in the ovary throughout the year. The formation of the ova from these cells (oögenesis) consists of two stages, the division of the oögonia, and the transformation of the resulting oöcytes into mature eggs. Oögonial division and the early phases in the maturation of the egg occur in the young fish at an age of seven weeks, in the second week of June, and oögonial division goes on until October. Some of the oöcytes reach maturity when the fish is two years old. In the succeeding years the division of the oögonia begins in May, lasting until October. " Thus each year after the first, a portion of the oögonia changes to oöcytes and increase the reserve supply, and at the same time a portion of the reserve supply enter the secondary growth phase and develop during the year into mature ova." (Hann, 1927.) The actual spawning time was found to be April. Thus the period of oögonial division occurs shortly after the breeding season and this is also true of other species. The growth period of the egg, however, varies with the species and in many cases occupies only one year (Cunningham, 1890 ; Craig-Bennett, 1931). Yolk formation in the eggs of *Cottus* goes on from midsummer to October.

Spermatogenesis with *Cottus* also occurs in two main stages, the division of the spermatogonia and the transformation of the spermatocytes so formed into spermatozoa. The division of the spermatogonia takes place when the male fish is 13 months old or nearly a year later than the corresponding phase in the female. " There result within the testis groups of spermatogonia within thin-walled cysts. With the beginning of maturation these cysts become very distinct and all cells of one cyst are practically at the same stage, though different cysts show different stages. Maturation continues until the spawning time in April."

The cyclical changes in the testis of the perch (*Perca flavescens*) have been described by Turner (1919). He states that there is an active migration of germ-cells from a cord outside the testis " to the ends of the lobules at the periphery of the testis," and that the spermatogonia are supplied from this cord. This process of translation of the germ-cells proceeds from March to August. The proliferation of these cells within the testis (a phase corresponding to the division of the spermatogonia in *Cottus*) extends from March to November. From December to March there is no spermatogenesis but the testes are full of spermatozoa. Parker (1942) states that in this fish the testes are united by a perforated septum so that their cavities communicate. A single duct from their posterior ends is enlarged to form a " vesicula seminalis " before it unites with the urinary duct just above the urinary orifice. Although the ducts have a common opening their junction is so close to the opening that sperm does not traverse any part of the urinary passage. The opening of the sperm duct appears to be formed by rupture caused by internal pressure, and there is no orifice until one becomes imperative for the discharge of the sperm. The same author states that in the female yellow perch there is a single median ovary with no oviduct or any connection between the urinary and reproductive systems. A membranous ovarian

G*

sac encloses the ovary ; the posterior ventral area of the sac, between the anus and the urinary orifice is fused with the body wall. Ripe eggs escape from their follicles into the central cavity of the ovary, where they become embedded in a gelatinous substance before they are discharged directly from the ovary to the exterior. As time for oviposition approaches, pressure from within causes a con-spicuous papilla to form on the ventral mid-line of the body in the area between the anus and the urinary orifice. This papilla, which marks the point at which the ovarian sac and the body wall fuse, becomes inflamed and greatly distended, concealing the urinary orifice and distorting the anus. Just prior to the rupture of the papilla the tissue covering its summit becomes so thin and transparent that the eggs can be readily seen through it. When the papilla ruptures, the eggs are dis-charged from the ovary in an unbroken ribbon-like gelatinous mass. There is no median abdominal pore between the anus and the urinary orifice through which the eggs are discharged as in some fish.

In *Lophius piscatorius*, Hammeter (1926) states that in fish from Wood's Hole, from September to May, the ova are minute and the large thin-walled hollow ovaries are collapsed. They are capable of great distension, and are filled with ripe ova during May and the early part of June. The terminal 30 to 40 cm. of the organs are the oviducts, that of each side joining its partner to end in a separate external orifice caudal to the anus. The extruded eggs form long pink ribbon-like gelatinous masses, 25 to 40 feet long, and 12 to 20 inches broad. They are found floating at the surface of the sea in quiet shallow water during June. In the mackerel, however, Steven and Corbin (1939) find that the spawning period of the individual fish is a long drawn-out process. The first indication of the spawning condition is the presence of ripe eggs, which appear at the outer surface of the ovary, widely scattered among unripe eggs. Later, these ripe eggs pass into the lumen of the ovary which, externally, reverts to an unripe appearance. The ripe eggs are shed, and this process recurs possibly many times before the ovary is fully spent, but the time taken to deliver all of one season's eggs is not known.

In the top-minnow (*Gambusia affinis*), an ovo-viviparous cyprinodont teleost, the spermatogonia are said to develop from inconspicuous germ-cells lying in the testicular stroma, between the spermatogonial cysts, these germ-cells migrating peripherally and giving rise to new spermatogonia. Spermatozoa are mostly produced from March to July (probably in response to rising temperature and increasing light) (Geiser, 1922). Spermatogenesis does not occur in the cold weather.

The seasonal changes in the testes of fish are also dealt with in an article by Oslund (1929) who refers to the existence of the interstitial tissue which is usually present, but in varying degrees of development, between the cysts of germ-cells (i.e. between spermatogenetic tissue). The significance of the interstitial tissue and its relative quantity in different species are discussed by Craig-Bennett (1931) who quotes the observations of other investigators. He remarks that whereas in cyprinodonts there is probably no correlation between the interstitial tissue and the secondary sexual characters with other genera, such as *Callionymus*, *Cottus* and *Gobius*, such a correlation exists and in *Callionymus*, at any rate, there is a close cyclical correlation, the interstitial tissue and the secondary male characters developing and regressing synchronously (Courrier, 1921a, b, c).

In *Gobius paganellus*, Vivien (1938a) describes the occurrence of large paired glands, communicating with the vas deferens, situated in the posterior part of the abdomen. These glands undergo cyclical enlargement. In this fish the male genital tract consists of two elongated testes in the dorsal part of the abdominal cavity ; the vasa deferentia, which unite to form an ejaculatory duct ; and an ampullary dilation of the latter, into which open the ducts from the paired accessory glands. The ejaculatory duct ends on an erectile urogenital papilla, where it opens to the exterior. Each accessory gland consists of a number of coiled tubes lined by a single layer of secretory cells with large nuclei. The tubes are separated from each other by feebly vascularised connective tissue, the whole forming two sacs, which, when in a state of full functional activity, surround the rectum. The cyclic activity seems to be closely correlated with the cycle in the testes. In August and September, when the testes are inactive, the tubes are reduced in size and empty of secretion. They are separated by masses of feebly vascularised connective tissue which form over two-thirds of the volume of the gland. In December and January, however, the months when spermatogenesis is very active, and the enlargement of interstitial tissue commences, the testes double their volume, but the glands become ten times larger. The tubes are dilated and filled with a secretion which appears to be of a colloid nature, and the connective tissue is reduced to thin laminae which are barely visible between the tubes. The function of these glands is unknown, but Vivien points out that they may be analogous to the coagulating glands of higher vertebrates and may retard the dispersion of the sperm in the surrounding water. In a later paper (Vivien, 1938b) he showed that their secretion does not act as a cement for fixing the eggs to a substratum, though Champy and Gley (1922) ascribe such a function to the secretion of a specialised glandular part of the testes in fishes of the genus *Blennius*. Here the glandular tissue is developed in the walls of the distal parts of the seminiferous tubules and is in a state of secretory activity in the spring. At this season, when pairing takes place, the tubules within the gland are increased in size and the glandular cells are diminished in volume in consequence of the excretion of their lipoid contents. After pairing, the volume of the gland cells gradually increases again. These investigators suggest that the secretion produces a reaction on the micropylar filaments of the egg so that they adhere to a substratum. The glandular part of the testis in these fishes is not to be confused with interstitial tissue, the presence of which between the seminiferous tubules has been demonstrated by Courrier (1922).

The changes in the internal reproductive organs throughout the breeding cycle have been studied in the three-spined stickleback (*Gasterosteus aculeatus*) and also in the nine-spined stickleback (*Pygosteus pungitius*) by a number of investigators (Courrier, 1921a, b ; Champy, 1923a, b ; van Oordt, 1923 ; Craig-Bennett, 1931). The following account is based chiefly on the work of Craig-Bennett upon *Gasterosteus aculeatus*.

In this fish, the germ-cells, interstitial and connective tissues of the testis undergo a definite annual cycle of development and regression, and in individuals from different habitats (a river, a pond or a canal) in the same latitude the commencement of the maturation of the germ-cells and the occurrence of the breeding season were noted about the same dates, maturation beginning in August and September and breeding taking place in April or May. In the male fish, the maximum development of the interstitial tissue of the testis occurred in all cases either prior to or coincident with the beginning of the breeding season.   All the germinal elements are present in the winter months and spermatogenesis at that time goes on actively, but it may be continued into the breeding season.   The spermatocytes occur within cysts (as in *Cottus*) and the spermatozoa escape from these cysts upon the approach of the breeding season.   Craig-Bennett considers that the rate of spermatogenesis is controlled by the temperature of the habitat, saying that if the temperature is high the completion of spermatogenesis follows more rapidly, although as stated above, it goes on in the winter ; moreover, if the fall of temperature is slow, spermatogenesis may be completed two or three months before the breeding season. In those male individuals in which spermatogenesis is completed prior to the beginning of the breeding season there is a period of " potential maturity " during which the spermatozoa are able to fertilise mature eggs, if given the opportunity experimentally under artificial conditions.   The change from potential maturity to functional maturity is induced in spring by a rise in the temperature of the water, but the rise itself, and not the temperature reached, is thought to be the important factor.   The development of the secondary sexual characters (*see* above, p. 19, Chapter 1) is coincident with the acquirement of the sexual instincts and takes place later.   There is no corresponding stage of " potential maturity " in the female.

In the female stickleback the division of the oögonia has been observed in July but may occur at other seasons.   The oögonia give rise to the oöcytes (primary growth phase) from July to September and the secondary yolk formation commences in October and continues until May which as we have seen is the time of breeding.   Nuclear maturation of the ovum and the discharge of the ripe eggs take place simultaneously during the breeding season from May to July.   There are no interstitial cells in the ovary of *Gasterosteus* and so no cyclical interstitial changes.

The annual changes in the volume of the ovaries are about seven times as great as those of the testes, the large size of the mature ovaries being due mainly to the size of the eggs which are from 70 to 150 in number.   The ripe ovary measures 10 mm. by 4 mm. ; after spawning it is only 6 mm. by 2 mm.   The increase in size occurs principally during the formation of the yolk.

Craig-Bennett records further that there are fat-bodies in *Gasterosteus* which undergo a cyclical development and regression, and that these are absent during the breeding season.   He regards this time relationship to breeding as being " accidental " and not functional.

In the male stickleback during the breeding season the posterior urinary tubules of the kidney secrete a mucous substance which is used in binding together the material of which the nest is formed.   This is in addition to their excretory function.   The epithelium of the lobules increases in depth prior to the production of the secretion.   The transformation is not accompanied by any other changes in the kidney, the blood supply being the same.   When the kidney passes back to the normal condition the modified lobules are invaded by blood corpuscles which appear to be broken down.

Bullough (1939) has studied the reproductive cycle in the minnow (*Phoxinus laevis*) and the environmental factors controlling it.   The gonads of this fish are paired elongated organs situated in the dorsal region of the body cavity just ventral to the air bladder. They are separate throughout their length, but the gonaducts issuing from the posterior end fuse immediately, and the single duct thus formed ends blindly, in the non-breeding condition, in the ventral wall of the kidney duct. In the male the wall separating these two ducts is never more than a few cells in thickness, and a month or more before the commencement of the breeding season it breaks down. In the female, however, the oviduct does not join the kidney duct, but acquires a separate opening to the exterior. The final break-through of this duct takes place immediately prior to spawning, so that many minnows taken in June with their ovaries almost mature still have undeveloped oviducts.

There is a considerable seasonal variation in the size of the gonads and immediately after spawning both testes and ovaries are slight, almost thread-like organs. Very little growth takes place through the summer months, but during late September and early October there is a considerable increase to about nine times the original volume in the ovary, and to about three times in the testis. The volume thus attained remains fairly constant throughout the winter, and the final increase to the maximum breeding size takes place in the following spring.

The interstitial elements of the ovary are poorly developed, and the connective tissue bounding the organ is very thin. Oögonia are often found in an epithelium which occurs in patches over the surface of the ovaries. They may also occur more centrally, when they are frequently associated with masses of small cells which are only found in the ovaries during the summer and early autumn. Oögonia have not been seen dividing, and it appears that they grow directly into primary oöcytes. The primary growth phase, a period of activity in the cytoplasm, then follows and there is a great increase in the size of the cell. Follicle cells are acquired early, but even at the end of this phase they do not form a complete covering to the oöcyte. With further growth a number of vacuoles appear between the periphery and a ring of darkly staining granules. These vacuoles enlarge and multiply as the granules fade and disappear. The secondary growth phase starts when yolk droplets arise in connection with the vacuoles. A vitelline membrane is then formed, and a long period of growth follows in which the yolk droplets increase in numbers and spread through the cytoplasm.

During July the production of new oögonia begins, but, as they have never been seen in division their mode of origin is uncertain. It is suggested that the follicle cells of the previous year provide a new supply of oögonia by direct growth as in the stickleback. During the summer there is a very slow growth of oögonia to form primary oöcytes which may develop to an early stage of the secondary growth phase. In October there is an acceleration of this process so that the number of eggs present is greatly increased. During the winter there is little change, but the maximum egg diameter increases slightly. In spring the completion of the secondary growth phase and maturation take place. There is a great increase in the diameter of the larger eggs until the mature size is reached.

The testes do not show a very definite structure, and the lobules which compose them are not well defined. After the breeding season, the primary germ-cells congregate in groups which are separated by a feebly developed interstitium, and each individual germ-cell, dividing many times, gives rise to a group of spermatogonia. These spermatogonia continue dividing, all the members of one group doing so simultaneously, until a cyst, or group of cells, is formed. The interstitial tissue, unlike that of the stickleback, is not greatly developed. The primary germ-cells are found at all times of the year lying quiescent along the sides of the lobules. They are occasionally seen dividing, but normally they appear to be in a resting phase. The change from primary germ-cell to spermatogonium is marked by a sudden affinity of the nucleus for stain. This is shown by both chromatin and ground substance. The nucleus also becomes smaller, and the cytoplasm has shrunk, and the cell elements are very difficult to distinguish in all the succeeding stages. Cell divisions occur rapidly, and, within each cyst, simultaneously.

A small decrease in size marks the change to primary spermatocyte, but otherwise the resting nucleus is very similar to that of the spermatogonium. The secondary spermatocytes are not frequently seen, and the stages appear to be of short duration. The second maturation division then occurs and the immediate result of this is the formation of the spermatids. The nucleus at first enters a typical resting stage with one nucleolus, and then the chromatin gathers to one side forming a cup-shaped mass, and a small spherical black body appears outside the nuclear membrane. A contraction of the cup-shaped chromatin mass produces a solid sperm head, a tail is formed, and the mature spermatozoön immediately makes its way towards the vas deferens.

During the summer there is a slow division of primary germ-cells to form cysts of spermatogonia. In October there is a rapid production of spermatogonia, and primary spermatocytes first make their appearance. During winter slow production of primary spermatocytes continues, but few spermatogonia are found. In spring there is almost complete cessation of the early developmental processes, but the production of secondary spermatocytes, spermatids and spermatozoa takes place. The fully mature testes of fish taken in June are distended with spermatozoa and all the maturation processes appear to have ceased. Primary germ-cells and spermatogonia are still present in appreciable numbers, but they are very rarely seen in division. Spermatocytes and spermatids are uncommon. A comparison of the testes of fish taken in June with those of fish taken at other times of the year shows that in the breeding season the proportion of interstitial cells to germ-cells is at its lowest, but, when allowance is made for the great increase in the numbers of germ-cells at this time, it appears probable that the total amount of interstitial tissue remains fairly constant throughout the year.

As a result of experimental work Bullough concludes that both water temperature and the amount of light to which the fish are subjected are factors controlling the cycle in the gonads. During winter a higher temperature alone stimulated early developmental stages of the gonads, these stages having been commenced in the previous autumn. Extra light has no effect at all unless the water temperature is high enough. If the temperature is above a certain threshold value then seventeen hours of daily light stimulate the later developmental phases and induce the maturation of the gonads. In the male, artificial stimulation of the testes to maturity is accompanied by the development of the vas deferens. In the female the development of the oviducts normally takes place immediately before spawning, and, probably because the experiments did not proceed long enough to induce spawning, no response was obtained in this sex. On the other hand, when groups of fish were kept either in total darkness or in seven hours of light a day (Bullough, 1940a), the experimental conditions, although not entirely preventing the development of the ovaries in the females, caused a delay. In the fish kept in total darkness the delay was more marked than in the fish allowed seven hours of light daily. In the males a slight delay was noticed in April, but all fish had reached full breeding condition by June. It is therefore claimed that an internal reproductive rhythm exists within the minnow, and is capable of acting in the absence of those external seasonal changes that may normally reinforce it, and render it more precise in the time of its action. A post-ovulatory mitotic activity has also been found in the ovary of the minnow (Bullough, 1942a). This activity can be artificially stimulated by a suitable injection of oestrone, and it is suggested that normal mitotic activity is induced by oestrone in high concentration only, as when the follicles burst and spill the follicular fluid with its contained oestrone over the germinal epithelium. A tendency towards masculinisation exists in the older female minnows (Bullough, 1940b), and this may result in complete sex reversal. It appears probable that, as the ovaries of these older fish cease to secrete oestrone, testis tissue is able to develop. The male hormone which is secreted by this testicular tissue induces the breakdown and total elimination of the ovary.

In the minnows of Windermere, Frost (1943) finds that the breeding season extends from May to July. Sexual maturity is reached by a few fish at the end of their first year, and the majority of the fish in their second year, and all older fish are mature. Among the three-year-old fish from this lake the females outnumbered the males by seven to one. Two-year-old fish contained 105 to 330 ripe eggs ; three-year-old fish from 293 to 550. The greatest reproductive activity was during the first half of May, followed by a gradual reduction to its end in the latter part of July. All the eggs of an individual fish are shed at once, so the long drawn-out breeding time is not due to the same individuals shedding eggs or sperm during a protracted period, but to a population of fish which mature at different times.

Merriman and Schedl (1941) studied the reproductive cycle in *Apeltes quadracus*, the American four-spined stickleback, a salt-water species that enters brackish, and, occasionally, fresh waters. In Connecticut, spawning takes place in late spring and early summer. The preliminary phases of spermatogenesis and oögenesis occur during the remainder of the summer and the early autumn when the water temperatures are high. The low temperatures of the autumn and winter slow down the rate of spermatogenesis, and also make possible the normal maturation of the oöcytes, a process which involves the addition of yolk material. The rising temperatures in the spring result in the completion of spermatogenesis, and the additional illumination from the increasing length of day at this season appears to play no part in the process. The slowly rising spring temperatures are not, however, sufficiently high to impede the last stages of oögenesis, involving the further increase in the bulk of the eggs. An added reaction from the increasing length of the day, probably, in the authors' opinion, stimulates the process of oogenesis to its final completion.

Orton and his colleagues investigated the paedogenetic male cycle in the salmon, *Salmo salar* (Orton, Jones and King, 1938 ; Jones and Orton, 1940). Half of a large number of salmon parr and smolts captured in English and Welsh rivers were males. All the females were immature virgins, but the males showed a seasonal sexual cycle in which the gonad develops in the summer, becomes mature in the autumn and is spent in the winter. After spawning a high proportion of the male parr migrate to the sea as smolts. All the male smolts examined had quiescent testes, being either spent, or immature and virgin ; there are thus two types of male smolts that migrate to the sea. It is practically certain that ripe male parr spawn on the salmon redds. A remarkable paucity of males among the younger classes of immigrating salmon recorded from the Wye may be general, and may be compensated by the abundant paedogenetic male parr. There is no doubt that paedogenesis occurs in the male of the Atlantic salmon (*Salmo salar*) throughout its geographical range. According to Jones (1940) the undeveloped tube-like gonad showed no changes other than the migration and growth of typical germ-cells : this type of testis is found throughout the year. The outer tunica is thin and the crypts poorly defined, but filled with large resting germ-cells. Smaller germ-cells are most numerous around the periphery of the testis, and migrate inwards along the walls of the crypts as they enlarge. These cells become spermatogonia, a decrease in size of the nucleus accompanying an increase in staining reaction of the cytoplasm. Each spermatogonium divides to give rise to a group of descendants which are enclosed in a cyst and undergo all subsequent divisions at the same time. The secondary spermatogonia appear early, before all the germ cells have given rise to primary spermatogonia. Spermatocytes appear in groups, and are spherical darkly staining cells with an uneven distribution of the nuclear chromatin giving them a mottled appearance. Sperm are produced very shortly after the appearance of spermatocytes and spermatids, and the colour of the testis changes from rosy to white. Further development of the testis consists mainly of an increase in size related to the formation of more sperm. The crypts, swollen with sperm, occupy the main mass of the testis, and the crypt walls are greatly attenuated. After the extrusion of the sperm the testes decrease in size and collapse, the crypts becoming empty. The outer tunica in the spent gonad becomes thicker owing to the contraction on emptying, and is thrown into longitudinal ridges. The crypt walls have the appearance of contracted elastic tissue, showing as relatively thick bands forming an open meshwork. The evacuated crypts are invaded by connective-tissue cells, and germ-cells again migrate inwards from the periphery to start the cycle once more. There is some indication that in the parr stage the testes may re-develop and that a second paedogenetic spawning may sometimes take place.

In a small percentage of female salmon the discharge of the ova at the normal time does not take place. Neill (1939) records an example in which the ova from a previous spawning season had been retained, and were in process of resorption while a new crop of young ova was in course of development. A similar resorption has been noted in *Gobius paganellus* by Vivien (1939) who states that the oöcytes in July, just after breeding, are 100 to 120 micra in diameter. By September they are 130 micra in diameter, and at this size the development of the peripheral granular vitelline zone commences in the cytoplasm of the oöcyte. This zone henceforth assumes increasing importance until maturity is reached. In October the oöcytes are 170 micra in diameter, in February 550, and in May, near the time for laying, 600 to 630 micra. After July those oöcytes which have not been discharged, but retained in the ovary, are rapidly and totally resorbed by the follicular elements.

Wheeler (1924) found that in the ovary of the dab (*Pleuronectes limanda*) a number of germ-cells are formed during the first two years of life. Some of these become oöcytes but the majority form follicle cells. This fish experiences at most eight annual spawning seasons, for it lives about ten years and does not mature until the third. At each spawning season the follicle cells enlarge as soon as the ripe eggs are shed. A few of these cells become ova and the rest return to their former condition as follicle cells. All the eggs of the growth period are shed at the conclusion of the spawning season, with the exception of a number of fully mature eggs which do not leave the ovary and are later reabsorbed. A few small oöcytes may also remain to survive and grow, or to degenerate in the following year. In May the ovary of the dab has completely recovered from the February spawning, but traces still remain of the degenerate oöcytes. Wheeler concludes that each yearly batch of eggs, after those of the first season, is formed from cells that were formerly follicle cells, and he found no sign of cell division for the production of new oöcytes. This author refers to the results of other workers, who found a similar condition in some other species of teleost fish.

The annual increase in the size of the generative organs in the salmon and other fish and the transference of substances from the muscles to the generative organs as the fish pass up the rivers to their breeding localities, and the comparable phenomenon shown by the herring are recorded in the first chapter (p. 17). It may be mentioned, further, in this connection that Graham (1923) records a reduction in weight in the cod following spawning, this reduction being followed by a steady increase from April to June. From June to August there is a further gradual fall, and a second rise which reaches its maximum in September or October, after which time the weight decreases until spawning is completed in April. Graham regards the fall in the fish's weight during the winter as connected with a transference of material from the liver and muscles to the growing generative organs (of. Heape, 1931, for the snoek). In the Pacific salmon, *Oncorhynchus nerka*, Satô (1939) records a yearly migration of the fish, returning to their breeding rivers, down the east side of the Kamchatka peninsula. During this migration, which takes about forty to sixty days, the gonads of the four- and five-year-old fish increase in weight. The weight of the ovary is doubled and that of the testis trebled. In *Plecoglossus altivelis* a common freshwater salmonid of Japan, Suzuki (1939) finds that fish hatched in one autumn spawn in the following one, and then die soon after. But in one Japanese lake the eggs are matured only in the right ovary and the posterior part of the left. The anterior part of the left ovary contains immature eggs from which the ovaries are regenerated, so that these fish survive for a further spawning season. In the males a new crop of germ-cells is not normally found in the lobules of the testis after the expulsion of the spermatozoa, but in the lake fish a new crop is produced within the previously existing lobules.

Evans (1938) has described the enlargement of the pituitary body in the eel in the month of September at the approach of the season for migration. This enlargement is presumably the expression of a correlation between the functional activities of the pituitary and those of the reproductive organs. This conclusion is supported by the experimental results of Fontaine (1936), who found that spermatogenesis and the liberation of spermatozoa followed the injection of urine of pregnancy (containing substances allied to, if not identical with, the hormones of the anterior lobe of the pituitary body) into " silver " eels, that is, freshwater eels at the beginning of their migration into the sea. Frost (1945) determined that the time spent in fresh water by female eels is nine to nineteen years, and by male eels an average of nine years. In females the commonest length for migration and the change to silver eels is 54 to 60 cm., though a small minority become silver when much older and larger. The average length of the male eel for migration is approximately 40 cm. Frost suggests that it is length and not age which controls migration. Presumably, therefore, length also controls the activity of the pituitary which is responsible for the development of the gonad and the assumption of the silver dress.

In viviparous elasmobranchs, too, Ranzi (1936) finds that there is an increase in the size of the pituitary body during pregnancy. At the same time the inter-renal bodies increase in size, and the histological appearance of the thyroid shows an augmented state of activity, during which, according to Bargmann (1939), many of the follicles of the thyroid become filled with blood cells, both erythro-cytes and leucocytes.

II. Amphibia

As indicated in the first chapter, amphibians, speaking generally, experience an annual breeding cycle, but there is great variability in passing from group to group or even from species to species. This is true both of the Urodela (newts) and of the Anura (frogs and toads). In both these orders the cyclical changes affect not only the production of the spermatozoa and ova but also the testicular interstitial cells and the secondary sexual characters.

Urodela

The cycle in urodeles has been well described by Aron (1926) who refers fully to both the older and the contemporaneous literature. In the male there is a marked spermatogenetic cycle, spermatogenesis generally occurring after the com-pletion of the breeding season, the spermatozoa being retained in the testes over a prolonged period. Thus, *Triton cristatus*, which together with other species was investigated by Aron, gradually discharges its spermatozoa from cysts during a spring breeding season (April to June). After breeding there is a pre-spermato-genetic period (in summer) during which the secondary spermatogonia multiply actively and new lobules are formed in the testes. The spermatogonia give rise to spermatocytes and the latter to spermatids which become spermatozoa in the typical manner. Spermatogenesis is terminated in the autumn when the animals leave the water and retire into their winter quarters for hibernation. The testes in the winter contain fully developed spermatozoa and these, as just mentioned, are discharged in the spring (Champy, 1913, 1921 ; Aron, 1924).

According to Adams (1940) the adult aquatic males of *Triturus viridescens* have a greater average total length but a smaller average body weight than the females. Large animals tend to have the heaviest gonads, and in the males multiple-lobed testes are more often present in large individuals than in small ones. Gametogenic activity takes place in the gonads during the summer and early autumn. The testes contain all stages in spermatogenesis, and are largest in July and August ; by September mature spermatozoa are abundant. The testis is divided into a cephalic section of transparent bluish hue separated by a fairly sharp division plane from a caudal section of whitish or yellowish opaque appearance ; the latter is often studded with golden-coloured tissue in the hilar region. Spermatogonia, spermatocytes and spermatids, according to the part of the yearly cycle, occur in the cephalic or immature part ; and cysts of mature spermatozoa and Sertoli cells, evacuated cysts and interstitial tissue in the caudal or mature part. The relative sizes of the mature and immature parts of the testes alternate cyclically with the sex cycle. The Wolffian ducts are coiled, and whitish in appearance from their contained spermatozoa, from September to May. During June they become straighter and often transparent. The straightening and transparency are characteristic of the conditions found in July and August. Ifft (1942) found that temperature is evidently the principal environmental factor influencing the sperm cycle in *T. viridescens*. In summer, spermatogenesis not only ceases at temperatures below 12° C., but spermatocytes and spermatids actually undergo degeneration. In winter, temperatures of 12° to 17° C. induce spermatocyte formation ; and higher temperatures of 21° to 25° C. at this season cause the discharge of sperm and the initiation of a new cycle. The cycle is not altered at any stage when the animals are kept under experimental conditions of constant light, gradually increasing light, or complete darkness ; nor is spermatogenesis inhibited when newts are starved experimentally.

The spermatogenetic cycle is different in *Cryptobranchus alleganiensis* (McGregor, 1899). In relation to the fact that the breeding season occurs in August and September, spermatogenesis takes place in July. It begins in the posterior end of the testis and proceeds in a wave to the anterior end. The spermatocytes give rise to the spermatids which become the spermatozoa in August, just before the female spawns. In October the testes having lost all their spermatozoa are much diminished in size. They contain small spermatogonia from which spermatozoa are produced in the following year.

Similar conditions exist in *Necturus maculosus* (Humphrey, 1921), breeding taking place in the late summer and early autumn. Spermatogenesis may occur in the winter, proceeding by a wave from the hind to the fore end of the testes as in *Cryptobranchus*. In the spring and summer it becomes more active, and in July the whole testis may be filled by cysts of secondary spermatocytes. The maturation processes take place in July and August, and spermatozoa are present in the hind part of the testis at the end of August, and are abundant throughout that organ in October. Later in the month or in November the spermatozoa have all disappeared. Aplington (1942) gives further details. From mid-December to mid-March the apices of the testis lobules, adjacent to the longitudinal superficial collecting duct, are filled with primary and secondary spermatogonia. Spermatogonial divisions are rare, and the lobules have not appreciably increased in depth as compared with the testis of autumn. Peripherally, throughout its entire length, the unexpanded testis is filled with stroma and interstitial cells, and no lobular boundaries exist in this region. In April there a few spermatogonial divisions, the April testis being otherwise in the winter condition ; but by May they occur throughout the testis, the greater number being in the posterior half. Secondary spermatogonia become more numerous, and in May some lobule formation is evident. In June, spermatogonial divisions have greatly increased throughout the testis, lobules are conspicuously further developed than in May, and interstitial cells are much less prominent. By August the testis has increased greatly in size, and its weight has almost doubled. The anterior half is in the first spermatocyte prophase, pachytene and diplotene figures predominating. First spermatocyte divisions become frequent at about the middle of the testis and are intermingled with many spermatocyte divisions a short distance posteriorly. The caudal third of the organ is filled with spermatids and transforming spermatids which are much elongated at the extreme caudal end of the testis, but no mature spermatozoa are present. In September there is only a small area at the anterior end of the testis which is filled with spermatids and transforming spermatozoa. Mature spermatozoa fill the lobules to about the middle of the organ. Below this point the lobules have begun to empty, particularly in the parts adjacent to the duct, and posteriorly many lobules are empty of spermatozoa. Sertoli cells remain in these empty lobules and some degeneration takes place. The formation and deposition of spermatophores begins during late August. By October sperm-filled lobules are confined to the anterior quarter of the testis, and even there the spermatozoa are few near the duct. In the caudal three-quarters of the testis the lobules are practically empty except for degenerating Sertoli cells and retained spermatozoa. At the extreme caudal end the lobules are collapsed and their boundaries are indistinguishable. Connective-tissue cells occupy the peripheral region, which approximates to the winter condition. In November the degeneration of the lobules has progressed in its caudo-cephalic wave to the anterior end of the testis, and the caudal half has reverted to the winter condition. Spermatogonial divisions have stopped, and the depth of the apical spermatogonial area remains constant until the following spring. In early December, except for the extreme anterior end, the testis has returned to the winter condition, and by the middle of the month has become completely inactive.

Aplington also finds a conspicuous correlation between the activity of the testis and the hypophysis. During the growth period of the testis marked alterations occur in the pars anterior of the hypophysis, where there is an increase in the number of the granular basophil cells. After the sperm has been discharged during the breeding season, the proportions of the numbers of basophil cells of different types alter, and a degranulation of the granular acidophil cells takes place.

In *Triton cristatus*, as described by Aron (1924), in addition to the changes affecting the spermatogenetic tissue, there is at the time of breeding a peculiar glandular development in the testis which he regards as being similar to the interstitial gland of other vertebrates. It is apparently formed from the walls of the testicular lobules and possibly also from the Sertoli cells which are ordinarily regarded as having a trophic function. The growth and regression of this interstitial tissue in the urodele occur in approximate correlation with the development and atrophy of the more obvious secondary male characters. Champy (1921, 1933) and Humphrey (1921), however, deny that there is any functional connection between them. Thus Champy regards the histological changes which occur in the testis at the time of breeding as a result of the altered condition of the organ consequent upon the release of the spermatozoa. And Humphrey states that the interstitial cells develop in a wave along the testes parallel to that shown by the spermatogenetic tissue. According to this account the so-called interstitial cells of the urodele testes are not glandular in function but are connective-tissue cells which develop a lipoid content. They are not formed until the spermatozoa are shed, and

Humphrey regards their development as a response to the collapsed state of the seminiferous lobules.

In addition to the gonadal changes, the seasonal nuptial coloration and the growth of the dorsal crest, Aron (1924) has described certain periodic changes in the internal organs of *Triton cristatus*. Of these the most marked are those of the collecting ducts of the kidney, the Wolffian duct through which the spermatozoa pass, and the walls of the cloaca.

The ducts of the kidney become conspicuously larger and their lumina are seen to be dilated. At the same time they develop a glandular function, their lining epithelial cells becoming cylindrical and containing secretory granules. The Wolffian duct also acquires a periodic glandular activity and produces a mucous secretion, the nuclei of many of the lining cells elaborating granulations which are discharged into the cytoplasm. The whole duct becomes much enlarged and is of an intense white colour. Contemporaneously the cloaca swells and its lips project behind the abdomen. The cloacal papilla increases in size and becomes modified into a structure suggestive of a rudimentary erectile organ. The epithelium which lines the cloacal chamber becomes cylindrical and its cells secrete a mucous product.

In *Triturus viridescens*, Adams (1940) was able to correlate the changes in the secondary sex characters, which are confined to the male, with the gonadal cycle. The varying characters are the thickened horny pads on the hind legs and toes of the males from September to June ; the height of the tail fin, which is lowest in July and August ; and the size of the cloaca. The latter is small during August and early September and large in winter and spring, reaching its greatest size in April and May ; the secretory activity of the glands of the cloacal region causes the increase in size. The secondary sex characters are much reduced during summer when the gonads are inactive, but from October onwards through the winter, until after the spermatozoa are released in the spring breeding season, they are highly developed. This latter period is characterised by an abundance of mature tissue in the gonads.

In the American salamander *Eurycea bislineata*, which breeds in late March and early April, Weichert (1945) states that about a month before the breeding season the spermatozoa have left the testis and distend the vasa deferentia. At the same time the tubules of the hedonic mental gland are filled with secretion. The vasa deferentia and the mental gland regress within two or three weeks of the end of the breeding period, and remain degenerate until August. Spermatogenesis begins in June, and spermatids first appear in late July and early August, when the mental gland begins to develop. Growth of the vasa deferentia soon follows, and at the end of September spermatogenesis is complete and spermatozoa enter the vasa deferentia. Secretion appears in the tubules of the mental gland late in October, when an autumn mating may take place, and spermatozoa first appear in the spermathecae of the females. The animals are thus capable of reproducing almost five months before the actual breeding period. Changes in the secondary sex characters, presumably caused by the action of male hormones, appear concurrently with the changes in the testes associated with the later stages of spermatogenesis.

It is thus seen that in the Urodela there is in the male animal a marked cycle of changes affecting a number of organs and structures. The cycle in the female apart from that affecting the ovaries, speaking generally, is not so conspicuous. In the ovaries of *Triton* and *Salamandra*, as in other amphibians, there is a great seasonal fluctuation in weight depending upon egg development and spawning, and the number of eggs produced increases with the size of the animals (March, 1937).

Accounts of the ovarian cycle in *Triturus viridescens* have been given by Hilsman (1934) and Adams (1940). The growth of the primary oöcytes is slow, and ovarian weights are smallest during the summer months. The oöcytes, differing from the oögonia by their large reticulated nuclei and relatively small amount of cytoplasm, are surrounded by sheaths of connective tissue and follicle cells. By September the oöcytes have increased greatly in size and the deposition of yolk has begun, the ovary now containing large yolk-laden eggs and many smaller oöcytes. In October the gonads of both sexes are mature and the autumn mating, or false breeding season, occurs, when spermatophores are deposited. From October through the winter, until the spring breeding season, the oöcytes continue to grow and form yolk so that each ovary contains about 250 large yolk-laden eggs each about 1·5 mm. in diameter. In animals with large ovaries the oviducts are convoluted and wide ; with the shedding of the eggs in early summer the ducts become less convoluted and narrower, and in July and August they are much reduced in size. Spermatozoa are found in the spermathecae in every month of the year, but they are especially abundant in autumn and spring. The cloacal glands also show secretory activity in every month, but it is least apparent in summer. The mature condition persists over the winter, with slight fluctuations in the size of the gonads, until the true breeding season starts in April. This lasts to the end of June, and thereafter a new growth cycle starts in both testes and ovaries.

Liebman (1945) studying the function of the leucocytes in the growth and regression of the egg of *Triturus viridescens*, found that lymphocytes are instrumental in the growth of the egg, but that neutrophils and eosinophils are involved in its involution. Lymphocytes serve as nurturing cells for the ovum, for they are attracted to, and ingested by, healthy growing eggs. But their function is not wholly trophic since they occur with ingested yolky material in the interovular spaces. Eosinophils appear to be concerned with starting the process of atresia in small yolkless ova, but the last remnants of corpora atretica are phagocytosed and removed by lymphocytes. Additional evidence that the eosinophils are involved in protoplasmic breakdown was given by observations on the involuting testis in captive *Triturus*, where a mass invasion by eosinophils followed the regression or dissolution of the testicular lobules.

Dunn (1923) has given a comparative account of the breeding organs and processes in the Urodela which he divides into two principal super-families according to their method of reproduction. In the Cryptobranchoidea, fertilisation is external, and presumably this is the primitive method. The females have no spermathecae or receptacles for the spermatozoa and the males have no cloacal papillae. In the Salamandroidea on the other hand, the females possess spermathecae and the males have cloacal papillae and form spermatophores, or packets of spermatozoa, by means of which internal fertilisation is accomplished.

The eggs are of two general types. In the more primitive species they are pigmented, with little yolk, and are usually abandoned in the water. The more advanced members of both super-families, however, have large non-pigmented eggs with much yolk which is formed in quantity at the approach of the breeding season. The larvae or young may issue in a relatively advanced state of development. Thus, live young are produced by *Salamandra*, *Oedipus* and other forms. *Proteus* also ordinarily produces live young, but under certain conditions it may lay non-pigmented eggs with a large yolk. The salamander, *Desmognathus fusca*, deposits its eggs, which are fertilised internally, under terrestrial conditions (Wilder, 1917). The mother then broods them, the incubation period varying, probably according to the outside temperature, from five to eight weeks. Unlike most other amphibians the number of eggs is small, being about twenty. This small number is no doubt correlated with the breeding habits. Paedogenesis, also, occurs in some urodeles, the best known example being the axolotl (*Amblystoma*), and it is sometimes found, at least under the artificial conditions of captivity, in some newts.

Anura

In its breeding cycle the common frog (*Rana temporaria*) is probably typical of most anuran amphibians, as already seen (p. 22, Chapter 1), there are other seasonal rhythms among the group. According to March (1937) the frog's testis reaches its maximum weight in autumn, just before hibernation. In the spring it was found to be lighter, and March suggests that this may be due to the transference of spermatozoa to the seminal vesicles at the ends of the Wolffian ducts.

According to Aron (1926) the primary and secondary spermatogonia are formed in the testes in May and June. The division of these (spermatogenesis) takes place in June and July. By the end of August the testes contain numerous spermatozoa within the spermatocysts. These are discharged in the spring breeding season (February to April) after being first passed into the seminal vesicles.

Aron has also described a contemporaneous cycle in the testicular interstitial tissue. He shows that in the functional region the interstitial cells of *R. esculenta* present their greatest dimensions in April and May. After mating they regress and show their minimal dimensions in August. They increase in size in the autumn. The nuclei of the cells undergo comparable fluctuations, their diameters nearly doubling as they pass from their smallest to their greatest dimensions. The protoplasmic contents and inclusions also increase greatly as the cells attain their problematical functional activity. Champy (1932), however, in a paper on the sexual characters of the frog, denies that the interstitial cells have a secretory function.

Gallien (1940) studied the reproductive cycle in *Rana temporaria* from Belgium and northern France, and found that it was divisible into three phases which together last the whole year. The reproductive phase, in which ovulation, spawning and fertilisation take place, immediately follows hibernation and takes place mostly in the first fortnight of March. The phase of genital activity extends from April to October, and coincides with the summer feeding activity after the frogs leave the breeding waters. In the first part of this phase, which lasts to June, the gonads resorb any ripe genital products which were not emitted in March. Thereafter a new spermatogenesis starts in the testis, and vitellogenesis in the ovary, so that at the end of September the animals reach their full genital maturity. The static phase starts in October, when the frogs hibernate at the bottom of ponds until February. During this phase they are sexually ripe, and ovulation and the production of tadpoles can be artificially stimulated by injections of pituitary extract.

In the males during the reproductive phase the testes are full of sperm, the seminal vesicles are considerably hypertrophied, and the digital callosity is at its maximum development. At the beginning of the phase of genital activity after breeding, the testes still hold masses of sperm. Involution occurs during April and May, and is followed by spermatogenesis in July and August when the volume of the testes increases again. The ampullae of the testes now contain spermatozoa grouped in bundles with the heads directed towards the exterior, and embedded in the mass of Sertoli cells lining the periphery of the ampullae. The seminal vesicles are in the resting stage. These conditions are maintained throughout the winter during the static phase until breeding in March. The callosity regresses rapidly after breeding, the highly keratinised papillae disappearing and the surface becoming smooth, until the following January when keratinisation and pigmentation start again. Sexual maturity is reached at the end of September in the fourth year, during the summer of which spermatogenesis has occurred for the first time. Breeding occurs in the following March, at the beginning of the fifth year. Until the March preceding puberty the testis remains small and shows only spermatogonial mitoses.

In the female after spawning the ovary is reduced to a thin band containing several generations of oöcytes of different sizes, none of which has undergone vitellogenesis. The oviduct is considerably reduced and nearly circular in section. As early as May there is a noticeable increase in the size of the oöcytes destined to form the next spawning. At the same time a number of ripe oöcytes which were not expelled in March degenerate and form atretic bodies. Vitellogenesis starts in June, and the oviduct enlarges and becomes elliptical in section. Development continues during the summer, so that in September the ovary and oviduct have the size and structure characteristic of sexual maturity. They remain in this state through the static phase and hibernation until the following March. Sexual maturity occurs in September of the fourth year, during which the first vitellogenesis and enlargement of the genital tract have taken place : the first spawning is in the following March, at the beginning of the fifth year.

In *Rana nigromaculata* of China, Ting and Boring (1939) report that spermatogenesis is most active during summer and early autumn, and that spermatozoa are already abundant during the winter. The amount of intertubular tissue is smallest in late summer when the spermatic tissue is greatest, and greatest during the mating period when the secondary sex characters are well developed. The region of the ureters behind the kidneys is enlarged during the mating season for the temporary storage of spermatozoa. The nuptial pads begin to grow in the autumn and reach their full size just before the mating period. The changes in the nuptial pads are parallel with the amount of intertubular tissue : during the summer the pads are much degenerated. The formation of ova in the female is most active after spawning, and rapid growth is found in the ovary in summer and early autumn. The oviducts are heaviest just before ovulation ; afterwards they are lightest, but a period of growth during the summer restores them by the autumn.

A state of incomplete paedogenesis has been found by Swingle (1921) in the larvae of *Rana catesbeiana*. A first sexual maturation cycle is found in the male larvae, but the cells degenerate and disappear gradually. A few cells, lineal descendants of the primordial germ-cells, persist unchanged through this cycle of maturation and degeneration, and give rise by repeated mitosis to a second germ-cell generation in larvae just ready for metamorphosis. Shortly before metamorphosis this second generation of germ-cells goes through a maturation cycle and normal spermatozoa are formed, despite the fact that the animal is a larva with the efferent ducts of the testes incompletely formed. The germ-cells of the female larvae at the time of metamorphosis are not mature, but are young growing oöcytes. There is, however, some evidence to show that sometimes the female larvae may show a precocious and abortive maturation cycle.

In the male of *Discoglossus*, Kehl (1944) reports that the weight of the testis is very large compared with the body weight, the ratio of interstitial tissue to body weight being the highest yet recorded. The nuptial pad of the thumb is an indicator of the state of the interstitial cells, and castration causes its rapid loss. In the female, genital activity is spread over a large period of the year, being greatest at the end of winter ; eggs can be laid at any time of the year if feeding is adequate, but not when fasting. The condition of the testis found by Kehl contradicts the findings of Champy (1923a) who thought that interstitial tissue was always very small in amount in *Discoglossus*, and sometimes totally absent, and that its presence had no correlation with the appearance of the nuptial pad. Benoit, Kehl and Leportois (1942), however, were able by careful measurement to show the real abundance of interstitial tissue in this anuran, and that the state of activity of the secondary sexual characters corresponds to an increase in the proportion of the weight of interstitial tissue to body weight.

The ovaries of the Cape clawed toad (*Xenopus laevis*) and the gross changes they undergo annually have been briefly described by Shapiro and Shapiro (1934). During the breeding season the ovaries fill to distension the whole of the body cavity. They are then composed mostly of masses of ova, mature and immature ; these are black at one pole and yellow at the other, and are often easy to see with the naked eye. The ovary has a mesenteric attachment all along the kidney and is invested with a thin connective-tissue capsule sending septa into its mass, these forming a supporting framework for the ova. The connective-tissue capsule contains small blood vessels with thin muscular walls. Some ova are large and central and others are small and peripheral. The large central eggs have pale clear-staining nuclei. The cytoplasm consists of ovoid discs, the largest of which are placed around the nucleus and the smallest around the periphery. A well-marked layer of pigment, several granules deep, can be seen lying most peripherally in those eggs which have been cut through the pigmented pole. This pigment is absent in the yellow hemisphere of the ovum. There appears to be a delicate reticulum supporting the ovoid discs of the cytoplasm. The peripheral ova are small and lie in direct relation to the thin investing connective-tissue capsule, which sends in slender septa. Their nuclei contain many dark-staining granules. The cytoplasm of such ova is hyaline and non-granular. These peripheral ova are the ones which can be seen with the naked eye. After retrogression the ovary appears as a gelatinous mass in which individual ova cannot readily be detected. The capsule is at this time thicker, and the vessels have thicker walls. The peripheral ova are numerous comparatively, but it is the central ova which at this time can be more readily recognised. According to Rugh (1935) follicular rupture in the frog is consequent upon copulation. In the Cape clawed toad, also, ovulation does not normally occur without copulation. Rugh states that the progress of the frog's egg into the oviduct depends entirely upon ciliary action ; the same is true for *Xenopus*.

As a result of experimental work, Alexander and Bellerby (1938) conclude that in *Xenopus* under natural conditions the seasonal decrease in the water volume of the ponds in which the toads live may induce, or at least contribute to the maintenance of, the retrogressive phase of activity which normally occurs. After the breeding season in July and August the ponds dry up, as a result of evaporation, and the toads aestivate in the mud at the bottom. During this period the vestigial ovary resulting from ovulation cannot grow because of the absence of food, and it is not until the seasonal rains begin, and the ponds fill up, that redevelopment takes place. In consequence of an increasingly abundant food supply the ovaries then grow rapidly, and the attainment of full maturity is followed once more by ovulation in June and July. Bellerby (1938) also shows that light is not essential for the maintenance of reproductive activity, and that seasonal variation in light intensity or wave length plays no part in the control of the sexual cycle under natural conditions. This author and his collaborators (Alexander and Bellerby, 1935 ; Bellerby and Hogben, 1938) conclude that the developmental condition of the ovary depends directly upon the amount of food available. The normal periods of ovarian growth and retrogression which occur in the toads under natural conditions can be explained on the basis of fluctuation in food supply alone.

March (1937) states that in *Rana* the ovaries and oviducts after the breeding season regress to juvenile proportions, but the ovaries in the succeeding season increase to a greater size than they were before and so in successive years in correlation with the increasing size of the frog. Similarly the number of ova produced increases with the size of the animals in an allometric manner.

As is well known, the oviducts of all frogs during the breeding season secrete a jelly-like substance which is spawned with the ova. With the tree-frogs of the genus *Rhacophorus*, which is terrestrial, laying its eggs on land, the jelly surrounding the eggs is described as being beaten by the hind legs into a frothy mass in which development takes place (Bhaduri, 1932). Such foam-nests have been recorded for three Indian species and some others ; Bhaduri's paper contains further references. This author describes the sperm as being massed together with some secretion which apparently contributes to the frothy mass. He suggests that this secretion, coming from a part of the urogenital duct of the male frog, may possibly be homologous with the prostatic secretion of mammals.

According to Kerr (1939), who bases his statements on so far unpublished observations by Spaul and Gladwell, the whole genital duct system in frogs has a cyclical series of changes, synchronising with the gonadal changes, and correlated with the pituitary. After spawning the ducts are at their lowest phase ; as summer proceeds they increase in size, and during the breeding season the wall of the oviduct releases mucous substances, and the vas deferens of the male similarly secretes. Kerr himself described comparable changes in the cloaca in both sexes. These changes occur in the epithelium and the connective tissue behind it, and consist of an enlargement of the folds, as well as of the individual cells, during summer and autumn, a final enlargement at the breeding season, and a post-spawning collapse. The changes are connected with alterations in the lymph content of the loose connective tissue. The function of the cloacal epithelium is thought to be to flush out and lubricate the passage during the spawning season, when the cells are engaged in active secretion.

In *Bufo arenarum* of Argentina, Allende (1939) finds that the ovary is in a resting state from January to October or November. Three generations of oöcytes are then present : small, clear and transparent ; medium, yellow in colour and about 0·5 mm. in diameter ; and large, pigmented and ready to be laid. In the period of activity, which occurs in the southern spring, the eggs are expelled and the ovary is reduced to a thread containing the two younger generations of oöcytes. The wall of the oviduct is thinner, its glands are reduced in size, and its lining epithelium is altered and at some points detached. The lumina of the glands are filled with a mass of granules which appear to be degenerating nuclei. After spawning, there is a period of recuperation when the remaining two stages of oöcytes grow, and a new generation of those of the smallest size is produced. The ovary is fully ripe at the beginning of winter and can be stimulated to ovulate by the administration of pituitary substances some months before the normal spawning season. The recuperation of the oviduct is more rapid than that of the ovary ; it occurs in summer when the animals are obtaining abundant food.

Rey (1939a) finds that in toads (*Bufo bufo*), collected near Paris, after spawning the ovary contains, besides occasional atretic follicles, a small number of young follicles, the largest of which is not more than 0·5 mm. in diameter. The follicles containing the oöcytes consist of two very thin layers of cells. In April and May the number of follicles increases and the smaller ones grow, but there is no increase in greatest diameter. During June some of the follicles increase greatly in size, and this growth continues until October, but with decreasing intensity. After October the ovary remains inactive and contains ripe follicles about 1·6 mm. in diameter, and a number of younger ones about half the size. Throughout the cycle, but especially towards the end of the growth period, numerous atretic follicles are present. In the testis of the toad, Rey (1939b) states that immediately after breeding, at the end of March, there is a multiplication of spermatogonia. At the beginning of May the cysts of the testis are full of spermatogonia and primary spermatocytes, numerous divisions of the latter to form secondary spermatocytes being visible by the beginning of June. After the end of this month the testes are filled with numerous spermatozoa, and from July to December all stages of spermatogenesis are present. The intensity of spermatogenesis decreases towards the end of the year, and in January and February the testes are resting and show no further change of structure until the time of breeding. During the resting stage each cyst contains numerous bundles of spermatozoa, and a few large spermatogonia which undergo no further development. In the toads examined by Rey the process of spermatogenesis continued longer than in those from which Champy (1913) gave an otherwise similar description of the cycle. Rey points out that the difference is probably due to the fact that he kept his toads at a higher temperature (above 15° C.) and fed them regularly.

In the Chinese *Bufo bufo*, Ting and Boring (1939) find a rapid growth of the reproductive tract during summer and early autumn, following the collapse which occurs on spawning. The gonads are actively maturing new germ-cells, and the accessory sex organs make rapid reparation and growth, while the secondary sex characters degenerate. In the late autumn and winter, growth of the gonads and accessory sex organs is retarded, but the secondary sex characters make their appearance again.

Cyclical changes have also been described in Bidder's organ in the toad. This structure, which is characteristic of toads, is histologically not unlike an ovary, and experimentally it has the potentialities of an ovary since removal of the testes in the male may result in Bidder's organ developing the structure and function of a female gonad (Harms, 1926). Rau and Gatenby (1923) found Bidder's organ in all males of *Bufo melanostictus*, but they could not find it in the females. Alexander (1932), however, definitely found Bidder's organ in at least eight female toads of this species. Harms found that Bidder's organ in *Bufo bufo* almost disappears between September and March, and is largest during the breeding season. On the other hand, Ting and Boring (1939) found no seasonal changes in Bidder's organ or the rudimentary oviducts in the males of the Chinese *Bufo bufo*.

The fat-bodies which consist of richly vascularised lymphatic tissue and lie alongside the gonads in both sexes of amphibians attain their fullest size in spring at the time when the reproductive organs are most active, and it is believed that they contribute to the discharge of the sexual functions, possibly by supplying nutriment. After the spawning season the fat-bodies become reduced to an inconspicuous size. Moreover, even in the tropical form *Bufo melanostictus* abovementioned, in which the breeding season extends throughout almost the whole year the size of the fat-bodies varies seasonally, these structures being quite small from October to January (Alexander, 1933). As already remarked October and November are the months when there is least evidence of breeding activity in this species. The fat-bodies of *Xenopus* are, according to Gitlin (1941), finger-like processes arising from a common stem attached to the upper poles of the gonads. They consist of typical fat-cells among which ramify the terminal divisions of blood vessels. The fat-bodies of the male are relatively heavier than those of the female. In both sexes there is a seasonal variation in the weight of the fat-bodies, the maximum being reached during aestivation and the minimum during the breeding season. There are subcutaneous fat deposits in *Xenopus*, which are larger in the female than in the male, and present seasonal variations similar to those of the fat-bodies.

The periodicity in the occurrence of the reflex responses displayed by frogs and other cold-blooded vertebrates has been already noticed (p. 22, Chapter 1).

Mayr (1942) summarises the work of Witschi (1930) and others who have described the occurrence of geographical sex races in some frogs and other amphibia. These races, which occur within a single species, may be differentiated or undifferentiated. In the first the males acquire their sexual characters at an early stage of development, but in the second the genetic males pass through a hermaphroditic condition, and do not acquire their male characters until the first year of life or later. Other races are known which are intermediate between these two extremes.

III. Reptilia

The changes which occur in the sexual organs have been investigated, more particularly in the male, in certain species of lizards and snakes. In the other reptiles, little attention has been paid to this subject. In most species there is

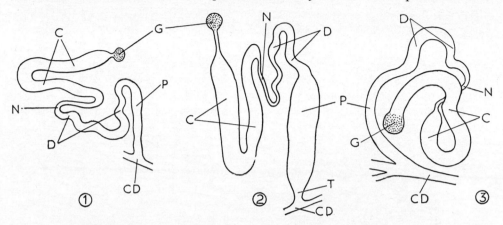

Fig. 3. 1—Diagrams showing the component parts of the uriniferous tubules of the kidney in reptiles (after Cordier, 1928). 1. Chelonia. 2. Ophidia. 3. Lacertilia.
C, convoluted tubule ; CD, collecting duct ; D, distal tubule ; G, glomerulus ; N, narrow segment ; P, pre-terminal segment ; T, terminal segment.

a well-marked male cycle affecting the spermatogenetic and interstitial tissue of the testis, the secretion of the epididymis, and the secretory activity of the pre-terminal segment of the renal tubules (the sexual segment) and sometimes also the external secondary sexual characters (coloration, etc.). There is also usually a female cycle affecting the ovaries and oviducts. Full references to the older

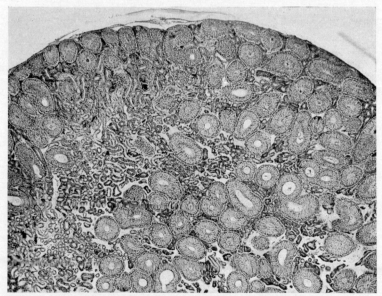

Fig. 3. 2—Adder *Pelias berus*. T.S. kidney of male, showing tubules and the enlarged glandular sexual (pre-terminal) segments of the tubules. Cf. Fig. 3. 6.

literature are given in the papers by Herlant (1933) and Regamey (1935). The uriniferous tubules of the reptilian kidney have been described in great detail by Regaud and Policard (1903a, b, c, d), who give references to the older literature, and by Cordier (1928). Each tubule consists of a glomerulus, followed by a convoluted tubule with ciliated epithelium, a short narrow segment, a distal convoluted tubule, and a pre-terminal segment which opens direct into the collecting ducts in the Chelonia and Lacertilia, but through a short terminal segment in the Ophidia (Fig. 3. 1). These segments have been further subdivided according to the structure of their epithelium. It is the pre-terminal segment of the uriniferous tubule that is modified as a sexual segment in the males of Ophidia and Lacertilia ; this modification does not occur in the Chelonia. In the kidney of male Lacertilia and Ophidia the sexual segments of the kidney tubules can be seen with the naked

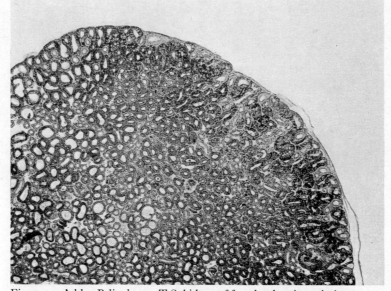

Fig. 3. 3—Adder *Pelias berus*. T.S. kidney of female, showing tubules. × 44.

eye as opaque yellow spots on the surface of the dark red organ. Microscopically this segment (Fig. 3. 2) consists of very high cylindrical cells, with basal nuclei, and alveolar cytoplasm containing very numerous granules. On their sides in contact with the lumen of the tubule the cells have no cell walls, and the granules escape in large masses direct from the cytoplasm of the cells into the lumen. In the kidney of the female (Fig. 3. 3) this great enlargement of the epithelium of the pre-terminal segment does not occur ; the cells are cubical with central nuclei, as are those of the adjacent segments, and produce a mucous secretion.

Lacertilia

Reiss (1923a, b) appears to have been the first to describe the sexual cycle in the lizards and to correlate the changes in the testes with those of the secondary male characters. The species he investigated were *Lacerta muralis* and *L. agilis*. Spermatogenesis appears to be normal and typical. The early processes begin to take place after the removal of the spermatozoa in the summer or earlier. The

spermatogonia proliferate and give rise to spermatocytes which in the processes
of maturation in time produce spermatids. These persist throughout the winter
and in the following spring (April and May) give rise to spermatozoa. The latter
quit the testicular canaliculi in May. The testis afterwards passes into a state of
relative inactivity until the spermatogenetic cycle is renewed. There is also an
interstitial cell cycle. During the winter these cells have the appearance of
ordinary connective-tissue cells. In the spring, however, they become large and
active and develop chondriosome granules. In the autumn they undergo regression. According to Reiss the development of the interstitial tissue in *Lacerta*
occurs synchronously with the growth and activity of the secondary sexual
characters, both internal (accessory sexual organs) and external. Thus, in the
spring there is a marked secretory activity on the part of the distal portions of the
renal tubules (pre-terminal or terminal, constituting the sexual segment of the
kidney tubules). The glands of this part of the organ are at this period not simply
mucous but some of their cells enlarge and form granules which are discharged
as an albuminous secretion at the same time as the discharge of the spermatozoa.
These periodic changes occur in the kidney of the male lizard only. The epididymis undergoes contemporaneous changes and secretes actively. The penes also
increase in size. The femoral organs which consist of scaly structures on the
under-surface of the thigh and are believed to serve some function, possibly
glandular, in copulation (being especially developed in the male), undergo a pronounced keratinisation and a secretion issues from the ducts of the organs which
open to the surface by papillae. Furthermore, at the season of sexual activity
the animal undergoes a colour change, a dark pigment developing in the skin.
After the sexual season is over all these organs and structures revert to their previous
condition. Reiss believes that there is a definite correlation between the interstitial cell cycle and that of the secondary sexual characters.

Frankenberger (1928) has also described the testicular cycle in *Lacerta agilis*.
According to this author there are two periods of spermatogenetic activity, the
first in April and May and the second in September, but the latter is abortive,
terminating after the first maturation division. There are also two maximal
periods of interstitial cell development, the first in spring when the spermatids
become transformed into spermatozoa, and the second at the end of the summer.
Between these two periods the interstitial cells diminish in number (that is, when
the spermatozoa have left the testicular canaliculi). After the second period of
activity they remain numerous until the beginning of hibernation when they
regress to a minimum in which condition they remain until the following spring.
Frankenberger is inclined to ascribe a trophic function to the interstitial cells,
stating that lipoid granules may be seen traversing their basal membranes presumably in process of passing to the spermatogenetic tissue.

Courrier (1929) has given an account of the male urogenital cycle in the spiny-
tailed lizard (*Uromastix*). He states that spermatogenesis and the hypertrophy
of the interstitial cells occur in May when also the sexual segment of the kidney
tubules and the epididymis actively secret. But he says further that there is a
second period of spermatogenetic activity in October, associated with a new
development of the interstitial tissue, whereas the sexual segment and the epididymis are in a state of quiescence. On the other hand, Kehl, Leportois and Benoit
(1942) find that in the female there is only one period of sexual activity during

the year. In May there are large eggs in the ovaries, ovulation occurs during June, and in July eggs are found in the oviducts. During the rest of the year the ovary is reported to be inactive. Secretory activity of the epithelium in the glands of the oviducts coincides with the presence of large eggs in the ovaries at the end of spring and during the summer.

Blount (1929) has given an account of the male cycle in the so-called " horned toad " (*Phrynosoma solare*). The testis being at a mimimum from November to March, when the lizard hibernates, increases later, first slowly and then in May rapidly, reaching its maximal dimensions in June or July ; afterwards it regresses gradually until the winter. The greatest size is about seven times the minimal one. The spermatogenetic cycle was not closely followed but sperm production is presumably active during the development of the seminal tubules which goes on after hibernation and more particularly in May when the organ is growing. Blount records the presence of spermatozoa in the tubules from the end of May until August. Copulation was especially noticeable in July. There was an interstitial cell cycle going on contemporaneously with the spermatogenetic cycle but its significance is not quite clear. The total number of cells was estimated to be greater after the mating season when the spermatozoa had been discharged, that is to say, it was greater in September than in July. In winter there was no reduction in the number. On the other hand, the size of the individual cells was found to be largest during the breeding season and to decrease afterwards. The maximal absolute volume of the tissue was also largest at the breeding season, being related to the cell size. The secondary sexual characters were not investigated, but one may presume that the accessory male organs are in a state of maximal activity at the breeding season. In a later paper, Blount (1934) further studied the seasonal changes in the interstitial cells of this lizard, using the staining reaction of the nucleus as an indication of change. In December and January, during hibernation, the nuclei of both the interstitial cells and the germinal epithelium showed no reaction. After hibernation, in February and March, the interstitial tissue nuclei first showed a positive reaction, which was later also shown by the germinal epithelium. The maximum reaction of the interstitial cells was found in May, after which there was a gradual reduction to none in July. In the middle of August a sudden increase in nuclear reaction occurred and continued through September, decreasing again to none with the onset of hibernation. The germinal epithelium nuclei reached a maximum reaction at the height of spermatogenesis in July, and after the discharge of sperm the reaction decreased. Blount adds that the first wave of interstitial reaction is accompanied by a cytoplasmic granulation maximum during July. This is correlated with increases in cell size, nuclear diameter and interstitial tissue volume, but a decrease in cell number, as already mentioned. The time of interstitial cell granulation maximum exactly corresponds with the time of spermatogenesis. The second wave of nuclear reaction in the interstitial cells is correlated with the increase in cell number in August.

Herlant (1933) has described the male sexual cycle in the lizard, *Lacerta muralis*, and has also recorded observations upon *L. vivipara*, upon *Chalcides ocellatus* and upon the gecko (*Hemidactylus mabuia*). The spermatogenetic cycle in these forms appears to be generally similar to that of *L. agilis*. Young spermatogonia occur in August and spermatocytes in September, and later, spermatids. Spermatozoa are extremely abundant in May (Fig. 3. 4), which is the most active month in the spermatogenetic cycle. The process is completed by June, when the spermatids have disappeared, but spermatozoa are still abundant in the male passages. There are definite interstitial cells in the lizard but these, according to Herlant, are more scattered than in other reptiles. Moreover, there is an interstitial cell cycle, which approximately corresponds to the spermatogenetic cycle. The number of interstitial cells in the lizard is greatest about mid-May. The increase begins in February. After May there is a steady decrease until August, after which month, with some variation, the number remains low until February. The accessory sexual organs and secondary male characters show closely parallel changes.

Dalcq (1920) briefly described the testicular cycle in the slow-worm, *Anguis fragilis*, and found that it was similar to that of mammals. The interstitial cell

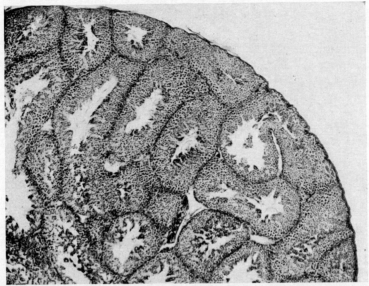

Fig. 3.4—Lizard *Lacerta vivipara*. T.S. testis. × 78. Active spermatogenesis.

development, according to this author, showed two peaks, one in spring, preceding sperm production, and the other in autumn. Herlant (1933) has also made a detailed study of the cycle in this animal. Here there is some dissociation between the spermatogenetic cycle and the interstitial cell cycle. Speaking broadly, the spermatogonia undergo division from June to September, after which time primary spermatocytes are found, the maturation division occurs in March and spermatozoa are formed in April and discharged in May. April may be said to be the time of greatest activity in the production of spermatozoa and the end of May and beginning of June the time of greatest quiescence. The interstitial cell cycle does not correspond very closely, for this tissue is not at its maximum until May. The cells which occur in small groups are not scattered as in the lizard. During the period of their greatest development they are characterised by an abundance of mitochondria and a poverty of lipoids, but their involution is accompanied by a formation of fat. It is noteworthy that the development and regression of the epididymis and sexual segment of the kidney tubules and other sexual characters run parallel with the interstitial cell cycle.

Lacerta agilis has also been the subject of detailed study by Regamey (1935) who has investigated the physiology of the generative organs and the sexual cycle not only in the male but also in the female.   His observations on the spermatogenetic cycle are in general agreement with those of Herlant.   Speaking generally, spermatogenesis was found to begin in July and to result in the formation of spermatids which are maintained during the winter.   A feeble abortive production of spermatozoa may occur in the autumn but the season of greatest production is in the spring, being at its height about April.   The spermatogenetic cycle, however, is not necessarily very marked, for all the stages in the process of sperm production may be observed at any time of the year.   According to Regamey the interstitial gland attains its maximal activity at the end of April and remains active until June, when it undergoes rapid regression.   Moreover, there is a complete conformity between the interstitial development and that of the accessory male organs and the secondary male characters.   The epithelial cells of the epididymis reach their maximal height in April and the organ secretes actively.   The sexual segment of the kidney tubules and the femoral organs likewise undergo their characteristic seasonal development and the penes simultaneously enlarge.   Moreover, the skin acquires the green colour of the mating period.

Regamey describes also a comparable cycle in the female of *L. agilis*.   The various stages in oögenesis were to be seen in the lizard's ovary at any time of the year, but it is not until April and May that ripe follicles were observed.   Ovulation, or the discharge of the ova, takes place in May.   Meanwhile the glandular epithelium of the oviduct increases in thickness and secretes actively.   The glands of the urogenital fossette with which the oviduct communicates behave similarly showing a maximal activity in May and June and a minimal in winter.   Regamey states that these glands play a part in connection with egg-laying and he suggests that in structure, function and cyclical activity they are analogous to the uterine glands of mammals.

Kehl (1935) has described briefly the sexual cycles of certain Saharan lizards ; namely, *Uromastix acanthinurus* (both male and female), *Varanus griseus* (male), *Scincus officinalis* (male) and *Acanthodactylus pardalis deserti* (male and female). The first three are closely similar to the cycles of European lizards, but that of *Acanthodactylus* differs considerably.   In the male, spermatogenesis may go on for the whole year and the accessory male organs and secondary male characters similarly present no definite cycle.   In some individuals, these organs go into complete quiescence in July, however, and again in the autumn and winter.   In the female, ripe eggs were observed in the oviduct in May, in July and in October. Large eggs were also seen in the ovary at the end of February.   In the winter (the end of November to the beginning of February) the female organs were in a state of quiescence.

Cowles and Burleson (1945) describe the male cycle in *Xantusia vigilis*, the Yucca night lizard.   In January the testis shows the first signs of activity by the appearance of numerous mitotic figures in the three to four peripherally placed rows of spermatogonia, and the five to six centrally placed layers of spermatocytes. During February and early March multiplication of these cells continues, and in late March spermatids begin to be formed.   The spermatocytes and spermatids increase in numbers, so that in late April only one or two rows of spermatogonia remain, but the spermatids are not transformed into spermatozoa until the middle of May. By the end of this month, however, this process is practically complete. The testis remains full of sperm until the middle of June when involution starts, so that by the end of the month the testis is reduced in size and shows no spermato-genetic activity, a state which continues throughout the summer until August, when there is a new wave of activity. The testes then increase in size, numerous mitoses occur and there is a production of primary and secondary spermatocytes, as also, apparently, of scattered spermatids. It is possible that a very few sperma-tozoa are produced, but the testes do not reach so high a level of activity as they do in the spring. The authors suggest that the autumnal activity is a direct result of the moderating summer temperature then found. They were able to produce an experimental degeneration of the testis by exposing the lizards to a temperature of 38° C. for a week, a temperature which the animals are liable to encounter during the height of the summer in their natural environment.

In the red-headed skink of America, *Eumeces fasciatus*, Reynolds (1943) found that early seasonal increases in epithelial height, lumen diameter and tubule diameter characterise the seminiferous tubules of the testis, the ductus epididymidis and the sexual segment of the kidney tubules. In the testis, maximal sizes in April are followed by regression, complete involution occurring in August, and by November the approximate sizes of January are restored. Primary spermato-cytes predominate in January, secondary spermatocytes and spermatids in February, and spermatids and metamorphosing sperm from March to the end of June. Mature sperm appear in small numbers in February, maximal numbers in April, and reduced numbers thereafter. Exhaustion of the current season germinal material in late June reduces the epithelium to a population of spermatogonia, which have been slowly proliferating since April. By November restoration of the epithelium is complete and some primary spermatocytes are present, a few of which reach, but none pass, the pachytene stage. In the ductus epididymidis and sexual segment of the kidney tubules secretion begins in February and reaches a maximum in May coincident with maximal size relations ; involution is complete in August. Experiments indicate that castration causes the epididymis and kidney to recede to an involute condition, while administration of testosterone propionate stimulates a condition in every way comparable to that of the height of normal seasonal activity.

Breckenridge (1943) records that the black-banded skink, *Eumeces septentrionalis*, breeds during late May in Minnesota. During the breeding season the testes are enlarged, and the malar region of the males is orange in colour, a secondary sexual character which is presumably developed in correlation with the seasonal activity of the testes. In late June and early July the eggs are laid in nests beneath stones and logs, the female remaining with them during the forty to fifty or more days of incubation. The lizards hibernate several feet below the surface of the ground from October to late April.

In *Anolis carolinensis*, Evans and Clapp (1940) found that seasonal changes were specially noticeable in the male genital tract. During the summer the testes weighed 74 per cent more, were 76 per cent longer and 81 per cent wider than in the winter. The diameter of the seminiferous tubules was 9 per cent greater, and that of the ductus deferens was 44 per cent greater in summer than in winter. The diameter of the cloaca, too, and the height of the cells of its epithelial lining were both about 17 per cent greater during the summer period of activity. The oviduct of the mature female during summer was 53 per cent heavier than in winter, and the thickness of the wall of the lower oviduct from mucosa to serosa was 39 per cent greater. The degree of folding of the mucosa and thickness of the muscular layer were also greater in summer, and the cloaca was similarly affected by seasonal changes.

Altland (1941) has described the annual reproductive cycle in the male of the fence lizard, *Sceloporus undulatus*, from North Carolina. The testis is smallest in July, just before the onset of the reproductive cycle. Primary and secondary spermatocytes and spermatids gradually increase in number during a period of very active growth in September, October and November. The testis reaches its maximum weight by November, at which time it is approximately 17 times as heavy as before the beginning of spermatogenesis. There is a gradual transformation of spermatids to form spermatozoa during December, January and February, after which, in March and April, spermatogenesis increases in intensity. The breeding season starts in May and goes on for about five weeks. Although maturation divisions are still prevalent in July, the testis is undergoing degeneration, except for the spermatogonia which are actively dividing in preparation for the next cycle. Involution is complete by the end of July. From November until June there is a gradual decrease in the size of the testis, with the greatest reduction occurring after March. No interstitial cells have been demonstrated in the testis ; at all times of the year there is very little intertubular space. The secondary sexual characters show seasonal alterations, with maximum development during the breeding season.

It has long been known that in various reptiles, as with certain species of viviparous fish, the ovarian follicles after ovulation become converted through the hypertrophy of the epithelial cells into bodies similar to the mammalian corpora lutea (see p. 468, Chapter 5, where full references are given). This statement in the case of lizards applies not only to viviparous species such as *Lygosoma quoyi*, *L. weekesae*, and *Egernia whitei*, but also to oviparous ones such as *Lacerta agilis* and *Amphibolurus muricatus*. (Weekes, 1934 ; this paper contains further references.) In the oviparous *A. muricatus*, however, the corpus luteum has an existence of only about three weeks, retrogression of the luteal cells beginning while the lizard is still carrying the eggs, and continuing until oviposition, when these cells are in the last stages of degeneration. In the viviparous lizards, on the other hand, the corpus luteum persists for approximately three and a half months, degeneration beginning at about the end of the second month of pregnancy and continuing until the birth of the young when the structure is in an advanced state of regression. Boyd (1941) has investigated the structure of the ovary and the formation of the corpus luteum in the viviparous New Zealand gecko, *Hoplodactylus maculatus*. The ovary, as in all geckos, has only one small localised area of germinal epithelium where oögonia are produced. The amount of stroma is small, the bulk of the ovary being composed of the enlarging oöcytes. Shortly after the breeding season every year, the largest oöcyte in each ovary, measuring about 1 mm. in diameter, enlarges rapidly and yolk spheres appear in it. By the following spring its diameter is about 8 mm., and it is ready for ovulation. Thus only two eggs are ovulated annually, one from each ovary. The germinal epithelium consists of a layer of cells about 0·01 mm. in height. The oögonia usually sink below the surface before undergoing transformation into oöcytes, and move deeper as they become larger, until they are surrounded by follicular epithelium. The egg is provided with a striated membrane composed of material similar to that of the zona pellucida. The epithelial wall of the follicle, originally many layered and exhibiting three different types of cells, is reduced to a single layer. Since only one egg is ovulated annually from each ovary, only one corpus luteum develops in each. In the fresh ovary it appears in early stages as a creamy-white, flattened body, the opening through which the oöcyte escaped being visible as a small, somewhat elongated depression stained with clotted blood. It is easily distinguishable from the more translucent-white young oöcytes, and forms rather more than half the volume of the ovary. At later stages its size is diminished and its surface becomes rounded. The shape of the corpus luteum in later stages varies considerably in individuals, being a matter of chance, and that which best fits the depression between the oöcytes. It consists of luteal cells invested by fibroblasts from the theca externa. Septa of fibroblasts are also present, but no blood vessels, although the theca is rich in capillaries. The theca interna plays no part in the development of the corpus luteum. A lipoid secretion is present in the luteal cells, but there is as yet no experimental evidence as to its functional significance. In such Lacertilia the conditions are clearly similar to those which exist in the Mammalia.

The progress of changes which occur in the accessory reproductive organs of lizards and more particularly in certain Australian species at the approach of and during breeding activity have also been described by Weekes (1935). The oviduct undergoes marked changes with the approach of the breeding season. The earliest indications are growth of the serous glands and the mitotic division of the epithelial cells lining the lumen, possibly in preparation for the stretching of the oviduct upon the entrance of the ova. At the time of ovulation the oviduct becomes divided into three regions, an anterior one in which the epithelial cells are granular, with their surface covered by mucus which presumably facilitates the passage of the ova ; a middle region in which the glands are numerous and particularly active ; and a posterior region communicating with the cloaca. During their passage down the oviduct the eggs are believed to absorb moisture through their vitelline membranes, and later through the shell membrane which is secreted by the walls of the uterine chambers. These chambers are formed from the oviduct as expanded parts of that organ and are separated from each other by short narrow strips of tissue which may be actual constrictions of the uterus.

Three types of structure by means of which the ova of lizards are attached to the wall of the uterus, that is, three types of placentation, have been described. There is first a simple type in which the maternal and embryonic epithelia are closely applied, presumably for purposes of respiration only. In lizards showing this type there is no reduction of the yolk in the eggs at ovulation (e.g. in *Lygosoma quoyi, Egernia whitei*) ; a similar type is seen in some ophidians, *Denisonia superba* and *D. sata*. There is a second type in which the maternal capillaries are borne on folds with grooves lined by glandular epithelium separating them. The function is possibly to supply water to the ova (e.g. in *Lygosoma pretiosum*). Thirdly, there is a more specialised type where portions of the uterine wall are raised into folds filled with capillaries and lined by a thickened glandular epithelium under which there is a well-developed chorionic epithelium (coming from the embryo). The lizards of this type have a reduced yolk at ovulation and the function of the placenta is almost certainly nutritive (e.g. in *Lygosoma weekesae*, and *Chaleides tridactylus*) (Weekes, 1935).

It has long been known that the Lacertilia grow fat-bodies presumably comparable to those of the Amphibia. These are largest in the spring at the beginning of the breeding season and afterwards become reduced (Gadow, 1901), at least in species inhabiting temperate climates. There can be little doubt that the material within these bodies is passed on to the organs of reproduction in the same way as is believed to occur in the amphibians.

Ophidia

Herlant (1933) has given an account of the male cycle in the ophidians and more particularly in the grass snake. There appears to be a spermatogenetic cycle

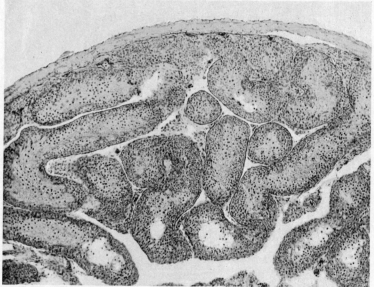

Fig. 3. 5—Grass snake *Natrix natrix*. T.S. testis. × 78. Active spermatogenesis. Interstitial tissue moderate in amount.

much like that of other reptiles. Thus, sperm production occurs in the spring (Fig. 3. 5). In winter in the grass snake, spermatocytes and a few spermatids can be observed and some spermatozoa may persist in the excretory ducts. The testicular interstitial tissue, according to this author, is present in voluminous masses and remains the same throughout the year. In correlation with this the male accessory organs likewise undergo little or no cyclical change. There is, however, a well developed sexual segment in the kidney tubules which in the male secrete freely. The epididymis forms a thin secretion. Volsøe (1944) has investigated the annual cycle in the adder, *Vipera berus*, of Denmark, more particularly in the male. Pairing takes place at the end of April or the beginning of May, some weeks after the adders have left their hibernating dens, and ovulation occurs towards the end of May. Parturition usually takes place in the first half of August, after a gestation period of about two months. The adder is ovo-viviparous and, although the egg-chambers of the oviduct become highly vascularised during pregnancy, nothing resembling a placenta is produced. During pregnancy the fat-body of the female is much reduced in size, but Volsøe does not think that its contents are used to provide material for the developing eggs or young. He considers that its function in this animal is primarily a mechanical one, to fill out the posterior part of the body and help the ventral scales to get a grip in locomotion. He suggests, therefore, that the diminution in size of the fat-body during pregnancy is due partly to its being used up in the metabolism of the mother, who is assumed to be at a disadvantage in procuring food, and partly to the necessity for providing space for the developing embryos. There are some indications that, in the more northerly parts of its range, the adder may have a two-yearly female reproductive cycle in correlation with the restricted yearly period of activity enforced by the long hibernation. The testis undergoes a small seasonal variation in size, its volume being about doubled at its maximum in March. Its minimum is reached in May, after mating, and thereafter there is a gradual return towards the maximum in the following breeding season. The variations in size are caused by corresponding variations in the diameters of the tubules.

" Apart from the pause which occurs during hibernation spermatogenesis is continuous, one spermatogenetic cycle starting even before the last has concluded. In the resting stage during hibernation the epithelium in the seminiferous tubules consists mainly of primary spermatocytes and spermatids. The ratio between these two types of cell varies from year to year, but generally the former outnumber the latter. Spermiogenesis may start in the autumn, but generally no large quantity of ripe spermatozoa are formed before hibernation, and those formed presumably degenerate during the winter. The essential part of spermiogenesis takes place just after hibernation, in March and April. There is a considerable variation in the course of spermatogenesis in different years. This variation is probably due to fluctuations in the climatic conditions, above all in the temperature. Cooling brings the process to a stop, or at least slows down its rate, while on the other hand, heat almost instantly renews the activity in the germinal epithelium."

The interstitial cells pass through an annual cycle in number, size and structure. In early spring they reach their maximum in numbers, size and cytoplasmic content. Parallel with the final stages of spermatogenesis there is a steep fall in all these points late in April, and they remain at a minimum until August (Fig. 3. 6). A slow increase in number and size then take place until hibernation, but the final growth and proliferation do not take place until the following spring, immediately after hibernation, but before copulation. There is a seasonal variation in both the diameter and the height of the epithelium of the ductus epididymidis. A maximum occurs in the winter and spring, a fall in May, a minimum in June, and a continuous rise during the summer and autumn. The amount of the seasonal variation in size is, however, small, and the secretory activity of the epithelium even at its maximum appears to be of little importance. Similarly the diameter of the ductus deferens is subject to considerable variation. The highest values occur late in April and in May, when the duct is distended with semen. The height of the epithelium is generally lowest when the diameter of the ductus is greatest, so the variation is probably only due to a passive distension of the duct, in which no signs of secretory activity have been found.

Volsøe found also an annual cycle in the activity of the sexual segment of the kidney tubules in the male. There is a maximum in the spring, a minimum in

June and July, and a slow rise in the autumn.   The average variation in diameter is from about 80 to about 140 micra, and in the height of the epithelium from about 30 to about 60 micra.   This is correlated with the occurrence of secretion granules in the cells and of secretion in the lumina of the tubules.   Secretion is present or even abundant in spring, but is absent in June and July, and sparse or absent during autumn and winter.   The function of the secretion is unknown ; it has been suggested that when mixed with the semen it provides nourishment for the spermatozoa ; that it helps to separate the semen from the urine, possibly by blocking the renal tubules or ureter during copulation ; or that it assists in the retention of the semen in the oviduct of the female, thereby resembling the vaginal plug found in some mammals.   None of these suggestions has been confirmed.

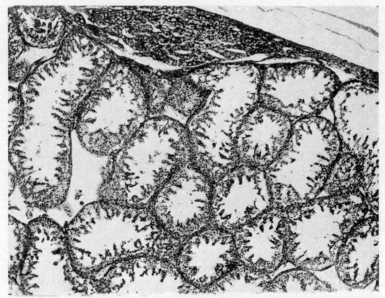

Fig. 3. 6—Adder *Pelias berus*. T.S. testis. × 78. Spermatogenesis complete.
Interstitial tissue extremely reduced.

In the garter-snake (*Thamnophis*) Hartmann (1944) found that in animals taken either in spring or in early autumn the testis size is nearly double that found in animals taken at other times of the year.   He suggests that the spermatogenetic activity at these periods may be correlated with an increase in the numbers of basophile cells found in the pars distalis of the pituitary in April and September.   This autumnal sexual activity has been found in several other snakes.

In the rattle-snake (*Crotalus viridis*) Rahn (1942) describes a two-year reproductive cycle.   He writes that the mature ripe female which is destined to ovulate in late spring is physiologically and morphologically nearly ready for this process in the preceding autumn, judging by the large ovarian follicles, the enlarged uterus, and the presence of motile sperm in the vagina.   Little change takes place in the reproductive tract during hibernation, and ovulation occurs upon emergence in the spring.   Before this the sperm must have travelled to the upper region of the uterus, and it seems doubtful whether an additional spring copulation is necessary for successful fertilisation because it is known that motile sperm are able to survive all the winter *in utero*.   During gestation corpora lutea develop in the ruptured follicles, and the growth of the next generation of follicles is inhibited. Beyond a slow degeneration of the corpora lutea after parturition this condition of the ovary prevails until the following spring, and during the ensuing summer the new follicles reach their large pre-ovulatory size.   During this ovarian growth the animal comes into oestrus and copulates, so that in the second autumn it is ready to produce another litter in the following year.   Rahn points out that this two-year cycle is characteristic of the rattle-snakes on the Wyoming plateau, but that in animals found at lower altitudes or further south there may be a yearly cycle, or even several ovulations a year in tropical zones.

Rahn states that while the ovary enlarges to its maximum size the uterus becomes larger and more coiled.   When it receives the eggs at ovulation it becomes enormously distended, especially after the large water-uptake of the embryos has greatly increased their size.   The regions of the uterus enveloping the embryos become highly vascularised, but the vascularity is not general for the uterus as a whole, and is restricted to the incubation chambers where the wall of the uterus has become stretched to transparency.   These may still be recognised in the spring following parturition, for they have not quite returned to their original shape and their great vascularity alternates with the anaemic regions of constriction. The hyperaemia gradually disappears and in ripe females with large ovaries it is no longer present.   In autumn and spring all ripe females contain motile sperm, but immature and post-partum snakes are without them.   The sperm are stored in the posterior part of the uterus, near the junction with the vagina, during the winter and have not been found in the uterus proper until just prior to ovulation. In a later paper Ludwig and Rahn (1943) state that the majority of sperms are stored in the anterior part of the vaginal pouch and in the vagina during hibernation.   Physiological reasons, rather than physical obstruction, appear to control the extent of penetration by the spermatozoa into the upper parts of the tract. The limited distribution of the spermatozoa posteriorly is explained by the plugging action of the bifurcate hemipenis which ensures deposition of spermatozoa only at the anterior end of each vaginal pouch.   Bogert (1942) reports observations indicating the probability of at least sporadic occurrences of autumn copulation in two other species of rattle-snake, *Crotalus cerastes* and *C. atrox*, in California.

Copulation in the autumn as well as in the spring appears to occur in many species of snakes, and a number of authors have shown that successful fertilisation of the eggs may take place with sperm stored in the genital tract of the female during the winter.   This phenomenon has been recorded in the garter-snake (*Thamnophis sirtalis*) by Rahn (1940) and Blanchard (1943), and in Dekay's snake (*Storeria dekayi*) by Trapido (1940).   Prolonged sperm viability and delayed fertilisation have also been found, though exceptionally, in *Elaphe dione* and *Natrix natrix* by Sosnovsky (1940), but the longest record of this kind is reported by Haines (1940) in a specimen of *Leptodeira annulata* which produced, in captivity, fertile eggs at least five years after the last possible copulation.

Bergman (1943) has studied the breeding cycle in sea-snakes from the Java Sea, and finds that ovulation takes place in May and June, delivery following by the end of October or the beginning of November.   There is one ovulation period a year, and different genera present similar states at the same season.   There is a correlation with the climatic cycle, even in these tropical countries.   The

H*

formation of the corpus luteum in various species of sea-snakes has been described by Samuel (1944). In *Enhydrina schistosa* of the Madras coast, a viviparous snake with a highly specialised allanto-placenta, gravid females were found in November and December. The luteal cells are formed exclusively from the small cells of the follicular epithelium. The theca is greatly thickened after ovulation and shows a clear distinction into theca interna and externa, and the latter into theca compacta and spongiosa. In later stages there is a gradual reduction of the theca, accompanied by a decrease in vascularity. Ingrowths of cells and fibres from the theca penetrate the luteal tissue but are not accompanied by blood vessels, and the fibroblasts do not occur between the individual luteal cells. The active phase of the corpus luteum is short and degeneration sets in early. In *Hydrophis cyanocinctus* the luteal cells are similarly derived by hypertrophy from the small cells of the follicular epithelium, but there is very slight distinction between the theca externa and interna. The fibroblast cells and the fibres of the theca show greater development, and in the later stages there is an increase in the number of blood vessels. Extensive ingrowths of connective-tissue septa carry the blood vessels into the luteal tissue, and the fibroblasts penetrate in between the luteal cells. The corpus luteum has a long life in this snake, and signs of the degeneration of luteal cells appear only after the birth of the young.

Fraenkel and Martins (1938) describe the corpus luteum in two species of South American Crotalidae (*Crotalus terrificus* and *Bothrops jararaca*) which are ovo-viviparous, as discoid or elliptical in shape, of soft consistence, and attached to the ovarian wall by a narrow zone, the periphery being free. The colour is yellow in contrast with the translucent appearance of the adjacent follicles. In number they are equal to that of the eggs in the oviducts ; they are absent or rudimentary in young or non-gravid animals. Microscopically they appear as a compact aggregation of granular cells, reminiscent of those in the walls of atretic follicles, much resembling the luteal cells of the corpus luteum of mammals. There is often a central or lateral cavity containing eosinophil material, and several connective-tissue trabeculae leave the wall and penetrate to the interior. Valle and Souza (1942) also find that the number of corpora lutea generally agrees with the number of eggs in the oviducts of ovo-viviparous South American snakes belonging to the genera *Dryophylax* and *Tomodon*. They find that the corpora lutea are less easy to recognise towards the end of gestation.

Rahn (1939) says that at ovulation, in snakes belonging to the genera *Storeria*, *Potamophis*, *Thamnophis* and *Natrix*, the granulosa becomes detached from the theca but remains inside the collapsed follicle, where it soon proliferates and re-establishes connection with the theca interna. The luteal tissue which is apparently derived entirely from the granulosa, almost completely fills the remaining follicular cavity. The theca interna is very active during the formation of the corpus luteum, and supplies supporting fibres, capillaries and blood vessels. The latter penetrate the luteal tissue and become very prominent towards the end of gestation. The completely differentiated organ, which is strikingly similar to that of a mammal, is maintained throughout pregnancy and slowly degenerates after parturition.

Cieslak (1945) describes the corpora lutea of *Thamnophis radix* as persisting during a nine-week gestation period. They regress after parturition in August, leaving corpus luteum scars. This author finds a correlation between the variations

in the cells of the pars anterior of the pituitary and the phases of the reproductive cycle which may be summarised as follows. Spermatogenesis occurs as
a complete wave during the late spring and summer, with most pronounced
activity during June and July. With this the testis reaches its maximum weight
and volume, which may be 990 per cent and 430 per cent, respectively, greater
than the minimum values. Spermatogenesis is pronounced in August, with a
secondary wave in late October. Sperm are stored in the ductus deferens during
hibernation and are used in the following spring. Interstitial cells show seasonal
changes in size and staining reaction. Three macroscopic groups of oöcytes
show differential growth, and are ovulated in successive seasons. In the pituitary
coarse acidophil cells are present throughout the year ; they are abundant during
the period of activity but scattered during hibernation. In both sexes there are
two peaks in the number of basophils ; they have nearly the same seasonal onset
and regression. Regression in spring is correlated with marked gonadal activity,
and in the autumn with oöcyte growth and an increase in interstitial cell size.
The hibernation peaks are similar and cannot be associated with gonadotrophic
activity.

Chelonia

Herlant (1933) states that he has examined the testes and kidneys of tortoises
belonging to the genera *Chrysemis, Emys* and *Testudo*, but he was able to pay little
attention to the sexual cycle. Interstitial tissue was found to be very abundant,
occupying a large part of the testes, and this was the case with animals killed in
both May and December. The terminal segment of the kidney tubules was
a solely mucus-secreting organ both in the male and in the female and at any time
of the year. According to Risley (1933, 1938) the spermatogenetic cycle of the
testis of the musk turtle, *Sternotherus odoratus*, is limited in Michigan to the
summer months, and closely parallels that of the anuran Amphibia. Spermatozoa
are present in the testis from September to May, and pairing may occur in autumn
or spring. A pronounced increase in the size of the epididymis and a corresponding decrease in size of the testis occurs in September at the end of the cycle.
During March, April and May all spermatozoa disappear from the seminal tubules,
and the germinal epithelium is built up in preparation for spermatogenesis.
Spermatogonial divisions occur in small numbers in May and the amount of division increases during June. Primary spermatocytes and maturation divisions
appear after the middle of June, and continue throughout July and August.
Formation of spermatozoa begins late in July, is in full progress in August, and is
practically complete by October. Laboratory specimens usually show an active
spermatogenesis in winter, but it is not probable that a second spermatogenetic
cycle occurs in specimens under normal hibernating conditions. During the autumn
and winter months the sperm are stored mainly in the epididymis, or in the oviducts
of the females. According to Risley's earlier paper (1933) the interstitial cells reach
a maximum in size and number during the autumn, winter and early spring, the
breeding and hibernation periods. Minimum development is associated with
spermatogenetic activity. But in his later communication (1938) he states that
no seasonal changes were observed in the interstitial cells of the testis, and that
no seasonally variable secondary sexual characters are known in turtles. Risley
also examined specimens of *Chelydra serpentina* from Iowa and of *Malaclemys*

centrata from North Carolina, and found no significant differences in the cycle in those species ; he concludes that the cycle is probably essentially similar in many species of Chelonia.

Cagle (1944) found that the female slider turtle, *Pseudemys scripta*, in southern Illinois may be sexually mature when a plastron length of 164 mm. is attained, but that some do not become mature until they reach a length of 230 mm. Old females become incapable of reproducing. In the mature ovary two to three groups of follicles are present and may represent successive clutches of eggs. The annual ovarian cycle is a slow increase in the size of the ovarian follicles resulting in one group reaching the ovulatory stage each season ; under favourable conditions more than one brood may perhaps be deposited in a season. In the steppe tortoise (*Testudo horsfeildi*) Sergeev (1941) finds that sexual maturity is reached by the tenth year, though the secondary sexual characters appear much earlier. The female lays several batches of eggs a year, each consisting of three to four eggs, the total reaching twelve to sixteen a year. Development lasts slightly over three months.

IV. AVES

The fact that the gonads of birds increase enormously in size in passing from the non-breeding to the breeding season has long been known and is commented on above in the first chapter.

Watson (1919) states that in the greenfinch (*Chloris chloris*) spermatogenesis is completed in May, when the testes are at their maximal size. At this season the interstitial cells are stated to be least numerous, but it is not clear whether they are absolutely or only relatively fewer.

Bissonnette (1930a) and Bissonnette and Chapnick (1930) made confirmatory observations for the European starling (*Sturnus vulgaris*) in America. These authors have given detailed accounts of the seasonal changes in the testes, describing both the phases of progression culminating in the spring and the phases of regression which follow. The testes are smallest in November and December, enlarge slowly through January and more rapidly through February and early March, and very rapidly between March 19 and April 1 ; they reach a maximum about April 19 to 23. On the latter date spermatozoa were found free in the lumina of the tubules.

" When the testes were at their smallest size, the cells in the tubules were of three types : one with small oval nuclei, Sertoli cells ; one with small round nuclei, judged to be undifferentiated germ-cells of the germinal epithelium ; and a few cells with larger round nuclei, more certainly germ-cells. From these three sorts, which, because of their inconstancy in relative numbers, are judged to be modifications of a single cell type, are derived all the cell types found during complete spermatogenesis. Interstitial cells are fewest relatively when the activity of the germ-cells is at its height and the birds are most active sexually. Whether they are converted into connective-tissue cells as the tubules are dilated could not be determined. They gave no indications of any secretory activity in their appearance at any time."

These authors suggest the possibility that the interstitial cells may nevertheless act as stimulators of the sexual and reproductive processes of the birds, releasing these activities and then disappearing while the activities go on, and reappearing again as the reproductive processes subside.

In a third paper (Bissonnette, 1930b) in which Bissonnette describes the regressive changes, it is stated that the testes become rapidly smaller in June. There is

" A disappearance of the later stages of the germ-cells in spermatogenesis from the seminiferous tubules in reverse order of their appearance in the progressive part of the sexual cycle. The cytoplasmic contents of the tubules become vacuolated and either walls or mucous strands appear to form round each nucleus with its attendant vacuo- lated cytoplasm as the later stages of the germ-cells undergo degeneration. These walls or strands stain blue with the aniline blue of Mallory's triple connective-tissue stain, like connective-tissue fibres or mucus. Interstitial cells are in inverse ratio to the degree of completeness of spermatogenesis. They are indistinguishable from connective-tissue cells at the height of the breeding season and are numerous, with rounded nuclei, when regression is evident in the tubule contents. In many, if not all, respects they behave like fibroblasts. The tunicae propriae of the tubules thicken considerably as the tubules shrink, and their nuclei assume the rounded appearance of interstitial nuclei as well as the oval and flattened shapes of the connective-tissue-cell nuclei. These nuclei are placed in a close ring just outside the connective-tissue fibre layer of the tubule wall. This thickening, with its nuclear changes, tends to disappear in many testes in late autumn and the tunic thins out to the condition found in young birds."

Crouch (1939) found a similar cycle in another passerine bird, *Phainopepla nitens lepida*. The testes gradually increased in size from a minimum of 1 mm. in length in November to a maximum of 8 mm. in May. No rapid increase in size was found until towards the end of March, and few spermatozoa were present in the lumina of the tubules until the second week in May. In the winter testis the tunica albuginea and the tunica propria are thick, the tubules are small and there is abundant inter-tubular material, chiefly connective tissue with a few interstitial cells. There are no lumina in the tubules, which in section show a ring of spermatogonia along the basement membrane. In February the testes are about 2 mm. in length, and lumina are beginning to appear in some of the tubules. The tunica albuginea and propria are thinner, interstitial material is less abundant, and spermatogonia are more plentiful. At the height of the breeding season the tubules contain all stages of spermatogenesis and clumps of mature sperm. There is little intertubular tissue ; only occasional connective tissue or interstitial cells are present. In early July regression has started with the vacuolation of some of the spermatogenetic cells and the appearance of debris in the lumina of the tubules. Later in the month complete disorganisation seems to set in. All stages of spermatogenesis are still to be found, but scattered at random throughout the tubules, the only regular feature being a ring of cells along the basement membrane. The tunica albuginea and propria are again thickening, and the interstitial elements are becoming prominent. At the end of the month, by which time the young are fledged, the testes are about 2 mm. in length, the tunica albuginea is as thick as in winter, and the lumina of the tubules have practically disappeared. A ring of nuclei lie along the basement membrane, and intertubular tissue is increasing in abundance.

The annual cycle in the male white-crowned sparrow (*Zonotrichia leucophrys*) of the Pacific seaboard of North America has been studied by Blanchard (1941). The changes in this species correspond more or less closely with those described in other passerine birds. In the birds of the southern subspecies (*Z. leucophrys nuttalli*), which is resident in California, this author found considerable year to year variation in the date of onset of the different stages of the cycle and was able to correlate it with climatic factors, especially with the temperature during the winter, which controls directly or indirectly the time when testicular development begins.   He adds, " light change is absent or negligible during the earlier part of development and cannot serve to initiate it.   The fact that so much early growth and change take place without the aid of any considerable increase in light hardly suggests the probability of the importance of light in later stages." · In the northern subspecies (*Z. leucophrys pugetensis*), which is migratory and may breed a thousand miles north of its winter quarters, the annual cycle is identical in histology though not in date or rate.   The bulk of the male gonad growth is divided more or less evenly between the flight north and the ensuing ten days on the breeding ground. Blanchard finds that it is impossible to say that spring migration is regulated and timed by rising temperatures and increasing daily periods of light.   Migration occurs in correlation with physiological development which has been proceeding for a long time and is in some degree controlled by remote climatic conditions. " Testis change has been in progress for at least eight weeks, moult for about four weeks, and the accumulation of fat for six weeks.   It is logical to conclude from the constancy of these correlative conditions that migration is not a last-moment effect of contemporaneous . . . climatic conditions."

In the red-winged blackbird, *Agelaius phoeniceus*, Wright and Wright (1944) state that the testes of the young are smaller throughout the year than those of the adults.   The testes of both adult and year-old birds undergo a period of rapid growth in the spring, but the maximum size attained by the testes of the young birds is two-thirds of that of the adults, and is reached three weeks later.   The testes of the young birds are actively producing spermatozoa, but most of these birds do not establish territories, and thus do not breed.   The testes of the adults during the quiescent period from August to January are larger, the seminiferous tubules have greater diameters, and there is more intertubular tissue than in the testes of the young.   A significant correlation was found between the state of regression of the testes and the progress of the post-nuptial moult.

Riley (1937) found in the house sparrow, *Passer domesticus*, in addition to the annual cycle, a diurnal spermatogenetic cycle during the breeding season.   He found that spermatogenetic activity occurs during darkness with a greatest frequency of cell division between 2 A.M. and 4 A.M.   The day temperature of the body in this bird was found to average 110° F. and the night temperature 103° to 104° F., and the reduced night temperature is essential for spermatogenetic activity.   A few mitotic figures were found in the testes during the day if the temperature of the bird was artificially lowered for several hours in full daylight. Conversely, enforced exercise during the night, with consequent high temperature, retards spermatogenesis.   Riley suggests that the dependence of spermatogenetic activity on low body temperature is comparable to the necessity for scrotal position of the testes in many mammals.

Witschi (1945) made quantitative studies on the seasonal development of the deferent ducts in passerine birds, using starlings and the paradise wydah (*Steganura paradisea*).   He concluded that the increase in weight of the deferent ducts during the breeding season is a composite of three factors : hormone stimulated growth of the walls ; accumulation of spermatic fluid in the ducts which serve as seminal

receptacles ; and growth, caused by mechanical stretching, of the epithelium
lining the lumen of the ducts.   Injection experiments indicated that the maximal
concentration of androgens in the blood of male starlings is not in excess of that
maintained by mammalian all-year breeders.   These seasonal breeders are
characterised mainly by the complete or nearly complete cessation of sex hormone
production during the eclipse season.

The periodic changes in the gonads and the factors controlling them are further
discussed in Chapter 13, where the researches of Rowan are described.

Burger (1938) has investigated the cyclic changes in the thyroid and adrenal
cortex of the male starling.   He found that there was no correlation between the
spermatogenetic cycle and the thyroid except a tendency to colloid resorption
at the mating period.   The adrenal cortex at spermatogenesis presented a characteristically uniform appearance with fully elaborated spongiocytes.   Bloom,
Bloom and McLean (1941) record that the bone marrow of pigeons undergoes
a series of striking transformations during the egg-laying cycle, all apparently
correlated with the need for storage and transport of calcium for the formation
of the egg shell.   While the follicle is maturing in the ovary during the pre-
ovulatory phase there is intense formation of medullary bone.   During the calcification of the first egg there is rapid destruction of bone, and this continues for
a short time after the first egg is laid.   Within a few hours after the first egg being
laid there is a return to bone formation, this process continuing until shortly after
the second egg reaches the shell gland.   Then follows a second period of bone
destruction, beginning while the second egg is in the shell gland, and continuing
on a diminishing scale after the second egg is laid, until all of the medullary bone
disappears.   Clavert (1942a, b) and Clavert and Benoit (1942) find that the administration of oestrogens has a strong osteogenetic effect and also raises the blood
calcium level.   They add that the daily injection of folliculin during several weeks
induces intense osteogenesis in the male pigeon, more than in the female at the
time of laying.   Kyes and Potter (1934) report that in the pigeon there is extreme
ossification if the ovary contains a follicle over 10 mm. in diameter, none if the
ovary contains no follicle greater than 2 mm. in diameter, and some ossification
if follicles of intermediate sizes are present.   On the other hand, Riddle, Rauch
and Smith (1944) state that it is only in virgin female pigeons close to the ovulation
of the first egg in life, and in carefully selected laying birds, that a significant
correlation between follicle size and degree of ossification can be found.   But
Kirschbaum and his colleagues (1939) report that

" The bones of adult female sparrows which were laying eggs during May were found
to contain osseous spicules in the marrow cavities.   Females trapped with their young at
the time when the latter leave the nest did not show this condition.   Unless the ovary
was near maximal activity, or eggs were found in the oviducts, hyperossification of the
long bones did not occur.   Hyperossification of the long bones represents a seasonal
cyclic physiological change in the female sparrow dependent on seasonal ovarian activity."

Bissonnette and Zujko (1936) have studied the progressive changes in the
ovary of the starling from December to the end of April, when ovulation first
takes place.   They found that in December, February and March the ovaries had,
respectively, three, four and five different sets of follicles, all the follicles in a set
being approximately similar in their degrees of development.   In April there

were also follicles in a sixth or final period of growth, that is, follicles apparently nearly ready to rupture.   Bissonnette and Zujko found further that :

" The number of follicles falling in a set or class decreases as the size of follicle in the class increases, and the larger the follicles in a set, the greater are the variations in size among them.   From December 7 to March 25, the average rate of growth of the largest follicle is about 0·009 mm. increase in diameter per day.   From March 25 to ovulation, the final growth period, after the follicle has reached a diameter of 1·65 mm., the average rate of growth of the largest follicle is about 0·285 mm. in diameter per day, about 31·6 times that of the preceding period.

" (Stage 1).   Primordial follicles (about 0·037 mm. diameter) contain the germinal vesicle and thin strands throughout the oögonial protoplasm.   The strands then thicken and multiply throughout the protoplasm, and collect near the centre of the follicle to form the yolk nucleus, a denser mass with rays extending into the surrounding protoplasm.   In follicles from about 0·04 to 0·2 mm. in diameter, the yolk-nucleus material spreads throughout the protoplasm of the maturing germ-cell.

" (Stage 2).   In follicles 0·2–0·5 mm. in diameter, a clearing develops either in the central region or in small regions scattered throughout the material of the yolk nucleus and expands until all of the material characteristic of the yolk nucleus has disappeared, leaving a central zone of clear substance surrounded by a homogeneous peripheral zone.

" (Stage 3).   In follicles from 0·5 to 1·20 mm. in diameter, from the April 3 ovaries, vacuolation begins at the periphery of the central zone and proceeds centripetally.

" (Stage 4).   When the central zone has become completely vacuolated, alternate concentric zones of small and of larger vacuoles are apparent in sections.   These are the result of unequal rates of growth of the vacuoles in these zones, the smaller ones having grown less rapidly than the larger.   Finally, however, the zonation tends to disappear as the smaller vacuoles in one type of zone approach those of the other in size.

" (Stage 5).   The appearance of round granules within the vacuoles next the peripheral zone suggests that precipitation of the original substance or ' clear yolk ' takes place.   These precipitation granules are referred to as ' white yolk.'   The fact that they appear in smaller follicles in more mature ovaries indicates that deposition of white yolk is not correlated with size of follicle directly, but with degree of development or maturity of the ovary as a whole.

" (Stage 6).   White yolk is laid down from the periphery inward, and, as in the case of vacuoles, thick zones of large granules are separated by thin zones of smaller ones, with the smallest granules at the centre of the follicle.   This indicates that the deposition of white yolk in a vacuole is related to the condition of the substance in it rather than to its size merely.   When white yolk granules have reached a diameter of about 0·016 mm., the material in the vacuole surrounding the granules becomes concentrated enough to stain. The granule loses its spherical form and either breaks up into many small granules, which mass together irregularly in an eccentric position in the vacuole or breaks up into small granules evenly dispersed throughout the vacuole.   These vacuoles are then referred to as ' transition forms ' between white and yellow yolk.   Their small granules then break up into minute particles evenly distributed through the vacuoles which then become the polyhedral bodies of yellow yolk.

" (Stage 7).   Near the periphery and separated from it by a thin zone of white yolk granules and transition forms, appears a zone of polyhedral bodies of yellow yolk with a zone of transition forms on its inner side next the white yolk which fills the centre of the follicle.

" (Stage 8).   Then another thick zone of transition-forms develops from white yolk farther toward the centre of the follicle, separated from the polyhedral-body and transition-form zones, previously formed, by a thin zone of white yolk granules.

" (Stage 9).   In the two largest follicles of the April 20 ovary, are three concentric zones of yellow yolk polyhedral bodies separated by zones of white yolk granules.   This results from conversion of transition forms into polyhedral bodies of yellow yolk.

" As the follicle increases in size, its peripheral zone decreases and eventually disappears, except in the blastodisc region.   In follicles nearing ovulation, the granulosa layer either disappears or becomes considerably reduced."

(For further information on oögenesis *see* Brambell (1925) and Chapter 5 below, *also* Conrad and Scott (1938), and Kummerlöwe (1930), for a comparative study of the female reproductive system in birds.)

Van Oordt (1928, 1931) and van Oordt and Bruyns (1938) in a series of studies on the state of the gonads and its relation to plumage changes in " summering " birds have described briefly the histology of the testes and ovaries in certain species of waders (knot, godwit, oyster-catcher, etc.) which migrate northwards for the purpose of seasonal breeding.   The progressive seasonal development of the interstitial tissue, as well as spermatogenetic tissue in both adults and young are included in these studies.   Bullough (1942b) finds that there are differences between the sedentary British starlings (*Sturnus vulgaris*) and the migratory continental birds, both subspecies wintering in Britain, in the seasonal variation of the reproductive systems of the male and female.   The gonads of the first year British and continental starlings begin to grow in February, but the rate of growth is greater in the British bird than in the continental.   The gonads of the adult British starlings do not regress so far in summer as those of the continental birds, and they start to grow precociously in early autumn.   The gonads of the adult continental starlings do not begin to grow until January or February, the time when the gonad growth of the British birds is accelerated.   In February and March the gonads of the adult British birds grow much more rapidly than those of the continental birds.   These differences in the degrees of regression and the times and rates of growth of the gonads of the British and continental starlings are reflected in the accessory sexual organs.   In the adult British males the rete testis and vas deferens show signs of growth in autumn, and although the other accessory sexual organs, apparently requiring a higher rate of sex hormone secretion, do not begin to grow until January or February, their growth is earlier and faster than that of the accessory sexual organs of the continental birds.

" In the adult British female the oviduct enlarges in autumn, and in some individuals the various organs of the Wolffian system also show signs of growth.   It is apparent that the ovary of the adult British female in autumn secretes both male and female sex hormones, but the amount of male sex hormone secreted by different individuals is very variable.   The secondary sexual characters of the starling are either permanent or vary according to the state of the reproductive cycle.   The browner colour of the iris of the male and the yellowish colour of that of the female are permanent distinguishing characters, and, in addition, the throat and breast feathers of the first year or adult male are narrower and more pointed than those of a female of the same age.   The colour of the beak is a varying secondary sexual character.   Owing to the secretion of the male sex hormone by the testes and ovaries of the adult British starlings in autumn, the beak turns from dark grey to yellow during this season.   No similar change in the beaks of the continental birds is noted until January or February.   When the beak is yellow, a grey base to both mandibles is a distinguishing feature of the male.   The behaviour of both races of birds was studied, and it was found that, coincident with the growth of the gonads in autumn, the adult British starlings showed sexual behaviour and close attachment to their nesting sites.   The habit of roosting in nest holes is seen all the year round in some

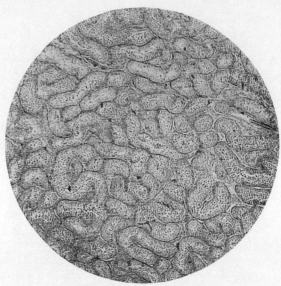

Fig. 3. 7—Gentoo penguin. T.S. testis. × 40. Stage before birds congregate at their rookeries. Many spermatocytes dividing but more mature stages absent. Tubules mostly occluded. (B. Roberts.)

birds of this race, and it becomes almost universal in early January. No similar behaviour was seen in the continental birds in this country, and none is described in the case of those birds which remain on the continent. At the end of February, when the gonads of the continental starlings are actively growing, the males begin to sing, and northward migration commences, and on the continent interest in nesting sites is first reported. It is evident that, as these two distinct races of starlings live together in the British Islands during autumn and winter, the differences in their reproductive cycles must be inherent and not dictated by environmental variations."

Bullough (1943) suggests that resident British birds are insular forms derived from the main continental species which were, and still are, migratory. He thinks that the southward migration urge, which is either induced or allowed by a deficiency of sex hormone, has been overcome by autumn activity of that part of the anterior pituitary gland which causes gonad growth and sex hormone secretion, and that this explains the otherwise incongruous appearance of sex display in autumn. Because of gonad growth the attachment to the nesting sites, territories, or areas is sustained throughout the entire autumn and winter. At the approach of the breeding season, when gonad growth is greatly accelerated, sexual behaviour merely becomes more diverse and intense, and the connection with the nesting places is further strengthened.

In a later paper (Bullough, 1945a) the same author expresses the opinion that the difference in the reproductive rhythm, which distinguishes the two races of starling in Europe, has proved sufficiently powerful to preserve their separate identities on the American continent for a period of fifty-five years of most

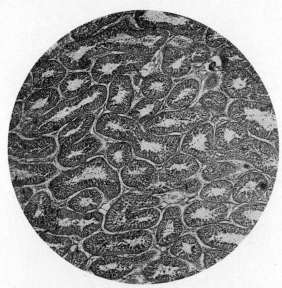

Fig. 3. 8—Gentoo penguin. T.S. testis. × 40. Early courtship activities at rookery. All stages to sperms with wavy tail, mostly held in clumps. Well defined lumen in nearly all tubules with small number of free spermatozoa. (B. Roberts.)

considerable increase in numbers and the most active spread of the species. All this time the breeding ranges of the two races have been either identical or have overlapped, but at least in the neighbourhood of Montreal, such mixing as may have taken place is inconsiderable. Bullough (1945b) gives an extensive review of what is known about the effects of sex hormones upon the breeding and social behaviour, and upon the migration of birds, in which further details may be found.

Roberts (1940) finds that in the Gentoo penguin (*Pygoscelis papua*) at South Georgia the testes (Figs. *3*. 7 to 12) are smallest from early December until late September. In mid-October they rapidly increase in size to approximately ten times

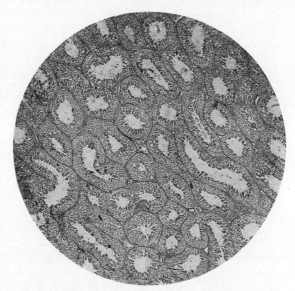

Fig. *3*. 9—Gentoo penguin. T.S. testis. × 40. Nest building. All stages present. Made incomplete attempt to copulate. Great nuclear activity in spermatocytes : many spermatids and a few free spermatozoa present. Some tubules still without lumen. (B. Roberts.)

their previous volume. The greater part of this increase in volume is made up by increase in the diameter and contents of the tubules. The volume of the testis, however, bears no direct relation to the stage of development reached, for the kind and arrangement of the cells within the tubules may be similar in testes of widely differing volumes taken on the same day. Free spermatozoa first appear in very small quantities at the beginning of October. The awakening of copulatory ability is not coincident with the first appearance of free spermatozoa in the tubules of the testis. Spermatogenesis may be completed in birds which are as yet unable to complete the sexual act, and copulation may occur long before spermatogenesis is complete.

The period during which free spermatozoa are available lasts for at least six weeks, and extends from the time when nest material is collected until incubation is well advanced, in the middle of November. None of the sections examined showed complete inactivity, but by December there

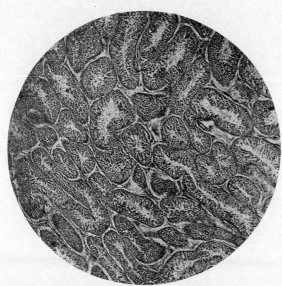

Fig. *3*. 10—Gentoo penguin. T.S. testis. × 40. Seen copulating. All stages present with many spermatozoa free in the lumen of most tubules. (B. Roberts.)

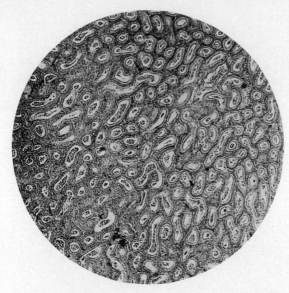

Fig. 3. 11—Gentoo penguin. T.S. testis. × 40. With chicks in the second down. A few spermatogonia show some activity. Very few spermatocytes. Lumen present in most tubules with sloughed-off degenerate cells in the centre. (B. Roberts.)

were no spermatids or later stages present in the testis. The diameter of the tubules is greatest at the height of spermatogenesis. There is no appreciable reduction in the number of tubules, nor a suppression of spermatogenesis during the early stages of incubation. Birds collected on any one day in the breeding season showed a considerable variation in gonad size. In over a hundred cases examined the left testis was larger than the right, the asymmetry ranging between 1·3 to 1 and 4 to 1. Even when widely different in size the two testes are equally functional as far as spermatogenetic activity is concerned. The amount of intertubular tissue present varies, but Roberts was unable to find any correlation between its quantity or quality and the stages of the sexual cycle. Examination of a fairly large series of ovaries from female Gentoo penguins captured shortly before egg-laying gave no indication of any marked behaviour phase correlated with the size of the more advanced follicle.

Testicular asymmetry has also been found by Test (1944) in the American woodpeckers *Colaptes cafer* and, to a lesser extent, in *C. auratus* and *C. chrysoides*. In these the left testis is always longer and more slender than the right, and decidedly different in shape. The lateral angulation of the left testis is individually variable ; it is usually greater in breeding adults than in juveniles and non-breeding birds. The testicular asymmetry is apparently a normal inherent condition, but it is suggested that the degree of asymmetry is influenced, at least in part, by the anatomical environment of the growing gonad.

In most species of birds there is only one ovary—the left ; the right ovary persists

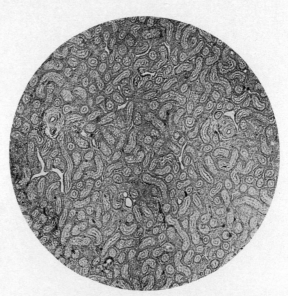

Fig. 3. 12—Gentoo penguin. T.S. testis. × 40. Moult just completed. Advanced retrogression, but some signs of activity in a few spermatogonia. Very few spermatocytes. Tubules mainly full of debris. (B. Roberts.)

merely as a vestige and the right oviduct similarly. In various species of hawks, however, both ovaries may persist, but the right oviduct is vestigial (Kummerlöwe, 1930 ; Witschi, 1932 ; Fitzpatrick, 1933 ; Stanley, 1937 ; Shaw, 1938). Stanley and Witschi (1940) summarise what is known on this point. They report that their quantitative studies on the sex glands of adult hawks prove that as a rule the right ovary is largest in the Accipitrinae. It is progressively smaller in the Falconinae, Butoeninae and Cathartinae ; in the Strigidae none was ever found. The species with the smallest right ovaries might often also show a marked reduction in the size of the right testes of the males. These authors also refer to the only known case of normal ovulation from the right ovary in a bird. A female *Accipiter gentilis* was shot while sitting on three eggs. Two ovulated follicles were found in the left, and one in the right ovary. The egg from the right ovary had passed down the left oviduct. Follicles of the right ovary often become atretic before attaining full maturity. Although it is generally assumed that the stock of oögonia laid down in the ovaries during embryonic life is not subsequently added to, Bullough and Gibbs (1941) have brought forward evidence which indicates that mitotic activity may occur in the germinal epithelium of adult animals, including birds. They find that the mitoses are at a maximum during a very short period following ovulation, and suggest that they may be stimulated by the oestrogens in the follicular fluid which is spilt over the surface of the ovary when a follicle bursts.

The changes which occur in the egg-producing apparatus of the fowl.—In the growth of the egg, which in the fowl as in all other birds contains much yolk, there are two main stages. The first stage begins in embryonic life, and at the time of hatching the ovary contains from 3,000 to 4,500 ova.

The several thousand ova present in the ovary of the hen at birth grow extremely slowly up to a diameter of 6 mm. When the hen approaches sexual maturity some of the ova pass into a second stage of growth which is very rapid. The ova at this period increase in diameter at the rate of 4 mm. a day. Thus, the 6 mm. diameter size develops to complete ripeness in only about seven days. During this second stage the ovum projects from the ovarian surface. It is enclosed by a capsule, the theca folliculi, which is attached to the ovary by a pedicle. This capsule is highly vascularised but has on its outer surface a clear area called the stigma. When the ovum which is now commonly called " the yolk " is ready to be shed in the process of ovulation, the capsule splits along the line of the stigma and the yolk or egg surrounded by the vitelline membrane is set free into the cavity surrounding the ovary (Halnan, 1936).

The occurrence of a definite periodicity in egg production in correlation with seasonal sexual activity, not only in birds in a state of nature, but also in the domestic fowl has been referred to and briefly described in the first chapter (p. 24). In conjunction with the marked variation which occurs in the size of the ovary in connection with the onset of breeding, there is a corresponding change in the size of the oviduct.

As already described in Chapter 2, the oviduct is divided into five main divisions, each having its own particular functions. There are (1) the infundibulum which starts as a funnel for receiving the egg and passes on to a part which secretes the two twisted cords of dense albumen known as the chalazae, (2) the main albumen-secreting region, (3) the isthmus which secretes the shell membrane,

(4) the isthmo-uterine junction, a transitional part which produces a fluid secretion, (5) the uterus in which the organic shell matrix is formed as well as thin albumen and the calcified shell, and (6) the vagina which opens into the cloaca. (Bradley 1915, 1928 ; Asmundson, 1931 ; Richardson, 1935. The last two give full bibliographies.)

The changes that occur in these regions as related more particularly by Richardson (1935) may now be briefly described. (*See also* Pearl and Curtis, 1912, 1914.)

The epithelium of the infundibulum is either ciliated or non-ciliated and the latter secretes a fluid during the period of activity. The funnel wall below the epithelium is richly vascular, and it has been suggested that through engorgement and erection and dilation, after ovulation, it serves the function of promoting the passage of the large-size yolk. Moreover, Coste (1874) stated long ago that the infundibulum clasps the follicle before ovulation and probably exerts pressure. The chalaziferous region of the infundibulum has also mucous epithelial cells lining the lumen and the mucus secreted serves as a lubricant. The mucous epithelium is folded after the manner of a mammalian Fallopian tube. There are in addition tubular glands which secrete the chalazae. During the active phase the epithelium of these hypertrophies and the apical cell walls rupture as the secretion is poured out, whereas in the empty stage the cells have clear unbroken margins.

The albumen region possesses a ciliated epithelium and a non-ciliated epithelium of goblet cells ; the latter secretes the glycoproteins of egg-white. There are also tubular glands which secrete the ovalbumen. When the glands are active the secretion shown is comparatively homogeneous and dark brown in staining. It forms a continuous stream or else a series of droplets which later coalesce. After the egg has passed down this part of the oviduct and into the uterus the presence of albumen in the glands and crypts of this region indicates that this substance is still being produced in some quantity. At this time the peripheral glands are granular in type, a condition which Richardson has shown to indicate the completion of the secretory phase several hours previously. In the resting state, prior to the recommencement of a fresh cycle of egg formation, the majority of the glands stain lightly, the glandular epithelium undergoing regeneration, but Richardson says it is doubtful whether complete regeneration is effected in all the glands before a fresh secretory phase is reached. There are, however, three fairly well marked stages of maximum secretion, regeneration of the gland cells, and rest, prior to the beginning of a new egg-cycle (cf. Surface, 1912).

As deposited upon the egg the albumen is differentiated in three layers, an outer layer, a middle thick layer and an inner thin layer immediately surrounding the yolk (Halnan, 1936). The chalazae become anchored to the thick layer.

In the isthmus apart from the lining epithelial cells which are partly secretory, presumably for purposes of lubrication, there are likewise tubular glands which give rise to the ovo-keratin material forming the fibrous two-layered shell membrane. (There is also a ciliated lining epithelium.) The secretion of the tubular glands exudes in the form of fine granules which coalesce into threads or fibre-like strands which come to project into the oviducal lumen. The secretory activity of the isthmal glands is slight as compared with those of the albumen region and the epithelial cells do not undergo three distinct secretory phases. The shell membrane commences to be deposited upon the naked egg-white as a thin layer as soon as the egg comes into contact with the isthmal wall and the inner layer of the shell membrane would then seem to be formed. The egg next becomes stationary for a time in this region and increased activity on the part of all the isthmal glands probably accounts for the formation of the outer layer.

In the isthmo-uterine junction some of the ciliated epithelial cells are granulated and are believed to contribute to the shell matrix. The tubular glands produce a thin albumen during the phase of activity.

Uterine activity appears to consist in the formation of the shell matrix with its mammillae and cuticle, the secretion of thin albumen added to the egg-white and the calcification of the shell. The mammillae are small dense ovoid bodies with a concentrically layered structure and are produced by cells belonging to modified epithelial pits. The cuticle is formed by basal vacuolated cells of the lining epithelium, and the shell matrix by apical ciliated, finely granular cells. There are further non-ciliated lining cells which secrete a lubricating substance. The tubular glands are uniform and faintly granular ; they secrete the thin fluid albumen, transporting calcium as well. It is evident that the uterine region enters into marked activity as soon as the egg enters it. There is every reason to suppose that the uterine mucosa lies always in intimate contact with the developing shell during the secretory process apart from transient periods when muscular activity may lead to a reorientation of different areas of epithelium in relation to the surface of the egg membrane (Richardson, 1935).

The epithelium of the vagina does not show any evidence of the secretory phases shown by the uterus. There are few tubular glands in this region which appear to be mucous in character and probably have a lubricating function, their secretory activity coinciding with egg-laying (Richardson, 1935). According to Asmundson (1931) the vagina takes no part in the formation of the hen's egg, but Halnan (1936) states that the shell cuticle and pigment are finally formed there.[1]

During the period of sexual activity when the ovary is fully functional the discharge of an ovum or ripe yolk, that is to say, ovulation, takes place from 14 to 75 minutes after the laying of a previous egg. According to the observations of Warren and Scott (1935) the average time is 30·7 minutes. (*See also* Conrad and Scott, 1938.) When the yolk comes into contact with the infundibulum, the rim of the latter undergoes wave-like recessions and advances over the yolk, which then becomes engulfed in the funnel. The yolk is so loosely enclosed in the vitelline membrane that it can assume the shape of the cavity into which it falls. The process of engulfment depends partly upon the original position of the yolk in the ovary ; it may take 25 minutes. When it is complete rhythmic

---

[1] Hill and Hill (1933) have described the oviduct of the egg-laying monotreme mammals, which although differing from the oviduct of birds is nevertheless broadly comparable as to its division into different regions. For about two-thirds of the total length of the oviduct in *Echidna* and *Ornithorhynchus* there are no tubular glands and the secretion of the albumen is associated with non-ciliated cells of the lining epithelium upon the upper region. Richardson, however, suggests that the secretion in this part may be a glycoprotein and not true albumen. The main glandular part is comparable to the fowl's isthmus and is similar in formation. The uterus is similar to that of the fowl, but the final layers of the egg shell which may be homologised with the shell matrix and cuticle come from the tubular glands and not from the lining epithelium. (*See* Hill and Hill, 1933, and Richardson, 1935.)

contractions are set up in the oviduct, these being serpentine in the infundibulum and wave-like further on. These muscular contractions propel the egg along the interior of the oviduct. Through their agency the yolk travels down in spirals, the albumen being wrapped in layers round the yolk as it passes forward in the albumen region which is by far the largest part of the duct.

The times of passage in the several regions are as follows : infundibulum 18 minutes, albumen region 174 minutes, isthmus 74 minutes, uterus and vagina 20 hours 40 minutes. (Warren and Scott, 1935 ; Halnan, 1936.) Asmundson (1931) states that the egg remains in the uterus for longer than 17 hours.

As regards the shape of the egg Asmundson considers that it is determined chiefly by the amount of albumen secreted in the albumen region, the calibre of

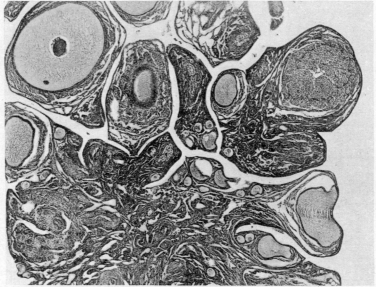

Fig. 3. 13—Manx shearwater. *Puffinus puffinus*. T.S. ovary (July). × 44.
Follicles in different stages of development, the older ones pedunculated.
A corpus luteum is present on the right of the photograph.

the lumen of the albumen part and the isthmus, and the muscular activity of these parts. The egg in the uterus is exposed to continuous waves of contraction in the walls, and these eventually force it out into the vagina, the exit being guarded by sphincter muscles. As a consequence the egg is usually laid with the broad end foremost. The general shape so formed may be more or less altered in the uterus which, with the isthmus, gives each egg its particular shape. Asmundson remarks further that the amount of albumen secreted by the oviduct must depend partly on the size of the bird and on the size of the oviduct.

The ovary of some species of birds, especially those of the order Procellarii-formes, such as the Fulmar petrel (Wynne-Edwards, 1939) and the Manx shear-water (Fig. 3. 13), are noteworthy for the large numbers of atretic follicles which they contain. These atretic follicles are filled with large cells apparently derived from the follicular epithelium. Similar cells fill the follicle after it is ruptured at ovulation, but it is uncertain whether the bodies thus produced persist for any considerable time. The ruptured follicle in most species of birds is usually described as disappearing within two to three weeks. Pearl and Boring (1918) describe the formation of a corpus luteum in the ovary of the domestic fowl. They find that the theca interna of the undischarged follicle contains nests of " lutear " cells. After ovulation the follicle is greatly reduced in size and the granulosa is expelled. The cavity is then invaded by a migration of the " lutear " cells, which become filled with luteal pigment. Loyez (1905) describes atresia as occurring by the thecal elements of the follicle invading the yolk from all sides after degeneration of the germinal vesicle. The invasion is followed by the penetration of capillaries. Resorption starts peripherally and progresses inwards, the atretic follicle being ultimately represented by a knot of connective tissue. But Fell (1924) states that the " luteal " cells of the bird ovary are derived from the medullary cords of the embryo, and thinks that Pearl and Boring are mistaken in homologising the " luteal " islets with the cells of the mammalian corpus luteum, because the numerous vacuolated cells of the discharged and large atretic follicles are found to be mainly the product of fatty degeneration of ordinary connective-tissue elements, and the yellow pigment seems to be derived from aborting blood vessels. This pigment is regarded as haemotoidin and is not found in true luteal cells. The regression of the post-ovulatory follicle has also been studied in the Argentine cowbird, *Molothrus bonariensis*, by Davis (1942b), who regards this structure as analogous to, but not homologous with, the mammalian corpus luteum because there is no proliferation or hypertrophy of the granulosa or theca and because the structure rapidly regresses and undergoes phagocytosis after ovulation. The regression occurs in distinct phases. During the process the granulosa becomes vacuolated and phagocytosed. The basement membrane becomes greatly hypertrophied and then disappears. The theca interna and externa deposit collagenous fibres and later become phagocytosed and eliminated. As regression continues the follicle decreases until merely a few vacuolated cells and phagocytes remain. The dense connective tissue in theca interna and externa becomes very conspicuous as two distinct layers, and then gradually disappears.

There is another type of atresia, first described by Rowan (1930) in *Junco hyemalis*, in which the follicle bursts into the stroma of the ovary, closely resembling the condition described in *Ornithorhynchus* by Hill and Gatenby (1926). It has since been found in many other species of birds by Davis (1942a, 1944), who points out that this type of atresia occurs only in large eggs from which a vast quantity of yolk must be eliminated. These burst atretic follicles bear some resemblance, particularly in later stages, to post-ovulatory follicles. The old burst atretic follicle is usually circular in cross section, but the post-ovulatory follicle is ellipsoid, and the residue of the yolk is visible outside the theca of the burst follicle. Further, the ovulation point of the ovulated follicle clearly opens through the mesothelium, but the break of the burst atretic follicle occurs through all layers except the mesothelium. Atresia takes place in stages, starting with convolution of the granulosa and the extrusion of the yolk. Phagocytosis then begins and eliminates the yolk, and the granulosa cells are no longer arranged in bands. The follicle then remains as merely a group of phagocytes surrounded by dense connective tissue, and at the end of atresia only a small body of phagocytes is left.

Bibliography

ADAMS, A. E. (1940). Sexual conditions in *Triturus viridescens*. III. The reproductive cycle of the adult aquatic form of both sexes. *Amer. J. Anat.*, **66**, 235.

ALEXANDER, G. (1932). Bidder's organ in *Bufo melanostictus* Schneider. *Copeia*, 1932, 78.

—— (1933). Secondary sexual characters of *Bufo melanostictus* Schneider. *Copeia*, **1933**, 204.

ALEXANDER, S. S., & BELLERBY, C. W. (1935). The effect of captivity upon the reproductive cycle of the South African clawed toad (*Xenopus laevis*). *J. exp. Biol.*, **12**, 306.

—— —— (1938). Experimental studies on the sexual cycle of the South African clawed toad (*Xenopus laevis*), I. *J. exp. Biol.*, **15**, 74.

ALLENDE, I. L. C. DE (1939). Cycle sexuel du crapaud *Bufo arenarum* femelle. *C.R. Soc. Biol.*, *Paris*, **130**, 676.

ALTLAND, P. D. (1941). Annual reproductive cycle of the male fence lizard. *J. Elisha Mitchell sci. Soc.*, **57**, 73.

APLINGTON, H. W., Jr. (1942). Correlative cyclical changes in the hypophysis and gonads of *Necturus maculosus* Rafinesque. I. The male. *Amer. J. Anat.*, **70**, 201.

ARON, M. (1924). Recherches morphologiques et expérimentales sur le déterminisme des caractères sexuels mâles chez les Urodèles. *Arch. Biol.*, *Paris*, **34**, 1.

—— (1926). Recherches morphologiques et expérimentales sur le déterminisme des caractères sexuels secondaires mâles chez les Anoures. *Arch. Biol.*, *Paris*, **36**, 1.

ASMUNDSON, V. S. (1931). The formation of the hen's egg. *Sci. Agric.*, **11**, 1.

BAILEY, R. J. (1933). The ovarian cycle in the viviparous teleost *Xiphophorus Helleri*. *Biol. Bull.*, *Wood's Hole*, **64**, 206.

BARGMANN, W. (1939). Über intrafolliculäre Blutüngen in der Schilddrüse der Selachier. *Anat. Anz.*, **88**, 41.

BELLERBY, C. W. (1938). Experimental studies on the sexual cycle of the South African clawed toad (*Xenopus laevis*), II. *J. exp. Biol.*, **15**, 82.

—— & HOGBEN, L. (1938). Experimental studies on the sexual cycle of the South African clawed toad (*Xenopus laevis*), III. *J. exp. Biol.*, **15**, 91.

BENOIT, J., KEHL, R., & LEPORTOIS, M. (1942). Sur l'interstitielle du testicule chez le discoglosse. *C.R. Soc. Biol.*, *Paris*, **136**, 522.

BERGMAN, A. M. (1943). The breeding habits of sea snakes. *Copeia*, **1943**, 156.

BHADURI, J. L. (1932). Observations on the urino-genital system of the tree-frogs of the genus *Rhacophorus* Kuhl, with remarks on their breeding habits. *Anat. Anz.*, **74**, 289.

BISSONNETTE, T. H. (1930a). Studies on the sexual cycle in birds, I. *Amer. J. Anat.*, **45**, 289.

—— (1930b). Studies on the sexual cycle in birds, III. *Amer. J. Anat.*, **46**, 477.

—— & CHAPNICK, M. H. (1930). Studies on the sexual cycle in birds, II. *Amer. J. Anat.*, **45**, 307.

—— & ZUJKO, A. J. (1936). Normal progressive changes in the ovary of the starling (*Sturnus vulgaris*) from December to April. *Auk*, **53**, 31.

BLANCHARD, B. D. (1941). The white-crowned sparrows (*Zonotrichia leucophrys*) of the Pacific seaboard : environment and annual cycle. *Univ. Calif. Publ. Zool.*, **46**, 1.

BLANCHARD, F. C. (1943). A test of fecundity of the garter snake *Thamnophis sirtalis sirtalis* (Linnæus) in the year following the year of insemination. *Pap. Mich. Acad. Sci.*, **28**, 313.

BLOOM, W., BLOOM, M. A., & MCLEAN, F. C. (1941). Calcification and ossification. Medullary bone changes in the reproductive cycle of female pigeons. *Anat. Rec.*, **81**, 443.

BLOUNT, R. F. (1929). Seasonal cycles of the interstitial cells in the testis of the horned toad (*Phrynosoma solare*), seasonal variation in the number and morphology of the interstitial cells and the volume of the interstitial tissue. *J. Morph.*, **48**, 317.

—— (1934). Seasonal changes in the activity of the interstitial cells of the testis of the horned toad, *Phrynosoma solare*. *Anat. Rec.*, **58** (Suppl.) 50.

BOGERT, C. M. (1942). Notes on the mating of desert rattlesnakes. *Copeia*, **1942**, 261.

BOYD, M. M. (1941). The structure of the ovary and the formation of the corpus luteum in *Hoplodactylus maculatus* Gray. *Quart. J. micr. Sci.*, **82**, 337.

BRADLEY, O. C. (1915). *The anatomy of the fowl*. London.

—— (1928). Notes on the histology of the oviduct of the domestic hen. *J. Anat., Lond.*, **62**, 339.

BRAMBELL, F. W. R. (1925). The oögenesis of the fowl. *Philos. Trans.* B, **214**, 113.

BRECKENRIDGE, W. J. (1943). The life history of the black banded skink *Eumeces septentrionalis septentrionalis* (Baird). *Amer. Midl. Nat.*, **29**, 591.

BULLOUGH, W. S. (1939). A study of the reproductive cycle of the minnow in relation to the environment. *Proc. zool. Soc. Lond.* A, **109**, 79.

—— (1940a). The effect of the reduction of light in spring on the breeding season of the minnow (*Phoxinus laevis* Linn.). *Proc. zool. Soc. Lond.* A, **110**, 149.

—— (1940b). A study of sex reversal in the minnow (*Phoxinus laevis* L.). *J. exp. Zool.*, **85**, 475.

—— (1942a). Effect of oestrin injections on the mouse ovary. *Nature, Lond.*, **149**, 271.

—— (1942b). The reproductive cycles of the British and Continental races of the starling (*Sturnus vulgaris* L.). *Philos. Trans.* B, **231**, 165.

—— (1943). Autumn sexual behaviour and the resident habit of many British birds. *Nature, Lond.*, **151**, 531.

—— (1945a). British and Continental races of the starling, *Sturnus vulgaris* L., in Canada *Nature, Lond.*, **155**, 757.

—— (1945b). Endocrinological aspects of bird behaviour. *Biol. Rev.*, **20**, 89.

—— & GIBBS, H. F. (1941). Oögenesis in adult mice and starlings. *Nature, Lond.*, **148**, 439.

BURGER, J. W. (1938). Cyclic changes in the thyroid and adrenal cortex of the male starling, *Sturnus vulgaris*, and their relation to the sexual cycle. *Amer. Nat.*, **72**, 562.

CAGLE, F. R. (1944). Sexual maturity in the female of the turtle, *Pseudemys scripta elegans*. *Copeia*, **1944**, 149.

CHAMPY, C. (1913). Recherches sur la spermatogènese des bactraciens et les eléments accessoires du testicule. *Arch. Zool. exp. gén.*, **52**, 13.

—— (1921). Sur les correlations entre les caractères sexuels mâles et les divers éléments du testicule chez les amphibians (*Triton alpestris*). *C.R. Acad. Sci., Paris*, **172**, 482.

—— (1923a). Sur la " source de l'hormone sexuelle " chez les poissons et en général. *C.R. Soc. Biol., Paris*, **88**, 1127.

—— (1923b). Observations sur les caractères sexuels chez les poissons. *C.R. Soc. Biol., Paris*, **88**, 414.

—— (1932). Observations sur les caractères sexuels de la grenouille. *Arch. Zool. exp. gén.*, **74**, 399.

—— (1933). Étude du mécanisme du développement de quelques caractères sexuels des Urodèles. *Arch. Zool. exp. gén.*, **76**, 59.

—— & GLEY, P. (1922). La glande du testicule des blennies et sa signification. *Bull. Soc. zool. Fr.*, **47**, 199.

CIESLAK, E. S. (1945). Relations between the reproductive cycle and the pituitary gland in the snake *Thamnophis radix*. *Physiol. Zoöl.*, **18**, 299.

CLAVERT, J. (1942a). Action hypercalcémiente et ostéogénétique de la folliculine chez le pigeon. *C.R. Soc. Biol., Paris*, **136**, 507.

—— (1942b). Action ostéogénétique de la folliculine chez le pigeon. *C.R. Soc. Biol., Paris*, **136**, 512.

—— & BENOIT, J. (1942). Enrichessement du squelette en calcium, chez le pigeon, sous l'action du dipropionate d'oestradiol. *C.R. Soc. Biol., Paris*, **136**, 509.

CONRAD, R. M., & SCOTT, H. M. (1938). The formation of the egg of the domestic fowl. *Physiol. Rev.*, **18**, 481.

CORDIER, R. (1928). Études histophysiologiques sur le tube urinaire des reptiles. *Arch. Biol., Paris*, **38**, 109.

COSTE, J. J. M. C. V. (1874). *Histoire du développement des corps organisés.* I. Paris.

COURRIER, R. (1921a). Sur le conditionnement des caractères sexuels secondaires chez les poissons. *C.R. Soc. Biol., Paris,* **85,** 486.

—— (1921b). Glande interstitielle du testicule et caractères sexuels secondaires chez les poissons. *C.R. Acad. Sci., Paris,* **172,** 1316.

—— (1921c). Sur l'existence d'une glande interstitielle dans le testicule des poissons. *C.R. Soc. Biol., Paris,* **85,** 939.

—— (1922). Sur l'existence d'une glande interstitielle dans le testicule des blennies. *Bull. Soc. zool. Fr.,* **44,** 458.

—— (1929). Les modifications saisonnières de l'appareil uro-génital chez *Uromastix acanthinurus* (Bell). *Arch. Anat. micr.,* **25,** 388.

COWLES, R. B., & BURLESON, G. L. (1945). The sterilising effect of high temperature on the male germ plasm of the Yucca night lizard *Xantusia vigilis. Amer. Nat.,* **79,** 417.

CRAIG-BENNETT, A. (1931). The reproductive cycle of the three-spined stickleback, *Gasterosteus aculeatus* Linn. *Philos. Trans.* B, **219,** 197.

CROUCH, J. E. (1939). Seasonal changes in the testes of the passerine bird *Phainopepla nitens lepida. Proc. Soc. exp. Biol., N.Y.,* **40,** 218.

CUMMINGS, J. B. (1943). Morphogenesis of the gonopodium in *Molliensia latipinna J. Morph.,* **73,** 1.

CUNNINGHAM, J. T. (1890). *A treatise on the common sole.* Plymouth.

—— (1931). *Hormones and heredity.* London.

—— & SMART, W. A. M. (1934). The structure and origin of *corpora lutea* in some of the lower vertebrates. *Proc. Roy. Soc.* B, **116,** 258.

DALCQ, A. (1920). Le cycle saisonnier du testicule de l'orvet. *C.R. Soc. Biol., Paris,* **83,** 820.

DAVIS, D. E. (1942a). The regression of the avian post-ovulatory follicle. *Anat. Rec.,* **82,** 297.

—— (1942b). The bursting of avian follicles at the beginning of atresia. *Anat. Rec.,* **82,** 153.

—— (1944). The occurrence of burst atretic follicles in birds. *Anat. Rec.,* **90,** 307.

DUNN, E. R. (1923). The breeding habits of salamanders and their bearing on phylogeny. *Copeia,* **1923,** 25.

EVANS, H. M. (1938). A note on the sexual changes in the pituitary gland of the eel. *Proc. zool. Soc. Lond.,* **107,** 471.

EVANS, L. T., & CLAPP, M. L. (1940). The effects of ovarian hormones and seasons on *Anolis carolinensis.* II. The genital system. *Anat. Rec.,* **77,** 57.

FELL, H. B. (1924). Histological studies on the gonads of the fowl. II. The histogenesis of the so-called " luteal " cells in the ovary. *Brit. J. exp. Biol.,* **1,** 293.

FITZPATRICK, F. L. (1933). Bilateral and unilateral ovaries in Raptorial birds. *Anat. Rec.,* **57** (Suppl.) 68.

FONTAINE, M. (1936). Sur la maturation complète des organes génitaux de l'anguille mâle et l'emission spontanée de ses produits sexuels. *C.R. Acad. Sci., Paris,* **202,** 1312.

FRAENKEL, L., & MARTINS, T. (1938). Sur les corps jaunes des serpents vivipares. *C.R. Soc. Biol., Paris,* **127,** 466.

FRANKENBERGER, Z. (1928). Études sur la spermatogénèse des reptiles. I. Sur le cycle saisonnier du testicule chez la *Lacerta agilis. Bull. int. Prague,* 1.

FRASER, E. A., & RENTON, R. M. (1940). Observations on the breeding and development of the viviparous fish, *Heterandria formosa. Quart. J. micr. Sci.,* **81,** 479.

FROST, W. E. (1943). The natural history of the minnow, *Phoxinus phoxinus. J. Anim. Ecol.,* **12,** 139.

—— (1945). The age and growth of eels (*Anguilla anguilla*) from the Windermere catchment area. Pt. 2. *J. Anim. Ecol.,* **14,** 106.

GADOW, H. (1901). *Amphibia and reptiles. Cambridge Natural History,* **8.** London.

GALLIEN, L. (1940). Récherches sur la physiologie hypophysaire dans ses relations avec les gonades et le cycle sexuel, chez la grenouille rousse, *Rana temporaria* L. *Bull. biol.,* **74,** 1.

GEISER, S. W. (1922).   Seasonal changes in the testis of *Gambusia affinis*, the top-minnow.
    Anat. Rec., **23**, 104.
GIACOMINI, E. (1896).   Contributo all' istologia dell' ovario dei Selaci con speciale
    riguardo sopra ad alcune particolarite di struttura riscontrati nell' ovario di
    Myliobatis bovina Geoff. St. Hil.   *Ric. Lab. Anat. norm. Univ. Roma*, **5**, 221.
GITLIN, G. (1941).   Seasonal variations and sexual differences in the fat bodies and other
    fat deposits of *Xenopus laevis* (the South African clawed toad).   *S. Afr. J.
    Med. Sci.*, **6**, 136.
GRAHAM, M. (1923).   The annual cycle in the life of the mature cod in the North Sea.
    Fish. Invest., Ser. 2, **6**, No. 6.
HAINES, T. P. (1940).   Delayed fertilisation in *Leptodeira annulata polysticta*.   *Copeia*,
    1940, 116.
HALNAN, E. T. (1936).   The scientific principles of poultry feeding.   4th ed.   *Bull.
    Minist. Agric. Lond.*, No. 7.
HAMMETER, J. C. (1926).   Oviduct of *Lophius* (Artedi) Linnæus.   *L. piscatorius* L.
    Anat. Rec., **33**, 311.
HANN, H. W. (1927).   The history of the germ-cells of *Cottus bairdii* Girard.   *J. Morph.*,
    43, 427.
HARMS, J. W. (1926).   *Körper und Keimzellen*.   2 vols.   Berlin.
HARTMANN, J. F. (1944).   Seasonal cytological changes in the anterior hypophysis of the
    garter snake.   *Amer. J. Anat.*, **75**, 121.
HEAPE, W. (1931).   *Emigration, migration and nomadism*.   Cambridge.
HERLANT, M. (1933).   Recherches histologiques et expérimentales sur les variations
    cycliques du testicule et des caractères sexuels secondaires chez les reptiles.
    Arch. Biol., Paris, **44**, 347.
HILL, C. J., & HILL, J. P. (1933).   The development of the Monotremata.   I. The histology of
    the oviduct during gestation.   II. The structure of the egg-shell.   *Trans. zool.
    Soc. Lond.*, **21**, 413.
HILL, J. P., & GATENBY, J. B. (1926).   The corpus luteum of the Monotremata.   *Proc.
    zool. Soc. Lond.*, **47**, 715.
HILSMAN, H. M. (1934).   The ovarian cycle in *Triturus viridescens*.   *Anat. Rec.*, **57** (Suppl.)
    82.
HISAW, F. L., & ABRAMOWITZ, A. A. (1938).   Physiology of reproduction in the dogfish
    Mustelus canis.   *Wood's Hole Oceanogr. Inst. Rep. for 1937*, 21.
—— —— (1939).   Physiology of reproduction in the dogfishes *Mustelus canis* and *Squalus
    acanthias*.   *Wood's Hole Oceanogr. Inst. Rep. for 1938*, 22.
HUMPHREY, R. R. (1921).   The interstitial cells of the urodele testis.   *Amer. J. Anat.*,
    29, 213.
IFFT, J. D. (1942).   The effect of environmental factors on the sperm cycle of *Triturus
    viridescens*.   *Biol. Bull., Wood's Hole*, **83**, 111.
JASKI, C. J. (1939).   Ein Oestruszyklus bei *Lebistes reticulatus* (Peters).   *Proc. Acad. Sci.,
    Amst.*, **42**, 201.
JONES, J. W. (1940).   Histological changes in the testes in the sexual cycle of male salmon
    parr (*Salmo salar* L. juv.).   *Proc. Roy. Soc. B*, **128**, 499.
—— & ORTON, J. H. (1940).   The paedogenetic male cycle in *Salmo salar* L.   *Proc. Roy
    Soc. B*, **128**, 485.
KEHL, R. (1935).   Étude préliminaire du cycle sexuel de quelques reptiles sahariens.
    Bull. Soc. Hist. nat. Afr. N., **26**, 61.
—— (1944).   Études de quelques problèmes d'endocrinologie genitale chez un batrachian
    Nord-Africain.   *Rev. Canad., Biol.*, **3**, 29.
—— LEPORTOIS, M., & BENOIT, J. (1942).   Biométrie du cycle génital normal et expéri-
    mental de *l'Uromastix* femelle.   *C.R. Soc. Biol., Paris*, **136**, 520.
KERR, T. (1939).   On the structure and function of the cloaca of the common frog (*Rana t.
    temporaria*).   *Proc. zool. Soc. Lond. B*, **109**, 63.
KIRSCHBAUM, A., PFEIFFER, C. A., VAN HEUVERSWYN, J., & GARDNER, W. V. (1939).   Studies
    on gonad-hypophyseal relationship and cyclic osseous changes in the English
    sparrow, *Passer domesticus* L.   *Anat. Rec.*, **75**, 249.

Kummerlöwe, H. (1930). Vergleichende Untersuchungen über das Gonadensystem weiblicher Vögel. I. and II. *Z. mikr.-anat. Forsch.*, **21**, 1 ; **22**, 259.

Kuntz, A. (1913). Notes on the habits, morphology of the reproductive organs and embryology of the viviparous fish *Gambusia affinis*. *Bull. U.S. Fish. Comm.*, **33**, 177.

Kyes, P., & Potter, T. S. (1934). Physiological marrow ossification in female pigeons. *Anat. Rec.*, **60**, 377.

Liebman, E. (1945). The function of the leucocytes in the growth and regression of the egg of *Triturus viridescens*. *Amer. J. Anat.*, **77**, 273.

Loukine, A. V. (1941a). La fréquence du frai chez le sterlet. *C.R. Acad. Sci. U.R.S.S.*, N.S., **32**, 166.

—— (1941b). Les stades de maturité sexuelle du sterlet. *C.R. Acad. Sci. U.R.S.S.*, N.S., **32**, 374.

Loyez, M. (1905). Récherches sur le développement ovarien des œufs meroblastiques à vitellus nutritif abondant. *Arch. Anat. micr.*, **8**, 69.

Ludwig, M., & Rahn, H. (1943). Sperm storage and copulatory adjustment in the prairie rattlesnake. *Copeia*, **1943**, 15.

McGregor, J. H. (1899). The spermatogenesis of *Amphiuma*. *J. Morph.*, **15** (Suppl.), 57.

March, F. (1937). Relative growth in amphibia. *Proc. zool. Soc. Lond.* A, 415.

Matthews, L. Harrison (1950). Reproduction in the Basking shark *Cetorhinus maximus* (Gunner). *Philos. Trans.* B, **234**, 247.

Matthews, S. A. (1938). The seasonal cycle in the gonads of *Fundulus*. *Biol. Bull Wood's Hole*, **75**, 67.

Mayr, E. (1942). *Systematics and the origin of species.* New York.

Mendoza, G. (1939). The reproductive cycle of the viviparous teleost, *Neotoca bilineata*, a member of the family Goodeidae. *Biol. Bull. Wood's Hole*, **76**, 359.

—— (1940). The reproductive cycle of the viviparous teleost, *Neotoca bilineata*, a member of the family Goodeidae. II. The cyclic changes in the ovarian stroma during gestation. *Biol. Bull. Wood's Hole*, **78**, 349.

—— (1941). The reproductive cycle of the viviparous teleost, *Neotoca bilineata*, a member of the family Goodeidae. III. The germ-cell cycle. *Biol. Bull. Wood's Hole*, **81**, 70.

—— (1943). The reproductive cycle of the viviparous teleost, *Neotoca bilineata*, a member of the family Goodeidae. IV. The germinal tissue. *Biol. Bull. Wood's Hole*, **84**, 87.

Merriman, D., & Schedl, A. P. (1941). The effects of light and temperature on gametogenesis in the four-spined stickleback *Apeltes quadracus* (Mitchill). *J. exp. Zool.*, **88**, 413.

Metten, H. (1939). Reproduction in the dog-fish. *Nature, Lond.*, **143**, 121.

—— (1944). The fate of spermatozoa in the female dogfish (*Scylliorhynus canicula*) *Quart. J. micr. Sci.*, **84**, 283.

Moltchanova, I. (1941). La structure histologique des œufs des sterlets aux stades différents de maturité sexuelle. *C.R. Acad. Sci. U.R.S.S.*, N.S., **32**, 163.

Neill, R. M. (1939). Reproductive cycle in *Salmo salar* Linn. *Nature, Lond.*, **144**, 332.

van Oordt, G. J. (1923). Secondary sex characters and testis of the ten-spined stickleback (*Gasterosteus pungitius*). *Proc. Acad. Sci., Amst.*, **26**, 309.

—— (1928). Studies on the gonads of summering birds. I. and II. *Tijdschr. ned. dierk. Ver.*, 3rd Ser., **1**.

—— (1931). Studien über die Gonaden ubersommernder Vögel. III. *Z. mikr.-anat. Forsch.*, **25**, 539.

—— & Bruyns, M. F. M. (1938). Studien über die Gonaden ubersommernder Vögel. IV. *Z. Morph. Ökol. Tiere*, **34**, 161.

Orton, J. H., Jones, J. W., & King, G. M. (1938). The male sexual stage in salmon parr (*Salmo salar* L. juv.). *Proc. Roy. Soc. Lond.* B, **125**, 103.

Oslund, R. (1929). Seasonal variations in the testes of vertebrates. *Quart. Rev. Biol.*, **3**, 254.

Parker, J. B. (1942). Some observations on the reproductive system of the yellow perch (*Perca flavescens*). *Copeia*, **1942**, 223.

PEARL, R., & BORING, A. M. (1918).   Sex studies.   X. The corpus luteum in the ovary of the domestic fowl.   *Amer. J. Anat.*, **23**, 1.

—— & CURTIS, M. R. (1912).   Studies on the physiology of reproduction in the domestic fowl.   V. Data regarding the physiology of the oviduct.   *J. exp. Zool.*, **12**, 99.

—— —— (1914).   Studies on the physiology of reproduction in the domestic fowl. VIII. On some physiological effects of ligation, section, or removal of the oviduct.   *J. exp. Zool.*, **17**, 395.

RAHN, H. (1939).   Structure and function of placenta and corpus luteum in viviparous snakes.   *Proc. Soc. exp. Biol., N.Y.*, **40**, 381.

—— (1940).   Sperm viability in the uterus of the garter snake, *Thamnophis*.   *Copeia*, **1940**, 109.

—— (1942).   The reproductive cycle of the prairie rattler.   *Copeia*, **1942**, 233.

RANZI, S. (1936).   Ghiandole endocrine, maturità sessuale e gestazione nei Selaci.   *R.C. Accad. Lincei*, 6, **24**, 528.

RAU, A. S., & GATENBY, J. B. (1923).   Notes on the distribution, morphology and cytology of the organ of Bidder.   *J.R. micr. Soc.*, **19**.

REGAMEY, J. (1935).   Les caractères sexuels du lézard (*Lacerta agilis* L.).   *Rev. suisse Zool.*, **42**, 87.

REGAUD, C., & POLICARD, A. (1903a).   Variations sexuelles de structure dans le segment préterminal du tube urinifère de quelques ophidiens.   *C.R. Soc. Biol., Paris*, **55**, 216.

—— —— (1903b).   Sur l'alternance fonctionnelle et sur les phénomènes histologiques de la sécrétion, dans le deuxième segment du tube urinipare, chez les serpents.   *C.R. Soc. Biol., Paris*, **55**, 894.

—— —— (1903c).   Sur les variations sexuelles de structure dans le rein des reptiles.   *C.R. Soc. Biol., Paris*, **55**, 973.

—— —— (1903d).   Recherches sur la structure du rein de quelques ophidiens.   *Arch. Anat. micr.*, **6**, 191.

REISS, P. (1923a).   Le cycle testiculaire du lézard.   *C.R. Soc. Biol., Paris*, **88**, 447.

—— (1923b).   Sur les caractères sexuels secondaires chez le lézard mâle.   *C.R. Soc. Biol., Paris*, **88**, 445.

REY, P. (1939a).   Modifications du cycle annuel de l'ovaire après ablation du lobe principal de l'hypophyse chez *Bufo vulgaris*.   *C.R. Soc. Biol., Paris*, **130**, 957.

—— (1939b).   Action de l'ablation du lobe principal de l'hypophyse sur le cycle annuel des cellules sexuelles mâles de *Bufo vulgaris*.   *C.R. Acad. Sci., Paris*, **208**, 1116.

REYNOLDS, A. E. (1943).   The normal seasonal reproductive cycle in the male *Eumeces fasciatus*, together with some observations on the effects of castration and hormone administration.   *J. Morph.*, **72**, 331.

RICHARDSON, K. C. (1935).   The secretory phenomena in the oviduct of the fowl, including the process of shell formation examined by the microincineration technique.   *Philos. Trans.* B, **225**, 149.

RIDDLE, O., RAUCH, V. M., & SMITH, G. C. (1944).   Changes in medullary bone during the reproductive cycle of female pigeons.   *Anat. Rec.*, **90**, 295.

RILEY, G. M. (1937).   Experimental studies on spermatogenesis in the house sparrow, *Passer domesticus* Linnæus.   *Anat. Rec.*, **67**, 327.

RISLEY, P. L. (1933).   The spermatogenetic and seasonal cycle of the testis of the musk turtle, *Sternotherus odoratus* (Latreille).   *Anat. Rec.*, **57** (Suppl.), 78.

—— (1938).   Seasonal changes in the testis of the musk turtle, *Sternotherus odoratus* L.   *J. Morph.*, **63**, 301.

ROBERTS, B. (1940).   The breeding behaviour of penguins.   *British Graham Land Expedition*, 1934–37, *Sci. Repts.*, **1**, 195.

ROBINSON, E. J., & RUGH, R. (1943).   The reproductive processes of the fish *Oryzias latipes*.   *Biol. Bull. Wood's Hole*, **84**, 115.

ROWAN, W. (1930).   A unique type of follicular atresia in the avian ovary.   *Trans. roy. Soc. Can.*, Sect. V, **24**, 157.

RUGH, R. (1935).   Ovulation in the frog.   II. Follicular rupture to fertilisation.   *J. exp. Zool.*, **71**, 163.

SAMUEL, M. (1943).   Studies on the corpus luteum in *Rhinobatus granulatus* Cuv.   *Proc. Indian Acad. Sci.* B, **18**, 133.

—— (1944).   Studies on the corpus luteum in *Enhydra schistosa* (Daudin) and *Hydrophis cyanocinctus* (Daudin) of the Madras coast.   *Proc. Indian Acad. Sci.* B, **20**, 143.

SATÔ, R. (1939).   On the condition of gonad of salmon (*Oncorhynchus*) reached the age of return in the Northern North Pacific.   I. Red salmon (*Oncorhynchus nerka* (Walb.)).   *Bull. Jap. Soc. sci. Fish.*, **8**, 72.

SELF, J. T. (1940).   Notes on the sex cycle of *Gambusia affinis affinis* and on its habits and relation to mosquito control.   *Amer. Midl. Nat.* **23**, 393.

SERGEEV, A. M. (1941).   On the biology of reproduction in the Steppe tortoise (*Testudo horsfieldi* Gray).   [In Russ., with Eng. summary.]   *Zool. Zh.*, **20**, 118.

SHAPIRO, B. G., & SHAPIRO, H. A. (1934).   Histological changes in the ovaries and ovarian blood-vessels of *Xenopus laevis* associated with hypophysectomy, captivity and the normal reproductive cycle.   *J. exp. Biol.*, **11**, 73.

SHAW, TSEN-HWANG (1938).   Double ovaries in some Chinese birds of prey.   *Nature, Lond.*, **142**, 1079.

SOSNOVSKY, I. P. (1940).   Breeding of *Elaphe dione* (Pall.).   [Russ. with Eng. summary.]   *Proc. Moscow zool. Park*, **1**, 169.

STANLEY, A. J. (1937).   Sexual dimorphism in North American hawks.   I. Sex organs   *J. Morph.*, **61**, 321.

—— & WITSCHI, E. (1940).   Germ-cell migration in relation to asymmetry in the sex glands of hawks.   *Anat. Rec.*, **76**, 329.

STEVEN, G. A., & CORBIN, P. G. (1939).   Mackerel investigations at Plymouth.   Preliminary report.   *Rapp. Cons. Explor. Mer.*, **111**, 15.

SURFACE, F. M. (1912)   The histology of the oviduct of the hen.   *Bull. Me. agric. Exp. Sta.*, **206**, 395.

SUZUKI, K. (1939).   Regeneration of gonads in *Plecoglossus altivelis* after spawning season   *Cytologia, Tokyo,* **10**, 113.

SWINGLE, W. W. (1921).   The germ-cells of anurans.   *J. exp. Zool.*, **32**, 235.

TEST, F. H. (1944).   Testicular asymmetry in the woodpecker *Colaptes*.   *Pap. Mich. Acad. Sci.*, **30**, 347.

TING, H., & BORING, A. M. (1939).   The seasonal cycle in the reproductive organs of the Chinese toad *Bufo bufo* and the pondfrog *Rana nigromaculata*.   *Peking nat. Hist. Bull.*, **14**, 49

TRAPIDO, H. (1940).   Mating time and sperm viability in *Storeria*.   *Copeia*, **1940**, 107.

TURNER, C. L. (1919).   The seasonal variation in the spermary of the perch.   *J. Morph.*, **32**, 681.

—— (1937a).   Reproductive cycles and superfetation in Poeciliid fishes.   *Biol. Bull. Wood's Hole*, **72**, 145.

—— (1937b).   The trophotaeniae of the Goodeidae, a family of viviparous cyprinodont fishes.   *J. Morph.*, **61**, 495.

—— (1938a).   The reproductive cycle of *Brachyraphis episcopi*, an ovoviviparous Poeciliid fish, in the natural tropical habitat.   *Biol. Bull. Wood's Hole*, **75**, 56.

—— (1938b).   Adaptations for viviparity in embryos and ovary of *Anableps anableps*.   *J. Morph.*, **62**, 323.

—— (1938c).   Histological and cytological changes in the ovary of *Cymatogaster aggregatus* during gestation.   *J. Morph.*, **62**, 351.

—— (1940a).   Superfetation in viviparous Cyprinodont fishes.   *Copeia*, **1940**, 88.

—— (1940b).   Pseudoamnion, pseudochorion, and follicular pseudoplacenta in Poeciliid fishes.   *J. Morph.*, **67**, 59.

—— (1940c).   Follicular pseudoplacenta and gut modifications in Anablepid fishes.   *J. Morph.*, **67**, 91.

—— (1940d).   Adaptations for viviparity in Jenynsiid fishes.   *J. Morph.*, **67**, 291.

—— (1942).   Diversity of endocrine function in the reproduction of viviparous fishes.   *Amer. Nat.*, **76**, 179.

VALLE, J. R., & SOUZA, P R. (1942).   Observações sobre o sistema endócrino dos Ofídios.   O corpo amarelo nas serpentes ovovivíparas não venenosas.   *Rev. Bras. Biol., Rio de J.*, **2**, 81.

VIVIEN, J. H. (1938a). Sur l'existence des glandes annexes du tractus génital chez le mâle de *Gobius paganellus* L. *C.R. Acad. Sci., Paris*, **206**, 938.

——(1938b). Étude préliminaire des annexes du tractus génital d'un gobiidé : *Gobius paganellus* L. *Trav. Sta. zool. Wimereux*, **13**, 713.

—— (1939). Rôle de l'hypophyse dans le déterminisme du cycle génital femelle d'un téléostéen, *Gobius paganellus* L. *C.R. Acad. Sci., Paris*, **208**, 948.

VOLSØE, H. (1944). Structure and seasonal variation of the male reproductive organs of *Vipera berus* (L.). *Spolia zool. Mus. Hauniensis*, **5**, 1.

WARREN, D. C., & SCOTT, H. M. (1935). The time factor in egg formation. *Poult. Sci.*, **14**, 195.

WATSON, A. (1919). Seasonal changes in avian testes. Greenfinch. *J. Physiol.*, **53**, 86.

WEEKES, H. C. (1934). The *corpus luteum* in certain oviparous and viviparous reptiles. *Proc. Linn. Soc. N.S.W.*, **59**, 380.

—— (1935). A review of placentation among reptiles with particular regard to the formation and evolution of the placenta. *Proc. zool. Soc. Lond.*, 625.

WEICHERT, C. K. (1945). Seasonal variation in the mental gland and reproductive organs of the male *Eurycea bislineata*. *Copeia*, **1945**, 78.

WHEELER, J. F. G. (1924). The growth of the egg in the dab (*Pleuronectes limanda*). *Quart. J. micr. Sci.*, **68**, 641.

WILDER, I. W. (1917). On the breeding habits of *Desmognathus fusca*. *Biol. Bull.*, *Wood's Hole*, **32**, 13.

WITSCHI, E. (1930). The geographical distribution of the sex races of the European grass frog (*Rana temporaria* L.). *J. exp. Zool.*, **56**, 149.

—— (1932). Sex deviations, inversions, and parabiosis. In E. Allen's *Sex and internal secretions*, 160. London.

—— (1945). Quantitative studies on the seasonal development of the deferent ducts in passerine birds. *J. exp. Zool.*, **100**, 549.

WRIGHT, P. L., & WRIGHT, M. H. (1944). The reproductive cycle of the male red-winged blackbird. *Condor*, **46**, 46.

WYNNE-EDWARDS, V. C. (1939). Intermittent breeding of the fulmar (*Fulmarus glacialis* (L.)) with some general observations on non-breeding in sea-birds. *Proc. zool. Soc. Lond.* A, **109**, 127.

CHAPTER 4

THE OESTROUS CYCLE IN THE MAMMALIA

By P. Eckstein and S. Zuckerman

I—Introduction : nature and phases of the cycle

In describing the sexual processes of the Mammalia, and the variations in the periodicity of breeding which occur in the different groups,[1] this chapter uses the terminology originally proposed by Heape (1900) and afterwards adopted by Marshall (1903, 1904, 1922), in giving an account of these phenomena in sheep and other animals.

The term *sexual season* is used by Heape to designate the particular time or times of the year at which the sexual organs exhibit a special activity. It is, in fact, employed in practically the same sense as the expression " breeding season." Heape suggests that it is better to adopt the latter term to denote " the whole of that consecutive period during which any male or female mammal is concerned in the production of young," since the expression is often used to include the period of pregnancy or even the period of lactation.

The sexual season is the time of the year during which mating takes place. In most female mammals this is restricted to definite periods of *oestrus* within a sexual season, but the males of many species are capable of copulating at any time and only rarely experience a true sexual season, known as the *rutting season*.

In the present chapter the terms mating and pairing are used synonymously with copulating, even though the two former expressions may be ambiguous in meaning.

The word " oestrus " or " oestrum " (in American spelling : " estrus " ; " estrum ") is a Latin adaptation of the Greek term : οῖστρος. This is defined by the Oxford English Dictionary as " something that stings or goads one on, a stimulus ; vehement impulse ; frenzy," and in its specific biological meaning as the " sexual orgasm " and the " rut of animals."

Heape (1900) adopted the masculine form of the term to describe the " special period of sexual desire of the female," distinguishing it from the rutting season of the male. He also employed it in its neuter form, in combination with such qualifying prefixes as Pro-, Di-, Met-, An(oestrum), and as the adjective " oestrous."

Heape's terminology met with universal approval. In the fifty-odd years since its first introduction it has been used widely, though not always correctly (either biologically or grammatically), by reproductive physiologists throughout

---

[1] As in Chapter 2, the classification is that of Simpson (1945), except in the case of Primates where, for convenience, Zuckerman's classification (1933) has been adopted, the Tupaiidae being considered separately.

the world.   In the following account the term " oestrus," in accordance with modern usage, will be employed exclusively in the nominative, whether alone or in combination with a prefix (hence " dioestrus," " metoestrus," etc.).

The non-breeding season or period of rest in a female mammal, when the ovaries and accessory reproductive organs are quiescent (at least relatively) and the animal shows no disposition to seek a mate, is called by Heape the *anoestrous period*, or simply the "anoestrum."   This period is generally very prolonged, and in many mammals occupies the greater part of the year.   Its close marks the beginning of the sexual season, and generally a change in the metabolism not only of the gonads and reproductive tract, but also of other endocrine organs, and of the body generally.

The first part of the sexual season is occupied by prooestrus.   This period is characterised by marked changes in the generative organs, the uterus growing and becoming congested.   Prooestrus is the period often referred to by breeders as the time when an animal is " coming on heat," or " coming in season."

The next period, *oestrus*, marks the climax of the process.   It is " during oestrus, and only at that time, that the female is willing to receive the male, and fruitful coition rendered possible in most, if not in all, mammals " (Heape, 1900). There is evidence that " heat " may occur occasionally during gestation.   This phenomenon has been observed in rabbits, cats, horses and other animals (*see* below). Coition during pregnancy may tend to occur periodically at times corresponding to what would have been the regular heat periods if the animal had remained non-pregnant, and may, exceptionally, result in superfoetation (*see* pp. 262, 304).

The periods of prooestrus and oestrus are commonly referred to together as the " heat " or " Brunst " period, and sometimes as the period of " rut," and no attempt is then made to distinguish the time occupied by " coming in season," and the time at which the female is ready to receive the male.   In Heape's terminology, as noted above, the term " rut " is restricted to the male sexual season.   The period of heat implies, it should be noted, not only the willingness of the female to accept the male, but also a number of concomitant anatomical and physiological changes in the reproductive organs, and metabolic changes in the body as a whole.

If conception takes place as a result of coition during oestrus, gestation follows. Gestation in its turn, after a short period of recovery, is followed by nursing or lactation, and the latter, in certain species, is succeeded by the next anoestrus. In other species (e.g. rat), parturition is followed almost immediately, in spite of lactation, by another prooestrus and oestrus.   In a third group, lactation is succeeded by another period of heat, and not by anoestrus.

If conception does not occur, oestrus is succeeded, either by a short recovery period called *metoestrus*, during which the oestrous changes in the generative system subside, or by a longer period, called pseudopregnancy, in which changes occur in the sexual organs that are basically similar to, but less pronounced than those which take place during true pregnancy.   The pseudopregnant period is then followed by another oestrus or, in some species, by anoestrus.

In some animals, as noted above, oestrus is succeeded by only a short interval of quiescence (e.g. the rat).   This short interval, which sometimes lasts for only a few days, is called *dioestrus*.   Dioestrus, in turn, is followed by another prooestrous period, and in this way the cycle may repeat itself until the sexual season is over. Such a cycle (consisting of a succession of the four periods : prooestrus, oestrus, metoestrus, and dioestrus, is known as the dioestrous or oestrous cycle. The number of dioestrous cycles in one sexual season depends upon the occurrence or non-occurrence of successful coition during oestrus. Thus, if conception takes place during the first oestrous period of the season, there can be no repetition of the cycle, at any rate until after parturition. If conception does not occur during any oestrus of the sexual season, the final metoestrous phase is succeeded by a prolonged anoestrous or non-breeding period. This is eventually followed by another prooestrus, marking the commencement of a new sexual season. It must be emphasised that dioestrus is not the same as anoestrus. Anoestrus is a period of physiological inactivity so far as the reproductive organs are concerned. Dioestrus is an abbreviated pseudopregnancy during which the reproductive organs undergo active, even if inconspicuous, changes.

The number of dioestrous cycles which can occur in a female mammal in the absence of the male, or in the absence of successful coition, varies according to species and between individuals within a species. Thus in some animals, such as the Scotch black-faced sheep in the Highlands, the number is usually 2. In many rodents, on the other hand, there may be 6 or 7 or even more cycles within the limits of a single sexual season.

Animals in which oestrus occurs only once during the sexual season are called monoestrous animals. Those in which several oestrous cycles occur are called polyoestrous. The polyoestrous condition may be regarded as a device (teleologically speaking) to increase the reproductive powers by providing more frequent opportunities for successful coition. There is no essential difference between the physiological changes which constitute the single oestrous cycle of a monoestrous animal and those which characterise one of the dioestrous cycles of a polyoestrous animal.

As Heape says, " the complication into which an otherwise simple story is thrown is due . . . to variation in the quiescent period." The two varieties of the quiescent period (anoestrus and dioestrus) " are homologous, the one is a modification of the other " ; and the modification is no doubt related to an increased or decreased power of reproduction. At the same time, for the purposes of the present chapter, " the difference between them must be regarded as essential, for their relation to the sexual season renders it necessary to discriminate clearly between them."

Although knowledge of mammalian reproduction is still far from complete, it has grown rapidly in past years, and is now much more extensive than it was when the last edition of this book appeared (1922). Out of the 18 living orders of mammals listed by Simpson (1945), there is adequate information about at least the more important representatives of 8 orders (Insectivora, Chiroptera, Primates, Lagomorpha, Rodentia, Carnivora, Perissodactyla, Artiodactyla) and moderate information about 5 orders (Monotremata, Marsupialia, Edentata, Cetacea, Proboscidea), while there is little or none about the remaining 5 (Hyracoidea, Dermoptera, Pholidota, Tubulidentata, Sirenia).

Most of our knowledge relates to domesticated or semi-domesticated species. Such information as is available about wild animals is, of necessity, mainly based on observation of captive specimens. This raises the issue of the influence of captivity on reproductive processes. Scientific opinion on this complex subject has passed through various phases. Darwin (1868) states that animals when first confined are " eminently liable to suffer in their reproductive systems " and adds that this tendency towards sterility cannot be attributed to a loss of health or vigour or to disease of the generative organs.   Heape (1900) realised that captive species vary considerably in breeding behaviour, some showing derangement or suppression, and others full maintenance or even enhancement of reproductive capacity. He also recognised the necessity of distinguishing between " wild animals in a state of nature, wild animals in captivity and domesticated animals."   For these reasons most subsequent authors have questioned the validity of inferences about the breeding habits of wild animals based upon observation of the same animals in captivity (Zuckerman, 1930 ; Baker and Baker, 1936 ; Baker, 1938).

The most recent study of the factors which influence the breeding of captive wild animals is that of Hediger (1950).   He shows, for example, that restriction of space, which has long been thought to be an important agent in suppressing reproduction, has less influence on breeding than external disturbances during the mating period.   By careful attention to such details, as well as to the physiological and psychological " readiness " of the mated individuals, species which have not bred before (e.g. the rhinoceros, elephant and hare) can be made to reproduce in confinement.   As Hediger puts it, failure or success in breeding wild animals is not so much a biological problem as a matter of organisation.   He adds, however, that certain mammals have so far defied all attempts at breeding when in captivity (e.g. gorillas, cheetahs).

According to him, successful breeding is the mark of adequate captive conditions.   If breeding does not occur, something is wrong with the way in which the animals are kept.   By implication, therefore, the occurrence of breeding might be taken to indicate normality or " naturalness " of the environment.   If this view were completely valid, it would be possible to infer the reproductive habits of free-living animals from their breeding records in captivity.   On the other hand, this can only be so in the case of certain species such as polar bears in which the seasonal sexual rhythm is fixed, and unaffected by captivity.   Other mammals (e.g. the ibex) appear to be more variable, the periodicity and duration of the breeding seasons changing easily and quickly under the influence of confinement.

II—PROTOTHERIA

MONOTREMATA (= Ornithodelphia)

Tachyglossus ; Echidna (Spiny anteater ; Echidna)
Ornithorhynchus (Duckbill ; Platypus)

The Monotremata constitute the lowest order of mammals and comprise two species, the duck-billed platypus (*Ornithorhynchus paradoxus*), and the spiny anteater (*Echidna aculeata*).   They are distinguished from all other mammals in being oviparous.   Their eggs are incubated either in a special brood pouch (*Echidna*) or in a nest (*Ornithorhynchus*).

The echidna as a rule lays only one egg, and in those few instances out of 140 records collected by Flynn and Hill (1938–40), in which two eggs were present, only one was normal, the other being small and degenerate.   The platypus usually lays two eggs, but occasionally one or three.

The eggs of *Echidna* are derived in equal numbers from both ovaries. In the duck-billed platypus, however, it is only the left gonad which is functional, the right one being morphologically and physiologically inactive, as in birds (*see* Chapter 2). The two eggs which are normally laid are derived from two follicles which mature at the same time in the left ovary. Flynn and Hill (1938–40) give the dimensions of twin-laid intra-uterine eggs of this animal as 17 × 14 and 16 × 15 mm., respectively.

Both species reproduce once a year, in the spring, and the onset of breeding appears to vary with the locality. Thus in Queensland platypus mates between July and August but in Victoria during October. Copulation occurs in the water (Burrell, 1927). The region of the reproductive tract in which fertilisation occurs is not known.

In Tasmania the breeding season of *Echidna* lasts from the beginning of July until September, and during August most females contain intra-uterine ova (Flynn and Hill, 1938–40). The pouch develops during the sexual season, and then regresses until the onset of the next season. It is present in the embryo, but is not apparent in the young animal until the beginning of the first prooestrus (Semon, 1899). When the *Echidna* egg is laid, the cloaca protrudes in such a way that the egg is almost immediately transferred to the pouch (Le Souef, Burrell and Traughton, 1926).

Solomons and Gatenby (1924) have found the corpus luteum of monotremes to be similar in structure to that of higher types of mammals. According to Hill and Gatenby (1926) the egg in both the echidna and platypus is laid when the embryo has reached a stage of development comparable to that of a chick of thirty-eight to forty hours' incubation. " After an unknown period of incubation, in the nest (*Platypus*) or in the pouch or incubatorium (*Echidna*), the young Monotreme, about 16·5 mm. in length in *Platypus* and about 12·5 mm. in *Echidna*, emerges from its enclosing shell and egg membranes with the aid of its caruncle or egg tooth, and proceeds to subsist on the milk which exudes from the mammary glands of the mother, the tubules of which have already attained a length of about five centimetres some time before the egg is laid."

The intra-uterine phase of embryonic development in *Echidna* lasts about 28 days, according to Broom (1895), but in Asdell's opinion (1946) Broom's evidence " only justifies the conclusion that it is between twelve and twenty-eight days."

The processes of maturation, fertilisation and early cleavage of the ovum have been described in detail by Flynn (1930b) and Flynn and Hill (1938–40). Hill's findings (1941) on the changes undergone by the reproductive tract during the sexual cycle are referred to on p. 544.

III—Metatheria

Marsupialia (= Didelphia)

Fam. *Didelphidae*
        Didelphis (Common opossum, Azara's opossum, etc.)

Fam. *Dasyuridae*
        Dasyurus (Native " cat ")

Fam. *Phalangeridae*

      Trichosurus (Common phalanger)
      Phascolarctos (Koala or native " bear ")
      Dromicia (" Dormouse " opossum)

Fam. *Macropodidae*

      Bettongia (Brush-tailed " rat " kangaroo)
      Dendrolagus (Tree kangaroo)
      Macropus (Wallaby)
      Potorous (Common " rat " kangaroo)

The young of Marsupialia are born after a very short gestation, and reach the pouch in a state of extreme immaturity. They spend the greater part of their development either within the pouch or, in those forms which do not possess a marsupium, hanging freely from the nipple (*see* p. 63). Such records as are available in the archives of zoological gardens in London and Australia (Zuckerman, 1953) suggest that most species of this order can breed at all times of the year, a conclusion which is supported by the few accurate observations that are available about these animals in the wild.

Family *Didelphidae*

Didelphis

The Virginian opossum (*Didelphis virginiana*) is polyoestrous (Hartman, 1923a, b ; 1928a). In Texas the sexual season lasts from January to October, and is preceded by a 3-month period of anoestrus and ovarian inactivity (October to December). Nelson (1946), however, has observed oestrus in captive females during August, and active ovaries in a wild specimen killed in September. By means of artificial illumination given during the autumn, anoestrus can be reduced, and in this way the Wistar Institute of Philadelphia has bred opossums and obtained several litters in December (*see* Farris, 1950). The natural breeding season begins early in the year, and reaches its height by the third week of January, when most ovulations and conceptions take place. After the fourth week, " all females brought in from the field may be expected to be pregnant or to carry pouch young " (Hartman, 1923a). The prevailing weather appears to have no effect on the onset of the season, which begins somewhat later in the northern parts of the species' range.

The oestrous cycle, as estimated by vaginal smears, and by palpation of the mammary glands, varies in length and averages about 28 days. The reproductive organs undergo well-marked cyclic changes (p. 545). Ovulation is spontaneous and is thought to occur shortly after oestrus, which lasts about 1 to 2 days (Hartman, 1923b). Copulation lasts for about 20 to 40 minutes (Farris, 1950). The rest of the cycle is made up of the luteal or " pseudo-pregnant " phase, during which the uteri, vaginal canals and mammary glands develop almost as much as they do in true pregnancy.

The average number of eggs shed by an opossum is 22. Usually, only about 10 young are born (Asdell, 1946), but Hartman has observed litters of 15, 17 and 18 new-born opossums in the pouch and removed " as many as twenty-two normal foetuses near term " from the pregnant uteri.   There are 13 teats in the pouch, of which usually only the lower 11 are functional (Hartman, 1920).   Young in excess of the number of teats presumably die.   The mother becomes pregnant again after her young are weaned, and if pouch young are removed or lost, the female soon returns to a state of oestrus.

In the opossum two annual litters are the rule, over three months being taken to rear each brood.   Three litters in one year have been reported, but are unlikely except in the case of an " unusually vigorous female " that begins breeding at the end of December and continues uninterruptedly until the following November (Hartman, 1923a).   Captive opossums breed well during their first and second years, but poorly during the third (Farris, 1950).

Hartman believes that the average interval between fertilisation and parturition is 12½ days.   The following description of the process of birth, which takes place through the median (pseudo-) vaginal passage, is based on his observations.

The female prepares for parturition by cleaning out the pouch several times, after which she assumes a sitting position with the body bent forward and legs extended.   On its emergence from the vulva the tiny foetus is licked free of fluid by the mother.   It immediately proceeds, without any other maternal assistance, to crawl " over the entanglement of hair into the pouch," a distance of fully three inches.   For their progress the young employ " a kind of ' overhand stroke,' as if swimming," and display a high degree of neuro-muscular co-ordination in finding the teats of the mammary glands, to which they attach themselves firmly for a stay of over two months' duration.   According to Hartman's data (1928a) a new-born opossum weighs about 0·13 g. and an average litter amounts to no more than one-thousandth of the body weight of the mature female.   When their eyes open at about the fiftieth day, the pouch young are about the size of small mice, but they continue to nurse for another thirty days.   They do not become independent for at least three months.   Hartman's account of the passage of the new-born from the vulva to the pouch has been confirmed by Dickerson (1928), who also states that the entire journey takes between 10 and 20 minutes.

Whether the male opossum experiences a period of reproductive rest like the female appears to be unknown.   Hartman (1928a) states that the male " seems to possess spermatozoa during the entire year," and Painter (1922) found mature sperm in four specimens killed between October and January, but cells showing maturation stages were most abundant in those collected in January.

The observations of Martinez-Esteve (1937) on *Didelphis azarae* are of particular interest in that they seem to show that in this species, unlike *D. virginiana*, the oestrous cycle is very short (approximately seven days), and that spontaneous ovulation (and hence pseudopregnancy), is the exception rather than the rule. The ovaries show marked follicular atresia and not a single corpus luteum was encountered in several females maintained in captivity and separated from males. Only one animal possessed ripe follicles and showed oestrous changes in the vagina and mammary glands similar to those described by Hartman in the American opossum.

The Gamba opossum, *D. aurita*, has two breeding seasons, one in June to July, and the other at the end of October (Hill, 1918).

Family *Dasyuridae*
Dasyurus

The Australian marsupial " cat " (*Dasyurus viverrinus*) is monoestrous, and has one breeding season a year beginning in May or early June and extending until the first fortnight in August (Sandes, 1903 ; O'Donoghue, 1911 ; Hill and O'Donoghue, 1913). Prooestrus lasts from 4 to 12 days, and during this time the lips of the cloaca become swollen, and the pouch enlarges slightly and becomes tumid and moist. There are corresponding internal changes (*see* p. 546). Oestrus lasts for 1 or 2 days, and ovulation probably occurs soon after its end (Hartman, 1923a), although Hill and O'Donoghue (1912) believe that heat may precede ovulation by as many as 5 days. The length of pregnancy is uncertain ; it probably lasts not less than 8 and not more than 14 days. In its absence pseudopregnancy occurs, and is associated with a series of changes in the reproductive tract and mammary glands, essentially similar to those which take place during gestation. The pouch enlarges, and the sebaceous, sweat and mammary glands, as well as the internal reproductive organs, hypertrophy. Marsupial cats, at the end of pseudopregnancy, have been seen to clean out the pouch for the reception of non-existent young, a fact which shows that the changes accompanying this condition may include even the behaviour normally associated only with parturition and the nursing of young. Anoestrus in *Dasyurus* lasts more than half the year.

Family *Phalangeridae*
Genera : *Trichosurus* ; *Phascolarctos* ; *Dromicia*

The silver-grey phalanger (*Trichosurus vulpecula*), according to Wood Jones (1924), breeds in June, but more recently Bolliger and Carrodus (1940) have stated that two mating periods occur, one in March and the other in August. Gestation lasts approximately 16 days, and a single young, which is retained in the pouch for five months, is the rule. Subsequently, the growing young can no longer be accommodated within the pouch itself, but continues to nurse from one of the greatly elongated nipples which protrude through the lips of the pouch.

According to Semon (1899), the sexual season of the native Australian " bear " or koala (*Phascolarctos cinereus*) in the Burnett River district, begins at the end of October. Since Semon failed to find pregnant females until the middle or end of November, it would seem that the mating season probably extends for at least 3 or 4 weeks. As in most marsupials, gestation is extremely short, the young arriving at a very early stage of development in the mother's pouch. The males experience a proper rutting season, during which they cry loudly, more frequently in the evening and night, but also during the day. This appears to be also true of *Trichosurus vulpecula* (*see* Hartman, 1923a). In this species and in certain other Australian types of marsupial, spermatorrhoea occurs frequently and must be considered as a physiological phenomenon (*see* Bolliger and Carrodus, 1938, and p. 60). Bolliger and Tow (1947) have reported that the scrotum of the adolescent castrate male *Trichosurus* can be transformed into a marsupial pouch by means of oestrogen and, temporarily and paradoxically, also by androgen.

The birth of two successive litters within a period of approximately six weeks in a *Dromicia concinna* Gould, a small Australian marsupial also belonging to the *Phalangeridae*, has been reported by Bowley (1939). The female had no access to males during this time, apart from her own very immature young, and the occurrence is considered by Bowley as an instance of delayed fertilisation.

Family *Macropodidae*
Genera : *Bettongia* ; *Dendrolagus* ; *Macropus* ; *Potorous*

The Tasmanian " rat " kangaroo (*Bettongia cuniculus*) has a breeding season which lasts at least from March to December (Flynn, 1930a), and during this period the animal is believed to be polyoestrous. This conclusion is not based on any direct evidence in captive specimens, but rests on the observation that most females taken during the breeding season are pregnant, and carry pouch young at the same time. Flynn did not obtain any material in January and February, but believes that these months are occupied by a period of reproductive rest or anoestrus.

Only a single young is produced at a time, and for this reason three of the four teats in *Bettongia* are usually unoccupied, unlike the condition in, e.g. *Didelphis* or *Dasyurus*, in which the number of new-born frequently exceeds that of the available teats in the pouch (*see* above).

Ovulation is spontaneous and unilateral, a single ovum being set free each time. Gestation lasts about 6 weeks, and lactation continues for about the same length of time.

An unusual feature of reproduction in this species is the fact, observed by Flynn, that during the first half of pregnancy the non-pregnant horn of the uterus is macroscopically and microscopically indistinguishable from the pregnant one. This condition of " pseudo-pregnancy " of the contralateral uterus persists until a few hours before term, when there is a sudden " convulsive expulsion of the contained lymph," accompanied by a partial breakdown of the glandular epithelium. Immediately after parturition the pseudopregnant horn undergoes prooestrous changes, and eventually pregnancy ensues in it. Thus, throughout the breeding season, there is an alternation between the two horns, one being pregnant while the other is in the pseudopregnant state (Fig. *4. 1*).

This finding is of considerable interest, since it is generally assumed that the non-pregnant horn of a bicornuate uterus does not undergo precisely the same changes as the horn containing embryonic sites (e.g. in the cow and ewe). A further inference from Flynn's observations is that in *Bettongia* one corpus luteum is responsible for the simultaneous development and maintenance of pregnancy and pseudopregnancy in the two horns of the uterus.

According to Matthews (1947b), there are reasons for believing that in the tree kangaroo, *Dendrolagus matschiei*, ovulation is not a spontaneous phenomenon, but depends on the stimulus of copulation. Matthews' observations were, however, based on the histological examination of a single specimen which had lived in captivity for about ten years.

Knowledge of reproduction in other members of the Macropodidae is both inadequate and conflicting. It is usually stated that pregnancy does not exceed six weeks in kangaroos and wallabies (Asdell, 1946), but several seemingly well-established cases reported by Wood Jones (1944) suggest that it may last very much longer. It is clear that more information is required about the length of time the spermatozoa may retain their fertilising capacity within the female reproductive tract.

On the other hand, there is now general agreement about the once very controversial subject of parturition in these animals.   The more pertinent information
about this process has been reviewed by Flynn (1928) and, more recently, by
Matthews (1943), who has himself contributed notes on the birth of a grey kangaroo
(*Macropus giganteus*).

The act of parturition resembles that outlined above for the opossum.   The
young kangaroo receives no direct help from the mother, and reaches the pouch by

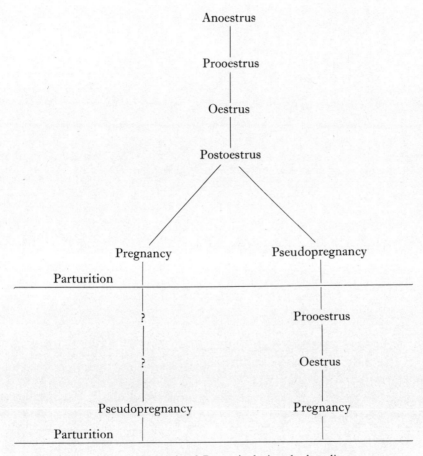

Fig. *4*. 1—The uterine cycle of *Bettongia* during the breeding season.
(Reproduced from Flynn, 1930a.)

its own exertions.   According to Matthews " the sole assistance rendered by the
female to the new-born is, apart from the assumption of a particular posture, the
preparation, by licking, of a moist track through the fur of the maternal abdominal
wall from cloaca to marsupium."   As shown in Fig. *4*. 2, the maternal cloaca protrudes markedly during parturition, thereby reducing the distance between it and
the pouch which the newly-born must traverse.   As already referred to, this is
also observed in *Echidna* (*see* Le Souef, Burrell and Traughton, 1926).   Lastly, in
some kangaroos, the dam is said to raise its tail, apparently with the object of
minimising the danger to the young of falling off before reaching the pouch (*see*

Vosseler, 1930). The total time taken by the young for this journey varies from 5 to about 30 minutes in different species of Macropodidae (Matthews, 1943).

The " median " mode of birth through a temporary or permanent median vaginal passage appears to be established for the great majority of marsupials

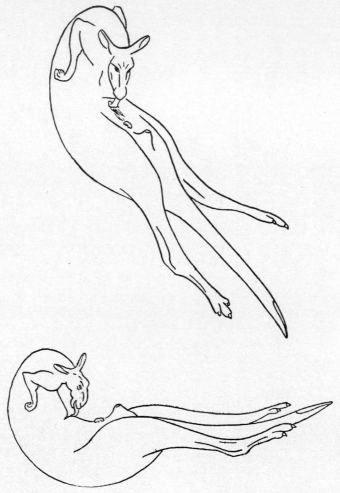

Fig. 4. 2—Birth in the kangaroo. The female licks a moist track in her fur, along which the new-born crawls to the pouch. (Reproduced from Matthews, 1943.)

(see Chapter 2). At least one well-authenticated case of delivery through the lateral vaginal canal in a dark " rat " kangaroo (Potorous tridactylus) is, however, on record (Flynn, 1923).

IV—Eutheria
(= Placentalia ; Monodelphia)

EDENTATA (= Xenarthra)

Fam. Dasypodidae
Dasypus (Armadillo)

Fam. *Bradipodidae*
Bradypus (Three-toed sloth)
Choloepus (Two-toed sloth)

The extraordinary facts of reproduction in some species of Edentata, though well established, are little known. The North and South American armadillos, *Dasypus* (*Tatusia*) *novemcinctus* and *D. hybridus*, have been extensively studied, but the sloths (Bradipodidae) and anteaters (Myrmecophagidae) appear to have received little attention.

In the Dasypodidae, the uterus is of the " simplex " type, as in primates, and a single pair of pectoral mammary glands is the rule.

Patterson (1913) and Hamlett (1932a, 1935a) have given detailed accounts of the mechanism of reproduction and early development of the nine-banded armadillo (*Dasypus novemcinctus*). One of the most interesting aspects of the sexual cycle in this species is the long interval which occurs between fertilisation and the attachment of the blastocyst to the uterus. Delay in implantation is known to occur in a variety of mammals (e.g. mustelids and deer), but *Dasypus* was one of the first species in which this phenomenon was firmly established.

In Texas the armadillo breeds during July, and most females are found to have ovulated by the end of this month (Hamlett, 1935a). Whether they do so spontaneously or only as a result of coitus appears to be unknown. Cleavage proceeds up to the formation of the blastocyst, and the ovum reaches the uterus in about the same stage of development as in other mammalian species. Further progress then ceases, and the embryonic vesicle remains quiescent in the uterine cavity without gaining attachment to its mucosa. This " free vesicle " stage lasts for $3\frac{1}{2}$ to 4 months, during which the corpus luteum, though of considerable size, appears to remain functionally inactive. In November the trophoblast and corpus luteum become active and implantation takes place, after which the blastocyst develops at a normal rate.

Birth of the litter occurs early in March or April, after a total length of pregnancy of almost 8 months, only half of which is taken up by the actual development of the young.

In the South American armadillo or " Mulita " (*D. hybridus*), implantation is stated to occur early in June, and parturition in October. The time of mating, and hence the duration of the quiescent stage, are unknown, but Hamlett (1935a) believes the latter lasts at least 2 months.

Polyembryony is a characteristic feature in both types of armadillo. It was first briefly reported in *D. hybridus* by von Ihering in 1895, and later confirmed and extensively investigated by Fernandez between 1909 and 1915 (*see* Wood Jones's comprehensive review, 1945). In *D. hybridus* there are usually eight in a litter, although as many as twelve young may be produced at a time. Only a single ovum from one follicle, and hence only one corpus luteum, are involved in each pregnancy, and the multiple embryos are derived by a process of budding from the originally single embryonic plate (*see* Record, 1951). According to Wood Jones, each of these segments " passes through all the stages of individual embryonic development," with the result that as many as 12 embryos of the same sex, each possessing its individual amnion, umbilical cord and placental area, are developed within a common chorionic cavity.

In the nine-banded armadillo of Texas (*D. novemcinctus*), the subdivision of the original ovum is less extensive, and in this species a set of identical quadruplets is usually produced in each pregnancy (Newman and Patterson, 1909, 1910).

Among other species of Dasypodidae, the one- and six-banded armadillos (*D. unicinctus* and *sexcinctus*), produce a single young at birth.   The hairy armadillo (*D. villosus*), however, is most remarkable in carrying two foetuses which externally appear to be monochorial, but which are actually derived from two separate ova. The investigations of Fernandez (1915) have shown that partial fusion of the foetal membranes occurs secondarily during embryonic development, thereby creating the impression of a single chorion containing twin embryos separated only by their respective amniotic vesicles (Wood Jones, 1945).

Sloths (Bradipodidae) are believed to breed throughout the year, but more usually during the dry season (Britton, 1941).   A single young is born after a gestation period, which probably lasts for between 4 and 6 months (Wislocki, 1927).   Parturition has been observed on a few occasions (*see* Britton, 1941).

PERISSODACTYLA

Fam. *Equidae*
>   *Equus* (Domestic horse ; donkey ; kiang ; zebra)

Fam. *Tapiridae*
>   *Tapirus* (Tapir)

Family Equidae

Heape (1900) was of the opinion that the mare is a " polyoestrous animal with a tendency towards monoestrum."   Some of the evidence now available for wild species of the genus *Equus* undoubtedly supports his view.   Thus, the kiang (*Equus kiang*) has its young only in June and July, both in captivity (Zuckerman, 1953), and in a state of nature (Lydekker, 1898b ; Blanford, 1881–91).   The semi-wild native mare of Saishuh Island, Japan, is also monoestrous (Satoh and Hoshi, 1932).   The breeding season lasts from April to September, ovulation apparently being limited to the period May–August.

Marshall (1936), in summarising unpublished observations by Dr. J. Hammond, writes : " In the case of horses, although in the more domestic breeds (i.e. in the ' better bred ' or more improved types) the dioestrous cycle may recur for a great part of the year, there is a definite tendency for foaling to occur in the spring. . . . In Canada, as with Britain, there is a very pronounced peak in May.   In the United States, which extends far down towards the Tropics, where the seasonal differences are less, there is for the whole country a definite peak, also in May, but not so pronounced as in Canada.   In Australia and New Zealand there are very marked peaks in October and November respectively, in the spring of these countries. . . .   The gestation period being eleven months the service peaks are in all cases a month later than the foaling peaks.   The results as a whole undoubtedly suggest a correlation between the sexual season and the incidence of daylight."

Oestrous cycles begin early in the spring and usually continue, in the unbred mare, well into the summer.   Breeding is also possible during the autumn and winter.   Recent studies (Seaborn, 1925 ; Aitken, 1927 ; Day, 1939a, b ; Heer,

1939 ; von Korff, 1939 ; Hammond and Wodzicki, 1941 ; Hirt, 1943 ; for review, *see* Asdell, 1946) show that the cycle varies greatly in length and that it averages about 22 days (the means collected by Asdell vary from 19 to 23 days). Exceptionally, oestrus may recur at four-weekly intervals. A belief that heavy mares have a longer cycle than light ones is not borne out by the facts (Asdell, 1946). The duration of heat (that is, the time when mares will mate) may vary from 3 to 54 days, but in most cases is 5 to 7 (McKenzie and Andrews, 1937; von Korff, 1939; Trum, 1940 ; Hammond and Wodzicki, 1941). In immature and senile mares it may continue for 10 to 15 days (Hammond, 1938a). Di- and metoestrus, i.e. the interval between the end of a previous heat period and the beginning of the following one, lasts about 16 days (Hammond, 1938b). In the spring and autumn, when food is less plentiful, mares tend to have longer oestrous and dioestrous periods (Day, 1939b).

Some authorities (Seaborn, 1925) divide the cycle in the mare into a period of rest lasting about 8 days, a prooestrus (" the preliminary period of refusal and delay ") of 3 days, oestrus (" the period of acceptance "), also lasting 3 days, and a metoestrus of approximately 10 days. Blood has been observed in the mare's prooestrous discharge, but is not generally present. The genitalia, however, are always swollen and congested during oestrus, and exude a glutinous secretion, while the clitoris and vulva often undergo a succession of spasmodic movements preceded by the discharge of small quantities of urine. Widening of the cervical canal is said to be a reliable sign of oestrus (von Korff, 1939).

The growth of the follicles can be followed by rectal palpation of the ovaries, and this method is frequently used to ascertain the most favourable time for service (Hirt, 1943). The size of the follicles may vary from that of a hazel nut to a fist, maximal dimensions being reached just before ovulation. Several follicles may mature simultaneously in the same ovary, but in most cases a single one ruptures, and only occasionally two (Gans, 1939).

Ovulation from the ovulation fossa (*see* p. 70) occurs spontaneously, and more frequently from the left ovary than from the right. Most observers agree that it usually takes place shortly before the end of heat (about the 6th day of oestrus ; *see* Hammond and Wodzicki, 1941 ; Asdell, 1946). Trum (1940), however, believes that conception is as frequent at the start as at the end of oestrus. Artificial insemination can be carried out up to 6 days before ovulation, but optimal results are obtained during the four preceding days. It is usually unsuccessful on the 7th day before, or from 2 to 24 hours after ovulation (Day, 1942). Fertilisation occasionally occurs 20 hours after the shedding of the egg (*see* Asdell, 1946), but as a rule the free ovum is not fertilisable for more than a few hours (Hammond, 1938a ; Day, 1942). Foetal migration from one horn of the uterus to the other is frequent (Amoroso, Hancock and Rowlands, 1948).

According to Young (1941), the mare is the only spontaneously ovulating species in which the common occurrence of heat without ovulation has been established. Ovulation may also occur in the absence of heat (Gans, 1939 ; Day, 1940), and it can be artificially provoked by various methods (*see* Hammond, 1946a).

The life-span of the corpus luteum is stated to be 15 to 17 days (Asdell, 1946). The corpus luteum which forms after the artificial rupture of a mature follicle reaches its maximum development by the 14th day and then gradually diminishes in size (Harrison, 1946). According to Hammond and Wodzicki (1941), the corpus luteum of the cycle persists anatomically " in a relatively inactive state " during the 2 or 3 oestrous cycles following its formation.

The urinary concentration of oestrogen during the normal cycle has been investigated by Mayer, Andrews and McKenzie (1940). These observers noted two peaks of excretion, one during oestrus, and a second and more marked one, between the 10th and 15th day after heat. Their study was, however, restricted to part of the cycle in a few mares.

Compared with other domestic animals, the anterior pituitary of the mare is exceptionally rich in follicle-stimulating hormone (Witschi, 1940), but relatively poor in luteinising hormone and prolactin (Chance, Rowlands and Young, 1939 ; West and Fevold, 1940). This is of particular interest in view of Asdell's suggestion (1946) that the long duration of oestrus may be directly related to the concentration of follicle-stimulating hormone in the pituitary gland.

Fillies reach sexual maturity when about one year old.

The length of gestation in the mare is very variable ; the averages for different breeds range from 329 to 345 days (see Asdell, 1946), with a standard deviation of about 9·5 days. According to the same author, lighter breeds tend to have longer gestation periods, while the age of the mare is of little significance. The duration of pregnancy may also vary seasonally (Hammond, 1938a).

Additional information about the duration of pregnancy in the *Equidae* has been provided by Ewart (1915).

Celtic pony	334–338 days.
Prjewalsky's horse	356–359 days.
Asses and zebras	358–385 days.

Two pregnancies in Burchell's zebra, recorded by Brown (1936), lasted 11 months and 6 days, and 11 months and 20 days, respectively. Matings between the horse and ass tend to produce gestation periods which lie about mid-way between those characteristic of each breed (Asdell, 1946).

As a rule one foal is born at a time. Twin pregnancies occur in 2–3 per cent of cases, but frequently result in abortion.

Heat sets in soon (as a rule one to two weeks : Hammond, 1938a ; Asdell, 1946) after parturition, or after surgical removal of the foetus. This post-partum oestrus, which is called the " foal heat," lasts on average 6 days. If the mare conceives at the foal heat, she may come into oestrus again 3 weeks later, and take the male (Wallace, 1907). The occurrence of heat during pregnancy has also been observed by Satoh and Hoshi (1933).

Suckling mares which come into heat tend to fail in their milk supply, and the quality of the milk appears to undergo some kind of change, for foals during the heat periods of their dams often suffer from diarrhoea. In non-suckling mares, the mammary gland becomes congested and increases in size during heat. At the same time some mares develop great excitability, and kick and squeal, becoming dangerous to approach and impossible to drive. There is, however, great variation, for other animals may pass through the " heat " periods without exhibiting any well-marked signs of their condition, which in a few instances can be determined only by the behaviour of the mare towards the stallion (see Wortley Axe, 1898 ; McKenzie and Andrews, 1937).

With the probable exception of the elephant, porcupine and the viscacha, a hystricoid rodent (*see* p. 283), the mare appears to be the only mammal in which the occurrence of ovulation and corpus luteum formation early during pregnancy is a normal and regular feature. Thus Day (1940) observed ovulation in a mare on the 23rd day of pregnancy, and Amoroso *et al.* (1948) have recovered tubal ova in 9 out of 14 mares which were between 46 and 73 days in foal. At about the same time gonadotrophic hormone can be first demonstrated in the serum (*see* below), and the corpus luteum of pregnancy begins to undergo degeneration. The newly formed corpora are stated to contain large amounts of progesterone and probably help to meet hormonal requirements during gestation. After 150 days the ovaries of the mare become fibrotic. They can be removed at 200 days without causing abortion (*see* Asdell, 1946). The interstitial cells of the foetal gonads undergo hypertrophy during intrauterine life (Cole, Hart, Lyons and Catchpole, 1933), and in consequence, the foetal gonads may be twice as heavy as the maternal ovaries during the second half of pregnancy (Amoroso and Rowlands, 1951). When they involute near term the interstitial cells disintegrate. Very similar findings in the ovaries of new-born fur seals have been reported by Amoroso (1951).

Gonadotrophic hormone is present in large amounts in the blood of the mare during the first half of pregnancy (Cole and Hart, 1930 ; Rowlands, 1947, 1949a). It appears about the 40th day, reaches a maximum between the 50th and 80th day, then diminishes gradually and cannot be identified after the 6th month (Day and Rowlands, 1940). Its concentration varies, but tends to be higher in small breeds and ponies than in larger breeds (Cole, 1938 ; Aylward and Ottoway, 1945 ; Day and Rowlands, 1947; Rowlands, 1949a). It is believed to be elaborated by the so-called " endometrial cups " of the pregnant horn of the uterus (*see* Rowlands, 1947 ; Amoroso, 1952).

Serum gonadotrophins are not excreted by the kidney, and hence no pregnancy test based on their presence in the urine is possible in the mare. On the other hand, the urine of pregnant females contains considerable amounts of oestrogen, though paradoxically less than that of the stallion, which is the richest known source of natural oestrogen (*see* Zondek, 1944). Other tests of pregnancy in the mare are discussed by Hammond (1938a), Miller and Day (1939) and Cowie (1948).

The breeding capacity of the horse is low compared with that of other domestic animals. According to data collected by Berliner (1946), only approximately 50 per cent of mares mated become pregnant and produce live foals. This reproductive inefficiency is at least partly due to biological factors residing in the male, and to merely technical ones such as the timing and duration of access of the stallion to the mare (*see* Hammond, 1938a).

Reproduction in the donkey (*Equus asinus* L.) appears to be essentially similar to that in the mare (Berliner, Streets, Means and Cowart, 1938 ; *see* Asdell, 1946).

Family *Tapiridae*

It is stated by Baker (1919) that the Brazilian tapir (*Tapirus terrestris*) gives birth at all times of the year, and that gestation lasts from 392 to 405 days, an astonishingly long period, considering the size of the animal.

ARTIODACTYLA

Suborder RUMINANTIA

Fam. *Bovidae*

    Subfam. *Bovinae*
- *Bos* (Domestic cattle)
- *Poëphagus* (Yak)
- *Bibos* (Gayal)
- *Bison* (American bison)
- *Bubalus* (Asiatic buffalo)
- *Syncerus* (African or Cape buffalo)

    Subfam. *Caprinae*
- *Ovis* (Domestic sheep, mouflon, argali, etc.)
- *Ammotragus* (" Maned " sheep)
- *Pseudois* (Nahur, Burrhel's wild sheep)

    Other genera of the Family *Bovidae* :
- *Capra* (Domestic goat, ibex, markhor)
- *Hemitragus* (Thar)
- *Cephalophus* (Duiker)
- *Antilope* (Antelope)
- *Redunca* (Reedbuck)
- *Tragelaphus* (Bushbuck)
- *Gazella* (Gazelle)
- *Oryx* (Oryx)
- *Taurotragus* (Eland)
- *Boselaphus* (Nilgai)

Fam. *Antilocapridae*
- *Antilocapra* (Pronghorn)

Fam. *Giraffidae*
- *Giraffa* (Giraffe)

Fam. *Cervidae*
- *Axis* (Axis deer)
- *Rusa* (Rusa deer, sambar)
- *Hyelaphus* (Hog deer)
- *Rucervus* (Thamin)
- *Cervus* (Red deer)
- *Dama* (Fallow deer)
- *Odocoileus* (American deer, mule deer)
- *Rangifer* (Reindeer)
- *Capreolus* (Roedeer)

Suborder TYLOPODA

Fam. *Camelidae*
- *Camelus* (Camel)
- *Lama* (Llama)

Suborder SUIFORMES (= Artiodactyla non-ruminantia)

Fam. *Suidae*
    Sus (Pig)

Fam. *Hippopotamidae*
    Hippopotamus (Hippopotamus)
    Choeropsis (Pygmy hippopotamus)

Suborder RUMINANTIA

Family *Bovidae*

Subfamily *Bovinae*

Genera : *Bos ; Bibos ; Poëphagus ; Bison ; Bubalus ; Syncerus*

Domestic cattle (*Bos taurus*) breed throughout the year, but under the conditions that prevail in the London and Whipsnade Zoological Gardens strains of
wild cattle, such as Highland cattle, breed only between February and November,
the greatest number of births occurring between March and June (Zuckerman,
1953). Under similar conditions the Zebu (*Bos indicus*) breeds throughout the
year, the Gayal (*Bibos frontalis*) from at least January to August, the Yak (*Poëphagus
grunniens*), the American bison (*Bison bison*), throughout the year. According to
Blanford (1888–91), however, wild yaks rut only in winter and bear their young in
the autumn, after a gestation period of 8·5 to 9 months (Brown, 1936). The wild
American bison is also said to have a limited sexual season and a definite season for
births (Catlin, 1841 ; Lydekker, 1898a ; Warren, 1910). It would seem therefore
that domestication raises the reproductive powers of wild cattle. As they get
older, however, an increasing proportion of domestic cows calve only in March,
April and May (Roberts, 1928). A similar seasonal incidence of calving is observed
in Zebu cattle in Africa, which calve mostly between June and September (Wilson,
1946). Analysis of a large series of data has also shown that breeding capacity in
the cow, although it may be continuous throughout the year, is always at its maximum during the summer months and weakest between November and January
(Hammond, 1927). True anoestrus (as distinct from ovulation with suppressed
symptoms of oestrus or " silent heat ") is confined to the winter months and
occurs almost exclusively among young animals, especially under hard feeding
conditions (Hammond, Jr., and Bhattacharya, 1944). During this time the ovary
as a rule contains only very small follicles.

The reproductive physiology of the cow has been extensively studied (Schmaltz,
1921 ; Zietzschmann, 1922 ; Murphey, 1924, 1926 ; Frei and Metzger, 1926 ;
Hammond, 1927 ; Cole, 1930 ; Anderson, 1936, 1941, 1944 ; Asdell, 1946). The
oestrous cycle is variable in length but usually lasts about 21 days, oestrus
itself occupying less than a day. In a recent account based on extensive records
from America, Asdell (1946) concludes that the mean length of the cycle in heifers
is 20·23 days with a standard deviation of 2·33 days (mode 20 days), and in cows
21·28 days with a standard deviation of 3·68 days (mode 21 days). Over 80 per
cent of all cycles in cows fall within a range of 18 to 24 days. Corresponding
figures for African Zebu cattle, given by Anderson (1944), are 23·03 days with a
standard deviation of 6·41 days (mode 22 days).

The heat period in cows is very short and lasts for about 13 to 14 hours (13·6 with a standard deviation of 3·9 hours ; Asdell, 1946). However, in Zebu cattle of Kenya the duration of oestrus is even shorter and averages only 4·8 hours with a standard deviation of 2·2 hours (Anderson, 1944). In this breed, the external signs of heat are so slight that vasectomised bulls are employed to establish the length of oestrus. Ovulation is spontaneous and is believed to occur regularly about 12 to 16 hours after the end of heat (Hammond, 1946a). Thus, both in respect to the shortness of the heat period and the occurrence of ovulation after, rather than during oestrus, the cow behaves in a very unusual way, compared with other mammals. In this connection Asdell (1946) points out that the follicle-stimulating hormone content of the pituitary gland and the output of oestrogen during the normal cycle and pregnancy are lower in the cow than in any other species investigated. In this author's opinion an effective level of oestrogenic stimulation prevails only in the earlier phases of follicular maturation, and ends before its completion, and hence before ovulation. The artificial induction of single and multiple ovulations in the cow has been reported by various workers (*see* Hammond, 1946a).

Vaginal bleeding occurs frequently after ovulation, especially in young cows and heifers (Trimberger, 1941 ; Weber, Morgan and McNutt, 1948). Neither the source nor the significance of this bleeding is entirely clear. It is about equally common in animals that conceive as in those that do not (Asdell, 1946). Most of the blood is thought to leave the uterus by a process of diapedesis, but epithelial disruption and direct capillary haemorrhage into the lumen of the uterus have been observed, especially in the intercotyledonary areas (Weber *et al.*, 1948 ; *see* p. 555). Hammond (1927) believes that at least some blood is of vaginal origin.

The average length of gestation in the cow is 280 days and ranges from 278 to 290 days in different breeds (Asdell, 1946). Approximately two natural services are required for conception (Anderson, 1941), but two-thirds of artificially inseminated cows conceive at the first opportunity. One calf is the rule, twins constituting 1·8 to 2·0 per cent of the total births. They are often of the " freemartin " type. Triplets and quadruplets may also occur, though much more rarely.

The ovarian cycle is as a rule unaffected by lactation, and cows are normally put to the bull soon after parturition (heat occurs from 3 to 7 weeks after calving). It is stated (Shortt, 1889) that in India cows do not seek the bull until 6 to 9 months after calving. Lactation can be artificially induced in heifers and cows by various experimental procedures (Folley and Malpress, 1944 ; Folley, Malpress and Young, 1944).

A periodic increase in the amount and acidity of the vaginal secretions takes place during the oestrous phase of the cycle. This is brought about by the action of the oestrogenic hormone, and manifests itself externally in the appearance of copious stringy mucus at the vulva. It is accompanied by liquefaction and increased penetrability of the highly viscous and tough mucous plug which closes the cervix at all other times (Blair, Folley, Malpress and Coppen, 1941 ; Brown, 1944).

Cyclical variations in the blood chemistry of the cow, correlated with the phases of the oestrous cycle, have been described by Frei and Demmel (1932). According to these workers the serum calcium of the cow, which is normally at a higher level than in bulls, is greater at oestrus than during dioestrus. The concentration of glucose shows corresponding changes.

Both the Indian and Cape buffalo (*Bubalus bubalis* and *Syncerus caffer*) appear to have restricted mating seasons in the wild, although in captivity they breed at all times of the year (Zuckerman, 1953). Blanford (1888–91) and Lydekker (1898a) state that the Indian buffalo pairs in the autumn, the young being born in the following summer after about ten months' gestation. The young of the Cape buffalo are born between January and March.

Subfamily *Caprinae*
Genera : *Ovis* ; *Ammotragus* ; *Pseudois*

Sheep present a complete gradation from the apparently monoestrous condition of some wild species to the extreme degree of polyoestrus of certain of the more domesticated breeds (Marshall, 1903).

The Barbary wild sheep (*Ammotragus lervia*) is said by Heape (1900) to be monoestrous. While it is true that most births occur between March and May in the London Zoological Gardens, young have, however, been born at all times of the year (Zuckerman, 1953). It is conceivable that different members of the species come into heat at different times of the year, but it is also possible that under the conditions of captivity some Barbary wild sheep become polyoestrous. Burrhel's wild sheep, *Pseudois nahoor*, breeds in captivity between May and August, and is almost certainly monoestrous. The mouflon, *Ovis musimon*, gives birth in the London Zoological Gardens between January and October, most young being dropped between March and May. It is believed that in captivity this species may experience two or more recurrent oestrous cycles each year. From Lydekker's account (1898a) it would seem, however, that *O. musimom*, *O. vignei*, *O. ammon* and *O. canadensis* in their wild condition are probably monoestrous, for their annual sexual season is of short duration, and occurs with great regularity. Similarly Prjewalsky's statements (1876) suggest that *O. poli*, *O. burrhel* and *O. argali* are monoestrous and breed only once a year.

In general the sexual season in wild sheep occurs in autumn, the actual time varying with the locality or climate. Thus *O. vignei* begins to breed in September in the Punjab, whereas, in Kashmir, its sexual season must be considerably later, since the young in that district are born about the beginning of June (Lydekker, 1898a).

Scotch black-faced sheep in the Highlands experience 2 oestrous cycles, each of 3 weeks' duration, so that the annual sexual season for these animals lasts 6 weeks. In the Lowlands, sheep of this breed may have at least 3 recurrent oestrous cycles in the absence of the ram, while according to flockmasters' personal observations, as many as 5 or 6 may occur under unusually favourable conditions. Grant (1934) states that the cycle in this breed of sheep lasts about 16 days and that heat continues for about 2 days. The reproductive behaviour of the Scotch black-faced sheep in the Highlands would seem to represent the natural habit of the breed more than its behaviour in the Lowlands, for sheep, in their wild state, are essentially mountain animals. Thus, in the Holarctic region, they are almost entirely confined to mountain districts, their range only just extending into the far warmer Oriental region. " The immense mountain ranges of Central Asia, the Pamir, and Thian-Shan of Turkestan may be looked upon as the centre of their habitat " (Flower and Lydekker, 1891).

The sexual season of hill sheep in Great Britain usually extends from about the middle of November until the end of the year. In exceptional circumstances individual sheep may experience oestrus at other times, such as April, after an early abortion in the winter. In other British breeds the sexual season is more prolonged. Thus in Suffolk cross Leicester-Cheviot sheep the season lasts from early October to late March and is fairly evenly spaced about the shortest day (Hammond, Jr., 1944). During the anoestrous period large follicles are commonly present in the ovaries and occasionally lambs are born at times which indicate that impregnation occurred in early August, an observation which shows that ovulation can occur well outside the normal limits of the breeding season (*see* Phillips, Fraps and Frank, 1946). Following lambing during the breeding season, there is also a lactation anoestrus, the length of which depends on the time of lambing (Hammond, Jr., and Bhattacharya, 1944). " Silent heat " (i.e. ovulation unaccompanied by overt oestrous manifestations) is believed to be frequent at the beginning of the sexual season (Grant, 1933), and may also occur towards its end.

Hampshire Down sheep are often given access to rams (or " tupped ") in the summer, but they do not, as a rule, breed more than once a year. The Limestone sheep of Westmorland and Derbyshire, and the Dorset Horn sheep of the south of England, are the only British sheep which are ordinarily capable of breeding more than once annually. Thus the main lambing season in the former is from the middle of February to the middle of March, but lambs are often born earlier, and when the ewes receive the ram soon after parturition a second crop of lambs may be born in August. Dorset Horn ewes frequently produce lambs twice a year, but the practice is discouraged as it is said to deteriorate the sheep. In this breed oestrus may continue to recur (in the absence of the ram) from the summer sexual season (when the sheep are tupped) until the late autumn or even longer.

Many foreign breeds of sheep lamb twice a year, e.g. the horned sheep which run half-wild in Patani, in the Malay Peninsula (Annandale, quoted by Marshall, 1922). A further example of high fecundity is provided by the indigenous sheep of India which, although scarcely ever supplied with any artificial food, produce lambs three times in two years. In this breed there is no definite season for lambing (Shortt, 1889).

Among the merino sheep in South Africa, the sexual season is April (the autumn month, corresponding to October in the northern hemisphere), but some sheep come into season earlier (Wallace, 1876). At high altitudes, however, where the sheep subsist entirely upon the natural produce of the veldt, the sexual season is May, or a month later than is the usual time in the Cape Province. On the other hand, in the low country below the second range of mountains, there are two seasons for " tupping," and lambs are produced twice a year. Under good conditions in the Transvaal, again, the merino has an uninterrupted series of oestrous cycles, but in years of drought, the succession of cycles is much curtailed (Quinlan and Maré, 1931). However, in the Western Free State merino ewes experience a prolonged anoestrous period (Küpfer, 1928).

In Argentina the merinos are reported to have two annual breeding seasons within the year (Wallace, 1904), but according to Phillips *et al.* (1946) this may only represent a single, though extensive, breeding season.

Probably the highest degree of sexual activity experienced by any sheep is displayed by certain Australian merinos. These are described as being able to breed throughout the year, a fact which implies, in the absence of gestation, an unbroken series of oestrous cycles. The report of the Chief Inspector of Stock for New South Wales (1891) divides the time of lambing into six periods which embrace the entire year.

The great variability in sexual activity which the sheep exhibits appears to depend largely on differences in food supply and climate, and the behaviour of black-faced sheep in Scotland and the merinos in Cape Colony affords direct evidence that this is the case. Indeed, the effect of the environment on the recurrence of breeding was noted long ago by Aristotle, who observes that " in some places where the weather is warm and fine and food is abundant," sheep may have lambs twice a year. The result of " flushing " (the practice of stimulating the generative system by supplying extra food or better pasture, and thereby increasing fertility) is further evidence of the effect of good nourishment upon sexual and reproductive powers. On the other hand, there can be no question that racial factors are also involved, as shown, for example, by English Limestone sheep, a mountain breed which can breed twice a year (*see* p. 246). Similarly, the indigenous sheep of India and the half-wild sheep of Patani show that an increase in the duration (or more frequent recurrence) of the sexual season is not necessarily an artificial condition resulting from increased food supply, etc.

Marshall (1937, 1942) has drawn attention to the relation which exists in sheep between the latitude of the habitat and the times of breeding. In general, the sexual season in the northern hemisphere begins in autumn, during the period of diminishing daylight, and continues into the winter. In the southern hemisphere, it occurs during the corresponding time of the year (i.e. spring). Marshall points out that sheep transferred from one hemisphere to the other rapidly adjust themselves to the changed seasons.

The first oestrus of the breeding season appears slightly later in ewe lambs than in mature ewes (McKenzie and Phillips, 1931 ; Cole and Miller, 1935 ; Hammond, Jr., 1944 ; Phillips *et al.*, 1946). According to Hammond, Jr., sexual activity begins at an age of about 180 days. If this age is attained after the middle of the season, heat does not occur until the next breeding period, when the animal may be 400 or more days old. The average age of lambs at sexual maturity is about 300 days.

The external physical signs of oestrus in the ewe are not very conspicuous, and often pass unnoticed. They consist of congestion of the vulva and a flow of mucus from the external genital aperture. These changes are more marked in Dorsets than in merinos. The length of the cycle can be determined by vaginal smears or by daily observation of the behaviour of the ewe with " teaser rams."

Observations on the duration of the cycle in sheep have been published by McKenzie and his associates (1931, 1933, 1937), Quinlan and Maré (1931), Bonfert (1933), Polovtzeva and Fomenko (1933), Grant (1934), Cole and Miller (1935), Hammond, Jr. (1944), and Phillips *et al.* (1946). All these observers found that the most frequent cycle-lengths are 16, 17 and 18 days. The available literature on the subject has been summarised by Asdell (1946), who states that the mean cycle length is 16·5 days and that merinos and rambouillets average about a day longer than most other breeds. The length of the cycle is not constant throughout the breeding season (McKenzie and Terrill, 1936 ; Hammond, Jr., 1944). Thus Hammond found that during the first half of the season cycle-length increases slowly but steadily from 16 to just over 17 days.   In the second half of the season it becomes more variable, but on the whole continues to lengthen further.

The duration of oestrus, according to McKenzie and Terrill (1937), ranges normally from 3 to 73 hours, with a mean of 29·3 hours and a mode of 21–27 hours. Asdell (1946) has concluded that it lasts normally not less than 24 hours or more than 48 hours, and on average 30–36 hours.   In the American rambouillet the duration of oestrus is usually 2 days (Cole and Miller, 1935), while in Australian merinos it is frequently less than 19 hours (Kelley, 1937).   The duration of the cycle in black-faced sheep is from 13 to 21 days, the variation appearing to depend partly upon the nature of the country in which they live and partly upon nutrition. Prooestrus and oestrus together do not as a rule occupy more than 2 or 3 days, and oestrus alone may last for only a few hours.

Ovulation is spontaneous, and is stated by different observers to occur between 18 and 24 hours, and 36 and 40 hours, from the beginning of heat or from 12 to 24 hours before its end (McKenzie and Terrill, 1937 ; Schott and Phillips, 1941). It is generally assumed that ovulation takes place before the end of heat, but in merino sheep of Australia and East Africa it is thought to occur shortly after the end of oestrus (Kelley, 1937 ; Anderson, 1938, 1941b).   Ovulation can be artificially induced in sheep by various types and combinations of pituitary gonadotrophin (Casida, 1946) and oestrogen (Hammond, Jr., Hammond and Parkes, 1942 ; Hammond, Jr., 1944), while the suppression of both oestrus and ovulation by adequate doses of progesterone has been reported by Dutt and Casida (1948).

According to McKenzie and Terrill (1937), the duration of the breeding season in the ewe, the duration of oestrus, the interval between the onset of heat and ovulation, and the number of follicles ruptured, increase from puberty to maturity. Grant has found, by means of the vaginal smear technique (*see* p. 557), that the length of cycle in the ewe is unaffected by sterile mating, which, on the other hand, shortens the duration of heat.   In the rat, as is well known, sterile mating prolongs dioestrus considerably.

Gestation in the sheep lasts 21 or 22 weeks (approximately 144 to 152 days ; Asdell, 1946).   The mean duration in the Tigai sheep is 154 days (Bonfert, 1933). As a rule 1 to 3 young are delivered at a lambing, but quadruplets are not infrequent in some breeds.   The incidence of multiple births increases from the beginning to the middle of the breeding season, after which it declines (Hammond, Jr., 1944).   Fecundity varies widely between different breeds, but tends to rise with the age of the ewe and reaches a peak at about the 6th year (Asdell, 1946 ; Hammond, 1952).   Normally oestrus does not occur during lactation, but exceptional instances in which it was observed are recorded by Cole and Miller (1935). From Casida and Warwick's data (1945) it appears that towards the end of the second month, pregnancy in the ewe may occasionally be maintained in the absence of the corpus luteum.

The reproductive capacity of Shropshire and Hampshire rams has been studied by McKenzie and Berliner (1937), and some of their observations are pertinent to the question of the breeding season of the sheep.   It appears that libido in these animals is relatively independent of spermatogenesis.   The actual number of spermatozoa ejaculated in a limited time is a good index of spermatogenic activity.   In Shropshire rams there are three periods : a distinct breeding season with high sperm production from October to January, a period of somewhat lower sex activity during the spring, and a season of greatly impaired breeding capacity in summer.   Hampshire rams show much less fluctuation in spermato-genesis, with a breeding season from August to January and only slightly impaired sex activity in summer.   A seasonal decline in sperm production towards the end of the breeding period has also been noticed in Suffolk and Leicester Cheviot rams (Chang, 1942).   According to Hafez (1951) the intensity of the sex drive of the ram is markedly influenced by the breed of the ewe.

Artificial insemination of sheep is widely practised throughout the world. Approximately 1,500 million spermatozoa are contained in an average ejaculate of 1 to 1·5 cc. volume (*see* Asdell, 1946).   As many as 30 ewes may be successfully inseminated from a single ejaculate (Hammond, Jr., 1944).   The free ovum is believed to be fertilisable for about 24 hours, while the fertilising power of the sperm within the female sex tract is approximately 14–40 hours (Hammond, 1946b).

Other genera of the family *Bovidae*

Genera : *Capra* ; *Hemitragus* ; *Cephalophus* ; *Antilope* ; *Redunca* ; *Tragelaphus* ; *Gazella* ; *Oryx* ; *Taurotragus* ; *Boselaphus*

Little is known of the breeding habits of other members of the *Bovidae*. Records of breeding in the London Zoological Gardens provide the following facts (Zuckerman, 1953) which, where indicated, are amplified by data from other sources.

The domestic goat, *Capra hircus*, and the strain known as the Cashmere goat, have fairly prolonged breeding seasons, but most births take place in April and May, suggesting that the peak of reproductive activity lies in the early winter months.   The Cretan goat, Angora goat and Grecian ibex give birth only between April and May.   The wild goat, *Capra caucasica* (Caucasian Tur) and *Capra falconeri* (Markhor) also have very restricted breeding seasons in captivity, all births occurring in May and June.

Kiesling (1923) gives the following information about the Saanen goat.   Sexual maturity is reached when the animals are 6 to 8 months old.   The mating season is in the autumn, and the animals kid in April and May after a gestation period of some 154 days.   Lactation continues for from 8 to 10 months.

The common goat, according to Hinterthür (1933), has a longer sexual season, which extends from July to February, but gestation lasts no longer than in the Saanen goat (approximately 150 days).   Turner (1936) found that domestic goats may become pregnant at any time of the year, but that the largest number of conceptions (30·5 per cent) occur in October, and the smallest (0·2 per cent) in May.

The most comprehensive survey of reproductive phenomena in the domestic goat is that of Phillips, Fraps and Frank (1946).   The length of the breeding season is about the same as in sheep.   Although a few mature animals can be bred late in July and August, the great majority do not come into oestrus until the latter part of September.   The peak of the sexual season lies between mid-September and mid-December.   Bissonnette (1941) has claimed that the onset of the season can be hastened by exposing goats to diminishing light.

The duration of the oestrous cycle varies considerably in different breeds and between kids and fully grown individuals of the same breed (*see* Phillips, Simmons and Schott, 1943 ; Asdell, 1946 ; Phillips *et al.*, 1946).   The usual cycle-length in mature goats is 20 to 21 days, approximately three-quarters of the cycles falling within a range of 18 to 24 days.   In kids, however, there is a large proportion of short cycles.

The average length of oestrus in goats is approximately 40 hours (Asdell, 1946).   Ovulation is spontaneous, as in the Bovidae generally, and occurs 30 to 36 hours after the beginning of heat (Harrison, 1948).   According to the same author, the development of the corpus luteum in the goat closely resembles that of the sheep and sow.   It reaches its largest size and probably greatest physiological activity on the 12th day after ovulation, and begins to degenerate histologically after the 15th day of the cycle.

In most temperate countries goats produce only a single litter of young, but in India and the Philippine Islands two kiddings may occur (Asdell, 1946).   Two kids are the rule, 1 to 3 are " common," while 4 and 5 are " rare."   Intersexual conditions of the reproductive tract and non-descent of the testes in males are frequent in this species.

The thar, *Hemitragus jemlahicus*, gives birth in captivity between May and September, but most young are born in June.   The peak of births in the London Zoological Gardens during the period 1891–1910 was in May, but in the next twenty-year period, 1911–30, it was in the first part of July (Zuckerman, 1953). In India this species is said to rut in September and October.

The Philantomba antelope or duiker, *Cephalophus maxwelli*, breeds in captivity throughout the year, as does the Indian blackbuck, *Antilope cervicapra*.   The latter animal also breeds continuously in the wild state, and has a gestation period of 6 months (Brown, 1936).   The reedbuck of Central Africa, *Redunca redunca bohor*, also gives birth at all times in the wild.   On the other hand, the closely-related bushbuck (*Tragelaphus roualigeni*), which lives in the same area, has a restricted breeding season (Schuster, 1929).

The Persian gazelle, *Gazella subgutturosa*, breeds in captivity only between May and September, most births occurring in May.   The sabre-horned oryx (*Oryx algazel*) and eland (*Taurotragus oryx*) likewise breed throughout the year in captivity, but in the latter species most births occur between May and July.

Marshall (1937, 1942), who has examined much of the naturalistic literature on the breeding habits of wild mammals, observes that with very few exceptions ruminants have their sexual season in the autumn, and thus differ from the majority of animals which mate in the spring.   The times of rut among the Bovidae are generally so arranged that young ruminants are born in the spring.   Exceptions to this rule appear to be the eland, which in the wild state is said to calve either in March (Hubbard, 1926) or between June and August (Sclater, 1900), and the Nilgai (*Boselaphus tragocamelus*) which in its native India and in the park at Woburn, England, ruts from March to May and drops its young in winter (Duke of Bedford and Marshall, 1942).   According to some observers (Fitzsimons, 1919–20) both these antelopes have lengthy and variable breeding seasons.

Family *Antilocapridae*

The pronghorn, *Antilocapra americana*, of North America, has its rutting season in September and October (Skinner, 1922).   These animals gather in bands, sometimes containing thousands of individuals, as the winter approaches (Nelson,

1925). Gestation lasts about 8 months, and the calving season is in May and June.

Family *Giraffidae*

No giraffe (*Giraffa camelopardalis*) has been born in the London Zoological Gardens outside the period February to September (Zuckerman, 1953). In South Africa the mating season in this species is said to be August to December (Fitzsimons, 1919–20). The period of gestation is approximately 14 to 15 months, and as a rule a single young is born. Gonadotrophic hormone is stated to have been detected in the urine of a pregnant female in which gestation lasted for 468 days (Wilkinson and de Fremery, 1940).

Family *Cervidae*

Genera : *Axis ; Rusa ; Hyelaphus ; Rucervus ; Cervus ; Dama ; Odocoileus ; Rangifer ; Capreolus*

With few exceptions members of the many genera of Cervidae are seasonal in their breeding habits both in the wild and in captivity (Zuckerman, 1953). Among the exceptions are the spotted deer of India, *Axis* (*Cervus*) *axis*, and the Molucca deer, *Rusa moluccensis*, which breed fairly evenly throughout the year. These species also breed continuously in the wild, although more young are said to be born in the cold season (Lydekker, 1898b, 1924). The hog deer, *Hyelaphus porcinus*, and the Sambar, *Rusa unicolor*, also breed without interruption in captivity in London, but in the former most young are born between February and June, and in the latter the peak of births occurs in May. The rutting season of the wild Sambar in Ceylon is very variable in its time of onset and may occur at any time of the year in different regions (Lydekker, 1924).

Unlike the species just referred to, the Javan Rusa deer (*Rusa hippelaphus*), and the Thamin (*Rucervus thamin*) of Upper Burma, consistently produce their young in late autumn and experience their rutting season in the spring. As pointed out by Bedford and Marshall, this is a " quite abnormal time for any deer which inhabit temperate countries." On the other hand, closely-allied species may exhibit quite different breeding habits in spite of living in identical environmental conditions (for instance, the reedbuck and bushbuck of South Africa ; *see* p. 250).

A detailed account of the breeding behaviour of red deer, *Cervus elaphus*, has been provided by Fraser Darling (1937). In Scotland rut and mating place take in September and October, and the young are born in June and July, the calves often suckling until they are yearlings. With the advent of the rutting season the behaviour of the stags changes profoundly. They wallow in peat bogs, fight, and roar—roaring being apparently correlated with the seasonal development of the larynx. Another characteristic of the rutting season is secretion of the infra-orbital glands. Casting of the antlers occurs long after the end of the rutting season, in April.

Wild fallow deer (*Dama dama*) rut in England in September and October (Lydekker, 1898b). The necks of the big bucks swell greatly during the first week, and the animals become more and more unsettled until about the fourth week, when the first calls are heard. The actual rut is as a rule short. The doe drops her calf about the beginning of June, and occasionally 2 or 3 young are born at a time. Sometimes, however, the females may come into heat at irregular times, and drop calves in any of the months after June—even as late as November (Millais, 1904–06). In the London Zoological Gardens young have been born in June, July and August.

The white-tailed deer of North America, *Odocoileus virginianus*, are said by Skinner (1929) to mate from mid-October to the end of November, the stags coming into season about two weeks before the hinds. In Florida mating occurs earlier. Gestation lasts about 7 months and the fawns, normally 2, are born late in May and June in the north and between January and March in the south (*see* Asdell, 1946). Barbour and Allen (1922) on the other hand, record the opinion of hunters that the subspecies *C. virginianus clavium* has no special season for breeding. Another species of the same genus, the mule deer, *Odocoileus hemionus*, gives birth in the wild in June and July (Gianini, 1932), as it also does in captivity in London (Zuckerman, 1953). The breeding season of the Lousiana deer is more variable. Mating usually occurs in February and most fawns are dropped in August. Reindeer, *Rangifer tarandus*, also, even in captivity, have a very restricted breeding season. In the London Zoological Gardens the season for births is May and June. Wild American elks or moose (*Alces gigas*) rut in September, and the young (frequently twins) are born late in May (Murie, 1944).

Heape (1900) has listed a variety of species which in the wild state experience a single annual sexual season, and give birth only during a very restricted part of the year, and which are therefore assumed to be monoestrous. Among the ungulates which belong to this category are the ibex, markhor, barasingha and thar, several species of Bovidae, as well as the black-tailed deer of Montana, red deer, roe deer, and fallow deer. However, no absolute proof of the monoestrous condition of these animals is available. Heape writes : " In all these cases there can be little over three weeks during which copulation takes place, and the extremely limited period during which parturition occurs strongly corroborates the view that this is the extent of the usual time during which sexual intercourse is possible. The fact that in captivity three weeks is the usual period which intervenes between two oestri in such animals, and the extreme probability that individual females do not all experience oestrus at exactly the same time . . . predispose one to believe that they are monoestrous in the wild state ; but, if the limit of time for coition is three weeks, there is still just time for the females to undergo two dioestrous cycles, and it is this possibility which prevents positive assertion on the matter."

As in the case of the red deer, the sexual season in many ruminants is a period of intense excitement, especially in those cases in which the males experience a definite rut. Thus, Catlin (1841), referring to the then not almost extinct American bisons, says : " The running season, which is in August and September, is the time when they congregate into such masses in some places as literally to blacken the prairies for miles together. It is no uncommon thing at this season, at these gatherings, to see several thousands in a mass, eddying and wheeling about under a cloud of dust, which is raised by the bulls as they are pawing in the dirt or engaged in desperate combats, as they constantly are, plunging and butting at each other in the most furious manner."

It has already been indicated that in stags the fighting weapons are the antlers, and that their growth is associated with the advent of the sexual season, after which they are cast off.

The seasonal changes in the state of the antlers and their correlation with the reproductive cycle in the male Virginia deer (*Odocoileus virginianus borealis*), have been studied by Wislocki (1943, 1949) and by Wislocki, Weatherford and Singer (1947). The testes and seminal vesicles are active and large at the time of the annual rut in autumn, and atrophic and small in the spring and early summer. Spermatogenesis begins in July, reaches a peak in October and diminishes by December and January. The interstitial cells of the testis in autumn give histo-chemical reactions which, in Wislocki's opinion, indicate the active formation of steroid hormones. In June these reactions are much less marked. The antlers begin their annual growth in this species (and almost all other types of deer in the northern hemisphere—with the only important exception of the European roe deer, *see* below) between the end of April and the beginning of May, i.e. at a time when the reproductive organs are most inactive. They reach their maximum degree of development, harden and shed their velvet in September, while the testes are rapidly enlarging, and are eventually lost in January, when the regression of the gonads has set in.

In view of these particular time relations, Wislocki concludes that the seasonal initiation of antler growth is independent of the testes. He assumes that it is brought about by an " antler-stimulating " hormone (probably not identical with the growth factor) of the anterior pituitary. This, he believes, is followed some months later by the release of gonadotrophic hormone which stimulates androgen production by the testes, and brings about, either alone or in combination with the pituitary factor, full maturation of the antlers. Shedding of the velvet occurs at the time of maximum testicular activity and can be experimentally brought about by androgen. Since the antlers are cast during the stage of gonadal involution in the winter, the process may be due to withdrawal of the testicular hormone. Casting can be precipitated by castration in the autumn, but at other times castration leads to the formation of deformed antlers which never shed their velvet. Androgen delays the process of casting (*see* also Marshall, 1922).

There is no direct evidence of the existence of an antler-growth promoting substance of non-testicular and possibly hypophysial origin, and Asdell (1946) has pointed out that if such a factor were involved, antler growth in the female might be expected, which is not normally observed in nature. This, however, may be due to the lack of an initial (" priming ") androgenic stimulus. Wislocki, Aub and Waldo (1947) have shown that testosterone can induce some antler growth in spayed does. Wislocki (1943) also refers to the well-known observation (*see* Donne, 1924) that the antler cycle as well as the breeding season is " shifted " when deer are taken across the equator.

The roe deer (*Capreolus capreolus*), which in England and Scotland is much rarer than the red deer, is peculiar in its reproductive behaviour and physiology. The stags are rarely separated from the hinds at any time of the year, and the social system is patriarchal rather than matriarchal, as it is in the red deer (Fraser Darling, 1937). The antlers of the male begin to regrow in January, and spermatogenesis starts in April (*see* Wislocki, 1943). According to Grohmann (1904) rut occurs in July and the beginning of August, and there is also a " false rut " in November. The young are born in May or June, and twinning is frequent.

Following the detailed researches of Bischoff (1854) and Keibel (1902), it is generally believed that the fertilised ovum remains dormant and unattached in the uterus for a considerable time before development proceeds, a phenomenon also observed in certain mustelids, the armadillo, etc. This view is supported by the results of breeding experiments in which females were isolated after service in the summer, and delivered their young in the following spring (*see* Grohmann, 1904 ; Prell, 1938).

Implantation is believed to be normally delayed until November or December (as in other species of deer), and the entire period of gestation lasts between 9 and 10 months (average 290 and range 273–318 days ; Prell, 1938). Of this total length approximately 140 days mark the period of non-attachment of the blastocyst, and the remaining 150 days the period of actual embryonic development. Exceptionally, however, implantation can occur immediately after the summer oestrus, in which case the length of pregnancy is reduced to its " basic " length (" Grundtragezeit ") of about 20 weeks (Prell, 1938).

Suborder TYLOPODA
Family *Camelidae*

All bactrian camels (*Camelus bactrianus*) bred in the London Zoological Gardens have been born in March and April. Leonard (1894) quotes Aristotle to the effect that in Arabia the camel ruts in November and early December, but his own observations suggest that the season is not fixed. Sven Hedin (1903) writes that wild camels in Tibet and Central Asia have their sexual season in December, January and February.

These findings suggest that the female camel may be polyoestrous, a conclusion which has been confirmed by more recent studies (reviewed by Asdell, 1946). The length of the oestrous cycle is variable, but appears to average 2 to 3 weeks, and heat is stated to last 3 to 4 days (range 1 to 7 days). The duration of gestation is about 12 to 13 months (Leonard, 1894). According to Asdell it varies from 370 to 440 days and averages 406 days. A single young is born at a time, and foal-heat is experienced by the female within 1 to 3 days of parturition, i.e. after a much shorter interval than in the mare and strictly comparable to the post-partum oestrus of rodents.

In the llama, *Lama glama*, pregnancy lasts 11 months (Brown, 1936), and in captivity in England these animals breed at any time of the year.

Suborder SUIFORMES
Family *Suidae*

Wild swine, *Sus scrofa*, have bred in captivity in London in all months of the year except January and February (Zuckerman, 1953), whereas in their natural state it is believed that these animals have only one annual sexual season. Whether or not the animals are monoestrous is unknown. The Indian wild pig (*S. cristatus*) may breed twice in the same year (Blanford, 1888–91).

In the domestic sow oestrus recurs throughout the year about every 21 days (Corner, 1921 ; Krallinger, 1933 ; Asdell, 1946), and lasts for 2 to 3 days, though it may continue up to 5 days. At the height of oestrus the vulva is often swollen and reddened, and there may be a serous or mucous vaginal discharge.

Ovulation is spontaneous, and takes place approximately 36 hours after the onset of heat, when there is also the highest percentage of fertile matings (*see* Asdell, 1946).

The development of the corpus luteum of the sow has been studied in detail by Corner (1915, 1919), while Kimura and Cornwell (1938) have assayed its hormone content. The last two workers found that " progestogen " is uniformly low from the 1st to the 10th day of the cycle, but that it rises sharply to a high peak between the 11th and 15th day and then drops abruptly to zero. These observations compare well with the results of Corner's (1921) histological studies on the life-span of the corpus luteum in this species (*see* also Eckstein, 1949).

The duration of pregnancy varies slightly in different breeds of pig, and averages 112–115 days. In wild sows, however, gestation is stated to last longer (127–128 days ; *see* Asdell, 1946). The size of the litter depends to a marked degree on the strain. Data collected by Asdell show that it may vary from 4 to 12 in different types of pig, both wild and domesticated.

Shortly after weaning, and less commonly after farrowing, sows come into heat.

The loss of litters from resorption of eggs or foetuses and stillbirths may amount to about 40 per cent and is " one of the major problems in pig breeding " (Asdell, 1946).

During pregnancy, oestrogen appears in the urine of the sow and reaches a maximum before parturition. Fluctuations in the gonadotrophic potency of the anterior pituitary in phase with the oestrous cycle have also been reported (*see* Asdell, 1946).

The domestic sow reaches sexual maturity before the age of one year, and sometimes as early as 4 months (Corner, 1921). According to Phillips and Zeller (1943) breeds differ in this respect, but the average age in " Poland-China " pigs is approximately 200 days with a range of 160 to about 250 days.

Sexual development in the male pig has been investigated by Phillips and Andrews (1936) and Phillips and Zeller (1943). Spermatozoa are first observed within the seminiferous tubules at 20–21 weeks, and are generally present in all boars after the age of 25 weeks.

Family *Hippopotamidae*

The Hippopotamus, *Hippopotamus amphibius*, has bred in captivity in London during the period August to November. In confinement it experiences oestrus at regular monthly intervals, but the basis for this conclusion appears to be somewhat slender (Wiltshire, 1883). Gestation lasts about 240 days (Brown, 1924 ; Vevers, 1926). The pigmy hippopotamus (*Choeropsis liberiensis* Morton) is said to be polyoestrous, and to have no regular breeding season (*see* Asdell, 1946). Gestation lasts for about 201 to 210 days, and the female comes into heat again within two weeks of parturition.

PROBOSCIDEA

Elephas (Asiatic elephant)
Loxodonta (African elephant)

The Indian elephant, *Elephas maximus* L., is believed to be polyoestrous, and the young are usually born in September, October and November (Blanford,

1888–91). The data assembled by Flower (1943) suggest, however, that births may occur throughout the year. In the African elephant, *Loxodonta africana*, most calves are delivered between November and March, but births also occur at other times of the year (Perry, 1953). In view of the length of gestation (about 22 months), it is clear that if a fixed sexual season does exist in this species, it cannot occur more frequently than once in two years.

The age at which sexual maturity is reached appears to vary considerably. Flower states that in the Indian elephant the usual age at which females produce their first calves is 15 to 16 years, while males are often sexually adult when 14 to 15 years old. Calving ages of 13, 10¼, 9 and 8 years have, however, been reported, and Perry's recent study indicates that wild African elephants first become pregnant at an age of about 10 years.

Reproductive maturity is reached before physical growth is complete. Full height, according to Flower, is generally attained between 19 and 20 years, but animals may continue to grow until the age of 23 or 24 years.

The " possible " length of the cycle in a captive female has been given as about 6 weeks (Perry, 1953). Pregnancy lasts 19 to 21 months in the Indian, and approximately 22 months in the African elephant (Flower, 1943). The mean duration of 15 pregnancies recorded by Burne (1943) in the African elephant is 20 months 27 days, with a range of 17 months 17 days to 24 months 13 days. A single young is the rule, but twins are occasionally born (Hundley, 1928). Three successive births in a captive female have been reported by Hvass (1932).

It is stated that Indian elephants have 3 to 5 calves during a lifetime (Williams, 1950), but Perry's more extensive observations (1953) suggest that, at any rate in wild African elephants, reproductive activity is more prolonged and extends over the greater part of the life-span. Out of a series of 81 females, 67 of them adult, Perry found not a single mature animal which was not either pregnant (with embryo *in utero*) or lactating. Many females were carrying as well as suckling young, and Perry believes that in individual females the mammary glands may be in continuous activity for a period of some 50 years, following the first pregnancy. A lactation interval approximately equal to the duration of gestation intervenes between successive pregnancies.

A striking feature of pregnancy in the African elephant is the formation and replacement of successive sets of corpora lutea, which recalls the cycle of events in the ovaries of the pregnant mare (*see* p. 241). According to Perry, the ovaries of females at any stage of gestation contain multiple corpora lutea of varying size, but the set present during early pregnancy is not identical with the one found near term. The first crop arises before conception, and consists of a number of small and relatively short-lived corpora, some formed by ovulation and others by luteinisation of non-ovulated follicles. It is followed by a second series of " accessory " corpora lutea during early pregnancy. These are replaced by a third set at about half-term. This last generation persists for the remainder of pregnancy and regresses rapidly after parturition.

In mature males swelling of the pre-orbital or " musth " glands occurs several times during the year. It subsides in old age. The phenomenon does not appear to be connected with sexual activity, since mating may take place when these glands are not secreting (Schneider, 1930 ; Williams, 1950).

HYRACOIDEA
Procavia (Hyrax ; Dassie)

Very little is known about the length of the breeding season in the dassie (*Procavia capensis*). According to van der Horst (1941), the young are born in November and December. Wislocki and van der Westhuysen (1940) refer to seven " quite advanced pregnancies " observed in specimens obtained from Kenya Colony during January, March and April. The possibility that two litters are produced annually cannot be discounted.

The characteristics of the oestrous cycle are not known, but the gestation period is stated to be $7\frac{1}{2}$ months (*see* Asdell, 1946). Litters vary in size, the modal number of embryos being 2 and the range 1 to 6 (Wislocki and van der Westhuysen, 1940).

LAGOMORPHA

Fam. *Leporidae*
        Oryctolagus (Rabbit)
        Sylvilagus (Cottontail rabbit)
        Lepus (Hare)

Oryctolagus

The rabbit, *O. cuniculus*, belongs to the small group of mammals in which it has been definitely established that ovulation is normally dependent on the coital stimulus. This peculiarity, which was first noted by Heape in 1905, and closely studied in the classical researches of Ancel and Bouin (1909a, b, c, etc. ; *see* Knaus, 1950) has permitted a variety of investigations and observations which cannot be made in spontaneously ovulating species. The only other animals which are known to behave similarly in this respect are the ferret, cat, ground squirrel, short-tailed shrew, and mink, and possibly the hare, weasel, Asiatic vole (*Microtus guentheri*), certain marsupials (e.g. *Didelphis azarae*), and a tropical fruit bat (*Pteropus giganteus*).

The wild rabbit has a fairly sharply defined breeding season. In Caernarvonshire, Wales, it begins in January and ends in June (Brambell, 1944–45). During this period reproductive activity is intense, and at the height of the season, in April and May, between 90 per cent and 100 per cent of females carry young. After July fewer than 10 per cent are pregnant and by November usually none. In exceptionally warm weather, however, some wild does may litter in late autumn or even in winter.

Under suitable conditions, domesticated rabbits in England may breed at all times of the year, although they frequently experience a period of sexual inactivity during autumn and winter.

Laboratory observation has shown that about 80 per cent of isolated does are in oestrus and will accept the male during April, but only 25 per cent in October and November (Hammond, 1925 ; Friedman, 1938). In the United States July to September are said to be the poorest months for breeding (Asdell, 1946).

There is no regular oestrous cycle in the rabbit, does " always being in a condition of oestrum when conditions of nutrition are favourable " (Hammond, 1925).

Short " dioestrous " periods may, however, occur during the breeding season when does will refuse the male, possibly as a result of adverse nutritional conditions.   Refusal consists in the assumption of a squatting position and avoidance of the male, rathei than in any truly antagonistic attitude towards the opposite sex (Young, 1941).

Oestrus is not as sharply demarcated in the rabbit as it is in most mammals, nor can it be determined by examination of vaginal smears (Kunde and Proud, 1929). Moreover, domesticated and wild does will accept the buck, although with reduced frequency, both in pseudopregnancy and pregnancy.   The only external sign of oestrus, congestion and purple coloration of the external genitalia, is also somewhat non-specific, for it can often be observed throughout pregnancy (Kunde and Proud, 1929), while on the other hand, it may be absent when the doe is ready to mate (Friedman, 1938).

In the absence of the buck the female remains in heat, and Hammond (1925) has observed does in this condition for up to 36 days.   During this time follicular maturation cycles of about 7 to 10 days' duration follow each other (Hill and White, 1933).   The duration of these cycles is not affected by variations in the amount of light to which the doe is exposed (Smelser, Walton and Whetham, 1934).   It is believed that heat in the rabbit depends on the presence of ovarian follicles of a certain, minimal size (see Young, 1941).

Following the stimulus of coitus, the maturing follicles grow and eventually rupture.   The exact mechanism of ovulation is unknown, but Markee and Hinsey (1936) believe that it is brought about by a rise in intra-follicular pressure, accompanied by " some local change in the wall of the ovary," whereby " a portion of it is removed at the time of rupture."

Usually, ovulation occurs about 10 hours after coitus.   Walton and Hammond (1928) have shown that the reaction is very precise in its time relations, which makes it possible to observe the process of ovulation during laparotomy carried out 10 hours following copulation.   The desire to mate, which persists for 12 to 30 hours after rupture of the follicles, is in abeyance for a short time, and then returns at various intervals after the 40th hour.   By the 14th day about 100 per cent of pregnant does will copulate.   Pseudopregnant rabbits also will accept the male, though less frequently.

Ovulation does not always follow coitus, and on the other hand it sometimes occurs after sexual excitement without coitus—for example, when does jump each other, or when the external genitalia of the doe are stimulated manually (see Fee and Parkes, 1930).   Ovulation does not, however, result from coitus during pregnancy, and Hammond believes that no authentic instances of natural superfoetation have been reported.   Ovulation also does not occur until the 16th to 20th days of pseudopregnancy, which is the time when the influence of the corpora lutea is waning (see below).   Observations made by Hammond to test the point showed that it is the corpus luteum which prevents ovulation during pregnancy and pseudo-pregnancy, and this conclusion has been confirmed in experiments in which corpus luteum hormone itself has been used (Makepeace, Weinstein and Friedman, 1937). More recently a direct inhibitory action of the corpus luteum on fertility (i.e. on the capacity of artificially ovulated ova to be fertilised) in the rabbit has been postulated by Casida (1946).

The nature of the exteroceptive stimulus which is responsible for ovulation is not fully understood. The afferent nervous pathways arising from the external genitalia do not seem to be involved, for Fee and Parkes (1930) have shown that a normal ovulatory response is obtained after local anaesthesia of the vulva and vagina. Hammond's analysis of the problem implies that any form of exteroceptive stimulation which leads to an orgasm may cause ovulation. But, apart from the diffuse conditions of excitement (noted above) by which it may be released, ovulation has also been reported as occurring after diverse experimental procedures such as electrical stimulation of the brain and lumbosacral cord (Marshall and Verney, 1936) ; pituitary gland and hypothalamus (Harris, 1937 ; Markee, Sawyer and Hollinshead, 1946) ; and tuber cinereum (Harris, 1948a) ; also as a result of injections of anterior pituitary in midbrain and midbrain-hypophysectomised animals (Hinsey and Markee, 1933a) ; as well as in rabbits whose superior cervical sympathetic ganglia and sympathetic trunks have been extirpated (Haterius, 1933 ; Hinsey and Markee, 1933b). On the other hand, Friedgood and Pincus (1935) observed ovulation after electrical stimulation of the superior cervical ganglia, a result which Haterius (1934) previously had failed to obtain. A review of this problem is given by Harris (1948b).

Ovulation itself, it is generally believed, depends on the release of gonadotrophin, in all probability the luteinising hormone, by the anterior pituitary. Removal of this gland within an hour of copulation prevents ovulation (Fee and Parkes, 1929). Coitus in the oestrous rabbit leads to an increase in the blood concentration of ovulation hormone (McPhail, Parkes and White, 1933), and to a rapid diminution of the gonadotrophic potency of the pituitary (Hill, 1935 ; Friedman and Friedman, 1939). Following copulation on the 9th day of pseudopregnancy, no such depletion is observed, indicating that the non-occurrence of ovulation during pseudopregnancy is due to the inadequate release of gonadotrophin from the hypophysis (Makepeace, Weinstein and Friedman, 1938). Ovulation can be artificially induced in intact oestrous and hypophysectomised does by suitable pituitary preparations (Hill and Parkes, 1931 ; McPhail, 1933b ; White and Leonard, 1933).

The mechanism responsible for the release of gonadotrophin from the pituitary has been closely studied. There is some evidence that the adenohypophysis is under neural, probably hypothalamic control (Harris, 1937 ; 1948b ; Brooks, 1938 ; Westman and Jacobsohn, 1940 ; Markee et al., 1946). The manner in which it is stimulated, and the pathways by which the stimulation is conveyed, are, however, not fully understood. Neither the cervical vagus and sympathetic trunk (Haterius, 1933 ; Markee et al., 1946), nor the greater superficial petrosal nerve (Vogt, 1942) are thought to be concerned. Most workers believe that very few nerve fibres end in the anterior lobe, but Vazquez-Lopez (1949) has claimed that well-developed bundles of fibres arising from the hypothalamic-hypophysial tract are distributed to the glandular cells in all parts of the adenohypophysis. His findings have been criticised on technical grounds by Harris (1950) and await confirmation.

Harris and Green suggest that the pathway by which the hypothalamus influences the adenohypophysis is the portal system of vessels which connect the infundibular stem with the pituitary body (see Green and Harris, 1947, 1949 ; Harris, 1949). Such a vascular network exists in a variety of mammalian species including man (Popa and Fielding, 1930, 1933 ; Wislocki and King, 1936 ; Green and Harris, 1947 ; Harris, 1950). On the strength of their anatomical findings, Harris and Green suggest that a humoral substance (or " chemotransmittor ") is liberated by the hypothalamus and carried *via* the portal vessels to the anterior hypophysial lobe, thereby regulating its activity. On the other hand, complete isolation of the pituitary is compatible with normal gonadotrophic function.

Ovulation can be artificially provoked by many diverse procedures (*see* Bradbury, 1944 ; Harris, 1948b).   It is easily induced by gonadotrophin (*see* above) and has been reported following mechanical stimulation of the vagina in oestro- genised does (Sawyer, 1949), and even, on occasion, " spontaneously " after com- bined oestrogen and progesterone treatment (Sawyer, Everett and Markee, 1950), though not, normally, after mechanical irritation of the vagina (Hammond, 1925). The length of pregnancy and pseudopregnancy may be considerably prolonged either by the production of new corpora lutea (with gonadotrophin : *see* Snyder, 1938), or by stimulating the maintenance of the corpora lutea of pregnancy by means of progesterone or oestrogen near term (Robson, 1940, 1947 ; Heckel and Allen, 1938, 1939).   Oestrous behaviour and ovulation can also be induced in pregnant or pseudopregnant rabbits (e.g. already possessing functional corpora lutea) injected with oestrogen before being mated with normal bucks (Klein, 1947).

The age of puberty varies with the breed (being earlier in small breeds : Farris, 1950), state of nutrition, and the time of year the doe is born.   The first coitus, which usually precedes the first ovulation by from 1 to 2 months, occurs at 8·5 months for does born in March and April, and at 5·3 months for does born from October to December (Hammond, 1925).

Pregnancy lasts from 30 to 35 days, 31 to 32 days being the average, and there is some indication that its length is influenced by the size and number of young that are carried (*see* Wishart and Hammond, 1933 ; Hammond, 1934a).   Pregnancy also appears to be shortest when breeding conditions are at their best.

The number of ova shed at each ovulation (and hence the size of the litter) varies with the genetic strain, averaging, for example, 1 in one and 12 in another, 7 being the rule (Hammond, 1925, 1928, 1930, 1933, 1934a ; Asdell, 1946).   In wild rabbits the modal number is 5, the range being 1 to 9 (Brambell, 1944–45).   Intrauterine mortality and failure of fertilisation are other factors which influence the number of young in a litter.   Thus in the domestic type of rabbit approximately 20 per cent of conceptions fail to develop to term, partly as a result of foetal absorption due to genetic factors acting through the maternal organism (Hammond, 1928, 1933, 1934b).   In wild rabbits in Wales, pre-natal mortality is even higher, and as many as 60 per cent of litters conceived may be lost through death and resorption of embryos (Brambell, 1942, 1944–45, 1948). In litters which survive to term the loss is estimated at between 9 and 10 per cent.

The onset of labour in the rabbit is thought to be related to the pressure exerted by the products of conception upon the placental vascular bed (*see* Reynolds and Foster, 1939 ; Reynolds, 1949).

Lactation lasts 50 to 60 days, and at the end of this period the doe can be re-bred at once (*see* Farris, 1950).

Rabbits, whether tame or wild, come into heat soon after parturition, and healthy post-partum females deprived of their litter can be consistently depended upon to be in oestrus (Friedman, 1938).   Well-fed rabbits suckling only one or two young easily become pregnant, implantation not being delayed as in the lactating rat or mouse.   If the suckled litter comprises more than three or four, the new set of embryos die in the blastocyst stage (*see* Hammond, 1925).

Pseudopregnancy, as indicated above, results when the ova liberated at ovulation are not fertilised.   In this condition, which is very rarely found in wild does (Brambell, 1944–45), corpora lutea develop and remain active for about two weeks (*see* below).   Their secretions cause changes in the uterus (*see* p. 563), and in the mammary glands, and the phase culminates between the 16th and 19th days with the production of milk and with nest-building.   Mating and ovulation may then recur (Hammond, 1925).

The work of Knaus (1927, 1929, 1930a, b ; for review *see* Robson, 1947, and Knaus, 1950) has clearly shown that the reactivity of the rabbit's uterus is regulated by, and varies markedly with, the type of hormonic stimulation to which it is sub-jected.   When under the influence of oestrogen (or during the follicular phase of the " cycle "), the myometrium shows spontaneous activity and a ready response to post-pituitary extract.   During pregnancy and pseudopregnancy (or following the injection of progesterone), spontaneous activity is diminished and the response to pituitrin abolished.   Physiologically, this " desensitisation " is induced very rapidly (about 32 hours after copulation ; *see* Knaus, 1950), and is thus a reliable index of luteal activity.   In this way Knaus has established that the active secretory phase of the corpus luteum of pseudopregnancy lasts about $13\frac{1}{2}$ days and that of pregnancy for at least twice this time.

As in the guinea-pig, the life of the corpus luteum of the rabbit can be prolonged by removal of the uterus, but quantitatively the effect is less marked in the latter species.   Thus Asdell and Hammond (1933) found that in hysterectomised pseudo-pregnant rabbits the corpus luteum functions for about 30 days, as compared with about 15 days in intact controls.   Similar results have been reported by Loeb and Smith (1936) and Chu, Lee and You (1944–46).   The last workers also found that the survival period of the corpora lutea of hysterectomised pseudopregnant does could be shortened and restored to approximately the normal span by the auto-implantation of uterine tissue.   On the other hand, removal of the uterus and its contents in pregnant animals causes a shortening of the functional life of the corpus luteum (Greep, 1941 ; Chu *et al.*, 1944).   The latter authors believe that this effect is due mainly to the removal of the placenta, since it can be abolished by the implantation of placental tissue and by the injection of oestrogen.

Eggs artificially ovulated in the pseudopregnant rabbit by means of pituitary extracts are generally unfertilisable (Murphree, Warwick, Casida and McShan, 1947).   According to Austin (1949a), this apparent infertility during pseudo-pregnancy is due partly to the inadequate transport of sperms along the female reproductive tract, and partly to the conditions existing within the Fallopian tubes, in particular their abnormal motility.

The fact that the rabbit normally ovulates only after mating has been taken advantage of in investigations of the survival of the sperm and of the time, in relation to ovulation, during which conception is possible (Hammond, 1925, 1930, 1934a, 1941 ; Hammond and Asdell, 1926 ; Walton and Hammond, 1928).   The findings obtained by these workers suggest that sperm deposited in the female reproductive tract retain their fertilising capacity for 30 hours in the rabbit, but that the free ovum remains in a fertilisable state for only 6 hours. More recently, the chemical composition of rabbit semen has been investigated (Davies and Mann,

1947 ; Mann and Lutwak-Mann, 1951), while Chang (1946) has discussed the relation between the concentration and fertilising capacity of sperm suspensions following artificial insemination (*see* also Walton, 1927). The suggestion that hyaluronidase may increase the fertilising capacity of dilute semen (McClean and Rowlands, 1942) has not been substantiated by subsequent work (Chang, 1950).

Certain aspects of reproduction in the wild rabbit have already been mentioned. According to Brambell (1944–45), the wild variety differs from the tame in " (a) the sharp delimitation of the breeding season, (b) the intensity of breeding during the season, (c) the maintenance of pregnancy during lactation normally, and (d) the extreme rarity of pseudopregnancy."

The successful crossing of wild bucks with domesticated does has been reported by Wilson (1936). Litters are, however, difficult to obtain, mainly because of the wild male's shyness when mated under laboratory conditions.

Sylvilagus

The North American cottontail rabbit (*S. floridanus* Allen), according to data collected by Asdell (1946), is polyoestrous and breeds from the middle of January to August, during which period several litters are produced. Gestation lasts approximately 4 weeks and 4 to 5 young are born as a rule. The testes of the male are stated to be scrotal only during the sexual season, as in the snowshoe hare.

Lepus

Several naturalistic studies have been made of the snowshoe hare, *L. americanus phaeonotus* (Grange, 1932 ; Aldous, 1937 ; *see* also Asdell, 1946). The females begin to breed in their second year, and from then on they have two and even three litters each year. The breeding season lasts from March to August, and gestation continues for about 36 days. The number of young in each litter varies according to the food supply, the average being about 2·4.

The testes of the male, which also first mates in its second season, undergo seasonal changes in size and position, being largest and fully descended in March, and smallest, as well as abdominal, in September.

Beyond the fact that litters have been obtained in England throughout the year (Barrett-Hamilton, 1910), little was known until recently about the reproductive habits of the common hare (*L. europaeus* Pallas). The animal is most difficult to maintain in captivity, but after a careful study of its characteristics and needs, and by keeping it free from infection, Hediger (1948, 1950) has raised three successive generations of hares at the Basle Zoological Gardens. He has confirmed that females breed at all times of the year, and established the length of gestation as 42 days. Hediger also noticed that pregnancy always occurs when a captive female is permitted to copulate, and he infers from this observation that ovulation in the hare, as in the domestic rabbit, is induced by the stimulus of mating. A gravid female frequently allows itself to be covered again shortly before delivery, and may then bear a second litter of young within 39 days of the first. The natural occurrence of ovulation during pregnancy has been noted in a few other species (e.g. mare, elephant), but the phenomenon of superfoetation as a " normal event " (Hediger, 1950) appears to be peculiar to the wild hare.

RODENTIA

Fam. *Sciuridae*
    Sciurus (Squirrel)
    Tamias (Chipmunk)
    Cynomys (Prairie " dog ")
    Citellus (Ground squirrel ; spermophile)
    Marmota (Woodchuck)
    Glaucomys (Flying squirrel)

Fam. *Castoridae*
    Castor (Beaver)

Fam. *Geomyidae*
    Geomys (Pocket gopher)
    Dipodomys (" Kangaroo rat ")
    Microdipodops (Dwarf pocket " rat ")

Fam. *Cricetidae*
  Subfam. *Cricetinae*
    Cricetulus (Chinese hamster)
    Cricetus (Golden hamster)
    Sigmodon (Cotton rat)
  Subfam. *Microtinae*
    Clethrionomys (Bank vole)
    Arvicola (Water vole)
  Other *Cricetidae*
    Microtus (Field mouse)
    Peromyscus (Deer mouse)
    Phenacomys (Tree mouse)
    Reithrodontomys (Harvest mouse)
    Onychomys (Grasshopper mouse)
    Neotoma (Wood rat)
    Synaptomys (Lemming mouse)
    Ondatra (Musk rat)

Fam. *Muridae*
    Rattus (Common rat)
    Mus (Common mouse)
    Mastomys (Multimammate mouse)

Fam. *Hystricidae*
    Hystrix (Old-world porcupine)

Fam. *Erethizontidae*
    Erethizon (New-world porcupine)

Fam. *Caviidae*
    Cavia (Guinea-pig ; cavy)

Fam. *Octodontidae*
    Octodon (Chilian bush rat ; degu)

Fam. *Capromyidae*
    Myocastor (Nutria ; coypu)

Fam. *Dasyproctidae*
>   *Dasyprocta* (Agouti)

Fam. *Chinchillidae*
>   *Chinchilla* (Chinchilla)
>   *Lagidium* (Mountain viscacha)

The rodents comprise a large number of species which differ widely in their reproductive patterns.

Most are polyoestrous, and have one annual breeding season which varies in length, and which in favourable environmental conditions may extend over the greater part of the year. Thus Baker (1930), in a study of the wild mouse, *Apodemus sylvaticus*, and the bank vole, *Clethrionomys* (*Evotomys*) *glareolus*, in the country around Oxford, observed the complete cessation of reproduction, affecting the males and females of both species, during the winter 1925–26, " a certain amount " of reproductive activity in the following winter, while breeding continued with only a small break throughout the winter 1927–28. The progressive increase in the rate of reproduction over the three winters was not correlated with any differences in such obvious environmental factors as temperature or length of day. Comparison of the functional condition of the male and female gonads and accessory organs in different months of the year showed that it is the female which in the main controls the length of the breeding season and the amount of reproduction. The onset and end of the breeding season of the female are gradual, whereas fecundity in the male is established more suddenly (about March). In both species the height of the season is reached during the summer months, when the size of litters is greatest.

In subsequent studies (Baker and Ranson, 1932a, b; 1933), specimens of the field mouse, *Microtus agrestis*, were trapped at three equidistant points on a north–south line in England, Scotland and Wales. During the two years 1930 and 1931, the breeding season lasted from February or March to September or October. Reproduction began latest in the most southerly of the three areas studied, and continued longest in the most northerly. There was some indication of a positive correlation between the hours of sunshine per month and the breeding condition of the mice, a conclusion which was strengthened by experimental study. Food and temperature appeared to be of secondary importance. Further analysis indicated that the majority of the mature animals, both male and female, die off in the autumn and early winter, and that each year's breeding community consists mainly of the previous year's young.

Family *Sciuridae*

Genera : *Sciurus* ; *Tamias* ; *Cynomys* ; *Citellus* ; *Marmota* ; *Glaucomys*

Sciurus

According to Klugh (1927), the red squirrel, *S. vulgaris*, mates in March, the young being born in May. In England it is said to breed early in spring and again in July and August (Millais, 1905). Rowlands (1938), however, collected pregnant females in every month from December to July, while the reproductive tract of females obtained between August and December was in an anoestrous condition. Since gestation in the red squirrel lasts from 32 to 40 days (*see* Asdell, 1946), it follows that the female is polyoestrous over the first half or so of the year. Sexually active males were found at all times between November and July, and Rowlands considers that the fertile period of the male may be even more extensive than this finding suggests.

According to data assembled by Asdell (1946), the fox squirrel of North America (*S. niger* L.) also has a prolonged breeding season, which begins in the winter and lasts until the summer. Two litters with a modal number of 3 young appear to be the rule, and gestation is thought to last for approximately 45 days.

Deanesly and Parkes (1933b) obtained pregnant grey squirrels, *S. carolinensis*, at all times between January and July, and in an analysis of the anatomical condition of all the specimens in their collection, concluded that in England "young are born in the spring and summer . . . and reach adult body weight by the autumn. When rather less than a year old, about February or June, according to their date of birth, they come into oestrus and become pregnant. Anoestrus eventually sets in and continues through the winter. In the spring of the next year these animals again become pregnant. It is not possible to say definitely whether all parous squirrels breed early in the year, possibly some remain quiescent till May or June so that their breeding period overlaps with that of the late first-year animals . . . animals breeding early may also have a second litter in the same year. . . . Those breeding in spring and failing to have a second litter presumably go into an early anoestrus." The material and data which were available to Deanesly and Parkes did not make it possible to decide whether the grey squirrel has one polyoestrous season or two monoestrous breeding seasons, but, as they point out, the latter conclusion is very unlikely. However, in America, grey squirrels are reported to experience two main breeding seasons, the first beginning in December and the second in May or early June (Asdell, 1946).

It is of interest that male grey squirrels, unlike the females, can be found at all times of the year with large testes in full spermatogenesis (Allanson, 1933).

Whether ovulation in the grey squirrel is spontaneous or dependent on copulation is not known. No post-partum oestrus occurs, and both the ovaries involute during lactation. Gestation in the American variety lasts approximately 44 days, and the interval between two litters, the average size of which is 3·6, appears to be about 3 months.

Deanesly and Parkes observe that during anoestrus the vulva is small and the vaginal orifice imperforate. As oestrus approaches, the surrounding tissue begins to swell and forms a papilla about 1 cm. long and 0·5 cm. wide which finally becomes perforated, a slit appearing at its clitoridal end and extending backwards. The prooestrous swelling probably lasts 2 weeks.

Tamias

The breeding habits of the eastern chipmunk of North America, *T. striatus lysteri*, have been studied by both Schooley (1934) and Condrin (1936). The breeding season lasts from March to October, with peaks of births occurring in April and July. The average number of young in a litter is 5. Older females appear to breed earlier in the season than younger ones, and there is a possibility that the first oestrous periods are unassociated with ovulation. The testes of the male are abdominal during anoestrus, and spermatogenesis is active by February.

K*

Cynomys

Wade (1928) writes that prairie dogs, *C. ludovicianus*, rut early in February, and that young are born in March. According to Stockard (1929), gestation in the related species *C. leucurus* lasts 27 to 33 days, and the male sexual season must be very short, since the size of the testes undergoes a sudden and pronounced reduction in April.

Citellus

Numerous studies have been made of the reproductive habits of American ground squirrels. In 1893 Bailey reported that *C. tridecemlineatus*, the thirteen-striped ground squirrel, and the related *C. franklini* and *C. richardsonii*, breed in May, after the animals emerge from hibernation, and that the number of young in a litter varies from 7 to 14. Shaw (1925) reports that *C. columbianus*, the Columbian ground squirrel, breeds during May and April. The animal is poly-oestrous, and each oestrous cycle takes 14 to 15 days, oestrus itself lasting 3 days.

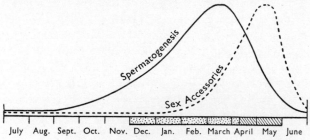

Fig. *4. 3*—The annual reproductive cycle of the male ground squirrel, *Citellus tridecemlineatus*. Cross hatching below the base line indicates the breeding season, and stippling the period of hibernation. (Reproduced from Turner, 1948.)

Gestation lasts about 24 days, as in the Douglas ground squirrel (*C. douglasii*), which is said to mate in March and April (Edge, 1931). The Californian ground squirrels: *C. grammurus* and *C. beecheyi* are stated to breed continuously in some years (Storer, 1930; Asdell, 1946).

Reproduction in the thirteen-striped ground squirrel has been closely studied in various American laboratories. The dates at which these animals emerge from hibernation, like the times of rut and birth, vary somewhat in different parts of their range. According to Wells (1935) the male appears above ground during the first ten days of April. The testes are then as a rule large and scrotal, but the accessory reproductive organs do not reach their maximum size until a few weeks later (Fig. *4. 3*). Full reproductive capacity is usually attained in April and May, when a short period of rut ensues. Between June and July spermatogenesis ceases, and the testes become smaller and recede into the abdominal cavity. Simultaneously the accessory reproductive organs involute. In the depth of hibernation only spermatogonia and primary spermatocytes are present (Johnson, Foster and Coco, 1933). Under natural conditions spermatogenesis restarts during March, but in animals confined to the laboratory it may begin as early as January. The regression of the reproductive tract cannot be retarded significantly by maintaining animals under conditions of additional illumination, but it can be prevented if animals are kept at a temperature of 4° C., provided treatment is begun during the sexual season. When applied during anoestrus, low temperature has little effect upon the onset of spermatogenesis (Wells, 1936; Wells and Zalesky, 1940).

The implantation of rat pituitaries into adult ground squirrels during the anoestrous period produces marked enlargement of the testes and seminiferous tubules, and stimulation of the germinal epithelium (Johnson, Gann, Foster and Coco, 1934). Similarly, the administration of gonadotrophic substances leads to the precocious formation of spermatozoa in immature animals, and to spermato-genesis and stimulation of the reproductive tract in adult males (Wells and Moore, 1936). Wells (1937) has shown that the scrotal sac grows under the influence of androgen, and that it does not develop fully when the testes are surgically restrained within the abdomen (artificial cryptorchidism). Another factor which seems to affect the size of the scrotum is the "mechanical stress produced by mere presence of the testis within the sac." On the other hand, the ascent of the testes at the end of rut is not due to a decrease in the size of the scrotum. Pigmentation of the scrotal sac shows a seasonal rhythm (Wells, 1935; Finkel, 1945).

It appears that the gonads secrete sex hormones, although at a much lower rate, even during anoestrus, for after gonadectomy the degree of involution of the accessory organs is greater than the physiological involution of the non-breeding season (Moore, Simmons, Wells, Zalesky and Nelson, 1934).

Seasonal variations occur in the size, cytology, and gonadotrophic potency of the pituitary (Moore et al., 1934; Wells, 1938), the adrenals (Zalesky, 1934), but not in the thyroid (Zalesky, 1935) of the ground squirrel. The anterior lobe of the pituitary becomes heavier with the onset of the breeding season, and coincidentally, there is a proportional increase in the number and granularity of basophiles. The gonadotrophic content of the hypophysis in both sexes runs parallel to these cyto-logical fluctuations. The increase in the size of the adrenal glands is due largely to the expansion of the reticularis zone of the cortex, and to the differentiation within this zone of an outer sub-zone, in which the cells become very large. This zone of cells can be experimentally developed by the injection of either oestrogen or androgen. Such cyclical changes as occur in the thyroid appear to be associated with fluctuations in general metabolism rather than in reproductive activity (e.g. during hibernation the gland is less active).

The period of sexual inactivity in the female ground squirrel lasts from July to the following April (Foster, 1934). The ovaries begin to hypertrophy in January while the animals are still hibernating. When the females emerge above the ground during the third week of April (shortly after the males make their appearance), the reproductive tract is fully developed (Moore et al., 1934). Simmons (1946b), by means of vaginal smears, has detected prooestrous changes during late March, and believes that full oestrus occurs for about two weeks in April and ends "usually within 10 days of May 3." Females isolated from males throughout the sexual season show an "oestrous-like" condition which persists for two to four weeks, and during which there is an irregular succession of short "pseudo-oestrous periods." These cease during anoestrus, when the vagina becomes occluded and its epithelial lining becomes cuboidal (Foster, 1934). During oestrus the vulval lips are swollen and projecting, the process of swelling being more gradual than the postoestrous regression.   In the absence of pregnancy the vulval swelling may continue for as many as 4 months.   Normally it probably lasts no more than 3 days (Foster, 1934 ; Moore *et al.*, 1934).

Foster has shown conclusively that ovulation in the ground squirrel, as in certain other mammals, is induced by mating.   Copulation, which lasts for about 10 minutes (Wade, 1927), is followed by ovulation 8 to 12 hours later.   A copulatory plug is formed.

In the wild only a single litter is produced each year.   Pregnancy lasts for 27 to 28 days, and is not followed by post-partum oestrus, except when lactation is interrupted.   In one female which had destroyed its litter, oestrus and successful copulation were observed 21 days after parturition (Foster, 1934).

In wild ground squirrels the litter comprises 5 to 13 (mean : 6 to 10, *see* Asdell, 1946).   The young develop with great rapidity, but usually do not breed until their second season (Simmons, 1946a).

Marmota

The woodchuck, *M. monax*, has a restricted breeding season in the spring, all births occurring in April or May (Merriam, 1884).   Each female gives birth to only one litter in the year.   The animals hibernate from September to March. Seton (1909) suggests, however, that there is some evidence that pairing also takes place in the autumn.

A detailed study of the testicular changes which take place in this rodent has been carried out by Rasmussen (1917).   The interstitial cells are minimal in size, and probably reduced in number during late summer and autumn.   In the spring, when the animals emerge from hibernation, the interstitial cells rapidly enlarge and apparently increase in number.   Their enlargement is primarily due to the development of a dense central mass of cytoplasm, and to the accumulation of fat globules peripherally.   These changes reach their maximum at the end of April, and by July regression sets in.

A spermatogenetic cycle is usually in progress just before hibernation begins, and during dormancy the tubules are filled with spermatocytes.   Spermatogenesis restarts suddenly in the spring, and free sperm are present by the end of March. Regression then sets in, and spermatogenesis is at a low ebb by the end of April. Early in May a new wave of sperm formation begins, and continues uninterruptedly throughout July.   Interstitial cell development does not, therefore, run exactly parallel to spermatogenesis.

At the beginning of the breeding season the seminiferous tubules enlarge, and at the same time they become widely separated as a result of the development of interstitial cells.   As they increase in size the testes descend into pouches which, though they remain in communication with the peritoneal cavity, represent a scrotum.   By July the testes have returned into the abdomen, and by August they have become reduced to about one-eighth of their maximum functional size.

Changes also occur in the interstitial cells of the ovary (Rasmussen, 1918). The greatest degree of hypertrophy of this tissue is observed in late breeding females, and, as in the male, is due mainly to the accumulation of lipoid and cytoplasmic secretion granules.

The corpora lutea persist for a long time after parturition, which occurs in the early summer, but by September all have involuted.

Glaucomys

According to Cowan (1936), the flying squirrel, *Glaucomys sabrinus*, has only one litter each year, the young being born either late in May or early in June. Hibbard (1935) writes that the related species, *G. volans volans*, gives birth in both September and March. This is confirmed by Sollberger (1943), who also suggests that in this species the vagina is normally closed by a membrane which opens only at oestrus (a condition also met in other types of squirrel, the guinea-pig and mole), and that the vulva becomes swollen during sexual activity, as in many carnivores. Gestation lasts about 40 days, and the usual size of the litter is 2. According to the same observer the testes of the male descend in January or February and are retracted in September.

Family *Castoridae*

In captivity in London the Canadian beaver, *Castor canadensis*, gives birth between May and August. Mating, which is believed to take place in the water, occurs between January and February, and litters are born in April or May (Seton, 1909 ; Bradt, 1939). There appears to be no accurate information about the length of gestation, which is believed to last about 4 months. The usual number of young is 3 or 4 with a range of 1 to 8. Litters of 6 may be reared successfully.

Family *Geomyidae*
Genera : *Geomys ; Dipodomys ; Microdipodops*

The reproductive habits of the genus *Geomys*, comprising the gophers, have been studied by numerous workers (Bailey, 1895 ; Dice, 1919 ; Dixon, 1922, 1929 ; Horn, 1923 ; Wight, 1930 ; English, 1932 ; Mossman, 1937). As a rule the breeding season is restricted to the spring and summer, and males become active before the females. According to Dixon, however, the Californian gopher mates in November and December. The usual number of young is 3, and 2 litters are raised in quick succession. Some species are said to have only 1 litter and others 3.

Among other species belonging to this family, the " kangaroo rat " (*Dipodomys ingens*) is stated to breed during the first half of the year (Grinnell, 1932), while the young of *Microdipodops sp.* are mostly born in May and June (Hall and Linsdale, 1929).

The symphysis pubis of the female pocket gopher (*Geomys bursarius*) is of particular interest (*see* Hisaw, 1925). During the first prooestrus and oestrus, it is resorbed, resorption being due to a secretion of the ovaries (" relaxin "), which Hisaw and his associates believe to be distinct from the oestrogenic and corpus luteum hormone. According to Mossman (1937), this substance is the specific product of what he calls the " thecal gland " of the ovary, a structure which is derived from the unusually well-developed theca interna of the follicles.

Apart from the pocket gopher, the guinea-pig and mouse appear to be the only rodents whose pubic bones normally separate during late pregnancy and parturition.

Family *Cricetidae*

Subfamily *Cricetinae*

Genera : *Cricetulus ; Cricetus ; Sigmodon*

The breeding season of the Chinese hamster (*Cricetulus griseus*) probably extends over the greater part of the year. According to Chang and Wu (1938), wild females confined to the laboratory show irregular cycles and fail to reproduce, whereas animals born in captivity have a regular oestrous cycle, averaging $4\frac{1}{2}$ days, and are able to breed. Parkes (1931), by means of the vaginal-smear technique, established a mean length of the oestrous cycle of $4 \cdot 3$ days. Ovulation is spontaneous and occurs towards the end of heat, about eight follicles rupturing at a time. The vaginal cycle is similar to that of the mouse, but the uterus does not show the same degree of oestrous distension. Well-developed myometrial glands occur in this species.

The golden hamster belongs to a different genus (*Cricetus auratus*) and, unlike the Chinese variety, reproduces freely in captivity. Deanesly (1938) states that animals breed throughout the year, but that pregnancies are less common in winter, although oestrous cycles continue regularly throughout the winter months. However, the animal usually stops breeding at the age of 10–11 months, and a certain proportion of females appears to be sterile (Peczenik, 1942 ; Farris, 1950).

The average length of the cycle of the golden hamster is about 4 days (e.g. Deanesly, 1938 ; Kent and Smith, 1945 ; Ward, 1946). Ovulation is spontaneous, and occurs at night towards the middle of oestrus (*see* Farris, 1950). The corpora lutea of ovulation are believed to be functionless.

Gestation lasts 16 days (Bruce and Hindle, 1934), and up to 12 young are born in a litter. There is no post-partum ovulation, and the lactation anoestrus lasts 2 to 4 weeks, depending on the number of young suckling. Sterile mating leads to pseudopregnancy, which lasts from 8 to 13 (usually 9 to 10) days. Fertilisation may take place in the hamster at the first mating.

The usual number of litters produced by a female during her reproductive phase is 5, but 6 can be obtained by selective breeding (*see* Farris, 1950). The normal life-span of this species under laboratory conditions is seldom more than a year ; occasionally it may be as much as 2 years.

Sexual development proceeds unusually rapidly (Ortiz, 1947). This author states that the first oestrus occurs at approximately 30 days, ovulation at 36 days, while opening of the vagina takes place at the extremely precocious age of about 10 days. This observation indicates that in the hamster, unlike the rat and mouse, the establishment of a patent vagina is not associated with the process of normal sexual maturation. It also shows that the hamster's vaginal membrane is unusually sensitive to the oestrogenic hormone. This is confirmed by Ortiz's finding that an identical amount of oestrogen produces opening of the vagina on the 18th day in the rat and on the 6th day of life in the hamster. The occurrence of fertile copulation in a 28-days-old golden hamster has been reported by Selle (1945). The routine employment of such young females for breeding purposes is not recommended (*see* Farris, 1950).

In the male the testes begin to descend into the scrotal pouches at about 26 days, and spermatogenesis is in progress at 36.

The cotton rat (*Sigmodon hispidus hispidus*), which occurs naturally in great abundance in Peru, Mexico and the southern United States, is a very prolific breeder, and produces young from early spring to late autumn and probably into the winter (Svihla, 1929). In the laboratory it breeds throughout the year, and no decrease in reproductive activity occurs during the winter months (Meyer and Meyer, 1944). According to these workers the length of the oestrous cycle varies markedly in different individuals and within a given female. It is also influenced by environmental factors, rats kept in a quiet laboratory having both shorter and more regular cycles than those maintained in a noisier room. In the former group the average length of the vaginal cycle was 7 days, of which oestrus accounted for 1·7 days ; in the second group it was 9 days, the difference being mainly due to the longer period of oestrus, which averaged 3·4 days. Clark (1936) who studied the same species, established the average length of the cycle as 8 days. It is clear that in the cotton rat the cycle is nearly twice as long as in the common rat or mouse.

Ovulation is spontaneous and occurs late during oestrus. Gestation in the cotton rat maintained in the laboratory lasts approximately 27 days, and the number of young averages 5·6 (range 2–10). According to Svihla (1929), the mean litter size in the feral animal is 4·75 and the normal variation 3–6.

Post-partum oestrus begins between 6 and 10 hours after littering, and is accompanied by ovulation. Many females copulate and conceive again within a few hours after parturition. Unlike the condition in the common rat or mouse (see p. 277), suckling does not seem to affect the length of pregnancy. The occurrence of pseudopregnancy has not been established.

Growth of the young is similar to that in laboratory rodents. The vagina opens at an average age of 30–40 days. In the male, the testes descend between 20–30 days, and spermatoza are stated to be present at 40–50 days of age (Clark, 1936).

Subfamily *Microtinae*
Genera : *Clethrionomys ; Arvicola*

The bank vole, *Clethrionomys* (*Evotomys*) *glareolus*, which has been extensively studied by Brambell and Rowlands (1936) and by Rowlands (1936), has a breeding season which lasts from the middle of April to October, although as noted by Baker (1930), it varies considerably from year to year (see p. 264). Females born early in the season mature and breed before its close, but it would seem that most of them live through two seasons. The animals are polyoestrous, and the mean number of young per litter is 4·43, the largest number of ruptured follicles being 12. Ovulation is spontaneous, but the number of ova liberated at each oestrus shows marked seasonal variation. Most females at the beginning of the breeding season appear to undergo a number of sterile cycles before they become pregnant. Ovulation, but not copulation, occurs during these cycles. Pseudopregnancy was not observed in any of the specimens studied by Brambell and Rowlands. Lactating animals are frequently pregnant, and anatomical evidence also shows that the bank vole, like the more common laboratory rodents, experiences a post-partum oestrus. The pregnancy which results if lactating bank voles again conceive is prolonged, as in the mouse and rat. This appears to be due to delayed implantation of the blastocysts, and is accompanied by a temporary arrest in the development of the corpora lutea (Brambell, 1937). One female may rear 4 or 5 litters in a single season.

Spermatogenesis in the vole occurs only during the breeding season, and the accessory organs exhibit the usual anoestrous regression.

The reproductive behaviour of the water vole (*Arvicola amphibius* L.) is very similar to that of the bank vole (Perry, 1942).

Other *Cricetidae*

Genera : *Microtus ; Peromyscus ; Phenacomys ; Reithrodontomys ;*
Onychomys ; Neotoma ; Synaptomys ; Ondatra

Numerous observations have been published by naturalists about the breeding habits of other wild mice and voles.

The European field vole (*Microtus agrestis hirtus*) closely resembles the bank vole in reproductive behaviour (Brambell and Hall, 1939). Fertility in the male, as judged by the presence of spermatozoa in the testes, begins in February, approximately a month before the onset of the sexual season in the female (and about 2 months before that of the female bank vole ; *see* p. 271). The end of the breeding season is unknown, but pregnant animals were obtained by Brambell and Hall on the 29th August in England, and in Scotland as late as October (Baker and Ranson, 1933). During the winter months the females are in anoestrus and the males are believed to be sterile. The species is polyoestrous, and ovulation occurs spontaneously. A hard plug is deposited in the vagina during copulation. The gestation period is about 21 days, and females regularly come into heat after parturition. If they do no conceive on that occasion, a period of lactation anoestrus follows, after which oestrous cycles may be resumed. An average of 5 embryos is present in the uterus, and the mean litter size is 4·8 ; in one female Brambell and Hall found 10 apparently healthy embryos.

Both males and females become fully reproductive during their first season, when only 5–6 weeks old. Following the attainment of puberty, the female may experience a few sterile cycles before her first pregnancy.

Microtus pennsylvanicus Ord, the American field mouse, breeds throughout the year in the captive state, but may experience a winter anoestrus in the wild. The female is polyoestrous, and may have as many as 17 litters in one year (Bailey, 1924). The average size of litter is 5. The vagina becomes patent at the first oestrus, but is closed between heat periods, as in the guinea-pig, certain squirrels and the mole. Post-partum oestrus occurs, and suckling does not prolong the subsequent gestation (Asdell, 1946).

Unlike the European and American types of *Microtus*, the Palestinian variety (*M. guentheri*) is thought to ovulate normally only after copulation, in this way resembling species like the rabbit, cat and ferret. This conclusion is based on the absence of corpora lutea and other oestrous manifestations in virgin and parous females isolated for one to two months (Bodenheimer and Sulman, 1946). This period of observation may not have been long enough to establish this conclusion, in so far as the possibility of a prolonged seasonal anoestrus was not excluded.

M. guentheri is also remarkable for its lack of a true vaginal cycle. Vaginal cornification can, however, be induced by means of large doses of oestrogen (Zondek and Sulman, 1940).

The average litter size of this species is 4 to 8 and the maximum observed under natural conditions, 14.

Female Californian meadow mice (*M. californicus*) start breeding when 21 to 22 days old, and the males when 42 days. Both gestation and lactation last about 21 days (Selle, 1928 ; Hatfield, 1935). Deer mice of the genus *Peromyscus* also tend to produce their young throughout the year, but in some parts of North America breeding is stated to be discontinuous. Gestation lasts about 23 days and in most other features of their reproductive life these animals appear to resemble the laboratory rat and mouse (*see* Dice, 1919 ; Seton, 1920 ; Scheffer, 1924 ; Svihla, 1932, 1935 ; Asdell, 1946). Harvest mice (genus *Reithrodontomys*), like tree mice (*Phenacomys longicaudus*, Howell, 1926 ; Benson and Borrell, 1931), also breed throughout the year, females only becoming mature when approximately 4 months old.

Gestation is unusually prolonged in the grasshopper mouse (*Onychomys leucogaster fuscogriseus*), lasting, according to Svihla (1936), 33 to 47 days. A post-partum oestrus occurs in this species as it does in the Asiatic mouse, *Mus bactrianus*. Green (1932) records the interesting observation that a male of the latter species sired a litter when 970 days old, and that a female of 648 days was still able to reproduce.

The breeding season of the wood rats (*Neotoma fuscipes* and *N. albigula*) appears to vary from region to region (Warren, 1926 ; Gander, 1929 ; Donat, 1933 ; Wood, 1935 ; Richardson, 1943). Most observers believe the species to be polyoestrous during the greater part of the year, but Donat writes that the female will not have cycles if isolated from males. Gestation lasts from 23 to 33 days in *N. fuscipes*, and as much as 37 or 38 days in the case of *N. albigula*. According to Wood, no vaginal plug is formed at copulation. The breeding season in the lemming mouse, *Synaptomys cooperi cooperi*, is restricted to the earlier half of the year (*see* Burt, 1928 ; Stegeman, 1930). Most musk rats (genus *Ondatra*) breed throughout the year. In some species, however, mating appears to be restricted, while the intensity of breeding shows marked seasonal variation in all (Dixon, 1922 ; Svihla and Svihla, 1931 ; Errington, 1937, 1946). Gestation lasts about 30 days, the average size of litter being 6.

Family *Muridae*

Genera : *Rattus* ; *Mus* ; *Mastomys*

Rattus and *Mus*

The rat and the mouse are the two mammals most frequently used in biological research, and numerous investigations have been made of their normal mechanisms of reproduction. The two classical studies are those of Long and Evans on the rat (1922) and of Allen on the mouse (1922). Both were made possible by the discovery that oestrus and ovulation can be readily detected in the living animal by daily examination of vaginal smears, a method first described in 1917 by Stockard and Papanicolaou (p. 280). Until then attempts to follow the oestrous cycle in the rat and mouse had been mostly unsuccessful (*see* Long and Evans, 1922 ; and Parkes, 1928a, for references to the earlier literature), and various devices had to be employed in order to obtain a fixed point from which to consider the various changes that occur in the cycle (e.g. dating from the immediate post-partum oestrus, the interval between sterile copulations, etc.). More recently, a series of studies published by Boling and Blandau and their associates have confirmed and extended Long and Evans' original findings on the rat.

Fertility in the Norway rat appears to be at its maximum in the first half of the year, and lowest in the second. King (1927), who has enquired into the question of whether or not variations in litter production occur under fairly uniform conditions of environment and nutrition, comes to the conclusion that there is only one pronounced cycle in fertility during the year. The data she analysed comprise 16,847 litters born in the animal colony of the Wistar Institute of Anatomy. There is, however, no correlation between seasonal variations in litter production and in average litter size, which remains fairly constant throughout the year (about 6 to 10).

Like the rat, the mouse breeds at all times of the year if environmental conditions are favourable, and fertility is higher in the second half of the year than in the first (Parkes, 1924, 1926b ; see also Laurie, 1946).

King has shown that " there is a yearly but not strictly seasonal cycle in the sex ratio. The highest point in the cycle (number of males to each hundred females) comes in the spring or early summer ; the lowest point in early autumn." The normal ratio is almost equality. Months of low fertility appear to be those when the sex ratio is low.

In both the normal unmated rat and mouse oestrus recurs approximately every 4 to 5 days. The average length of 1,999 cycles in the rat was found by Long and Evans to be 5·4 days, with a total range of 3 to 38 days. Excluding all cycles of more than 8 days' length the average was 4·8 days, which compares with a mean of 4·4 days (range 2 to 19 days) in Blandau, Boling and Young's series (1941). Over 80 per cent of all cycles fall within the 4 to 6-day group, and Asdell (1946) concludes that the mode is 4 days and the mean approximately 4·8 days. The cycle of the rat is subject to marked individual variations (Long and Evans, 1922 ; Ishii, 1922).

In the mouse the usual duration of cycle, as given by Allen (1922) is 4 to 6 days, the mode being $4\frac{1}{2}$ days and the range 2 to 14 days (563 cycles). In another study based on 1,000 cycles, Parkes (1928b) found that the average length was 6·213 ± 0·0554 days, the range being 2 to 28 days and the mode 5 days. According to Allen (1922), the dioestrous interval shows a greater variation than any other stage of the cycle.

The histological characteristics of the oestrous cycle are considered on p. 565. The duration of its various phases, according to Astwood (1939a), is as follows (in hours) : " preoestrus " (a short stage during which the typical nucleated cells of prooestrus are missing), 4 ; prooestrus, 14 ; prooestrus to oestrus, 3 ; oestrus, 25 ; metoestrus, 8 ; dioestrus, 55 ; total cycle length, 109. These findings agree substantially with those of Long and Evans. Astwood also established periodic changes in the water content of the uterus during the normal cycle. This is highest at prooestrus, falls off abruptly during oestrus, and reaches a minimum early in dioestrus.

The spontaneous occurrence of persistent oestrus associated with deficient ovulation and corpus luteum formation in a laboratory strain of rats has been reported by Everett (1939). The vaginal and ovulatory cycle in such animals can be restored to normal by progesterone (Everett, 1940), and deoxycorticosterone (Marvin, 1947).

The average age at which rats become sexually mature depends on the strain and the particular criterion of maturity used, as well as on dietary conditions. According to Long and Evans (1922), rats mate for the first time at 92·7 days, but most subsequent studies have yielded much lower means.   Thus, Blandau and Money (1943), using the " copulatory response " test, established an average age of 49·4 ± 5·46 days (range 37–67 days) for the occurrence of the first heat period. When mated or artificially inseminated at this period, a high percentage of females conceived, thus showing that the first oestrus was accompanied by ovulation. During the transition from puberty to full sexual maturity, the cycle of the rat becomes gradually shorter (Blandau and Money, 1943).

In the prepubertal rat and mouse the vagina is non-canalised, and in most cases a complete lumen does not appear until the first heat period.   In the rats studied by Blandau and Money, vaginal patency was established as a rule from 48 hours before, to 12 hours after the first appearance of heat, although exceptionally it preceded oestrus by as many as 19 days.   Other findings summarised by Asdell (1946) show that the age at which the vaginal closure membrane breaks down varies from 41 to 76·5 days in different strains.   In specially fed animals it may occur between 32 and 40 days (Ishii, 1922).   On the other hand, when growth is retarded through faulty nutrition, sexual maturity is delayed (Asdell and Crowell, 1935). Neither body length nor weight appear to be more reliable indices of puberty than age (see also Leslie, Perry and Watson, 1945–46).

The mouse becomes sexually mature somewhat earlier than the rat (29 to 56 days, Mirskaia and Wiesner, 1930 ; Mirskaia and Crew, 1930b ; Parkes, 1925), and, as in the rat, the first cycles are somewhat longer than those of the mature animal. According to Mirskaia and Crew (1930a), variations in the time of puberty in the mouse have a genetic basis.

The cessation of reproductive function in the rat is a gradual process, and usually sets in when the animals are 15 to 18 months old (see Farris, 1950).   The average life-span of rats in the laboratory is about 3 years (Donaldson, 1924).

Before it is fully canalised the vaginal wall in the mouse is lined by two to four layers of columnar cells.   Mucification of this epithelium often sets in just before the first oestrus (Mirskaia and Wiesner, 1930).

Ovulation can be brought about in hypophysectomised rats by means of gonadotrophin (Rowlands and Williams, 1946), and 60 per cent of the released ova can be fertilised after mating the females to normal males.   On the other hand, if ovulation is induced in intact immature rats by the same method (Austin, 1950), only 25 per cent are found to have fertilised ova within one day of mating.   This low fecundity is due partly to the lack of oestrus (only 34 per cent of the treated females mated), and partly to the inadequate fertilisation and abnormality of the ova.   Austin (1949b) has also observed that a high proportion of such artificially ovulated eggs undergo spontaneous divisions, but can be distinguished satisfactorily from normally segmenting fertilised eggs by means of phase contrast microscopy.

The surgical opening of the ovarian bursa in the rat is said to reduce fecundity on the operated side (Kelly, 1939).

Striking changes are observed in the reproductive cycle of rats and mice that are mated but do not become pregnant. This was first noticed by Long and Evans, who found that after non-fertile mating (e.g. with a vasectomised male), the succeeding oestrus was delayed until the 14th day, the average length of the cycles concerned being 13·1 days.   Comparable observations on the mouse are reported (Parkes, 1926a), the average length of the prolonged cycle in this species being 11 days.   The increase in the length of the cycle is due to the prolongation of the dioestrous interval.   Observations that are reported elsewhere show that in the unmated rat and mouse the corpora lutea of the normal cycle are only slightly functional, and that the uterus is little, if at all, influenced by their secretions (e.g. trauma of the endometrium does not lead to deciduoma formation ; p. 570). On the other hand, if sterile mating occurs the corpora become functional, and the endometrium is sensitised, so that deciduomata can be produced (Parkes, 1926a, 1929).   In the rat this is only possible before the 5th or 6th day of pseudopregnancy (Long and Evans, 1922), and between the 4th and 7th day of pregnancy (Allen, 1931 ; Peckham and Greene, 1947).   The implication of these observations is that after the time at which the embryos normally implant, the uterus loses its sensitivity to a traumatic stimulus, even though neither the corpus luteum nor the uterus itself then show any histological signs of retrogression (Allen, 1931).

Pseudopregnancy lasting approximately 14 days can be induced in the rat not only by sterile mating but also by mechanical stimulation of the cervix uteri (Long and Evans, 1922 ; Slonaker, 1929).   In normal copulation a vaginal plug is formed. Its solidity is due to the coagulating secretions of certain lobes of the prostate (Walker, 1910 ; see Mann and Lutwak-Mann, 1951), and its effect, according to Long and Evans, is not only to keep the sperm within the reproductive tract of the female, but also to stimulate the vagina and cervix uteri so that the corpora lutea become functional and pseudopregnancy results.   The conditions are the same if fertilisation occurs, for the changes of pseudopregnancy are identical with those of the first part of pregnancy.   In the mouse the copulation plug does not appear to be essential for fertilisation (Merton, 1938–39), but in the rat removal of the male accessory reproductive glands usually leads to infertility (Blandau, 1945 ; Mann and Lutwak-Mann, 1951).

Pseudopregnancy and functional corpora lutea in the rat can also be induced by a variety of experimental procedures, such as electrical stimulation of the cervix (Shelesnyak, 1931) or of the head (Harris 1936) ; mechanical stimulation of the nipples (Selye and McKeown, 1934) ; local anaesthetisation of, or application of silver nitrate to the nasal mucosa during heat (Rosen and Shelesnyak, 1937 ; Shelesnyak and Rosen, 1938) ; and by the injection of prolactin (Evans, Simpson and Lyons, 1941).   Pseudopregnancy occurs less frequently when mechanical stimulation of the cervix is performed under deep anaesthesia (Meyer, Leonard and Hisaw, 1929).   An interesting series of experiments by Haterius (1933) suggests that these artificial methods of provoking pseudopregnancy differ in the manner of their action from mating with vasectomised males.   Two series of rats were used to demonstrate the difference, one in which the abdominal sympathetic chains and pelvic parasympathetic nerves had been removed, an operation which does not affect the normal cycle (Herren and Haterius, 1932), and the other in which the superior cervical ganglia had been extirpated.   It was found that sterile mating of both groups of animals always resulted in pseudopregnancy, whereas mechanical or electrical stimulation of the vagina and cervix uteri gave uniformly negative results.   The fact that the operated animals respond to infertile mating Haterius explains as being due to generalised sexual excitement—a factor which is absent under experimental conditions. These findings are in keeping with those of Vogt (1931).

Removal of the uterus in the mature rat does not lead to a prolongation of the cycle, unlike the condition in the guinea-pig (Long and Evans, 1922).

The sudden appearance of blood in the vagina near the cervix (the " placental sign ") constitutes the earliest external indication of pregnancy in both rats and mice (Long and Evans, 1920, 1922 ; Parkes, 1926a). In the rat the bleeding is of uterine origin, and continues from the 12th to the 16th day of gestation (see Stafford, 1930 ; Venable, 1939). Gross external uterine haemorrhage is also observed in pseudopregnant rats possessing deciduomata (Astwood, 1939b). This author believes that it indicates the involution of the deciduomata and heralds the next oestrus.

In the pregnant mouse the symphysis pubis separates, and the gap becomes bridged by a long interpubic ligament (Gardner, 1936 ; Hall and Newton, 1946). According to Hall (1947), who has also described the histological changes accompanying this process, the pubic bones begin to separate on the 13th day of gestation, and the gap widens an average of 1 mm. per day until parturition on the 19th or 20th day. Subsequently, the gap closes rapidly, and " is usually less than 2 mm. on the third or fourth day post-partum, but does not completely return to the virgin condition."

Gestation in the rat normally lasts 21·5 to 22 days (Long and Evans, 1922), and in the mouse (in which, as in the rat, copulation and parturition normally occur at night), 19 to 20 days (Parkes, 1926a ; Crew and Mirskaia, 1930a). Oestrus occurs in both species within 24 hours of parturition, when females may conceive again, the interval between post-partum oestrus and the next oestrus in the lactating mouse lasting 24·8 days (Parkes, 1926a ; Crew and Mirskaia, 1930b), and in the rat from 25 to 40 days (Long and Evans, 1922). If only one or two young are being suckled, oestrous cycles are not suppressed for as long a period. Young rats can be weaned after 21 days, but lactation will often continue for twice as long if the young are left with the mother. Oestrus occurs within 3 to 12 days after the young are removed, the time depending on the number of young suckled (Long and Evans, 1922). Destruction of the corpora lutea by electrocautery during early pregnancy and pseudopregnancy leads to the reappearance of heat within about 4 days. If carried out during the second half of pregnancy, it causes abortion or partial resorption of foetuses without a return of heat, but exceptionally gestation may proceed normally (McKeown and Zuckerman, 1938).

Both Parkes (1926a) and Crew and Mirskaia (1930b) have shown that the prolongation of lactation, by the foster-mothering of young litters, does not extend the normal lactation interval. On the other hand, if mice or rats become pregnant at the first post-partum oestrus, and are thereby both pregnant and lactating at the same time, pregnancy may be much prolonged (Lataste, 1887, 1891 ; Daniel, 1910 ; King, 1913 ; Kirkham, 1916, 1918). The last author showed that the prolongation is due to a delay in the implantation of the embryos which may last up to 20 days. Once embedded in the uterus, the blastocysts develop normally, and the birth weights of the young are comparable to those of litters born after a normal gestation period. Suckling rats and mice do not conceive readily if mated at the first post-partum oestrus, and there is no direct correlation between the number of lactating young and the extent of the prolongation of pregnancy

(Mirskaia and Crew, 1930c ; Hain, 1934 ; Brambell, 1937 ; Bloch, 1948). In spite of numerous investigations (Weichert, 1940, 1943; Krehbiel, 1941a, b; Bloch, 1943, 1948), the mechanism responsible for the delay is still largely unknown (for discussions *see* Brambell, 1937, and Courrier, 1945).

Oestrus occasionally occurs during pregnancy (Long and Evans, 1922 ; Nelson, 1929). Swezy and Evans (1930) relate this finding to the continuation of the ovarian cycle, and they state that mature follicles and corpora lutea are developed during pregnancy in the same way as at other times. Normally, the presence of fairly large follicles neither leads to oestrous changes in the accessory organs nor to oestrous behaviour. That it may do so, with superfoetation resulting, is indicated by two observations reported by Slonaker (1934), who has also shown that although " typical oestrual rhythm " in muscular activity is usually absent during gestation and lactation, oestrus may sometimes occur on the 14th day of pregnancy.

Slonaker (1924, 1925) has also carried out an interesting series of investigations in both rats and guinea-pigs on the relation of muscular activity and food consumption to reproductive mechanisms. It appears that rhythmical changes occur in the activity of mature female rats, and that these changes cannot be demonstrated either in ovariectomised mature females, prepubertal females, or in males which are isolated from females. The maximum of muscular activity and the least intake of food coincide with oestrus. It has also been shown, by Kinder (1927) and by Sturman-Hulbe and Stone (1929), that cyclical changes take place in nest-building activity. The maximum amount of building occurs at the time of the greatest food intake, and the minimum at oestrus. These studies indicate the profound effects reproductive processes can have on social behaviour.

The observations which have been reviewed above refer to rats and mice kept under good nutritional conditions. Disturbances in the cycle occur when certain dietary factors are lacking (*see* p. 568). The only aspect of this question which will be referred to here is that of electrolyte metabolism. Evans and Bishop (1922) and Wolfe (1930) have shown that the oestrous cycle is usually prolonged when rats and mice are kept on a diet low in salts. It is also well known that cycles normally cease after adrenalectomy, and both Kutz, McKeown and Selye (1934) and Martin and Fazekas (1937) have shown that the cycle can be restored after this operation if adequate amounts of sodium chloride are administered.

Various other observations indicate that the suprarenal glands are of importance in maintaining the reproductive rhythm in rodents. Thus both in the mouse (Masui and Tamura, 1926) and in the rat (Andersen and Kennedy, 1932 ; Bourne and Zuckerman, 1941) the adrenals increase in size during oestrus ; this change is due to enlargement of the cortex. Bourne and Zuckerman have also shown that the greater size of the adrenal cortex at oestrus is due in the main to hypertrophy of the zona fasciculata, and that it is associated with an increase in the size, but not in the number, of the fasciculata cells.

In the wild brown rat (*Rattus norvegicus* Erxleben), reproduction does not proceed at an even rate throughout the year (Perry, 1945–46). The percentage of pregnant adult females rises steadily from December to a peak between March and June, and then falls off abruptly. Breeding continues from then on, but on a lower, though fairly uniform, level. Perry believes individual brown rats experience phases of greater breeding activity interspersed by periods of reproductive rest. It is of some interest that in the wild rat even at the height of the breeding season the pregnancy rate does not exceed 50 per cent, whereas in the wild rabbit it may approach 100 per cent (Brambell, 1944–45).

Another difference between the wild and domesticated type of rat is the great frequency with which pregnancy in *R. norvegicus* is accompanied (and consequently prolonged) by lactation. In the laboratory rat conception occurs only rarely at the post-partum oestrus. Approximately 10 ova are ovulated at a time in the wild brown rat, but the average size of the litter is only 7 to 8.

The male in this species, as in other Muridae, remains fully fertile throughout the year, so that the observed seasonal variation in the rate of reproduction appears to depend upon changes in the female generative system (Perry, 1945–46 ; Davis and Hall, 1948). On the other hand, in the bank vole (*Clethrionomys*), musk rat (*Ondatra*) and possibly the wood rat (*Neotoma*), which belong to the *Cricetidae*, the testes undergo regression during part of the year (*see* Asdell, 1946).

Matthews (1947a) has described an intersexual wild brown rat.

Mastomys

The reproductive habits of the multimammate mouse of Sierra Leone (*Mastomys erythroleucus* Temm.) have been investigated by Brambell and Davis (1941). No conclusive evidence of a true breeding season was obtained, but the greatest number of mature females and of pregnancies were found in October and November, towards the end of the rainy season. Thus, like the brown rat and other wild rodents, *Mastomys* appears to breed most intensively during a restricted part of the year.

The mean litter size is 11·5 but as many as 17 apparently healthy embryos were seen in one uterus. This, the unusually large number of mammary glands (ten pairs), and the fact that most females conceive at the first post-partum oestrus, account for the very high fertility of this species.

Family *Hystricidae*

The crested porcupine of Africa, *Hystrix cristata*, has bred during all months of the year in the London Zoological Gardens, most births taking place between April and September (Zuckerman, 1953).

Family *Erethizontidae*

The North American porcupine, *Erethizon dorsatum*, has a short, clearly demarcated breeding season which lasts from the beginning of November to the beginning of December. A single young is born in the spring, after a gestation period of some 16 weeks (Struthers, 1928 ; Shadle, 1948). Whether the animal is mono- or seasonally polyoestrous appears to be unknown.

A feature of the ovarian cycle in this species is the presence of large numbers of accessory corpora lutea, in addition to the single primary corpus luteum (Mossman and Judas, 1949). These "satellite" corpora are formed at oestrus and in early pregnancy as a result of luteinisation of atretic follicles. They develop in both ovaries, but persist only on the side carrying the primary (ovulatory) corpus luteum, an observation which suggests that the latter is concerned in their maintenance.

The formation of additional corpora lutea during pregnancy has been reported in a variety of mammals (e.g. the rhesus monkey, mare and elephant ; *see* Mossman and Judas ; and this Chapter), but the unilateral persistence of such lutein tissue in only one gonad appears to be peculiar to the porcupine.

Family *Caviidae*

Cavia

The guinea-pig (*Cavia porcellus*) is distinguished in the history of reproductive physiology by the fact that it was the subject of the now classical study by Stockard and Papanicolaou (1917) which showed for the first time that the phases of the ovarian cycle are correlated with periodic changes both in the vaginal epithelium and the vaginal " secretion." This observation provided a method for following the oestrous cycle in living animals, thus opening the way for the isolation and assay of the follicular (oestrogenic) hormone.

In captivity the guinea-pig breeds throughout the year with little variation in fecundity, and gestation lasts for over 2 months. The size of litters usually varies from 2 to 4, and the young are born in a well-developed state, being able to fend for themselves.

Pioneer workers such as Bischoff (1844, 1852), Rein (1883), Sobotta (1906) and in particular Loeb (1911a, b, 1914, 1917) had established that ovulation occurs spontaneously and is closely related to oestrus.

By means of the vaginal smear technique, Stockard and Papanicolaou showed that the length of the oestrous cycle, i.e. the interval between successive ovulations, is approximately 16 days. It was no accident that the vaginal cycle was first discovered in the guinea-pig, for in this species the vagina is closed by an epithelial membrane on all except 4 days of the oestrous cycle, when mating can occur. The periodicity of this phenomenon led to the study of the vaginal mucosa, and so to the establishment of the correlation of the ovarian phases with the cyclical changes in the accessory reproductive organs. Stockard and Papanicolaou's observations have been confirmed by Selle (1922), Nicol (1933a, b) and Young (1937).

Asdell (1946) has summarised various findings on the length of the oestrous cycle and quotes an average of 16½ days, with modes varying in different studies from 15 to 17 days. According to the same author, prooestrus lasts from 1 to 1½ days, and the period of sexual receptivity 8 to 10 hours, and rarely more than 20 hours. In Squier's opinion (1932) a female is actually " in heat " for a mere 2 to 3 hours, or for less than 1 per cent of the length of the entire 16-day cycle.

Oestrus is characterised by straightening of the back and elevation of the pelvis (Young, 1941). A " guttural vocalization," as well as " pursuit and mounting of other females and even males " are frequently observed, but can also occur independently of oestrus. These manifestations are most intense at the beginning of heat and subside gradually towards its end.

Ovulation occurs about 10 hours after the beginning of the heat phase and, except when oestrus is short in duration, before it ends (Myers, Young and Dempsey, 1936). The same authors point out that oestrus, as identified by means of the vaginal smear, does not always coincide exactly with the period of acceptance of the male. In a subsequent study (Young, Dempsey, Myers and Hagquist, 1938), they have shown that there is no close correlation between the ovarian condition (such as general follicular development and the number of maturing follicles) and the character and duration of heat, an observation which is important because of the widespread belief that the follicular and vaginal cycles in rodents run a parallel course. In the opinion of these authors sexual behaviour in the female guinea-pig varies from individual to individual, and in the same animal from cycle to cycle. In certain females heat is of the intermittent or " split " type first described by Young, Dempsey and Myers (1935). This consists of two or three heat periods of variable length separated by one or two intervals lasting normally less than 24 hours.

Loeb has demonstrated that in the guinea-pig, unlike the rat, sterile copulation does not induce a state of pseudopregnancy. This is due to the fact that the corpora lutea which develop in the non-pregnant cycle of the guinea-pig are fully functional (e.g. they permit the experimental induction of deciduomata, Loeb, 1907, 1917). If the corpora lutea of ovulation are removed immediately after oestrus, the cycle is shortened to about 11 days (Dempsey, 1937). Conversely, the normal life-span of the corpora lutea of the guinea-pig is greatly increased if the uterus is removed, thereby delaying the next cycle by as much as 5 or 6 months (Loeb, 1923, 1927). If the corpora lutea of an hysterectomised animal are extirpated, a new ovulation soon occurs. Additional observations that bear on these findings have been published by Freksa and Spiegel (1935).

Cyclical changes in the cervix uteri correlated with those in other parts of the reproductive tract have been described by Jurow (1943).

Pregnancy, according to recent investigations, varies from 58 to 72 days with a mode of 68 days (Blandau and Young, 1939 ; Rowlands, 1949b). The usual number of young is said to be 2 or 3 (range 1 to 8 ; Asdell, 1946), but Rowlands (1949b) has reported an average litter size of $3 \cdot 69 \pm 0 \cdot 07$ in a laboratory colony.

Nicol (1933a) states that the vaginal closure membrane (see p. 581) may open during pregnancy, and that vaginal oestrous signs may occur once or twice during the period of gestation. According to Young (1941), this is an extremely rare occurrence (see also Ford, Webster and Young, 1953).

Relaxation of the pelvic girdle is a normal feature of parturition in the guinea-pig (Hisaw, 1926). This author and his associates (1929, 1944) claim to have established that the responsible endocrine factor, relaxin, is distinct from either the oestrogenic or progestational hormone, both of which are also able to produce pelvic relaxation (Courrier, 1945 ; Talmage, 1947 ; Zarrow, 1948).

In about two-thirds of females, heat and ovulation occur almost immediately after littering. The duration of this post-partum oestrus averages only $3 \cdot 5$ hours, or about half that in the non-pregnant animal (Boling, Blandau, Wilson and Young, 1939). Three in four guinea-pigs will mate at the post-partum oestrus if males are present (Bruce and Parkes, 1948). The number of young born after conceptions taking place at the post-partum oestrus is usually high, and in this way a 60 per cent increase in the annual output of young is possible without a deterioration in the quality of litters. Owing, however, to the possible dangers to the health of does bred in this intensive fashion, their reproductive life should be restricted to one year, thus necessitating a higher rate of replacement of stock (Rowlands, 1949b).

Lactation in the guinea-pig is stated to last about 3 weeks (Farris, 1950). As a rule there are only two functional mammary glands, and hence a litter of more than two young can never be nursed at the same time by one female. Oestrous cycles are reported to continue during the lactation interval (Ishii, 1920). This fact may be associated with the highly developed condition of new-born guinea-pigs, which to some extent find their own food, and with the relatively small demand they make upon the mother. Females are stated to reach puberty at about 50–60 days (Asdell, 1946), but breeding at much earlier ages has been reported (*see* Farris, 1950). Males attain sexual maturity when about 70 days old.

Families : *Octodontidae ; Capromyidae ; Dasyproctidae ; Chinchillidae*

In captivity in London the following species breed throughout the year (Zuckerman, 1953).

> *Octodon degus :* Chilian bush rat
> *Myocastor coypus :* Coypu, nutria
> *Dasyprocta agouti :* Golden agouti
> *Dasyprocta prymnolopha :* Hairy-rumped agouti
> *Lagidium (Viscaccia) :* Viscacha

Births in the species *Chinchilla laniger*, the chinchilla, are restricted to the period April to December, while the Patagonian cavy, *Dolichotis magellanica* breeds only between April and October. In the wild state, however, the chinchilla is believed to breed, though probably not uniformly, at all times of the year (Asdell, 1946). Gestation in the chinchilla is relatively long, as in Hystricoidea generally, and lasts about 111 days. The litter comprises 1 to 4 young.

The South American coypu or nutria, which is commercially bred for its fur, is polyoestrous. The length of the cycle is about 4 weeks, as in the chinchilla, and oestrus itself lasts about 2 to 4 days (Asdell, 1946). The period of gestation is 135 to 150 days, and the litter comprises 9 to 10 young. The female comes into heat shortly after parturition. In the golden agouti (*Dasyprocta agouti*) pregnancy lasts 104 days (Brown, 1936).

The reproductive habits of another hystricoid, the wild mountain viscacha (*Lagidium peruanum* Meyer), have been studied in detail by Pearson (1949). This rabbit-sized diurnal rodent inhabits Peru and Chile at heights from 12,000 to 17,000 feet, and presents various unusual features. There is a clearly defined breeding season which reaches a peak between the end of October and the beginning of November. By mid-December all females appear to be pregnant. Gestation is stated to last 3 months, and some, possibly most, females may breed again later in the season. During September and early October all are in anoestrus. On the other hand, the male viscacha appears to be fertile throughout the year.

Hard waxy plugs of some 40 mm. length are deposited in the vagina after copulation, but remain there for only a short time. In view of the length of gestation and the likelihood of an anoestrous period, it is believed that no more than three young are produced by an adult female each year.

Ovulation takes place near the time of copulation—whether as its result or spontaneously is uncertain. Only a single ovum is released at a time, and almost always from the right ovary. Implantation occurs predominantly in the right horn of the uterus. On the other hand, there is no histological difference between the two ovaries, and if the right gonad is removed, both the left ovary and uterine horn function normally, as they do very occasionally in the natural state. Normally, therefore, the left ovary is in a state of physiological suppression, unlike the condition in certain types of bat in which the left ovary is grossly atrophic, and apparently incapable of functioning.

Another remarkable feature in the viscacha is the appearance, about half-way through pregnancy, of accessory corpora lutea in the right ovary, probably as a result of luteinisation of unruptured follicles. At the time of parturition there may be a dozen of such secondary corpora (in addition to the primary and apparently functional corpus luteum) present. The only other mammalian species in which a comparable sequence of events has been established so far are the Canadian porcupine, mare and elephant (*see* this Chapter).

CETACEA

Fam. *Balaenopteridae*
      Balaenoptera (Blue, Fin whale)
      Megaptera (Humpback whale)

Fam. *Physeteridae*
      Physeter (Sperm whale)

Fam. *Balaenidae*
      Balaena : Eubalaena (Right whale)

Fam. *Rachianectidae*
      Rachianectes (Grey whale)

Fam. *Phocaenidae*
      Phocaena (Common porpoise)

Fam. *Delphinidae*
      Lagenorhynchus (Striped dolphin)
      Platanista (Ganges dolphin)
      Delphinus (Common dolphin)
      Monodon (Narwhal)
      Globicephala (Ca'ing whale ; " Blackfish ")
      Orcinus (Killer whale)
      Pseudorca (False killer whale)

Knowledge of the breeding habits of the larger and smaller Cetacea has accumulated rapidly in more recent years, mainly owing to the growing opportunities for research provided by the whaling industry. Since 1925 much of this work has been fostered by the *Discovery* Committee (*see* Mackintosh, 1946), and the results have been embodied in a number of its reports (Mackintosh and Wheeler, 1929 ; Wheeler, 1930 ; Ommanney, 1932 ; Matthews, 1937a, 1938a, b, c ; etc. ; *see* Mackintosh, 1946). Additional information is contained in the volume *Giant Fishes, Whales and Dolphins*, by Norman and Fraser (1937), and in two papers by Matthews (1948) and Harrison (1949).

Families : *Balaenopteridae ; Physeteridae ; Balaenidae ; Rachianectidae*

In their monograph on the blue whale (*Balaenoptera musculus*) and the fin whale (*B. physalus*), Mackintosh and Wheeler (1929) define the difficulties of drawing definite conclusions about the breeding habits of whales. Such general statements as can be made are derived from three sources of information : " 1. the examination of the reproductive organs themselves ; 2. the study of the occurrence of foetuses ; and 3. the correlation of the sexual movements and other habits of whales, with the reproductive processes." These authors also point out that nearly all the conclusions which can be drawn about the breeding habits of whales " ultimately rest on the assumption that there is an annual migration of these whales towards the equator in winter into warmer waters for purposes of breeding, and southwards in summer into colder waters where food is more plentiful."

According to Matthews' analyses, the sex ratio in most species of whale is about equal. Earlier statements to the contrary are to be attributed, so Matthews suggests, to the fact that a preponderance of either males or females will be found in given waters when the sexes segregate during different phases of their breeding cycle.

The available evidence suggests that blue whales usually pair in June, July and August, and fin whales in June, July, August and September, these months constituting the winter in the southern hemisphere. The height of the sexual season in blue and fin whales is about June and July, but in isolated cases copulation (and hence the start of pregnancy) may occur at any time. Indirect observations suggest that pregnancy as a rule occurs only every two years. Gestation lasts about one year, and a single young is born at a time, although the occurrence of twins has been reported (*see* Asdell, 1946).

Examination of the reproductive organs (Mackintosh, 1946) indicates that the female is polyoestrous and that ovulation occurs spontaneously. The changes undergone by the uterine mucosa during the reproductive cycle have been described in detail by Matthews (1948) and are referred to on p. 584.

In the male, spermatogenesis appears to continue throughout the year, but Mackintosh and Wheeler (1929) believe that an increased production of spermatozoa takes place during early winter (from April to June or July).

The blue whale calf is born when about 7, and that of the fin whale when 6 metres long. Weaning occurs after a lactation of about 6 to 7 months, when the blue whale measures approximately 16 metres and the fin whale 12 metres. Both types of whale become mature at an age of nearer 3 than 2 years (Mackintosh, 1946), when their dimensions are about 24 metres and 20 metres respectively.

Although an increase in size continues for a considerable time after the attainment of sexual maturity in whales, these facts suggest that in general the rate of growth in marine mammals is much faster than in the larger terrestrial ones. In the elephant, for example, gestation lasts about 20 months, and full maturity is not reached before the animals are about 25 years old. There are indications, too, that whales live for a much shorter period than the larger land mammals. On the other hand Wheeler (1930) reports that the fin whale does not reach its sexual prime until 10 years old and that it is still reproducing actively when 20. Laurie (1937) even maintains that the female blue whale may breed at 30.

In humpback whales (*Megaptera nodosa*) most pregnancies start between August and November, September being the height of the season of conception. On the other hand, breeding may occur throughout the year. It has been pointed out by Matthews, as well as by other workers, that some of the small number of pregnancies which begin outside the regular breeding season " may be those of whales belonging to schools of the northern hemisphere, which have crossed the equator and joined those of the southern hemisphere and are consequently in a state of pregnancy different from that of the majority of their companions." Gestation in this species lasts about 11 months, when the foetus reaches a length of about 4·5 to 5 metres (a quarter of the length of its mother), and lactation is estimated to continue for approximately 5 months. According to data given by Asdell (1946), twins are common in this species. The female may experience several oestrous cycles before pregnancy occurs (Matthews, 1937a). It seems that

" the majority of female humpback whales breed once every two years, with a period of anoestrus between lactation and the following pregnancy, but that a minority go into oestrus and are impregnated after lactation, during the months when the majority are in anoestrus." It may be noted that the evidence does not suggest that oestrus takes place before the end of lactation.

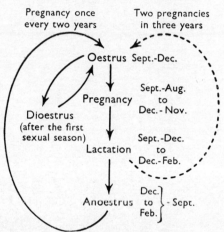

Fig. 4. 4—The oestrous cycle in the humpback whale. (Reproduced from Matthews, 1937a.)

The relation of the breeding cycle of the humpback whale to migration is described as follows by Matthews : there is " a southern feeding migration, as far south as there is open water in the southern summer, followed by a migration towards the north which is pursued mainly in the coastal waters of the continents. The northward migration reaches the neighbourhood of the equator in August, when most of the females give birth to their calves, and the return migration begins at once ; pairing takes place during its course and is, for the most part, over by the end of the year when the whales are on their southern feeding grounds. Some humpbacks are present on the South Georgia whaling grounds during the winter and may be non-migrating individuals which have spent the summer farther to the south. The migration is not restricted only to breeding whales, but includes immature as well as mature whales, pregnant as well as non-pregnant females."

Matthews' diagram of the oestrous cycle in the humpback whale is shown in Fig. 4. 4.

Male humpback whales become sexually mature when they are about 12 metres long, and the state of the testes examined by Matthews suggests that the male sexual season of this southern species falls between March and December. A few observations by Engle (1927) also point towards the occurrence of a spermatogenetic cycle.

The male sperm whale (*Physeter catodon*), unlike the humpback whale, does not appear to have a sexual season. Testes collected in all months of the year except May, September and December and examined by Matthews (1938a) all showed spermatogenesis. Nevertheless breeding in this species is not continuous. Indirect observations show that the majority of copulations take place between August and December, with a peak in October. The season of parturition extends from December to April, with a maximum in February, pregnancy lasting about 16 months. Lactation is believed to continue for 6 months. Examination of ovaries shows that ovulation takes place at or a little before the end of lactation, and it appears that pregnancy usually begins immediately after weaning. Females breed every other year, and so far as can be determined, there is either no anoestrus or only a very short one, the females being in some active phase of the reproductive cycle at all times. There are, however, indications that a series of at least 4 oestrous cycles may occur without pregnancy taking place. As in other whales, only one young is born at a time, but there have been records of twins (Norman and Fraser, 1937). Sexual maturity, it is believed, occurs at about 2 years in the male and at about 15 months in the female. Full physical maturity, according to Matthews, is probably not reached before an age of 8 to 9 years.

The relation of the phases of breeding to migratory movements is stated by Matthews to be as follows. The headquarters of the species is in the tropics. " In summer there is a movement towards the temperate regions of the hemisphere concerned. Pairing mainly takes place during this migration and the females give birth to their young in subtropical and temperate waters. A small proportion of the males, though fully active sexually, leave the females at the height of the pairing season and migrate alone into high latitudes, later returning to temperate waters and joining the general movement of the schools towards the equator during winter."

The sei whale (*Balaenoptera borealis*) differs from the species already discussed in so far as its sex ratio shows an excess of males from early foetal life onwards. As Matthews (1938b) writes, this fact implies unbalanced sex ratio at conception, unless it be assumed that there is a differential foetal mortality at the early stages of life. Examination of testicular tissue suggests that spermatogenesis occurs at all times of the year. In the female, however, there is a definite, if rather prolonged, breeding season. The animals are polyoestrous, and ovarian examinations suggest that in this species, too, as many as four oestrous cycles may occur before fertilisation takes place. Matthews points out that unfruitful cycles may be due as much to the absence of males in the neighbourhood of the female at the time of oestrus as to unsuccessful impregnation. Pairing mainly takes place during May and August, with the maximum in July, and gestation lasts approximately 12 months. Lactation continues on an average for about 5 months. Sexual maturity in the female (according to Hayasi, 1927) is reached at a mean body size of 12 metres, or at the relatively early age of about 18 months (Matthews, 1938b), and breeding is believed to begin at the end of the second year of life.

Matthews summarises the information on the relation of the breeding cycle of the sei whale to its migratory habits as follows : " The migrations of the sei whale consist of a feeding migration to the south in the southern summer and a breeding migration towards the north in the winter. Parturition and pairing occur mainly in tropical and sub-tropical waters. Lactation is mainly finished by the time the whales arrive on their southern feeding grounds. Pregnant whales are the first to arrive at and leave the southern grounds, and are followed by whales in anoestrus."

Some information on other species of *Balaenoptera* is given by Norman and

Fraser (1937). *Balaenoptera acutorostrata* usually calves in November, December and January. Information on the southern right whale, *Eubalaena australis*, is limited. A few observations made by Matthews (1938c) merely suggest that the species, like other whales, is polyoestrous and that the animals reach sexual maturity long before they are fully grown. The Greenland right whale, *Balaena mysticetus*, pairs towards the end of summer, and gives birth after a gestation period lasting 9 to 10 months. The few remarks made by Norman and Fraser about the Californian grey whale, *Adochianectes* (*Rhachianectes*) *glaucus*, suggest that this species is not very different in its reproductive habits from other whales.

Families : *Phocaenidae ; Delphinidae*

In general the breeding habits of the smaller Cetacea would appear to resemble those of the larger whales. The common porpoise, *Phocaena phocaena*, is usually said to pair in summer and to give birth after a year's gestation. But according to information recorded by Asdell (1946), the porpoise copulates at any time between July and October, and the period of gestation lasts approximately 183 days. Meek (1918) states that in this species the testes enlarge enormously in summer. The white-sided dolphin (*Lagenorhynchus*) is said to copulate in late summer, pregnancy being about 10 months.

Pregnancy in the Ganges dolphin, *Platanista gangetica*, a fresh-water species, lasts 8 to 9 months, the young being born between April and July. A similar length of pregnancy (276 days) has been reported in the common ocean dolphin (*Delphinus delphis*) (*see* Asdell, 1946).

The ovarian cycle of the Ca'ing whale (*Globicephala melaena*) has been studied in detail by Harrison (1949). This author concludes that *Globicephala* is polyoestrous, and that ovulation, which is spontaneous, occurs from one follicle at a time. Corresponding conclusions have been drawn from a study of the false killer whale (*Pseudorca crassidens*) by Comrie and Adam (1938).

It is well established that in whalebone whales (*Mysticeti*) the old corpora lutea persist for very long periods (Mackintosh and Wheeler, 1929 ; Wheeler, 1930). It has, therefore, been suggested (Mackintosh, 1946) that the number of corpora albicantia accumulated over the years can give an indication of the age of an adult whale. This worker states that there is a " fairly steady annual increment " of these structures in the ovary. Harrison was unable to find any evidence supporting this view. He states that in the Ca'ing whale the corpora albicantia, although persisting for long periods, eventually regress and become invisible to the naked eye, so that without serial sections through the entire ovary their exact number cannot be ascertained. Harrison points out that even if this were possible, there is no means of distinguishing a corpus albicans of the cycle from one of pregnancy. Hence, to count the number of these structures is " of little use in estimating the age of an individual adult *Globicephala*."

Porsild's observations (1922) on the narwhal or sea unicorn, *Monodon monoceros*, show that this species, unlike other small Cetacea such as the true killer whale (*Orcinus orca*), has no definite rutting season. In this it appears to resemble the false killer whale, *Pseudorca crassidens*, which is thought to breed over a very extensive period of the year, but which in the northern hemisphere experiences an anoestrous period during the winter months (Comrie and Adam, 1938).

CARNIVORA

Suborder FISSIPEDIA

    Fam. *Canidae*

        Canis (Domestic dog ; dingo ; wolf ; coyote)
        Vulpes (Fox)
        Lycaon (Cape hunting dog)

    Fam. *Ursidae*

        Ursus (Common bear)
        Thalarctos (Polar bear)

    Fam. *Procyonidae*

        Ailuropoda (Giant panda)

    Fam. *Mustelidae*

        Mustela (Stoat ; weasel ; mink ; ferret)
        Martes (Marten ; fisher)
        Meles (Badger)
        Mephitis (Skunk)
        Lutra (Otter)

    Fam. *Hyaenidae*

        Crocuta (Spotted hyaena)

    Fam. *Felidae*

        Felis (Cat ; lion ; tiger ; etc.)

Suborder PINNIPEDIA

        Phoca (True or common seal)
        Callorhinus (Fur seal)
        Leptonychotes (Weddell seal)
        Halichoerus (European grey seal)
        Eumetopias (Northern sea-lion)
        Otaria (Southern sea-lion)
        Mirounga (Elephant seal)

Suborder FISSIPEDIA

Family *Canidae*

Genera : *Canis ; Vulpes ; Lycaon*

Canis

The dog

The reproductive habits of the domestic dog (*C. familiaris*) have been the subject of considerable study.

It is generally assumed that bitches have two sexual seasons a year, which fall in spring and autumn, during each of which they experience one heat period. Thus Heape (1908) writes that the best breeding times for the greyhound are April and September, and his data suggest that breeding is at its maximum in the spring. Evans and Cole (1931), however, state that they did not encounter obvious seasonal differences in the incidence of heat in female dogs which they studied in California. This view is corroborated by Asdell (1946) and by Hancock and Rowlands (1949). Records of litters in kennel clubs show a unimodal distribution, peaks of conception occurring in the spring, but whether this reflects a natural tendency or results from breeding practices is not clear (Asdell).

There appear to be differences in the frequency of heat between large and small breeds of dog. Thus in Irish terriers oestrus may occur every 4 months, while in great danes the interval between successive heat periods is often as much as 8 months (Marshall and Jolly, 1906). Stonehenge (1887) writes that there is much individual variability in the periodicity of oestrus, and that heat may recur at any interval from 4 to 11 months, but that 6, 5 and 4 months are the most usual periods. Hancock and Rowlands observed that in their colony of foxhounds, airedales and mongrels, the most frequent interval between successive cycles was 7 to 8 months. Each bitch as a rule has her own peculiar period to which she remains constant, unless systematically prevented from breeding, in which case the periods tend to recur irregularly or cease altogether (Heape, 1900). It has also been noted that the recurrence of the sexual season tends to become irregular with advancing age, whether or not the animal is permitted to become pregnant. The periodicity depends also to some extent upon climate, for in Greenland dogs usually breed only once a year (Rink, 1877).

If bitches are not mated during the season, they gradually pass into anoestrus. Prooestrus, which lasts 8 to 10 days, is characterised by swelling and congestion of the vulva, and a clear yellow mucous discharge often tinged with blood. Oestrus lasts for another week or 10 days (mean : $9 \cdot 0 \pm 0 \cdot 5$ days, range 4–13 days : Evans and Cole, 1931). Hancock and Rowlands (1949) found that the average length of the combined bleeding and heat periods ranged in different breeds from 18 to 28 days. The bleeding phase (" prooestrus ") alone usually varied from 5 to 12 days (range 2 to 27 days), and the period of acceptance (" oestrus ") from 10 to 12 days (range 6 to 24 days). The mean duration of heat in 45 fertile cycles was $10 \cdot 4 \pm 0 \cdot 4$ days compared to $14 \cdot 5 \pm 1 \cdot 3$ days in 10 non-fertile cycles. Interrupted heat (" split-oestrus ") was encountered in about 8 per cent of cycles.

As a rule there is no sanguineous discharge during oestrus, but there is frequently some overlapping in the external signs of the two phases. Thus Evans and Cole (1931) and Griffiths and Amoroso (1939) observe that bleeding does not cease until after the second day of true oestrus, while in Hancock and Rowland's series bleeding frequently persisted even beyond the end of heat. Heape (1900) states that the winter oestrus in some breeds does not last as long as the summer oestrus.

The symptoms of heat disappear rapidly. If conception does not occur, a condition of pseudopregnancy supervenes and lasts for approximately 2 months, during the greater part of which corpora lutea persist in the ovaries, and the uterus and mammary glands undergo proliferative changes. The end of pseudopregnancy is heralded by a milky, fluid vaginal discharge, unaccompanied by external bleeding. Milk secretion and nest formation may occur late in pseudopregnancy, as at the end of true pregnancy (Marshall and Halnan, 1917). Anoestrus succeeds pseudopregnancy and lasts about 2 months.

The period of gestation varies considerably in different breeds of dog, but generally ranges from 58 to 63 days. Owing to the uncertainty in the timing of ovulation its length may be difficult to calculate accurately.

Neonatal mortality is high in dogs, and probably no more than two-thirds of pups are successfully reared (Hancock and Rowlands, 1949). Litter size is also very variable, but averages between 5 and 7, a common range being 4 to 10 (Asdell, 1946). In some breeds as many as 14 pups may be born at a single birth. The size of the litter does not seem to be affected by variations in the onset of the sexual season, for Dighton's records (1921) show that the number of young is practically the same at all times of the year. Lactation is very variable in duration, and may continue until the beginning of the next prooestrus.

There is much individual and breed variation in the age at which bitches attain sexual maturity. Thus Hancock and Rowlands found that in four colony-bred mongrels the first oestrus occurred at between 12–24 months, and in an Airedale litter at ages ranging from 18–24 months. In this connection it is of interest that the average age of a dog in England, without counting deaths as young puppies, is probably well under 4 years (Flower, 1931). Very exceptionally, dogs may reach the age of 20 or even more years.

It is generally accepted that ovulation in the dog is spontaneous (*see* Evans and Cole, 1931). According to Marshall and Jolly (1906), it occurs after external bleeding has been in progress for several days, or when bleeding is almost or quite finished, and about the time the bitch first accepts the male. In the opinion of other investigators it usually takes place between the first and second days after the first acceptance of the male (Gerlinger, 1925 ; Evans and Cole, 1931 ; Evans and Swezy, 1931; Griffiths and Amoroso, 1939). Hancock and Rowlands (1949) obtained the highest conception rates by mating bitches twice, once during the first 4 days of oestrus and again 48 hours later. They state that conception is less likely if service is withheld until the 5th day of oestrus. In all other spontaneously ovulating mammals ovulation is thought to take place towards the end of heat.

Evans and Cole believe that the ovum of the bitch remains viable and capable of fertilisation for at least 4 days after ovulation, a much longer period than in other species of mammal.

The Dingo

The dingo (*C. familiaris dingo*) is generally believed to be a strain of domestic dog that went wild after its introduction into Australia. According to Wood Jones (1923–25), its breeding season in South Australia is August and September, most pups being born in the winter months. In captivity in London dingos generally produce their young between February and May, the implication being that the animal is monoestrous and that it has a single breeding season in the year. In this it resembles the wild dog of South America (*Pseudalopex gymnocercus*) (Rengger, 1830), and the wolves.

The Wolf

In captivity in London the common wolf (*C. lupus*) gives birth only between April and July ; the timber wolf of North America (*C. lupus occidentalis*) between March and May ; the Tibetan wolf (*C. niger*) in April ; and the Indian wolf (*C. pallipes*) between March and May. In India wild wolves are stated to pair between December and April (Blanford 1888–91), and in North America during March, the female remaining in heat for about 2 weeks (Murie, 1944). Gestation lasts for about 63 days, and litters of 4 to 6 pups are born in the spring and early summer. Jackals, which are members of the genus *Canis*, also have a very restricted breeding season. Thus the North African jackal (*C. anthus*) gives birth in captivity in London only between March and June.

The Coyote

In captivity in London the prairie wolf, or coyote (*C. latrans*), also litters between March and June. In the wild state in America it usually mates during February, and the young are produced in late March or April, gestation lasting approximately 60 to 65 days. The average litter size is 5 to 6. Vulval swelling and vaginal bleeding have been observed in captive coyotes (*see* Asdell, 1946). At the end of April the reproductive organs of the female become inactive, and the ovaries show marked thinning and degeneration of the cortex (Hamlett, 1938). Very exceptionally, a second litter may be produced in one season (Dixon, 1920).

The male coyote also has a sharply defined sexual season, which extends approximately from January to late April. By May the testes no longer contain spermatozoa.

Vulpes

According to Bischoff (1863), the sexual season of the fox (*V. vulpes*) varies with the country which it inhabits, animals which live at high altitudes breeding later than those residing in the lowlands. Millais (1904) states that fox cubs in most parts of Britain are born at the end of March or the beginning of April, but that in the south of England they are often produced as early as January.

The youngest fox cubs collected by Rowlands and Parkes (1935) were received in May. In the opinion of these authors the female attains sexual maturity in the season after birth, at an age of about 10 months. Oestrous changes in the vulva, such as swelling or bleeding, could not be established. Ovulation is spontaneous and, if the animals are not mated, is followed by a phase of pseudopregnancy, as in the bitch. The usual litter size for the British red fox is 3 to 7 (Millais, 1904), and the average number of corpora lutea per animal in six pairs of fox ovaries examined by Rowlands and Parkes was 5·7.

Owing to its commercial value numerous studies have been made of the reproductive habits of the silver fox (*V. fulva*), which is a mutant of the red fox of North America. According to Seton (1909), the wild Canadian variety, like the red fox, is monoestrous, and mates at the end of January or early February. Stoss (1933) states that the breeding season of the silver fox in captivity is January and February, and that it may extend until July. According to him the duration of prooestrus and oestrus is 14 days, mating taking place on the 12th and 13th days.

Similar conclusions were reached by Pearson and Bassett (1946) in an analysis of data collected at the silver fox experiment station at Saratoga Springs, New York. Over a period of 14 years the mean mating date of adult vixens was February 12th, with a standard deviation of about 10 days. In most years a few vixens bred as early as January, while a few others did not do so until March. Yearling females tended to mate about a week later than adult ones.

All births recorded by the Silver Fox Breeding Association of Great Britain during the period 1925-31 occurred between March and the first week of June, the maximum number of litters being produced in April (*see* Rowlands and Parkes,

1935). There was no significant difference between the times of birth for the English and Scottish farms—a fact which, as Rowlands and Parkes point out, is of interest in view of the suggestion that foxes breed earlier in the south than in the north of Great Britain. On the other hand, Johansson (1940) states that oestrus occurs earlier in the south of Sweden than in the north.

There is some doubt about the occurrence of external signs of oestrus in the silver fox. Many authors do not believe that there are any. Kakushkina (1937), however, notes that oestrus is associated with a swelling of the vulva and the presence of cornified cells in vaginal smears. Pearson and Bassett (1946) also state that the vulva increases in size and turgidity on the approach of oestrus.

Sexual receptivity of the vixen varies between 1 and 5 days, and lasts on an average for 3. Ovulation usually occurs late on the first or early on the second day of the period of acceptance (Pearson and Enders, 1943). According to Pearson and Bassett (1946), copulation lasts approximately 25 minutes, and there is no correlation between its duration and litter size. Many females fail to mate, and an even larger percentage tend to destroy their litters. This is more marked in young females than in older ones. Pregnancy lasts about 52 days (range 49 to 55 days : Asdell, 1946), and an average of 4 to 5 cubs, in exceptional cases as many as 11, are born in a litter. The animals continue breeding until they are 14 years old.

According to Bishop (1942), gonadal activity in the male silver fox undergoes a marked decline outside the breeding season.

Lycaon

Some information about the breeding habits of the Cape hunting dog (*Lycaon pictus*) has been recorded by Cunningham (1905). A single pair of this species which lived in the Zoological Gardens in Dublin produced 6 litters between January 1896 and January 1900. The first three litters were born in January, the fourth in November 1898, the fifth in May 1899, and the sixth in January 1900. Cunningham writes " It is not easy to offer a satisfactory explanation of the irregularity of the fourth and fifth litters. I am inclined to believe, however, in the absence of definite information on this point obtained from the animals in a state of nature, that the lycaon breeds only once a year, and that the irregularity noticeable in the fourth and fifth litters is due to a tendency on the part of the Dublin specimens to adapt themselves to the climatic conditions of Ireland. At the same time it should be mentioned that certain indications were observed in connection with the demeanour of the parents towards each other which seemed to indicate that the sexual instinct was excited at more than one period of the year." The period of gestation was ascertained to be about 80 days, or nearly three weeks longer than in the domestic dog. On one occasion, when the litter produced was unusually large, the gestation period was 86 days.

Family *Ursidae*

Ursus

Studies of the breeding habits of European bears have been published by Prell (1930a) and Popoff (1934). The brown bear (*Ursus arctos*) usually comes into heat between April and June, but if unsuccessfully mated it may breed again during

July and August.   The grizzlies of North America are believed to mate only every two years, usually in May and June (Murie, 1944).

Gestation in the brown bear lasts about 7 to 8 months, and in Europe the young (normally two) are born between December and February.   According to Blanford (1888–91), the sexual season of wild bears in the Himalayas lasts from September to November, and the cubs are born in April or May.   Hamlett (1935a) suggests that embryonic development in bears is delayed or slowed down during part of intra-uterine life, and observes that macroscopically-visible blastocysts cannot be demonstrated until about two months before delivery.

Thalarctos

Polar bears (*Ursus thalarctos maritimus*) in captivity in London give birth only during the restricted period of November and December (Zuckerman, 1953). Mating is believed to take place at essentially the same times as in brown bears (Prell, 1930b), but according to Lönnberg (1928) and Heller (1930) it may also occur in February and March.   Pregnancy lasts approximately 8 months.

Family *Procyonidae*
Ailuropoda

Sheldon (1937) states that the giant panda (*Ailuropoda melanoleuca*) mates in early spring, and that the young are born in the following January.

Family *Mustelidae*
Genera : *Mustela* ; *Martes* ; *Meles* ; *Mephitis* ; *Lutra*
Mustela
The Stoat

The breeding habits of the stoat (*Mustela erminea*) have been studied by Deanesly (1935, 1943).   Stoats in England generally have one litter a year, either in March or April.   The young female becomes reproductively mature before reaching its maximum body size.   Thus twenty-three of twenty-five first-year stoats collected by Deanesly in June, and hence about three months old, had ovulated.   These young animals frequently mate, presumably with adult males, since the reproductive organs of the males of their own season remain undeveloped until the end of the year in which they are born.   The fact that ovulation in these animals is spontaneous has been established by observations of isolated females kept in the laboratory.   The vulva of the stoat, like that of the ferret, swells during oestrus.

In her original report (1935) Deanesly was puzzled by the apparent absence of pregnancies after the late spring and summer matings, and attributed this to a failure in luteal function, itself due to reduced activity of the pituitary gland. Since then she has re-examined her material (1943), and established that delay in the implantation of the blastocysts is a regular phenomenon in stoats (as well as in many other mustelids).   Deanesly found unattached blastocysts in first-year and parous females " in every month of the year."   They resemble those of the American weasel (Wright, 1942a), marten (Marshall and Enders, 1942) and fisher or pekan (Enders and Pearson, 1943) in being bilaminar and possessing a conspicuous zona pellucida. They appear to undergo no marked changes during their long period of non-attachment, which Deanesly estimates to last for 10 months or more in parous animals and for 9 months in those breeding for the first time. This is borne out by one observed pregnancy which is stated to have lasted 10 months (*see* Asdell, 1946).

At the beginning of the active period of embryonic development in spring, the previously small corpora lutea and uterus enlarge, and the endometrium undergoes decidual changes. In first-year females the rudimentary mammary glands proliferate and form discrete nipple areas. Thus the true length of gestation, excluding the quiescent phase, is only about 6 weeks, much as in the closely-allied ferret (Deanesly, 1943).

The number of young in a litter varies from 6 to 13, the average being 9. Lactation lasts about 5 weeks, after which ovulation and heat occur. More than one oestrus a year is possible, but in the great majority of females, reproductive activity appears to be suspended until March (Deanesly, 1943).

Young males reach their adult weight and become sexually mature in the year following their birth. The male fertile period lasts from February or March until July. Enlargement of the testes begins towards the end of February, and in March spermatogenesis is active. It continues into June and July and is associated with descent of the testes into the scrotal sacs. Most fertile matings take place in late spring and summer, at a time when the testes have usually not yet reached their maximal dimensions. From July onwards they regress in size and leave the scrotal sacs. They are very small and aspermatic from October until January. The epididymis and vas deferens show corresponding seasonal changes.

The Weasel

Many observations (Pohl, 1910 ; Simpson, 1924 ; Thompson, 1931) suggest that the European weasel (*M. nivalis*), unlike the stoat, may breed more than once a year. This is also confirmed by the more recent studies of Hill (1939) and Deanesly (1944). On the other hand, the American weasels, *M. frenata* and *cicognanii* (Wright, 1942a, b) appear to have a more restricted breeding season and a gestation period of approximately 9 months, which precludes the delivery of more than one litter per year. In view of these differences, the reproductive cycle of the European and American varieties will be described separately.

(a) The European Weasel (*M. nivalis*)

The breeding season in England and Wales lasts roughly from April to August (Hill, 1939), but first matings have been reported in January and February. The onset of the season is spread over several months, probably because of differences in the times of birth of the young during the previous year. Thus Deanesly (1944) found that five out of six weasels obtained in March were anoestrous, whereas the sixth contained large blastocysts. In April, two of ten females were anoestrous, four oestrous, and four pregnant. Pregnancies, according to Deanesly, are most frequent in April and May, but they occur in any month from March till August. Some females, breeding early in the year, can have their second litter in the summer. Weasels coming on heat again after the end of lactation were taken between May and

July, and a second pregnancy was actually observed in June. The young resulting from these second pregnancies are born between July and August and even as late as September. Hill (1939) points out that late litters from first matings and early litters from second matings tend to overlap, and hence there is a " continuous but decreasing supply of young animals from June to the end of the year." The end of the breeding season is followed by a period of anoestrus, which lasts as a rule from September to February. In some females the first oestrus may not occur until May or June.

Deanesly mentions that a single female kept unmated in the laboratory for nearly a year failed to ovulate. This observation, and the fact that only pregnant or parous weasels trapped in the field contain corpora lutea, inclines her to believe that in the weasel ovulation depends on copulation, as in such species as the ferret, rabbit and cat.

The exact length of gestation is unknown, but according to Deanesly (1944) the combined duration of pregnancy and lactation is about 10 weeks, and that of pregnancy alone 6 weeks, as in the ferret. The early phase of embryonic development is stated by Deanesly to be relatively slow, but " there is no actual period of delayed implantation."

The number of corpora lutea in both ovaries varies from 4 to 11 ; the average is 7 and the mode 6. The size of the litter is usually 4, but may be 5 or 6.

Females reach sexual maturity at the age of 4 to 5 months, and the majority do not breed until their second season. A small proportion of females born in spring may be found pregnant in late summer and autumn.

The sexual cycle in the male weasel has been described in detail by Hill (1939). Males born early in the breeding season reach adult body weight and sexual maturity when about 4 months old, i.e. during their first year of life. Animals born later do not become sexually mature until their second season. The testes of adult animals (over 7 months) are fully active from March to the end of August, but occasionally, fertile males are seen as early as February or as late as October. There follows a short but well-marked anoestrous period. Retrogression of the gonads is rapid and " comparative quiescence " lasts from October until the beginning of the next year. According to Hill, the production of spermatogonia and spermatocytes never ceases entirely, while the renewed onset of spermatogenesis during January and February is even more rapid than that of anoestrous regression. In the captive male spermatogenesis may continue during the winter when the wild animal is in anoestrus.

Marked seasonal changes correlated with the spermatogenetic cycle are exhibited by the interstitial cells, the epididymis and vas deferens.

(b) The American Weasel (*M. frenata* and *cicognanii*)

According to Wright (1942a, b), the large brown or long-tailed weasel of North America (*M. frenata*) breeds in July and August, and the young are born in the following April or May. During the greater part of this period the embryonic vesicles lie freely in the lumen of the uterine cavity. Blastocysts have been recovered by Wright in the long-tailed weasel in each month from September to January, and in the short-tailed variety (*M. cicognanii*) between October and February. Implantation of the embryos is believed to occur about 3 to 4 weeks before parturition. Thus the active phase of intra-uterine development lasts probably for no more than 4 to 6 weeks, while the total length of gestation, including the quiescent stage, is of the order of 8 to 9 months. In one animal isolated after being mated in the summer, the observed length of pregnancy was at least 252 days (Wright, 1942a). During the quiescent period the corpora lutea are small, and do not protrude externally from the surface of the ovary.

Females first mate when 3 to 4 months old, and may produce litters during the following spring.

The male experiences a seasonal regression of the gonads during the autumn and winter, similar to, but more prolonged than that shown by the European weasel (*see* above). Spermatozoa reappear in the epididymides in March but do not become abundant until mid-April. Moulting is closely correlated with the resumption of testicular activity (Wright, 1942b).

It is clear from these descriptions that the reproductive physiology of the European weasel resembles that of the ferret, whereas that of the American weasel (*M. frenata* and *M. cicognanii*) corresponds more to that of the stoat, marten and badger.

The Mink

The mink (*M. vison*) breeds during only a restricted part of the year (Law, 1930 ; Fritz, 1937 ; Enders, 1952). In North America the season begins in the second part of February and continues throughout March until early April, mating taking place mainly in March. Most of the kits are born in the first part of May (Enders, 1952). During the breeding season mink may experience several oestrous periods, separated from each other by intervals of variable length. Since one service does not always lead to conception, many breeders re-mate their females from 7 to 10 days after an earlier mating, but not all females will copulate again following ovulation. Oestrus lasts about 2 days, and many females accept the male two or three times on each of these days. Preliminary signs of heat may be shown by females a week before oestrus begins. The onset of the sexual season can be modified by variations in illumination (Hammond, Jr., 1951).

According to Enders (1940 ; 1952), ovulation does not occur spontaneously in the mink, but is induced by copulation, sexual struggle with a male, and even by the taking of a vaginal smear or mechanical stimulation of the cervix. Coitus, as in the ferret, is prolonged and usually lasts for 30–40 minutes (range 20 minutes to 2 hours). It is followed by ovulation after an interval of about 40 hours (36–37 hours : Hansson, 1947 ; 42–50 (average 48) hours : Enders, 1952). If conception does not occur, pseudopregnancy results. Artificial insemination has been successfully accomplished on a few occasions (Enders, 1952).

Gestation averages about 51 days but is most variable in length (Fritz, 1937 ; Bowness, 1942 ; Hansson, 1947 ; Enders, 1952). Some delay in the implantation of the blastocysts is likely, and Pearson and Enders (1944) believe that the period of embryonic attachment (i.e. true pregnancy) lasts for less than 31 days. Average litter size is 3 to 4, but litters as large as 17 have been reported (Enders, 1952).

The Ferret

The female

The mating and breeding season of the ferret, *Mustela* (*Putorius*) *furo*, in England normally lasts from April to August. The ovaries always contain ripe follicles, and ovulation will occur at any time during this period, provided copulation takes place. At the beginning of the breeding season, when the ferret comes into heat, the vulva becomes considerably swollen, enlarging to about fifty times its anoestrous size (Hammond and Marshall, 1930 ; Marshall, 1933). It remains in this condition and oestrus continues until pregnancy occurs, or in the absence of pregnancy, until the end of the breeding season, the onset of which varies in different individuals. During pregnancy, pseudopregnancy, and lactation the vulva resumes its unswollen anoestrous condition.

Slight fluctuations sometimes occur in the size of the vulva of unmated ferrets during the breeding season. When the vulva is swollen, a variable amount of serous discharge may be observed from the vagina. This discharge usually contains numerous leucocytes, a few vaginal epithelial cells and sometimes red blood corpuscles (Hammond and Walton, 1934a). Subsidence of the swelling occurs at variable times up to 4 days after coitus (Thomson, unpublished observations).

It was established by Marshall in 1904 that the ferret ovulates as a result of coitus. Robinson (1918) held that the actual mating in itself does not lead to follicular rupture, ferrets sometimes failing to ovulate although mated in full heat, and came to the conclusion that the ferret does not ovulate unless it is properly inseminated. This view is not shared by Hammond and Marshall, who have shown clearly that ovulation occurs after mating with vasectomised males. The average duration of coitus in the ferret is 2 hours (Murr, 1931 ; Farris, 1950), ovulation occurring some 30 hours later (Hammond and Walton, 1934a). Ovulation may also occur if coitus is artificially interrupted after 15 to 20 minutes (McPhail 1933a), and occasionally even if vaginal penetration by the male is prevented (McPhail, 1933a ; McKeown and Zuckerman, 1937). It may be concluded that copulation for the normal full period is not essential, and that the exteroceptive stimulus necessary for ovulation is not as specific as is often assumed.

If a female in heat is not mated, the mature follicles undergo atresia, although the usual signs and symptoms of heat may continue. Because of this, females mated late in the breeding season may fail to become pregnant.

Removal of the pituitary gland $1\frac{3}{4}$ hours after the beginning of copulation does not inhibit ovulation (Hill and Parkes, 1932), but it will do so if carried out within the first hour, copulation itself being interrupted after 20 minutes (McPhail, 1933a). McPhail concluded that the anterior pituitary liberates its ovulation-producing hormone some time during the second hour after the beginning of coitus.

Hysterectomy during anoestrus does not affect the cycle of ovarian changes associated with oestrus and pseudopregnancy (Deanesly and Parkes, 1933a). In this respect, the ferret differs from the guinea-pig, in which removal of the uterus leads to a considerable alteration of the ovarian cycle (Loeb, 1927).

Gestation in the ferret lasts from 41 to 43 days, 42 being the usual period. The process of parturition has been described by Murr (1932), and litter size varies between 5 and 13, 9 being the most frequent. Lactation as a rule lasts about 5 weeks.

When mated with vasectomised males, ferrets in heat become pseudopregnant, a condition which lasts $5\frac{1}{2}$ to 6 weeks, as determined by histological examination of the uterus and ovaries. The termination of pseudopregnancy is followed after

L*

a further interval of 2 weeks by a new oestrous period (Hammond and Marshall, 1930). If a ferret's young are removed immediately after their birth, the animal begins to come on heat about 9 days later. There is no basis for the popular belief that if ferrets are not mated during the breeding season they die.

If a female breeds and rears a litter early in the season, she may come into heat again and raise a second litter. Hammond and Walton (1934b) state that the last day on which they observed a ferret in heat was August 28th, and they note that since gestation normally lasts 6 weeks it may extend into what is usually the anoestrous period. According to Murr (1933), ferrets have been known to breed three times within one year.

Ferrets transferred from the northern to the southern hemisphere adapt themselves rapidly to the changed external conditions, and may experience two full breeding seasons during the year of transition (Duke of Bedford and Marshall, 1942).

The male

The changes which occur in the male ferret during the sexual season have been studied by Allanson (1931, 1932). The testes and accessory sexual organs are fully functional only from March to July. Regression takes place between August and October and continues until December, when changes preparatory for the next breeding season can be observed. Between October and November the testes of mature male ferrets have a prepubertal appearance, the majority of tubules being lined by a single layer of cells made up of Sertoli cells and occasional spermatogonia. Parallel changes occur in the weight of the testes and epididymides, in the diameters of the seminiferous and the epididymal tubules, and in that of the vas deferens. According to Allanson, the interstitial cells begin to increase in size in December and attain a maximum by May, after which they decrease again to reach their lowest level in November. Detailed histological study suggests that these cells are most functional in January, February and March. Unlike those of many other mammals, the interstitial cells of the ferret rarely contain pigment.

It is of interest that normally spermatogenesis in the ferret begins between the second half of February and the beginning of March (Allanson, 1932 ; Habib, 1950), which is several weeks before the females are ready for breeding.

Although ferrets in natural conditions breed only between April and August, they can be made reproductively potent during anoestrus by exposure to additional daily illumination (Bissonnette, 1932, 1935 ; Hart, 1951 ; Hammond, Jr., 1951). The relation between light and the activity of the reproductive tract in this species is highly complex and far from adequately understood (Rowan, 1938 ; Le Gros Clark, McKeown and Zuckerman, 1939 ; Thomson, 1951). Thus the seasonal reactivation of the testes starts during winter, at a time when the incidence of light may be presumed to be minimal. In the female the recurrence of sexual activity begins in the spring. In both sexes, the response to normal and additional illumination varies greatly in different individuals. Females kept in darkness for almost 24 hours per day from the end of January, or those made blind by, for example, the cutting of the optic nerve fibres, will exhibit external oestrous changes and (frequently irregular) oestrous cycles at the usual time of the year (Hill and Parkes, 1934 ; Thomson, 1950). This subject is discussed in greater detail in Chapter 13.

Martes

The Pine Marten

According to Cocks (1900), the English pine marten (*Martes martes*) pairs about January, but the European varieties (e.g. *M. pinel* and *M. foina*) are reported to breed in July and August (Prell, 1927 ; Schmidt, 1934). In North America, too, the mating season appears to be later than in England. In the Alaska marten (*M. americana actuosa*) it occurs during March (Dice, 1921), while the common American marten (*M. americana*) breeds during July, August and September (Enders and Leekley, 1941).

Oestrus may last approximately a fortnight, and is accompanied by conspicuous swelling and turgidity of the vulva (Enders and Leekley, 1941). The swelling persists for a variable period of time (from 6 to 31 days, according to Enders and Leekley), and does not regress immediately after copulation. In this respect the marten resembles the mink, and differs from the ferret.

Reports on the length of gestation differ considerably (94 to 106 days : Cocks, 1900 ; 220 to 230 days : Brassard and Bernard, 1939 ; 259 to 273 days : Enders and Leekley, 1941), and suggest that there may be much natural variation in this species. In the European pine marten pregnancy is stated to last for 270 to 285 days (Schmidt, 1934). Correspondingly long gestation periods have been reported in a variety of allied species such as the sable, stoat, American weasel and badger (*see* Asdell, 1946, and p. 296), and are generally believed to be due to delayed implantation of the embryos. That this also occurs in the marten is indicated by the finding of unattached blastocysts in the uteri of females taken during the winter months (Wright, 1942a ; Marshall and Enders, 1942).

It is believed that the male undergoes a period of anoestrus in winter. Thus Ehrlich (1949) found completely inactive and aspermatic testes in an adult stone marten (*M. foina*) killed in January, and active spermatogenesis in another obtained in June.

The Fisher

The fisher or pekan (*Martes pennanti*), a native of North America, is believed to reach sexual maturity at the age of two. Breeding occurs between April and May, and the young are delivered after a gestation period of between 338 and 358 days or roughly 51 weeks (Laberee, 1941 ; Hall, 1942). The litter varies between 1 and 5, with a mean of 3, and the female mates again shortly after parturition.

The prolongation of pregnancy is thought to be due to delayed implantation of the embryos. Enders and Pearson (1943) found unimplanted blastocysts in two females killed in January and February. Since there is no evidence of delayed ovulation or fertilisation, these authors conclude that in the fisher, as in a variety of other mustelids, the blastocysts remain free and unattached in the uteri for a period of nine or more months following copulation.

Meles

According to Neal (1948), the European type of badger (*M. meles*) mates only in July and August. The only exception he quotes is a mating observed in Sweden on May 27th (Lönnberg, 1928). Similar findings, fixing the time of breeding for August and September, have been reported for the American badger by Hamlett (1932b).

Following conception, the blastocysts remain dormant in the uteri for a period of four to five months. Thus Fischer (1931) found unattached blastocysts from the end of July until January. Implantation and resumption of embryonic development usually take place in late December and January, and the cubs (mostly 2 or 3) are born between February and March, but occasional births as early as January or as late as April are on record. In the American badger implantation occurs in the middle of February (Hamlett, 1932b).

According to Neal, the total duration of pregnancy is 7 months. Actual development, however, is confined to a period of only 6 weeks. As Hamlett (1932b) points out, this agrees closely with the length of gestation in ferrets which do not have a " free-vesicle stage interpolated in their embryology." There are, however, reputable statements that badgers have given birth after a year of solitary confinement (Fairfax-Blakeborough and Pease, 1914 ; Neal, 1948) and it may be that, exceptionally, the period of quiescence can be prolonged beyond the more usual 5 months.

Sexual maturity appears to be attained by the female during the second year, and normally one litter is produced each year—not every other year as commonly thought.

Mephitis

Observations on the reproductive habits of skunks (*Mephitis misomilas varians*, the striped skunk ; and *M. mephitis nigra*, the Eastern skunk) have been published by Cuyler (1924) and by Wight (1931). The mating season in this genus appears to be very restricted, occurring in the latter species between March 1st and 15th. The female accepts the male only when she is in full oestrus, when, as in ferrets, the vulva becomes swollen. Coupling lasts from 5 to 25 minutes, and the vulval swelling disappears shortly afterwards. Gestation lasts about 62 days, the young being born in the second week of May.

Lutra

Wild European otters (*Lutra vulgaris*) breed once a year, in the winter, and the young are usually born in spring and early summer, but litters may occur at any season (Millais, 1905 ; Lloyd, 1951). Cocks (1881) writes that in captivity the isolated female comes in season " nearly every month," and that gestation lasts approximately 62 days. According to Barabash-Nikiforov (1935), the sea otters of the genus *Enhydra* have no definite breeding season. Their courtship and mating activities have been described by Fisher (1939).

North American otters (*L. canadensis*) are said to mate in February and to bear their young in April. Gestation lasts about 2 months, and the usual size of the single litter is 3 to 4 (*see* Asdell, 1946).

Family *Hyaenidae*

Crocuta

Matthews (1941b) states that there is no indication of a sexual season in the spotted hyaena (*C. crocuta*), and that breeding occurs at all times. This is confirmed by the few records of copulations observed in captive animals (Schneider,

1926), and by the fact that in the London Zoological Gardens spotted hyaenas have bred during all months of the year (Zuckerman, 1953).

The duration of the oestrous cycle is not accurately known, but a few isolated observations by Grimpe (1917) in captive females suggest that it lasts about 14 days. Ovulation is spontaneous but, in the absence of mating or conception, does not result in a lengthy pseudopregnancy, as in the bitch. Under natural conditions the species is only potentially polyoestrous, and Matthews states that any female coming into oestrus quickly becomes pregnant.

Gestation lasts approximately 110 days (Schneider, 1926), and the number of young in each litter is 1 or 2.

Both copulation and parturition take place by way of the urogenital canal, which opens at the tip of the clitoris. In spite of the extreme narrowness of this passage, the young are stated to be born in an advanced stage of development. In the striped hyaena, whose genital organs show no unusual features, the new-born are said to be " small, blind and completely toothless and helpless " (Matthews).

Two to four corpora lutea are present in the ovaries of the pregnant female. These remain functional throughout gestation and lactation (which may continue for over 6 months), after which they slowly regress. The entire sexual cycle occupies approximately one year, of which pregnancy and lactation together account for about $9\frac{1}{2}$ months, and post-lactation anoestrus for a variable period of 1 to 2 months. At least 4 complete reproductive cycles may occur in a female, and in the feral animal the duration of life is probably about 10 years.

The female is believed to reach sexual maturity at about 2 years, rather later than the male (Matthews).

Family *Felidae*

The Domestic Cat

In spite of many detailed studies, a number of points about the reproductive processes of cats still remain unsettled. The main controversy is whether ovulation in this species occurs spontaneously or only after the stimulus of coitus.

The domestic cat (*Felis catus*) breeds two or three times a year. There is some doubt about the times when females come into heat, and earlier statements (for example, that of Spallanzani) about the occurrence of fixed or sexual seasons for all cats are no longer accepted to-day. Heape (1900) believed that there may be as many as four sexual seasons in one year, provided, of course, the cats are not allowed to become pregnant. Marshall's observations and more recent ones by Liche (1939) show that the usual number of litters is 2—the first in the spring and the second in autumn. There may be some overlapping during the summer months and, in addition, climatic and nutritional factors are known to influence the breeding periods. Thus in Algiers the mating seasons both begin and end earlier than in the northern parts of Europe and America (Gros, 1936). Winter is usually a period of rest from sexual activity. Foster and Hisaw (1935) established the existence of a definite anoestrous period lasting from September to January, which can be identified histologically and physiologically (e.g. uterine motility) as well as by sexual behaviour. This period of anoestrus can be shortened by exposing females to artificial illumination (Farris, 1950).

The cat is a seasonally polyoestrous animal, and during each breeding period experiences a succession of oestrous cycles, each cycle lasting approximately 14 days.   Some females may experience regular 2-weekly cycles for several months (Farris).

The most extensive studies of the sexual cycle are those of Bourg (1935) and Gros (1936).   Gros' investigation was carried out in Algeria, where cats reach puberty at about 15 to 18 months of age, and the two main sexual seasons last from 15th July to the end of August, and from 15th December to the end of January, respectively.

For the first day or two of oestrus the cat is restive and miaows, and during this period it consistently refuses the male.   The external signs of oestrus then appear, and during this period, which lasts 4 days, the animals can be made to assume the mating position by stroking of the neck.   The receptivity of the animal increases up to the third day of the oestrous period and generally ceases abruptly after the fourth.   In cats which have been isolated, however, symptoms of heat may continue for 9 to 10 days.   There then follows in such animals a period of complete repose which lasts from 15 to 21 days, to be followed in turn by another period of heat.   According to Bard (1939), actual copulation of the oestrous cat comprises two separate phases.   The first, described by Bard as " courtship activities," includes " playful rolling, excessive rubbing, a curious low vocalisation (calling) not heard at other times, and crouching and treading."   The female accepts the male in her characteristic crouch position, resting on chest and forelegs with the pelvis and tail elevated, and treading vigorously with the hindlegs.   The second stage (or " after-reaction ") consists of " more or less vigorous rolling, sliding, rubbing, squirming and licking," and generally coitus is not permitted again until this phase has passed.   Cats will accept the male a second time 48 hours after an initial coitus (Longley, 1911), and occasionally later during pregnancy (Marshall, 1922).

Recent observers such as Gros and Liche are convinced that the cat ovulates only as the result of coitus.   Gros states that in 150 isolated cats under his observation no case of spontaneous ovulation occurred.   Furthermore, he points out that cats in heat will not ovulate if penetration does not take place when they are covered and, although cats will accept the male for a second time after the first copulation, it is the first coitus which provokes ovulatory changes in the ovary.   Ovulation, he also states, occurs from 27 to 30 hours after successful copulation.   This conclusion is based on direct observation of the ovaries of 33 cats.   An exploratory laparotomy was performed and a vaginal smear was taken both when these cats came into heat, and again after successful mating (established by the presence of spermatozoa in the vagina).   In 29 of Gros' 33 experimental observations, which were made between the 27th and the 152nd hour after copulation, it was found that ovulation had occurred.   The four remaining laparotomies were performed 26, 25, 27 and $7\frac{1}{2}$ hours, respectively, after the mating.   In none of these cases had ovulation occurred.   Other investigations (Courrier and Gros, 1933 ; Dawson and Friedgood, 1940) also indicate that ovulation takes place between 24 and 30 hours following copulation, but Liche (1939) estimates the time interval at between 40 and 54 hours.

Other workers have made observations which, although not so extensive, are consistent with those of Gros.   For example, Longley (1911) found that of ten cats killed at times ranging from 23 to 50 hours after pairing, six had ovulated, whereas in a second series of five animals which were not allowed to pair none had ovulated within 50 hours. Manwell and Wickens (1928) in a study of twenty adult cats, also report that no corpora lutea were to be found in those animals which had not been mated and which were sacrificed at various times during oestrus, whereas unsegmented ova, blastocysts, and early embryos were recovered from eight animals following copulation.

Gros was unable to induce ovulation artificially, but Greulich (1934) accomplished this in nine out of twelve animals by mechanical stimulation of the cervix with a glass rod. He removed the ovaries at varying periods after such stimulation, and found that the minimal interval between it and ovulation was about 25 hours.

As already stated, the dependence of ovulation upon the stimulus of coitus remains, in spite of all these carefully undertaken investigations, a disputed point. It is clear that Gros' observations are open to no other interpretation than the one he provides, unless it be that ovulation had occurred in the interval between his first laparotomy and the mating of his experimental animals. From his descriptions it appears that this interval was at least 2 and may have been 5 days. The possibility that ovulation did occur in this period cannot therefore be excluded —in spite of the fact that ovulation was found not to have taken place in four animals which were laparotomised less than 27 hours after coitus.

The view that the cat may ovulate spontaneously is based upon such findings as Bonnet's (1897) report of a tubal ovum in a cat which had been so carefully segregated that there was no possibility of its having mated, as well as corresponding observations by Sadler (quoted by Evans and Swezy, 1931) and by Parkes (unpubl. observations). The general view to-day (Dawson and Friedgood, 1940 ; Asdell, 1946 ; Knaus, 1950) is that spontaneous ovulation occurs very rarely, and that induced ovulation is the usual event.

Ovulation can be induced both in anoestrous and immature cats by the combined use of the follicle-stimulating and luteinising hormones of the anterior pituitary (Foster and Hisaw, 1935 ; van Dyke and Li, 1938).

Gestation is stated to last 62–63 days (*see* Farris, 1950) or 64–65 days (Gros, 1936). The average number of follicles which ovulate is $4 \cdot 12$ (Gros) and the mean litter size is $3 \cdot 88$ (Farris). However, the number of young varies with the age and size of the female, and sometimes 8 or 9 kittens are born in a litter. Lactation may continue for 2 months and there is no post-partum oestrus. Heat frequently recurs within 2–4 weeks of weaning (Farris, 1950).

A female served by a vasectomised male exhibits pseudopregnancy, which is variable in duration, but on an average lasts approximately 36 days (Gros, 1935 ; Liche, 1939). The experimental pseudopregnancy which follows hormone-induced ovulation may last up to 44 days (Foster and Hisaw, 1935).

An interesting case of superfoetation in the cat has been described by Markee and Hinsey (1935). The cat concerned delivered two kittens on June 6th, 1932, and two more 13 days later. Examination of the uterus showed that the two earlier kittens had occupied the right uterine horn and the two later ones the left. Two corpora lutea were found in the left ovary and none in the right, and because both pairs of kittens were normally developed, Markee and Hinsey infer that ovulation had occurred in the left ovary 13 days after the first pregnancy had begun. Another point of interest in this case was the fact that the cat was able to nurse the first two kittens before the other two were born. Additional instances of probable superfoetation in the cat are referred to by Farris (1950).

Mivart (1881) reports that the cat becomes reproductively mature when it is about a year old and that it is still prolific at nine.   Most cats die when fourteen or fifteen, although there have been reports of cats living until thirty-one (Flower, 1931).

The Wild Cat

The extent to which the breeding behaviour of the wild cat (*F. sylvestris*) differs from that of the domestic cat (*F. catus*) is not known.   It would seem that most wild cats are conceived in a mating season during March, and are born early in May.   Another heat period may occur towards the end of lactation late in May or at the beginning of June, and a second litter is then born about August.   This statement is based on the repeated observation of young wild cats in late autumn, which could not have been more than a few weeks old (Cocks in a personal communication to Millais, 1904), and on Matthews' finding (1941a) of a lactating female with its kittens on August 29th.   Matthews also states that, very rarely, a third oestrus can occur late in the year, possibly after the loss of the second litter, the resulting young being born during the winter (November to January).   More usually, however, there is a winter anoestrus which lasts until the end of February.

Oestrus lasts about 5 days, as in the domestic cat, and gestation approximately 68 days (Cocks).

The wild cat breeds first when about 12 months old (Matthews, 1941).

Marshall (1922) has recorded a statement by Cocks that the male wild cat has a definite season of rut, during which it calls loudly and continuously and makes far more noise than the female.   Matthews (1941a) could not confirm this, and concluded that the reported noisiness of the males during the mating season is caused by " the occurrence of oestrus in the female rather than by any physiological change in the male."   A recurrent rutting season is unknown among other species of *Felidae*, such as the common cat.

Other *Felidae*

All the larger Felidae appear to be polyoestrous in captivity. In the London Zoological Gardens young lions have been born at all times of the year, most births occurring between June and September.   In South Africa most cubs are born in the warm season between November and March.

In the absence of the male the lioness may experience 3 or 4 sexual seasons during which oestrus (lasting for about 7 days) may occur every 3 to 4 weeks. If successfully mated, she may raise two litters in each year.   Gestation lasts 108 to 111 days, and the usual number of young is 2 or 3, although up to 6 may be born at a time (Blanford, 1888–91 ; Sclater, 1900 ; Brown, 1936).

Captive tigers also breed throughout the year, gestation lasting from 98 to 109 days (Zuckerman, 1953).   According to Ridley (1895), wild tiger cubs are born in December and January.   The leopard also breeds at all times in captivity (Zuckerman), but it has been stated that in India the young are born between February and March (Blanford, 1888–91), and in South Africa between October and December (Sclater, 1900).

Records of births among other species of Felidae in captivity in London are not as extensive as those already discussed, but most that have bred have done so throughout the greater part of the year.   An exception is the puma (*F. concolor*), 17 births of which have all fallen between April and November.   Grinnell, Dixon and Linsdale (1937) state that pumas in the wild mate at all times.   In California most puma cubs are born in April, although there is a second peak of births in August.   Gestation in this species is said to last 3 months.

Suborder PINNIPEDIA

Genera : *Phoca ; Callorhinus ; Leptonychotes ; Halichoerus ; Eumetopias ; Otaria ; Mirounga*

Seals produce their single offspring at roughly annual intervals, and appear to be monoestrous.   The pups of the harp seal (*Phoca groenlandica*) in Newfoundland, and in Greenland, are born each year between 8th and 10th March (Millais, 1904).   Farther north, at Jan Mayen, they are not born until about 23rd or 24th March.   The fur seal (*Callorhinus ursinus* L.) produces its young between June 20th and July 20th (*see* Enders, Pearson and Pearson, 1946), and the Weddell seal (*Leptonychotes weddelli*) between October 5th and November 10th (Lindsey, 1937). This suggests that the sexual season in these animals is restricted to regular periods of comparatively short duration.   On the other hand, both the common (harbour) seal (*Phoca vitulina* L.) of the Pacific coast of North America (*see* Asdell, 1946) and the European grey seal, *Halichoerus grypus* (Davies, 1949) have much more extensive breeding seasons.   In the latter species there may be an interval of as many as 4 months between the birth of the first and last calves.   This, Davies suggests, is due to the need of the young to spend the first few weeks of life out of the sea, a requirement which is difficult to obtain in the cramped breeding quarters on small Atlantic islands frequented by this species.   In other types of seal the young are able to take to the sea at once, and can be born on tidal sandbanks.

According to Davies, female grey seals arrive at their nurseries " from three days to three weeks before giving birth."   During this waiting period they frequently indulge in sexual play with the bulls, which usually reach the breeding grounds some weeks earlier.   The main calving season is in September and October, but some young are born in mid-August, and calving probably continues sporadically into November.   The sex-ratio of the calves is equal.   The young are not suckled for at least 6 hours after birth, and the average total lactation period lasts for 15 to 17 days.   During this time the mother remains near the pup, but does not feed herself and consequently loses much weight (Amoroso, Goffin, Halley, Matthews and Mathews, 1951).   After weaning around the 17th day, the calves are deserted by the cows and a little later take to the sea themselves.

After parturition the females quickly come into heat.   In one case observed by Davies, this occurred on the 12th day of lactation.   In the fur seal, females are stated to mate within 6 days of giving birth (Enders *et al.*, 1946).

Coition appears to occur mainly at sea.   In grey seals Davies observed it on three occasions, and each time it took place in and largely under the water.   According to Darling (1947), the grey seal in Scotland may copulate either on land, in shallow pools of water, or in the sea.   During the mating season males and females eat little and get noticeably thinner.   The male fur seal has even been reported to live for over 100 days without taking food.

In most seals pregnancy lasts approximately one year. It is likely that implant-ation of the ovum is delayed, since the uteri of females collected as late as 4 months after the mating season do not contain any visible embryos. Thus Enders and Pearson (1945) and Enders *et al.* (1946) who studied the fur seal (*Callorhinus ursinus cynocephalus*), which mates in June, July and August, found unattached ova of an estimated age of 2 to 3 weeks in 4 females caught between July and August. The ovaries of each of these animals showed a recently ovulated follicle. No embryos were obtained from specimens collected later in the season, and hence in more advanced stages of pregnancy. The seal blastocyst resembles that of other species in which delayed implantation is an established occurrence (e.g. mustelids). Enders *et al.* state that ovulation in the fur seal occurs near the time of mating, and that after fertilisation the ovum segments at about normal speed for at least a few days. The free (or unattached) stage of embryonic development lasts at least two months. Corresponding views have been expressed about Antarctic types of seal (*see* Bertram, 1940 ; Matthews and Harrison, 1949). Harrison and Matthews (1951) have found free blastocysts in crab-eater seals (*Lobodon carcino-phagus*) in late December and January, and implanting blastocysts from late January onwards.

In the fur seal the post-parturient horn of the uterus involutes rapidly, and the succeeding pregnancy involves the opposite horn. The ovaries are surprisingly large, but do not appear to show the extensive system of subsurface crypts described in Antarctic seals by Matthews and Harrison (1949). Ovulation occurs alternately from each ovary in successive years. The corpus luteum is conspicuously lobu-lated and may be nearly as large as the entire ovary. Possibly as a result of this mechanical pressure, follicular development is greatly reduced, although it is practically unaffected in the opposite ovary. Not surprisingly (in view of the likelihood of a delay in implantation and foetal development), the corpus luteum is smaller during the early stages of pregnancy than towards its end, and traces of it may persist for two months after whelping. The foetal gonads show marked hypertrophy of the interstitial cells, as they also do in the horse (Amoroso, 1951 ; Harrison, 1951).

Seals reach sexual maturity at an age of about two years. Cows deliver their first young during the following year (e.g. Weddell's seal, Lindsey, 1937 ; and the grey seal, Davies, 1949). Puberty in the male harbour seal is said to occur towards the end of the third year (Asdell, 1946), but in both sexes physical growth is not complete until several years after the attainment of reproductive maturity.

Male seals experience rut at the time of the female sexual season, and spermatogenesis in the harbour seal is said to " begin " in July (Asdell, 1946). Whether the male generative organs are functional during the remainder of the year does not appear to be known.

The walrus affords an example of a mammal which bears young only once in 3 years. Parturition takes place about May or June, and the sexual season is believed to recur about 2 years later. Thus the nursing or lactation period extends for nearly 2 years, while gestation lasts about 1 year.

According to Rowley (1929), the Californian or Northern sea-lion (*Eumetopias stelleri*) has a breeding season that extends from June 15th to July 15th, and a gestation period of about 11 months. The cows arrive in the neighbourhood of the rookery during the latter part of May and are joined by the adult males early in June.   By the middle of the month breeding activities are in full swing, and within a week or so of giving birth the cows come into heat and seek the bull. As soon as every female has been served, the animals take to the sea and the sexes separate.   According to Evermann and Hanna (1925) the Californian sea-lion has the same breeding season over a north-south range of 2,000 miles.

The breeding season of the Southern sea-lion, *Otaria bryonia*, lasts from December to February, and only one young is born (Hamilton, 1934).   Post-partum oestrus is the rule in this species, as in all the Pinnipedia.   Both the male and the female become sexually mature when about 4 years old.

The elephant seal, *Mirounga leonina*, gives birth during a brief season beginning with the last week of August and continuing for 6 weeks (Matthews, 1929). Gestation lasts 11 months and one pup is born at a time.

CHIROPTERA

I. The Fruit-eating bats

Fam. *Pteropidae*
Pteropus (Fruit bat)
Rousettus (Collared fruit bat ; rousette bat)

II. The Insectivorous bats

Fam. *Vespertilionidae*
Pipistrellus (Pipistrelle)
Myotis (Common bat)
Eptesicus (Big brown bat)
Nyctalus (Noctule bat)
Miniopterus (Long-winged bat)
Lasiurus (Red bat)

Fam. *Rhinolophidae*
Rhinolophus (Horse-shoe bat)

Fam. *Nycteridae*
Nycteris (Hispid bat)

Fam. *Molossidae*
Tadarida : Nyctinomus (Free-tailed bat)

Fam. *Phyllostomatidae*
Glossophaga (Long-tongued " vampire ")

I. The Fruit-eating Bats

Family *Pteropidae*

Genera : *Pteropus ; Rousettus*

The most comprehensive review of information about the breeding of wild fruit bats is that of Baker and Baker (1936), to which complementary data have been added by Marshall (1948, 1949).

From Baker and Baker's survey it is clear that north of latitude 4° N. Pteropidae tend to produce their young in March and April, and south of latitude 3° N. in September. Thus a demarcation line or " biological equator " appears to exist for this family just north of the true equator. In spite of the stable character of the climate in which they live, these equatorial species have sharply defined breeding seasons corresponding with those of mammals living near the borders of the tropics. In general the Pteropidae, like sheep and deer, tend to mate in the " autumn " while the days are growing shorter, and to give birth to their young in the " spring." The only certain exception appears to be *Pt. scapulatus*, which in Australia copulates while the days are lengthening (Marshall, 1948).

Gestation in the larger fruit bats lasts about 5 to 6 months (Baker and Baker). In the smaller African collared fruit bat, *Rousettus leachi*, it is said to continue for only 15 weeks from the last copulation (Anderson, 1912). Baker and Baker's own studies of fruit bats were confined to two species, *Pt. geddiei* and the smaller *Pt. eotinus*, collected in the New Hebrides in all months of the year.

The social habits of *Pt. geddiei* vary with the season of the year. " Both sexes congregate together in large ' camps ' during the daytime from about September to about January. These camps are often in large Casuarina trees near the shore. When the females become pregnant, about February, they leave these camps and it becomes difficult for a time to obtain female specimens. For a time the males continue to live a social life. . . . Later in the year, about June, when pregnancy is far advanced, the females may be found in inland camps which contain few or no males. At this season the males have given up their social life and live separately, and it is now difficult to obtain males." Similar findings have been reported by Andrews (1900) from Christmas Island (East Indies) and by Ratcliffe (1932) for the Australian types of fruit bat.

Detailed examination of the specimens which were collected by Baker and Baker showed clearly that in spite of the constancy of the climate, *Pt. geddiei* and *eotinus* experience a distinct breeding season. Copulation occurs in January or February, and most conceptions take place in February and March, but occasionally impregnation may occur as late as June or July. The young are mostly born in August and September, a single one being delivered at a time. The duration of lactation is unknown.

The " flying fox " (*Pt. giganteus*), which lives in the equable tropical climate of Western Ceylon at 7° N., experiences a single annual breeding season of sudden onset and short duration (Marshall, 1948, 1949). Copulation takes place during late November and December, and in any particular colony all mature females "appear to become pregnant or contain sperms in the uterus or Fallopian tubes within a few days." As a rule conception occurs during December and a single young is born in May.

This indicates that there is an important difference in reproductive behaviour between tropical fruit bats and the hibernating insectivorous bats of the Old and New World. In both, mating takes place late in the year (in autumn or at the beginning of winter), but while ovulation and conception occur shortly after copulation in fruit bats (with pregnancy following immediately and continuing through the winter), they are deferred until the next spring in the great majority of insectivorous bats. This point is discussed more fully in the following section.

Fruit bats have bred freely in captivity in the London Zoo. The African collared fruit bat, *Rousettus leachi*, has given birth throughout the year, like the related species *R. aegyptiacus* in Giza (Flower, 1932), but most young have been born between March and May. The "flying fox" (*Pt. giganteus*) has bred on only thirteen separate occasions—all births falling in the period between December and June (Zuckerman, 1953).

Marshall's study of the reproductive cycle in *Pt. giganteus* revealed several unusual features. Apparently, ovarian follicles are formed " in successive waves of hundreds " in which all ova are of approximately equal size. Most of these degenerate but a small number undergo maturation. As one set of follicles becomes atretic the next one arises, and in general any given ovary contains the " comparatively few large survivors of one wave " side by side with the " primary oöcytes of the succeeding batch." Ovum formation, unaccompanied by ovulation, continues throughout pregnancy.

Ovulation, according to Marshall, is not spontaneous but is induced during sexual congress. In eight specimens examined at a preovulatory stage copulation had preceded ovulation. From this and the fact that corpora lutea were found only during pregnancy, Marshall (1949) concludes that *Pt. giganteus* probably belongs to the small group of mammals in which ovulation is conditioned by coitus or the sexual play accompanying mating.

Following conception, the uterine horn next to the functioning ovary develops a progestational endometrium and becomes appreciably swollen. The opposite horn remains relatively inactive and consequently the uterus presents a marked external asymmetry. The localised endometrial reaction, which appears to depend on the presence of an active corpus luteum, is confined to a small region just below the tubo-uterine junction, and implantation occurs only in this restricted area. It occurs equally frequently on the right and left sides, and both sets of ovaries and uterine horns appear to be fully functional. A very similar condition has been described in the elephant shrew, *Elephantulus* (*see* van der Horst and Gillman, 1941a ; and p. 326).

It is remarkable that although the female fruit bat experiences so clear a seasonal restriction in reproduction, the epididymis of the male contains sperms throughout the year (e.g. in *Pt. giganteus*). The male, nevertheless, does show a seasonal change in the size of the testes. In *Pt. geddiei* these are at their maximum size in January and then decrease to a minimum in July. In *Pt. giganteus* the gonads are best developed in November when copulation takes place, but then decline sharply in weight during the next 1–2 months, reaching their lowest values in April (Marshall, 1948). Groome (1940) has made a study of the interstitial cells in the testes of *Pt. geddiei*. He found that there is a close parallelism between the degree of development of this tissue and the animal's social and sex life. From October to February when this bat is social and sexual, the interstitial cells are largest and most numerous, while in July and August, when the males are solitary and asexual, interstitial cell activity is at a minimum.

In some species the testes are partly or wholly intra-abdominal during the greater part of the year, and descend into scrotal pouches only during the copulating season (e.g. in Australian fruit bats ; Ratcliffe, 1932), but this was not observed in *Pt. geddiei* by Baker and Baker.

II. The Insectivorous Bats

Families : *Vespertilionidae ; Rhinolophidae ; Nycteridae ; Molossidae ; Phyllostomatidae*

The fact, first observed by Pagenstecher in 1859, that sperms may live for long periods in the reproductive tract of the female insectivorous bats, has led to a considerable literature on the breeding habits of these animals. Pagenstecher's own observations were made on the pipistrelle (*Pipistrellus pipistrellus*), in one female of which he found the uterus distended with live sperms in spite of the fact that ovulation did not appear to be imminent. Since Pagenstecher's study, numerous investigations have been made of the breeding habits of other insectivorous bats, and the literature on the subject has been repeatedly reviewed (Hartman, 1933a ; Baker, in Baker and Bird, 1936 ; Wimsatt, 1942 ; Wood Jones, 1944).

The essential facts of the reproductive cycle in insectivorous bats can be summarised as follows :—

Spermatogenesis in vespertilionid and rhinolophid bats occurs during the summer, but ceases rapidly during the autumn, when the testes and seminiferous tubules begin to involute, as does the head and body of the epididymis. Spermatozoa, however, persist in large numbers in the hypertrophied tail of the epididymis throughout the period of hibernation. During the same time the accessory organs of the male are in a highly active state (Courrier, 1927 ; Nakano, 1928 ; Matthews, 1937b ; Miller, 1936, 1937, 1939). Mating generally takes place in autumn when the animals enter upon the period of hibernation, but in certain species (e.g. *Myotis*) it may also recur sporadically throughout the winter and early spring (Robin, 1881b ; Vogt, 1881 ; Duval, 1895 ; Guthrie, 1933a, b ; Caffier and Kolbow, 1934 ; Wimsatt, 1942). Ovulation does not usually occur until the spring, and the sperm deposited during the autumn inseminations survive in the female reproductive tract through the winter. In the Vespertilionidae they are retained either within the distended uterus or in the uterine glands, while in the Rhinolophidae they are stored as a solid mass (the " bouchon vaginal ") in a ventral pocket of the vagina (Fries, 1879 ; Vogt, 1881 ; Rollinat and Trouessart, 1895a, b; Courrier, 1924 ; Matthews, 1937b). Ovulation and fertilisation occur shortly after the animals emerge from hibernation (*see* Guthrie, 1933b ; Baker and Bird, 1936 ; Wimsatt, 1944b), but experimentally, hibernating females can be made to ovulate and conceive by raising the temperature of the room and feeding them (Rollinat and Trouessart, 1896, 1897).

Most insectivorous bats whose breeding habits have been investigated are monoestrous, and produce their young once a year. *Nycteris luteola* Thos., an East African bat, appears to be an exception, in that more than one pregnancy can occur in this species (Matthews, 1941c). This worker found half-term foetuses in females which at the same time were in full lactation. From his material Matthews was unable to deduce whether breeding is continuous throughout the year, but he states that " it is certain that in December at least two pregnancies occur in quick succession." The state of the ovaries and accessory organs of reproduction, as well as the occurrence of post-partum oestrus in *Nycteris luteola* previously reported by Matthews (1939), support such a view. These findings imply that in the *Nycteridae* gestation must be of unusually short duration. So far as is known, pregnancy in other insectivorous bats varies considerably but lasts for not less than 6 weeks (e.g. in the common pipistrelle : Deanesly and Warwick, 1939), and may be up to 12 weeks in length.   In most bats a single young is the rule, but in the big brown bat of North America (*Eptesicus fuscus*) 2 are normally produced ; one instance of 4 embryos is on record for this species (Harper, 1929).

As shown in the comprehensive reviews of Hartman (1933a) and Baker and Bird (1936), many of these facts have been known for a long time.   There has, how-ever, always been considerable doubt about the validity of the conclusion that the ova liberated in the spring are fertilised by sperms stored from the preceding autumn.

Indirect evidence in support of this view is substantial.   The fact established by Courrier (1927) and Nakano (1928) that the testes become inactive after the mating season in autumn has already been referred to.   Courrier (1927) and Matthews (1937b) have made a close study of the " bouchon vaginal " in species in which it fills the whole of the vagina or distends the anterior vaginal pocket, thereby blocking the entire passage (Fig. *4*. 5).   Matthews describes this plug in British horse-shoe bats as having the consistency of soft cartilage with an outer layer of inspissated mucus and a softer, inner core entirely composed of densely packed sperm.   The outer cover is thought to be derived from the accessory sexual glands of the male during the act of copulation, and so is presumably homologous with the vaginal plug of rodents.   The plug begins to liquefy in spring, and disappears alto-gether during the summer months.   In the horse-shoe bat (*Rhinolophus ferrum-equinum insulinus*) the bouchon vaginal may be shed entire with some loss of blood due to laceration of the vagina (Rollinat and Trouessart, 1896, 1897), but before that, sperms occasionally leak into the bladder and so into the urine (*see* Hartman, 1933a).

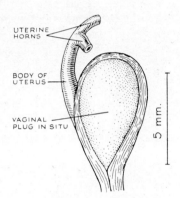

Fig. *4*. 5—Lateral aspect of the uterus and vagina of a horse-shoe bat, with the vagina opened to show the vaginal plug. (Redrawn from Matthews, 1937b.)

Because of this obstruction of the vagina, Matthews denies the possibility of winter copulations in British horse-shoe (rhinolophid) bats.   Since the penis of the male possesses a baculum, and is further reinforced by an accessory corpus cavernosum (*see* p. 113), this conclusion may not be fully justified.   On the other hand, in certain vespertilionid bats narrowing or " atresia " of the vaginal lumen may occur which would seem to constitute a more effective barrier to subsequent penetration.   This observation was first made by Grosser (1903) in *Nyctalus noctula*, in which the hypertrophied cornified epithelium of the proximal vagina separates from the subjacent connective tissue.   This epithelial plug remains *in situ* throughout hibernation, and is cast out only in spring, when the denuded epithelium regenerates, thereby restoring the lumen of the cervico-vaginal canal. Similar vaginal plugs were noted by Courrier (1924) in the European pipistrelle. Since they consist of cornified epithelial cells, they cannot be homologous with the " bouchon vaginal " of rodents (Hartman, 1933a).   It is noteworthy that in the common pipistrelle of Great Britain no vaginal plug is found at copulation (Deanesly and Warwick, 1939).

Another argument frequently quoted in support of the view that ova liberated in the spring are fertilised by sperms deposited in the previous autumn is the presence of active sperm in the female genital tract throughout the period of hibernation.   This has been shown both under natural conditions (for a summary of the observations of Nakano, 1928, and Redenz, 1929, *see* Hartman,1933a), and in bats kept isolated from males for over five months after the autumn mating season (Wimsatt, 1942, 1944a).

None of these findings can be said to constitute direct evidence of the ability of spermatozoa deposited in the autumn to initiate conception and embryonic development of ova released in the spring.   The crucial experiment, involving the maintenance of isolated inseminated females in artificial hibernation for several months has, however, been successfully carried out in recent years.   Gates (1936), in *Myotis sodalis* and *M. lucifugus*, and Folk (1940) in *Eptesicus f. fuscus* were the first to accomplish this, after separating females from males for 68 and 90 days respectively.   Since then Wimsatt (1942 and 1944a) has extended the period of isolation to 138 days in the case of *M. lucifugus* and to 156 days in that of *Eptesicus f. fuscus*.

These experiments show clearly that sperms can survive and retain full fertilising capacity within the female reproductive tract for very considerable lengths of time.   On the other hand, they do not prove that the spermatozoa introduced with the autumn copulations are necessarily the ones which in Nature bring about fertilisation in the spring.

The fact that additional winter and spring copulations can occur in various American and continental types of bat has already been referred to.   For instance, in the vespertilionid cave bats (*Myotis* and *Pipistrellus*) studied by Guthrie (1933a) it seems fairly certain that copulation occurs not only in the autumn, but regularly also in the spring when the animals emerge from hibernation, as well as in the winter if the animals are aroused or have migrated as a result of abnormal seasonal changes.   According to Guthrie sperm can remain alive in the uterus for at least a month, but she believes that the spermatozoa which are introduced in the autumn are in part ingested by leucocytes and in part expelled from the vagina by muscular movements of the reproductive tract.   Fertilisation in her opinion is normally effected by the sperm deposited at the spring copulation immediately before ovulation.

Guthrie's cave bats would thus appear to differ in their habits from those bats whose vaginae remain occluded by solid mucous or epithelial plugs until after fertilisation has occurred in the spring.   More recently, however, it has been reported (Reeder, 1939 ; Wimsatt, 1944a) that the vaginal plug is not a constant feature in *Myotis l. lucifugus* (a species in which winter and spring inseminations have been repeatedly observed).   According to Wimsatt the plug, when present, consists almost entirely of a cheesy mass of cornified epithelial cells.   Whether or not this could be penetrated by the penis of the male is uncertain.   Moreover, as Wimsatt points out, the winter matings may only involve females without a plug.

The interpretation of the chain of events in species in which copulation occurs both in the autumn and sometimes or frequently in the spring as well is obviously very difficult—a fact which explains the conflict of opinions expressed by different reviewers.   Baker (in Baker and Bird, 1936) points out that it is more or less impossible to come to any definite conclusion as to which batch of sperm introduced into the female actually fertilises the ovum, in view of the fact that even in such species as those examined by Guthrie, the autumn sperm are apparently still being eliminated immediately before the spring copulation occurs.

That the male remains capable of mating during the hibernating period in spite of the occurrence of testicular involution is well established. As a rule sperms continue to be stored in the greatly enlarged epididymis while the accessory reproductive organs remain in full development during winter and spring (Courrier, 1927 ; Miller, 1936, 1937, 1939). In this connection Courrier's observation (1927) that in the common pipistrelle (*P. pipistrellus*) the interstitial cells of the testis remain functional after the seminiferous tubules have degenerated, which has been confirmed by Burbank (cited by Baker and Bird, 1936), is of considerable interest.

Since it must be accepted that at least in some types of hibernating bats winter and spring copulations may occur in addition to the earlier autumn inseminations, the biological significance of these supplementary matings needs to be considered.

Most workers (Matthews, 1937b ; Deanesly and Warwick, 1939) believe that the young females born during one year do not experience oestrus during the same year, and only pair during their second season. It seemed, therefore, reasonable to suggest, as was done by the earlier workers, that the supplementary matings serve the purpose of impregnating these young females which had not mated in the preceding autumn (*see* Hartman, 1933a). The only exception appears to be *Myotis grisescens*, females of which may be inseminated at the end of their first summer, although they have not reached full maturity by then (Guthrie, 1933b).

A more significant fact, also reported by Guthrie, is the continuous elimination of spermatozoa from the female reproductive tract during the hibernation period (*see* above, p. 312). This, and the results of their experimental studies, led Guthrie and Jeffers (1938) to the conclusion that only recently deposited sperm introduced during supplementary inseminations can fertilise the ova released in the spring. This view is controverted by Folk and Wimsatt's more recent findings. Wimsatt (1944a) suggests that the supplementary copulations serve to maintain the concentration of sperm within the female reproductive tract at a level sufficient for fertilisation after ovulation in the spring. Wimsatt adds that the winter and spring inseminations are probably of irregular occurrence and do not necessarily involve all the females later found pregnant. They do, however, serve as a safety device of " multiple assurance," enabling those females whose sperm complement has been temporarily reduced, to restore their supplies to a level ensuring conception. Wimsatt concludes as follows : " The important fact is that the fall sperm are able to initiate normal development of the ovum, and in many individuals probably do so, while in the unknown percentage of individuals that mate later, these matings serve to supplement or replenish the supply previously received during the fall."

It must be stressed, however, that this applies only to a small number of species in which the occurrence of winter and spring copulations in addition to the ones in the autumn has been definitely established. In the majority of bats no such supplementary inseminations are thought to take place (*see* Baker and Bird, 1936).

If doubt remains about the sequence of events in species which copulate in both the autumn and the spring, none can be said to exist about the reproductive habits of those bats which both copulate and ovulate either in the autumn or in the spring. *Miniopterus schreibersii* (Courrier, 1927) belongs to the former category, while *Nyctinomus* (*Tadarida*) *mexicanus* (Hartman and Cuyler, 1927) is a representative of the latter. In *M. schreibersii* pregnancy follows immediately upon copulation in the autumn and continues through the winter into the spring. In the male, however, the testes and accessory reproductive organs become atrophic after the mating period in autumn, and remain completely inactive from then on until the next breeding season in the subsequent year.

In several species of bat spring copulations are the rule and are at once followed by fertilisation. This was first described by Hartman and Cuyler in *N. mexicanus*, studied in Texas at 30° N., where mating takes place only in March. At no other time of the year are spermatozoa found in the uterus or in the testes and genital tract of the male of this species.

A similar type of reproductive behaviour is exhibited by the small black vespertilionid bat, *Miniopterus australis*, investigated by Baker and Bird (1936) in the New Hebrides at 15° S., in the Pacific Ocean. In this species all the females conceive within a few days at the beginning of September (a remarkably sharply defined breeding season in view of the fact that these animals live in caves, the climate of which is almost perfectly equable, thereby recalling the breeding habits of certain equatorial fruit bats : *see* above). In *Miniopterus* the weight of the testis is at its maximum in August, after which it decreases considerably and remains low until about the following June. The epididymides are still large and full of sperm in September, but by December they are small and aspermatic. A third bat belonging to this group is the free-tailed bat (*Tadarida cynocephala*) of Florida (Sherman, 1937). The first ovulations in this species occur about the middle of March, and the females are fertilised at this time. Births take place during June after a period of gestation lasting apparently between 11 and 12 weeks. A fourth species with habits similar to those of *N. mexicanus* is the South American phyllostomid bat, *Glossophaga soricina*, in which, moreover, the sexual cycle presents some very unusual features (*see* Hamlett, 1934, 1935b, and below).

The foregoing account of reproduction in insectivorous bats has been concerned mainly with the question of the relation of copulation and insemination to ovulation. The following further facts of general interest have emerged in the various studies that have been made of these animals.

As already mentioned, in most species of bat only a single young is born at a time, but among certain insectivorous bats such as *Eptesicus fuscus*, twins are the rule, and it, as well as the American red bat, *Lasiurus borealis*, may produce a litter of 4 (Lyon, 1903). The developing foetus usually occupies the right uterine horn, which is frequently bigger than the left.

In some species, in which implantation occurs on the right side, the ova are also produced by the right gonad (for instance, in the British lesser horse-shoe bat, in which the left ovary appears to be functionally atrophic ; Matthews, 1937b). By contrast, in *Miniopterus dasythrix*, a South African type of bat, the ova are released from the left ovary, but pregnancy invariably develops in the right uterine horn (Matthews, 1941c). Again, in the British common bat (*P. pipistrellus* : Deanesly and Warwick, 1939), and in the American species *Myotis* and *Eptesicus* (Wimsatt, 1944b), both gonads function.

As already pointed out, the length of gestation varies greatly in different types of bat, and lactation appears to be completed shortly before the autumn period of acceptance.   It would thus appear that there is no true anoestrus in most bats, the period of the year which would correspond to anoestrus in other mammals being constituted by the interval which intervenes between the autumn copulation and the spring fertilisation.

The bat is often considered as an animal in which oestrus, i.e. the autumn receptivity, is widely separated from the spring follicular maturation and rupture. However, the studies of Guthrie and Jeffers (1938a) and Wimsatt (1944b) have shown that in *Myotis lucifugus lucifugus*, a single Graafian follicle is present in the ovary, which even at the time of the autumn matings is of conspicuous size and persists almost unchanged throughout the period of hibernation.   Moreover, the presence of a cornified vaginal epithelium and the state of secretory activity of the endometrium in hibernating bats (Courrier, 1924) imply clearly that the ovary produces sufficient oestrogen during this period.

The single Graafian follicle present in *Myotis* in autumn is destined to rupture in the spring.   Ovulation is spontaneous and occurs under natural conditions in this species in April, after the end of hibernation.   Bats removed from hibernation in the spring will ovulate within a few days after being brought into a warm laboratory.   The fact that they will not regularly do so when removed during early winter (Wimsatt, 1944b) seems to indicate that increased illumination and temperature are not the only factors conditioning ovulation in these animals.

The occurrence of a menstruation-like degeneration of the endometrium has been reported both in fruit and insectivorous bats.   It was claimed for the Japanese fruit bat *Xantharpya amplexicaudata* by Kohlbrugge (1904, 1913), and more recently in the insectivorous phyllostomid species, *Glossophaga soricina*, by Hamlett (1934).   As pointed out by Hamlett, Kohlbrugge's description appears to refer to a discharge of mucus and leucocytes rather than to true haemorrhagic disintegration of the endometrium.   Such a process apparently occurs in the species observed by Hamlett.

Most observers believe that European bats of both sexes born in the spring, although mature by the same autumn, do not breed until the next mating season in the following year.   This view is also held about many American species. One exception to this rule, *Myotis grisescens*, has already been referred to.   Another appears to be *Tadarida cynocephala* (Sherman, 1937), a non-hibernating type of bat, in which the young are born late in May or June and begin to reproduce in the following spring.

It has also been stated (Rollinat and Trouessart, 1897) that young females may not experience their first oestrus until their third autumn.   If true, this is remarkable, since bats are stated to live probably for no more than four or five years (Andersen, 1917).

INSECTIVORA

Fam. *Erinaceidae*
        Erinaceus (Hedgehog)
Fam. *Talpidae*
        Talpa (Old-world mole)
        Scalopus (American mole)
        Parascalops (Hairy-tailed mole)
        Condylura (Star-nosed mole)

Fam. *Soricidae*
> *Sorex* (Common and lesser shrew)
> *Blarina* (Short-tailed shrew)
> *Cryptotis* (Little shrew)

Fam. *Macroscelididae*
> *Elephantulus* (Elephant shrew)

Fam. *Tenrecidae* (= *Centetidae*)
> *Tenrec ; Centetes* (Tenrec)
> *Hemicentetes* (Streaked tenrec)
> *Setifer ; Ericulus* (" Hedgehog " tenrec)

Family *Erinaceidae*

Erinaceus

The reproductive habits of the European hedgehog (*E. europaeus* L.) have been the subject of considerable study (Marshall, 1911 ; Courrier, 1927 ; Herter, 1933 ; Deanesly, 1934 ; Allanson, 1934 ; Allanson and Deanesly, 1934 ; Skowron, 1938 ; Ranson, 1941 ; Skowron and Zajaczek, 1947).

The female

The animal generally hibernates from the late autumn until the spring, but the length and extent of hibernation vary considerably (Deanesly, 1934 ; Skowron and Zajeczek, 1947). In England the female emerges from anoestrus (during which follicular activity does not cease entirely) at the end of March, and breeding occurs between the end of April and June. Pregnant specimens are found between May and September, and the first litters are born in June.

More than one investigator has attempted to breed hedgehogs in captivity, but of the authors cited above, only Herter and Ranson have been successful, and both obtained two litters from single females in the same season. Gestation lasted between 5 and 6 weeks and lactation continued for about $1\frac{1}{2}$ months.

The observation that hedgehogs may breed twice in one season agrees with analyses of the distribution of pregnancies in animals collected in the wild, and with an observation of Deanesly that females in early stages of gestation may have well developed and recently functional mammary glands. Deanesly points out, however, that it is unlikely that all hedgehogs have two litters a year since some, including parous animals, do not come into their first oestrus until June or even later. Herter, it may be noted, did not observe sexual behaviour in his captive animals until the middle of May. The actual season of mating can therefore be taken as falling between the end of March and the end of July, although it is normally supposed to terminate at the beginning of June. Copulation does not usually occur at the first oestrus, but occasionally at the second (Deanesly).

Ovulation is spontaneous and successive ovulations take place before pregnancy occurs. The average size of the litter is 5. The maximum number of foetuses observed by Deanesly was 7, although she states that as many as 10 ruptured follicles may be found in the two ovaries. Herter gives records of 9 young in a litter.

The hedgehog appears to be remarkably infertile in the wild, in spite of the fact that it may be repeatedly impregnated. Conception does not invariably occur

after the first mating, and repeated pseudopregnant cycles are common.   In
Deanesly's series pseudopregnancy was not related to age, parity, low body weight
or low uterine weight.   She suggests that the eggs are often fertilised, but that
they fail to become implanted because of insufficient progestational transformation
of the uterus.   The endometrium appears to become more sensitive after repeated
matings.

The occurrence of numerous corpora lutea of different ages in non-pregnant
hedgehogs suggests that the intervals between successive ovulations are fairly
short, and, as in the rat and mouse, it is likely that the interval is increased by
sterile copulation.   Deanesly estimates the interval between a sterile mating and the
next ovulation as about 7 to 10 days.   Both pregnancy and the lactation interval
(during which ovulation does not occur) are believed to last about one month, and
there is no immediate post-partum oestrus.

The deposition of a copulatory plug has been described by Camus and Gley (*see*
Eadie, 1948b).   This was not confirmed by Deanesly (1934) who, however, found
that spermatozoa persist throughout the uterus for considerable periods of time,
thereby providing evidence of copulation.

Young hedgehogs acquire adult body weight about the time of the beginning of
the anoestrous period, but the females do not appear to reach sexual maturity
until the second season.

The male

The sexual cycle is as sharply demarcated in the male hedgehog as it is in the
female (Marshall, 1911 ; Courrier, 1927 ; Allanson, 1934).

Spermatogenesis occurs between the beginning of April and the end of August,
but Skowron (1938) and Skowron and Zajaczek (1947) state that it is at its height
only between the middle of April and the middle of June.   Rapid testicular
regression sets in during September.   Between October and December the
seminiferous tubules contain only spermatogonia, Sertoli nuclei and primary
spermatocytes, many of which eventually degenerate.   The tubules resume activity
from about the end of January.

These changes in the spermatogenic function of the seminiferous tubules are
reflected in gross changes in the size of the testis, which is always intra-abdominal,
but which increases during the breeding season from two to five times its anoestrous
size.   The anoestrous quiescence of the testis of the hedgehog is less marked than
in either the ferret (Allanson, 1934) or the bat (Courrier, 1927).

The interstitial cells undergo seasonal changes in size which parallel those in the
seminiferous tubules.   They are large and in a fully active condition from April to
the end of June, after which they regress, and reach their lowest functional state in
October.   They begin to develop again in December, but their increase in size is
most rapid at the end of March.   These findings indicate that the interstitial cells
begin to decrease in size before active spermatogenesis has stopped.

The secretory activity of the interstitial cells is reflected in changes in their
content of lipids.   In June many of these cells are heavily charged with fat, which
then decreases in amount, to reach a low level in October.   They never contain
pigment.

The fact that these cells are most active during the breeding season is probably
connected with the enormous hypertrophy which the accessory organs undergo

during that period. At the height of the breeding season these organs may account for almost 10 per cent of the body weight, and some authorities have stated that relative to the size of the animal as a whole, they become more markedly developed than in any other mammal.

The cycle of changes in the epididymis, according to Allanson, is closely related to that of the testis, but the development of the seminal vesicles, prostate, and Cowper's glands is at first slow and then rapid relative to that of the testis. There appears to be no marked seasonal fluctuation in the size of the penis. The increase in size of the seminal vesicles is particularly marked, and the glandular cells lining its acini become tall and cylindrical and secrete actively, so that all lumina are full of a glairy, milky secretion which consists of numerous crystalloid particles of a phospho-protein nature (Hopkins, 1911). These may be identical with the " sympexia " or concretions identified in the seminal vesicles by Courrier (see Eadie, 1948b). They appear to resemble the corpora amylacea found in the prostatic secretions of a variety of insectivores. Spermatozoa are never present in the seminal vesicles.

The internal prostate, which has a characteristic yellow colour, and the external prostate, also secrete freely during the breeding season, and their glandular elements undergo marked proliferation (Griffiths, 1890 ; Marshall, 1911). Courrier (1927) has confirmed Linton's original observations (1907) on the external prostate, which show that the central more deeply staining parts of the gland from which the main ducts arise have a very different epithelium from the peripheral more lightly staining zone. The external zone contains simple tubular glands lined by cylindrical epithelium. As these tubular glands pass to the central zone, their cylindrical epithelium becomes abruptly transformed into a deep stratified epithelium consisting of small cells poor in cytoplasm. These cells show considerable mitotic activity, and their most superficial layers are in process of degeneration and continuous desquamation, so that the lumina of the tubules become filled with material containing chromophylic granules. Courrier therefore likens the external prostate to a gland which excretes its nuclei.

According to the same author both the external and internal prostates elaborate a ferment (termed by him " vesiculaise E ") which coagulates the protein of the secretion of the seminal vesicles and agglutinates formed bodies such as spermatozoa. More detailed cross-coagulation tests indicate that the secretion of the external prostate is essential for the formation of the copulatory plug. When mixed with fluid from the internal prostate it forms a gelatinous clot which is more solid and homogeneous if the products of the seminal vesicles are present as well. No other combination will result in clot formation, nor do the three individual secretions coagulate spontaneously (Zuckerman, unpublished observations).

Some interesting observations of Skowron (1938) suggest that the sensitivity of the accessory organs of the hedgehog to androgenic stimulation varies. It appears that the central stratified part of the external prostate is the most sensitive, and that the order of sensitivity then decreases in the following sequence : inner prostate ; seminal vesicles ; epididymis ; peripheral part of outer prostate.

According to Skowron and Zajaczek (1947), cyclical histological changes corresponding to those displayed by the gonads can be demonstrated in the thyroid and adrenal glands.

The male hedgehog does not breed in the season of its birth.   The period of immaturity is not less than 9, and probably not more than 11 months (Allanson, 1934).

Family *Talpidae*

Genera : *Talpa ; Scalopus ; Parascalops ; Condylura*

Talpa

The female

The reproductive habits of the European mole (*Talpa europaea* Linnaeus : *see* Schwarz, 1948) have always been the subject of great interest.   This is due to the fact that it is almost impossible to distinguish the female from the male by its external appearance, except during the breeding season, when a vaginal orifice appears behind the peniform clitoris, which is traversed by the urethra.   This orifice closes again after parturition.   Geoffroy St.-Hilaire (1829), who was the first to describe this peculiarity, assumed that the vaginal orifice actually resulted from the efforts of the male in the act of copulation, and it was Adams (1903, 1909), who first described the true process by which the opening appears.   " My observations show," he writes, " that about March 1st a wrinkle appears at the base of the clitoris which in a few days assumes a purple hue and by the middle of March a perforation appears in this livid wrinkle on each side of the middle line.   Towards the end of March these two perforations coalesce and the vagina is then open for penetration in the usual way.   I have not found any internal hymen whatever." Since Adams' paper the main contributions to our knowledge of reproduction in the female mole are those of Wood Jones (1914), Matthews (1935) and Godet (1949).   Those aspects of the two former studies which refer essentially to the formation and alterations of the reproductive tract have already been discussed (*see* p. 120).

From Matthews' study, which is based on an analysis of the condition of the reproductive tract at different times of the year, it appears clear that anoestrus lasts from early in June till early in February.   During this period the distance between the base of the clitoris and the anal papilla is much reduced, and the cortical or ovarian part of the ovary is small and inactive.   On the other hand, the interstitial gland is active during this time.   It seems to reach its peak of activity in the middle of winter.   In older animals it becomes so hypertrophied that the ovarian part of the organ appears to be merely a small cap of tissue.   The annual cycle undergone by the medullary segment has been recently re-investigated by Godet (1947), who showed that the medulla attains its greatest weight towards the end of January, and then regresses gradually until it reaches a minimum in July or August.   Parallel cyclic changes take place in the degree of development and secretory activity of the interstitial tissue.

Prooestrus, according to Matthews, begins either in February or in March with swelling and vascularisation of the genital region, and is associated with proliferation of the ectodermal vaginal strands (*see* p. 120). These strands become canalised and final opening of the utero-vaginal canal to the exterior marks the onset of oestrus, which in most animals in England appears to occur in the last week of March. Oestrus is associated with swelling and hyperaemia of the region surrounding the vaginal orifice (Fig. 4. 6).   After copulation, the swelling appears to be intensified on account of a mucoid mass, apparently the coagulated secretions of the accessory glands of both sexes, which oozes from the vaginal orifice. The swelling disappears shortly after the onset of pregnancy.

Oestrus appears to last a very short time. All females in heat in the series examined by Matthews were collected in the same month, and each individual female is thought to be impregnated almost immediately after coming into heat. Coitus takes place from the middle of March onwards. It is not known whether or not ovulation is spontaneous, but it is clear that it occurs very shortly after coitus. Pregnancy lasts about 4 weeks or slightly longer, parturition occuring in the last days of April and the first few days of May. The vaginal orifice begins to close immediately after the young are born, and by about the first week of June, when lactation has ended, it is completely obliterated, a scar being left to mark its site.

The young usually number 3 or 4, and are almost fully grown in about 3 weeks.

Although it is plain that the mole is monoestrous and that it has a very restricted breeding season, it has been stated by Adams (1903) that litters of young moles have occasionally been found in September. Whether or not such an occurrence indicates a second oestrus in older animals or a precocious sexual development of the young, has not been determined. In Russia the breeding season appears to be more extensive, and to last from mid-April until August, but litters are usually produced at the end of May (Baskirov and Zarkov, 1934).

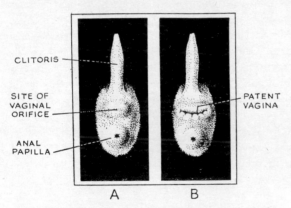

CLITORIS

SITE OF
VAGINAL
ORIFICE

ANAL
PAPILLA

PATENT
VAGINA

A   B

Fig. 4. 6—The genital region of the female mole during anoestrus (A) and at oestrus (B). (Slightly modified from Matthews, 1935.) Observe the swelling surrounding the fully-formed vaginal orifice at oestrus.

Matthews, like others before him, regards the female mole as an animal which represents a high degree of intersexuality, and in support of this view he cites the following facts :—

1. The division of the ovary into an ovarian part which functions only during the breeding season, and an interstitial part which is least active during the breeding season and most active during anoestrus in the depth of winter.

2. The origin of the interstitial gland from the germinal epithelium.

3. The development of female form and function concurrently with the decline in activity of the interstitial gland and increase in activity of the ovarian part of the ovary.

4. The assumption of a male facies and regression in female function concurrently with a hypertrophy of the interstitial gland and the atrophy of the ovarian part of the ovary.

5. The male form of the external genitalia.

Matthews also suggests that the interstitial part of the ovary is homologous with the testis and that it elaborates male hormone. According to him the adult female mole is " a glandular hermaphrodite or female intersex during the period of anoestrum, but during the breeding season it becomes a functional female. The gonad is in effect an ovotestis in which the ovarian and testicular portions alternate in their activity. While the ovarian part is active and the testicular part quiescent the animal is a functional female ; when the ovarian part is quiescent, and the testicular part active, the animal is intersexual, with male facies.''

More recently, Godet (1949) has discovered a way of keeping moles alive in captivity over prolonged periods, and has re-examined the problem experimentally. He finds that the reproductive tract of the female is completely ambisexual at birth and that it loses some, but not all of its male characters during postnatal development. The ovarian part of the gonad elaborates oestrogen which is responsible for oestrous changes, including the opening of the vagina. The medullary ("testicular") elements produce a secretion which resembles, but is not identical with the androgenic hormone. In Godet's opinion closure of the vaginal orifice at the end of the reproductive cycle is not due to the production of androgen, but to the cessation of the oestrogenic stimulus. Thus from a functional or hormonal point of view the female mole is incompletely ambisexual. It may be added that the apparent lack of an external sexual dimorphism which characterises the mole outside the mating period is also observed in the spotted hyaena (*Crocuta crocuta*) and to some extent in *Ateles*, a platyrrhine monkey. Similarly, the opening of the vagina during the breeding season in the mole can be compared with the establishment of a median (pseudovaginal) passage in the bandicoot (*Parameles*) during pregnancy and to its disappearance soon after parturition (*see* p. 62).

The male

The sexual cycle of the male mole owes much of its interest to the relation of the cycle in spermatogenesis to that of the interstitial cells—a problem which has been investigated in detail by several workers (among others : Griffiths, 1890 ; Tandler and Grosz, 1912, 1913 ; Courrier, 1927 ; Schwarz, 1928 ; Matthews, 1935). The testes and accessory organs become enormous during the breeding season. The former do not migrate into scrotal sacs, although according to Owen (1868) " they are protruded into serous sacs which look like a continuation of the abdominal cavity beneath the base of the tail." The atrophy of the accessory organs and of the testes starts at the beginning of May, and in July they have reached their most involuted condition. Between July and December the average weight of the testis is 0·1 g., while at the height of the sexual season it is about 2 g. (Koller, 1936).

Spermatogenetic activity begins in November, and by January the seminiferous tubules are enlarged and contain a number of primary and secondary spermatocytes (Koller, 1936). By the beginning of March spermatozoa are being produced, and during that month the testes slowly become reduced in size, some seminiferous tubules returning to their resting state. In mid-April, many are still producing spermatozoa, but the process of involution continues rapidly By June all the seminiferous tubules present an embryonic appearance, containing only Sertoli cells and resting spermatogonia.

The facts about the changes in the interstitial cells are somewhat obscure. According to Courrier (1927), large interstitial cells rich in cytoplasm and lipoid are present throughout the year and do not vary conspicuously in number or size. He observes, however, that the cells become slightly pigmented during April. On the other hand, Pellegrini (1926) believes that the male mole shows annual variations in the character of the interstitial cells. According to him, they increase in size and lipoid content during the period of spermatogenesis. A completely opposite view was stated by Tandler and Grosz (1912, 1913), according to whom the interstitial cells vary in an inverse way with the activity of the seminiferous tubules, being smallest and least numerous during the period of maximum spermatogenesis, and largest and most numerous during the anoestrous period. This remarkable conclusion, however, was based upon what seems to have been rather a superficial study of the testicular changes, for the cells appear to have been neither measured nor counted in the histological preparations examined by these investigators. Since the testes and seminiferous tubules decrease considerably in size after the breeding season, it is obvious that if the interstitial cells do not vary significantly, as Courrier suggests, they will nevertheless appear to be greatly increased in number and size during anoestrus.

Tandler and Grosz' views obtain little support from the facts of the cycle of changes in the accessory reproductive organs. These are functional and active only during the period of spermatogenesis, a finding which suggests that any cycle of functional activity of the interstitial cells runs parallel to that in the seminiferous tubules. Thus, in March, the vasa efferentia, epididymis, vasa deferentia, prostate, and Cowper's glands are greatly hypertrophied, and their epithelial elements are in general tall, columnar and secreting. The prostatic tubules, for example, when quiescent, are lined by a single layer of small cuboidal cells, but during March, the epithelium of the hypertrophied prostate is of the tall columnar type and its total surface area is " enormously increased " through the extensive folding of the underlying stroma (Griffiths, 1890). At this time, too, the lumina of the tubules are distended by secretion in which numerous small crystalloid bodies are suspended.

Regression of the accessory organs at the end of the mating season is very rapid. It is already apparent in April, and complete by June.

As noted above, a vaginal plug appears in the mole after coitus. This plug, as in most other mammalian species, is formed as a result of the action of the prostatic secretion which is able to agglutinate the spermatozoa. The prostatic secretion in turn is coagulated by the secretion of Cowper's glands (Courrier, 1927 ; Eadie, 1948b).

Other *Talpidae*

Such observations as have been published on other species of mole include few references to changes in the reproductive tracts comparable to those which occur in the European mole (*Talpa europaea*).

The star-nosed mole of North America (*Condylura cristata*) and the common American mole (*Scalopus aquaticus machrinus*) are said to breed in April and May and to have one litter per season (Hamilton, 1931 ; Arlton, 1936).

The hairy-tailed mole (*Parascalops breweri*) mates as a rule between the end of March and the beginning of April, and produces 1 litter a year after a gestation period of between 4 and 6 weeks. In this species the external orifice of the vagina is stated to be patent only during the breeding period, as in the European mole. It is open in March and closed by September.

The testes and accessory reproductive organs of the male undergo marked hypertrophy during early spring, and regress rapidly in size after the middle of May (Eadie, 1939).

In both *Condylura* and *Parascalops* the secretion of the prostate gland consists of masses of suspended amyloid bodies (corpora amylacea). These make up the bulk of the copulatory plug which is deposited in the utero-vaginal canal of the female (Eadie, 1948a). A copulatory mass similar to the natural one can be produced by mixing fluid of the excised prostatic and Cowper's glands (Eadie, 1948b).

Family *Soricidae*

Genera : *Sorex* ; *Blarina* ; *Cryptotis*

The female

The most important studies of the reproductive habits of the family Soricidae are those of Brambell (1935) and Brambell and Hall (1936) on the common shrew (*Sorex araneus*) and lesser shrew (*S. minutus*).

All the Soricidae appear to be polyoestrous and to breed over a long period of the year. Jackson's (1928) taxonomic review of the American long-tailed shrews of the genera *Sorex* and *Microsorex* contains the observation that the animals do not hibernate and that their breeding season extends from March until the end of September. The breeding season of the short-tailed shrew (*Blarina brevicauda*) varies in different regions, but in New York State it continues from February till June (Hamilton, 1929). In this species the young are delivered between April and May, but a second litter may be born in the autumn. In a subsequent study (1944) Hamilton has shown that in the little short-tailed shrew (*Cryptotis parva*) the sexual season extends from early March to November in the northern parts of the United States, but may continue through the whole year in Florida.

The extensive material studied by Brambell shows that the breeding seasons of the common shrew and of the lesser shrew begin, in Great Britain, early in May and in mid-April respectively, and that both species cease breeding in October. The onset of the season, as indicated by pregnancy, appears to take place with remarkable suddenness. In both species the height of the season appears to be in June.

Brambell's analysis shows clearly that females do not normally breed in the season in which they are born, and also gives strong support to the well-known view that shrews usually die after they have survived only one winter and one breeding season. Within their short lives, however, these animals appear to be exceedingly fertile, the female shrew normally producing several litters in a season. Ovulation is almost inevitably associated with pregnancy, and the animals usually conceive again at the post-partum oestrus. The mean number in a litter is $6 \cdot 45$ with a range of 1 to 9. The largest litters occur in June. Since the mean number of corpora lutea in a set is $7 \cdot 5$, and the mean number of maturing follicles is $8 \cdot 5$, it would also seem that only about 10 per cent of the maturing follicles fail to ovulate. A small number of embryos do not develop healthily, the number increasing as the end of the breeding season approaches.

The changes associated with the first oestrus of the breeding season are gradual in onset, and the vagina seems to become cornified long before the animals mate. Copulation normally precedes ovulation, and since it is almost always fertile, pseudopregnancy is not thought to occur in these animals. Indirect calculations made by Brambell suggest that the duration of gestation and the post-partum oestrus together " does not exceed 20 days and is probably 18 days or less," and that lacta-tion lasts as long as gestation. Brambell also believes that implantation may be delayed during lactation, with a consequent increase in the duration of pregnancy. An unexpectedly large number of specimens were found with unattached blasto-cysts. Since most females conceive at the post-partum oestrus and are thus gravid and lactating at the same time, Brambell (1937) explains this finding by assuming an arrest in the development of the embryos and a delay in implantation during suckling similar to that which occurs in the rat and mouse (p. 277).

Lactation in shrews which do not become pregnant at the post-partum oestrus continues in the absence of corpora lutea, and it seems probable that at the end of the season animals in lactation and oestrus pass directly into winter anoestrus. It is of interest that while ovulation does not normally occur during pregnancy, one of the animals examined by Brambell manifested the rare condition of super-ovulation.

The reproductive habits of the lesser shrew (*Sorex minutus*) are practically identical with those of the common shrew (Brambell and Hall, 1936), the only important difference between the two species being the absence of parous lesser shrews during the winter. Presumably none survive the breeding season, and hence it is unlikely that a true winter anoestrus occurs.

The reproductive habits of the North American short-tailed shrew (*Blarina brevicauda*) appear to differ in several important respects from those of the com-mon and lesser shrews. According to Pearson (1944), ovulation, as in the rabbit and ferret, is induced by copulation. Repeated matings are necessary for the release of ova, which occurs about 64 hours after the beginning of coitus. In the absence of the male the female may remain continuously in heat for periods of several weeks. Gestation lasts approximately 18 days, while pseudopregnancy is stated to occur and to last for 9 to 10 days. Post-partum heat appears to be absent, and no copulation plug is deposited in the vagina.

The male

Brambell observed mature sperms in the testes of the common shrew between the middle of March and the beginning of November, a period considerably in excess of that during which pregnant females are found. Hence both the onset and the end of the breeding season appear to be determined by the female of the species. At the end of the mating season the adult males die, and only young males can be caught between mid-November and the following March. There is no evidence that these young males become sexually mature during the season in which they are born. On the other hand, male short-tailed shrews reach sexual maturity at an age of 50–80 days, and may breed in their first year, if born early enough (Pearson, 1944).

Further observations by Brambell have shown that the various accessory organs of the common shrew undergo an enormous increase in size before the beginning of the breeding season, their increase being directly correlated with the increase in size and functional activity of the testes. The vasa deferentia, prostate, and Cowper's glands appear, however, to lag behind the testes, epididymides and penis in their initial development.

The sexual cycle of the male lesser shrew (*S. minutus*) appears to be identical with that of the common shrew.

Family *Macroscelididae*

Elephantulus

Taxonomically, the elephant shrew (*Elephantulus myurus jamesoni*) belongs to the family Macroscelididae, the systematic position of which is still under dispute, being assigned to the Insectivora by most authorities, but showing sufficient resemblance to the Tupaiidae for some to suggest their inclusion with the latter in a subfamily Menotyphla, which is related to the Lemuroidea of the Primates (*see* Simpson, 1945). The three most important genera included in it are *Macroscelides*, *Nasilio* and *Elephantulus* (Thomas and Schwann, 1906). There is only a single species in each of the first two of these genera, whereas many species and subspecies are assigned to *Elephantulus*. They are distributed throughout the African continent.

From the reproductive point of view, two main groups of species can be distinguished within the family Macroscelididae. In the first, which includes such well-studied species as *Elephantulus myurus jamesoni*, and *E. capensis* and *Macroscelides proboscideus*, a large number of ova are shed at ovulation, but only two embryos are implanted. In the second group, comprising *Elephantulus rupestris* and *E. intufi*, no more than two eggs are liberated at a time, associated with the formation of a corresponding number of corpora lutea, and with the implantation of either one or two embryos in the uterus (van der Horst, 1944).

The sexual cycle in the elephant shrew (*E. myurus jamesoni*) has been investigated by van der Horst and Gillman in a series of studies pub-

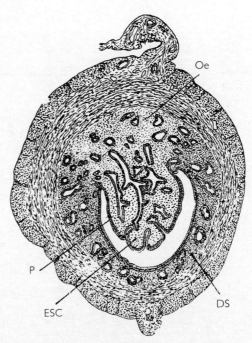

Fig. 4. 7—The endometrial "polyp" of *Elephantulus*. × 40. (Reproduced from van der Horst and Gillman, 1942b.) DS, Dense stroma in the antimesometrial part of the uterus. Oe, Oedema. P, Polyp. ESC, Enlarged stromal cells.

lished between 1940 and 1944. Owing to the difficulty of breeding or maintaining these delicate animals in captivity, the exact length of the oestrous cycle and of its different stages are unknown. From a study of histological material van der Horst and Gillman (1941a) have deduced that in the Transvaal High Veldt *Elephantulus* is seasonally polyoestrous during the spring and summer months, and that it goes into anoestrus between May and July. Apparently the anoestrous animal passes again into oestrus towards the end of July and the beginning of August, but van der Horst and Gillman do not make it clear whether this is to be considered as the beginning of a second breeding season. That this may be the case is indicated by the occurrence of pregnant elephant shrews in September in South-West Africa (Shortridge, 1934). The length of gestation in the elephant shrew is not known.   Its duration of life is thought to be at most two years.

The histological changes in the reproductive tract during the different stages of the cycle are described on p. 614.   It is useful to note here certain remarkable changes that occur in one area of the uterus (van der Horst and Gillman, 1941a). In an area a millimetre in diameter on the mesometrial aspect of each uterine horn, a " polyp-like outgrowth " of the endometrium is formed during the late luteal phase of the cycle, which eventually ruptures and discharges its contents of cells, glandular secretions and blood into the cavity of the uterus in a manner which van der Horst and Gillman consider analogous to the process of menstruation of

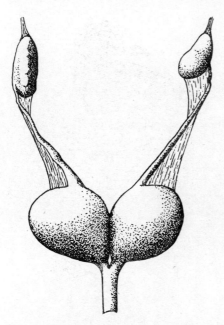

higher primates.   The fully formed endo-metrial " polyp " presents at the outside of the uterus as an elongated local swelling, and internally it may form a " pendulous mass " which protrudes into the uterine cavity (Fig. 4. 7).   Morphologically, there is a marked contrast between the parts of the endometrium which undergo " menstrual " breakdown and the adjacent unchanged tissue.

Ovulation is spontaneous but presents some very unusual features.   As observed on p. 125, as many as 60 ova are set free from each ovary (and hence a total of some 120) at a time, by far the greatest number of eggs normally ovulated by any mammal (van der Horst and Gillman, 1941b).   On the other hand, the gravid female never contains more than 2 embryos, which are sym-metrically implanted, one in each horn, 2 or

Fig. 4. 8—The gravid reproductive tract of *Elephantulus*, showing the two sym-metrical implantation sites. (Repro-duced from the original of Fig. 1 ; C. J. van der Horst and Joseph Gillman, *Anat. Rec.* **80**, 444.)

3 millimetres above their junction with the median uterus (Fig. 4. 8).   The astonishing discrepancy (between the number of liber-ated ova and those actually developing) can be related to the fact that there is only a single minute area in each uterus which undergoes decidual proliferation, and which permits the implantation of a blastocyst.   Van der Horst and Gillman suspect, but have not established, that the sites of implantation and " menstruation " are identical.

The mechanism of ovulation, too, is unlike that observed in other mammalian species, with the possible exception of *Centetes* (van der Horst and Gillman, 1940a, b; Feremutsch and Strauss, 1949), in so far as the corpus luteum is formed before the ovum is discharged from the Graafian follicle.   The granulosa cells at the deep pole of the follicle enlarge and proliferate, and encroach upon the follicular cavity, which is thus gradually obliterated.   At the same time the theca interna proliferates and in turn invaginates the heaped-up granulosa cell mass.   In this way the ovum is pushed out of the follicle through the peripheral layers of the ovarian cortex, and the original granulosa lining of the follicular cavity is everted so as to project from the surface of the ovary.   Luteinisation and vascularisation by the vessels of the theca interna in time transform the exposed mass of granulosa cells into a corpus luteum, which is later covered by epithelium continuous with that on the surface of the ovary.

After ovulation, the ova pass rapidly through the ampullary part of the oviduct, and then collect in a non-ciliated local dilatation of the middle part of the tube or " egg chamber," which forms about the time of ovulation.   All ova remain in this chamber for a considerable period, during which they may be fertilised.   Subsequently, they are transported rapidly through the narrow isthmic part of the tube by wave-like muscular contractions (van der Horst, 1943).   Although the majority of the ova (about 60) which are present in each Fallopian tube may be fertilised, only one adheres to the restricted implantation area and continues to develop : the remainder die.   This circumstance provides an unusually good opportunity to study the relations between uterus and embryo, and van der Horst and Gillman (1944) have concluded that in *Elephantulus* there exists a mutual interaction between both, whereby the blastula is " indispensable for the normal development of the decidual reaction at the implantation site," and the latter in turn is " necessary for the normal development of the embryo."

Family Tenrecidae (= Centetidae)

Genera : Tenrec ; Hemicentetes ; Setifer

The reproductive physiology of this little-known family of Mascarene insectivores presents various unusual features, an outline of which has been given by Feremutsch and Strauss (1949).   According to these authors, the females are seasonally polyoestrous, but a long dioestrous period intervenes between two successive sexual seasons.   The main breeding activities of *Hemicentetes semispinosus* occur from the second half of August to the end of September, and those of *Setifer* (*Ericulus*) *setosus* between October and November, but the latter species may experience a second sexual season in February.   This is confirmed by Rand (1935), who found a female *Tenrec* (*Centetes*) *ecaudatus* early in March with a litter of young approximately one-third grown.   Rand also states that tenrecs usually breed in October, at the end of their period of hibernation, and give birth after a short pregnancy.

Nothing is known of the length of the oestrous cycle, but from Feremutsch and Strauss' estimate that the entire reproductive cycle lasts about 4 to 6 weeks (*see* below) it may be inferred that it is very short.   Ovulation, corpus luteum formation and fertilisation present some very unusual features (*see* Strauss, 1938, 1939).   The mature follicle is characterised by the absence of liquor, and the oöcyte is slowly displaced towards the periphery by the pressure of the granulosa cells.   Fertilisation is intrafollicular, and may be observed in follicles which show only the earliest signs of ovulation.   Following extrusion of the fertilised ovum into the periovarial space (within the ovarian bursa), the entire mass of luteinising granulosa cells is everted and eventually protrudes from the surface of the ovary in the shape of a mushroom.   The process of corpus luteum formation resembles that in *Elephantulus* (van der Horst and Gillman, 1942).

The fertility of tenrecs is most remarkable.   In *Centetes* Bluntschli (1937) observed 32 embryos in an advanced stage of development, while 30 to 32 corpora lutea were counted by Strauss (1939) in a single ovary of a pregnant *Hemicentetes*. In this species, therefore, as many as 60 follicles may be assumed to ovulate in a female at oestrus. However, most fertilised ova are eliminated before implantation, and only 6 to 8 (possibly 10) blastocysts reach maturity. In *Ericulus*, the uterus is stated to contain only 3 to 4 embryonic sites.

The complete reproductive cycle is believed to occupy about 4 weeks in *Centetes* and *Hemicentetes* and 1 to 2 weeks more in *Ericulus*, by far the greater part of these periods being due to pregnancy itself (Feremutsch and Strauss).

TUPAIIDAE

An analysis of the condition of the reproductive organs of the tree shrew, *Tupaia* sp., collected in Java and preserved in the Hubrecht collection in Utrecht, shows that this species has a breeding season of at least 8 months' duration—June to January (Zuckerman, 1932a). There are no data for the other 4 months of the year.

From the accounts of Stratz (1898) and Schultz (1948) it appears that the number of young in tree shrews varies between 1 and 4. In *T. chinensis* Schultz found a range of 2 to 4 embryos, the rule being 3.

There is some equivocal evidence that prooestrous or menstrual uterine haemorrhage occurs in *T. javanica* (*see* Stratz, 1898 ; van Herwerden, 1905 ; van der Horst and Gillman, 1941a). Van Herwerden (1905) also states that uterine hyperaemia and extravasation of red blood cells into the stroma takes place in the " flying lemur," *Galeopithecus volans*.[1]

PRIMATES [2]

Suborder LEMUROIDEA

Fam. *Lemuridae*
    Lemur (Common lemur)
    Microcebus (Dwarf lemur)

Fam. *Lorisidae*
    Nycticebus (Slow loris)
    Loris (Slender loris)

Fam. *Galagidae*
    Galago (Bush baby ; galago)

Suborder TARSIOIDEA

    Tarsius (Spectral tarsier)

[1] Simpson (1945) has assigned this animal to the genus *Cynocephalus*, of the order *Dermoptera*.

[2] The classification of this order is that followed by Zuckerman (1933). Such observations in this section as are made without reference to the literature are based on personal findings previously unpublished.

Suborder PITHECOIDEA

The Platyrrhine (New World) Monkeys

Fam. *Cebidae*
    Cebus (Capuchin)
    Saimiri (" Squirrel " monkey)
    Ateles (" Spider " monkey)
    Alouatta (Howling monkey)

Fam. *Hapalidae*
    Hapale ; Callithrix (Marmoset)

The Catarrhine (Old World) Monkeys

Fam. *Cercopithecidae*
  Subfam. *Cercopithecinae*
    Macaca (Macaques ; Rhesus, bonnet monkey, etc.)
    Cercocebus (Mangabeys)
    Papio (Baboons)
    Mandrillus (Drills ; mandrills)
    Cercopithecus (Common African monkeys)
    Miopithecus (Talapoin monkey)
  Subfam. *Colobinae* (Leaf monkeys ; langurs)
    Semnopithecus ; Presbytis (Langurs)
    Kasi (Purple-faced monkeys)

The Anthropoid Apes

Fam. *Hylobatidae*
    Hylobates (Gibbon)

Fam. *Pongidae*
    Pan (Chimpanzee)
    Pongo (Orang-utan)
    Gorilla (Gorilla)

Fam. *Hominidae*
    Homo (Man)

Suborder LEMUROIDEA

Family *Lemuridae*

Genera : *Lemur ; Microcebus*

The lemuriform (true) lemurs of Madagascar all seem to have a very restricted breeding season. Some of these animals breed freely in captivity, and an analysis of sixty-six birth records of various species belonging to the genus *Lemur* which lived in the London Zoological Gardens shows that almost all births occur between March and June (Zuckerman, 1932a). A similarly restricted breeding season was demonstrated by the birth records of lemurs which lived in the Giza Zoological Gardens of Egypt (Flower, 1933). It would seem, however, that the breeding season of lemurs in the northern hemisphere is the reverse of the natural breeding season, for

Rand (1935) reports from Madagascar that most lemurs in the wild are pregnant in August and September, the young being born in October and November. All females of the mouse lemur, *Microcebus murinus murinus*, taken in October and November were pregnant, the number of embryos carried being two or three (*see* also Schultz, 1948).

Most lemurs give birth to a single young at a time, twins being an exception. Schultz found only 8 instances of twinning recorded in the literature, as compared with 57 single births, while Flower (1933) reported 3 cases of twins and 1 of triplets out of a total of 120 young in diverse species of lemur.

The length of gestation is believed to be 4 to 5 months (*see* Hartman, 1932 ; Zuckerman, 1933).

Families : *Lorisidae ; Galagidae*
Genera : *Nycticebus ; Galago ; Loris*

The breeding habits of the African species of the lorisiform lemurs appear to be different from those of the Asiatic ones. Records of births in the African genus *Galago* suggest that these animals may have a restricted breeding season, whereas the Hubrecht data for the slow loris (*Nycticebus coucang*), an Asiatic species, show that this animal breeds at all times, but with a peak of fertility towards the end of the year (Zuckerman, 1932a).

Lowther (1940), who has made a detailed study of a pair of *Galago senegalensis moholi*, and of their twin offspring, reports that this animal, like the lemur, has a restricted breeding season which lasts from April to October. Unless her use of the term " breeding season " differs from the usual one, this statement is at variance with her own observation that the female in her possession experienced oestrus mainly during the winter and spring. Birth took place in April after a gestation of 4 months, and nursing continued for $3\frac{1}{2}$ months. Twins appear to be common in this species.

In the slow loris (*Nycticebus malaïanus*), gestation is believed to last " at least over three months," and in the slender type from Ceylon and Southern India (*Loris tardigradus tardigradus*) for about 6 months (Hill, 1935, 1937a). This is confirmed by Nicholls (1939) who established a length of 171 days in *L. tardigradus*, an astonishingly long period for so small an animal.

Narayan Rao (1927, 1932) suggests, and Hill (1933, 1935) somewhat reservedly agrees, that *Loris* has a biannual breeding season, unlike its close relations *Nycticebus* and *Tarsius*, both of which are believed to reproduce throughout the year. According to Narayan Rao, the sexual season of *Loris tardigradus lydekkerianus* extends from April to May and from October to November. During these periods two oestrous cycles can occur, after which, in the absence of conception, the females return to " sleepy anoestrum." Correspondingly, the male loris is said to experience two rutting seasons a year, during which descent of the previously abdominal testes takes place " overnight " (Hill, 1935).

Lactation in these animals continues for at least 6 months (Hill, 1933, 1937a, b), and the young, of whom many are twins (Narayan Rao, 1927 ; Schultz, 1948) develop with remarkable rapidity. A female loris may conceive again while suckling a young baby (Hill, 1933).

Little is known about the details of the oestrous cycle in lemurs. Lowther, in the study mentioned above, established that the female galago will accept the male only during periods of oestrus, which may last as long as 5 or 6 days. Copulation takes place at night or, exceptionally, in the morning. When not in heat the female is either indifferent towards or actively discourages the attentions of the male. In the absence of fertilisation oestrus may recur at intervals of 1 to 2 months, " thus establishing the galago as poly-oestrous within the limits of their sexual season."

In the slender loris of Southern India, prooestrus and oestrus last for approximately one week (Narayan Rao, 1927). Prooestrus is " marked by a slight sanguincous discharge through the genital orifice " and by a swelling of the pendant clitoris and the adjacent skin. In a subsequent study (1932) the same author demonstrated the occurrence of menstruation-like changes in the uterus of this species. Following upon a phase of growth and vascular congestion, patches of mucous membrane and its epithelial lining peel off in shreds, and the resultant discharge of extravasated red cells, glandular secretions and oedema fluid escapes into the lumen of the uterus. The total amount of blood appearing at the vulva is, however, small, possibly because the process of endometrial hypertrophy and subsequent degeneration seems to be confined to the cranial ends of the uterine horns.

Unfortunately, Narayan Rao did not correlate the state of the endometrium with that of the ovaries. For this reason a detailed interpretation of the changes he describes is impossible. From his statement that the vaginal haemorrhage occurs during the " prooestrum," it may, however, be inferred that the degenerative process is associated with a ripening follicle and that it is analogous with the prooestrous bleeding of the bitch, rather than the true menstruation of higher primates.

Hill (1933), who studied captive animals, failed to confirm Narayan Rao's findings, but does not deny the possibility that some form of cycle occurs in a state of nature. Zuckerman (1933) suggests that the indications are that the Lemuroidea do not experience menstrual cycles.

Suborder TARSIOIDEA

Tarsius

An examination of the reproductive organs of over 900 tarsiers showed that the females of this species can become pregnant at all times of the year, and that there is little if any seasonal variation in the birth rate (van Herwerden, 1905, 1925 ; Zuckerman, 1931a, 1932a). Only a single young is born at a time.

Tarsiers have been successfully kept in captivity in their natural habitat (Melanesia), in California (see Catchpole and Fulton, 1939, 1943), and in the London Zoological Gardens. They do not appear to have produced any viable young in confinement, but one female maintained at the London Zoo conceived and is stated to have aborted early during pregnancy (Hill, Porter and Southwick, 1952). Catchpole and Fulton (1943) noted cyclical congestion and regression of the labia minora, and well-marked vaginal cornification at the time of oestrus. This phase lasts for 24 hours, and is followed by deturgescence of the vulva and replacement of cornified cells by leucocytes. The vaginal cycle, defined as the interval between two successive peaks in vaginal cornification, lasts for $23 \cdot 5 \pm 0 \cdot 7$ days (average of 12 cycles) with a range of 23 to 28 days.

Uterine haemorrhage was not observed by Catchpole and Fulton either on macroscopical or microscopical examination, although they noted isolated red blood cells in the lavage fluid at various times. On the other hand, Hill *et al.* observed definite external bleeding on a few occasions in one female, blood being present between the labia and in the vaginal lavage.

A laminated vaginal plug is deposited by the male during copulation (Hill *et al*).

Suborder PITHECOIDEA

The Platyrrhine (New World) Monkeys

Families : *Cebidae ; Hapalidae*

Genera : *Saimiri ; Cebus ; Ateles ; Alouatta ; Hapale* (= *Callithrix*)

The earlier accounts of naturalists suggested that New World monkeys of the family Cebidae have restricted breeding seasons. This is possibly true in the case of the squirrel monkey (*Saimiri oerstedii*, Wislocki, 1930). On the other hand, Wislocki's findings in the spider monkey, *Ateles geoffroyi*, the capuchin, *Cebus capucina*, and the howler monkey, *Alouatta palliata*, indicate that these species breed at all times. Hamlett (1939) found that ovulatory cycles occur in *Cebus azarae* for at least 9 months of the year, and hence the non-breeding season, if it exists at all, cannot be longer than 2 to 3 months. Most births in this species are stated to occur during two distinct and restricted periods, May–June and October–November, respectively. The reason for this bimodal distribution of conceptions, which is also observed in marmosets (*Hapale jacchus*), is at present obscure.

From Lucas, Hume and Smith's observations (1927, 1937), it is clear that the common marmoset breeds continuously throughout the year, although there is a tendency for more births to occur in spring and autumn even when a comparatively long interval elapses between the pregnancies of any particular female.

There is a long-standing and widely-accepted belief that New World monkeys do not undergo menstrual cycles. While it seems to be true that they differ in this respect from Old World primates, the observation needs to be qualified. Rengger (1830) noted that females of the species *Cebus azarae* occasionally exhibited a slight vaginal bleeding which lasted 2 to 4 days and recurred in 3, 6 or even 10 weeks. Pallas, quoted by Breschet (1845) records a similar bleeding " à chaque époque du rut " in marmosets. On the other hand, Lucas *et al.* (1927, 1937), who bred a considerable number of common marmosets (*Hapale jacchus*), observed vaginal bleeding in an animal of this species on only one occasion. Moreover, according to these observers, there are no external genital changes which can be correlated with the oestrous cycle (e.g. no cyclic variation in the conformation of the genital area), and none are referred to by Fitzgerald (1935), who also succeeded in breeding these animals in captivity. An exceptional and contrary observation is reported by Russell and Zuckerman (1935).

Histological evidence of the occurrence of " menstrual " changes in the uterus, in the absence of external bleeding, has been reported by Howard (1930) and Dempsey (1939) for *Cebus*, *Ateles* and *Alouatta*. More recently, Kaiser (1947b) has published a detailed study of the menstruating endometrium in the same three species and concluded that " there can be no serious question that platyrrhine monkeys do exhibit periodic cycle desquamation of the endometrium accompanied by haemorrhage, fitting thereby the definition of menstruation offered by Bartelmez (1937)." Goodman and Wislocki (1935) studied a fully-mature spider monkey (*Ateles geoffroyi*) for about 6 months, and found that the animal had successive phases of slight uterine haemorrhage, recurring at intervals of 24 to 27 days, and maintained for 3 to 4 days at a time. The bleeding consisted of a mere " tingeing " of the vaginal washings with red cells and was never externally visible. There were no cyclical changes of the genitalia.

Menstruation of a similar scanty type was also observed by Hamlett (1939) in capuchins believed to be of the species *Cebus azarae*. The bleeding was not a regular feature, but of 6 animals investigated daily for 6 or more weeks, all menstruated at least once, while one female experienced 5 successive cycles with a mean duration of 17·8 days (range 15–20 days). Even in this animal the amount of blood lost was rarely " sufficient to appear externally," and in most instances was visible only in the lavages. The average duration of bleeding was 1 to 5 days. Hamlett also found that there is a well-marked vaginal cycle in *Cebus* with an average length of 18 days and an approximate range of 16 to 20 days. Ovulation is thought to coincide with the time of maximal, and menstruation with that of minimal vaginal cornification.

Copulation is believed by Hamlett to be restricted to the time of, or shortly before, ovulation. In each of 10 cases the presence of a vaginal plug and spermatozoa in the lavage fluid suggested that it took place either at, or at most 3 days prior to, the peak of the vaginal cycle. According to Hill (1941) it takes place only at night, usually at dusk, and lasts up to 20 minutes. The existence of a definite oestrous period in other platyrrhines is indicated by Lucas *et al.*'s observations (1927) in captive marmosets, and by Carpenter's field studies of wild howler and red spider monkeys (1934, 1935). In the last two species copulation is mainly confined to a short " oestrus " lasting for 2 or 3 days, but sporadic mating may also occur at other times. The particular conditions of his study prevented Carpenter from making any accurate observations on the length of the sexual cycle.

Pregnancy in *Cebus*, according to Hamlett, lasts about 6 and certainly less than 7 months. In the howling (*Alouatta seniculus*) and spider monkey (*Ateles ater*) gestation is stated to average 139 days (*see* Kenneth, 1947). In captivity marmosets produce young twice a year, and pregnancy, during which oestrus is suppressed, lasts about 140 days. Twins are the rule, but occasionally single young, and rarely triplets, are born (*see* Wislocki, 1939 ; Schultz, 1948). Lucas *et al.* (1937) refer to a set of four full-term foetuses in a young female which died during delivery. Wislocki has shown clearly that the twins are biovular in origin, and that the two blastocysts undergo early fusion with the resulting formation of a common chorion and exocoelom. In spite of the development of early and adequate anastomotic connections between the two embryonic sites, " free-martin " effects are not evident in heterosexual twin marmosets, unlike the condition in cattle.

Marmosets reach sexual maturity when about 14 months old.

Sexual behaviour and ovulation are suppressed in lactating howler monkeys (Carpenter, 1934) and spider monkeys (Dempsey, 1939), but in the former oestrus may recur long before the young are weaned.

The Catarrhine (Old World) Monkeys

Only the more important and best-studied species of catarrhine monkeys are dealt with in the following sections. Some information on certain of the less-known species has been given by Zuckerman (1930, 1937a) and Hill (1937a).

Family *Cercopithecidae*

Subfam. *Cercopithecinae*

Genera : *Macaca ; Cercocebus ; Papio ; Mandrillus ; Cercopithecus*

Macaca

The Rhesus Monkey

Captive rhesus monkeys (*M. mulatta*) breed at all times of the year (*see* e.g. Corner, 1923a ; Zuckerman, 1930, 1931a, 1932b). There is, however, a seasonal variation in the rate of conceptions and births, as emphasised by Hartman (1931b, 1932). This author holds that the reduced fertility of the female rhesus in the summer months (the " non-breeding " or " non-ovulating " season, as it should more properly be termed), is due to a failure of ovulation, and not to temporary sterility of the male. During this phase menstrual cycles may continue with perfect regularity (Heape, 1896; Corner, 1923a). In a series of 24 births recorded during captivity in England, 16 (66 per cent) were observed in the period April to August, and 7 (*ca.* 30 per cent) between November and February. This observation implies that most conceptions must have taken place between December and February, but that ovulatory cycles do not entirely cease in the summer months.

Some writers believe that wild rhesus monkeys have a restricted breeding season. This is claimed by Heape (1894, 1896, 1897) and Hartman (1931b), who obtained female macaques direct from India relatively soon after their capture in the wild state, and by Hingston (1920) who, apparently, based his views on personal observations in Himalaya. According to them, the season is restricted to September or October. Carpenter (1942a, b), who investigated the behaviour of some 350 semi-domesticated and free-ranging *M. mulatta* on Santiago Island, off Puerto Rico, reports that matings occurred mainly between February and April, and were then followed by a " lack of primary sexual behaviour " during the ensuing months, most births being recorded in August, September and October.

The sexual cycle

Menstrual periodicity. The largest series of observations on the length of the menstrual cycle in *M. mulatta* are those of Corner (1923a : 125 cycles), Hartman (1932 : 712 cycles), and Zuckerman (1937a : 167 cycles), all referring to females maintained in captivity in the northern temperate zone. In these conditions rhesus monkeys show fairly regular cycles from October to April, and less regular and frequent ones during the remainder of the year (Corner, Hartman and Bartelmez, 1945). The modal length is 28 days, but there is very marked variability within and between different individuals. Thus Hartman (1932) records individual means ranging from 22·5 to 33 days in 33 animals, and a total range in cycle length of 14–42 days in 22 selected females (the " best of the colony "). Some 75 per cent of cycles are stated to fall between 23 and 33 days (Asdell, 1946).

Zuckerman (1937a) has analysed one thousand cycles recorded by three different observers, and relating to some 80 different females of diverse ages (including adolescents) observed at all times of the year. The average cycle length was $33 \cdot 5 \pm 0 \cdot 6$ days, the mode (represented by only 10 per cent of all cycles) being 28 days and the overall range 9 to 200 days. This series of records includes long and irregular cycles characteristic of pubertal animals (see p. 338), as well as instances of what would be regarded clinically as polymenorrhoea.

From a comparison of records obtained in North America, England and China, Zuckerman has also concluded that the cycle of rhesus monkeys kept under laboratory conditions does not vary significantly in relation to geographical environment. On the other hand, the distribution of cycles in this species is not a normal one, cycles of less than " modal " length tending to be suppressed.

Menstruation usually lasts for 4 to 6 days. The individual means of 33 of Hartman's females varied from $1 \cdot 7$ to $6 \cdot 6$ days (1932), and the total range has been given by Corner as 2 to 11 days. Even longer menorrhagic periods occasionally occur in apparently normal females.

Ovulation. The time of ovulation in the menstrual cycle of *M. mulatta* has been closely studied by Hartman (1932, 1933, 1944) and by van Wagenen (1945a, b, 1947). By an analysis of breeding records and by palpation of the ovaries *in situ*, Hartman showed that almost all ovulations occur between days 10 and 16 of the cycle, and most between the 11th to 14th days. These findings are corroborated by van Wagenen's data on the number of conceptions which follow single 48-hour matings on specified days of the cycle, and by Farris (1946) on the basis of the ovarian hyperaemia test. Exceptionally, ovulation may occur outside these limits, e.g. from the 9th to 20th day (Hartman, 1933, 1944). Van Wagenen (1947) obtained a conception rate of $4 \cdot 3$ per cent in females mated only on the 6th day. There is evidence that ovulation may occasionally be delayed in healthy, normally cyclic macaques until the 3rd to 5th week (21st to 36th day) after the onset of the preceding menstruation (Rossman and Bartelmez, 1946), and it is suggested that this is due to a phase of ovarian inactivity at the beginning of a cycle. While such cycles are naturally of unusual length, they cannot necessarily be considered as abnormal. Instances of conception on the 19th and 17th day have been recorded by Hartman (1932) and by van Wagenen (1945b).

Ovulation in the rhesus macaque occurs spontaneously (Corner, 1923a, 1932b). It is frequently accompanied by, but not necessarily causally related to, the appearance of a few red cells in the vaginal lavage, the so-called mid-cycle bleeding (Hartman, 1928b, 1932).

Assuming that ovulation occurs approximately on the 13th day in cycles of normal (i.e. about 28 days) duration, it follows that the follicular and luteal phases last about 13 and 15 days respectively. Although Hartman (1933) has expressed a contrary view, it is well established that the luteal or progestational phase of the cycle is more constant in length than the preovulatory or proliferative phase (see Zuckerman, 1936, 1937a ; Corner, Hartman and Bartelmez, 1945). Gross irregularities in the follicular part of the cycle are of relatively frequent occurrence (Rossman and Bartelmez, 1946). Normally, regression of the corpus luteum can be demonstrated histologically around the 13th day after its formation, menstruation following a day or two later (Corner *et al.*, 1945).

The fact that ovulation may sometimes fail to occur during the cycle in *M.*

mulatta was first noted by Sutton (1886) and Heape (1896, 1897). It was systematically investigated by Corner (1923a, 1927), who proved conclusively that pubertal and young mature animals do not ovulate regularly (*see* also Hartman, 1932, 1938b; Smith and Rubenstein, 1940). Later, Hartman (1932) drew attention to the frequency with which non-ovulatory cycles occur in fully adult females during the summer months (the so-called " non-breeding " season). He also showed (1938b) that out of a total of 136 healthy mature and well-acclimatised females kept in his experimental colony and observed for several years, 11 never ovulated at any time in the course of a total of 175 cycles. A second group of 18 females (175 recorded cycles) did so only very occasionally, and a further 11 (100 cycles) ovulated " on the average about half of the cycles of the breeding season." It would seem that even during the " breeding " part of the year more than one-fifth of mature rhesus monkeys ovulate so rarely as to be virtually sterile (*see* also p. 334). These observations on captive subjects do not necessarily apply to animals living in their natural habitat.

Unfertilised tubal ova were first recovered in rhesus monkeys by Corner (1923a) and Allen (1927). Subsequently, Lewis and Hartman (1933, 1941) succeeded in obtaining fertilised living eggs and in following early segmentation changes by means of cinematography. The average size of these ova was 138 μ, which compares with a value of 121 μ for ovarian eggs obtained from ripe Graafian follicles by Hartman and Corner (1941). The findings of these workers confirm the conclusions about the time relations of ovulation referred to above (*see* also Hartman, 1936).

Manifestations of reproductive activity may continue for at least 15 years in macaques. Hartman (1938b) refers to two females which reached the ages of 18 and 17 years respectively and continued menstruating " nearly until the last." However, ovulation was believed to have ceased between $1\frac{1}{2}$ and 3 years respectively before death. Assuming that puberty occurred in them at about the age of 3 (*see* p. 338), this suggests a reproductive life-span of some 12 years. The average duration of life of captive rhesus monkeys is thought to be about 15 years (*see* Zuckerman, 1933), but exceptional specimens have lived for much longer periods (Flower, 1931 ; Hill, 1937c).

Other cyclic phenomena. Mature female rhesus monkeys are characterised by a vivid red coloration of their hindquarters. The area so affected encloses the external genitalia and is called the sexual skin (Heape, 1896 ; Corner, 1923a ; Collings, 1926 ; Allen, 1927 ; Zuckerman, 1930, 1937a ; Hartman, 1932). Posteriorly it extends from the iliac crests to within about an inch of the popliteal space, and may spread on to the back of the legs, the outer sides of the thighs and up the back. It extends on the ventral aspect of the body as a sharply-demarcated triangle over the pubes. The face and nipples are also usually a bright red.

The colour of the sexual skin does not undergo regular cyclic changes, but it usually reaches its maximum intensity during the third week after the onset of menstruation, that is to say, about the time of ovulation or soon after, and fades before the next flow (*see* Zuckerman, 1937a). Hartman (1932) states that as a means of diagnosing the condition of the reproductive organs the colour " has only an accessory use." He also stresses the intense reddening of this region in the pregnant female, which may surpass anything observed during the normal cycle.

Allen (1927) showed that the coloration is due to stimulation by oestrogen.   It is, therefore, interesting to note that reddening may persist throughout lactation (when the ovaries are involuted).   It may also be present in old females past the reproductive phase of life (*see* Hartman, 1932, 1942a).   Likewise, the scrotum and circumanal skin of many fully mature male rhesus monkeys are conspicuously red (Zuckerman, 1937a).   Coloration can be induced by a variety of hormonal agents (*see* Zuckerman, van Wagenen and Gardiner, 1938 ; Hartman, 1942a), and to some extent may be regarded as an expression of general bodily health.

Sexual activity.   There have been numerous investigations of the sexual behaviour of rhesus monkeys, most of them based on the observation of captive animals.   The general conclusions emerging from such studies have been reviewed from time to time (Zuckerman, 1930, 1932b ; Young, 1941), and can be sum-marised as follows.

Manifestations of sexual desire and mating occur at all times.   They tend, however, to be more frequent and intense during the period of maximum coloration of the sexual skin, and hence roughly coincide with the fertile phase of the cycle. At this time, females welcome or actively solicit the advances of, and appear to be more attractive to, the males (Ball and Hartman, 1935). Periodic changes in sexual behaviour have also been observed in wild macaques.   Thus Carpenter (1942a, b) writes that in free-ranging macaques coitus is mainly restricted to oestrous periods, which last for approximately one-third of the length of a cycle.   Their average duration in 45 cycles observed in 40 individual females was $9 \cdot 2 \pm 2 \cdot 90$ days, and the range 4 to 15 days.   " Sporadic " copulations occurred at other times.   They may represent mere submission on the part of a female to a particularly dominant and aggressive male and, in Carpenter's opinion, may lack true sexual motivation (" pseudo-receptivity ").   A similar conditioning of sexual behaviour by non-specific factors such as social relationships, fear, desire of food or protection, is known to exist in the case of other primates, such as chimpanzees (*see* Zuckerman, 1930, 1932b ; Yerkes, 1939).   Their influence is particularly manifest in conditions of captivity, and may overshadow or obscure the basic cyclical pattern in sexual behaviour displayed by free-living animals.

Physiological investigations.   From a study of the total solids in the genital tract at different times of the menstrual cycle, Van Dyke and Ch'en (1936, 1940) inferred that the water content of the uterus is at its highest during the pre-ovulatory phase of the cycle, and that dehydration occurs at the time of menstrua-tion.   Conversely, the lipoid and cholesterol content of the endometrium is at its maximum during the luteal and menstrual phases.

The structure and chemical composition of the sexual skin in the macaque have been extensively studied (Collings, 1926 ; Zuckerman, 1935b ; Fisher and Zuckerman, 1937 ; Akroyd and Zuckerman, 1938 ; Ogston, Philpot and Zucker-man, 1939 ; Chain and Duthie, 1940 ; Duran-Reynals, Bunting and van Wagenen, 1950 ; Rienits, 1951).   The active sexual skin appears to contain oestrogenic sub-stances, and a compound which is readily acted upon by hyaluronidase, and which has been chemically identified as hyaluronic acid (Chain and Duthie ; Rienits). Swelling, which is normally observed only in pubertal and adolescent animals, is due to the deposition of water in the intercellular spaces and to imbibition of the connective-tissue elements.   The tissue fluid is reabsorbed following the injection of hyaluronidase (Duran-Reynals *et al.*).   Day-to-day variations in water balance and in the concentration of red cells are both less conspicuous and less clearly related to the cycle in *M. mulatta* than in the pig-tailed monkey (*M. nemestrina*), a species which regularly exhibits well-marked sexual skin oedema (Krohn and Zuckerman, 1937 ; Guthkelch and Zuckerman, 1937a, b ; *see* also p. 342).

The concentration of sex hormones in the body fluids during the menstrual cycle has not been systematically investigated, but Fish, Young and Dorfman (1941) and Dorfman and van Wagenen (1938, 1941) report that the immature animal excretes very little, if any, substance having androgenic or oestrogenic potency, but that measurable amounts are present in the urine of adult males and females. The concentration of urinary oestrogen in mature females varies from about 7 to 12 I.U./24 hours in different specimens and at different times of the cycle ; no continuous assays were carried out.   A very marked increase in the excretion rate of both substances takes place during the first half of pregnancy.   The maximum is reached at about the 110th day, when 460 I.U. oestrogen may be eliminated per day. The concentration of sex hormones is not significantly altered by removal of the foetus or by ovariectomy at various stages of pregnancy (*see* also p. 340).

Progesterone is present in the blood in measurable quantities (De Allende, 1940).   The greatest concentration occurs about the middle of the cycle (days 10 to 11).   According to Hooker and Forbes (1949), about 5 μg. per ml. blood is present during the luteal phase of the cycle, practically all of it being contained in the plasma.

The hormonal basis of the process of menstruation has been discussed in several recent reviews (*see* Reynolds, 1947 ; Zuckerman, 1949, 1951 ; Hamilton, 1949 ; Corner, 1951).

Using the glass electrode method of estimation, Mai and van Dyke (1934) have studied the vaginal pH in different phases of the cycle in normal rhesus monkeys. Except for a tendency towards slightly higher values about the time of the menstrual flow, they could not find any clear evidence of cyclical variation in pH.

Puberty and the attainment of sexual maturity

The process of sexual maturation in the female rhesus is characterised by the onset of menstruation, and by a series of remarkable changes in the sexual skin (*see* Hartman, 1932 ; Zuckerman, van Wagenen and Gardiner, 1938 ; Eckstein, 1948).

External changes in the sexual skin (an outline of which was given on p. 139) usually precede the first menstrual bleeding, but occasionally ménarche occurs suddenly, unaccompanied by a phase of swelling.   In 6 females of known age, the first signs of activity in the sexual skin (reddening and swelling) were noticed at a mean age of 27·6 months and a mean body weight of about 3,400 g., while ménarche occurred at an average age of 31 months (range 27 to 32 months) and a weight of 3,600 g. (range 2,450 to 5,400 g.).   Similar findings have been reported by Allen (1927), Hartman (1932), Schultz (1933) and Smith and Rubenstein (1940), but in van Wagenen's closely inbred colony the average age at ménarche was only 2 years, its earliest occurrence being observed in a female aged 1 year and 5 months (van Wagenen, 1949, 1950).   The last stage in the sexual skin development (disappearance of all traces of roll swelling) is reached at an approximate age of 5 years and a body weight of well over 5,000 g.

After the ménarche, the rhesus monkey passes through a phase of ovarian and uterine instability.   This period of so-called " adolescent sterility " (Hartman,

1931a, 1932 ; Ashley Montagu, 1939, 1946) is characterised by menstrual irregularities, frequent anovular cycles (Corner, 1923a ; Hartman, 1932, 1938b), and by a
high rate of abortion following conception (Smith and Rubenstein, 1940).

The average body weight at the first conception is about 5,000 g., which corresponds to an age of approximately 5 years (Hartman, 1932 ; Eckstein, 1948).
Thus the usual interval between the beginning and completion of the sexual
maturation process, and hence the length of the period of relative sterility, appears
to be of the order of about 2 years. It may, however, be much shorter, as shown by
the occasional occurrence of conception during the first few cycles following
ménarche (Smith and Rubenstein). Inbreeding may lower the age of both
puberty and maturity (van Wagenen, 1950).

Pregnancy

The average length of some 30 pregnancies studied by Hartman (1932) was
163·9 days (range 146 to 180 days), and that of 26 gestations resulting in viable
offspring 165·2 (range 149 to 180 days). Twenty-three out of the total of
30 cases fall within the range of 155 to 171 days. Van Wagenen (1945b) records
an average of about 168 days. An unusually long gestation of 191 days in a
primiparous female has been recorded by Eckstein (1944).

A frequent but not invariable indication of pregnancy is the " placental sign "
described by Hartman (1928b ; 1929, 1932), and believed by him to be associated
with implantation of the ovum. It consists of a slight (usually microscopic)
bleeding from the vagina, which begins about the 14th day after conception (or
about 29 days after the onset of the last menstrual period), and lasts approximately
3 weeks. The blood can be traced to the uterine glands at the periphery of the
placenta (Wislocki and Hartman, 1929). The haemorrhage sets in at about the
time of the next expected menstrual period.

Unlike the condition in man, the excretion product of progesterone, pregnanediol, is not found in the urine of pregnant macaques (Marker and Hartman,
1940). Gonadotrophic hormones are present in the urine for a few days only
(from the 19th to the 25th day) during pregnancy (Hamlett, 1937 ; Delfs,
1941).

Pregnancy should be suspected in the presence of a heightened purplish-red
colour of the sexual skin ; the formation of intensely red secondary areolae around
the nipples ; translucent, acellular vaginal washings, abdominal enlargement ;
increased weight and persistent amenorrhoea. It can be established by repeated
palpation of the uterus (Hartman, 1932) and by X-rays as early as the second or
third month.

Rhesus monkeys exhibit an increase of sexual interest in the earliest stages of
gestation (Ball, 1937). Considerable relaxation of the pelvic ligaments can be
demonstrated during the last month of normal gestation. This occurs also in
monkeys whose ovaries are removed early during pregnancy and after death of the
foetus (Hartman and Straus, Jr., 1939).

The specific morphological changes undergone by the genital tract during
pregnancy and parturition were described by Hartman (1932) and by Danforth,
Graham and Ivy (1942), while Ramsey (1949) has given an account of vascular
phenomena in the gravid uterus. Birth itself was witnessed by Hartman (1928c),
Hartman and Tinklepaugh (1930, 1932 ; *see* Hartman, 1932), and Philipp (1931),

and certain physiological observations concerning parturition and the state of the new-born have been published by Ivy, Hartman and Koff (1931) and Hartman, Squier and Tinklepaugh (1930).

Ovariectomy can be performed as early as the 25th day of pregnancy without abortion resulting (Hartman, 1941). If the foetus is removed between the 70th and 157th day, and the placenta left undisturbed, the female rhesus remains "physiologically pregnant." In these circumstances labour associated with delivery of the placenta occurs after a normal period of gestation (van Wagenen and Newton, 1943). A central placenta praevia in a pregnant *M. mulatta* has been reported by Palmer (1938–39).

Usually a single young is born, but twins occur very occasionally. Hartman (1932, 1943) has recorded double ovulation in one ovary and the delivery of a double-headed monster.

There are no accurate data about the duration of lactation. Hartman (1932) states that it lasts about 7 months on the average, but adds that it may vary " as much as among cattle." In two of his females milk was still plentiful after a whole year's nursing. Amenorrhoea is the rule during lactation. According to Hartman's records it usually lasts for 7 to 8 months when a baby is suckled, and approximately 3 to 4 months in cases of stillbirth. Shorter intervals can occur. Non-ovulatory cycles are also stated to be frequent in lactating animals (Hartman, 1938b). A female may, however, conceive while suckling a young, and Hartman (1931b, 1932) believes that this is a regular feature among animals living in a state of nature.

Intense proliferation of the cervical mucous membrane takes place during pregnancy, when the organ becomes a thin-walled and highly labyrinthine glandular structure which produces abundant mucus (Hamilton, 1949). On the other hand, the most superficial part of the vaginal mucosa (the " functionalis ") undergoes pronounced atrophy during the later stages of pregnancy, until it resembles that of the castrate animal (Davis and Hartman, 1935). After parturition it gradually reforms and is completely restored in thickness within 4 weeks.

The Common Macaque

Reproduction in the common macaque (*M. irus*) has been closely studied by Spiegel (1930, 1931, 1950), while Corner (1932a) has contributed important data on the length of the cycle in this species.

In his latest report (1950) Spiegel gives details about 345 cycles recorded in 19 females. The mean duration was 31 days with a mode of 28 and a range of 23–42 days. Corner's corresponding observations for 63 cycles in four females yielded a mean of 40·1 days and a modal length of 35 days. The difference between these means is significant, but with a larger and more evenly distributed set of observations the modal cycle in Corner's series would probably have been shorter. The difference may also be partly due to the fact that Spiegel observed mature animals, while Corner's females were pubertal or at most sub-adult.

The only other information on the duration of the cycle in this species is Joachimovits' statement (1928) that females observed by him in Java menstruated about every 25 to 29 days, but that occasionally much longer cycles (" at least 45 days ") can occur. Zuckerman (1930) also reported fairly regular bleeding in one captive female in the London Zoological Gardens, the average of 4 cycles being 41 days. Menstruation lasts for 2 to 7 days, the rule being 3 to 4 days (Spiegel, 1931, 1950 ; Corner, 1932a). The presence of erythrocytes in vaginal lavages around the middle of the cycle (usually the 14th to 21st day in cycles of average duration) has been observed by Spiegel (1931, 1950). The sign was absent in a number of cycles during which conception took place, and hence cannot be considered a reliable index of ovulation.

Spiegel also refers to the occurrence of cyclical swelling and reddening of the skin of the perineum and root of the tail (1930, 1931, 1950). According to him these changes are most marked and definitely related to the menstrual cycle in pubertal or young mature females. In older animals they are inconstant and subject to much individual variation. Thus in some females oedema is not accompanied by coloration and vice versa. Zuckerman (1930) observes similar swellings in captive *M. irus*, but was unable to establish that they occurred in phase with the cycle.

Females caged continuously with males tend to copulate mainly during the follicular part of the cycle.

Pregnancy in the common macaque lasts on average for 167 days (range 153–179 days), and a " placental sign " can be demonstrated after conception (Spiegel, 1930, 1931, 1950). Parturition has been described by the same author, who also states that lactation continues for 1 to 1½ years. If the female conceives again lactation may continue uninterruptedly for years. Amenorrhoea is the rule during lactation and lasts from 2 to 13 months. The shortest interval between parturition and the next fertile copulation observed by Spiegel was 4 months.

The available evidence (Zuckerman, 1930, 1931a ; Spiegel, 1950) indicates that captive common macaques conceive at any time of the year.

Puberty, as shown by the occurrence of the first menstrual period, occurs at an average age of 2½ to 3 years, the earliest instance being 2 years 3 months (Spiegel, 1950). The interval between ménarche and the first conception lasts from 3 months to 2 years. These figures agree well with corresponding findings in rhesus monkeys. The male *M. irus* acquires sexual maturity at an age of approximately 4–4½ years.

The Bonnet Monkey (subgenus *Zati*)

According to Hill (1932), two separate species of bonnet monkey can be recognised, the true bonnet macaque of Southern India (*Macaca radiata*), and the toque (*M. sinica*) which occurs in Ceylon.

A characteristic of both species is a copious vaginal discharge of mucus which originates from a highly glandular cervix and which occurs intermittently throughout the cycle. Menstruation varies considerably in duration and intensity, and has been thought to be absent altogether (Pocock, 1906). In the toque monkey it lasts from 1 to 4 days (Hill, 1939a), but in *M. radiata* it may occasionally continue for 10 (Hartman, 1938a).

There is little accurate information about menstrual periodicity in *M. radiata*. Zuckerman (1930) observed three consecutive cycles of 31, 33 and 29 days' duration in one female, and refers to two of 38 and 34 days respectively, in another animal. Hartman (1938a) recorded four cycles of 25, 26, 31 and 36 days' length, and both he and Hill (1939a) state that a monthly menstrual period is the rule for both types of bonnet monkey.

Sexual skin activity is very slight both in toque and true bonnet monkeys, and consists of a mere puffiness of the circumanal and vulvar regions. The area is dark purple rather than red in colour. Swelling and marked purple-red coloration of the sexual skin may be observed during pregnancy (Hartman, 1938a). The same author also states that captive mature bonnet macaques mate predominantly, though " not quite exclusively," around the middle of the cycle.

Hartman estimated the length of three consecutive pregnancies in one female *M. radiata* as 153, 166, and 169 days, respectively. On each occasion the pelvic ligaments became relaxed shortly before parturition, just as in the rhesus monkey (*see* Hartman and Straus, Jr., 1939). Interbreeding between *M. radiata* and *M. sinica* and between bonnet monkeys and other species of macaque is not uncommon (Zuckerman, 1931a ; Hill, 1937a).

Puberty is thought to be reached by the female toque monkey at approximately three years (Hill, 1939a). Its earliest manifestation is the secretion of cervical mucus, and this is followed by the ménarche after a variable interval. An interesting observation of Hill is that the vagina is imperforate throughout the greater part of its extent, until the first appearance of the mucoid discharge.

The Pig-tailed Macaque

The average length of 75 cycles recorded in 13 mature and young-mature pig-tailed monkeys, *M. nemestrina*, was $32 \cdot 08 \pm 0 \cdot 8$ days, the mode being 30 and the range 24 to 66 days. Almost two-thirds of all cycles fell within a range of 29 to 33 days. Similar findings, derived from an analysis of 30 cycles observed in five females, have been previously reported by Zuckerman (1937a).

Pig-tailed monkeys, like baboons and mangabeys, but unlike most other types of macaque, exhibit pronounced cyclical swelling of the sexual skin (Zuckerman, 1930). These periodic changes are closely correlated with, and hence reflect the phases of the ovarian and menstrual cycle (*see* Zuckerman, 1937a). The follicular and luteal phases of the cycle are respectively demarcated by the swelling and subsequent deturgescence of the sexual skin. The onset of deturgescence is abrupt and easily recognised.

Analysis of 75 cycles shows that the luteal phase in the pig-tailed macaque is both shorter and less variable than the follicular phase (Table I).

TABLE I

THE FOLLICULAR AND LUTEAL PHASES OF THE CYCLE IN *M. nemestrina* (DAYS)

No. of cycles	Phases	Mean	Mode	Range
75	Swelling (follicular) Subsidence (luteal)	$18 \cdot 29 \pm 1 \cdot 32$ $14 \cdot 35 \pm 0 \cdot 82$	14 14–15	11–47 8–39

The development and regression of the oedema of the sexual skin are associated with a rise and fall in body weight, and with cyclical fluctuations in the daily water balance (Krohn and Zuckerman, 1937). The decline in body weight coincides to within a day with the onset of sexual skin subsidence and with a dramatic rise (up to 645 per cent) in the daily output of urine. The observed increase in weight during the follicular phase may amount to as much as 18 per cent of the entire body weight, and is accounted for by the volume of water retained by the animal during this part of the cycle.

These changes in the sexual skin and water metabolism are also accompanied by variations in the concentration of erythrocytes. The red cell count seems to be lowest during menstruation and highest in the middle of the cycle when genital oedema is maximal. Its fall coincides with the time of regression of the sexual skin (Gutchkelch and Zuckerman, 1937a, b).

Puberty, as indicated by the occurrence of menstruation and regular phases of sexual skin oedema, was reached by a pig-tailed macaque at the known age of 50 months (Zuckerman, 1937a). The length of pregnancy in a single case was 171 days, and the lactation interval, during which there was neither menstruation nor swelling of the genital skin, lasted for approximately 7 months.

Hybrids between *M. nemestrina* and other macaques are known to occur (*see* Zuckerman, 1931a).

Cercocebus

A total of 86 cycles has been recorded in 9 sooty mangabeys (*C. torquatus atys*), of which 7 (responsible for 83 cycles) were fully mature. The mean cycle length is 29·44 ± 0·75 days, and the group mean (based on collective means from each of the 9 females) 30·65 ± 4·50 days. The most common duration is 24 and 28 days (the great majority falling between 24 and 32 days) ; and the overall range 18 to 58 days. These figures compare with a mean of 33·4 ± 1·1 and a mode of 30 days based on 22 cycles previously reported by Zuckerman (1937a).

The menstrual flow is externally visible, but not always profuse, and may be discontinuous. As in rhesus monkeys, it usually lasts for 4 to 5 days.

All members of the genus *Cercocebus* undergo marked cyclical changes of the sexual skin, of a kind similar to those manifested by the pig-tailed macaque (*see* Zuckerman, 1930).

Papio

The reproductive physiology of baboons has been extensively studied and reviewed (*see* Zuckerman, 1930, 1931a, b, 1932a, 1937a ; Zuckerman and Parkes, 1932 ; Gillman, 1935, 1937 ; Gillman and Gilbert, 1946 ; Cohen, 1950).

The menstrual cycle

Zuckerman (1930, 1937a) and Zuckerman and Parkes (1932) have reported on a total of 127 cycles (in two series) in the sacred baboon (*Papio hamadryas* ; *Comopithecus*), 32 cycles in the yellow baboon (*P. cynocephalus*), and 20 in the Anubis baboon (*P. anubis*), while Gillman and Gilbert (1946) have given details about 507 (404 selected normal) cycles in the Chacma baboon (*P. porcarius*). Comparison of these data indicates that in their menstrual cycles all four species of baboon closely resemble each other as well as the chimpanzee (Table II).

The menstrual flow lasts approximately 3 to 4 days in both *P. hamadryas* and *P. porcarius*, being most intense on the first day and diminishing subsequently.

Menstrual cycles may continue for at least 20 years in baboons. Zuckerman

(1947) has reported on one Anubis baboon (*P. anubis*) and a yellow baboon (*P. cynocephalus*) in which regular cycles had occurred for approximately 20 and 17 years, respectively.

TABLE II

COMPARISON OF THE LENGTH OF THE CYCLE IN DIFFERENT SPECIES OF BABOON AND THE CHIMPANZEE (DAYS)

Species	No. of Cycles	No. of Animals	Range	Mode	Mean ± S.D. of Distribution
P. porcarius					
all	507	34*	17–238	35	39·63 ± 16·20
selected	404	—	29–42	35	35·61 ± 3·206
P. hamadryas					
1st series	72	10†	22–46	33	31·4 ± 5·18
2nd series	55	5†	25–84	33	36·2 ± 11·3
P. cynocephalus	32	2†	25–41	31–32	33·3 ± 3·48
P. anubis	20	1†	28–38	35	34·75 ± 2·38
Chimpanzee (Young and Yerkes, 1943)	653	22‡	22–187	33	37·28

* = 28 of the 34 were mature and 6 pubescent females. Gillman and Gilbert do not say how many cycles refer to the immature animals.
† = adult females.
‡ = mixed colony of mature and pubertal animals ; exact composition not stated.

The sexual skin cycle

Baboons experience cyclical phases of sexual skin swelling. These have been described in detail by Pocock (1906), Gear (1926), Zuckerman (1930, 1937a), Zuckerman and Parkes (1932) and Gillman and Gilbert (1946).

In the sacred baboon (*P. hamadryas*) swelling begins either during or immediately after the menstrual period, and reaches a maximum in about a week. The sexual skin consists of an anterior (" prevaginal ") and a posterior (" post-vaginal ") part. The posterior swelling is much the larger of the two and soon overlaps its attached base, hiding the ischial callosities and distorting the anal orifice. When fully formed, the sexual skin is bright-red in colour, is turgid and shiny and contains large quantities of fluid. According to Pocock (1906) and Zuckerman (1930), it is better developed in *P. cynocephalus* than in *P. hamadryas*, and most conspicuous in *P. porcarius*, where it may reach a maximum breadth of 18 inches (Gillman, 1937), and appears as a veritable " outgrowth." The swelling is maintained until about the middle of the cycle, when it regresses with great suddenness, so that most of the oedema is resorbed within 24 to 48 hours. As in the pig-tailed macaque, this is associated with a greatly increased output of urine (Krohn and Zuckerman, 1937).

The perineum then assumes a quiescent appearance which lasts for a variable length of time until the end of the cycle, when the menstrual flow begins and sexual skin activity is resumed. Table III summarises data that have been provided by

Zuckerman (1937a) and by Gillman and Gilbert (1946) regarding the length of the two phases of the sexual skin cycle.

TABLE III

THE FOLLICULAR AND LUTEAL PHASES OF THE CYCLE IN *P. porcarius*
AND *P. hamadryas* (DAYS)

	No. of Cycles	Phases	Range	Mode	Mean ± S.D. of Distribution
P. porcarius	404	(Follicular (Luteal	10–32 6–25	19 17	19·45 ± 3·55 16·07 ± 2·77
P. hamadryas 1st series	72	(Follicular (Luteal	8–26 10–21	15–19 14	17·1 ± 3·49 15·1 ± 2·47
2nd series	55	(Follicular (Luteal	12–69 9–22	17 15	21·8 ± 10·1 14·4 ± 1·88

The time relations of ovulation

On the basis of timed laparotomies in *P. hamadryas*, Zuckerman (1930, 1937a) and Zuckerman and Parkes (1932) concluded that ovulation coincides with sexual skin subsidence. Gillman and Gilbert (1946) believe that in the Chacma baboon ovulation may precede deturgescence " by at least two or three days," but their evidence is not entirely conclusive.

Séguy and Bullier (1935) have drawn attention to periodic changes in the composition of the cervical mucus of the Hamadryas baboon. They point out that the secretion first appears towards the 12th day of the cycle, when it is thick and opaque. It increases in quantity as well as fluidity until the 19th–20th day, and subsequently diminishes again in amount and transparency until its disappearance around the 28th day.

Puberty

Puberty in the baboon, as in other catarrhine monkeys, starts with activity of the sexual skin. According to Gillman and Gilbert, the first appearance of perineal turgescence can be observed in Chacma baboons between $3\frac{1}{2}$ and 4 years old (*see* also Zuckerman, 1932b). This is usually followed by the first menstrual haemorrhage after a short interval, but occasionally, ménarche occurs without any signs of previous oedema. The sexual skin swelling increases progressively with successive cycles, and reaches adult proportions approximately 1 to 2 years after its first appearance. During puberty the length of the cycle and its component phases shows many eccentricities. These usually disappear on the attainment of reproductive maturity, but in some females they may persist into adult life. The menstrual flow, too, tends to be longer and more profuse in pubertal than in fully grown animals.

Pregnancy

In the Hamadryas baboon (Zuckerman and Parkes, 1932) the mean gestation period is 172·2 days (range 154 to 183 days), and in the Chacma baboon (Gilbert and Gillman, 1951) 187 days (range 173 to 193), counted from the approximate day of conception. A single young is the rule, but twins are stated to occur (*see* Shortridge, 1934 ; Wislocki, 1939). The length of lactation is not accurately known, but may be more than a year. During the greater part of gestation and lactation the ovaries and uterus as well as the sexual skin are in a state of quiescence (Zuckerman, 1931a, b ; Gilbert and Gillman, 1951). The interval between parturition and the resumption of activity in the generative organs (the " lactation interval ") is of the order of 5 to 6 months. Hence a complete reproductive cycle in the baboon, i.e. the shortest interval between two successive births in the same female, is thought to be about one year (Zuckerman, 1931a).

There is good evidence that the Chacma baboon has no annual breeding season either in the wild or in the captive state (Zuckerman, 1931a ; Gillman and Gilbert, 1946). This is probably also true of the Hamadryas baboon.

Mandrillus

One of the first records of the cycle in the drill is that of Percy (1844), who observed regular menstruation " at intervals of about six weeks " in a *Papio leucophaeus* (= *Mandrillus leucophaeus*). He adds that " the labia become enormously swelled and protuberant, and during the subsidence of the swelling a sanguineous discharge appears." More recently, Zuckerman (1937a) recorded a mean cycle length of $32 \cdot 6 \pm 0 \cdot 9$ days, based on 18 cycles in two drills.

Both drills and mandrills exhibit sexual skin changes similar in general character to those of baboons.

A few observations on the establishment of puberty in a female drill (*M. leucophaeus*) have been published by Zuckerman (1930).

Cercopithecus

There is very little information about the menstrual habits of this genus.

In a group of 12 green monkeys (*C. aethiops sabaeus*) Zuckerman (1935c) observed menstruation once only in each of 3 animals. In another female, observed subsequently, 4 successive cycles were recorded at intervals of 16, 32, 52 and 32 days. Similarly, an animal belonging to the closely related subspecies *C. aethiops aethiops* menstruated fairly regularly at intervals of 31 days, the flow lasting for about 2 days. In green monkeys, the bleeding is not externally visible at the vulva but can be detected by means of vaginal lavages. It lasts from 2 to 4 days.

With the notable exception of the Talapoin monkey (*see* below), species of the genus *Cercopithecus* are distinguished by the absence of all external cyclical changes other than menstruation itself. As in the toque monkey (p. 341), the vagina of the green monkey is not fully canalised until puberty (Zuckerman, 1938).

According to data collected by Asdell (1946) the grivet monkey breeds throughout the year. A single young is the rule and gestation is said to last approximately 7 months (e.g. 213 days in guenons ; *see* Kenneth, 1947). This seems to be a very long time, considering that the usual duration in most other catarrhine monkeys is about $5\frac{1}{2}$ to 6 months.

The Talapoin monkey

This very small monkey, *Miopithecus (Cercopithecus) talapoin*, exhibits well-marked external cyclical changes, unlike other members of the genus *Cercopithecus*.

They are easily noted, since in Talapoin monkeys the perineum is not obscured by hair.

Sexual skin activity was first reported by Zuckerman (1930) in an adult female. It consists of typical swelling and folding of the circumgenital skin areas, unaccompanied by changes in colour.   Later, Zuckerman (1937b) described the menstruating endometrium of this species, and in 1940 Tomilin reported confirmatory findings based on 20 months' daily observation of a mature female.   This author noted 5 consecutive menstrual cycles of 27, 28, 32, 36 and 43 days' duration, haemorrhage lasting from 1 to 4 days.   There appeared to be no correlation between the onset of bleeding and the state of the sexual skin, with menses occurring variously during phases of growth and regression of this area.

Subfamily *Colobinae*

Genera : *Semnopithecus ; Kasi*

According to Heape (1894) and Hill (1936b), females of the genera *Semnopithecus* (langurs) and *Kasi* (purple-faced monkeys) menstruate at approximately monthly intervals for 2 to 4 days.   The flow is slight (Hill, 1936b), and is not accompanied by changes in the external genitalia.   Heape believes that " slight swelling " of the vulva and occasionally of the nipples may occur.   Zuckerman (1930) observed an adult female of the genus *Pithecus* (= *Kasi*), and was unable to detect any cyclical changes in the size of its otherwise turgid and prominent pudendum.

Heape (1894) assumed the existence of " one or more limited breeding seasons " in *Semnopithecus entellus*.   His evidence on this point is of doubtful value (*see* Zuckerman, 1931a), and is not supported by the records of births in Zoological Gardens and private breeding colonies in India (Zuckerman, 1931a, 1932b ; Hill, 1936b).

McCann (1933) holds that langurs and lutongs (*Trachypithecus pileatus*) residing in those parts of India which experience an annual cold season breed periodically instead of continuously throughout the year.   According to this author, mating occurs during the winter months and most babies are born in February and March.

Twins are said to be not uncommon in langurs (*see* Blanford, 1888-91 ; Hill, 1936b), and hybrids between different types of leaf-monkey have been reported on several occasions (Hill, 1939c).

The Anthropoid Apes

Family *Hylobatidae*

Hylobates

Information about the sexual behaviour and breeding habits of gibbons has been provided by Pocock (1905), Carpenter (1940, 1941) and Matthews (1946). Carpenter (1940) states that wild gibbons do not have a " discrete " breeding season, an opinion with which Matthews agrees.   Carpenter's field observations were restricted to only 4 months (February to June).

According to Pocock (1905) and Matthews (1946), gibbons begin to menstruate at approximately 7 years, while Carpenter (1940) estimates that puberty occurs at a minimal age of 8 years.   The menstrual cycle of captive gibbons varies greatly in length, and its continuity is frequently broken by long periods of amenorrhoea (Pocock, 1905 ; Zuckerman, 1930 ; Carpenter, 1940 ; Matthews, 1946). Continuous cycles during the greater part of one year were, however, observed by Carpenter (1941) in two fully mature females.

The mean of 27 menstrual periods reported in the literature is 31·33 days (range 20–57) with a mode of about 28 days. Menstruation itself is generally believed to be slight and to last for a little over 2 days. According to Pocock (1905) and Carpenter (1941) the haemorrhage is visible externally. In a Siamang (*Symphalangus syndactylus*) which was observed for many months, Zuckerman (1930) was unable to detect menstruation or any variation in the appearance of the genital region. In gibbons, according to Kaiser (1947a), the menstruating endometrium is usually well preserved histologically, and shows no oedema or leucocytic infiltration and relatively little bleeding.

The external genitalia and surrounding skin areas do not swell during the cycle (Pocock, 1905 ; Schultz, 1938 ; Matthews, 1946), but Carpenter (1941) has reported some changes in the colour and degree of eversion and turgidity of the labia, which he thinks may be homologous with the sexual skin swelling in other types of primates. He does not give any details about the relation of these changes to the menstrual cycle.

There appear to be no significant fluctuations in the temperature and cell content of the vagina correlated with the cycle (*see* Carpenter, 1941 ; Matthews, 1946). Periodic changes in the histological texture of the vaginal wall have been claimed to occur (Dempsey, 1940).

The copulatory behaviour of captive and wild gibbons has been described by various observers (Coolidge, Jr., 1933 ; Carpenter, 1940). Gestation lasts approximately 7 months (Ogilvie, 1923 ; Robinson, 1925 ; Rode, 1942), and a single young seems to be the rule.

Family *Pongidae*

Genera : *Pan ; Pongo ; Gorilla*

Pan

The sexual cycle

The mean length of the menstrual cycle in fully mature chimpanzees was found to be about 36 days (range 29 to 53), and the mode 35 (Elder and Yerkes, 1936a). About 20 per cent of the total of available cycles were omitted from Elder and Yerkes' final analysis (*see* Zuckerman, 1937a) ; if all data had been included the mean would have been higher. In a subsequent study based on 653 cycles in 22 females of all ages, Young and Yerkes (1943) established an average of 37·3 ± 0·1 days with a median of 35 days, a mode of 33 days, and a total range of 22 to 187 days (*see* Table II, p. 344). The cycle is very variable in length both between different individuals and in the same female from time to time. Among the most important causes of this variability are age, pregnancy and season (Young and Yerkes, 1943 ; *see* also Clark and Birch, 1948, for a study of the factors operative in atypical cycles).

Cycles may continue for over 20 years in the chimpanzee. Yerkes (1943) refers to one female who at an estimated age of 29 years was still menstruating and breeding regularly.

A conspicuous feature of the cycle is the occurrence of marked sexual skin swelling. At its height the swelling has a volume of about 1,400 ml. (Elder and Yerkes, 1936a) and, if exceptionally large, may reach four to five times the size of a man's clenched hand (Yerkes, 1943). Changes in the size and degree of turgidity of the sexual skin permit the subdivision of the menstrual cycle into four unequal parts (see Young and Yerkes, 1943 ; Clark and Birch, 1948). The first or " pre-swelling " phase represents a period of genital and ovarian follicular inactivity, and lasts about 7 days. The second or " swelling " phase, which averages 18 days, is characterised by genital tumescence and coincides with active follicular growth, and the third, or " post-swelling " (i.e. detumescent) phase, 10 days long, with the luteal stage of the ovarian cycle. The final stage is represented by menstruation, and lasts for 3 days. The first two phases (" pre-swelling " and " swelling ") are stated by Young and Yerkes to be the most variable ones, and the last two " post-swelling " and " menstruation " the least. In this respect, the chimpanzee resembles other members of the *Catarrhini*, in most of whom the luteal part of the cycle is thought to be relatively more constant than the follicular part (see Zuckerman, 1937a ; Young and Yerkes, 1943 ; and above, p. 335).

In 1930 Zuckerman pointed out that in various types of monkeys ovulation is closely associated with the collapse of the sexual skin. Elder and Yerkes (1936a) and Young and Yerkes (1943), suggest on the basis of direct inspection of the ovaries in a few animals, that ovulation may occur " shortly before detumescence." In another communication, Nissen and Yerkes (1943), apparently basing themselves on Young and Yerkes' findings, state that conception (and hence presumably ovulation) occurs on average 2·7 days before the beginning of sexual subsidence. It is difficult to see how this conclusion could be reached, in the absence of systematic examination of the state of the gonads at the time of deturgescence. It is also possible that the character and timing of subsidence may differ in fertile and non-fertile cycles, since the occurrence of irregular sexual skin cycles during the early stages of pregnancy in the chimpanzee is well established (see p. 351). The fact that conception has been observed to take place at varying times between the 12th and 32nd day in cycles of presumably ordinary length emphasises the great irregularity of the cycle in this species.

The sexual behaviour of chimpanzees has been repeatedly studied and reviewed (Zuckerman, 1930, 1932b; Yerkes and Elder, 1936 ; Yerkes, 1939, 1943). According to the last author, the female " exhibits desire to mate only during the interval of maximum genital swelling." Her sexual receptivity parallels the degree of swelling of the sexual skin and increases from zero during the menstrual and preswelling phases to a climax (" oestrus ") during the stage of maximal swelling. With the subsidence of the genital oedema sexual interest disappears. The female also permits coitus at other times of the cycle, even when the sexual skin is quiescent. According to Yerkes, however, this is largely conditioned by external factors such as restriction of space and should not be confused with true physiological receptivity. A vaginal plug is deposited during copulation (Tinklepaugh, 1930).

Oestrogen is present in the urine of the female and varies in concentration in phase with the menstrual cycle (Allen, Diddle, Burford and Elder, 1936 ; Fish, Young and Dorfman, 1941). There are two peaks, one during the phase of maximal swelling of the sexual skin, and a second, equally marked one, during the pre-menstrual period. The pattern of excretion thus resembles that found in normal women (Frank, 1935).

Puberty and adolescence

Puberty in the female begins with swelling of the sexual skin. In this, as in all other sexual characteristics of the chimpanzee, there is marked variation between different individuals (*see* Schultz and Snyder, 1935 ; Ashley Montagu, 1939 ; Clark and Birch, 1948). Thus in three adolescent females in which the first appearance of sexual skin oedema was noted, swelling lasted for 3 weeks, 8 months and 14 months respectively (Schultz and Snyder). The first swelling may be followed by a period of sexual skin quiescence, but usually irregular and repeated phases of swelling and deturgescence supervene and continue until the onset of menstrual cyclicity (Tinklepaugh, 1933 ; Zuckerman and Fulton, 1934). According to Clark and Birch (1948) ménarche occurs between $4\frac{1}{2}$ months and 3 years after the first sign of genital oedema.

The average age at the first menstruation has been given by Young and Yerkes (1943) to be about 9 years.

During the first years after the ménarche menstruation is irregular (Young and Yerkes). This applies particularly to the earlier part of the cycle in which sexual skin swelling occurs. Young and Yerkes have shown that this phase becomes shorter during the first year, while the succeeding phase of collapse becomes gradually longer. As a result, the length of the cycle as a whole decreases from an average of $50 \pm 4 \cdot 38$ days shortly after the onset of reproductive life to $35 \pm 0 \cdot 79$ days during the 7th year following ménarche.

The period of " adolescent sterility " is believed to last for 1 to $1\frac{1}{2}$ years in the chimpanzee (Young and Yerkes). The interval between ménarche and first conception ranged in 7 animals from 4 months to 17 months, the average being $11 \cdot 33$ months. These findings agree with earlier observations of Schultz and Snyder (1935). In two cases the interval between ménarche and the first fertile mating was 3 years $9 \cdot 5$ months and 5 years 1 month respectively. It may be concluded that full reproductive maturity is as a rule reached between 10 and 11 years. In the male active spermatogenesis is thought to begin at an age of about 8 years (Yerkes, 1943).

The physical growth and development of the chimpanzee has been described by Schultz (1940) and Yerkes (1943). The average weight of the new-born is a little over $1 \cdot 5$ kg. (range 1–2 kg.) ; that of the adult female 40 kg. ; and that of the adult male 50 kg. Sexual dimorphism in weight does not become apparent until about puberty (approximately 7 years), and full physical maturity is believed to be attained early in the 11th year.

Pregnancy

The duration of pregnancy from the first day of the last menstrual period to delivery is about 250 days. By subtracting 21 days to allow for the occurrence of ovulation (*see* p. 349), Nissen and Yerkes (1943) have established a mean conception age at parturition in 48 pregnancies of $227 \cdot 5 \pm 12 \cdot 6$ days (median 228 and range 202–260 days). In 6 cases of single-day matings the average (conception) length was 228 days. The process of delivery, placentophagia and the postnatal infant-mother relationships have been described by Tinklepaugh (1932), Tomilin and

Yerkes (1935), Elder and Yerkes (1936b), Yerkes (1943) and Nissen and Yerkes (1943).

A single young is the rule, but a few instances of twins have been reported (Yerkes, 1934 ; Tomilin and Yerkes, 1935 ; Schultz, 1948).

Diagnosis of pregnancy by means of the Aschheim-Zondek and Friedman tests is possible in the chimpanzee (Zuckerman, 1935a ; Schultz and Snyder, 1935). Elder and Bruhn (1939) have obtained positive results from the 2nd to the 4th month inclusive, but not at any other times during gestation.

Chimpanzees resemble man in the frequency with which accidents and complications occur during pregnancy. These range from abortions and stillbirths, to post-partum haemorrhage and puerperal sepsis (see Tinklepaugh, 1932 ; Schultz and Snyder, 1935 ; Yerkes, 1943). On the other hand, toxaemia comparable to that which occurs in man does not seem to have been observed.

Menstrual cycles normally cease during pregnancy, but periods of sexual skin oedema may occur (Tinklepaugh, 1933 ; Elder and Yerkes, 1936b ; Yerkes, 1939 ; Nissen and Yerkes, 1943 ; Clark and Birch, 1948). Most of these swellings are observed during the first 2 or 3 months, although occasionally they may be present in the 5th or 6th month.

Sexual receptiveness and copulation may occur during pregnancy, but in Yerkes' opinion (1939, 1943) should be considered as " artificial " and essentially " protective " in character, and due to the conditions of experimental mating in which the pregnant female is unable to escape the attentions of the male.

During lactation, which may last for over 2 years (see Zuckerman, 1932b), the sexual skin is atrophic and may be hardly more conspicuous than in the immature female (Elder and Yerkes, 1936b). Following the resumption of ovarian activity it gradually increases to full size (Clark and Birch, 1948). Post-parturitional bleeding from the vagina is common. It is stated to occur between 10 and 28 days after delivery and to last on average for 3·7 days. The first true menstruation follows childbirth after an interval of about 3 months in females which nurse only for short periods. One female which was allowed to nurse for 12 months experienced her first menstrual bleeding 6 months after parturition (Nissen and Yerkes, 1943). The first cycle after pregnancy tends to be longer than those preceding conception. The alteration is due to a prolongation of the pre-swelling and swelling phases and is usually of very short duration (Young and Yerkes, 1943).

Pongo

The first reliable record of the menstrual cycle and pregnancy in the orang was given by Aulmann in 1932.

The animal concerned was approximately $9\frac{1}{2}$ years old when first studied, but had previously menstruated regularly for an unspecified period. Four complete cycles were observed, lasting 32, 32, 32 and 31 days, respectively. No details are given about the amount and duration of the bleeding, or about the appearance of the genital region. The animal became pregnant during the 5th cycle and aborted after 3 months. She appears to have conceived again within one week following the abortion, and this time delivered a healthy infant after a total length of gestation estimated at 275 days. Milk production was copious immediately after delivery. According to Zuckerman (1932b) orangs may nurse for about 4 years. The same author (1937a) also records menstrual bleeding in an orang at intervals of

29, 59 and 58 days, but adds that owing to discontinuous observation phases of haemorrhage may have been missed during the two longer periods.

Although a true sexual skin does not appear to be present in the non-pregnant orang, there are various reports to show that slight to marked swelling of the genital regions may occur during pregnancy. Thus Schultz (1938) observed a para-vulval swelling measuring about 12 × 10 × 6 cm. in a parous and pregnant female and refers to 4 similar instances reported in the literature. The swelling is usually slight during the early months of pregnancy, increases to a maximum in the last trimester, and shrinks after parturition.

Gorilla

The only detailed study of the menstrual cycle in the gorilla appears to be that of Noback (1939).

The subject was a young lowland gorilla (*G. gorilla*) which had been in captivity for over 7 years, and whose estimated age at the first observed menstruation (probably coincident with ménarche) was 9 years. Visible menstruation was first reported in this animal in 1936. Eight complete cycles occurred, which ranged from 36 to 72 days in length with an average of 49 days. Two of these cycles were very prolonged (60 and 72 days, respectively), and may each have represented two intermenstrual periods. If they are omitted from the total, the mean for the remaining 6 cycles becomes 43 days.

Slight cyclic changes occur in the external genitalia. At the time of menstruation the labia are shrunk and the vulvar cleft measures approximately 1 to 1·5 cm. in length. During the follicular part of the cycle, the vulva enlarges and becomes swollen. It reaches a maximum during the ovulatory phase, when the cleft may be 3 to 4 cm. long. This is maintained for 3 to 8 days, after which rapid shrinking of the genital cleft takes place. There are no external changes in the anogenital region, and no correlation exists between body temperature and the phases of the menstrual cycle.

It is of interest that Raven (1936) has reported the presence in a female wild gorilla of a pale and tumid swelling of the genital region " similar in size to that of a female chimpanzee during maximum enlargement." He was unable to establish whether this particular female was pregnant or not.

There is no evidence that gorillas have ever bred in captivity, although young specimens brought from Africa have been reared successfully. It is likely that the male rather than the female is responsible for this apparent sterility. The external genitalia of even fully grown males are very inconspicuous, and various autopsy findings have shown the testes to be remarkably small and atrophic and, in at least one instance, to lack any germinal epithelium (*see* Hill and Matthews, 1949; Hediger, 1950).

Family *Hominidae*

Homo

The sexual cycle

Menstrual periodicity. The literature on the length of the human menstrual cycle is very extensive. Among the more important recent contributions to the subject are those of Gunn, Jenkin and Gunn (1937), Haman (1942), Latz and Reiner (1942), Goldzieher and Hamblen (1947), Knaus (1950), and Mazer and Israel

(1951).   All carefully conducted studies have confirmed the wide variability of the cycle both between different women and in the same individual from time to time. The most common (modal) duration of the cycle is 26 to 29 days, and the overall mean (represented by only 10 per cent to 15 per cent of all cycles) lies close to 28. The range in healthy women is approximately 24 to 35 days (Goldzieher and Hamblen, 1947; Mazer and Israel, 1951).   An absolutely " regular " woman may be said not to exist.   Most women tend to adhere fairly closely to their individual means, but over 80 per cent experience cycles which vary in length by at least 5 days throughout the year, some 10 per cent exceeding 8 days (Gunn et al., 1937; Latz and Reiner, 1942).   The length of the flow is usually 4 to 5 days; anything from 3 to 7 may be regarded as physiological.

After the ménarche (p. 356) and during the years immediately preceding the menopause, the cycle is more irregular and longer than during the main period of reproductive life.   In adult women emotion and fear may be associated with irregularities of the cycle, and sudden anxiety can precipitate a phase of uterine bleeding after prolonged amenorrhoea (O'Neil, 1952; Stieve, 1952).

Menstrual cycles cease, either gradually or abruptly, at the menopause (p. 359). In the great majority of women this occurs during the second half of the fifth decade (see Lancet, 1933; Hamblen, 1947; Cameron, 1947).

Ovulation.   There are no very obvious signs of ovulation in women, but a wide variety of observations suggest that it occurs at about the middle of the cycle (most frequently about day 13 in 28-day cycles), and that it is more closely bound in time to the onset of the subsequent than that of the preceding menstrual period. The direct and indirect evidence bearing on this subject has been frequently reviewed, more recently by Hartman (1936, 1939), Zuckerman (1949), Knaus (1950), Mazer and Israel (1951) and Corner (1952).

Among the more important considerations which support these views are (1) the recovery of tubal ova and early embryos in women whose menstrual history was accurately known (Allen, Pratt, Newell and Bland, 1930; Hertig and Rock, 1944, 1945, 1946, 1949; Rock and Hertig, 1944, 1948); (2) cases of pregnancy following upon a single artificial insemination on a known day of the cycle (Cary, 1948); (3) the evidence of controlled matings based on the assumption that both male and female gametes survive for only short periods inside the female reproductive tract (Latz and Reiner, 1942; Knaus, 1950); (4) the occurrence in some women of mid-menstrual bleeding (" spotting ") or pain (" Mittelschmerz ") (Krohn, 1949); (5) a large number of indirect tests believed to indicate the occurrence of ovulation such as (a) specific changes in the endometrium and vagina (p. 637); (b) the excretion of gonadotrophin in the urine (Farris, 1946, 1948; Corner, Farris and Corner, Jr., 1950, and see p. 355, below); (c) the excretion of pregnane-diol glucuronidate in the urine (Venning and Browne, 1937; Venning, 1952, and see p. 355, below); (d) characteristic changes in basal temperature (Palmer, 1942; and see below); (e) changes in the cervical mucus (Séguy and Vimeux, 1933; Palmer and Marcille, 1941; Pommerenke and Viergiver, 1947 and see p. 356, below); (f) changes in the vaginal *p*H (Rakoff, Feo and Goldstein, 1944); (g) changes in the cytology of the vagina (de Allende & Orías, 1950).

Few workers now believe that ovulation occurs invariably 14 to 15 days before the next menstruation, and all agree that its timing, like that of other biological phenomena, is subject to individual variation.   What is still at issue is the extent of this variability. Until an easy and reliable indirect test becomes available, the exact plotting of the " time of ovulation " will not be possible.

At present the most convenient practical method of establishing the approximate day of ovulation in an individual woman is by taking the basal body temperature. This is at a lower level in the first than in the second half of the cycle (Van de Velde, 1928 ; Palmer, 1942 ; Tompkins, 1945 ; Barton and Wiesner, 1945). As a rule the transition between the two phases occurs abruptly about the middle of the cycle, and this is taken to indicate the occurrence of ovulation. No clear-cut temperature changes can be observed in anovulatory and atypical cycles (Buxton, 1950). Another way of making a rough estimate of the time at which ovulation is most likely to occur in a given cycle is the so-called Knaus-Ogino method, which assumes that ovulation usually occurs about 14 days before the onset of the next menstruation, regardless of the length of the cycle (Knaus, 1934, 1950). This method has received impressive clinical support. Latz and Reiner (1942) have published an analysis of over 11,000 cycles in 1,000 women who first successfully used the so-called " sterile " or " safe " period of the cycle to avoid pregnancy, and later cohabited in the " fertile " period and conceived.

Some reliable, if exceptional, cases are on record in which ovulation must have taken place at times other than the middle of the cycle. Thus Seymour (1947) found that a small proportion of women conceived only if artificially inseminated before the seventh day of the cycle. Similar findings have been reported by Cary (1948) and Greulich (1952).

Although menstrual cycles with either unusually short or long luteal phases may occur (Brewer and Jones, 1947, 1948 ; Buxton, 1950), it is generally held that the pre-ovulatory phase is more variable in length than the post-ovulatory, and that the known inconstancy of the human cycle is mainly due to irregularities of the follicular stage (Latz and Reiner, 1942 ; Rock and Hertig, 1944, 1948 ; Rossman and Bartelmez, 1946 ; Goldzieher and Hamblen, 1947). The possibility that the progestational part of the cycle may be no less variable than the follicular has recently been raised by Corner (1952).

Anovular cycles, that is to say, menstrual cycles in which ovulation does not occur, are relatively frequent at the beginning and end of reproductive life (Hamblen, 1947 ; Cameron, 1947), as well as after abortion (Sharman, 1950) and during lactation (Lass, Smelser and Kurzrok, 1938). They are also stated to occur in about 10 per cent of sterile but menstruating women (Jeffcoate, 1935 ; Sharman, 1944; Mazer and Israel, 1951). They may occur more frequently in fertile or potentially fertile women than is commonly believed (see Corner, 1951, 1952). According to Rock and Hertig (1948), only 25 per cent of 104 women who cohabited at the expected time of ovulation conceived.

Anovular menstrual cycles do not differ in length from ovulatory cycles, and anovular menstruation which occurs from an endometrium in the follicular or " interval " state (p. 637) exhibiting no, or only few signs of luteinisation (see Steinberg, 1951), is indistinguishable from ovulatory menstruation. Very rarely, a non-secretory type of mucosa may be associated with a recent corpus luteum, thus indicating a lack of responsiveness by the endometrium to luteal stimulation (Mazer, Israel and Kacher, 1937).

Sexual activity. Sexual behaviour in women very rarely manifests any rhythmic pattern. Some workers assert that there is such an inherent cycle, and that libido is maximal either just before or after menstruation (*see* Beach, 1948 ; Corner, 1952).

Other cyclic phenomena

Cyclic variations occur in the concentration of sex hormones in the body fluids of non-pregnant women, but their significance is still far from clear.

Oestrogen. According to most workers, the maximal concentration of oestrogens in the blood and urine occurs at about the time of ovulation (Frank, 1935 ; *see* also Clauberg, 1936 ; Fluhmann, 1936 ; Gustavson, Mason, Hays, Wood and D'Amour, 1938 ; D'Amour, 1940, 1943 ; Markee, 1947). A second peak, occurring at the height of the luteal phase and lasting until shortly before the onset of menstruation, has been identified by some workers (Frank, 1935 ; D'Amour, 1940 ; Jayle and Crépy, 1952). A somewhat different view is put by Smith, Smith and Schiller (1943) and Smith and Smith (1952), who found a high urinary concentration of total oestrogens between the 14th and 21st day and much lower values at other stages of the cycle. According to these workers most of the overall variations are accounted for by changes in the oestriol and oestrone fractions, the excretion of oestradiol remaining at a constant low level throughout the cycle.

Luteal hormone. The amounts of progesterone present in the blood during the cycle are extremely small, which suggests that this hormone is utilised immediately after secretion (Venning, 1952). The degree of luteal stimulation present is therefore assessed by determining the urinary concentration of pregnanediol, one of the principal metabolic products of progesterone. Pregnanediol is present in the urine in measurable amounts during the luteal part of the cycle and throughout pregnancy (p. 358). It becomes demonstrable a day or so after ovulation, soon reaching a maximum, and then disappearing, usually about 1 to 4 days before the onset of the menstrual flow (Venning and Browne, 1937 ; Stover and Pratt, 1939 ; Wilson, Randall and Osterberg, 1939 ; Venning, 1952). No pregnanediol is detectable in anovulatory cycles.

The time of maximal excretion of a given steroid does not necessarily coincide with its maximal biological effects (Krohn and Zuckerman, 1937), the concentration of female sex hormones in the blood and urine depending on many factors other than the level of ovarian (or placental) secretion (de Watteville, 1950). Thus the amount of oestrogen in the body fluids is also affected by the activity of the liver and adrenal cortex, by the rate of (oestrogen) metabolism, as well as by the presence or absence of progesterone. Similarly, many factors are known to affect the metabolism of progesterone (for instance, the rate of conversion of progesterone into pregnanediol, the production of metabolites like pregnanolone in addition to pregnanediol, and the elimination of the latter by routes other than the kidney). Hence inferences about corpus luteum function, based on pregnanediol assays in the urine, are rarely justified (*see* Venning, 1952 ; Pearlman, 1952).

Gonadotrophin. A marked increase in the urinary concentration of gonadotrophin occurs at about the time of ovulation. This rise is slightly preceded by the peak in oestrogen excretion referred to above (D'Amour, 1940, 1943 ; Levin, 1941). At all other times the level of gonadotrophin excretion is very low, and close to the limits of sensitivity of available assay methods (Evans and Simpson, 1950). Most or all of the gonadotrophin excreted is FSH (Evans and Simpson,

1950).   Its presence in the urine is the basis of the ovarian hyperaemia test for the occurrence of ovulation (Farris, 1946 ; Corner, Farris and Corner, Jr., 1950).

There are no constant or marked cyclic changes in the concentration of haemoglobin or red blood cells in women (see Guthkelch and Zuckerman, 1937a, b ; Hamblen, 1947).   Plasma sodium and chloride have been found to rise during the follicular phase of the cycle and then to fall gradually until the onset of menstruation (Eckstein, Lubran and McKeown, 1940–41).

The reactivity of the uterine musculature changes during the menstrual cycle. According to Knaus (1934, 1950), the myometrium contracts spontaneously and vigorously during the follicular phase, but is less active and becomes refractory to post-pituitary extracts during the luteal phase, as in the rabbit (p. 261).   Other workers have been unable to confirm this finding (Henry and Browne, 1943 ; Moir, 1944 ; Henry, Browne and Venning, 1950).

Periodic alterations occur in the amount, composition and sperm penetrability of the cervical mucus.   This was recognised over a hundred years ago (Pouchet, 1847), and rediscovered subsequently (Séguy and Vimeux, 1933 ; Séguy and Simmonet, 1933), and has since been confirmed and extended by many workers (Lamar, Shettles and Delfs, 1940 ; Viergiver and Pommerenke, 1944 ; Pommerenke and Viergiver, 1947).   The mucus becomes more plentiful and thinner (glairy) around the time of ovulation, thereby facilitating the ascent of spermatozoa to the upper parts of the reproductive tract (Barton and Wiesner, 1946).   At other times only a small amount of highly viscid and tough mucus is present in the cervical canal.

Puberty and the attainment of maturity

The time at which girls begin to menstruate is influenced by genetic, socio-economic, nutritional and, apparently, climatic factors.   A secular trend towards progressively lower ages at the ménarche has also been claimed (Mills, 1937).

Recent surveys have shown that in the northern hemisphere menstrual cycles begin at an average of $13\frac{1}{2}$ years, some 75 per cent of individuals falling within an age group of 12 to 15 years (Ellis, 1947 ; Wilson and Sutherland, 1949 ; Mazer and Israel, 1951).   The ménarche occurs in a small proportion of girls either before the age of 10 or after 17.   Those in which it is greatly delayed are said to be more likely to be sterile and to develop amenorrhoea than those in whom menstrual cycles begin at the usual time (Mazer and Israel, 1951).   According to Mills, ménarche is consistently later in both the colder northern and warmer southern parts than in the intermediate, more temperate region, of the United States.

Surveys also indicate that in tropical races the average age at ménarche is a little higher than in European races (Kark, 1943 ; Ellis, 1950 ; Wilson and Sutherland, 1950).   The usual view that in the tropics women mature earlier than in temperate zones is clearly not consonant with these findings.

Instances of a so-called congenital or constitutional type of sexual precocity in the human female have been described by Novak (1944) and Hain (1947a).   Some, at least, of the individuals concerned not only begin to menstruate but also to ovulate at abnormally early ages, a fact which explains the remarkable cases that have been reported of young children becoming mothers.

Shortly before the time of the first physical manifestations of puberty, and some $1\frac{1}{2}$ to 2 years before the onset of menstruation, oestrogen appears in the urine in amounts which vary cyclically (Nathanson, Towne and Aub, 1941). The amount of 17-ketosteroids excreted increases very gradually during childhood and adolescence in both boys and girls, and shows no marked change at the time of puberty (Talbot, Butler, Berman, Rodriguez and MacLachlan, 1943 ; Hain, 1947b; Dorfman, 1948). In sexually precocious girls the level of excretion of these substances usually equals or exceeds that in normal pubertal girls (Nathanson and Aub, 1943 ; Hain, 1947b). Gonadotrophin can be detected in the urine as early as the 7th year in girls (Hain, 1947a).

Menstrual irregularities, prolonged cycles and periods of amenorrhoea are not uncommon during puberty and adolescence. Thus Engle and Shelesnyak (1934) found a mean cycle length of 33·9 days ± 14·28 (s.d.) and a total range of 7 to 256 days in 3,140 cycles recorded in pubertal girls, while Gunn, Jenkin and Gunn (1937) established a progressive decrease in the average length of cycle with increasing age, amounting to about one day in every five to six years (see also Larsen, 1947).

It is now generally recognised that puberty cannot be equated with sexual maturity, and that full reproductive capacity, as defined by the ability to bear and rear children, is preceded by a phase of so-called " adolescent sterility " (Hartman, 1931a ; Miculicz-Radecki and Kausch, 1935 ; Mills and Ogle, 1936 ; Ashley-Montagu, 1939, 1946). This usually lasts for at least two to three years, during which ovulation is said to be irregular or not to occur at all. Should pregnancy take place during this time, it is said to be characterised by high maternal and infant mortality (Ashley-Montagu, 1939).

Circumstantial sociological and anthropological evidence provides the main basis for the concept of adolescent sterility, and anatomical proof of the failure of ovulation is very limited (see Corner, 1927 ; Laqueur, 1945).

Pregnancy

The duration of pregnancy in women is usually calculated from the first day of the last menstruation preceding the gestational amenorrhoea. The accuracy of such estimates is affected by irregularities of the cycle, and by variations in the interval between the onset of menstruation and ovulation. In spite of these and other theoretical objections (see Gibson and McKeown, 1950 ; McKeown and Gibson, 1952), the method remains the only practicable one for dealing with large series of data. A recent analysis of over 17,000 single normal births in England, carried out in this way, showed that the mean duration is approximately 281 days (Gibson and McKeown, 1950), corresponding to a true (conception) length of gestation of about 267 days. About 28 per cent of all births occurred during the 40th week of gestation ; roughly two-thirds between the 39th and 41st weeks ; and approximately one-third earlier than the 39th or after the 41st week. There was no consistent correlation between the mean duration of pregnancy and maternal age or parity in this series of records.

Because of the great medico-legal importance of this problem, McKeown and Gibson (1952) also analysed the longest cases of gestation in their series for which sufficiently reliable data were available. In five instances in which an estimate could be made with " fair confidence," the duration of pregnancy calculated from coitus to birth ranged from 319 to 328 days, and McKeown and Gibson conclude that even longer gestation periods " cannot be said to be impossible." Their figures compare with estimates of a mean (conception) length of gestation of 266–270 days, and a maximum of 285 days in 135 women in whom the approximate day of ovulation had been determined from the basal temperature charts (Stewart, Jr., 1952).

Multiple births are an infrequent but regular feature of human reproduction. Twins occur once in about 83 births, triplets once in 83^2, and higher numbers in still increasing powers, following what is known as Hellin's law (1895) (*see* Asdell, 1946). This long-accepted relationship defines the frequency of triplets as being equal to the square of the frequency of twins, and that of quadruplets to its cube (or, where *f* is the frequency of twins, the frequency of multiple births of size *n* is equal to f^{n-1}). A recent analysis by Record (1952) of multiple births has yielded conclusions which disagree with Hellin's hypothesis, and Record believes that at present no accurate prediction of the relative frequencies of human multiple births. is possible. Further details of human population statistics are given in Chapter 23 (Vol. II).

The relation between the number in a birth and the mean duration of pregnancy in human multiple pregnancies has been examined by McKeown and Record (1952). They find that there is a progressive reduction in the length of gestation as the number of foetuses increases, and they believe that the earlier onset of labour in multiple pregnancy is due to the distension of the uterus, the time of onset being determined by the " relation between total foetal weight and the tolerance of the uterus at any given period of gestation."

The concentrations of steroid hormones and gonadotrophin present in the body fluids increase during pregnancy. Zondek (1931) was the first to show, and others have since confirmed, that the level of total oestrogen in the urine rises steadily during the first months of gestation. It increases to a maximum and then falls rapidly just before parturition. Most of the oestrogen in the blood appears to be in conjugated form, and to be held in the β-globulin fraction of the plasma (Roberts and Szego, 1946). The corpus luteum of pregnancy is believed to be essential in the early stage of gestation, but the ovaries can be removed about the end of the first month without abortion occurring (Melinkoff, 1950). This operation does not result in any marked fall in the amount of oestrogen excreted, and it is therefore believed that the placenta begins to excrete oestrogens very soon after its formation.

The amount of pregnanediol excreted during the early months of pregnancy is roughly the same as in the luteal phase of the cycle. It then increases greatly, and reaches a " plateau " during the last third of gestation, disappearing from the urine within a few days after delivery (Venning, 1952). Hooker and Forbes (1949), by means of their uterine stromal-cell test (1947), found a concentration of about 5 μg./ml. progesterone in the blood in early human pregnancy, almost all of it free in the plasma, only about 10 per cent being bound to protein. Other workers have been unable to corroborate their findings (*see* Morris, 1952).

The changes that occur in the excretion of gonadotrophin during pregnancy have been described in detail by Evans and Simpson (1950). The concentration in the blood and urine is high at about the time of the first missed period, or from two to three weeks after ovulation and conception (Levin, 1941). This is the biological basis of the Aschheim-Zondek, Friedman, and similar pregnancy tests, which become positive at about that time, and of which a comprehensive account is given by Cowie (1948). After the sixth week, excretion of gonadotrophin rises abruptly, and is maintained at a peak between the second and third months of gestation. After the 90th day or so the titre declines almost as rapidly as it had risen previously. Only relatively small amounts are excreted during the remainder of pregnancy, and within a few days after parturition, the hormone disappears completely from the urine (Albert and Berkson, 1951). The persistence of or return to a high gonadotrophin titre in the urine after childbirth is indicative of the survival of trophoblastic tissue.

Gonadotrophin, consisting predominantly of FSH, can be detected in increasing amounts in the urine after the menopause or bilateral ovariectomy.

An account of adrenal function during human pregnancy is provided by Venning (1946).

Further information about the physiology of pregnancy and lactation in women is given in the appropriate sections in Vol. II of this book, and by Snyder (1938) ; Newton (1939, 1949), Courrier (1945), Reynolds (1949), and Folley and Malpress (1948).

Menopause

The word menopause, meaning cessation of the menses, is applied to that period in the life of women during which menstrual cycles become irregular and eventually cease (p. 353). Subsequently, all cyclic activity in the reproductive organs ends, and women become adjusted to the " change of life." The pheno-menon appears to be peculiar to the human species, and may be related to the progressive increase in longevity that is associated with improved living conditions.

In lower mammals the decline of reproductive function in the female occurs late and very gradually. Even in primates menstrual cycles may persist for almost the whole span of life (pp. 336, 348). The physiological basis of the process and its atten-dant psychological and other manifestations in women are described in Chapter 23 (*see* also Novak and Richardson, 1941 ; Engle, 1947 ; Newell and Rock, 1952).

Bibliography

ADAMS, L. E. (1903). A contribution to our knowledge of the mole (*Talpa europaea*). *Mem. Manchr. lit. phil. Soc.*, **47**, 1.
—— (1909) Some notes on the breeding habits of the common mole. *Mem. Manchr. lit. phil. Soc.*, **54**, 1.
AITKEN, W. A. (1927). Some observations on the oestrous cycle and reproductive pheno-mena of the mare. *J. Amer. vet. med. Ass.*, **70**, 481.
ALBERT, A., & BERKSON, J. (1951). A clinical bio-assay for chorionic gonadotropin. *J. clin. Endocrinol.*, **11**, 805.
ALDOUS, C. M. (1937). Notes on the life history of the snowshoe hare. *J. Mammal.*, **18**, 46
ALLANSON, M. (1931). The reproductive cycle in the male ferret. *J. Physiol.*, **71**, 20 P.
—— (1932). The reproductive processes of certain mammals. III.—The reproductive cycle of the male ferret. *Proc. Roy. Soc. B*, **110**, 295.
—— (1933). The reproductive processes of certain mammals. Part V. Changes in the reproductive organs of the male grey squirrel (*Sciurus carolinensis*). *Philos Trans. B*, **222**, 79.
—— (1934). The reproductive processes of certain mammals. Part VII. Seasonal variation in the reproductive organs of the male hedgehog. *Philos. Trans. B*, **223**, 277.

ALLANSON, M., & DEANESLY, R. (1934). The reaction of anoestrous hedgehogs to experimental conditions. *Proc. Roy. Soc.* B, **116**, 170.

ALLEN, E. (1922). The oestrous cycle in the mouse. *Amer. J. Anat.*, **30**, 297.

—— (1923). Racial and familial cyclic inheritance and other evidence from the mouse concerning the cause of oestrous phenomena. *Amer. J. Anat.*, **32**, 293.

—— (1927). The menstrual cycle in the monkey, *Macacus rhesus* : observations on normal animals, the effects of removal of the ovaries and the effects of injections of ovarian and placental extracts into the spayed animals. *Contr. Embryol. Carneg. Instn.*, **19**, 1.

—— DIDDLE, A. W., BURFORD, T. H., & ELDER, J. H. (1936). Analyses of urine of the chimpanzee for estrogenic content during various stages of the menstrual cycle. *Endocrinology*, **20**, 546.

—— PRATT, J. P., NEWELL, Q. U., & BLAND, L. J (1930). Human tubal ova ; related early corpora lutea and uterine tubes. *Contr. Embryol. Carneg. Instn.*, **22**, 45.

ALLEN, J. A. (1922). The American Museum Congo Expedition Collection of *Insectivora. Sciuridae, Anomaluridae* and *Idiuridae* collected by the American Museum Congo Expedition. *Bull. Amer. Mus. Nat. Hist.*, **47**, 1 ; 39.

ALLEN, W. M. (1931). I. Cyclical alterations of the endometrium of the rat during the normal cycle, pseudo-pregnancy, and pregnancy. II. Production of deciduomata during pregnancy. *Anat. Rec.*, **48**, 65.

ALLENDE, I. L. C. de (1940). Blood progesterone during sexual cycle of *Macaca rhesus* ; quantitative assay. *Proc. Soc. exp. Biol., N.Y.*, **44**, 534.

—— & ORÍAS, O. (1950). *Cytology of the human vagina.* New York.

AMOROSO, E. C. (1951). Chairman's summary. Symposium on endocrinological aspects of fertility. *J. Endocrinol.*, **7**, LVI.

—— (1952). In *Marshall's physiology of reproduction* ; 3rd ed., Vol. II. London.

—— GOFFIN, A., HALLEY, G., MATTHEWS, L. H., & MATHEWS, D. J. (1951). Lactation in the grey seal. *J. Physiol.*, **113**, 4 P.

—— HANCOCK, J. L., & ROWLANDS, I. W. (1948). Ovarian activity in the pregnant mare. *Nature, Lond.*, **161**, 355.

—— & ROWLANDS, I. W. (1951). Hormonal effects in the pregnant mare and foetal foal. *J. Endocrinol.*, **7**, XLV.

ANCEL, P., & BOUIN, P. (1909a). Sur la fonction du corps jaune (première note préliminaire) Methodes de recherches. *C. R. Soc. Biol., Paris*, **66**, 454.

—— —— (1909b). Sur la fonction du corps jaune (troisième note préliminaire). Action du corps jaune vrai sur la glande mammaire. *C. R. Soc. Biol., Paris*, **66**, 605.

ANDERSEN, D. H., & KENNEDY, H. S. (1932). Studies on the physiology of reproduction. IV. Changes in the adrenal gland of the female rat associated with the oestrous cycle. *J Physiol.*, **76**, 247.

ANDERSEN, K. (1912). *Catalogue of the chiroptera in the collection of the British Museum.* Vol. I. London.

—— (1917). On the determination of age in bats. *J. Bombay nat. Hist. Soc.*, **25**, 249.

ANDERSON, J. (1936). Studies on reproduction in cattle. I. The periodicity and duration of oestrus. *Emp. J. exp. Agric.*, **4**, 186 ; 198.

—— (1938). Ovulation in the ewe. *J. agric. Sci.*, **28**, 64.

—— (1941). Further investigations on artificial insemination of cattle. *J. agric. Sci.*, **31**, 348 ; 354.

—— (1944). The periodicity and duration of oestrus in zebu and grade cattle. *J. agric. Sci.*, **34**, 57.

ANDREWS, C. W. (1900). *A monograph of Christmas Island.* London. (Quoted by Baker, J. R., & Baker, Z., 1936.)

Argentine shows and livestock (1904). Edinburgh. (Quoted by Marshall, F. H. A., 1922.)

ARISTOTLE. *History of animals.* (Quoted by Heape, W., 1900.)

ARLTON, A. V. (1936). An ecological study of the mole. *J. Mammal.*, **17**, 349.

ASDELL, S. A. (1929). *J. agric. Sci.*, **19**, 382. (Quoted by Marshall, F. H. A., 1937.)

—— (1946). *Patterns of mammalian reproduction.* New York.

ASDELL, S. A., & CROWELL, M. F. (1935). The effect of retarded growth upon the sexual development of rats. *J. Nutrit.*, **10**, 13.

—— & HAMMOND, J. (1933). The effects of prolonging the life of the corpus luteum in the rabbit by hysterectomy. *Amer. J. Physiol.*, **103**, 600.

ASTWOOD, E. B. (1939a). Changes in the weight and water content of the uterus of the normal adult rat. *Amer. J. Physiol.*, **126**, 162.

—— (1939b). An assay method for progesterone based upon the decidual reaction in the rat. *J. Endocrinol.*, **1**, 49.

AULMANN, G. (1932). Geglückte Nachzucht eines Orang-utan im Düsseldorfer Zoo. *Zool. Gart. Lpz.*, **5**, 81.

AUSTIN, C. R. (1949a). Fertilization and the transport of gametes in the pseudo-pregnant rabbit. *J. Endocrinol.*, **6**, 63.

—— (1949b). The fragmentation of eggs following induced ovulation in immature rats. *J. Endocrinol.*, **6**, 104.

—— (1950). The fecundity of the immature rat following induced superovulation. *J. Endocrinol.*, **6**, 293.

AXE, J. W. (1898). The mare and the foal. *J. R. agric. Soc.*, **9**, 213.

AYKROYD, O. E., & ZUCKERMAN, S. (1938). Factors in sexual-skin oedema. *J. Physiol.*, **94**, 13.

AYLWARD, F., & OTTOWAY, C. W. (1945). The collection and examination of plasma from pregnant mares for gonadotrophic hormone. *J. comp. Path.*, **55**, 159.

BAILEY, V. O. (1893). The prairie ground squirrels or spermophiles of the Mississippi valley. *U.S. Dept. Agric. Bull.* **4**.

—— (1895). The pocket gopher of the United States. *Wash. Dept. Agric. Divisn. Ornith. & Mammal.*, Washington.

BAILEY, V. (1924). Breeding, feeding and other life habits of meadow mice (*Microtus*). *J. agric. Res.*, **27**, 523.

—— (1926). *A biological survey of North Dakota.* (Quoted by Murie, A., 1944.)

BAKER, A. B. (1919). Breeding of the Brazilian tapir at National Zoological Park. *J. Mammal.*, **1**, 143.

BAKER, J. R. (1930). The breeding season in British wild mice. *Proc. zool. Soc. Lond.*, **1**, 113.

—— (1937). Light and breeding season. *Nature, Lond.*, **139**, 414.

—— (1938). The evolution of breeding seasons. In *Evolution : essays on aspects of evolutionary biology.* Ed. G. R. de Beer. Oxford.

—— & BAKER, Z. (1936). The seasons in a tropical rain-forest (New Hebrides). Part 3. Fruit-bats (*Pteropidae*). *J. linn. Soc. (Zool.)*, **40**, 123.

—— & BIRD, T. F. (1936). The seasons in a tropical rain-forest (New Hebrides). Part 4. Insectivorous bats (*Vespertilionidae* and *Rhinolophidae*). *J. linn. Soc. (Zool.)*, **40**, 143.

—— & RANSON, R. M. (1932a). Factors affecting the breeding of the field mouse (*Microtus agrestis*). Part I. Light. *Proc. Roy. Soc. B*, **110**, 313.

—— —— (1932b). Factors affecting the breeding of the field mouse (*Microtus agrestis*). Part II.—Temperature and Food. *Proc. Roy. Soc. B*, **112**, 39.

—— —— (1933). Factors affecting the breeding of the field mouse (*Microtus agrestis*). Part III.—Locality. *Proc. Roy. Soc. B*, **113**, 486.

BALL, J. (1937). Sexual responsiveness and temporally related physiological events during pregnancy in the rhesus monkey. *Anat. Rec.*, **67**, 507.

—— & HARTMAN, C. G. (1935). Sexual excitability as related to the menstrual cycle in the monkey. *Amer. J. Obstet. Gynec.*, **29**, 117.

BARABASH-NIKIFOROV, I. (1935). The sea-otters of the Commander Islands. *J. Mammal.*, **16**, 255.

BARBOUR, T., & ALLEN, G. H. (1922). The white-tailed deer of Eastern United States. *J. Mammal.*, **3**, 65.

BARD, P. (1939). Central nervous mechanisms for emotional behaviour patterns in animals. *Res. Publ. Ass. Nerv. Ment. Dis.*, **19**, 190. (Quoted by Young, W. C., 1941.)

BARRETT-HAMILTON, G. E. H. (1910). *A history of British mammals.* London.

BARTELMEZ, G. W. (1933). Histological studies on the menstruating mucous membrane of the human uterus. *Contr. Embryol. Carneg. Instn.*, **24**, 141.

—— (1937). Menstruation. *Physiol. Rev.*, **17**, 28.

BARTON, M., & WIESNER, B. P. (1945). Waking temperature in relation to female fecundity. *Lancet*, ii, 663.

—— —— (1946). The receptivity of cervical mucus to spermatozoa. *Brit. med. J.*, **2**, 606.

BASKIROV, I. S., & ZARKOV, J. V. (1934). (Quoted by Asdell, A. S., 1946.)

BEACH, F. A. (1948). *Hormones and Behaviour.* New York and London.

BEDFORD, DUKE OF, & MARSHALL, F. H. A. (1942). On the incidence of the breeding season in mammals after transference to a new latitude. *Proc. Roy. Soc.* B, **130**, 396.

BENECKE, B. (1879). Über Reifung und Befruchtung des Eies bei den Fledermäusen. *Zool. Anz.*, **2**, 304.

BENSON, S. B., & BORRELL, A. E. (1931). Notes on the life history of the red tree mouse, *Phenacomys longicaudus. J. Mammal.*, **12**, 226.

BERLINER, V. R. (1946). The biology of equine spermatozoa. In *The problem of fertility*. Ed. E. T. Engle. Princeton.

—— SHEETS, E. W., MEANS, R. H., & COWART, F. E. (1938). The oestrous cycle of jennets and sperm production of jacks. *Proc. Amer. Soc. Anim. Prod.*, 295. (Quoted by Asdell, A. S., 1946.)

BERTRAM, G. C. L. (1940). The biology of the Weddell and crabeater seals with a study of the comparative behaviour of the *Pinnipedia*. *Sci. Rep. Brit. Graham Land Exped. 1934-37*, **1**, 1.

BISCHOFF, T. L. W. (1844). *Beweis der von der Begattung unabhängigen periodischen Reifung und Loslösung der Eier der Säugetiere und des Menschen als der ersten Bedingung ihrer Fortpflanzung.* Giessen. (Quoted by Stockard, C. R. & Papanicolaou, G. N., 1917.)

—— (1852). *Entwicklungsgechichte des Meerschweinchens.* Giessen. (Quoted by Stockard, C. R., & Papanicolaou, G. N., 1917.)

—— (1854). *Entwicklungsgeschichte des Rehes.* Giessen.

—— (1863). Über die Ranzzeit des Fuchses und die erste Entwicklung seines Eies. *Sitzg. Math.-phys. Gesell. Wien.* (Quoted by Marshall, F. H. A., 1922.)

BISHOP, D. W. (1942). Germ cell studies in the male fox (*Vulpes fulva*). *Anat. Rec.*, **84**, 99.

BISSONNETTE, T. H. (1932). Modification of mammalian sexual cycles; reactions of ferrets (*Putorius vulgaris*) of both sexes to electric light added after dark in November and December. *Proc. Roy. Soc.* B, **110**, 322.

—— (1935). Modification of mammalian sexual cycles. III. Reversal of the cycle in male ferrets (*Putorius vulgaris*) by increasing periods of exposure to light between October second and March thirtieth. *J. exp. Zool.*, **71**, 341.

—— (1941). Experimental modification of breeding cycles in goats. *Physiol. Zoöl.*, **14**, 379.

BLAIR, G. W. S., FOLLEY, S. J., MALPRESS, F. H., & COPPEN, F. M. U. (1941). Variations in certain properties of bovine cervical mucus during the oestrous cycle. *Biochem. J.*, **35**, 1039.

BLANDAU, R. J. (1945). Is the copulation plug necessary for the en masse transport of spermatozoa into the uterine cornua of the albino rat? *Anat. Rec.* (*Abstr.*), **91**, 266.

—— BOLING, J. L., & YOUNG, W. C. (1941). The length of heat in the albino rat as determined by the copulatory response. *Anat. Rec.*, **79**, 453.

—— & MONEY, W. L. (1943). The attainment of sexual maturity in the female albino rat as determined by the copulatory response. *Anat. Rec.*, **86**, 197.

—— & YOUNG, W. C. (1939). The effects of delayed fertilization on the delevopment of the guinea-pig ovum. *Amer. J. Anat.*, **64**, 303.

BLANFORD, W. T. (1888-91). *The fauna of British India, including Ceylon and Burma. Mammalia.* London.

BLOCH, S. (1943). Über die Wirkung der Milchdrüsensekretion auf die Nidation bei der Maus. *Schweiz. med. Wschr.*, **73**, 245.

BLOCH, S. (1948). Zum Problem der Nidationsverzögerung bei der säugenden Maus. *Bull schweiz. Akad. med. Wiss.*, **4**, 309.

BLUNTSCHLI, H. (1937). Die Frühentwicklung eines Centetinen (*Hemicentetes semispinosus* Cuv.). *Rev. Suisse. Zool.*, **44**, 271.

BODENHEIMER, F. S., & SULMAN, F. (1946). The oestrous cycle of *Microtus guentheri* D. and A. and its ecological implications. *Ecology*, **27**, 255.

BOLING, J. L., BLANDAU, R. J., WILSON, J. G., & YOUNG, W. C. (1939). Post-parturitional heat response of newborn and adult guinea pigs. Data on parturition. *Proc. Soc. exp. Biol.*, *N.Y.*, **42**, 128.

BOLLIGER, A., & CARRODUS, A. L. (1938). Spermatorrhoea in *Trichosurus vulpecula* and other marsupials. *Med. J. Aust.*, **25**, 1118.

—— —— (1940). The effect of oestrogens on the pouch of the marsupial *Trichosurus vulpecula*. *J. roy. Soc.*, *N.S.W.*, **73**, 218.

—— & TOW, A. J. (1947). Late effects of castration and administration of sex hormones on the male *Trichosurus vulpecula*. *J. Endocrinol.*, **5**, 32.

BONFERT, A. (1933). Contributiuni la studiul vietii sexuale a orlor. *Bul. Asoc. Med. vet. Român.*, **45**, 215.

BONNET, R. (1897). Beiträge zur Embryologie des Hundes. *Anat. Hefte*, **9**, 419.

BOUIN, P., & ANCEL, P. (1909a). Sur la fonction du corps jaune. Action du corps jaune vrai sur l'uterus (Deuxième note préliminaire). *C. R. Soc. Biol., Paris*, **66**, 505.

—— —— (1909b). Sur la fonction du corps jaune (quatrième note préliminaire). Démonstration experimentale de l'action du corps jaune sur l'uterus et la glande mammaire. *C. R. Soc. Biol., Paris*, **66**, 689.

—— —— (1909c). Sur les homologies et la signification des glandes à sécretion interne de l'ovaire. *C. R. Soc. Biol., Paris*, **67**, 464.

BOURG, R. (1935). Étude des modifications provoquées par la gravidine au niveau de l'ovaire et du tractus génital chez la chatte. *Arch. Biol., Paris*, **46**, 47.

BOURNE, G., & ZUCKERMAN, S. (1941). Changes in the adrenals in relation to the normal and artificial threshold oestrous cycle in the rat. *J. Endocrinol.*, **2**, 283.

BOWLEY, E. A. (1939). Delayed fertilization in *Dromicia*. *J. Mammal.*, **20**, 499.

BOWNESS, E. R. (1942). Duration of pregnancy in mink. *Fur Trade J. Canada*, **19**, 16. (Quoted by Pearson, O. P., & Enders, R. K., 1944.)

BRADBURY, J. T. (1941). Rabbit ovulating factor of plant juice. *Amer. J. Physiol.*, **142**, 487.

BRADT, G. W. (1939). Breeding habits of beaver. *J. Mammal.*, **20**, 486.

BRAMBELL, F. W. R. (1935). Reproduction in the common shrew (*Sorex araneus* Linnaeus) I. The oestrous cycle of the female. *Philos. Trans. B*, **225**, 1.

—— (1937) The influence of lactation on the implantation of the mammalian embryo. *Amer. J. Obstet. Gynec.*, **33**, 942.

—— (1942). Intra-uterine mortality of the wild rabbit, *Oryctolagus cuniculus* (L). *Proc. Roy. Soc. B*, **130**, 462.

—— (1944–45). The reproduction of the wild rabbit, *Oryctolagus cuniculus* (L). *Proc. zool. Soc. Lond.*, **114**, 1.

—— (1948). Prenatal mortality in mammals. *Biol. Rev.*, **23**, 370

—— & DAVIS, D. H. S. (1941). Reproduction of the multimammate mouse (*Mastomys erythroleucus* Temm.) of Sierra Leone. *Proc. zool. Soc. Lond. B*, **111**, 1.

—— & HALL, K. (1936). Reproduction in the lesser shrew (*Sorex minutus* Linnaeus). *Proc. zool. Soc. Lond.*, **1936**, 957.

—— —— (1939). Reproduction of the field vole, *Microtus agrestis hirtus* Bellamy. *Proc. zool. Soc. Lond. A*, **109**, 133.

—— & ROWLANDS, I. W. (1936). Reproduction of the bank vole (*Evotomys glareolus* Schreber). I. The oestrous cycle of the female. *Philos. Trans. B*, **226**, 71.

BRASSARD, J. A., & BERNARD, R. (1939). *Canad. Field Nat.*, **53**, 15. (Quoted by Asdell, S. A., 1946.)

BRESCHET, G. (1845). Recherches anatomiques et physiologiques sur la gestation des quadrumanes. *Mem. Acad. Sci., Paris*, **19**, 401.

Brewer, J. I., & Jones, H. O. (1947). Studies on the human corpus luteum. Histologic variations in corpora lutea and in corpus luteum. Endometrial relationships at the onset of normal menstruation. *Amer. J. Obstet. Gynec.*, **54**, 561.

—— —— (1948). Studies of the human corpus luteum. Corpus luteum—endometrial relationships in functional uterine bleeding. *Amer. J. Obstet. Gynec.*, **55**, 18.

Brooks, C. McC. (1938). A study of the mechanism whereby coitus excites the ovulation-producing activity of the rabbit's pituitary. *Amer. J. Physiol.*, **121**, 157.

Broom, R. (1895). *Proc. Linn. Soc., N.S.W.*, **10**, 576. (Quoted by Asdell, S. A., 1946.)

Brown, C. E. (1924). Rearing hippopotamuses in captivity. *J. Mammal.*, **5**, 243.

—— (1936). Rearing wild animals in captivity, and gestation periods. *J. Mammal.*, **17**, 10.

Brown, P. C. (1944). *Amer. J. Vet. Res.*, **5**, 99. (Quoted by Asdell, S. A., 1946.)

Bruce, H. M., & Hindle, E. (1934). The golden hamster, *Cricetus (Mesocricetus) auratus*, Waterhouse. Notes on its breeding and growth. *Proc. zool. Soc. Lond.*, **1934**, 361.

—— & Parkes, A. S. (1948). Feeding and breeding of laboratory animals. VIII. Breeding of guinea pigs. *J. Hyg., Camb.*, **46**, 434.

Burne, E. C. (1943). A record of gestation periods and growth of trained Indian elephant calves in the Southern Shan States, Burma. *Proc zool. Soc. Lond.*, **113**, 27.

Burrell, H. (1927). *The Platypus. Its discovery, zoological position, form and characteristics, habits, life history, etc.* Sydney.

Burt, W. H. (1928). Additional notes on the life history of the Goss lemming mouse. *J. Mammal.*, **9**, 212.

Buxton, C. L. (1950). The atypical secretory phase. In *Menstruation and its disorders*. Ed. E. T. Engle. Springfield, Ill.

Caffier, P., & Kolbow, H. (1934). Anatomisch-physiologische Genitalstudien an Fledermäusen zur Klärung der therapeutischen Sexual-hormonwirkung. *Z Geburtsh. Gynäk.*, **108**, 185.

Cameron, A. T. (1947). *Recent advances in endocrinology.* 6th ed. London.

Camus, L., & Gley, E. (1899). Action coagulante du liquide de la prostate externe du hérisson sur le contenu des vesicules séminales. *C. R. Acad. Sci.*, **128**, 1417. (Quoted by Eadie, W. R., 1948b.)

Carpenter, C. R. (1934). A field study of the behavior and social relations of howling monkeys (*Alouatta palliata*). *Comp. Psychol. Monog.*, **10** (No. 2).

—— (1935). Behavior of red spider monkeys in Panama. *J. Mammal.*, **16**, 171.

—— (1940). A field study in Siam of the behavior and social relations of the gibbon (*Hylobates lar*). *Comp. Psychol. Monog.*, **16** (No. 5).

—— (1941). The menstrual cycle and body temperature in two gibbons (*Hylobates lar*). *Anat. Rec.*, **79**, 291.

—— (1942a). Societies of monkeys and apes. *Biol. Symp.*, **8**, 177.

—— (1942b). Sexual behavior of free ranging monkeys (*Macaca mulatta*). I. Specimens, procedures and behavioral characteristics of oestrus. Sexual behavior of free ranging monkeys (*Macaca mulatta*). II. Periodicity of estrus, homosexual, autoerotic and non-conformist behavior. *J. comp. Psychol.*, **33**, 133 ; 143.

Cary, W. H. (1948). Results of artificial insemination with an extramarital specimen (semi-adoption). *Amer. J. Obstet. Gynec.*, **56**, 727.

Casida, L. E. (1946). Induction of ovulation and subsequent fertility in domestic animals. In *The problem of fertility*. Ed. E. T. Engle. Princeton.

—— & Warwick, E. J. (1945). The necessity of the corpus luteum for maintenance of pregnancy in the ewe. *J. Anim. Sci.*, **4**, 34.

Catchpole, H. R., & Fulton, J. F. (1939). Tarsiers in captivity. *Nature, Lond.*, **144**, 514.

—— —— (1943). The oestrous cycle in *Tarsius* : observations on a captive pair. *J. Mammal.*, **24**, 90.

Catlin (1841). *North American Indians.* 2nd ed. Vol. I. London. (Quoted by Marshall, F. H. A., 1922.)

Chain, E., & Duthie, E. S. (1940). Identity of hyaluronidase and spreading factor. *Brit. J. exp. Path.*, **21**, 324.

CHANCE, M. R. A., ROWLANDS, I. W., & YOUNG, F. G. (1939). Species variation in thyro-
trophic, gonadotrophic, and prolactin activities of the anterior hypophyseal tissue.
J. Endocrinol., **1**, 239.

CHANG, C.-Y., & WU, H. (1938). Growth and reproduction of laboratory bred hamsters,
Cricetulus griseus. *Chin. J. Physiol.*, **13**, 109.

CHANG, M.-C. (1942). Effects of oestrogen (stilboestrol) on the sperm production of adult
rams. *J. Endocrinol.*, **3**, 192.

—— (1946). Fertilizing capacity of rabbit spermatozoa. In *The problem of fertility*.
Ed. E. T. Engle. Princeton.

—— (1950). Fertilization, male infertility and hyaluronidase. *Ann. N.Y. Acad. Sci.*, **52**,
1192.

CHU, J. P., LEE, C. C., & YOU, S. S. (1944–46). Functional relation between the uterus and
the corpus luteum. *J. Endocrinol.*, **4**, 392.

CLARK, F. H. (1936). The oestrous cycle of the cotton rat, *Sigmodon hispidus*. *Contr.
Lab. Vert. Genetics, Univ. Michigan*, **2**, 1.

CLARK, G., & BIRCH, H. G. (1948). Observations on the sex skin and sex cycle in the chimpanzee. *Endocrinology*, **43**, 218.

CLARK, W. E. LE GROS, MCKEOWN, T., & ZUCKERMAN, S. (1939). Visual pathways concerned in gonadal stimulation in ferrets. *Proc. Roy. Soc.* B, **126**, 449.

CLAUBERG, C. (1936). Ovarium, Hypophyse, Placenta und Schwangerschaft in ihrer
innersekretorischen Beziehung zur Frauenheilkunde. In Veit-Stoeckel, *Handb.
Gynäk.*, Bd. 9. München.

COCKS, A. H. (1881). Note on the breeding of the otter. *Proc. zool. Soc. Lond.*, **1881**, 249.

—— (1891). (Quoted by Tetley, H., 1941a.)

—— (1900). Note on the gestation of the pine marten. *Proc. zool. Soc. Lond.*, **1900**, 836.

—— (1903). On the gestation of the badger. *Zoologist*, **7**, 441.

—— (1904). The gestation of the badger. *Zoologist*, **8**, 108.

COHEN, S. (1950). Variations in serum protein concentration during the menstrual cycle
of the baboon (*Papio ursinus*). *S. Afr. J. med. Sci.*, **15**, 101.

COLE, H. H. (1930). A study of the mucosa of the genital tract of the cow, with special
reference to the cyclic changes. *Amer. J. Anat.*, **46**, 261.

—— & HART, G. H. (1930). The potency of blood serum of mares in progressive stages of
pregnancy in effecting the sexual maturity of the immature rat. *Amer. J. Physiol.*,
93, 57.

—— —— LYONS, W. R., & CATCHPOLE, H. R. (1933). The development and hormonal
content of foetal horse gonads. *Anat. Rec.*, **56**, 275.

—— & MILLER, R. F. (1935). Changes in the reproductive organs of the ewe with some
data bearing on their control. *Amer. J. Anat.*, **57**, 39.

COLLINGS, M. R. (1926). A study of the cutaneous reddening and swelling about the
genitalia of the monkey, *M. rhesus*. *Anat. Rec.*, **33**, 271.

COMRIE, L. C., & ADAM, A. B. (1938). The female reproductive system and corpora lutea
of the false killer whale, *Pseudorca crassidens* Owen. *Trans. Roy. Soc. Edinb.*, **59**,
521.

CONDRIN, J. M. (1936). Observations on the seasonal and reproductive activities of the
eastern chipmunk. *J. Mammal.*, **17**, 231.

COOLIDGE, H. J., Jr. (1933). Notes on a family of breeding gibbons. *Hum. Biol.*, **5**, 288.

CORNER, G. W. (1915). The corpus luteum of pregnancy, as it is in swine. *Contr.
Embryol. Carneg. Instn.*, **2**, 69.

—— (1919). On the origin of the corpus luteum of the sow from both granulosa and theca
interna. *Amer. J. Anat.*, **26**, 117.

—— (1921). Cyclic changes in the ovaries and uterus of the sow, and their relation to the
mechanism of implantation. *Contr. Embryol. Carneg. Instn.*, **13**, 117.

—— (1923a). Ovulation and menstruation in *Macacus rhesus*. *Contr. Embryol. Carneg.
Instn.*, **15**, 73.

—— (1923b). Oestrus, ovulation, and menstruation. *Physiol. Rev.*, **3**, 457.

—— (1927). The relation between menstruation and ovulation in the monkey. *J. Amer.
med. Ass.*, **89**, 1838.

CORNER, G. W. (1932a).   The menstrual cycle of the Malayan monkey, *Macaca irus*.   *Anat. Rec.*, **52**, 401.

—— (1932b).   In the rhesus monkey ovulation is spontaneous.   *Proc. Soc. exp. Biol., N.Y.*, **29**, 598.

—— (1951).   Our knowledge of the menstrual cycle, 1910–1950.   *Lancet*, i, 919.

—— (1952).   The events of the primate ovarian cycle.   *Brit. med. J.*, **2**, 403.

—— FARRIS, E. J., & CORNER, Jr., G. W. (1950).   The dating of ovulation and other ovarian crises by histological examination in comparison with the Farris test.   *Amer. J. Obstet. Gynec.*, **59**, 514.

—— HARTMAN, C. G., & BARTELMEZ, G. W. (1945).   Development, organization and breakdown of the corpus luteum in rhesus monkey.   *Contr. Embryol. Carneg. Instn.*, **31**, 117.

COURRIER, R. (1924).   Le cycle sexuel chez la femelle des mammifères.   Etude de la phase folliculaire.   *Arch. Biol., Paris*, **34**, 369.

—— (1927).   Etude sur le déterminisme des caractères sexuels secondaires chez quelques mammifères à activité testiculaire périodique.   *Arch. Biol., Paris*, **37**, 173.

—— (1945).   *Endocrinologie de la gestation*.   Paris.

—— & GROS, G. (1933).   Données complémentaires sur le cycle génital de la chatte.   *C. R. Soc. Biol., Paris*, **114**, 275.

COWAN, I. McT. (1936).   Nesting habits of the flying squirrel, *Glaucomys sabrinus*.   *J. Mammal.*, **17**, 58.

COWIE, A. T. (1948).   *Pregnancy diagnosis tests : a review*.   Commonwealth Agricultural Bureaux Jt. Publ. No. 13.   Edinburgh, Shinfield, Weybridge.

CREW, F. A. E., & MIRSKAIA, L. (1930a).   On the effect of removal of the litter upon the reproductive rate of the female mouse.   *Quart. J. exp. Physiol.*, **20**, 263.

—— —— (1930b).   The lactation interval in the mouse.   *Quart. J. exp. Physiol.*, **20**, 105.

CUNNINGHAM, D. J. (1905).   Cape hunting dogs (*Lycaon pictus*) in the gardens of the Royal Zoological Society of Ireland.   *Proc. Roy. Soc. Edinb.*, **25**, 843.

CUYLER, W. K. (1924).   Observations on the habits of the striped skunk (*Mephitis mesomelas varians*).   *J. Mammal.*, **5**, 180.

D'AMOUR, F. E. (1940).   Further studies on hormone excretion during the menstrual cycle.   *Amer. J. Obstet. Gynec.*, **40**, 958.

—— —— (1943).   A comparison of methods used in determining the time of ovulation.   *J. clin. Endocrinol.*, **3**, 41.

DANFORTH, D. N., GRAHAM, R. J., & IVY, A. C. (1942).   The functional anatomy of labour as revealed by frozen sagittal sections in the macacus rhesus monkey.   *Surg., Gynec., Obstet.*, **74**, 188.

DANIEL, J. F. (1910).   Observations on the period of gestation in white mice.   *J. exp. Zool.*, **9**, 865.

DARLING, F. F. (1937).   *A herd of red deer*.   London.

—— (1947).   *Natural history in the Highlands and Islands*.   London.   (Quoted by Davies, J. L., 1949.)

DARWIN, C. (1868).   *The variation of animals and plants under domestication*.   London.

DATHE, H. (1934).   Eine neue Beobachtung des Känguruhgeburtsaktes.   *Zool. Gart., Lpz.*, **7**, 223.

DAVIES, D. V., & MANN, T. (1947).   Functional development of accessary glands and spermatogenesis.   *Nature, Lond.*, **160**, 295.

DAVIES, J. L. (1949).   Observations on the grey seal (*Halichoerus grypus*) at Ramsay Island, Pembrokeshire.   *Proc. zool. Soc. Lond.*, **119**, 673.

DAVIS, D. E., & HALL, D. (1948).   The seasonal reproductive condition of male brown rats in Baltimore, Maryland.   *Physiol. Zoöl.*, **21**, 272.

DAVIS, M. E., & HARTMAN, C. G. (1935).   Changes in vaginal epithelium during pregnancy in relation to the vaginal cycle.   *J. Amer. med. Ass.*, **104**, 279.

DAWSON, A. B., & FRIEDGOOD, H. B. (1940).   The time and sequence of preovulatory changes in the cat ovary after mating or mechanical stimulation of the cervix uteri.   *Anat. Rec.*, **76**, 411.

DAY, F. T. (1939a).   Ovulation and the descent of the ovum in the Fallopian tube of the mare after treatment with gonadotrophic hormones.   *J. agric. Sci.*, **29**, 459.

—— (1939b).   The oestrous cycle of the mare following removal of the foetus at various stages of pregnancy.   *J. agric. Sci.*, **29**, 470.

—— (1940).   Clinical and experimental observations on reproduction in the mare.   *J. agric. Sci.*, **30**, 244.

—— (1942).   Survival of spermatozoa in the genital tract of the mare.   *J. agric. Sci.*, **32**, 108.

—— & ROWLANDS, I. W. (1940).   The time and rate of appearance of gonadotrophin in the serum of pregnant mares.   *J. Endocrinol.*, **2**, 254.

—— —— (1947).   Serum gonadotrophin in Welsh and Shetland ponies.   *J. Endocrinol.*, **5**, 1.

DEANESLY, R. (1934).   The reproductive processes of certain mammals.   Part VI.   The reproductive cycle of the female hedgehog.   *Philos. Trans.* B, **223**, 239.

—— (1935).   The reproductive processes of certain mammals.   Part IX.   Growth and reproduction in the stoat (*Mustela erminea*).   *Philos. Trans.* B, **225**, 459.

—— (1938).   The reproductive cycle of the golden hamster (*Cricetus auratus*).   *Proc. zool. Soc. Lond.* A, **108**, 31.

—— (1943).   Delayed implantation in the stoat (*Mustela mustela*).   *Nature, Lond.*, **151**, 365.

—— (1944–45).   The reproductive cycle of the female weasel (*Mustela nivalis*).   *Proc zool. Soc. Lond.*, **114**, 339.

—— & PARKES, A. S. (1931).   The functions of the corpus luteum.   V.   Changes in the sterile horn during pregnancy, and their relation to changes in the corpus luteum.   *Proc. Roy. Soc.* B, **109**, 196.

—— —— (1933a).   The effect of hysterectomy on the oestrous cycle of the ferret.   *J. Physiol.*, **78**, 80.

—— —— (1933b).   The reproductive processes of certain mammals.   IV.   The oestrous cycle of the grey squirrel (*Sciurus carolinensis*).   *Philos. Trans.* B, **222**, 47.

—— & WARWICK, T. (1939).   Observations on pregnancy in the common bat (*Pipistrellus pipistrellus*).   *Proc. zool. Soc. Lond.* A, **109**, 57.

DELFS, E. (1941).   Serum chorionic gonadotropin in the rhesus monkey.   *Anat. Rec.* (Suppl.), **79**, 17.

DEMPSEY, E. W. (1937).   Follicular growth rate and ovulation after various experimental procedures in the guinea-pig.   *Amer. J. Physiol.*, **120**, 126.

—— (1939).   The reproductive cycle of New World monkeys.   *Amer. J. Anat.*, **64**, 381.

—— (1940).   The structure of the reproductive tract in the female gibbon.   *Amer. J. Anat.*, **67**, 229.

DICE, L. R. (1919).   The mammals of Southeastern Washington.   *J. Mammal.*, **1**, 10.

DICKERSON, L. M. (1928).   Observations on parturition in the opossum, *Didelphys virginiana*.   *Science*, **68**, 111.

DIGHTON, A. (1921).   *The greyhound and coursing*.   London.

DIXON, J. (1920).   Control of the coyote in California.   (Quoted by Hamlett, G. W. D., 1938.)

—— (1922).   Rodents and reclamation in the Imperial Valley.   *J. Mammal.*, **3**, 136.

—— (1929).   The breeding season of the pocket gopher in California.   *J. Mammal.*, **10**, 327.

DONALDSON, H. H. (1924).   *The rat : date and reference tables*.   2nd ed.   Philadelphia.

DONAT, F. (1933).   Notes on the life history and behaviour of *Neotoma fuscipes*.   *J. Mammal.*, **14**, 19.

DONNE, T. E. (1924).   *The game animals of New Zealand : an account of their introduction, acclimatization and development*.   London.

DORFMAN, R. I. (1948).   Biochemistry of androgens.   In *The hormones*.   Ed. G. Pincus and K. V. Thimann.   Vol. 1.   New York.

—— & WAGENEN, G. VAN (1938).   Excretion of sex hormones in urine of adult male monkeys.   *Proc. Soc. exp. Biol., N.Y.*, **39**, 35.

—— —— (1941).   The sex hormone excretion of adult female and pregnant monkeys   *Surg. Obstet. Gynec.*, **73**, 545.

Duran-Reynals, F., Bunting, H., & Wagenen, G. van (1950). Studies on the sex skin of *Macaca mulatta*. *Ann. N.Y. Acad. Sci.*, **52**, 1006.

Dutt, R. H., & Casida, L. E. (1948). Alteration of the estrual cycle in sheep by use of progesterone and its effect upon subsequent ovulation and fertility. *Endocrinology*, **43**, 208.

Duval, M. (1895). Sur l'accouplement des chauve-souris. *C. R. Soc. Biol., Paris*, **47**, 135.

Dyke, H. B. van, & Ch'en, G. (1936). Observations on the biochemistry of the genital tract of the female macaque particularly during the menstrual cycle. *Amer. J. Anat.*, **58**, 473.

—— —— (1940). The distribution of lipoids in the genital tract of the monkey at different stages of the menstrual cycle. *Amer. J. Anat.*, **66**, 411.

—— & Li, R. C. (1938). The secretion of progesterone by the cat's ovary following the formation of corpora lutea due to the injection of anterior pituitary extract or prolan. *Chin. J. Physiol.*, **13**, 213.

Eadie, W. R. (1939). A contribution to the biology of *Parascalops breweri*. *J Mammal.*, **20**, 150.

—— (1948a). The male accessory reproductive glands of *Condylura* with notes on a unique prostatic secretion. *Anat. Rec.*, **101**, 59.

—— (1948b). Corpora amylacea in the prostatic secretion and experiments on the formation of a copulatory plug in some insectivores. *Anat. Rec.*, **102**, 259.

Eckstein, P. (1944). Unusually long pregnancy in a macaque. *J. Anat., Lond.*, **78**, 147.

—— (1948). The growth and development of the rhesus monkey. M.D. Thesis, University of Cambridge.

—— (1949). Patterns of the mammalian sexual cycle. *Acta Anat.*, **7**, 389.

—— Lubran, M., & McKeown, T. (1940–41). Fluctuations in the blood electrolytes in relation to the menstrual cycle. *Guy's Hosp. Rep.*, **90**, 28.

Edge, E. R. (1931). Seasonal activity and growth in the Douglas ground-squirrel. *J. Mammal.*, **12**, 194.

Ehrlich, I. (1949). Über Chromosomenzahl, Hodenzyklen und Brunft bei *Martes foina*, Erxl. *Rev. Suisse Zool.*, **56**, 621.

Elder, J. H., & Bruhn, J. M. (1939). Use of the Friedman test for pregnancy with chimpanzees. *Yale J. Biol. Med.*, **12**, 155.

—— & Yerkes, R. M. (1936a). The sexual cycle in the chimpanzee. *Anat. Rec.*, **67**, 119.

—— —— (1936b). Chimpanzee births in captivity : a typical case history and report of sixteen births. *Proc. Roy. Soc. B*, **120**, 409.

Ellis, R. W. B. (1947). *Child health and development*. London.

—— (1950). Age of puberty in the tropics. *Brit. med. J.*, **1**, 85.

Enders, R. K. (1940). Ovulation in the mink (*Mustela vison*). *Anat. Rec. (Abstr.)*, **76**, 20.

—— (1941). *Amer. Fur Breeder*, **14**, 6. (Quoted by Asdell, S. A., 1946.)

—— (1952). Reproduction in the mink (*Mustela vison*). *Proc. Amer. philos. Soc.*, **96**, 691.

—— & Leekley, J. R. (1941). Cyclic changes in the vulva of the marten (*Martes americana*). *Anat. Rec.*, **79**, 1.

—— & Pearson, O. P. (1943). The blastocyst of the fisher. *Anat. Rec.*, **85**, 285.

—— —— (1945). Some reproductive phenomena of the fur seal. *Anat. Rec. (Abstr.)*, **91**, 271.

—— —— & Pearson, A. K. (1946). Certain aspects of reproduction in the fur seal. *Anat. Rec.*, **94**, 213.

Engle, E. T. (1927). Notes on the sexual cycle of the Pacific *Cetacea* of the genera *Megaptera* and *Balaenoptera*. *J. Mammal.*, **8**, 48.

—— (1946). *The problem of fertility*. Princeton.

—— (1947). Endocrine changes at the menopause. In *Progress in gynecology*. Ed. J. V. Meigs & S. H. Sturgis. London.

—— & Shelesnyak, M. C. (1934). First menstruation and subsequent menstrual cycles of pubertal girls. *Hum. Biol.*, **6**, 431.

ENGLISH, P. F. (1932). Some habits of the pocket gopher, *Geomys breviceps breviceps*. *J. Mammal.*, **13**, 126.

ERRINGTON, P. L. (1937). The breeding season of the muskrat in northwest Iowa. *J. Mammal.*, **18**, 333.

—— (1946). Predation and vertebrate populations. *Quart. Rev. Biol.*, **21**, 144.

EVANS, H. M., & BISHOP, K. S. (1922). On the relations between fertility and nutrition. II. The ovulation rhythm in the rat on inadequate nutritional regimes. *J. metab. Res.*, **1**, 335.

—— & COLE, H. H. (1931). An introduction to the study of the oestrous cycle in the dog. *Mem. Univ. Calif.*, **9**, 65.

—— & SIMPSON, M. E. (1950). Physiology of the gonadotrophins. In *The hormones*. Ed. G. Pincus & K. V. Thimann. Vol. 2. New York.

—— & LYONS, W. R. (1941). Influence of lactogenic preparations on production of traumatic placentoma in the rat. *Proc. Soc. exp. Biol., N.Y.*, **46**, 586.

—— & SWEZY, O. (1931). Ovogenesis and the normal follicular cycle in adult Mammalia. *Mem. Univ. Calif.*, **9**, 119.

EVERETT, J. W. (1939). Spontaneous persistent estrus in a strain of albino rats. *Endocrinology*, **25**, 123.

—— (1940). The restoration of ovulatory cycles and corpus luteum formation in persistent-estrus rats by progesterone. *Endocrinology*, **27**, 681.

EVERMANN, B. W., & HANNA, G. D. (1925). The Steller sea lion rookery on Ano Nuevo Island, California, in 1924. *J. Mammal.*, **6**, 96.

EWART, J. C. (1915). Studies on the development of the horse. *Trans. Roy. Soc. Edinb.*, **51**, 287.

FAIRFAX-BLAKEBOROUGH, J., & PEASE, A. E. (1914). The life and habits of the badger. *The foxhound*. London. (Quoted by Neal, E., 1948.)

FARRIS, E. J. (1946a). The time of ovulation in the monkey. *Anat. Rec.*, **95**, 337.

—— (1946b). A test for determining the time of ovulation and conception in women. *Amer. J. Obstet. Gynec.*, **52**, 14.

—— (1948). The prediction of the day of human ovulation by the rat test as confirmed by fifty conceptions. *Amer. J. Obstet. Gynec.*, **56**, 347.

—— (1950). *The care and breeding of laboratory animals*. New York ; London.

FEE, A. R., & PARKES, A. S. (1929). Studies on ovulation. I. The relation of the anterior pituitary body to ovulation in the rabbit. *J. Physiol.*, **67**, 383.

—— —— (1930). Studies on ovulation. Effect of vaginal anaesthesia on ovulation in the rabbit. *J. Physiol.*, **70**, 385.

FEREMUTSCH, K., & STRAUSS, F. (1949). Beitrag zum weiblichen Genitalzyklus der madagassischen Centetinen. *Rev. Suisse Zool.* (Fasc. Suppl. 1), **56**, 1.

FERNANDEZ, M. (1915). Dasypus villosus. *Anat. Anz.*, **48**, 303. (Quoted by Jones, F. W., 1945.)

FINKEL, M. P. (1945). The relation of sex hormones to pigmentation and to testis descent in the opossum and ground squirrel. *Amer. J. Anat.*, **76**, 93.

FISCHER, E. (1931). Die Entwicklungsgeschichte des Dachses und die Frage der Zwillingsbildung. *Verh. anat. Ges. Jena.*, **72**, 22.

FISH, W. R., YOUNG, W. C., & DORFMAN, R. I. (1941). Excretion of estrogenic and androgenic substances by female and male chimpanzees with known mating behavior records. *Endocrinology*, **28**, 585.

FISHER, E. M. (1939). Habits of the Southern sea otter. *J. Mammal.*, **20**, 21.

FISHER, R. B., & ZUCKERMAN, S. (1937). The distribution of water in the sexual skin of monkeys. *J. Physiol.*, **89**, 15 P.

FITZGERALD, A. (1935). Rearing marmosets in captivity. *J. Mammal.*, **16**, 181.

FITZSIMONS, F. W. (1919–20). *The natural history of South Africa, Mammals.* **1–4**. London.

FLOWER, S. S. (1931). Contribution to our knowledge of the duration of life in vertebrate animals. V. Mammals. *Proc. zool. Soc. Lond.*, **1931**, 145.

—— (1932). Notes on the recent mammals of Egypt, with a list of the species recorded from that kingdom *Proc. zool. Soc. Lond.*, **1932**, 369.

Flower, S. S. (1933). Breeding season of lemurs. *Proc. zool. Soc. Lond.*, **1933**, 317.

—— (1943). Notes on age at sexual maturity, gestation period and growth of the Indian elephant, *Elephas maximus*. *Proc. zool. Soc. Lond.*, **113**, 21.

—— & Lydekker, R. (1891). *Mammals living and extinct.* London.

Fluhmann, C. F. (1936). Estrogenic substances in the blood of women. *Amer. J. Obstet. Gynec.*, **32**, 612.

Flynn, T. T. (1923). Remarks on the method of parturition in *Potoroüs tridactylus*. *Proc. Linn. Soc., N.S.W.*, **47**, 28.

—— (1928). *Searchlight Series (Workers' Education Assoc. of Tasmania).* **1**, 1. (Quoted by Matthews, L. H., 1943.)

—— (1930a). The uterine cycle of pregnancy and pseudo-pregnancy as it is in the diprotodont marsupial *Bettongia cuniculus*. *Proc. Linn. Soc., N.S.W.*, **55**, 506.

—— (1930b). On the unsegmented ovum of Echidna (*Tachyglossus*). *Quart. J. micr. Sci.*, **74**, 119.

—— & Hill, J. P. (1938–40). The development of the Monotremata. Part IV. Growth of the ovarian ovum, maturation, fertilisation and early cleavage. *Trans. zool. Soc. Lond.*, **24**, 445.

Folk, G. E., Jr. (1940). The longevity of sperm in the female bat. *Anat. Rec.*, **76**, 103.

Folley, S. J., & Malpress, F. H. (1944–46). Artificial induction of lactation in bovines by oral administration of synthetic oestrogens. *J. Endocrinol.*, **4**, 23.

—— —— (1948). Hormonal control of lactation. In *The hormones.* Ed. G. Pincus and K. V. Thimann. Vol. 1. New York.

—— —— & Young, F. G. (1944–46). Induction of lactation in goats and cows with synthetic oestrogens and anterior pituitary extracts. *J. Endocrinol.*, **4**, 181.

Ford, D. H., Webster, R. L., & Young, W. C. (1951). Rupture of the vaginal closure membrane during pregnancy in the guinea pig. *Anat. Rec.*, **109**, 707.

Foster, M. A. (1934). The reproductive cycle in the female ground squirrel, *Citellus tridecemlineatus* (Mitchill). *Amer. J. Anat.*, **54**, 487.

—— & Hisaw, F. L. (1935). Experimental ovulation and the resulting pseudo-pregnancy in anoestrous cats. *Anat. Rec.*, **62**, 75.

Frank, R. T. (1935). Sex-endocrine factors in blood and urine in health and disease. *J. Amer. med. Ass.*, **104**, 1991.

Frei, W., & Demmel, M. (1932). Beziehungen zwischen Blut und Sexualzustand beim weiblichen Rind. *Schw. Arch. Tierheilk.*, **74**, 469.

—— & Metzger, E. (1926). Die Sexualperiodizität in der Vagina des Rindes. *Berl. tierärztl. Wschr.*, **42**, 645.

Freksa, H. F., & Spiegel, A. (1935). Über die Hemmung des Brunstzyklus nach Hysterektomie beim Meerschweinchen. *Zool. Anz.*, **112**, 283.

Friedgood, H. B., & Pincus, G. (1935). Studies on conditions of activity in endocrine organs. XXX. The nervous control of the anterior hypophysis as indicated by maturation of ova and ovulation after stimulation of cervical sympathetics. *Endocrinology*, **19**, 710.

Friedman, M. H. (1938). Criteria for the selection of oestrous rabbits. The significance of seasonal factors. *Endocrinology*, **22**, 354.

—— & Friedman, G. S. (1939). Seasonal variations in the gonadotropic hormone content of the rabbit pituitary. *Endocrinology*, **24**, 626.

Fries, S. (1879). Über die Fortpflanzung der einheimischen Chiropteren. *Zool. Anz.*, **2**, 355.

—— (1880). Über die Fortpflanzung von *Meles taxus*. *Zool. Anz.*, **3**, 486.

Fritz, B. (1937). Kanadische Winke für Nerzzüchter. *Dtsch. Pelztierz.*, **12**, 128.

Gander, F. F. (1929). Experiences with wood rats, *Neotoma fuscipes macrotis*. *J. Mammal.*, **10**, 52.

Gans, O. (1939). Untersuchungen über den Zyklus der Stuten. V. Beitrag: Eierstöcke und Gebärmutter. (Quoted in *Vet. Bull.*, Weybridge, 1943, **13**, 224.)

Gardner, W. U. (1936). Sexual dimorphism of the pelvis of the mouse, the effect of oestrogenic hormones upon the pelvis and upon the development of scrotal hernias. *Amer. J. Anat.*, **59**, 459.

GATES, W. H. (1936). Keeping bats in captivity. *J. Mammal.*, **17**, 268.

GEAR, H. S. (1926). The oestrous cycle of the baboon. *S. Afr. J. Sci.*, **23**, 706.

GEOFFROY SAINT-HILAIRE, E. (1829). *Cours de l'histoire naturelle des Mammifères.* Paris.

GERLINGER, H. (1927). *Le cycle sexuel chez la femelle des mammifères. Recherches sur la chienne.* Strasbourg.

GIANINI, C. A. (1932). Birth date of the mule deer. *J. Mammal.*, **13**, 80.

GIBSON, J. R., & MCKEOWN, T. (1950). Observations on all births (23,970) in Birmingham. I—Duration of gestation. *Brit. J. soc. Med.*, **4**, 221.

GILBERT, C., & GILLMAN, J. (1951). Pregnancy in the baboon (*Papio ursinus*). *S. Afr. J. med. Sci.*, **16**, 115.

GILLMAN, J. (1935). The cyclical changes in the external genital organs of the baboon (*P. porcarius*). *S. Afr. J. Sci.*, **32**, 342.

—— (1937). The cyclical changes in the vaginal smear in the baboon and its relationship in the perineal swelling. *S. Afr. J. med. Sci.*, **2**, 44.

—— & GILBERT, C. (1946). The reproductive cycle of the chacma baboon (*Papio ursinus*) with special reference to the problems of menstrual irregularities as assessed by the behaviour of the sex skin. *S. Afr. J. med. Sci.*, **11** (Biol. Suppl.), 1.

GODET, R. (1947). Variations périodiques de l'interstitielle médullaire dans l'ovaire de la taupe. *C. R. Soc. Biol., Paris*, **141**, 1102.

—— (1949). Recherches d'anatomie, d'embryologie normale et expérimentale sur l'appareil génital de la taupe (*Talpa europaea* L.). *Bull. biol.*, **83**, 25.

GOLDZIEHER, J. W., & HAMBLEN, E. C. (1947). Characteristics of the normal menstrual cycle. *Amer. J. Obstet. Gynec.*, **54**, 668.

GOODMAN, L., & WISLOCKI, G. B. (1935). Cyclical uterine bleeding in a new world monkey (*Ateles geoffroyi*). *Anat. Rec.*, **61**, 379.

GRANGE, W. B. (1932). Observations on the snowshoe hare, *Lepus americanus phaeonotus* Allen. *J. Mammal.*, **13**, 1.

GRANT, R. (1933). Occurrence of ovulation without 'heat' in ewe. *Nature, Lond.*, **131**, 802.

—— (1934). Studies on the physiology of reproduction in the ewe. Part I. The symptoms, periodicity, and duration of oestrus. Part II. Changes in the vagina and cervix. Part III. Gross changes in the ovaries. *Trans. Roy. Soc. Edinb.*, **58**, 1.

GREEN, C. V. (1932). Breeding habits in captivity of *Mus bactrianus* Blyth. *J. Mammal.*, **13**, 45.

GREEN, J. D., & HARRIS, G. W. (1947). The neurovascular link between the neuro-hypophysis and adenohypophysis. *J. Endocrinol.*, **5**, 136.

—— —— (1949). Observation of the hypophysio-portal vessels of the living rat. *J. Physiol.*, **108**, 359.

GREEP, R. O. (1941). Effects of hysterectomy and of oestrogen treatment on volume changes in the corpora lutea of pregnant rabbits. *Anat. Rec.*, **80**, 465.

GREULICH, W. W. (1934). Artificially induced ovulation in the cat (*Felis domestica*). *Anat. Rec.* **58**, 217.

—— (1952). A probable case of human ovulation on day six of the menstrual cycle. *Anat. Rec.*, **112**, 336.

GRIFFITHS, T. (1890). Observations on the function of the prostate gland in man and the lower animals. II. *J. Anat. Physiol.*, **24**, 27. (Quoted by Marshall, F. H. A., 1911.)

GRIFFITHS, W. F. B., & AMOROSO, E. C. (1939). Prooestrus, oestrus, ovulation and mating in the greyhound bitch. *Vet. Rec.*, **51**, 1279.

GRIMPE, G. (1917). Hyänologische Studien. *Zool. Anz.*, **48**, 49.

GRINNELL, J. (1932). Habitat relations of the giant kangaroo rat. *J. Mammal.*, **13**, 305.

—— DIXON, J. S., & LINSDALE, J. M. (1937). *Fur bearing mammals of California.* Berkeley.

GROHMANN (1904). *Sport in the Alps.* Edinburgh. (Quoted by Marshall, F. H. A., 1922.)

GROOME, J. R. (1940). The seasonal modification of the interstitial tissue of the testis in the fruit-bat (*Pteropus*). *Proc. zool. Soc. Lond.* A, **110**, 37.

GROS, G. (1935). Evolution de la muqueuse utérine chez la chatte. *C. R. Soc. Biol., Paris*, **118**, 1575.

GROS, G. (1936). Contribution a l'endocrinologie sexuelle. Le cycle génital de la chatte. *These, Université d'Alger. No. 21.*

GROSSER, O. (1903). Die physiologische bindegewebige Atresie des Genitalkanals von *Vesperugo noctula* nach erfolgter Kohabitation. *Anat. Anz.,* **23,** 129. (Quoted by Hartman, C. G., 1933.)

GULDBERG, G., & NANSEN, F. (1904). *On the structure and development of the whale.* Bergen. (Quoted by Marshall, F. H. A., 1922.)

GUNN, D. L., JENKIN, P. M., & GUNN, A. L. (1937). Menstrual periodicity ; statistical observations on a large sample of normal cases. *J. Obstet. Gynaec., Brit. Emp.,* **44,** 839.

GUSTAVSON, R. G., MASON, L. W., HAYS, E. E., WOOD, T. R., & D'AMOUR, F. E. (1938). Quantitative determination of estrogenic substances in normal female urine during menstrual cycle. *Amer. J. Obstet. Gynec.,* **35,** 115.

GUTHKELCH, A. N., & ZUCKERMAN, S. (1937a). Concentration of the blood in relation to the menstrual cycle in monkeys. *J. Physiol.,* **89,** 51 P.

—— —— (1937b). The red cell count of macaques in relation to the menstrual cycle. *J. Physiol.,* **91,** 269.

GUTHRIE, M. J. (1933a). Notes on the seasonal movements and habits of some cave bats. *J. Mammal.,* **14,** 1.

—— (1933b). The reproductive cycles of some cave bats. *J. Mammal.,* **14,** 199.

—— & JEFFERS, K. R. (1938). Growth of follicles in the ovaries of the bat *Myotis lucifugus lucifugus. Anat. Rec.,* **71,** 477.

HABIB, G. G. (1950). Studies on the response of anoestrous male and female ferrets to added illumination. B.Sc. Thesis, University of Birmingham.

HAFEZ, E. S. E. (1951). Mating behaviour in sheep. *Nature, Lond.,* **167,** 777.

HAIN, A. M. (1934). The effect of suckling on the duration of pregnancy in the rat (Wistar Albino). *J. exp. Biol.,* **11,** 279.

—— (1947a). Constitutional type of precocious puberty. *J. clin. Endocrinol.,* **7,** 171.

—— (1947b). The excretion of 17-ketosteroids and gonadotrophin in children : normal and abnormal cases. *Arch. Dis. Child.,* **22,** 152.

HALL, E. R. (1942). Gestation period in the fisher with recommendations for the animal's protection in California. *Calif. Fish. and Game,* **28,** 143. (Quoted by Pearson, O. P., & Enders, R. K., 1944.)

—— & LINSDALE, J. M. (1929). Notes on the life history of the kangaroo mouse (*Microdipodops*). *J. Mammal.,* **10,** 298.

HALL, K. (1947). The effects of pregnancy and relaxin on the histology of the pubic symphysis in the mouse. *J. Endocrinol.,* **5,** 174.

—— & NEWTON, W. H. (1946). The normal course of separation of the pubes in pregnant mice. *J. Physiol.,* **104,** 346.

HAMAN, J. O. (1942). The length of the menstrual cycle. A study of 150 normal women. *Amer. J. Obstet. Gynec.,* **43,** 870.

HAMBLEN, E. C. (1947). *Endocrinology of woman.* Springfield, Ill.

HAMILTON, C. E. (1949). Observations on the cervical mucosa of the rhesus monkey. *Contr. Embryol. Carneg. Instn.,* **33,** 81.

HAMILTON, J. E. (1934). The southern sea lion, *Otaria bryonia* (de Blainville). *Discovery Rep.,* **8,** 269.

HAMILTON, W. J., Jr. (1929). Breeding habits of the short-tailed shrew, *Blarina brevicauda. J. Mammal.,* **10,** 125.

—— (1931). Habits of the star-nosed mole, *Condylura cristata. J. Mammal.,* **12,** 345.

—— (1944). The biology of the little short-tailed shrew, *Cryptotis parva. J. Mammal.,* **25,** 1.

HAMLETT, G. W. D. (1932a). The reproductive cycle in the armadillo. *Z. wiss. Zool.,* **141,** 143.

—— (1932b). Observations on the embryology of the badger. *Anat. Rec.,* **53,** 283.

—— (1934). Uterine bleeding in a bat, *Glossophaga soricina. Anat. Rec.,* **60,** 9.

—— (1935a). Delayed implantation and discontinuous development in the mammals. *Quart. Rev. Biol.,* **10,** 432.

HAMLETT, G. W. D. (1935b). Breeding habits of the phyllostomid bats. *J. Mammal.*, **16,** 146.

—— (1937). Positive Friedman tests in the pregnant rhesus monkey, *Macaca mulatta. Amer. J. Physiol.*, **118,** 664.

—— (1938). The reproductive cycle of the coyote. *U.S. Dept. Agric. Techn. Bull.*, 616.

—— (1939). Reproduction in American monkeys. I. Oestrous cycle, ovulation and menstruation in *Cebus. Anat. Rec.*, **73,** 171.

HAMMOND, J. (1925). *Reproduction in the rabbit.* London.

—— (1927). *The physiology of reproduction in the cow.* Cambridge.

—— (1928). Die Kontrolle der Fruchtbarkeit bei Tieren. *Züchtungskunde*, **3,** 523.

—— (1930). The control of fertility in the rabbit. *World's Poultry Congr.*, 876.

—— (1933). Factors producing sterility, with special reference to genetic causes. *Proc. R. Soc. Med.*, **26,** 1183.

—— (1934a). The fertilisation of rabbit ova in relation to time. A method of controlling the litter size, the duration of pregnancy and the weight of the young at birth. *J. exp. Biol.*, **11,** 140.

—— (1934b). The inheritance of fertility in the rabbit. *Harper Adams Util. Poult. J.*, **19,** 557.

—— (1938a). Recent scientific research on horse breeding problems. *Trans. Yorks. agric. Soc.*, **95,** 11.

—— (1938b). Oestrus and ovulation in the mare. *Sechenov J. Physiol. U.S.S.R.*, **21,** 193.

—— (1941). Fertility in mammals and birds. *Biol. Rev.*, **16,** 165.

—— (1946a). The induction of ovulation in domestic animals. In *The problem of fertility.* Ed. E. T. Engle. Princeton.

—— (1946b). Methods for determining the time of ovulation in domestic animals. In *The problem of fertility.* Ed. E. T. Engle. Princeton.

—— (1952). In *Marshall's physiology of reproduction* ; 3rd ed., Vol. II. London.

—— & ASDELL, S. A. (1926). The vitality of the spermatozoa in the male and female reproductive tracts. *Brit. J. exp. Biol.*, **4,** 155.

—— & MARSHALL, F. H. A. (1930). Oestrus and pseudopregnancy in the ferret. *Proc. Roy. Soc.* B, **105,** 607.

—— & WALTON, A. (1934a). Notes on ovulation and fertilization in the ferret. *J. exp. Biol.*, **11,** 307.

—— —— (1934b). Pregnancy during the anoestrous season in the ferret. *J. exp. Biol.*, **11,** 320.

—— & WODZICKI, K. (1941). Anatomical and histological changes during the oestrous cycle in the mare. *Proc. Roy. Soc.* B, **130,** 1.

HAMMOND, J., Jr. (1944). On the breeding season in the sheep. *J. agric. Sci.*, **34,** 97.

—— (1951). Control by light of reproduction in ferrets and mink. *Nature, Lond.*, **167,** 150.

—— & BHATTACHARYA, P. (1944). Control of ovulation in the cow. *J. agric. Sci.*, **34,** 1.

—— HAMMOND, J., & PARKES, A. S. (1942). Hormonal augmentation of fertility in sheep. I. Induction of ovulation, superovulation and heat in sheep. *J. agric. Sci.*, **32,** 308.

HANCOCK, J. L., & ROWLANDS, I. W. (1949). The physiology of reproduction in the dog. *Vet. Rec.*, **61,** 771.

HANSSON, A. (1947). The physiology of reproduction in mink (*Mustela vison* Schreb.) with special reference to delayed implantation. *Acta zool., Stockh.*, **28,** 1.

HARPER, F. (1929). Mammal notes from Randolph County, Georgia. *J. Mammal*, **10,** 84.

HARRIS, G. W. (1936). The induction of pseudopregnancy in the rat by electrical stimulation through the head. *J. Physiol.*, **87,** 1 P.

—— (1937). The induction of ovulation in the rabbit, by electrical stimulation of the hypothalamo-hypophysial mechanism. *Proc. Roy. Soc.* B, **122,** 374.

—— (1948a). Electrical stimulation of the hypothalamus and the mechanism of neural control of the adenohypophysis. *J. Physiol.*, **107,** 418.

—— (1948b). Neural control of the pituitary gland. *Physiol. Rev.*, **28,** 139.

—— (1949). The relationship of the nervous system to (a) the neurohypophysis and (b) the adenohypophysis. *J. Endocrinol.*, **6,** xvii.

HARRIS, G. W. (1950).   Hypothalamo-hypophysial connexions in the *Cetacea.   J. Physiol.*, **111**, 361.

HARRISON, R. J. (1946).   The early development of the corpus luteum in the mare. *J. Anat., Lond.*, **80**, 160.

—— (1948).   The changes occurring in the ovary of the goat during the oestrous cycle and in early pregnancy.   *J. Anat., Lond.*, **82**, 21.

—— (1949).   Observations on the female reproductive organs of the Ca'ing whale, *Globiocephala malaena* Traill.   *J. Anat., Lond.*, **83**, 238.

—— MATTHEWS, L. H., & ROBERTS, J. M. (1951).   Reproduction in some Pinnipedia. *Trans. zool. Soc. Lond.*, **27**, 437.

HART, D. S. (1951).   Photoperiodicity in the female ferret.   *J. exp. Biol.*, **28**, 1.

HARTMAN, C. G. (1920).   Studies on the development of the opossum *Didelphys virginiana* L. V. The phenomena of parturition.   *Anat. Rec.*, **19**, 251.

—— (1923a).   Breeding habits, development, and birth of the opossum.   *Rep. Smithson. Instn. 1921*, 347.

—— (1923b).   The oestrous cycle in the opossum.   *Amer. J. Anat.*, **32**, 353.

—— (1928a).   The breeding season of the opossum (*Didelphis virginiana*) and the rate of intrauterine and postnatal development.   *J. Morph.*, **46**, 143.

—— (1928b).   A readily detectable sign of ovulation in the monkey.   *Science*, **68**, 452.

—— (1928c).   The period of gestation in the monkey, *Macacus rhesus*, first description of parturition in monkeys, size and behaviour of the young.   *J. Mammal.*, **9**, 181.

—— (1929).   Uterine bleeding as an early sign of pregnancy in the monkey (*Macacus rhesus*) together with observations on the fertile period of the menstrual cycle. *Johns Hopk. Hosp. Bull.*, **44**, 155.

—— (1931a).   On the relative sterility of the adolescent organism.   *Science*, **74**, 226.

—— (1931b).   The breeding season in monkeys, with special reference to *Pithecus (macacus) rhesus.   J. Mammal.*, **12**, 129.

—— (1932).   Studies in the reproduction of the monkey (*Macacus (Pithecus) rhesus*, with special reference to menstruation and pregnancy.   *Contrib. Embryol. Carneg. Instn.*, **23**, 1.

—— (1933a).   On the survival of spermatozoa in the female genital tract of the bat. *Quart. Rev. Biol.*, **8**, 185.

—— (1933b).   Pelvic (rectal) palpation of the female monkey, with special reference to the ascertainment of ovulation time.   *Amer. J. Obstet. Gynec.*, **26**, 600.

—— (1936).   *Time of ovulation in women.*   London.

—— (1938a).   Some observations on the bonnet macaque.   *J. Mammal.*, **19**, 468.

—— (1938b).   Menstruation without ovulation (" Pseudomenstruation ") : incidence and treatment, with special reference to the rhesus monkey.   In *Les Hormones Sexuelles.*   Ed. L. Brouha.   Paris.

—— (1939).   Studies on reproduction in the monkey and their bearing on gynecology and anthropology.   *Endocrinology*, **25**, 670.

—— (1941).   Non-effect of ovariectomy on the twenty-fifth day of pregnancy in the rhesus monkey.   *Proc. Soc. exp. Biol., N.Y.*, **48**, 221.

—— (1942).   Contributions of studies on primate animals to gynecological thought. *Amer. J. Obstet. Gynec.*, **44**, 156.

—— (1943).   Birth of a two-headed monster in the rhesus monkey.   *Science*, **98**, 449.

—— (1944).   Recovery of primate eggs and embryos ; methods and data on time of ovulation.   *West. J. Surg.*, **52**, 41.

—— & CORNER, G. W. (1941).   The first maturation division of the macaque ovum. *Contr. Embryol. Carneg. Instn.*, **29**, 1.

—— & CUYLER, W. K. (1927).   Is the supposed long life of the bat spermatozoa fact or fable ?   *Anat. Rec.*, **35**, 39.

—— SQUIER, R. R., & TINKLEPAUGH, O. L. (1930).   The fetal heart rate in the monkey (*Macacas rhesus*).   *Proc. Soc. exp. Biol., N.Y.*, **28**, 285.

—— & STRAUS, W. L., Jr. (1939).   Relaxation of the pelvic ligaments in pregnant monkeys. *Amer. J. Obstet. Gynec.*, **37**, 498.

HATERIUS, H. O. (1933).   Partial sympathectomy and induction of pseudopregnancy. *Amer. J. Physiol.*, **103**, 97.

HATERIUS, H. O. (1934). The genital-pituitary pathway. Non-effect of stimulation of superior cervical sympathetic ganglia. *Proc. Soc. exp. Biol., N.Y.*, **31**, 1112.

HATFIELD, D. M. (1935). A natural history study of *Microtus californicus*. *J. Mammal.*, **16**, 261.

HAYASI, K. (1927). Über den Zeitpunkt des Eintretens der Geschlechtsreife beim Seiwal und über den Follikelinhalt des Seiwalovariums. *Jap. J. med. Sci. (Biochem.)*, **1**, 221.

HEAPE, W. (1894). The menstruation of *Semnopithecus entellus*. *Philos. Trans.* B, **185**, 411.

—— (1896). The menstruation and ovulation of *Macacus rhesus*. *Proc. Roy. Soc.*, **60**, 202.

—— (1897). The menstruation and ovulation of *Macacus rhesus*, with observations on the changes undergone by the discharged follicle.—Part II. *Philos. Trans.* B, **188**, 135.

—— (1900). The " sexual season " of mammals, and the relation of the " pro-oestrum " to menstruation. *Quart. J. micr. Sci.*, **44**, 1.

—— (1905). Ovulation and degeneration of ova in the rabbit. *Proc. Roy. Soc.* B, **76**, 260.

—— (1908). Notes on the proportion of the sexes in dogs. *Proc. Camb. phil. Soc.*, 14.

HECKEL, G. P., & ALLEN, W. M. (1938). Prolongation of pregnancy in the rabbit by the injection of progesterone. *Amer. J. Obstet. Gynec.*, **35**, 131.

—— —— (1939). Maintenance of the corpus luteum and inhibition of parturition in the rabbit by injection of estrogenic hormone. *Endocrinology*, **24**, 137.

HEDIGER, H. (1948). Die Zucht des Feldhasen (*Lepus europaeus* Pallas) in Gefangenschaft. *Physiol. comp. oecol.* **1**, 46.

—— (1950). *Wild animals in captivity*. London.

HEDIN, S. (1903). *Central Asia and Tibet*. London.

HEER, R. (1939). Untersuchungen über den Zyklus der Stute. II. Beitrag : Eierstöcke und Gebärmutter. (Quoted in *Vet. Bull., Weybridge*, 1943, **13**, 223.)

HELLER, E. (1930). Polar bears reared in Milwaukee. *Bull. Wash. Park Zool. Soc., Milwaukee*, 1.

HENRY, J. S., & BROWNE, J. S. L. (1943). The contractions of the human uterus during the menstrual cycle. The effect of progesterone and posterior pituitary extract upon the motility of the human uterus. *Amer. J. Obstet. Gynec.*, **45**, 927.

—— —— & VENNING, E. H. (1950). Some observations on the relations of estrogens and progesterone to the contractions of the nonpregnant and pregnant human uterus. *Amer. J. Obstet. Gynec.*, **60**, 471.

HERREN, R. Y., & HATERIUS, H. O. (1932). On the mechanism of certain ovarian hormonal influences on the central nervous system. *Amer. J. Physiol.*, **100**, 533.

HERTER, K. (1933). Gefangenschaftsbeobachtungen an europäischen Igeln. II. *Z. Säugetierk.*, **8**, 195.

—— (1938). *Die Biologie der europäischen Igel*. Leipzig. (Quoted by Feremutsch, K., & Strauss, F., 1949.)

HERTIG, A. T., & ROCK, T. (1944). On the development of the early human ovum, with special reference to the trophoblast of the pre-villous stage : a description of 7 normal and 5 pathological human ova. *Amer. J. Obstet. Gynec.*, **47**, 149.

—— —— (1945). Two human ova of the pre-villous stage, having a developmental age of about seven and nine days respectively. *Contr. Embryol. Carneg. Instn.*, **31**, 65.

—— —— (1946). On a human blastula recovered from the uterine cavity 4 days after ovulation. *Anat. Rec.*, **94**, 469.

—— —— (1949). Two human ova of the pre-villous stage, having a developmental age of about eight and nine days respectively. *Contr. Embryol. Carneg. Instn.*, **33**, 169.

HERWERDEN, M. A. VAN (1905). *Bijdrage tot de Kennis van den menstrueelen Cyclus*. Leiden.

—— (1925). Some remarks on the polyoestrus of primates. *Anat. Rec.*, **30**, 221.

HIBBARD, C. W. (1935). Breeding seasons of gray squirrel and flying squirrel. *J. Mammal.*, **16**, 325.

HILL, C. J. (1933). The development of *Monotremata*. Part I. The histology of the oviduct during gestation. *Trans. zool. Soc. Lond.*, **21**, 413.

HILL, J. P. (1918). Some observations on the early development of *Didelphis aurita*. Contributions to the embryology of the Marsupialia—V. *Quart. J. micr. Sci.*, 63, 91.

—— & GATENBY, J. B. (1926). The corpus luteum of the Monotremata. *Proc. zool. Soc. Lond.*, **1926**, 715.

—— & O'DONOGHUE, C. H. (1912). The reproductive cycle in the marsupial *Dasyurus viverrinus*. *Quart. J. micr. Sci.*, **59**, 133.

—— & TRIBE, M. (1924). The early development of the cat (*Felis domestica*). *Quart. J. micr. Sci.*, **68**, 513.

HILL, M. (1939). The reproductive cycle of the male weasel (*Mustela nivalis*). *Proc. zool. Soc. Lond.* B, **109**, 481.

—— & PARKES, A. S. (1931). Studies on ovulation. IV. Induction of ovulation in the hypophysectomised rabbit by administration of anterior lobe extracts. *J. Physiol.*, **71**, 36.

—— —— (1932). Studies on the hypophysectomised ferret. I. Technique. *Proc. Roy. Soc.* B, **112**, 138.

—— —— (1934). Effect of absence of light on the breeding season of the ferret. *Proc. Roy. Soc.* B, **115**, 14.

—— & WHITE, W. E. (1933). The growth and regression of follicles in the oestrous rabbit. *J. Physiol.*, **80**, 174.

HILL, R. T. (1935). Variation in the activity of the rabbit hypophysis during the reproductive cycle *J. Physiol.*, **83**, 129.

HILL, W. C. O. (1932). The external characters of the bonnet monkeys of India and Ceylon. *Ceylon J. Sci.* B, **16**, 311.

—— (1933). A monograph on the genus *Loris*. With an account of the external, cranial and dental characters of the genus : a revision of the known forms ; and the description of a new form from Northern Ceylon. *Ceylon J. Sci.* B, **18**, 89.

—— (1935). Breeding of *Loris* in captivity. *Nature, Lond.*, **136**, 107.

—— (1936a). Supplementary observations on purple-faced leaf-monkeys (genus *Kasi*). *Ceylon J. Sci.* B, **20**, 115.

—— (1936b). On a hybrid leaf-monkey, with remarks on the breeding of leaf-monkeys in general. *Ceylon J. Sci.* B, **20**, 135.

—— (1937a). On the breeding and rearing of certain species of primates in captivity. *Ceylon J. Sci.* B, **20**, 369.

—— (1937b). Treatment of the slender loris in captivity. *Loris*, **1**, 85.

—— (1937c). Longevity in a macaque. *Ceylon J. Sci.* B, **20**, 255.

—— (1939a). The menstrual cycle of the toque macaque (*Macaca sinica* Linn.), with observations on its uterine structure, compared with that of other macaques. *Ceylon J. Sci.* D, **5**, 21.

—— (1939b). An annotated systematic list of the leaf-monkeys. *Ceylon J. Sci.* B, **21**, 277.

—— (1939c). A new leaf-monkey hybrid (*Trachypithecus obscurus flavicauda* ♂ × *Semnopithecus priam thersites* ♀). *Ceylon J. Sci.* B, **21**, 265.

—— (1941). Reproduction in capuchin monkeys. *Nature, Lond.*, **148**, 408.

—— & MATTHEWS, L. H. (1949). The male external genitalia of the gorilla, with remarks on the os penis of other Hominoidea. *Proc. zool. Soc. Lond.*, **119**, 363.

—— PORTER, A., & SOUTHWICK, M. D. (1952). The natural history, endoparasites and pseudoparasites of the tarsier (*Tarsius carbonarius*). *Proc. zool. Soc. Lond.*, **122**, 79.

HINGSTON, R. W. G. (1920). *A naturalist in Himalaya*. London. (Quoted by Zuckerman, S., 1930.)

HINSEY, J. C., & MARKEE, J. E. (1933a). Studies on prolan-induced ovulation in mid-brain and mid-brain-hypophysectomised rabbits. *Amer. J. Physiol.*, **106**, 48.

—— —— (1933b). Pregnancy following bilateral section of the cervical sympathetic trunks in the rabbit. *Proc. Soc. exp. Biol.*, N.Y., **31**, 270.

HINTERTHÜR, E. (1933). Die Tragezeit der Ziege. *Züchtungskunde*, **8**, 55.

HIRT, E. (1943). Über den Brunstzyklus und die Unfruchtbarkeit der Stute. *Schweiz. Arch. Tierh.*, **85**, 353. (Quoted in *Vet. Bull.*, Weybridge, 1945, **15**, 274.)

HISAW, F. L. (1925). The influence of the ovary on the resorption of the pubic bones of the pocket gopher, *Geomys bursarius* (Shaw). *J. exp. Zool.*, **42**, 411.

HISAW, F. L. (1926). Experimental relaxation of the pubic ligament in the guinea pig. *Proc. Soc. exp. Biol., N.Y.*, **23**, 661.

—— (1929). The corpus luteum hormone. I. Experimental relaxation of the pelvic ligaments in the guinea-pig. *Physiol. Zoöl.*, **2**, 59.

—— ZARROW, M. X., MONEY, W. L., TALMAGE, R. V. N., & ABRAMOWITZ, A. A. (1944). Importance of the female reproductive tract in the formation of relaxin. *Endocrinology*, **34**, 122.

HOOKER, C. W., & FORBES, T. R. (1947). A bio-assay for minute amounts of progesterone. *Endocrinology*, **41**, 158.

—— —— (1949). The transport of progesterone in blood. *Endocrinology*, **44**, 61.

HOPKINS, F. G. (1911). A note on the chemistry of the vesicular fluid of the hedgehog. *J. Physiol.*, **43**, 259.

The Hormones. Physiology, chemistry and applications (1948 ; 1950). Vols. 1, 2. Ed. G. Pincus & K. V. Thimann. New York.

HORN, E. E. (1923). Some notes concerning the breeding habits of *Thomomys townsendi*, observed near Vale, Malheur County, Oregon, during the spring of 1921. *J. Mammal.*, **4**, 37.

HORST, C. J VAN DER (1941). On the size of the litter and the gestation period of *Procavia capensis. Science*, **93**, 430.

—— (1943). The mechanism of egg transport from the ovary to the uterus in *Elephantulus S. Afr. J. med. Sci.*, **8**, 41.

—— (1944). Remarks on the systematics of *Elephantulus. J. Mammal.*, **25**, 77.

—— & GILLMAN J. (1940a). Mechanism of ovulation and corpus luteum formation in *Elephantulus. Nature, Lond.*, **145**, 974.

—— —— (1940b). Ovulation and corpus luteum formation in *Elephantulus. S. Afr. J. med. Sci.*, **5**, 73.

—— —— (1941a). The menstrual cycle in *Elephantulus. S. Afr. J. med. Sci.*, **6**, 27.

—— —— (1941b). The number of eggs and surviving embryos in *Elephantulus. Anat Rec.*, **80**, 443.

—— —— (1942a). Pre-implantation phenomena in the uterus of *Elephantulus. S. Afr. J. med. Sci.*, **7**, 47.

—— —— (1942b). A critical analysis of the early gravid and pre-menstrual phenomena in the uterus of *Elephantulus, Macaca,* and the human female. *S. Afr. J. med. Sci.*, **7**, 134.

—— —— (1944). On abnormal blastulas in *Elephantulus. Anat. Rec.*, **90**, 101.

HOWARD, E. (1930). The X-zone of the suprarenal cortex in relation to gonadal maturation in monkeys and mice and to epiphyseal unions in monkeys. *Anat. Rec.*, **46**, 93.

HOWELL, A. B. (1926). Voles of the genus *Phenacomys*. I. Revision of genus *Phenacomys*. II. Revision of the red tree mouse (*Phenacomys longicaudus*). Washington.

HUBBARD, W. D. (1926). Notes on the antelopes and zebra of northern Rhodesia and Portuguese East Africa. *J. Mammal.*, **7**, 184.

HUNDLEY, G. (1928). Twin elephant calves. *J. Bombay nat. Hist. Soc.*, **32**, 214.

HVASS, H (1932). Von der indischen Elefantin Ellen und ihren drei in Gefangenschaft geborenen Jungen. *Zool. Gart., Lpz.*, **5**, 191.

ISHII, O. (1920). Observations on the sexual cycle of the guinea-pig. *Biol. Bull., Wood's Hole*, **38**, 237.

—— (1922). Observations on the sexual cycle of the white rat. *Anat. Rec.*, **23**, 311.

IVY, A. C., HARTMAN, C. G., & KOFF, A. (1931). The contractions of the monkey uterus at term. *Amer. J. Obstet. Gynec.*, **22**, 388.

JACKSON, H. H. T. (1928). A taxonomic review of the American long-tailed shrews (Genera *Sorex* and *Microsorex*). *N. Amer. Fauna* No. 51.

JAYLE, M. F., & CRÉPY, O. (1952). The excretion and measurement of urinary phenol-steroids. *Ciba Foundation Colloquia on Endocrinology*, **2**, 84.

JEFFCOATE, T. N. A (1935). Sterility due to ovarian dysfunction. *Brit. med. J.*, **1**, 345.

JOACHIMOVITS, R. (1928). Studien zu Menstruation, Ovulation, Aufbau und Pathologie des weiblichen Genitales bei Mensch und Affe (Pithecus fascicularis mordax). Biol. gen., **4**, 447.

JOHANSSON, I. (1940). Minkens Fortplanting. Varapälsdjur., **11**, 73. (Quoted by Pearson, O. P., & Enders, R. K., 1944.)

JOHNSON, G. E., FOSTER, M. A., & COCO, R. M. (1933). The sexual cycle of the thirteen-lined ground squirrel in the laboratory. Trans. Kans. Acad. Sci., **36**, 250. (Quoted by Ruth, E. B., 1934.)

—— GANN, E. L., FOSTER, M. A., & COCO, R. M. (1934). The effect of daily heteropituitary implants into adult but sexually inactive male ground squirrels. Endocrinology, **18**, 86.

JONES, F. WOOD (1921). On the habits of Trichosurus vulpecula. J. Mammal., **2**, 187.

—— (1923–25). The mammals of South Australia. Adelaide.

—— (1944). Some curiosities of mammalian reproduction. Part I.—Mammals that have triumphed over anatomical handicaps. Part II. Concerning the life of the sperm. J. Obstet. Gynaec., Brit. Emp., **51**, 416 ; 553.

—— (1945). Some curiosities of mammalian reproduction. Part III.—Mammals that produce uniovular litters. J. Obstet. Gynaec., Brit. Emp., **52**, 55.

JUROW, H. N. (1943). Cyclic variations in the cervix of guinea-pig Amer. J. Obstet. Gynec., **45**, 762.

KAISER, I. H. (1947a). Histological appearance of coiled arterioles in the endometrium of rhesus monkey, baboon, chimpanzee and gibbon. Anat. Rec., **99**, 199.

—— (1947b). Absence of coiled arterioles in the endometrium of menstruating New World monkeys. Anat. Rec. **99**, 353.

KAKUSHKINA, E. A. (1937). The normal reproductive cycle of silver foxes. Bull. Biol. Med. Exp. **4**, 26.

KARK, E. (1943). Menarche in South African Bantu girls. S. Afr. J. med. Sci., **8**, 35.

KEIBEL, F. (1902). Die Entwicklung des Rehes bis zur Anlage des Mesoblast. (Quoted by Prell, H., 1938.)

KELLEY, R. B. (1937). Studies in fertility of sheep. Bull. Coun. sci. industr. Res. Aust. No. 112.

KELLY, G. L. (1939). Effect of opening of the ovarian bursa on fecundity in the albino rat. Anat. Rec., **73**, 401.

KENNETH, J. H. (1947). Gestation periods. 2nd ed. Imp. Bur. Anim. Breedg. Genet. Tech. Comm. 5.

KENT, G. C., Jr., & MIXNER, J. P. (1945). Use of vaginal smears in mating the golden hamster. Proc. Soc. exp. Biol., N.Y., **59**, 251.

—— & SMITH, R. A. (1945). A study of the estrous cycle in the golden hamster Cricetus (Mesocricetus) auratus Waterhouse. Anat. Rec., **92**, 263.

KIESLING, A. (1923). Studien zur Monographie der Schweizer Saanen-Ziege. Züchtungskunde B, **27**, 141.

KIMURA, G., & CORNWELL, W. S. (1938). The progestin content of the corpus luteum of the sow (Sus scrofa) during successive stages of the oestrous cycle and pregnancy. Amer. J. Physiol., **123**, 471.

KINDER, E. E. (1927). A study of the nest-building activity of the albino rat. J. exp. Zool., **47**, 117.

KING, H. D. (1913). Some anomalies in the gestation of the albino rat (Mus norvegicus albinus). Biol. Bull., Wood's Hole, **24**, 377.

—— (1927). Seasonal variations in fertility and in the sex ratio of mammals, with special reference to the rat. Arch. EntwMech. Org., **112**, 61.

KIRKHAM, W. B. (1916). The prolonged gestation period in suckling mice. Anat. Rec., **11**, 31.

—— (1918). Observations on the relation between suckling and the rate of embryonic development in mice. J. exp. Zool., **27**, 49.

KLEIN, M. (1947). Oestrogen level and ovarian hypophysial relationship during pseudopregnancy and pregnancy in the rabbit. J. Endocrinol., **5**, xxv.

KLUGH, A. B. (1927). Ecology of the red squirrel. J. Mammal., **8**, 1.

KNAUS, H. (1927). Experimentelle Untersuchungen zur Physiologie und Pharmakologie der Uterusmuskulatur in der Schwangerschaft. *Arch. exp. Path. Pharmak.*, **124,** 152.

—— (1929). Zur Physiologie des Corpus luteum. I. Mitteilung. *Arch. Gynaek.*, **138,** 201.

—— (1930a). Zur Physiologie des Corpus luteum. II. Mitteilung. *Arch. Gynaek.*, **140,** 181.

—— (1930b). Zur Physiologie des Corpus luteum. III. u. IV. Mitteilung. *Arch. Gynaek.*, **141,** 374 ; 395.

—— (1934). *Die periodische Fruchtbarkeit und Unfruchtbarkeit des Weibes.* Wien.

—— (1950). *Die Physiologie der Zeugung des Menschen.* 3. Aufl. Wien.

KOHLBRUGGE, J. H. F. (1904). Das bei der Menstruation ausgestossene Ei. 3. *Z. Morph. Anthr.*, **12,** 579. (Quoted by Hamlett, G. W. D., 1934.)

—— (1913). Befruchtung und Keimbildung bei der Fledermaus " *Xantharpya amplexicaudata.*" *Verh. Akad. Wet., Amst.* Sect. 2, *Deel 17*, 1.

KOLLER, P. C. (1936). Chromosome behaviour in the male ferret and mole during anoestrus. *Proc. Roy. Soc.* B, **121,** 192.

KORFF, K. VON (1939). Untersuchungen über den Zyklus der Stuten. IV. Beitrag : Äussere Rosse und Scheidenbild. (Quoted in *Vet. Bull., Weybridge*, 1943, **13,** 223.)

KRALLINGER, H. (1933). Untersuchungen über Geschlechtsleben und Fortpflanzung der Schweine. *Arch. Tierernähr. Tierz.*, **8,** 436.

KREHBIEL, R. H. (1941a). The effects of lactation on the implantation of ova of a concurrent pregnancy in the rat. *Anat. Rec.*, **81,** 43.

—— (1941b). The effects of theelin on delayed implantation in the pregnant lactating rat. *Anat. Rec.*, **81,** 381.

KROHN, P. L. (1949). Intermenstrual pain (the " Mittelschmerz ") and the time of ovulation. *Brit. med. J.*, **1,** 803.

—— & ZUCKERMAN, S. (1937). Water metabolism in relation to the menstrual cycle. *J. Physiol.*, **88,** 369.

KUNDE, M. M., & PROUD, T. (1929). The ineffectiveness of vaginal smears in predicting the oestrous cycle in the rabbit. *Amer. J. Physiol.*, **88,** 446.

KÜPFER, M. (1928). The sexual cycle of female domesticated mammals. The ovarian changes and the periodicity of oestrum in cattle, sheep, goats, pigs and horses. (Observations on animals in Central Europe and South Africa). 13th and 14th *Rep. vet. Res. S. Afr.*, Pt. 2, 1209.

KUTZ, R. L., McKEOWN, T., & SELYE, H. (1934). Effect of salt treatment on certain changes following adrenalectomy. *Proc. Soc. exp. Biol., N.Y.*, **32,** 331.

LABEREE, E. E. (1941). Breeding and reproduction in fur bearing animals. *Fur. Tr. J. Can.* (Quoted by Enders, R. K., & Pearson, O. P., 1943.)

LAMAR, J. K., SHETTLES, L. B., & DELFS, E. (1940). Cyclic penetrability of human cervical mucus to spermatozoa *in vitro*. *Amer. J. Physiol.*, **129,** 234.

The Lancet (1933). An investigation of the menopause in one thousand women. *Lancet*, i, 106.

LANGE, D. DE (1931). Distribution of different stages of pregnancy and of the oestrous cycle in *Tarsius spectrum*. *Rep. Hubrecht Lab.*, Utrecht.

LAQUEUR, G. L. (1945). Anatomical demonstration of anovulatory menstrual cycle. *Calif. West. Med.*, **63,** 268. (Quoted by Reynolds, S. R. M., 1949.)

LARSEN, M. S. (1947). The menstrual cycle length and variability of young adult women. *Amer. J. Obstet. Gynec.*, **54,** 1069.

LASS, P. M., SMELSER, J., & KURZROK, R. (1938). Studies relating to time of human ovulation. III. During lactation. *Endocrinology*, **23,** 39.

LATASTE, F. (1887). Recherches de zoöetique sur les mammifères de l'ordre des rongeurs. *Act. Soc. Linn., Bordeaux*, **10,** 291. (Quoted by Knaus, H., 1950.)

—— (1891). Des variations de durée de la gestation chez les mammifères et des circonstances qui déterminent ces variations. Théorie de la gestation retardée. *C. R. Soc. Biol., Paris*, **43,** 21.

LATZ, L. J., & REINER, E. (1942). Further studies on the sterile and fertile periods in women. *Amer. J. Obstet. Gynec.*, **43,** 74.

LAURIE, A. H. (1937).   The age of female blue whales and the effect of whaling on the stock. *Discovery Rep.*, **15**, 223.

LAURIE, E. M. O. (1946).   The reproduction of the house-mouse (*Mus musculus*).   *Proc. Roy. Soc.* B, **133**, 248.

LAW, R. G. (1930).   The mink in captivity.   Ontario Gov. Pamphlet.

LEONARD, A. G. (1894).   *The camel*.   London.

LESLIE, P. H., PERRY, J. S., & WATSON, J. S. (1945–46).   Determination of the median body weight at which female rats reach maturity.   *Proc. zool. Soc. Lond.*, **115**, 473.

LEVIN, L. (1941).   Quantitative precipitation of the urinary gonadotropin of normal men and women.   *Endocrinology*, **28**, 378.

LEWIS, W. H., & HARTMAN, C. G. (1933).   Early cleavage stages of the egg of the monkey. *Contr. Embryol. Carneg. Instn.*, **24**, 187.

—— —— (1941).   Tubal ova of the rhesus monkey.   *Contr. Embryol. Carneg. Instn.*, **29**, 7.

LICHE, H. (1939).   Oestrous cycle in the cat.   *Nature, Lond.*, **143**, 900.

—— & WODZICKI, K. (1939).   Vaginal smears and the oestrous cycle of the cat and lioness. *Nature, Lond.*, **144**, 245.

LINDSEY, A. A. (1937).   The Weddell seal in the Bay of Whales, Antarctica.   *J. Mammal.*, **18**, 127.

LINTON, R. G. (1907).   A contribution to the histology of the so-called Cowper's glands of the hedgehog.   *Anat. Anz.*, **31**, 61.   (Quoted by Eadie, W. R., 1948b.)

LLOYD, J. I. (1951).   When do otters breed ?   *The Field*, 1035.

LOEB, L. (1907).   Über die experimentelle Erzeugung von Knoten von Decidualgewebe in dem Uterus des Meerschweinchens nach stattgefundener Copulation.   *Zbl. allg. Path. path. Anat.*, **18**, 563.

—— (1911a).   The cyclic changes in the ovary of the guinea-pig.   *J. Morph.*, **22**, 37.

—— (1911b).   Über die Bedeutung des Corpus luteum für die Periodizität des sexuellen Zyklus beim weiblichen Säugetierorganismus.   *Dtsch. med. Wschr.*, **37**, 17.

—— (1914).   The correlation between the cyclic changes in the uterus and the ovaries in the guinea-pig.   *Biol. Bull., Wood's Hole*, **27**, 1.

—— (1917).   The relation of the ovary to the uterus and mammary gland from the experimental aspect.   *Surg. Gynec. Obstet.*, **25**, 300.

—— (1923).   The effect of extirpation of the uterus on the life and function of the corpus luteum in the guinea-pig.   *Proc. Soc. exp. Biol., N.Y.*, **20**, 441.

—— (1927).   The effects of hysterectomy on the system of sex organs and on the periodicity of the sexual cycle in the guinea-pig.   *Amer. J. Physiol.*, **83**, 202.

—— & SMITH, M. G. (1936).   The effect of hysterectomy on the duration of life and retrogression of the corpora lutea and on secondary sex organs in the rabbit.   *Amer. J. Anat.*, **58**, 1.

LONG, J. A., & EVANS, H. M. (1920).   A characteristic sign of pregnancy in the rat detectable from the thirteenth to the sixteenth day.   *Anat. Rec.*, **18**, 249.

—— —— (1921).   Further studies in the physiology of reproduction.   *Anat. Rec. (Abstr.)*, **21**, 56.

—— —— (1922).   The oestrous cycle in the rat and its associated phenomena.   *Mem. Univ. Calif.*, **6**.

LONGLEY, W. H. (1911).   The maturation of the egg and ovulation in the domestic cat. *Amer. J. Anat.*, **12**, 139.

LÖNNBERG, E. (1928).   Contributions to the biology and morphology of the badger, *Meles taxus*, and some other Carnivora.   *Ark. Zool.*, **19A** (No. 26).

LOWTHER, F. DE L. (1940).   A study of the activities of a pair of *Galago senegalensis moholi* in captivity, including the birth and post-natal development of twins.   *Zoologica, N.Y.*, **25**, 433.

LUCAS, N. S., HUME, E. M., & SMITH, H. H. (1927).   On the breeding of the common marmoset (*Hapale jacchus* Linn.) in captivity when irradiated with ultra-violet rays.   *Proc. zool. Soc. Lond.*, **1927**, 447.

LUCAS, N. S., HUME, E. M., & SMITH, H. H. (1937). On the breeding of the common marmoset (*Hapale jacchus* Linn.) in captivity when irradiated with ultra-violet rays. II. A ten years' family history. *Proc. zool. Soc. Lond.* A, **1937**, 205.

LYDEKKER, R. (1898a). *Wild oxen, sheep and goats of all lands.* London.

—— (1898b). *The deer of all lands.* London.

—— (1924). *The game animals of India.* 2nd ed. London.

LYON, M. W., Jr. (1903). Observations on the number of young of the lasiurine bats. *Proc. U. S. nat. Mus.*, **26**, 425.

MacGILLIVRAY, J. (1860). Zoological notes from Aneiteum. *Zoologist*, **18**, 7133.

MACKINTOSH, N. A. (1946). The natural history of whalebone whales. *Biol. Rev.*, **21**, 60.

—— & WHEELER, J. F. G. (1929). Southern blue and fin whales. *Discovery Rep.*, **1**, 257.

MAI, M. Y. CH'EN, & DYKE, H. B. VAN (1934). The hydrogen-ion concentration of the vaginal fluid during the menstrual cycle of the macaque. *Chin. J. Physiol.*, **8**, 203.

MAKEPEACE, A. W., WEINSTEIN, G. L., & FRIEDMAN, M. H. (1937). The effect of progestin and progesterone on ovulation in the rabbit *Amer. J. Physiol.*, **119**, 512.

—— —— —— (1938). Effect of coitus on gonadotropic content of pituitary glands of pseudopregnant rabbits. *Endocrinology*, **22**, 667.

MANN, T., & LUTWAK-MANN, C. (1951). Secretory function of male accessory organs of reproduction in mammals. *Physiol. Rev.*, **31**, 27.

MANWELL, E. J., & WICKENS, P. G. (1928). The mechanisms of ovulation and implantation in the domestic cat. *Anat. Rec. (Abstr.)*, **38**, 54.

MARKEE, J. E. (1947). The morphological and endocrine basis for menstrual bleeding. In *Progress in gynecology*. Ed. J. V. Meigs & S. H. Sturgis. London.

MARKEE, J. E., & HINSEY, J. C. (1935). A case of probable superfetation in the cat. *Anat. Rec.*, **61**, 241.

—— —— (1936). Observations on ovulation in the rabbit. *Anat. Rec.*, **64**, 309.

—— SAWYER, C. H., & HOLLINSHEAD, W. H. (1946). Activation of the anterior hypophysis by electrical stimulation in the rabbit. *Endocrinology*, **38**, 345.

MARKER, R. E., & HARTMAN, C. G. (1940). Assays of urine from rhesus monkeys for pregnanediol and other steroids. *J. biol. Chem.*, **133**, 529.

MARSHALL, A. J. (1948). The breeding cycle of an equatorial bat (*Pteropus giganteus* of Ceylon). *Proc. Linn. Soc., Lond.*, **159**, 103.

—— (1949). Pre-gestational changes in the giant fruit bat (*Pteropus giganteus*), with special reference to an asymmetric endometrial reaction. *Proc. Linn. Soc., Lond.*, **161**, 26.

MARSHALL, F. H. A. (1903). The oestrous cycle and the formation of the corpus luteum in the sheep. *Philos. Trans.* B, **196**, 47.

—— (1904). The oestrous cycle in the common ferret. *Quart. J. micr. Sci.*, **48**, 323.

—— (1911). The male generative cycle in the hedgehog ; with experiments on the functional correlation between the essential and accessory sexual organs. *J. Physiol.*, **43**, 247.

—— (1922). *The physiology of reproduction.* 2nd ed. London.

—— (1933). Cyclical changes in the vagina and vulva of the ferret. *Quart. J. exp. Physiol.*, **23**, 131.

—— (1936). The Croonian lecture ; sexual periodicity and the causes which determine it. *Philos. Trans.* B, **226**, 423.

—— (1937). On the change-over in the oestrous cycle in animals after transference across the equator, with further observations on the incidence of the breeding seasons and the factors controlling sexual periodicity. *Proc. Roy. Soc.* B, **122**, 413.

—— (1942). Exteroceptive factors in sexual periodicity. *Biol. Rev.*, **17**, 68.

—— & HALNAN, E. T. (1917). On the post-oestrous changes occurring in the generative organs and mammary glands of the non-pregnant dog. *Proc. Roy. Soc.* B, **89**, 546.

—— & JOLLY, W. A. (1906). Contributions to the physiology of mammalian reproduction. Part I. The oestrous cycle in the dog. *Philos. Trans.* B, **198**, 99.

—— & VERNEY, E. B. (1936). The occurrence of ovulation and pseudopregnancy in the rabbit as a result of central nervous stimulation. *J. Physiol.*, **86**, 327.

Marshall, F. H. A., Verney, E. B., & Vogt, M. (1939). The occurrence of ovulation in the rabbit as a result of stimulation of the central nervous system by drugs. *J. Physiol.*, **97**, 128.

Marshall, W. H., & Enders, R. K. (1942). The blastocyst of the marten (*Martes*). *Anat. Rec.*, **84**, 307.

Martin, S. J., & Fazekas, J. F. (1937). Effect of sodium chloride therapy on oestrous cycle and hypophysis of bilaterally suprarenal-ectomised rats. *Proc. Soc. exp. Biol., N.Y.*, **37**, 369.

Martinez-Esteve, P. (1937). Le cycle sexuel vaginal chez le marsupial *Didelphys azarae*. *C. R. Soc. Biol., Paris*, **124**, 502.

Marvin, H. N. (1947). Diestrus and the formation of corpora lutea in rats with persistent estrus, treated with desoxycorticosterone acetate. *Anat. Rec.*, **98**, 383.

Masui, K., & Tamura, Y. (1926). *J. Coll. Agric., Tokio*, **7**, 353. (Quoted by Bourne, G., & Zuckerman, S., 1941.)

Matthews, L. H. (1929). The natural history of the elephant seal, with notes on other seals found at South Georgia. *Discovery Rep.*, **1**, 233.

—— (1935). The oestrous cycle and intersexuality in the female mole (*Talpa europaea* Linn.). *Proc. zool. Soc. Lond.*, **1935**, 347.

—— (1937a). The humpback whale, *Megaptera nodosa*. *Discovery Rep.*, **17**, 7.

—— (1937b). (1) The form of the penis in the British rhinolophid bats, compared with that in some of the vespertilionid bats ; and (2) the female sexual cycle in the British horse-shoe bats, *Rhinolophus ferrum-equinum insulanus* Barrett-Hamilton and *R. hipposideros minutus* Montagu. *Trans. zool. Soc. Lond.*, **23**, 213.

—— (1938a). The sperm whale, *Physeter catodon*. *Discovery Rep.*, **17**, 93.

—— (1938b). The sei whale, *Balaenoptera borealis*. *Discovery Rep.*, **17**, 183.

—— (1938c). Notes on the southern right whale, *Eubalaena australis*. *Discovery Rep.*, **17**, 169.

—— (1939). Post-partum oestrus in a bat. *Nature, Lond.*, **143**, 643.

—— (1941a). Reproduction in the Scottish wild cat, *Felis silvestris grampia* Miller. *Proc. zool. Soc. Lond.*, **111**, 59.

—— (1941b). Reproduction in the spotted hyaena, *Crocuta crocuta* (Erxleben). *Philos. Trans.* B, **230**, 1.

—— (1941c). Notes on the genitalia and reproduction of some African bats. *Proc. zool. Soc. Lond.*, **111**, 289.

—— (1943). Parturition in the kangaroo. *Proc. zool. Soc. Lond.* A, **113**, 117.

—— (1946). Notes on the genital anatomy and physiology of the gibbon (*Hylobates*). *Proc. zool. Soc. Lond.*, **116**, 339.

—— (1947a). On an intersexual wild brown rat, *Rattus norvegicus* (Erxleben). *Proc. zool. Soc. Lond.*, **117**, 44.

—— (1947b). A note on the female reproductive tract in the tree kangaroos (*Dendrolagus*). *Proc. zool. Soc. Lond.*, **117**, 313.

—— (1948). Cyclic changes in the uterine mucosa of balaenopterid whales. *J. Anat., Lond.*, **82**, 207.

—— & Harrison, R. J. (1949). Subsurface crypts, oogenesis and the corpus luteum in the ovaries of seals. *Nature, Lond.*, **164**, 587.

Mayer, D. T., Andrews, F. N., & McKenzie, F. F. (1940). The estrin content of the follicular fluid and urine of the mare and its relation to phenomena of the estrual cycle. *Endocrinology*, **27**, 867.

Mazer, C., & Israel, S. L. (1951). *Diagnosis and treatment of menstrual disorders and sterility.* 3rd ed. New York.

—— —— & Kacher, L. (1937). Pseudomenstruation in the human female. *Surg. Gynec. Obstet.*, **65**, 30.

McCann, C. (1933). (Quoted by Hill, W. C. O., 1936b.)

McClean, D., & Rowlands, I. W. (1942). Role of hyaluronidase in fertilization. *Nature, Lond.*, **150**, 627.

McKenzie, F. F. (1926). The normal oestrous cycle in the sow. *Univ. Miss. Coll. Agric. Res. Bull.* No. 86.

McKENZIE, F. F., ALLEN, E., GUTHRIE, M. J., WARBRITTON, V., TERRILL, C. E., CASIDA, L. E., NAHM, L. J., & KENNEDY, J. W. (1933). Reproduction in the ewe. *Proc. Amer. Soc. Anim. Prod.*, 278.

—— & ANDREWS, F. N. (1937). Estrus and ovulation in the mare. *Proc. Amer. Soc. Anim. Prod.*, 64.

—— & BERLINER, V. (1937). The reproductive capacity of rams. *Univ. Miss. Coll. Agric. Res. Bull.* No. 265.

—— & PHILLIPS, R. W. (1931). Some observations on the estrual cycle in the sheep. *Proc. Amer. Soc. Anim. Prod.*, 138.

—— & TERRILL, C. E. (1937). Estrus, ovulation and related phenomena in the ewe. *Univ. Miss. Coll. Agric. Res. Bull.* No. 264.

McKEOWN, T., & GIBSON, J. R (1952). The period of gestation. *Brit. med. J.*, **1**, 938.

—— & RECORD, R. G. (1952). Observations on foetal growth in multiple pregnancy in man. *J. Endocrinol.*, **8**, 386.

—— & ZUCKERMAN, S. (1937). The stimulation to ovulation. *J. Anat., Lond.*, **72**, 153.

—— —— (1938). The suppression of oestrus in the rat during pregnancy and lactation. *Proc. Roy. Soc.* B, **124**, 464.

McPHAIL, M. K. (1933a). Studies on the hypophysectomised ferret. VII. Inhibition of ovulation in the mated oestrus ferret. *Proc. Roy. Soc.* B, **114**, 124.

—— (1933b). Induction of ovulation in the unmated oestrous ferret. *J. Physiol.*, **80**, 78.

—— (1934). The assay of progestin. *J. Physiol.*, **83**, 145.

—— PARKES, A. S., & WHITE, W. E. (1933). Ovulation after blood dilution & cross circulation. *J. Physiol.*, **79**, 180.

MEADE-WALDO, E. G. (1894). The badger : its period of gestation. (Quoted by Cocks, A. H., 1903.)

MEEK, A. (1918). The reproductive organs of the *Cetacea*. *J. Anat., Lond.*, **52**, 186.

MELINKOFF, E. (1950). Questionable necessity of the corpus luteum. *Amer. J. Obstet. Gynec.*, **60**, 437.

MERRIAM, C. H. (1884). Vertebrates of the Adirondack region, northeastern New York. *Trans. Linn. Soc., New York*, Vol. II.

MERTON, H. (1938–39). Studies on reproduction in the albino mouse. III. The duration of life of spermatozoa in the female reproductive tract. *Proc. Roy. Soc. Edinb.*, **59**, 207.

MEYER, B. J., & MEYER, R. K. (1944). Growth and reproduction of the cotton rat, *Sigmodon hispidus hispidus*, under laboratory conditions. *J. Mammal.*, **25**, 107.

MEYER, R. K., LEONARD, S. L., & HISAW, F. L. (1929). Effect of anaesthesia on artificial production of pseudopregnancy in the rat. *Proc. Soc. exp. Biol., N.Y.*, **29**, 340.

MICULICZ-RADECKI, F. VON, & KAUSCH, E. (1935). Beziehungen zwischen Kohabitation und Gravidität in jugendlichem Alter und der daraus erkannte physiologische Follikelzyklus beim Mädchen. *Zbl. Gynäk.*, **59**, 2290.

MILLAIS, S. G. (1904–06). *The mammals of Great Britain and Ireland.* London.

MILLER, R. E. (1936). The reproductive cycle in the males of some cave bats. *Anat. Rec.* (*Abstr.*), **67**, 62.

—— (1937). Further observations on the reproductive system in male bats. *Anat. Rec.* (*Abstr.*), **70**, 84.

—— (1939). The reproductive cycle in male bats of the species *Moyotis lucifugus lucifugus.* and *Myotis grisescens*. *J. Morph.*, **64**, 267.

MILLER, W. C., & DAY, F. T. (1939). The diagnosis of equine pregnancy (Quoted in *Vet. Bull., Weybridge*, 1940, **10**, 470.)

MILLS, C. A. (1937). Geographic and time variations in body growth and age at ménarche. *Hum. Biol.*, **9**, 43.

—— & OGLE, C. (1936). Physiologic sterility of adolescence. *Hum. Biol.*, **8**, 607.

MIRSKAIA, L., & CREW, F. A. E. (1930a). On the genetic nature of the time of attainment of puberty in the female mouse. *Quart. J. exp. Physiol.*, **20**, 299.

—— —— (1930b). Maturity in the female mouse. *Proc. Roy. Soc. Edinb.*, **50**, 179.

—— —— (1930c). On the pregnancy rate in the lactating mouse and the effect of suckling on the duration of pregnancy. *Proc. Roy. Soc. Edinb.*, **51**, 1.

MIRSKAIA, L. & WIESNER, B. P. (1930). On the occurrence and mechanism of prepubertal mucification. *Proc. 2nd internat. Congr. Sex. Res.*, 408.

MIVART, ST. G. (1881). *The cat.* London.

MOIR, J. C. (1944). The effect of posterior lobe pituitary gland fractions on the intact human uterus. *J. Obstet. Gynaec., Brit. Emp.*, **51**, 181.

MONTAGU, M. F. A. (1939). Adolescent sterility. *Quart. Rev. Biol.*, **14**, 13 ; 192.

—— (1946). *Adolescent sterility.* Springfield, Ill.

MOORE, C. R., SIMMONS, G. F., WELLS, L. J., ZALESKY, M., & NELSON, W. O. (1934). On the control of reproductive activity in an annual-breeding mammal (*Citellus tridecemlineatus*). *Anat. Rec.*, **60**, 279.

MORRIS, C. J. O. R. (1952). Blood progesterone in pregnancy. *Ciba Foundation Colloquia on Endocrinology*, **2**, 359.

MOSSMAN, H. W. (1937). The thecal gland and its relation to the reproductive cycle. A study of the cyclic changes in the ovary of the pocket gopher, *Geomys bursarius* (Shaw). *Amer. J. Anat.*, **61**, 289.

—— & JUDAS, I. (1949). Accessory corpora lutea, lutein cell origin, and the ovarian cycle in the Canadian porcupine. *Amer. J. Anat.*, **85**, 1.

—— LAWLAH, J. W., & BRADLEY, J. A. (1932). The male reproductive tract of the Sciuridae. *Amer. J. Anat.*, **51**, 89.

MURIE, A. (1944). *The wolves of Mount McKinley.* Fauna of the National Parks of the United States. Fauna series No. 5. Washington.

MURPHEY, H. S. (1924). Studies of the oestrous or genital cycle of the ox. *J. Amer vet. med. Ass.*, **65**, 598.

—— (1926). Studies of the oestrous cycle in the ox. *Iowa St. Coll. Vet. Pract. Bull.* No. 25, 153.

MURPHREE, R. L., WARWICK, E. J., CASIDA, L. E., & McSHAN, W. H. (1947). Influence of reproductive stage upon the fertility of gonadotrophin-treated female rabbits. *Endocrinology*, **41**, 308.

MURR, E. (1931). Beobachtungen über die Paarung des Frettchens. *Zool. Gart., Lpz.*, **4**, 289.

—— (1932). Beobachtungen über den Geburtsvorgang beim Frettchen. *Zool. Gart., Lpz.*, **5**, 37.

—— (1933). Aus der Fortpflanzungsbiologie des Frettchens (*Putorius furo*). *Z. Säugetierk.*, **8**, 26.

MYERS, H. I., YOUNG, W. C., & DEMPSEY, E. W. (1936). Graafian follicle development throughout the reproductive cycle in the guinea-pig, with especial reference to changes during oestrus (sexual receptivity). *Anat. Rec.*, **65**, 381.

NAKANO, O. (1928). Über die Verteilung des Glykogens bei den zyklischen Veränderungen in den Geschlechtsorganen der Fledermaus und über die Nahrungsaufnahme der Spermien in dem weiblichen Geschlechtswege. *Folia anat. jap.*, **6**, 777.

NARAYAN RAO, C. R. (1927). Observations on the habits of *Loris lydekkerianus*. *J. Mysore Univ.*, **1**, 57.

—— (1932). On the occurrence of glycogen and fat in liquor folliculi and uterine secretion in *Loris lydekkerianus* (Cabr.). *J. Mysore Univ.*, **6**, 140.

NATHANSON, I. T., & AUB, J. C. (1943). Excretion of sex hormones in abnormalities of puberty. *J. clin. Endocrinol.*, **3**, 321.

—— TOWNE, L. E., & AUB, J. C. (1941). Normal excretion of sex hormones in childhood. *Endocrinology*, **28**, 851.

NEAL, E. (1948). *The badger.* London.

NELSEN, O. E. (1946). Variability of the anoestrous condition in the opossum, *Didelphys virginiana*. *Anat. Rec. (Abstr.)*, **94**, 402.

NELSON, E. W. (1925). Status of the pronghorned antelope 1922–1924. *U.S. Dept. Agr. Dept. Bull.* No. 1346. Washington.

NELSON, W. O. (1929). Oestrus during pregnancy. *Science*, **70**, 453.

NEWELL, J. W., & ROCK, T. (1952). Upper age limit of parturition. A review of the literature. *Amer. J. Obstet. Gynec.*, **63**, 875.

NEWMAN, H. H., & PATTERSON, J. T. (1909). A case of normal identical quadruplets in the nine-banded armadillo, and its bearing on the problems of identical twins and of sex determination. *Biol. Bull., Wood's Hole*, **17**, 181.

NEWMAN, H. H., & PATTERSON, J. T. (1910). The development of the nine-banded armadillo from the primitive streak stage to birth : with especial reference to the question of specific polyembryony. *J. Morph.*, **21**, 359.

NEWTON, W. H. (1939). In *Sex and internal secretions.* Ed. E. Allen. London.

—— (1949). *Recent advances in physiology.* 7th ed. London.

NICHOLLS, L. (1939). Period of gestation of *Loris*. *Nature, Lond.*, **143**, 246.

NICOL, T. (1933a). Studies on the reproductive system in the guinea-pig : variations in the oestrous cycle of the virgin animal, after parturition, and during pregnancy. *Proc. Roy. Soc. Edinb.*, **53**, 220.

—— (1933b). Studies on the reproductive cycle in the guinea-pig : post-partum repair of the uterus, and the associated appearances in the ovaries. *Trans. Roy. Soc. Edinb.*, **57**, 765.

NISSEN, H. W., & YERKES, R. M. (1943). Reproduction in the chimpanzee : report on forty-nine births. *Anat. Rec.*, **86**, 567.

NOBACK, C. V. (1936). 1. Note on menstruation in the gorilla (*Gorilla gorilla*). 2. Note on gross changes observed in the external genitalia of the female gorilla just before, during and after menstruation. *Amer. J. phys. Anthrop.*, **21**, 9.

—— (1939). The changes in the vaginal smears and associated cyclic phenomena in the lowland gorilla (*Gorilla gorilla*). *Anat. Rec.*, **73**, 209.

NORMAN, J. R., & FRASER, F. C. (1937). *Giant fishes, whales and dolphins.* London.

NOVAK, E. (1944). The constitutional type of female precocious puberty with a report of 9 cases. *Amer. J. Obstet. Gynec.*, **47**, 20.

—— & RICHARDSON, E. H., Jr. (1941). Proliferative changes in the senile endometrium. *Amer. J. Obstet. Gynec.*, **42**, 564.

O'DONOGHUE, C. H. (1911). The growth-changes in the mammary apparatus of *Dasyurus* and the relation of the corpora lutea thereto. *Quart. J. micr. Sci.*, **57**, 187.

OGILVIE, A. W. (1923). Breeding of the gibbon in captivity. *J. nat. Hist. Soc., Siam*, **6**, 137.

OGSTON, A. G., PHILPOT, J. ST. L., & ZUCKERMAN, S. (1939). Observations related to the swelling of sexual skin in rhesus monkeys. *J. Endocrinol.*, **1**, 231.

OMMANNEY, F. D. (1932). The urino-genital system of the fin whale (*Balaenoptera physalus*). *Discovery Rep.*, **5**, 363.

O'NEIL, D. (1952). Uterine bleeding in tension states. *J. Obstet. Gynaec., Brit. Emp.*, **59**, 234.

ORTIZ, E. (1947). The postnatal development of the reproductive system of the golden hamster (*Cricetus auratus*) and its reactivity to hormones. *Physiol. Zoöl.*, **20**, 45.

OWEN, R. (1868). *On the anatomy of vertebrates.* Vol. III. Mammals. London.

PAGENSTECHER, H. A. (1859). Über die Begattung des *Vesperugo pipistrellus*. *Verh. naturh.-med. Ver. Heidelb.*, **1**, 194. (Quoted by Hartman, C. G., 1933a.)

PAINTER, T. S. (1922). Studies in mammalian spermatogenesis. I. The spermatogenesis of the opossum (*Didelphys virginiana*). *J. exp. Zool.*, **35**, 13.

PALMER, A. (1938–39). Placenta praevia in a rhesus monkey. *J. Anat., Lond.*, **73**, 626.

—— (1942). Basal body temperature in disorders of ovarian function and pregnancy. *Surg. Gynec. Obstet.*, **75**, 768.

PALMER, R., & MARCILLE, S. (1941). Le mucus cervical normal et pathologique. *Gynéc. et Obstét.*, **41**, 11. (Quoted by Knaus, H., 1950.)

PARKES, A. S. (1924). Fertility in mice. *Brit. J. exp. Biol.*, **2**, 21.

—— (1925). The age of attainment of sexual maturity in the albino mouse. *J. R. micr. Soc.*, **45**, 315.

—— (1926a). Observations on the oestrous cycle of the albino mouse. *Proc. Roy. Soc. B*, **100**, 151.

—— (1926b). Studies on the sex ratio and related phenomena : (9) Observations on fertility and sex ratio in mice, 1922–5. *Brit. J. exp. Biol.*, **4**, 93.

—— (1928a). The physiology of ovarian activity. *Biol. Rev.*, **3**, 208.

—— (1928b) The length of the oestrous cycle in the unmated normal mouse : record of one thousand cycles. *Brit. J. exp. Biol.*, **5**, 371.

PARKES, A. S. (1929). The functions of the corpus luteum. II. The experimental pro-
    duction of placentomata in the mouse. *Proc. Roy. Soc.* B, **104**, 183.

—— (1931). The reproductive processes of certain mammals. Part I. The oestrous
    cycle of the Chinese hamster (*Cricetulus griseus*). *Proc. Roy. Soc.* B, **108**, 138.

PATTERSON, J. T. (1913). Polyembryonic development in *Tatusia novemcincta*.
    J. Morph., **24**, 559.

PEARLMAN, W. H. (1952). Progesterone metabolism—a review. *Ciba Foundation Col-
    loquia on endocrinology*, **2**, 309.

PEARSON, O. P. (1944). Reproduction in the shrew (*Blarina brevicauda* Say). *Amer. J.
    Anat.*, **75**, 39.

—— (1949). Reproduction of a South American rodent, the mountain viscacha. *Amer.
    J. Anat.*, **84**, 143.

—— & BASSETT, C. F. (1946). Certain aspects of reproduction in a herd of silver foxes.
    Amer. Nat., **80**, 45.

—— & ENDERS, R. K. (1943). Ovulation, maturation and fertilization in the fox. *Anat.
    Rec.*, **85**, 69.

—— —— (1944). Duration of pregnancy in certain mustelids. *J. exp. Zool.*, **95**, 21.

PECKHAM, B. M., & GREENE, R. R. (1947). Attempts to produce deciduomata in the
    pregnant rat. *Endocrinology*, **41**, 273.

PECZENIK, O. (1942). Actions of sex hormones on oestrous cycle and reproduction of the
    golden hamster. *J. Endocrinol.*, **3**, 157.

PELLEGRINI, G. (1926). Sulle modificazioni degli elementi interstiziali del testicolo negli
    animali ad attività sessuale periodica. *Arch. ital. Anat. Embriol.*, **22**, 550.

PERCY, Professor (1844). On the management of various species of monkeys in confine-
    ment. *Proc. zool. Soc. Lond.*, **82**. (Quoted by Zuckerman, S., 1930.)

PERRY, J. S. (1942). Reproduction in the water-vole, *Arvicola amphibius* Linn. *Proc.
    zool. Soc. Lond.* A, **112**, 118.

—— (1945–46). The reproduction of the wild brown rat (*Rattus norvegicus* Erxleben).
    Proc. zool. Soc. Lond., **115**, 19.

—— (1953). The reproduction of the African elephant, *Loxondonta africana*. *Philos.
    Trans.* B, **237**, 93.

PHILIPP, E. (1931). Physiologie und Pathologie der Geburt bei Affen. *Zbl. ges. Gynäk.*,
    55, 1776.

PHILLIPS, R. W., & ANDREWS, F. N. (1936). The development of the testes and scrotum
    of the ram, bull and boar. *Mass. Agric.*, 331.

—— FRAPS, R. M., & FRANK, A. H. (1946). Ovulation and oestrus in sheep and goats. In
    The problem of fertility. Ed. E. T. Engle. Princeton.

—— SIMMONS, V. L., & SCHOTT, R. G. (1943). Observations on the normal oestrous cycle
    and breeding season in goats and possibilities of modification of the breeding season
    with gonadotrophic hormones. *Amer. J. vet. Res.*, **4**, 360.

—— & ZELLER, J. H. (1943). Sexual development in small and large types of swine. *Anat.
    Rec.*, **85**, 387.

POCOCK, R. I. (1905). Observations upon a female specimen of the Hainan gibbon (*Hylo-
    bates hainanus*), now living in the Society's gardens. *Proc. zool. Soc. Lond.*, **2**, 169.

—— (1906). Notes upon menstruation, gestation and parturition of some monkeys that
    have lived in the Society's gardens. *Proc. zool. Soc. Lond.*, **2**, 558.

POHL, L. (1910). Wieselstudien. *Zool. Beob.*, **51**, 234. (Quoted by Deanesly, R., 1944.)

POLOVTZEVA, V., & FOMENKO, M. (1933). The determination of the time of ovulation
    in the sheep by vaginal smears. *Probl. Zlinotn.* No. 5, 95. (Quoted by Asdell,
    S. A., 1946.)

POMMERENKE, W. T., & VIERGIVER, E. (1947). Relationship between cervical mucus and
    basal temperature cycles. *Amer. J. Obstet. Gynec.*, **54**, 676.

POPA, G. T., & FIELDING, U. (1930). A portal circulation from the pituitary to the hypo-
    thalamic region. *J. Anat., Lond.*, **65**, 88.

—— —— (1933). Hypophysio-portal vessels and their colloid accompaniment.
    J. Anat., Lond., **67**, 227.

POPOFF, N. (1934). L'ovaire d'une ourse (*Ursus arctos*) de 4 ans. *C. R. Ass. Anat.*, **29**, 471.

PORSILD, M. P. (1922). Scattered observations on narwhals. *J. Mammal.*, **3**, 8.

POUCHET, F. A. (1847). *Théorie positive de l'ovulation spontanée et de la fécondation des mammifères et de l'espèce humaine, Texte et Atlas.* Paris. (Quoted by Knaus, H., 1950.)

PREJEWALSKY (1876). *Mongolia, the Tangut country and the solitudes of northern Tibet.* Morgan's translat. London. (Quoted by Heape, W., 1900.)

PRELL, H. (1927). Über doppelte Brunstzeit und verlängerte Tragzeit bei den einheimischen Arten der Mardergattung *Martes pinel*. *Zool. Anz.*, **74**, 122.

—— (1930a). Über die Fortpflanzungsbiologie der europäischen Bären. *Zool. Gart.*, *Frankfurt*, **3**, 168.

—— (1930b). Über doppelte Brunstzeit und verlängerte Tragzeit bei den europäischen Arten der Gattung *Ursus* Linné. *Biol. Zbl.*, **50**, 257.

—— (1931). Über die Tragzeitverhältnisse der arctoiden Raubtiere. *Z. Säugetierk.*, **6**, 57.

—— (1938). Die Tragzeit des Rehes. *Züchtungskunde*, **13**, 325.

QUINLAN, J., & MARÉ, G. S. (1931). The physiological changes in the ovary of the merino sheep in South Africa, and their practical application in breeding. *17th Rep. vet. Res. S. Afr.*, 663.

RAKOFF, A. E., FEO, L. G., & GOLDSTEIN, L. (1944). The biologic characteristics of the normal vagina. *Amer. J. Obstet. Gynec.*, **47**, 467.

RAMSEY, E. M. (1949). The vascular pattern of the endometrium of the pregnant rhesus monkey (*Macaca mulatta*). *Contr. Embryol. Carneg. Instn.*, **33**, 113.

RAND, A. L. (1935). On the habits of some Madagascar mammals. *J. Mammal.*, **16**, 89.

RANSON, R. M. (1941). New laboratory animals from wild species. Breeding a laboratory stock of hedgehogs (*Erinaceus europaeus* L.). *J. Hyg., Camb.*, **41**, 131.

RASMUSSEN, A. T. (1917). Seasonal changes in the interstitial cells of the testis of the woodchuck (*Marmota monax*). *Amer. J. Anat.*, **22**, 475.

—— (1918). Cyclic changes in the interstitial cells of the ovary and testis in the woodchuck (*Marmota monax*). *Endocrinology*, **2**, 353.

RATCLIFFE, F. (1932). Notes on the fruit bats (*Pteropus* spp.) of Australia. *J. anim. Ecol.*, **1**, 32. (Quoted by Baker, J. R., & Baker, Z., 1936.)

RAVEN, H. C. (1936). Genital swelling in a female gorilla. *J. Mammal.*, **17**, 416.

RECORD, R. G. (1952). Relative frequencies and sex distribution of human multiple births. *Brit. J. soc. Med.*, **6**, 192.

REDENZ, E. (1929). Das Verhalten der Säugetierspermatozoen zwi·ch·n Begattung und Befruchtung. *Z. Zellforsch.*, **9**, 734. (Quoted by Guthrie, M. J., 1933b.)

REEDER, E. (1939). Cytology of the reproductive tract of the female bat *Myotis lucifugus lucifugus*. *J. Morph.*, **64**, 431. (Quoted by Wimsatt, W. A., 1944a.)

REIN, G. (1883). Beiträge zur Kenntnis der Reifungserscheinungen und Befruchtungsvorgänge am Säugetierei. *Arch. mikr. Anat.*, **22**, 233. (Quoted by Young, W. C., 1941.)

RENGGER, J. R. (1830). *Naturgeschichte der Säugetiere von Paraguay.* Basel.

Report of the Chief Inspector of Stock for New South Wales (1891). *The rural economy and agriculture of Australia and New Zealand.* London. (Quoted by Marshall, F. H. A., 1922.)

REYNOLDS, S. R. M. (1947). The physiologic basis of menstruation : a summary of current concepts. *J. Amer. med. Ass.*, **135**, 552.

—— (1949). *Physiology of the uterus.* 2nd ed. New York.

—— & FOSTER, F. I. (1939). Physical conditions in the uterus governing the duration of pregnancy. *Anat. Rec.*, **75**, 175.

RICHARDSON, W. R. (1943). Wood rats (*Neotoma albigula*) : their growth and development. *J. Mammal.*, **24**, 130.

RIDLEY, H. N. (1895). The mammals of the Malay Peninsula. *Nat. Sci.*, London. (Quoted by Zuckerman, S., 1932b.)

RIENITS, K. G. (1951). Hyaluronic acid in exudate from oedematous sexual skin in rhesus monkeys. *Biochem. J.*, **48**, lviii.

Rink (1877).   *Danish Greenland, its people and products.*   London.   (Quoted by Heape, W., 1900.)

Roberts, E. J. (1928).   Int. Dairy Congr. Rep., 281.   (Quoted by Marshall, F. H. A., 1937.)

Roberts, S., & Szego, C. M. (1946).   The nature of circulating estrogen ; lipoprotein-bound estrogen in human plasma.   *Endocrinology*, **39**, 183.

Robin, H. A. (1881a).   Recherches anatomiques sur les mammifères de l'ordre des Chiroptères.   *Ann. Sci. nat. (Zool.)*, 6ᵉ Sér., **11**, 1.

—— (1881b).   Sur l'époque de l'accouplement des chauve-souris.   *Bull. Soc. philom., Paris*, 7ᵉ Sér., **5**, 88.

Robinson, A. (1918).   The formation, rupture and closure of ovarian follicles in ferrets and ferret-polecat hybrids, and some associated phenomena.   *Trans. Roy. Soc. Edinb.*, **52**, 303.

Robinson, S. M. (1925).   *J. Bombay nat. Hist. Soc.*, **30**, 201.   (Quoted by Rode, P., 1942.)

Robson, J. M. (1940).   Prolongation of pregnancy in the hypophysectomised rabbit by progesterone and oestrogens.   *J. Physiol.*, **97**, 517.

—— (1947).   *Recent advances in sex and reproductive physiology.*   3rd ed.   London.

Rock, J., & Hertig, A. T. (1944).   Information regarding the time of human ovulation derived from a study of 3 unfertilised and 11 fertilised ova.   *Amer. J. Obstet. Gynec.*, **47**, 343.

—— —— (1948).   The human conceptus during the first two weeks of gestation.   *Amer. J. Obstet. Gynec.*, **55**, 6.

Rode, P. (1942).   A propos de la durée de gestation chez les gibbons.   *Mammalia.*   No. 1, 46.

Rollinat, R., & Trouessart, E. (1895a).   Sur la reproduction des chiroptères.   *C. R. Soc Biol., Paris*, 10ᵉ Sér. **2**, 53.

—— —— (1895b).   Sur la reproduction des chauve-souris.   *Bull. Soc. zool. Fr.*, **20**, 25.

—— —— (1896).   Sur la reproduction des chauve-souris.   Le vespertilion murin (*Vespertilio murinus* Schreber).   *Mém. Soc. zool. Fr.*, **9**, 214.

—— —— (1897).   Sur la reproduction des chauve-souris.   Les Rhinolophes.   *Mém. Soc. zool. Fr.*, **10**, 114.

Rosen, S., & Shelesnyak, M. C. (1937).   Induction of pseudopregnancy by silver nitrate on nasal mucosa.   *Proc. Soc. exp. Biol., N.Y.*, **36**, 832.

Rossman, I., & Bartelmez, G. W. (1946).   Delayed ovulation, a significant factor in the variability of the menstrual cycle.   *Amer. J. Obstet. Gynec.*, **52**, 28.

Rowan, W. (1938).   Light and seasonal reproduction in animals.   *Biol. Rev.*, **13**, 374.

Rowlands, I. W. (1936).   Reproduction of the bank vole (*Evotomys glareolus* Schreber).   II. Seasonal changes in the reproductive organs of the male.   *Philos. Trans.* B, **226**, 99.

—— (1938).   Preliminary note on the reproductive cycle of the red squirrel (*Sciurus vulgaris*).   *Proc. zool. Soc. Lond.* A, **108**, 441.

—— (1947).   Anterior pituitary-like hormones.   *J. Endocrinol.*, **5**, xx.

—— (1949a).   Serum gonadotrophin and ovarian activity in the pregnant mare   *J. Endocrinol.*, **6**, 184.

—— (1949b).   Post-partum breeding in the guinea-pig.   *J. Hyg., Camb.*, **47**, 281.

—— & Parkes, A. S. (1935).   The reproductive processes of certain mammals.   VIII. Reproduction in foxes (*Vulpes spp.*).   *Proc. zool. Soc. Lond.*, **1935**, 823.

—— & Williams, P. C. (1946).   Fertilization of eggs in hypophysectomized rats.   *J. Endocrinol.*, **4**, 417.

Rowley, J. (1929).   Life history of the sea-lions on the California coast.   *J. Mammal.*, **10**, 1.

Russell, A. E., & Zuckerman, S. (1935).   A " sexual skin " in a marmoset.   *J. Anat., Lond.*, **69**, 356.

Ruth, E. B. (1934).   The os priapi : a study in bone development.   *Anat. Rec.*, **60**, 231.

Sandes, F. P. (1903).   The corpus luteum of *Dasyurus viverrinus*, with observations on the growth and atrophy of the Graafian follicle.   *Proc. Linn. Soc., N.S.W.*, **28**, 364.

SATOH, S., & HOSHI, S. (1932). A study of reproduction in mares. *J. Jap. Soc. vet. Sci.*, 11, 257.

—— —— (1933). A study of reproduction in the mare. II. The study of the oestrus. *J. Jap. Soc. vet. Sci.*, 12, 200.

SAWYER, C. H. (1949). Reflex induction of ovulation in the estrogen-treated rabbit by artificial vaginal stimulation. *Anat. Rec.*, 103, 502.

—— EVERETT, J. W., & MARKEE, J. E. (1950). " Spontaneous " ovulation in the rabbit following combined estrogen-progesterone treatment. *Proc. Soc. exp. Biol.*, N.Y., 74, 185.

SCHEFFER, T. H. (1924). Notes on the breeding of *Peromyscus*. *J. Mammal.*, 5, 258.

SCHMALTZ, R. (1921). *Das Geschlechtsleben der Haussäugetiere.* 3. Aufl. Berlin.

SCHMIDT, F. (1934). Über die Fortpflanzungsbiologie von sibirischem Zobel (*Martes zibellina* L.) und europäischem Baummarder (*Martes martes* L.). *Z. Säugetierk.*, 9, 392.

SCHNEIDER, K. M. (1926). *Pelztierzucht*, 2, 1. (Quoted by Matthews, L. H., 1941b.)

—— (1930). Einige Beobachtungen über das Geschlechtsleben des indischen Elefanten. *Zool. Gart., Frankfurt*, 3, 305.

SCHOOLEY, J. P. (1934). A summer breeding season in the Eastern chipmunk, *Tamias striatus*. *J. Mammal.*, 15, 194.

SCHOTT, R. G., & PHILLIPS, R. W. (1941). Rate of sperm travel and time of ovulation in sheep. *Anat. Rec.*, 79, 531.

SCHULTZ, A. H. (1933). In *The anatomy of the rhesus monkey*. Ed. C. G. Hartman & W. L. Straus, Jr. London.

—— (1938). Genital swelling in the female orang-utan. *J. Mammal.*, 19, 363.

—— (1940). Growth and development of the chimpanzee. *Contr. Embryol. Carneg. Instn.*, 28, 1.

—— (1948). The number of young at a birth and the number of nipples in primates. *Amer. J. phys. Anthrop.*, 6, 1.

—— & SNYDER, F. F. (1935). Observations on reproduction in chimpanzees. *Johns Hopk. Hosp. Bull.*, 57, 193.

SCHUSTER, L. (1929). Ein Beitrag zur Frage der Brunst- und Setzzeiten der Säugetiere in den Tropen. *Zool. Gart., Lpz.*, 2, 114.

SCHWARZ, E. (1948–49). Revision of the Old-world moles of the genus *Talpa* Linnaeus *Proc. zool. Soc. Lond.*, 118, 36.

SCHWARZ, F. (1928). Die Harnkeim-(Urogenital)-Gegend der Nabeltiere (*Amniota*). 1. Die Entwicklung des Harnkeimwerkes (Urogenitalia) beim Maulwurf (*Talpa europaea*) *Z. Anat. EntwGesch.*, 88, 181.

SCLATER, W. L. (1900). *The fauna of South Africa*. Mammals, 1. London.

SEABORN, E. (1925). The oestrous cycle in the mare and some associated phenomena *Anat. Rec.*, 30, 277.

SÉGUY, J., & BULLIER, P. (1935). Recherche du cycle menstruel de l'*Hamadryas papion* L. *Arch. Mus. Hist. nat.*, Paris, 12, 309.

—— & SIMMONET, H. (1933). Recherche de signes directs d'ovulation chez la femme. *Gynéc. et Obstét.*, 28, 657.

—— & VIMEUX, J. (1933). Contribution à l'étude des stérilités inexpliquées : étude de l'ascension des spermatozoïdes dans les voies génitales basses de la femme. *Gynéc. et Obstét.*, 27, 346.

SELLE, R. M. (1922). Changes in the vaginal epithelium of the guinea-pig during the oestrous cycle. *Amer. J. Anat.*, 30, 429.

—— (1928). *Microtus californicus* in captivity. *J. Mammal.*, 9, 93.

—— (1945). Hamster sexually mature at twenty-eight days of age. *Science*, 102, 485.

SELYE, H., & McKEOWN, T. (1934). Production of pseudo-pregnancy by mechanical stimulation of the nipples. *Proc. Soc. exp. Biol.*, N.Y., 31, 683.

SEMON, R. (1899). *In the Australian Bush and on the coast of the coral sea*. London.

SETON, E. T. (1909). *Life histories of northern animals. An account of the mammals of Manitoba.* 1–2. New York.

—— (1920). Notes on the breeding habits of captive deermice. *J. Mammal.*, 1, 134.

Seymour, F. I. (1947).   In *Recent advances in sex and reproductive physiology*.   Ed. J. M. Robson.   3rd ed., p. 201.   London.

Shadle, A. R. (1948).   Gestation period in the porcupine, *Erethizon dorsatum dorsatum*. *J. Mammal.*, **29**, 162.

Sharman, A. (1944).   Some recent studies and investigations in sterility.   *J. Obstet. Gynaec., Brit. Emp.*, **51**, 85.

—— (1950).   Re-establishment of ovulation post-partum and post-abortum.   *Proc. Soc. Study of Fertility*, **1**, 26.

Shaw, W. T. (1925).   Breeding and development of the Columbian ground-squirrel. *J. Mammal.*, **6**, 106.

Sheldon, W. G. (1937).   Notes on the giant panda.   *J. Mammal.*, **18**, 13.

Shelesnyak, M. C. (1931).   The induction of pseudopregnancy in the rat by means of electrical stimulation.   *Anat. Rec.*, **49**, 179.

—— & Rosen, S. (1938).   Naso-genital relationship : induction of pseudopregnancy in rat by nasal treatment.   *Endocrinology*, **23**, 58.

Sherman, H. B. (1937).   Breeding habits of the free-tailed bat.   *J. Mammal.*, **18**, 176.

Shortridge, G. C. (1934).   *The mammals of South-West Africa*.   London.

Shortt, J. (1889).   *A manual of Indian cattle and sheep*.   3rd ed.   Madras.   (Quoted by Marshall, F. H. A., 1922.)

Simmons, G. F. (1946a).   The problem of delayed puberty in a monoestrous wild mammal (*Citellus tridecemlineatus*).   *Anat. Rec. (Abstr.)*, **94**, 368.

—— (1946b).   Reproductive cycle of the female ground squirrel.   *Anat. Rec. (Abstr.)*, **94**, 385.

Simpson, G. G. (1945).   The principles of classification and a classification of mammals. *Bull. Amer. Mus. Nat. Hist.*, Vol. 85.

Simpson, J. J. (1924).   *Chats on British mammals*.   London.   (Quoted by Hill, M., 1939.)

Skinner, M. P. (1922).   The prong-horn.   *J. Mammal.*, **3**, 82.

—— (1929).   White-tailed deer formerly in the Yellowstone Park.   *J. Mammal.*, **10**, 101.

Skowron, M. St. (1938).   Untersuchungen über das endokrine System des Igels (*Erinaceus*).   1. Histologische Veränderungen in den Hoden und in den akzessorischen Drüsen des männlichen Genitalapparates, die periodisch oder unter dem Einfluss von endokrinen Reizen auftreten.   *Bull. Nat. Acad. Polon. Sci. Lett., Classe Sci. Math. Nat., Sér.* B, Sci. Nat. (II), **2**, 129.

—— & Zajaczek, S. (1947).   Modifications histologiques des glandes endocrines durant le cycle annuel chez le hérisson.   *C. R. Soc. Biol., Paris*, **141**, 1105.

Slonaker, J. R. (1924).   The effect of pubescence, oestruation and menopause on the voluntary activity in the albino rat.   *Amer. J. Physiol.*, **68**, 294.

—— (1925).   The effect of copulation, pregnancy, pseudopregnancy and lactation on the voluntary activity and food consumption of the albino rat.   *Amer. J. Physiol.*, **71**, 362.

—— (1929).   Pseudopregnancy in the albino rat.   *Amer. J. Physiol.*, **89**, 406.

—— (1934).   Superfetation in the albino rat.   *Amer. J. Physiol.*, **108**, 322.

Smelser, G. K., Walton, A., & Whetham, E. O. (1934).   The effect of light on ovarian activity in the rabbit.   *J. exp. Biol.*, **11**, 352.

Smith, O. W., & Smith, G. V. (1952).   Endocrinology and related phenomena of the human menstrual cycle.   *Rec. Progr. Horm. Res.*, **7**, 209.

—— Smith, G. van S., & Schiller, S. (1943).   Clinical experiments in relation to the excretion of the estrogens.   III. Urinary estrogens in a normal menstrual cycle and in a case of essential dysmenorrhoea.   *Amer. J. Obstet. Gynec.*, **45**, 15.

Smith, R. M., & Rubenstein, B. B. (1940).   Adolescence of macaques.   *Endocrinology*, **26**, 667.

Snyder, F. F. (1938).   Factors concerned in the duration of pregnancy.   *Physiol. Rev.*, **18**, 578.

Sobotta, J. (1906).   Über die Bildung des Corpus luteum beim Meerschweinchen.   *Anat. Hefte*, **32**, 89.

Sollberger, D. E. (1943).   Notes on the breeding habits of the Eastern flying squirrel (*Glaucomys volans volans*).   *J. Mammal.*, **24**, 163.

SOLOMONS, B., & GATENBY, J. W. B. (1924). Notes on the formation, structure and physiology of the corpus luteum of man, the pig and the duck-billed platypus. *J. Obstet. Gynaec., Brit. Emp.*, **31**, 580.

SOUEF, A. S. LE, BURRELL, F., & TRAUGHTON, E. LeG. (1926). *The wild animals of Australasia ; embracing the mammals of New Guinea and the nearer Pacific Islands.* London.

SPIEGEL, A. (1929). Biologische Beobachtungen an Javamakaken, *Macacus irus* F. Cuv. (*Cynomolgus*, L.). Geburt und Entwicklung während der ersten Lebensmonate. *Zool. Anz.*, **81**, 45.

—— (1930). Beobachtungen über den Sexualzyklus, die Gravidität und die Geburt bei Javamakaken (*Macaca irus mordax* Thomas × Wroughton [*cynomolgus* L.]). *Arch. Gynaek.*, **142**, 561.

—— (1931). Untersuchungen über die Fortpflanzung bei Javamakaken. *Zbl. Gynäk.*, **55**, 1762.

—— (1950). Weitere Beobachtungen und Untersuchungen über die Fortpflanzung bei Javamakaken [*Macaca irus mordax* Th. und Wr. (*cynomolgus* L.)]. *Arch. Gynaek.*, **177**, 590.

SQUIER, R. R. (1932). The living egg and early stages of its development in the guinea-pig. *Contr. Embryol. Carneg. Instn.*, **23**, 223.

STAFFORD, E. S. (1930). The origin of the blood of the " placental sign." *Anat. Rec.*, **47**, 43.

STEGEMAN, L. C. (1930). Notes on *Synaptomys cooperi cooperi* in Washtenaw County, Michigan. *J. Mammal.*, **11**, 460.

STEINBERG, W. (1951). Modern concepts of the anovulatory cycle. *J. Med. Soc. New Jersey*, **48**, 326. (Quoted in *Quart. Rev. Obst. Gynec.*, **10**, 125.)

STEWART, Jr., H. L. (1952). Duration of pregnancy and postmaturity. *J. Amer. med. Ass.*, **48**, 1079.

STIEVE, H. (1952). Eine Schreckblutung im Klimakterium. *Anat. Anz.*, **98**, 361.

STOCKARD, A. H. (1929). Observations on reproduction in the white-tailed prairie-dog (*Cynomys leucurus*). *J. Mammal.*, **10**, 209.

STOCKARD, C. R., & PAPANICOLAOU, G. N. (1917). The existence of a typical oestrous cycle in the guinea-pig—with a study of its histological and physiological changes. *Amer. J. Anat.*, **22**, 225.

" STONEHENGE " (1887). *The dog in health and disease.* 4th ed. (Quoted by Heape, W., 1900.)

STORER, T. I. (1930). Summer and autumn breeding of the California ground squirrel. *J. Mammal.*, **11**, 235.

STOSS, A. O. (1933). Über das Geschlechtsleben der Silberfüchse. *Dtsch. Pelztierz.*, **4**, 181.

STOVER, R. F., & PRATT, J. P. (1939). Progestin studies ; pregnandiol excretion. *Endocrinology*, **24**, 29.

STRATZ, K. H. (1898). *Der geschlechtsreife Säugethiereierstock.* Den Haag.

STRAUSS, F. (1938). Die Befruchtung und der Vorgang der Ovulation bei *Ericulus* aus der Familie der Centetiden. *Bio-Morphosis*, **1**, 281.

—— (1939). Die Bildung des Corpus luteum bei Centetiden. *Bio-Morphosis*, **1**, 489.

STRUTHERS, P. H. (1928). Breeding habits of the Canadian porcupine (*Erethizon dorsatum*). *J. Mammal.*, **9**, 300.

STURMAN-HULBE, M., & STONE, C. P. (1929). Maternal behaviour in the albino rat. *J. comp. Psychol.*, **9**, 203.

SUBBA RAU, A., & HIRIYANNAIYA, S. (1930). Contributions to our knowledge of the anatomy of the *Lemuroidea*. II. The urino-genital systems of *Loris lydekkerianus*. *J. Mysore Univ.*, **4**, 149.

SUTTON, J. B. (1886). Menstruation in monkeys. *Brit. gynaec. J.*, **2**, 285 ; 303.

SVIHLA, A. (1929). Life history notes on *Sigmodon hispidus hispidus*. *J. Mammal.*, **10**, 352.

—— (1932). A comparative life history study of the mice of the genus *Peromyscus*. *Univ. Mich. Misc. Publ. Mus. Zool. No. 24.*

SVIHLA, A. (1935). Development and growth of the prairie deermouse, *Peromyscus maniculatus bairdii*. *J. Mammal.*, **16**, 109.

—— & SVIHLA, R. D. (1931). The Louisiana muskrat. *J. Mammal.*, **12**, 12.

SVIHLA, R. D. (1931). Notes on desert and dusky harvest mice (*Reithrodontomys megalotis megalotis* and *R. m. nigrescens*). *J. Mammal.*, **12**, 363.

—— (1936). Breeding and young of the grasshopper mouse (*Onychomys leucogaster fuscogriseus*). *J. Mammal.*, **17**, 172.

SWEZY, O., & EVANS, H. M. (1930). Ovarian changes during pregnancy in the rat. *Science*, **71**, 46.

TALBOT, N. B., BUTLER, A. M., BERMAN, R. A., RODRIGUEZ, P. M., & MacLACHLAN, E. A. (1943). Excretion of 17-ketosteroids by normal and by abnormal children. *Amer. J. Dis. Child.*, **65**, 364.

TALMAGE, R. V. N. (1947). Changes produced in the symphysis pubis of the guinea pig by the sex steroids and relaxin. *Anat. Rec.*, **99**, 91.

TANDLER, J., & GROSZ, S. (1912). Über den Saisondimorphismus des Maulwurfhodens. *Arch. EntwMech. Org.*, **33**, 297.

—— —— (1913). Über den Saisondimorphismus des Maulwurfhodens. *Arch. Entw-Mech. Org.*, **35**, 132.

TETLEY, H. (1941a). On the Scottish wild cat. *Proc. zool. Soc. Lond.* B, **111**, 13.

—— (1941b). On the Scottish fox. *Proc. zool. Soc. Lond.* B, **111**, 25.

THOMAS, O., & SCHWANN, H. (1906). The Rudd exploration of South Africa. V. List of mammals obtained by Mr. Grant in N.E. Transvaal. *Proc. zool. Soc. Lond.*, **1906**, 575.

THOMPSON, A. R. (1931). *Nature by night*. London. (Quoted by Hill, M., 1939.)

THOMSON, A. P. D. (1954). The onset of oestrus in normal and blinded ferrets. *Proc. Roy. Soc.* B, **142**, 126.

—— (1951). The relation of retinal stimulation to oestrus in the ferret. *J. Physiol.*, **113**, 425.

TINKLEPAUGH, O. L. (1930). Occurrence of vaginal plug in a chimpanzee. *Anat. Rec.*, **46**, 329.

—— (1932). Parturition and puerperal sepsis in a chimpanzee. *Anat. Rec.*, **53**, 193.

—— (1933). Sex cycles and other cyclic phenomena in a chimpanzee during adolescence, maturity and pregnancy. *J. Morph.*, **54**, 521.

TOMILIN, M. I. (1940). Menstrual bleeding and genital swelling in *Miopithecus talapoin*. *Proc. zool. Soc. Lond.*, **110**, 43.

—— & YERKES, R. M. (1935). Chimpanzee twins : behavioural relations and development. *J. gen. Psychol.*, **46**, 239.

TOMPKINS, P. (1945). Basal body temperature graphs as an index to ovulation. *J. Obstet. Gynaec., Brit. Emp.*, **52**, 241.

TRIMBERGER, G. (1941). Menstruation frequency and its relation to conception in dairy cows. *J. Dairy Sci.*, **24**, 819.

TRUM, B. F. (1940). The days of oestrus during which a mare will conceive. (Quoted in *Vet. Bull.*, 1942, **12**, 426.)

TURNER, C. D. (1948). *General endocrinology*. Philadelphia : London.

TURNER, C. W. (1936). Seasonal variation in the birth rate of the milking goat in the United States. *J. Dairy Sci.*, **19**, 619.

VAZQUEZ-LOPEZ, F. (1949). Innervation of the rabbit adenohypophysis. *J. Endocrinol.*, **6**, 158.

VELDE, T. H. VAN DE (1928). *Ideal marriage. Its physiology and technique*. London.

VENABLE, J. H. (1939). Intra-uterine bleeding in the pregnant albino rat. The " Placental Sign." *Anat. Rec.*, **74**, 273.

VENNING, E. H. (1946). Adrenal function in pregnancy. *Endocrinology*, **39**, 203.

—— (1952). Progesterone metabolism : a review. *Ciba Foundation Colloquia on Endocrinology*, **2**, 1.

—— & BROWNE, J. S. L. (1937). Studies on corpus luteum function. I. The urinary excretion of sodium pregnanediol glucuronidate in the human menstrual cycle. *Endocrinology*, **21**, 711

VEVERS, G. M. (1926). Some notes on the recent birth of a hippopotamus (*H. amphibius*) in the Gardens. *Proc. zool. Soc. Lond.*, **1926**, 1897.

VIERGIVER, E., & POMMERENKE, W. T. (1944). Measurement of the cyclic variations in quantity of cervical mucus and its correlation with basal temperature. *Amer. J. Obstet. Gynec.*, **48**, 321.

VOGT, C. (1881). Recherches sur l'embryogénie des chauve-souris (Chiroptères). *C. R. Ass. franç. Av. Sci.*, **10**, 655.

VOGT, M. (1931). Über den Mechanismus der Auslösung der Gravidität und Pseudo-gravidität, zugleich ein physiologischer Beweis für die sympathische Innervation des Hypophysenvorderlappens. *Arch. exp. Path. Pharmak.*, **162**, 197.

—— (1942). Ovulation in the rabbit after destruction of the greater superficial petrosal nerves. *J. Physiol.*, **100**, 410.

VOSSELER, J. (1930). Zur Fortpflanzung des Känguruhs. *Zool. Gart., Lpz.*, **3**, 1.

WADE, O. (1927). Breeding habits and early life of the thirteen-striped ground squirrel, *Citellus tridecemlineatus* (Mitchill). *J. Mammal.*, **8**, 269.

—— (1928). Notes on the time of breeding and the number of young of *Cynomys ludovicianus*. *J. Mammal.*, **9**, 149.

WAGENEN, G. VAN (1945a). Mating in relation to pregnancy in the monkey. *Yale J. Biol. Med.*, **17**, 745.

—— (1945b). Optimal mating time for pregnancy in the monkey. *Endocrinology*, **37**, 307.

—— (1947). Early mating and pregnancy in the monkey. *Endocrinology*, **40**, 37.

—— (1949). Accelerated growth with sexual precocity in female monkeys receiving testosterone propionate. *Endocrinology*, **45**, 544.

—— (1950). In *The care and breeding of laboratory animals*. Ed. E. J. Farris. New York.

—— & NEWTON, W. H. (1943). Pregnancy in the monkey after removal of the fetus. *Surg. Obstet. Gynec.* **77**, 539.

WALKER, G. (1910). A special function discovered in a glandular structure hitherto supposed to form a part of the prostate gland in rats and guinea pigs. *Johns Hopk. Hosp. Bull.*, **21**, 182.

WALLACE, R. (1876). *Farming industries of Cape Colony*. London. (Quoted by Marshall, F. H. A., 1922.)

—— (1904). *Argentine shows and live stock*. Edinburgh. (Quoted by Marshall, F. H. A., 1922.)

—— (1907). *Farm live stock of Great Britain*. 4th ed. London. (Quoted by Marshall, F. H. A., 1922.)

WALTON, A. (1927). The relation between " density " of sperm-suspension and fertility as determined by artificial insemination of rabbits. *Proc. Roy. Soc.* B, **101**, 303.

—— & HAMMOND, J. (1928). Observations on ovulation in the rabbit. *Brit. J. exp. Biol.*, **6**, 190.

WARD, M. C. (1946). A study of the oestrous cycle and the breeding of the golden hamster, *Cricetus auratus*. *Anat. Rec.*, **94**, 139.

WARREN, E. P. (1910). *The mammals of Colorado*. New York.

WARREN, E. R. (1926). Notes on the breeding of wood rats of the genus *Neotoma*. *J. Mammal.*, **7**, 97.

WATTEVILLE, H. DE (1950). Clinical use of hormone determinations in urine. *Edinb. med. J.*, **57**, 403.

WEBER, A. F., MORGAN, B. B., & McNUTT, S. H. (1948). A histological study of metrorrhagia in the virgin heifer. *Amer. J. Anat.*, **83**, 309.

WEICHERT, C. K. (1940). The experimental shortening of delayed pregnancy in the albino rat. *Anat. Rec.*, **77**, 31.

—— (1943). Effect of environmental stilbestrol in shortening prolonged gestation in the lactating rat. *Proc. Soc. exp. Biol., N.Y.*, **53**, 203.

WELLS, L. J. (1935). Seasonal sexual rhythm and its experimental modification in the male of the thirteen-lined ground squirrel (*Citellus tridecemlineatus*) *Anat. Rec.*, **62**, 409.

—— (1936). Prolongation of breeding capacity in males of an annual breeding wild rodent (*Citellus tridecemlineatus.*). *Anat. Rec.* (*Abstr.*), **64**, 138.

—— (1937). The fibro-muscular scrotal sac under normal and experimental conditions in an annual breeder (*Citellus*). *Proc. Soc. exp. Biol., N.Y.*, **36**, 625.

Wells, L. J. (1938). Gonadotropic potency of the hypophysis in a wild male rodent with annual rut. *Endocrinology*, **22**, 588.

—— & Moore, C. R. (1936). Hormonal stimulation of spermatogenesis in the testis of the ground squirrel. *Anat. Rec.*, **66**, 181.

—— & Zalesky, M. (1940). Effects of low environmental temperature on the reproductive organs of male mammals with annual aspermia. *Amer. J. Anat.* **66**, 429.

West, E., & Fevold, H. L. (1940). A comparison of interstitial cell-stimulating, ovarian stimulating, and inhibiting actions of pituitary glands of different species. *Proc. Soc. exp. Biol., N.Y.*, **44**, 446.

Westman, A., & Jacobsohn, D. (1940). Endokrinologische Untersuchungen an Kaninchen mit durchtrenntem Hypophysenstiel. *Acta. obstet. gynec. scand.*, **20**, 392.

Wheeler, J. F. G. (1930). The age of fin whales at physical maturity with a note on multiple ovulations. *Discovery Rep.*, **2**, 403.

White, W. E., & Leonard, S. L. (1933). Ovarian responses to prolan and anterior pituitary extract in hypophysectomized rabbits with particular reference to ovulation. *Amer. J. Physiol.*, **104**, 44.

Wight, H. M. (1930). Breeding habits and economic relations of the Dalles pocket gopher. *J. Mammal.*, **11**, 40.

—— (1931). Reproduction in the Eastern skunk (*Mephitis mephitis nigra*). *J. Mammal.*, **12**, 42.

Wilkinson, J. F., & Fremery, P. de (1940). Gonadotropic hormones in the urine of the giraffe. *Nature, Lond.*, **146**, 491.

Williams, J. H. (1950). *Elephant Bill*. London.

Wilson, D. C., & Sutherland, I. (1949). The age of the ménarche. *Brit. med. J.*, **2**, 130.

—— —— (1950). Age at the ménarche. *Brit. med. J.*, **1**, 1267.

Wilson, R. B., Randall, L. M., & Osterberg, A. E. (1939). Studies on pregnandiol. *Amer. J. Obstet. Gynec.*, **37**, 59.

Wilson, S. G. (1946). The seasonal incidence of calving and of sexual activity in zebu cattle in Nyasaland. *J. agric. Sci.*, **36**, 246.

Wilson, W. K. (1936). A tamewild rabbit cross. *J. Hered.*, **27**, 127.

Wiltshire, A. (1883). Lectures on the comparative physiology of menstruation. *Brit. med. J.*, **1**, 395 ; 446 ; 500.

Wimsatt, W. A. (1942). Survival of spermatozoa in the female reproductive tract of the bat. *Anat. Rec.*, **83**, 299.

—— (1944a). Further studies on the survival of spermatozoa in the female reproductive tract of the bat. *Anat. Rec.*, **88**, 193.

—— (1944b). Growth of the ovarian follicle and ovulation in *Myotis lucifugus lucifugus*. *Amer. J. Anat.*, **74**, 129.

Wishart, J., & Hammond, J. (1933). A statistical analysis of the interrelations of litter size and duration of pregnancy on the birth weight of rabbits. *J. agric. Sci.*, **23**, 463.

Wislocki, G. B. (1927). On the placentation of the tridactyl sloth (*Bradypus griseus*) with a description of some characters of the fetus. *Contr. Embryol. Carneg. Instn.*, **19**, 209.

—— (1928). The placentation of hyrax (*Procavia capensis*). *J. Mammal.*, **9**, 117.

—— (1930). On a series of placental stages of a platyrrhine monkey (*Ateles geoffroyi*) with some remarks upon age, sex, and breeding period in platyrrhines. *Contr. Embryol. Carneg. Instn.*, **22**, 173.

—— (1939). Observations on twinning in marmosets. *Amer. J. Anat.*, **64**, 445.

—— (1943). Studies on growth of deer antlers. II. Seasonal changes in the male reproductive tract of the Virginia deer (*Odocoileus virginianus borealis*) with a discussion of the factors controlling the antler-gonad periodicity. In *Essays in Biology*. Berkeley : Los Angeles.

—— (1949). Seasonal changes in the testes, epididymides and seminal vesicles of deer investigated by histochemical methods. *Endocrinology*, **44**, 167.

—— Aub, J. C., & Waldo, C. M. (1947). The effects of gonadectomy and the administration of testosterone propionate on the growth of antlers in male and female deer. *Endocrinology*, **40**, 202.

WISLOCKI, G. B., & HARTMAN, C. G. (1929). On the placentation of a macaque (*Macaca rhesus*) with observations on the origin of the blood constituting the placental sign. *Johns Hopk. Hosp. Bull.*, **44**, 165.

—— & KING, L. S. (1936). The permeability of the hypophysis and hypothalamus to vital dyes, with a study of the hypophyseal vascular supply. *Amer. J. Anat.*, **58**, 421.

—— WEATHERFORD, H. L., & SINGER, M. (1947). Osteogenesis of antlers investigated by histological and histochemical methods. *Anat. Rec.*, **99**, 265.

—— & WESTHUYSEN, O. P. VAN DER (1940). The placentation of *Procavia capensis*, with a discussion of the placental affinities of the *Hyracoidea*. *Contr. Embryol. Carneg. Instn.*, **28**, 65.

WITSCHI, E. (1940). The quantitative determination of follicle stimulating and luteinizing hormones in mammalian pituitaries and a discussion of the gonadotropic quotient, F/L. *Endocrinology*, **27**, 437.

WOLFE, J. M. (1930). Effect of a diet low in salts on oestrous cycle of albino mouse. *Proc. Soc. exp. Biol., N.Y.*, **27**, 333.

WOOD, F. D. (1935). Notes on the breeding behaviour and fertility of *Neotoma fuscipes macrotis* in captivity. *J. Mammal.*, **16**, 105.

WOOD JONES, F.—see under Jones, F. Wood.

WRIGHT, P. L. (1942a). Delayed implantation in the long-tailed weasel (*Mustela frenata*), the short-tailed weasel (*Mustela cicognanii*) and the marten (*Martes americana*). *Anat. Rec.*, **83**, 341.

—— (1942b). A correlation between the spring molt and spring changes in the sexual cycle in the weasel. *J. exp. Zool.*, **91**, 103.

YERKES, R. M. (1934). Multiple births in anthropoid apes. *Science*, **79**, 430.

—— (1939). Sexual behavior in the chimpanzee. *Hum. Biol.*, **11**, 78.

—— (1943). *Chimpanzees. A laboratory colony.* New Haven : London.

—— & ELDER, J. H. (1936). Oestrus, receptivity, and mating in chimpanzees. *Comp. Psychol. Mon.*, **13** (No. 5).

—— & YERKES, A. W. (1929). *The great apes. A study of anthropoid life.* New Haven.

YOUNG, W. C. (1937). The vaginal smear picture, sexual receptivity, and the time of ovulation in the guinea-pig. *Anat. Rec.*, **67**, 305.

—— (1941). Observations and experiments on mating behavior in female mammals. *Quart. Rev. Biol.*, **16**, 135 ; 311.

—— DEMPSEY, E. W., & MYERS, H. I. (1935). Cyclic reproductive behavior in the female guinea-pig. *J. comp. Psychol.*, **19**, 313.

—— —— —— & HAGQUIST, C. W. (1938). The ovarian condition and sexual behavior in the female guinea-pig. *Amer. J. Anat.*, **63**, 457.

—— & YERKES, R. M. (1943). Factors influencing the reproductive cycle in the chimpanzee ; the period of adolescent sterility and related problems. *Endocrinology*, **33**, 121.

ZALESKY, M. (1934). A study of the seasonal changes in the adrenal gland of the thirteen-lined ground squirrel (*Citellus tridecemlineatus*), with particular reference to its sexual cycle. *Anat. Rec.*, **60**, 291.

—— (1935). A study of the seasonal changes in the thyroid gland of the thirteen-lined ground-squirrel (*Citellus tridecemlineatus*), with particular reference to its sexual cycle. *Anat. Rec.*, **62**, 109.

ZARROW, M. X. (1948). The role of the steroid hormones in the relaxation of the symphysis pubis of the guinea-pig. *Endocrinology*, **42**, 129.

ZIETZSCHMANN, O. (1922). Über Funktionen der weiblichen Genitale bei Säugetier und Mensch. *Arch. Gynaek.*, **115**, 201.

ZONDEK, B. (1931), *Die Hormone des Ovariums und des Hypophysenvorderlappens : Untersuchungen zur Biologie und Klinik der weiblichen Genitalfunktion.* Berlin.

—— & SULMAN, F. (1940). Vaginal cycle of *Microtus guentheri* and its responses to estrogenic and gonadotropic hormones. *Proc. Soc. exp. Biol., N.Y.*, **43**, 86.

ZONDEK, H. (1944). *The diseases of the endocrine glands* 4th (2nd English) ed. Baltimore.

ZUCKERMAN, S. (1930). The menstrual cycle of the primates. I. General nature and homology. *Proc. zool. Soc. Lond.*, **1930**, 691.

—— (1931a). The menstrual cycle of the primates. Part III. The alleged breeding-season of primates, with special reference to the Chacma baboon (*Papio porcarius*). *Proc. zool. Soc. Lond.*, **1931**, 325.

—— (1931b). The menstrual cycle of the primates. IV. Observations on the lactation period. *Proc. zool. Soc. Lond.*, **1931**, 593.

—— (1932a). The menstrual cycle of the primates. VI. Further observations on the breeding of primates, with special reference to the suborders *Lemuroidea* and *Tarsioidea*. *Proc. zool. Soc. Lond.*, **1932**, 1059.

—— (1932b). *The social life of monkeys and apes.* London.

—— (1933). *Functional affinities of man, monkeys and apes.* London.

—— (1935a). The Aschheim-Zondek diagnosis of pregnancy in the chimpanzee. *Amer. J. Physiol.*, **110**, 597.

—— (1935b). The menstrual cycle of the primates. IX. The effect of oestrin on the denervated sexual skin. *Proc. Roy. Soc.* B, **118**, 22.

—— (1935c). Variation in the sensitivity of different species of monkeys to oestrin. *J. Physiol.*, **84**, 191.

—— (1936). The physiology of fertility in man and monkey. *Eugen. Rev.*, **28**, 37.

—— (1937a). The duration and phases of the menstrual cycle in primates. *Proc. zool. Soc. Lond.* A, **1937**, 315.

—— (1937b). The menstrual cycle of the primates. XI. The part played by oestrogenic hormone in the menstrual cycle. *Proc. Roy. Soc.* B, **123**, 457.

—— (1938). Development of the vagina in the green monkey *Cercopithecus aethiops sabaeus.* *J. Anat., Lond.*, **72**, 471.

—— (1947). Duration of reproductive life in the baboon. *J. Endocrinol.*, **5**, 220.

—— (1949). The menstrual cycle. *Lancet*, ii, 1031.

—— (1951). The hormonal basis of uterine bleeding. *Acta endocrinol., Copenhagen*, **7**, 378.

—— (1953). The breeding seasons of mammals in captivity. *Proc. zool. Soc. Lond.*, **122**, 827.

—— & FULTON, J. F. (1934). The menstrual cycle of the primates. Part VII. The sexual skin of the chimpanzee. *J. Anat., Lond.*, **69**, 38.

—— & PARKES, A. S. (1932). The menstrual cycle of the primates. V. The cycle of the baboon. *Proc. zool. Soc. Lond.*, **1932**, 139.

—— WAGENEN, G. VAN, & GARDINER, R. H. (1938). The sexual skin of the rhesus monkey. *Proc. zool. Soc. Lond.* A, **108**, 385.

CHAPTER 5

OVARIAN CHANGES

By F. W. R. Brambell

I. Development of the Ovary and Oögenesis

A broad conception of the fundamental structure of the ovary of an adult vertebrate animal and an appreciation of the significance of the changes proceeding therein are dependent largely on an adequate knowledge of the development of this organ. This introductory section, therefore, is devoted to an outline description of the embryology and post-natal development of the ovary up to the time of puberty.

The Primordial Germ-cells

The formation of the definitive gonads begins at a very early stage in the development of all vertebrates. Waldeyer (1870) expressed the view, held by many of the earlier workers, that the germ-cells arise in the rudiments of the gonads from the cells of the peritoneal or germinal epithelium covering them. Goette (1875) appears to have been the first to recognise that the primordial germ-cells arise from undifferentiated cells, before the formation of the genital ridges and at some distance from where they will be formed. Nussbaum (1880), also, was of opinion that the primordial germ-cells are differentiated before the formation of the germ-layers is completed and that they can be traced back even to the cleavage stages. This view met with early opposition but, with the appearance of Weismann's (1885) theory of the " continuity of the germ-plasm," it became widely accepted. It is now recognised by a large majority of embryologists that the primordial germ-cells do arise exceedingly early, long before the rudiments of the gonads are formed and at a distance from the sites which they will occupy. They originate, at least in many instances, from the primitive endoderm and subsequently migrate through the tissues to the sites of the definitive gonads. Their subsequent fate within the gonads, whether they give rise to all, some or none of the definitive germ-cells, is still disputed.

Primordial germ-cells have been described in representatives of all the classes of vertebrates. The following are the more important papers, in addition to those referred to in the text, dealing with the subject ; in cyclostomes, Butcher (1929) ; in teleosts, Eigenmann (1891), Böhi (1904), Fedorow (1907), Richards and Thompson (1921), Essenberg (1923), Reinhard (1924), Stromsten (1929), Wolf (1931) and Goodrich, Dee, Flynn and Mercer (1934) ; in urodeles, Hall (1904), B. M. Allen (1911b), Schapitz (1912), Spehl and Polus (1912), Beccari (1929), Humphrey (1928, 1929a), McCosh (1930), Fischer (1935) and Burger (1937) ; in anurans, M. Bouin (1900), Hall (1904), B. M. Allen (1907b), King

(1908), Swingle (1921, 1926), Beccari (1924, 1925), Humphrey (1927b), Perle (1927) and Cheng (1932) ; in reptiles, Hoffmann (1889), Gasparro (1908) and Dustin (1911) ; in birds, Rubaschkin (1907), Dantschakoff (1908, 1931a and b, 1932a), Firket (1913), Defretin (1924), Hulpieu (1925), Goldsmith (1928), Dants-chakoff, Dantschakoff and Bereskina (1931), Matsumoto (1932) and Blocker (1933) ; and in mammals, Rubaschkin (1909), Fuss (1911, 1913), Jenkinson (1913), Kirkham (1916), Kohno (1925), Rauh (1926), Brambell (1927a), Fischel (1930), Florian (1931), Goldsmith (1932), Politzer (1933), Hamlett (1935a), and West (1937).   Critical reviews of the literature are provided by Firket (1920a), Brambell (1930), Heys (1931), Risley (1933), Bounoure (1934) and Brachet (1935).

Origin of the primordial germ-cells

It has been established that the primordial germ-cells are distinguishable first in the entoderm, in the lateral splanchnic mesoderm, or in the mesentoderm, before the separation of these two layers.   In the lampreys, *Petromyzon* (Wheeler, 1900) and *Entosphenus* (Okkelberg, 1921), they arise in the primitive entoderm posteriorly, symmetrically on each side of the embryo, before the separation of the lateral plate mesoderm.   They are situated in elasmobranchs in the ento-derm on each side of the embryo at the junction of embryonic and extra-embryonic regions (Woods, 1902).   Beard (1900, 1902a and b, 1904) claimed to distinguish them in the pre-embryonal blastoderm immediately beneath the area where the embryonic rudiment arises later.   But Woods (1902) points out that at this stage all the cells, save those of the ectoderm, resemble primordial germ-cells.   They are found in small numbers in the primitive entoderm, before the separation of the mesoderm, in teleosts, but they increase in number subsequently (Dodds, 1910). Hann (1927) distinguished large cells, probably primordial germ-cells, in the pre-intestinal entoderm.   Johnston (1951) describes their very early origin in the region of the dorsal lip of the blastopore in the black bass.   According to B. M. Allen (1910), they are seen first in the entoderm at the level of the hind-gut in ganoids, scattered ventrally and laterally in the wall of the gut in *Lepidosteus* but laterally in the extra-embryonal entoderm in *Amia* in still earlier stages.   They are found first in the entoderm in *Acipenser* also (Maschkowzeff, 1934).   This author observed that the primordial germ-cells of the sturgeon are of two sizes, large and small, according to the amount of yolk present.   The large cells become oögonia and the small transform into interstitial cells in females.   The small cells become the spermatogonia in males.   Among the amphibians the site of origin of the primordial germ-cells appears to differ in the Urodela and Anura.   The majority of authors are agreed that in the urodeles the primordial germ-cells arise in the mesoderm of the lateral plate medio-dorsally, where it joins that of the somitic region.   They thus arise close to the entoderm but apparently not from it. Abramowicz (1913) and Bounoure (1925) both claimed to find them in the ento-derm, but Humphrey (1925), who recognised their entodermal origin in anurans, was unable to find any evidence of it in urodeles.   The early location of the primordial germ-cells in the entoderm of anurans is well established and has been repeatedly confirmed.   The views of Dustin (1907), who alone attempted to describe their origin from the mesoderm, have not received support.   The primordial germ-cells occur in a single median band in the dorsal crest of the entoderm of the archenteric roof of anuran embryos in the earliest stage in which they have been recognised by the majority of investigators. Bounoure (1934) claims to have traced them back to the blastula about to gastrulate, and states that at this time they are segregated from the somatic cells and are situated between the blastocoel and the lower pole, scattered around the embryonic axis. Fifteen to twenty primordial germ-cells are differentiated, and this number is not increased sub-sequently until they have reached the definitive gonads. They come to lie, in consequence of gastrulation, in the anterior part of the yolk-mass, which forms the ventral wall of the archenteron, and they migrate posteriorly and laterally around the archenteron to reach from both sides the dorso-median position in the ento-derm of the archenteric roof. Bounoure describes the presence of specialised cytoplasmic bodies in these cells, which are characteristic, and by means of which their lineage can be traced back to the ovum. This characteristic germinal cyto-plasm in the fertilised egg consists of little homogeneous masses, measuring about 10μ across, which are clearly differentiated by their chromophility from the sur-rounding cytoplasm and are always associated with mitochondria. A number of these bodies are situated close to the vitelline membrane at the lower pole of the ovum. They are distributed to all the blastomeres of the 4-cell stage but the third cleavage results in their segregation in the macromeres. Within the macro-meres they tend to fuse into slightly larger plates and subsequent cleavages result in their distribution to a number of blastomeres around the embryonic axis and between the blastocoel and the lower pole. These bodies remain peripheral in position within the cells until the final cleavage in the late blastula which results in their segregation in the primordial germ-cells. Each then moves inwards and forms a crescentic cap around the nucleus with which the mitochondria and Golgi bodies are associated. Although their exact cytological nature could not be deter-mined, they clearly constitute a germ-cell determinant comparable to that found in certain insect eggs. This work represents so substantial an increase in our know-ledge of the lineage of the primordial germ-cells of vertebrates, and its implications are so far-reaching, that it is very desirable that it should receive independent confirmation.

The primordial germ-cells of reptiles and birds differentiate very early in the extra-embryonic entoderm of the yolk-sac wall, around the margin of the area pellucida. They are formed in a crescentic area around the posterior third of the embryo in Chelonia (B. M. Allen, 1906; Risley, 1933), although Dustin (1910) was unable to find them posterior to the embryo. They are formed all around the embryo in the lizards (Jarvis, 1908; Pasteels, 1953) and in *Sphenodon* (Tribe and Brambell, 1932), although in the latter species they are much more numerous in a crescentic region in front and around the anterior part of the embryo. Their origin is confined to a crescentic area anterior and lateral to the embryo in birds (Swift, 1914). Dustin (1910) found that primordial germ-cells were differentiated in *Chrysemys* before the formation of the medullary groove and notochord, and in *Sphenodon* (Tribe and Brambell, 1932) they were recognisable in the earliest stage examined, in which the medullary plate was not differentiated. They are recognisable in birds (Fig. 5. 2) from the primitive streak stage onwards (Swift, 1914).

Extra-regional primordial germ-cells have been described frequently in the entoderm and splanchnic mesoderm of the yolk-sac stalk and of the gut and in the mesentery of mammalian embryos (Fig. 5. 1). They have been observed in the entoderm of the allantoidean region in presomitic stages of guinea-pig (Celestino da Costa, 1932a and b) and human embryos (Debeyre, 1933 ; Politzer, 1933). The fullest accounts of the entodermal origin and migration of the primordial germ-cells in human embryos is that of Witschi (1948), and of their subsequent history in the developing gonads that of Gillman (1948). They have been recognised at still earlier stages in the embryos of the armadillo, *Tatusia novemcincta*, by Van-neman (1917). They occur in the blastocysts of this species prior to the polyem-bryonic differentiation of the four embryonic rudiments. Not more than two of these cells for each embryonic vesicle are found, lying against the entoderm, between it and the ectoderm outside the region of the formation of the two first

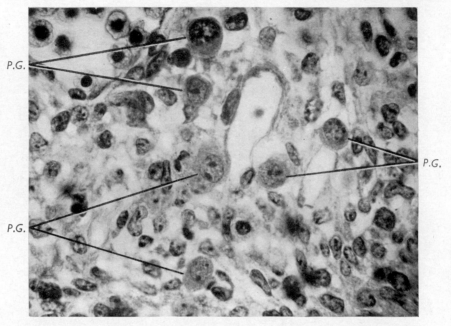

P.G.

P.G.

P.G.

Fig. 5. 1—Photomicrograph of six primordial germ-cells (P.G.) in the mesenchyme above the genital ridge of a 10-day p.c. mouse embryo. × 1000. (From Brambell, 1927a.)

embryonic buds. They are more numerous at the time when the first buds double to form the four embryonic rudiments.

Thus the primordial germ-cells have been shown to arise in the entoderm, before or after the separation of the lateral plate mesoderm, in representatives of all the classes of vertebrates. The weight of evidence favours a mesodermal origin, in the lateral plate after its separation, in the Urodela alone. Their site of origin is extra-regional in all instances, and in the amniotes and some of the fishes it is extra-embryonic. The earliest time in development at which they have been dis-tinguished varies in the different species, but they have been described in pre-somitic stages in representatives of all the classes of vertebrates and their origin prior to the formation of the embryonic rudiment in all three classes of Amniota may be regarded as established. Bounoure's claim that their lineage can be traced throughout cleavage and that a germ-cell determinant is recognisable in the cytoplasm of the unsegmented ovum of the frog is unique.

The primordial germ-cells, from the time of their formation until they reach the definitive gonads, are readily distinguished from the surrounding cells by their cytological characters. They are commonly larger in size than the surrounding entodermal or mesodermal elements, often considerably so as, for example, in the cyclostomes (Wheeler, 1900) and the reptiles (Tribe and Brambell, 1932). The nucleus is usually large, either spherical or slightly crenated, and contains as a rule one or more nucleoli. The cytoplasm is clear in stained preparations, in comparison to the somatic cells conspicuously so, and the cell boundary is sharply

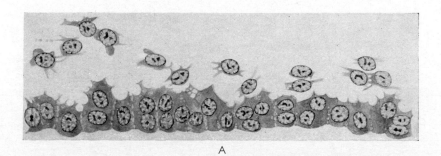

A

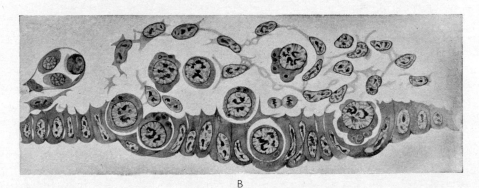

B

Fig. 5. 2—The primordial germ-cells are seen in and beneath the germinal epithelium in a transverse section of the genital ridge of a 3 to 3½-day chick embryo in B. A transverse section of the region of the genital ridge of a chick embryo in which the extra-regional primordial germ-cells had been destroyed previous to migration by the operative removal of the germ-cell crescent is shown in A. The absence both of primordial germ-cells and of thickening of the germinal epithelium is evident. (After Dantschakoff, 1932b.)

defined. The shape of the cell may be either rounded or irregular owing to the presence of blunt pseudopodial-like lobes. The cytoplasm of the primordial germ-cells, except in the mammals, contains numerous yolk-globules, often notably uniform in size (Tribe and Brambell, 1932), which are retained long after the yolk has disappeared from the surrounding cells, and which provide a useful means of identification. The mitochondria, which are small and granular, have been described by Aunap (1913) in teleosts, by Tschaschin (1910), Berenberg-Gossler (1913), Firket (1914) and Swift (1914) in birds, and by Rubaschkin (1910, 1912), Kingery (1917) and Rauh (1929) in mammals. The Golgi apparatus in the primordial germ-cells of the chick has been described by Woodger (1925). The centrosphere and Golgi bodies are situated close to the nuclear membrane and the mitochondria are clustered around them, forming a crescentic cap on one side of the nucleus. The primordial germ-cells are not specialised and they resemble in their cytological characters undifferentiated cells, such as the blastomeres of the egg during the later stages of cleavage. They do not, as a rule, multiply mitotically after their formation, until they have reached the forming gonads, but Swift (1914), Jordan (1917) and Risley (1933) observed that they do so both before and during migration in birds and reptiles, and Beccari (1921) noted mitoses before migration in anurans.

Migration of the primordial germ-cells

The primordial germ-cells, migrating from their site of origin to the forming genital ridges, follow either of two main routes. First, they may migrate through the entoderm, or adjoining splanchnic mesoderm, or both, to the dorsal median line of the entoderm or to the mesentery. Thence they migrate up the mesentery and outwards on each side to the genital ridges, formed between the mesentery and the Wolffian ducts on the ventro-median border of each mesonephros. Second, from the extra-embryonic entoderm into the blood-islands of the area vasculosa and thence via the blood-stream to the mesonephric region of the dorsal aorta. There the primordial germ-cells wander out of the vessel, through its walls and the intervening mesoderm, to the genital ridges. The first is the route followed in the majority of vertebrates, including the Chelonia (Risley, 1933), but the latter is used in birds and in lizards (Pasteels, 1953) and by many, but not all, of the primordial germ-cells in *Sphenodon*. Dustin (1910) laid great stress upon the grouping of the primordial germ-cells ; first in the entoderm at the margin of the area pellucida on each side of the embryo, forming bilaterally symmetrical cords of cells ; then in a single median cord in the mesentery or adjoining entoderm ; finally in the genital ridges. He distinguishes these three successive stages at which concentration of the primordial germ-cells occurs as " glandes paires primaires," " glande impaire médiane," and " glandes paires secondaires ou définitives." B. M. Allen (1911a) denied that these three locations had any special significance, except as points on the migration path of the primordial germ-cells. The concentration of the primordial germ-cells to form the primary paired cords, as undoubtedly occurs in chelonian embryos is not a universal phenomenon, but the median unpaired concentration is more general and is shown remarkably clearly by anuran embryos.

The means by which the apparent migration of the primordial germ-cells is effected may be (a) growth resulting in passive changes in their relative position ; (b) active movements, presumably amoeboid, of the individual cells through the tissues ; and (c) passive transport in the blood-stream. Berenberg-Gossler (1913) attributed migration entirely to unequal growth. Probably this factor plays a large part in the apparent change in position. The growth in size of the embryo itself, with its consequent lateral extension, would result in cells, at first extra-embryonic, being drawn within the embryo. The median approximation of the splanchnopleur on each side above the gut, to form the mesentery, would account for further relative movement. Humphrey (1925) attributes the migration of the primordial germ-cells in Amphibia entirely to such growth changes. Dantschakoff (1931a) speaks of the displacement of the gonad as a whole as being due to the differential growth of the mesonephros and the gut. Apart from growth changes, amoeboid movement of the primordial germ-cells has been invoked by many authors, including B. M. Allen (1906), Jordan (1917) and Swift (1915). Swift maintained that the primordial germ-cells show selectivity because, in the chick, larger numbers reach the left ovary than the right, which remains rudimentary. The evidence for amoeboid movement rests partly on the pseudopodial processes observed in the cells, especially in those in the vessels of the chick where the blood provides a favourable fluid medium for the protrusion of such processes, and partly on the difficulty in accounting fully for the movement in any other way. Pseudopodial processes have been observed in the living germ-cells of the chick cultured *in vitro* by the hanging-drop method (Muratori, 1937). Thus the transference of the primordial germ-cells in the chick from the entoderm to the blood-islands of the area vasculosa, and their subsequent escape from the blood-stream by penetrating the aortic wall, must involve active movement of the individual cells. The passive transport of the primordial germ-cells in the blood-stream in the embryos of *Sphenodon* and of birds is indisputable, since they have been observed in the vessels of all parts of the body but especially in the vitelline veins, heart and aorta.

Not all the primordial germ-cells attain their goal in the gonads, since many get lost on the way and, presumably, degenerate ultimately. B. M. Allen (1907a) finds, from statistical investigation, that only about 50 per cent of the primordial germ-cells complete their migration and reach the genital ridges. Aberrant primordial germ-cells have been found in almost all the embryonic tissues. They occur frequently in *Sphenodon* (Tribe and Brambell, 1932) in the smaller vessels of the head, in which they appear to have jammed in the lumen, completely occluding it.

Fate of the primordial germ-cells

There has been, and still is, much diversity of opinion regarding the functional significance and fate of the primordial germ-cells. Some authors have maintained that the primordial germ-cells all degenerate and that the definitive germ-cells are differentiated later, being derived exclusively from the mesodermal elements of the peritoneal or germinal epithelium covering the genital ridges. Simkins (1923, 1925, 1928) and Simkins and Asana (1930) deny the germinal nature of the so-called primordial germ-cells altogether. Berenberg-Gossler (1913) regarded them as entodermal wandering cells, which become transformed into mesodermal elements, although he recognised their migration and admitted that some of them reach the genital ridges. Kuschakewitsch (1190) maintained that, while the oögonia are derived from the primordial germ-cells, the spermatogonia are derived exclusively from mesodermal elements. De Winiwarter and Sainmont (1909), de Winiwarter (1910), Felix (1912), Kingery (1917), Hargitt (1924, 1925, 1930a, b and c) and Stieve (1927), amongst others, stated that the primordial germ-cells all degenerate and that the definitive germ-cells have a mesodermal origin later.

Many other authors have recognised the possibility of a dual origin of the definitive germ-cells, maintaining that while some are, or may be, derived from the primordial germ-cells, others are certainly derived from mesodermal elements, which differentiate later within the gonads.

Finally, the view that the definitive germ-cells are derived exclusively from the primordial germ-cells has received quite as much support from competent observers.

This diversity of opinion is due largely to the fact that the primordial germ-cells, soon after entering the genital ridges, lose the cytological characteristics which render their identification so easy during migration. The yolk-globules, when present, are absorbed and disappear from the cytoplasm ; in the mammals, in which yolk is absent, they were never present. However, in certain instances (Tribe and Brambell, 1932), some of the primordial germ-cells, before losing their yolk-content and while still identifiable, enter upon the characteristic stages of the prophase of the heterotypic division. Thus their germinal nature may be regarded as established, whatever their subsequent fate may be, despite the contrary conclusions of Simkins. The germ-cells within the genital ridges enter upon a phase of mitotic multiplication and the resulting oögonia are not much larger than some of the surrounding epithelial elements. Moreover, in consequence of the difficulty of estimating accurately the rates of multiplication and degeneration, counts at successive stages of the germ-cells in the genital ridges have failed to throw much light on the problem.

It must be admitted that, so far, the histological method alone has failed to solve the problem of the fate of the primordial germ-cells, though clearly establishing their early extra-regional origin, migration, presence in the genital ridges and germinal nature. Fortunately the experimental method has been applied successfully to amphibian and avian embryos and has thrown much further light on the problem.

The gonads develop abnormally slowly in frog embryos derived from eggs that were over-ripe when fertilised. Kuschakewitsch (1910) came to the conclusion that this was because no primordial germ-cells were differentiated from the entoderm and that the spermatogonia (the offspring of these cultures being all males), which appeared later, arose from mesodermal elements. Witschi (1915, 1929a) confirmed the observation that the germ-cells are late in appearing in the gonads of the embryos from such cultures, but he attributed this to a slowing-up of the migration of the primordial germ-cells. The most convincing results obtained with the Amphibia are those described by Humphrey (1927a), using embryos of *Amblystoma*, in which the superficial position of the primordial germ-cells in the intermediate mesoderm on each side renders their operative removal possible. The intermediate mesoderm, together with the adjacent parts of the axial and lateral mesoderm, the pronephric duct and the overlying ectoderm from the 7th to the 16th somite, were excised on one side only. Approximately two-thirds of the operated animals survived ; the primordial germ-cells were found to have been completely removed in many instances and no gonad was developed on the operated side. Bounoure (1935a and b, 1937a, b, c and d) has extended his investigations (see p. 399) of the germ-cell determinant of the frog's egg by experimental means. He has shown that irradiation with ultra-violet rays of the vegetative pole of the egg, before cleavage, results in the production of individuals with reduced gonads. The atrophic gonads in the experimental animals, at the time of metamorphosis, consist of thin strands of tissue, the same length as, but of much smaller diameter than, the gonads of control animals from the same batch of eggs. Histological examination revealed that the number of germ-cells in the gonads of the experimental animals was small and never more than 10 per cent of the normal ; in each of two animals germ-cells were absent in one gonad and only one or two were present in the other. The rete-cords were differentiated and exhibited sexual dimorphism, enabling the atrophic gonads to be identified as ovaries or testes. It was shown that this sterilisation resulted from the irradiation of the germ-cell determinant and not from the effects on the egg as a whole, since the gonads developed normally in animals raised from eggs in which the animal pole had been irradiated. These results appear to provide conclusive proof of the presence of a germ-cell determinant in the cytoplasm of the vegetative pole of the unsegmented egg of the frog. Monroy (1939) has shown experimentally that the primordial germ-cells of Discoglossus are localised in the ventral entoderm at an early stage of development. Removal of this part of the entoderm results in the absence of germ-cells from the embryo.

Reagan (1916) was the first to attempt operative removal of the extra-regional primordial germ-cells of chick embryos. He excised the area of extra-embryonic blastoderm in front of the embryo in which the primordial germ-cells are localised in presomitic stages. None of the operated embryos survived more than five days, but at that stage primordial germ-cells were absent from the gonads, which were completely sterile and consisted only of stromal tissue with its peritoneal covering. Goldsmith (1935) repeated these experiments and found no primordial germ-cells in embryos in which the germ-cell region was destroyed entirely, but none of the embryos lived beyond the fifth day of incubation. Benoit (1930, 1931) succeeded in destroying the primordial germ-cells in 18- to 22-hour chick embryos by irradiation with ultra-violet rays ; the embryos being protected by a suitable screen and the crescentic extra-embryonic area containing the gonocytes exposed. Germ-cells were absent from some of the surviving embryos treated in this way. Dantschakoff (1932b), reviewing a series of experimental researches, states that the operative destruction of the extra-regional primordial germ-cells results in the absence of germ-cells from the embryo, and also in the genital ridges failing to develop (Fig. 5. 2). It was concluded that the primordial germ-cells upon reaching the genital ridge act as an organiser, which is responsible for provoking the further differentiation of the gonad. This conclusion left unsolved the problem of whether the primordial germ-cells themselves gave rise to the definitive germ-cells or whether they induced the formation of the latter from the germinal epithelium. The destruction was attempted of the germinal epithelium before the arrival in the genital ridges of the primordial germ-cells, with a view to the solution of this problem. This was attained by the operative removal of the caudal part of the embryo at about the 20-somite stage. The primordial germ-cells in such half-embryos subsequently accumulate in the region medioventral to the mesonephros. This region contains, with the exception of the " germinal epithelium," all the component tissues of an embryonic gonad : viz. nephrogeneous tissue, peritoneal epithelium and mesenchyme. Perfect gonad rudiments were developed in this region in the half-embryos, which did not survive more than six and a half days. The further development of such rudiments was obtained by grafting them on to the chorio-allantoic membrane of other embryos. These experiments demonstrate that the particular field of peritoneal epithelium, known as the germinal epithelium, which normally covers the genital ridges, is not essential for the differentiation of a gonad rudiment but it does not preclude the possibility of the induction by the primordial germ-cells, acting as an organiser, of germ-cell formation from any part of the peritoneal epithelium beneath which they lie. Willier (1937) investigated the development of gonads in chorio-allantoic grafts of isolated pieces of chick blastoderms at stages before, during and after the migration of the primordial germ-cells. He found that sterile gonads developed in the grafts irrespective of whether primordial germ-cells were, or were not, included in the original explant. These sterile gonads were composed of medullary cords, no cortical tissue ever developing. This result indicates that the development of a gonad may be initiated but cannot proceed far and cannot produce a cortex in the absence of germ-cells. The fact that rudimentary gonads are formed in the frog after the majority of the primordial germ-cells have been destroyed by the irradiation of the egg with ultra-violet light (see p. 404) and that these gonads exhibit incipient differentiation of sex, appears to conflict with the conception that the primordial germ-cells act as organisers in the organogenesis of the gonad. It should be remembered, however, that germ-cells, though greatly reduced in number, were never found to be absent from both gonads at the time of metamorphosis. Moreover, it is possible that they were more numerous at an earlier stage when the gonads were differentiating, and subsequently degenerated before metamorphosis ; such delay in the effect of irradiation on tissue-components being a well-known phenomenon.

It has been shown by Martinovitch (1938) that germ-cells are not formed from the germinal epithelium and arise exclusively from the mitotic division of previously differentiated oögonia in ovaries of embryo and new-born rats and mice excised and cultured *in vitro* for periods of up to one month.

Everett (1943) found that transplants of the prospective genital ridges of mice, removed before the primordial germ-cells have reached them, will differentiate into mesonephric and genital ducts but remain devoid of germ-cells. Similar transplants made after the primordial germ-cells have reached the genital ridges, differentiate into typical ovarian and testicular tissue as well as into ducts.

Other experimental evidence regarding the fate of the primordial germ-cells in mammals is that female mice can be sterilised at or before their birth by exposure to X-rays (Brambell, Parkes and Fielding, 1927b), the ovaries remaining permanently free from germ-cells. The evidence for the later formation of germ-cells from the germinal epithelium can be dealt with more conveniently (see p. 421) after the organogenesis of the ovary has been described.

Differentiation of the Ovary

Formation of the genital ridges

The formation of the genital ridges begins with the arrival of the primordial germ-cells in and beneath the peritoneal epithelium on each side, midway between the base of the mesentery and the Wolffian duct. The peritoneal epithelium in this region thickens and becomes more clearly differentiated from the underlying mesenchyme. Its cells, usually resting upon a distinct basement membrane, become cubical or columnar and begin to proliferate actively. Sometimes the cell boundaries are indistinct and the tissue appears syncytial (B. M. Allen, 1904). The primordial germ-cells become embedded in this thickened epithelium although some may remain for a time beneath it, free in the underlying mesenchyme. The germinal epithelium is clearly differentiated from the squamous epithelium of adjoining regions of the peritoneum and soon forms a definite longitudinal germinal ridge projecting into the splanchnocoel. The development of the germinal ridges, as of the other organs in the vertebrate embryo, begins anteriorly and extends posteriorly. The anterior extremities always are slightly more advanced in development than the posterior. The longitudinal extent of the genital ridges varies in different forms, beginning behind the anterior extremity of the mesonephros and extending posteriorly a variable distance beyond its caudal end. The anterior and posterior extremities of the genital ridges gradually taper away. The definitive gonad arises from the middle region of the genital ridge to which the germ-cells are confined. The anterior and posterior regions of the genital ridge lack germ-cells and remain permanently sterile. The anterior sterile region gives rise to the suspensory ligament of the ovary and, in the Amphibia, to the fat-body. The posterior sterile region in mammals becomes the utero-ovarian ligament.

The continued proliferation of the germinal epithelium of the middle region of the genital ridge leads to the gonad rudiment projecting more and more into the coelom and thickening progressively. The gonad becomes in this way cylindrical in form. The base by which it is attached to the body wall, at first relatively broad, becomes constricted to form a narrow mesentery, the mesovarium. During these growth processes, leading to the delimitation of the gonad, a core of mesenchymal tissue becomes included within it. Thus the gonad consists at first of the thickened germinal epithelium, actively proliferating and containing the germ-cells, enclosing a central core of mesenchymal cells. The growth in length of the gonad as development proceeds is not as rapid as that of the adjoining tissue and hence it becomes progressively relatively shorter and broader.

The correct interpretation of the organogenesis of the vertebrate gonad began with the recognition by Janosik (1885, 1890) that the epithelial cords arise by proliferation directly from the peritoneal or germinal epithelium covering the site of the future gonad, and with the description, simultaneously, by Mihálkovics (1885) of the origin of the rete-cords from outgrowths of the mesonephric epithelium of the walls of Bowman's capsules. Yet the full significance of these discoveries was not realised until the appearance of the series of papers by the Belgian embryologists de Winiwarter and Sainmont on the development of the gonads of mammals and, in particular, of their joint paper (1909) on the ovary of the cat. This classical work provided the basis for all modern researches on the development of the ovary. The earlier work has become of little, save historic, interest and may be virtually disregarded. Existing knowledge of the organogenesis of the mammalian ovary is far more complete than that of the ovaries of other vertebrates, although fairly complete and consistent accounts are available for the amphibians, reptiles and birds. With the exception of the papers by Okkelberg (1921) on the lamprey, *Entosphenus wilderi* Gage, and by Essenberg (1923) on the teleost, *Xiphopherus helleri* Heckel, there has been little recent work on gonadogenesis in cyclostomes and fishes.

The early development of the indifferent gonad, before its differentiation into ovary or testis, is effected mainly by (*a*) proliferation of the germinal epithelium accompanied by multiplication of the germ-cells contained in it, and (*b*) the formation of the rete-cords from mesonephric elements resulting in the establishment of the urino-genital connection. These two processes,

although for convenience reviewed in sequence, proceed simultaneously in
development.

The medullary cords

The initial proliferation of the germinal epithelium results in the production
of the sex-cords of epithelial and germ-cells. These give rise to the spermatic
tubules, if the gonad differentiates into a testis, and to the medullary cords, if it
becomes an ovary. Hence the spermatic tubules of the testis are homologous
to the medullary cords of the ovary. The sex-cords arise in some species, including
the rabbit (de Winiwarter, 1901), cat (Sainmont, 1906 ; de Winiwarter and
Sainmont, 1909 ; Kingsbury, 1913), pig (B. M. Allen, 1904), fowl (Swift, 1916 ;
Firket, 1914, 1920b ; Dantschakoff, 1933) and turtle (B. M. Allen, 1905 ; Risley,
1933) by the ingrowth of finger-shaped processes or invaginations from the proliferating germinal epithelium into the underlying mesenchyme. These cords of
cells, which do not branch, lengthen both by the proliferation of their component
cells and by continued formation from the epithelium, to which they remain
attached for a time. The proliferation of the germinal epithelium in other species,
such as the mouse (Brambell, 1927a) and the rat (Torrey, 1945), results in the
formation of a solid epithelial nucleus or core, which later becomes split up into
cords of cells by the downgrowth into it from the genital ridge of mesenchymal
elements. A similar method of formation of the medullary cords in the human
embryo has been described by Felix (1912) and by Gruenwald (1942), but their
ingrowth from the epithelium, as in most other species, was noted by de Winiwarter
(1910), Simkins (1928) and Stieve (1927). The formation of the genital ridges
in the human embryo has been investigated also by Higuchi (1932). The development of the gonad in Amphibia, in which the adult ovary contains little,
if any, medullary tissue, proceeds somewhat differently (Witschi, 1915, 1929a).
The germ-cells of the genital ridge become localised in the germinal epithelium.
The mesenchymal core becomes gelatinous, appearing in sections almost transparent and consequently resembling a large central cavity. The epithelium
exhibits some proliferation but does not give rise to definite sex-cords or to a
massive epithelial nucleus as in amniotes. The germ-cells and some epithelial
cells become detached from the germinal epithelium, move through the mesenchyme and attach themselves to the developing rete-cords in embryonic testes,
but in ovaries they retain permanently their continuity with the germinal
epithelium.

During the formation of the sex-cords the germ-cells multiply. They can be
observed frequently in mitosis, which may account for the whole of the increase
in numbers. It is extremely difficult to distinguish the primordial germ-cells,
which contain no yolk, from the larger and more differentiated epithelial cells,
especially when these are in the early stages of mitosis, in mammals. There is no
doubt that such epithelial cells may present an appearance intermediate between
the undifferentiated peritoneal epithelial cells and the germ-cells. These have
frequently been interpreted as transitional stages in the formation of germ-cells
from the germinal epithelium ; that is, from mesodermal elements (see p. 423).
It is difficult to deny that a second generation of germ-cells may arise in this way
in mammals. The methods of descriptive morphology have failed so far to solve
this problem, and appear to be inadequate to do so. Moreover, in vertebrates

other than mammals, once the characteristic yolk-globules have disappeared from the primordial germ-cells, a similar difficulty in determining whether or not new germ-cells arise from epithelial elements presents itself. Since this problem is bound up with that of the formation of germ-cells in the adult ovary further reference will be made to it (see p. 427).

Many of the germ-cells, whatever their origin, become included in the sex-cords, both in males and females. Some germ-cells remain in the germinal epithelium in embryonic ovaries after the formation of the medullary cords has been completed. No germ-cells are found in the germinal epithelium of embryonic testes as a rule after the sex-cords are formed and have lost their connection with the epithelium. Either all the germ-cells were included in the sex-cords or else those that remained in the germinal epithelium rapidly degenerated, the germinal epithelium in the male becoming thin and sterile in consequence. Exceptions to this are found, such as in the salamander, *Amblystoma* (Humphrey, 1929b), and in the turtle, *Sternotherus* (Risley, 1933), in which germ-cells remain for a time in the germinal epithelium of the male, as well as in that of the female.

The sex-cords become separated from the germinal epithelium, when their formation is completed, by the down-growth of mesenchymatous elements from the base of the gonad which form a layer, the primitive tunica albuginea, immediately within the germinal epithelium. This tunica isolates the germinal epithelium without from the sex-cords within and its formation marks the termination of the first epithelial proliferation. The primitive tunica albuginea thickens and persists in the embryonic testis, becoming the definitive tunica albuginea. The germinal epithelium in the male becomes reduced in thickness, ceases to proliferate and forms the thin peritoneal covering of the definitive testis. In the embryonic testes of the salamander (Humphrey, 1929b), lizard (Simkins and Asana, 1930), turtle (Risley, 1933), sparrow (Witschi, 1935), rat (Torrey, 1945), and mouse (Brambell, 1927a), the germinal epithelium proliferates for a short time after the formation of the tunica albuginea, forming a rudimentary cortex, corresponding to the cortical proliferation to be described in the ovary. This cortex is abortive and the epithelium soon becomes stretched, thin and inactive. A similar insipient formation of cortical cords in the embryonic testes of man and cat has been described by Gruenwald (1942). The primitive tunica albuginea differentiates in embryonic ovaries also, resulting in the separation of the medullary cords. It is, however, a transitory structure in the female and the degree to which it is developed varies in different species. It is so slight a structure in some that the medullary cords tend to retain their connection with the germinal epithelium, so that no sharp line can be drawn between the first proliferation, which gives rise to them, and the second, which produces the cortical cords.

The ovarian stroma is derived mainly from the mesenchymatous core of the germinal ridge. Later ingrowths of connective and vascular tissues from the hilus may contribute to it. Epithelial elements included in it may be derived either from isolated cells budded off from the germinal epithelium or from the medullary cords (see p. 510 for origin of interstitial cells). Both B. M. Allen (1904) and Risley (1933) expressed the view that the ovarian stroma, in mammals and turtles respectively, was derived entirely from elements of the germinal epithelium.

The urinogenital connection

The efferent ducts of the testis or vasa efferentia in gnathostomes,[1] by means of which the spermatozoa are conveyed from the spermatic to the epididymal tubules, arise in the embryo as a network or rete of cords which connect the sex-cords with some of the mesonephric tubules. The development of the rete and the establishment of the urinogenital connection begins before the differentiation of the embryonic gonad into either an ovary or a testis. Consequently the rete is present in the embryonic ovary as well as in the testis. Although the ova are discharged directly into the coelom in all vertebrates and the ovarian rete does not give rise to functional ducts, it is of importance in the organogenesis of the ovary.

The precise origin of the rete is difficult to determine and appears to vary somewhat in the different orders. The views of the various authors who have investigated the problem may be summarised under four main headings : their formation from (1) condensation of the undifferentiated mesenchyme between the base of the gonad and the mesonephros, (2) an undifferentiated core of epithelial cells of peritoneal origin, at the base of the gonad, (3) epithelial downgrowths from the nephrostomes or nephrostomial canals of the mesonephric tubules, (4) epithelial downgrowths from the walls of Bowman's capsules.

The evidence in favour of a mesenchymal origin is derived chiefly from amphibians and birds. There is substantial agreement amongst those (M. Bouin, 1900 ; Kuschakewitsch, 1910 ; Witschi, 1929a ; Deal, 1931 ; Cheng, 1932), who have investigated the origin of the rete in amphibians. The rete-cords in *Rana sylvatica* (Witschi, 1929a), which are solid at first, are formed in the region of the hilus by the aggregation of single cells of the mesonephric blastema. These cells break away from the blastema and move into the hilus of the gonad. The rete-cords in the female grow slowly, become hollow distally and, the cavities expanding, give rise to the characteristic ovarian sacs which occupy the centre of the hollow amphibian ovary. The rete-cords in the male grow rapidly but remain compact. The germ-cells and epithelial cells, proliferated from the epithelium, migrate through the mesenchyme and become attached to the rete-cords, in connection with which they differentiate into the spermatic tubules. The rete-cords thus are separate primarily both from the gonad and the mesonephric tubules, their connection with these being secondary. In the female the connection of the rete-cords with the mesonephric tubules disappears. Among the birds, Prenant (1890), Firket (1914) and Swift (1915), considered that the rete-cords are derived from a condensation of the mesenchyme lying between the Malpighian corpuscles of the mesonephros and the hilus of the gonad. Sixteen cords are formed in the chick, the first being at the level of the 17th glomerulus. A similar origin has been attributed to the rete in the pig and the dog by Wichmann (1912). Simkins (1923) described the origin of the rete in the rat and the mouse from a blastema formed in the hilus of the gonad by a condensation of connective-tissue cells.

Felix (1912) and Wilson (1926) consider that the rete in the human embryo arises from a core of epithelial cells, lying in the region of the hilus of the gonad. This rete blastema is therefore of peritoneal origin. Thus on this view, as on that of their mesenchymal origin, the connection of the rete-cords with the Malpighian corpuscles is secondary. De Burlet and de Ruiter (1920) similarly derive

[1] The modifications of the male genital ducts in Anamnia and especially in Osteichthyes are reviewed by Goodrich (1930).

the rete in the mouse from a longitudinal core of cells, to which the spermatic tubules are attached, and from an epithelial ridge which is joined to the core. These descriptions lead on to the third theory of the origin of the rete from the nephrostomes or nephrostomial canals.

Fraser (1919) described the origin of the rete in marsupials from a core of cells lying within the genital ridge in front of the rudiment of the gonad. She considered that in *Perameles*, and probably also in *Trichosurus* and other marsupials, this core of cells is derived from the nephrostomial canals of the mesonephros, which lose their connection with both the coelomic epithelium and the Malpighian corpuscles and unite into a continuous mass of cells. Van Beek (1924) also traces the rete in the cow to the pregonal germinal ridge and in the mouse Agduhr (1927) finds that it is formed by downgrowth of epithelial cords from the cranial end of the genital ridge.

In the elasmobranchs (Borcea, 1906 ; Brachet, 1935) the anterior mesonephric tubules, the number varying according to the species, lose their nephrostomes and the free ends of their nephrostomial canals then become connected with the hilus of the testis. These extremities, anastomosing, give rise to a longitudinal canal or system of lacunae, from which epithelial outgrowths arise, become hollow and unite with the seminal accini to form the efferent ducts. The Malpighian corpuscles of the genital region of the mesonephros then atrophy. B. M. Allen described the origin of the rete-cords in the turtle, *Chrysemys* (1905), and in the pig and the rabbit (1904) from the union of invaginations of the coelomic epithelium, which he called funnel cords, with epithelial evaginations from the walls of the Malpighian corpuscles. These funnel cords were evidently nephrostomial canals. They arise in the anterior part of the genital ridge in the mammals and, growing back to the cranial end of the gonad, branch and anastomose. Risley (1933) accepts Allen's derivation of the rete of the turtle from " funnel cords " but denies that any outgrowths from the walls of Bowman's capsules occur. The urinogenital connection in the mouse (Brambell, 1927b) is effected by the downgrowth of strands of cells from the nephrostomial canals which fuse with the epithelial nucleus of the gonad and form the rete. The view that the rete arise from nephrostomial canals in elasmobranchs and amniotes has led to the interesting suggestion (Brachet, 1935) that in primitive ancestral forms open nephrostomes provided the channels by which the spermatozoa, shed into the coelom, escaped to the exterior. The origin of the rete from epithelial outgrowths of the walls of Bowman's capsules described by Mihálkovics (1885) has been supported by Hoffmann (1889, 1892), working on reptiles and birds, and by Peter (1904) on reptiles. These outgrowths growing down through the hilus of the gonad unite with the sex-cords. According to this view, the connection of the rete with the mesonephric tubules is primary but that with the sex-cords is secondary. A similar origin has been ascribed to the rete in the cat (de Winiwarter and Saintmont, 1909), rabbit (de Winiwarter, 1901), mouse (Kingery, 1917 ; Bovy, 1928) and man (de Winiwarter, 1910).

The number of mesonephric tubules involved in the urinogenital connection in mammals varies in different species. The sixth to the twentieth are involved in the pig, and the twelfth to the twentieth in the rabbit (B. M. Allen, 1904). Six to eight tubules are concerned in the mouse (Brambell, 1927b).

The rete in the ovary, after differentiating, soon retrogresses and loses its connection with the tubules of the mesonephros. The rete remains, however, even in the adult, as a few small cords of epithelial cells distinguishable in the region of the hilus of the ovary. The mesonephros in the amniotes, owing to the development of the metanephros, functions as an excretory organ at most for a short period during embryonic life. Consequently, the posterior mesonephric tubules, not involved in the urinogenital connection, retrogress in both sexes. They are represented only by remnants in the adult, forming the paradidymis in the male and the parovarium in the female. The anterior tubules in the female, corresponding to the epididymis in the male, also retrogress, but not so completely as the parovarium. They form the epovarium, a bundle of small blind tubules situated in the mesovarium near the hilus of the ovary, in the adult.

Formation of the ovarian cortex

The formation of the ovarian cortex from a second proliferation of the germinal epithelium, succeeding that which produced the medullary cords, occurs in the ovaries of Amphibia and Amniota. This cortical proliferation is less intense in the amphibians, in which the adult ovary is a hollow sac with relatively thin walls, than in the development of the more massive ovaries of amniotes. Whether the proliferation of the germinal epithelium in cyclostomes and fishes is continuous or can be divided into medullary and cortical phases remains to be determined, but if two distinct proliferations occur then the earlier workers failed to differentiate between them.

Among the Amphibia, Witschi (1915, 1929a) does not distinguish between cortical and medullary proliferations in frogs. However, the germinal epithelium does continue to thicken in the ovaries, chiefly owing to mitotic multiplication of the germ-cells, after the ovaries are distinguishable from testes. This continued multiplication of the germ-cells, accompanied by rearrangement and some multiplication of the epithelial cells, results in the formation of the definitive cortex and obviously corresponds to the cortical proliferation in amniotes. A definite cortical proliferation occurs in *Amblystoma*, since Humphrey (1929b) has shown that even in males in many cases an ovarian cortex is formed outside the sex-cords, which constitute the testis proper. This incipient cortex, usually limited to the ventral surface only, is a transitory structure and does not persist in the testis.

A definite cortical proliferation appears to occur invariably in reptiles, birds and mammals. The growth of the cortex in the musk turtle (Risley, 1933) is due to the differentiation of the deeper cells of the epithelium, multiplication of the epithelial cells and, especially, multiplication of the germ-cells. Lobules of cortical tissue, containing germ-cells, are formed in this way and appear to retain their connection with the germinal epithelium permanently. They are not in the form of definite cortical cords which are separated from the epithelium by the downgrowth of the stroma. A distinct cortical proliferation occurs also in the alligator (Forbes, 1940).

The cortical proliferation in birds (d'Hollander, 1904; Firket, 1914, 1920b; Swift, 1915; Koch, 1926; Dantschakoff, 1933) and in the majority of mammals gives rise to thick, discrete cortical cords of epithelial cells, enclosing many germ-cells. Since Pflüger first showed that the cortical cords originate as epithelial invaginations they are known sometimes as " tubes of Pflüger." The cortical cords as they grow into the ovary break up the primitive tunica albuginea, the mesenchymatous cells of which are carried in around them and contribute to their stromal sheaths.   The growth of the cortical cords also results in the progressive compression of the medullary cords, which are confined to the centre of the gonad. The formation of the cortex continues for a considerable time, until after birth in all mammals and even until the approach of puberty in some.   The cortical proliferation in the mouse is continuous with the medullary, no primitive tunica albuginea being formed.   It does not give rise to separate cords in the mouse (Brambell, 1927a), as it does in the dog (Jonckheere, 1930), cat, rabbit, man (de Winiwarter, 1901, 1910 ; de Winiwarter and Sainmont, 1909), etc.   Probably this is a specialisation due to the small size and rapid development of the mouse.

The medullary cords, after the beginning of the cortical proliferation, undergo a phase of development varying in degree and duration in different species.   The contained germ-cells multiply and then enter upon the characteristic prophase changes of the heterotypic division.   By the time they have reached the resting or dictyate stage, a simple follicle of epithelial cells has differentiated around each. Many of the oöcytes enter upon the growth phase and the follicles may develop antra and may attain a considerable size in some species before retrogression takes place.

Ultimately, all the germ-cells contained in the medullary cords retrogress and the strands of epithelial cells gradually atrophy.   Some of the epithelial cells of the medullary cords may give rise to interstitial cells (see p. 511) and persist as such.

The germ-cells of the cortex multiply and then enter on the prophase of the heterotypic division soon after they have been included in the growing cortical cords.   Consequently, the oöcytes in the deeper parts of the cortex, which was formed first, are in more advanced stages of development than those nearer the germinal epithelium.   Each oöcyte, as in the medullary cords, becomes surrounded by a follicle.   Although diversity of opinion existed among the earlier workers, it is generally recognised now that the cells of the follicular epithelium are derived from the germinal epithelium (Okamoto, 1928).   Some of the oöcytes enter on the growth phase soon after birth, but these are destined to degenerate, like those of the medullary cords, before puberty (Engle, 1931 ; Sneider, 1937 ; Duke, 1941). This pre-pubertal wave of growth and subsequent degeneration of oöcytes is a striking phenomenon in avian and many mammalian ovaries.   It has been suggested that it results in the degeneration of all the primordial germ-cells and that only germ-cells of secondary origin survive, but if the germ-cells have a dual origin there is no means of distinguishing the two kinds or of testing this suggestion.

The completion of the cortical proliferation is marked by the formation of the secondary or definitive tunica albuginea, which separates the cortical cords from the germinal epithelium, to which they were attached previously.   The definitive tunica albuginea is formed, like the primary, by the downgrowth of mesenchymatous elements.   These differentiate into connective tissue.   Smooth muscle cells are present also in the tunica albuginea of the adult ovary.

The cortical proliferation gives rise to the whole of the cortex in reptiles and birds.   The germinal epithelium is said to become active again, at least in some mammals, after the proliferation of the cortical cords has stopped, and to produce a third and final set of epithelial invaginations (Fig. 5. 3). This appears to be the case in the opossum (Nelsen and Swain, 1942), cat (de Winiwarter and Sainmont, 1909), dog (Jonckheere, 1930), rabbit (de Winiwarter, 1901) and man (de Winiwarter, 1910). These epithelial invaginations invade the cortex and are said to be the exclusive source of the definitive germ-cells. Their formation begins some time after birth and continues until puberty, during which time the oöcytes in the cortical cords are said to degenerate completely, like those of the medullary cords. The formation of these invaginations may be delayed in the vicinity of the hilus, and, in the adult ovary, may still be in progress there after it has ceased elsewhere (de Winiwarter, 1920). The nests of young oöcytes, with nuclei in the characteristic stages of the heterotypic prophase, present in the ovaries of adult lemurs (Gérard, 1920, 1932) may be similar. The formation of

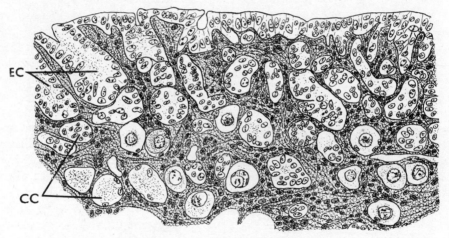

Fig. 5. 3—Epithelial invaginations (EC) and cortical cords (CC) in the ovary of a rabbit six weeks old. × 480. (From Brambell, 1930, after de Winiwarter, 1901.)

ova from epithelial invaginations during adult life in other species (see p. 423), if substantiated, would belong also to this definitive proliferation.

Differentiation of sex

The differentiation of the indifferent gonad into an ovary or a testis does not begin until after the completion of the medullary proliferation and the formation of the primitive tunica albuginea. It occurs soon afterwards in mammals, there being no prolonged indifferent period. The testes differentiate first, the spermatic tubules develop from the medullary cords and the tunica albuginea thickens and persists. The germinal epithelium, which has stopped proliferating, remains inactive and forms the thin peritoneal investment of the organ. The rudiments of the essential components of the testis are present, in fact, in the embryonic gonad immediately before the differentiation of sex. The ovaries remain indifferent for a short time after the testes have differentiated, but they can be identified by elimination. Then the cortical proliferation begins and marks the positive differentiation of the ovary. Thus the " anlage " of the ovary cannot be considered complete until after the formation of the cortex has begun.

Many of the lower vertebrates during development pass through a phase of rudimentary hermaphroditism, when the gonads are ovotestes, before sex is finally differentiated. This appears to be the rule among the Cyclostomata, occurring in *Myxine* (Schreiner, 1904; Cole, F. J., 1905), *Bdellostoma* (Conel, 1917) and *Entosphenus* (Okkelberg, 1921). Okkelberg found that the gonads of all individuals from 35 to 70 mm. long are ovotestes. Oöcytes and spermatic pockets are differentiated throughout the gonads, and the future sex can only be diagnosed by the relative frequency of these. The gonads in some individuals appear to develop first in the direction of one sex and then in that of the other before finally differentiating into either an ovary or a testis. The developing gonad is, at first, hermaphrodite in character in *Acipenser*, as in other fishes, although in this genus there is a remarkable sexual dimorphism in size among the primordial germ-cells (Maschkowzeff, 1934; see p. 398).

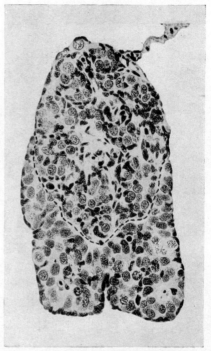

Fig. 5. 4—Photomicrograph of the testis of a larval Amblystoma showing the thickened cortical zone below. The membrane separating the cortex from the spermatic region has been picked out in black. The germ-cells in the cortex have leptotene and pachytene nuclei, unlike the spermatogonia in the spermatic region. × 100. (From Humphrey, 1929b.)

The formation of a cortex, although it is rudimentary and transitory, in the testes of the salamander, lizard, turtle, sparrow and mouse (see p. 409 and Fig. 5. 4) may be interpreted similarly as incipient hermaphroditism. At least it provides in the gonads of both sexes all the essential rudiments of both ovary and testis. The development of ovarian tissue, which gives rise to Bidder's organ in the adult, in the males of all species of *Bufo* examined, is another and better-known example of rudimentary, though not transitory, hermaphroditism. The significance of Bidder's organ in toads is discussed and the relevant literature is cited by Ponsé (1924, 1927), Brambell (1930) and Witschi (1933a) among others.

The occurrence of juvenile or Pflügerian hermaphroditism, both natural and experimentally induced, in Amphibia is well known (see Witschi, 1915, 1921, 1929a, etc.; Willier, 1932). It involves as a rule the transformation of ovaries into testes, not *vice versa*. Some or all of the males in certain species and geographical races of frogs normally undergo such indirect development. The sex-reversal of the gonad takes place at different times during development and even in adult life, according to the species or race. The transformation is brought about, according to Witschi (1921, 1929a), by the migration of germ-cells from the base of the germinal epithelium into the walls of the ovarian sacs, where they form nests which differentiate into spermatic tubules. The cortical or ovarian part of the gonad degenerates at the same time, leaving only a thin peritoneal epithelium covering the gonad. The ovarian sacs then transform into the rete and vasa efferentia of the testis. The basal and central regions of the gonad become testicular before the peripheral ovarian tissue has degenerated, but ultimately the whole gonad is transformed completely into a testis. Similar results have been produced experimentally, both in urodeles and anurans, by racial and specific crosses, by parabiosis, by grafting and other means (see series of papers by Witschi, by Humphrey, by Burns, and that by Uchida, 1937).

The transformation of testes into ovaries has been produced experimentally in *Amblystoma* (Burns, 1931, 1935). The development of an incipient cortex in the testes of this animal (see p. 412 and Fig. 5. 4) probably is significant in this connection, since it supplies a rudiment from which the ovarian tissue could be developed. Its absence in most species may account for ♂→♀ sex-reversal not occurring in them.

Oöcytes are developed frequently in the spermatic tubules of the testes of amphibians, both in natural and experimental conditions. Ichikawa (1937) describes the occurrence of masses of such oöcytes in testis-grafts in newts.

Burns (1938 and 1939) has shown that the injection of male and female hormones in larval Amblystoma at the time of sexual differentiation of the gonads modifies their development, as do grafts and parabiosis. Thus the injection of oestrone causes transformation of testes in genetic males into ovaries but does not appreciably affect the development of the ovaries in genetic females. Similarly, the injection of testosterone propionate produces ovotestes in genetic females but does not affect the gonads of genetic males. The effect appears to be brought about by directing the differentiation of the rete-cords towards that of the appropriate sex and inhibiting medullary or cortical development, rather than by direct stimulation of the development of the cortex in the case of oestrone or of the medulla in the case of testosterone. If it be assumed that medulla and cortex are mutually inhibitory in the normal differentiating gonad, then injection of oestrone enhances this effect of the cortex and injection of testosterone that of the medulla.

General Morphology of the Adult Ovary

The ovaries of adult marsupials and placentals are small in proportion to the size of the animal. Thus the ovary of a cow may weigh 10–15 grms. approximately. The ovary is smooth in contour or slightly lobed, only mature follicles or large corpora lutea projecting from the surface (Fig. 5. 33). It is spherical, ovate or partially flattened in shape. Both ovaries of a pair are functional and are equal or sub-equal in size. They are firm in texture, both on account of the thickness of the cortex and the large amount of stromal tissue in it and because of the relatively small volume of the more spongy medullary region. The whole organ is invested by the peritoneal or germinal epithelium, which is cubical or low columnar and has a well-developed basement membrane. Here and there small folds or pits in the epithelium form slight invaginations projecting into the underlying cortex (Harrison and Matthews, 1951). The basement membrane of the germinal epithelium rests immediately upon the cortex, the superficial tissues of which usually are differentiated as the tunica albuginea, consisting of fibrous connective tissue and smooth muscle cells. It varies widely in different species, being thin and scarcely distinguishable from the underlying stroma in some and forming a well-differentiated and relatively thick layer in others. The cortex is thick and forms the major part of the ovary.   It contains the oöcytes in all stages of growth.   The smallest are contained in primordial follicles consisting of only a few flattened epithelial cells and are peripheral in position (Fig. 5. 5).   The larger follicles are more deeply situated and contain an antrum filled with fluid, the liquor folliculi.   The term " Graafian follicle " should be applied only to such follicles in which an antrum is present.   The wall of the Graafian follicle consists of a membrana granulosa, which is epithelial, several cells thick and surrounds the antrum, and an outer theca of connective tissue.   The theca in the larger follicles is differentiated into two layers, theca externa and theca interna.   The largest follicles, owing to their size, project somewhat from the surface.   Mossman (1938)

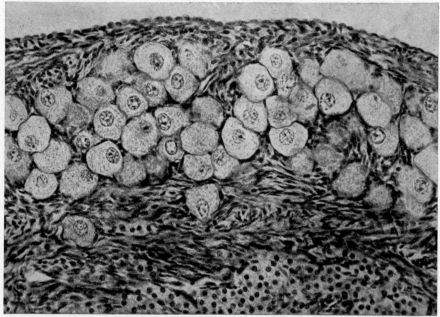

Fig. 5. 5—Photomicrograph of the ovary of a cat showing the thick zone of small oöcytes in
primordial follicles immediately beneath the periphery.   Strands of interstitial tissue
are visible in the stroma in the lower part of the picture.   × 290.

points out that the follicular-epithelium is to be regarded as a modified coelomic epithelium, and the follicular cavities as isolated portions of the peritoneal cavity filled with slightly modified peritoneal fluid.   The corpora lutea formed from the discharged follicles are present also in the ovaries of adult animals during the breeding season.   They are, at their maximum, as large as or larger than mature Graafian follicles and also project from the surface.   The stroma is a dense tissue and occupies the space between the follicles and corpora lutea.   It consists of connective tissue, often fibrous, smooth muscle cells and interstitial cells, which appear to be glandular in nature.   Changes in the stromal connective tissue of the ovary of the bird have been investigated by Hett (1931) and those of the human ovary by Mainland (1931b).   The structure and significance of the follicles, corpora lutea and interstitial cells will be dealt with in detail in the succeeding sections of this chapter.   Blood-vessels, lymphatics and bundles of nerve fibres are numerous in the cortex, and their distribution is described (see p. 451, also Peter, 1929).   The changes during adult life of the arteries in the human ovary are described by Ferroni and Ferri (1939).

The medulla adjoins the hilus and occupies the centre of the ovary. It is loose and spongy in texture, containing numerous large lymphatic sinuses and the larger blood-vessels. The tissue between these vessels is chiefly connective, but some strands of epithelial elements are present. These epithelial strands represent the remnants of the rete-cords and medullary cords of the embryo. Changes in the rete during adult life have been described by Wallart (1930a). Certain large cells, the *cellules sympathicotropes* of Berger (1923, 1928) and *cellules phéochrome* of de Winiwarter (1924), resembling interstitial cells in appearance but apparently differing from them in becoming brown after fixation in fluids containing chromic acid or its salts, occur in the region of the hilus of the human ovary. These cells are in close association with, and even in, the bundles of sympathetic nerve fibres. Both in chromophility and in their association with sympathetic nerves they resemble the chromaffin cells of the adrenal medulla, the sympathetic ganglia and the chromaffin bodies or paraganglia in the vicinity of the dorsal aorta. It has been suggested in consequence that they may be true chromaffin cells. Wallart (1927, 1930b) confirms de Winiwarter's finding (1924) that these cells occur in the broad ligament and mesovarium as well as in the hilus and medulla of the ovary. They arise during development from sympathetic nervous elements and are present in the ovary at birth. They atrophy thereafter but reappear at puberty and are present in the adult (Wallart, 1927, 1930b; Neumann, 1927, 1928, 1929). Their nature has been investigated also by Brannan (1927), Pawlowski (1929), Kohn (1928), Cieri (1932) and Watzka and Eschler (1933). It is significant, in relation to the sympathetic nervous mechanism of the ovary, that cells so closely resembling true chromaffin tissue should be present in the hilus.

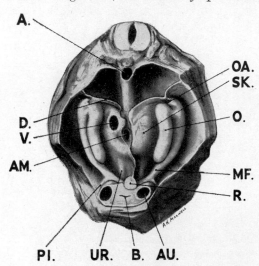

FIG. 5. 6—Drawing of a dissection of a 12½-day p.c. female mouse embryo. The long narrow ovaries are seen attached to the small mesonephric folds. Medial to each ovary is a swelling in the body-wall produced by the developing adrenal bodies and the kidneys. The cephalic extremity of each mesonephric fold, showing the ostium abdominal tubae, is attached to the diaphragm, which is cut across, by the short plica diaphragmatica. A, aorta; AM, superior mesenteric artery; AU, umbilical artery; B, bladder; D, diaphragm; MF, mesonephric fold (tubal portion); O, ovary; OA, ostium abdominal tubae; PI, plica inguinalis; R, rectum; SK, ridge formed by the developing adrenal and kidney; UR, ureter; V, inferior vena cava. × 28. (From Brambell, 1927b.)

The ovaries of other vertebrates are larger in proportion to the size of the animal and have less stroma in the cortex. Consequently the larger follicles project more from the surface. The mature follicles in elasmobranchs, reptiles, birds and monotremes are so large that they confer on the ovary an appearance resembling a bunch of grapes. They are pedunculate, being attached to the ovary only by narrow necks. The medullary region of the ovary in monotremes, birds and reptiles is extensive and very spongy, containing a network of large lymph spaces. The ovaries of amphibians contain a number of large cavities, the ovarian sacs, formed by the expanded ends of the rete-cords. These ovarian cavities occupy the centre of the gonads, which consequently are hollow. The ovarian tissue only forms their relatively thin walls. The large follicles project into these cavities, being attached to the wall only over a relatively small area at one pole. Cavities into which the ova are discharged, found in the ovaries of many teleosts, are of a different nature, being coelomic in origin. This cystovarian condition arises during development by the fusion of folds, formed by the ovaries, with one another or with the body wall, thus shutting off tubular cavities from the remainder of the splanchnocoel.

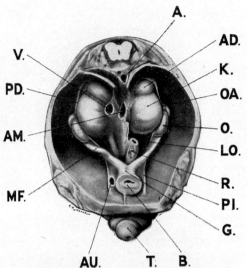

Fig. 5. 7—Drawing of a dissection of a 15-day p.c. female mouse embryo. The ovaries are being pushed laterally by the developing kidneys. The plica diaphragmatica has lengthened. The ovarian ligament and plica inguinalis are shown. Only one umbilical artery could be distinguished in this specimen. AD, adrenal; G, genital cord; K, kidney; LO, ovarian ligament; PD, plica diaphragmatica; T, genital tubercle; other letters as in Fig. 5. 6. × 17. (From Brambell, 1927b.)

The ovaries of cyclostomes and fishes are very large, and are attached throughout their length by a mesentery or mesovarium to the dorsal body wall between the kidney and the mesentery of the gut. They extend longitudinally throughout the greater part of the splanchnocoel. The ovaries in Amphibia also are large but they are not so long; the insertion of the mesovarium extending from the cranial end of the kidney two-thirds or more of the distance towards its caudal extremity. The ovaries of Sauropsida are also dorsal in position and far forward, being attached at the level of the anterior end of the metanephros. The region of attachment of the ovaries of marsupial and placental mammals is contracted to form the short hilus, where the mesovarium is inserted and the vessels and nerves enter. The ovaries in these mammals tend to move posteriorly and sometimes ventrally as well, during development (Figs. 5. 6 and 5. 7). This descent of the ovary doubtless corresponds to that of the testis to the scrotum, but is more limited. The degree of descent attained in the different orders varies widely. Thus, in the Rodentia the ovary in the adult lies close to the dorsal body wall immediately lateral to the posterior end of the kidney (Fig. 5. 7). The Carnivora show a greater descent, the ovary being posterior to the kidney though still close to the dorsal body wall. The ovaries in the Cheiroptera, Insectivora and Primates move still further back and ventrally as well. The ventral movement accompanies ventral flexure of the uterus. The extreme descent illustrated by the human female results in the ovaries in the virgin lying within the pelvic region immediately below the external iliac vessels. Descent of the ovary is accompanied by lengthening of the suspensory ligament, ovarian artery and vein and the ovarian nerves, and by shortening of the ovarian ligament, which corresponds to the posterior sterile region of the genital ridge.

Although the ovaries are primitively symmetrical paired organs, a condition which is retained in the majority of vertebrates, an asymmetrical condition due to arrest in the development of one ovary is not uncommon, and occurs especially in forms producing very large oöcytes. The cyclostomes have a single gonad only, which is median in *Petromyzon* and on the right side in *Myxine*. The single gonad in the brook lamprey arises from paired primordia which fuse (Okkelberg, 1921), but in *Myxine* the condition probably arises through failure of the left gonad to complete its development. Both ovaries are developed and functional in some elasmobranchs, but in the majority, including *Scyllium, Galeus, Mustelus, Zygaena, Charcharias, Pristiophorus*, etc., only the right is functional and the left is rudimentary. Many teleosts also have only a single ovary, but in some instances this is due to fusion of paired rudiments (Essenberg, 1923), as in the lamprey, and in others to arrested development of one. The left ovary is functional and the right rudimentary as a rule in birds. There are, however, many exceptions, notably in the birds of prey, in which the left ovary is frequently functional as well the right and may be as large. The degree of development of the right ovary in a number of species has been investigated by Kummerlöwe (1930a and b, 1931a and b), to whose papers reference may be made for the earlier literature. The asymmetry of the ovaries in North American hawks has been dealt with recently by Stanley (1937) who found nearly symmetrical paired ovaries in three species. Brode (1928) investigated the development of the right ovary in the hen and found that in 60 per cent of individuals it consisted entirely of medullary tissue, whereas in the remaining 40 per cent a rudimentary cortex was present. This conforms with expectation in that both gonads might be assumed to develop equally until after the time of differentiation of sex since the testes are symmetrical. Wolff and Haffen (1952) have succeeded in culturing *in vitro* excised whole gonads of duck and chick embryos. The explants were taken before the differentiation of sex and continued to develop normally *in vitro* for several days. It was found that, if the left gonad differentiated into a testis, then the right gonad did so, but if the left gonad differentiated into an ovary, then the right gonad atrophied and became a typical rudimentary right ovary. The ovaries in the Monotremata are asymmetrical also, the left being the larger in *Ornithorhynchus*, and sometimes the left, sometimes the right, in *Echidna* (Hill and Gatenby, 1926 ; Flynn, 1930).

Oögenesis

The germ cells in the embryonic ovary, after an initial period of mitotic multiplication, enter upon the prophase of the heterotypic division soon after their inclusion in the cortical cords. Before or shortly after birth in mammals all the germ-cells contained in the ovaries are primary oöcytes which have completed the prophase changes. Similar changes may be observed in the oöcytes in the medullary cords before they begin to degenerate. Thus the characteristic prophase changes take place in all the germ-cells formed during embryonic life irrespective of whether they arise from the primordial germ-cells or from somatic elements of the germinal epithelium.

The prophase of the heterotypic division

The terminology employed in this outline [1] of the prophase in the primary oöcytes is based on that of de Winiwarter (1901) and de Winiwarter and Sainmont (1909) in their classical descriptions of oögenesis in the rabbit and the cat.

The prophase of the heterotypic division in the primary oöcytes of vertebrates is essentially similar to that in invertebrates and in the primary spermatocytes of both vertebrates and invertebrates. Although this similarity is not limited to any one phase of the process, its essence lies in the occurrence of syndesis, the significance of which in relation to the genetical theory of crossing-over is fundamental.

Our knowledge of this process has been greatly extended, and modified in some important respects, in recent years owing to researches, chiefly on insects. These advances have been due in part to improvements in the technique of nuclear cytology, in part to the discovery of the giant chromosomes of the salivary glands of dipterous insects, and to the application of genetical knowledge to the interpretation of nuclear phenomena. Although much that has been learned regarding meiosis in insects is undoubtedly relevant also to vertebrates, including mammals, comparatively little attention has been paid to them recently since they do not provide such favourable material. Reference should, however, be made to such general accounts of nuclear phenomena as that provided by White (1945).

One important difference in the nuclear changes during the prophase of the heterotypic division in spermatogenesis and oögenesis of vertebrates does exist. Each primary spermatocyte, having entered upon the prophase, completes the heterotypic division without the interpolation of a prolonged resting phase. This is associated with the continued production of primary spermatocytes from spermatogonia and consequently of the whole process of spermatogenesis throughout the sexually functional life of the male. Although spermatogenesis may be temporarily in abeyance during the non-breeding season, in species in which this is restricted, it recurs at the beginning of, and continues uninterruptedly throughout, each succeeding season. On the other hand, in the ovary the earlier stages of the prophase are completed and the dictyate stage has been attained by all the oöcytes at an early stage in development. This is true of vertebrates with few exceptions. Thus in mammals, all the oöcytes have reached the dictyate stage soon after birth and thereafter, with certain exceptions to be mentioned, none of the earlier stages are to be found in the ovaries. It follows that, if these are the definitive oöcytes, they persist until either they become atretic or are ovulated. Those that are ultimately ovulated must remain in the resting phase for very different periods according to whether they mature early or late in life. Ultimately each enters upon the growth phase culminating in the completion of the heterotypic division and ovulation. Thus, in the human ovary, an oöcyte which has completed the initial stages of the prophase soon after birth may be destined to be ovulated at any period between puberty and the menopause.

Formation of oöcytes during adult life

Among the mammals, in a few instances, oöcytes have been observed in the initial stages of the prophase of the heterotypic division after puberty. De Winiwarter (1920) found oöcytes exhibiting these nuclear stages in the immediate

[1] Full descriptions and references to the literature are available in the standard text books on cytology (e.g. Wilson, 1928 ; White, 1945).

vicinity of the hilus in the ovaries of cats shortly after puberty. He concluded that the formation of oöcytes in this region is delayed and that it may still be in progress there after it has ceased elsewhere in the ovary. Many years after he reinvestigated this problem and reaffirmed his conclusions (1942). Refusing to accept the alleged formation of oöcytes in the adult ovary, except in those instances where the characteristic prophase changes could be recognised, he states : " Les seuls auteurs qui aient réellement démontré une néoformation chez l'adulte, sont Gérard et Hamlett." Hamlett (1935b) described the occurrence of oögonia and oöcytes in the prophase of the heterotypic division in an epithelial mass attached to the surface of the ovary of an adult *Dasypus novemcinctus*. This mass was interpreted as a late formation of epithelial cords which were unable to penetrate the dense tunica albuginea of the adult ovary and consequently grew outwards. Gérard (1920) described and figured the occurrence of oögenesis in the ovaries of a single lactating lemur, *Galago senegalensis moholi* (= *G. mossambicus*). The germ-cells, which exhibited all the characteristic nuclear phases of the transformation of oögonia into primary oöcytes, were grouped in epithelial invaginations or Pflüger's tubes formed by mitotic proliferation of the germinal epithelium. The formation of primordial follicles, by the ingrowth of connective tissue breaking up the masses of epithelial and germ-cells, was proceeding in the deeper parts of these cords. The whole process was very intense and presented a similar appearance to that proceeding in the ovaries of the female offspring which the mother was suckling. The same author has described since (1932) the ovaries of four non-pregnant adult and eight pregnant females of *Galago demidoffi* and one non-pregnant adult and four pregnant females of *Galago senegalensis moholi*, in all but two of which active oögenesis was proceeding. It may be concluded therefore that oögenesis occurs normally in the ovaries of *Galago* during adult life. Since it was not proceeding in the ovaries of two adults and varied in intensity in the others, it was concluded that the process was discontinuous and probably cyclic. A similar formation of oöcytes and their passage through the characteristic initial stages of the prophase of the heterotypic division is described in the ovaries of the adult lemur, *Loris lydekkerianus* Cabr., especially during pregnancy, by Rao (1927). Moreover, this phenomenon has been observed in the ovaries of pregnant females of this species (Brambell, 1930). It must be concluded, therefore, that new primary oöcytes do arise by oögonial multiplication in the peripheral regions of the ovaries of lemurs throughout adult life. Moreover, these oöcytes undergo the characteristic prophase changes of the heterotypic division before entering upon the growth phase. We are unaware of the occurrence of this phenomenon in any other mammal. Whether the new germ cells arise by the transformation of epithelial cells, as was concluded by Gérard and by Rao, and as seems probable, or from oögonia, derived from primordial germ-cells, which have persisted as such into adult life, as is possible at least theoretically, requires further investigation.

During recent years a number of authors have described what they believe to be the formation of oöcytes during adult life in several species of mammals. Yet their results fall into a different category from those referred to above since they failed admittedly to observe the characteristic stages of the prophase of the heterotypic division in the nuclei and concluded that these do not occur. The acceptance of this contention, therefore, involves the admission that syndesis does not necessarily occur in mammalian oögenesis. Yet the occurrence of syndesis in gametogenesis is otherwise universal. It occurs in invertebrates and in spermato-genesis of all vertebrates. Moreover, it occurs in mammalian oögenesis during embryonic life. Its non-occurrence in oögenesis, if this proceeds in the adult mammal, would be exceptional cytologically and not in accordance with the established principles of genetics.

It is unnecessary, in reviewing the recent literature on the formation of oöcytes in the adult mammalian ovary, to go back further than the work of Kingery (1917). This author, using the white mouse, concluded that the definitive oöcytes arise exclusively from proliferations of the germinal epithelium extending almost from birth to puberty. Stages in the transformation of the epithelial cells into primary oöcytes were described and the absence of syndesis and synizesis was noted. Syndesis was found only in the oöcytes formed before birth, all of which were said to degenerate subsequently. Robinson (1918) came to the conclusion that oöcytes are formed continuously from the germinal epithelium in adult ferrets. Edgar Allen (1923) described the stages in the formation of oöcytes from the germinal epithelium in the adult mouse. First, mitoses occur in the epithelium, secondly, germ cells are found immediately beneath it, and thirdly, they are seen at a depth of a few cells from the surface. Allen found that this proliferation of germ-cells was cyclical, occurring at oestrus when the ovaries were hyperaemic and being in abeyance during dioestrus. He concluded that the incidence of the three stages named in relation to the oestrous cycle showed that they were successive stages in the transformation of epithelial cells into germ-cells and that the process took from four to six days. He estimated that 400–500 oöcytes were formed in each ovary at each oestrus in this way, of which only about 1 per cent ultimately sur-vived. Sun (1923) concluded, from counts of young oöcytes at various stages of the oestrous cycle, that they are formed in the adult guinea-pig from the germinal epithelium. Cowperthwaite (1925) examined the ovaries of rats with a view to determining if post-pubertal oögenesis occurs and concluded that it does not. Butcher (1927), using the same material, arrived at the opposite conclusion. He found that the formation of the definitive germ-cells from the epithelium begins at six or seven days after birth and continues until old age. The process is some-what retarded after puberty but is accelerated during oestrus. The successive stages in the transformation were described and the absence of the typical prophase stages was recognised. Swezy (1929) and Hargitt (1930a, b and c), also using the rat, arrived at similar conclusions. Evans and Swezy (1931) have given an elaborate account of the formation of oöcytes from the epithelium during maturity in the rat, guinea-pig, dog, cat, monkey and man. The oöcytes arise by prolifera-tions from the germinal epithelium in the form of invaginations or cords which become cut off from the epithelium and pass through the tunica albuginea. One or more cells in each group enlarge and transform into oöcytes, the remaining cells forming the follicular epithelium. The typical prophase changes of the heterotypic division are not encountered in these oöcytes. The formation of oöcytes is cyclic, beginning after ovulation and increasing gradually to a maximum at the end of the oestrous cycle. The rhythmic production of oöcytes continues during pregnancy. The majority of the oöcytes so formed degenerate at the onset of prooestrus, before the next oögenetic wave begins. Thus the number of oöcytes in the ovaries reaches a maximum at the end of dioestrus and during late pregnancy and is at a minimum at oestrus.   These conclusions, so far as the dog is concerned, are not in accord with those of Jonckheere (1930) who states emphatically that no formation of oöcytes ever occurs in the adult.   Pincus and Enzmann (1937) found no appreciable formation of new oöcytes during sexual maturity in the rabbit.

Guthrie and Jeffers (1938) claim that oöcytes arise from the cells of the germinal epithelium in the ovaries of bats during adult life.   The formation of oöcytes from the germinal epithelium has been described by Everett (1942) in the adult opossum and by Duke (1944) in a pregnant harvest mouse.   Flynn and Hill (1939) found no evidence of the formation of oöcytes during adult life in monotremes.

Edgar Allen and Creadick (1937) have reinvestigated oögenesis during sexual maturity in the mouse.   They have demonstrated the occurrence of active mitosis, which they claim to be the first stage in oögenesis, in the germinal epithelium, using colchicine, which arrests mitosis.   Bullough (1942b) claims to have obtained similar results.   Schmidt and Hoffman (1941), using colchicine, found that mitotic activity in the germinal epithelium of the guinea-pig ovary is much less than in the mouse ovary, but they observed a doubling of the rate of mitosis during oestrus as compared to other stages of the oestrous cycle.   Schmidt (1942) in the guinea-pig and Allen et al. (1943) in the rat have observed, by means of the colchicine technique, cyclic changes in the mitotic activity of follicular tissue during the oestrous cycle.   Bullough (1946) has observed in the mouse a great increase in the mitotic activity of the germinal epithelium in the vicinity of the ruptured follicles immediately after ovulation.   He has shown also that great mitotic activity is associated with follicular growth.

Clearly, if all the definitive oöcytes are present in the ovaries at birth, there must be then a sufficient number to account for the continual loss by degeneration throughout life as well as for those that are ultimately ovulated.   Various estimates have been made of the number of ova in the ovaries.   Arai (1920a) states that in the rat about 35,000 are present at birth, 11,000 at 23 days, 7000 at 70 days and 2000 at 31 months.   Slater and Dornfeld (1945) estimated that there are 160,000 oöcytes in the ovaries of young rats two days before birth, and 23,000 at eleven days after birth.   Swezy (1933) found numbers ranging from 1738 to 6483 in a single ovary in adult female rats.   Both authors maintain that new oöcytes are formed during adult life.   Schotterer (1928) found 700,000 follicles in the ovaries of dogs at birth, 355,000 at puberty, 34,000 at 5 years and 500 at 10 years of age. Since it is impossible to arrive at a satisfactory estimate of the number that degenerate, and since in all these counts the numbers present were greatly in excess of the number that could ultimately be ovulated, no conclusion can be arrived at regarding the formation of new oöcytes.   Swezy (1933) gives data of the numbers of oöcytes in the ovaries of rats during the unmated oestrous cycle, pregnancy and pseudopregnancy, which tend to show that there is an increase during pregnancy and pseudopregnancy.   Such an increase, if statistically significant, would prove that oöcytes are formed during adult life.   Unfortunately, the range of variation is so great, presumably due to individual variation and experimental errors, that the total number of counts necessary to provide statistically significant results would be extremely laborious to obtain.   Much careful work has been done in this field recently by Zuckerman and his colleagues.   He has reviewed critically

(Zuckerman, 1951) the numerical work, his own and other people's, on the number of oöcytes in the ovaries and he has shown convincingly that it does not provide a statistically significant basis for the assumption of the formation of oöcytes in the adult ovary.

The cyclic nature of the oögenetic processes described by Allen, Butcher, Evans and Swezy suggests that they, as well as the other rhythmic ovarian phenomena, may be influenced by the hormones of the anterior lobe of the pituitary. The effects of various preparations of anterior lobe substance and of other sex hormones on oögenesis in the rat has been investigated by Swezy (1933). The results varied according to the preparations employed, some being claimed to have a stimulating, and others a depressing, effect on oögenesis. It was concluded that the anterior lobe of the pituitary has no causal relation to oögenesis. Marx (1941) claims that in young rats injections of gonadotropic extracts or of oestrogens stimulate the formation of oöcytes in the ovary. Stein and Allen (1942) injected oestrone in sesame oil into the left ovarian capsules and sesame oil alone into the right ovarian capsules of normal young mice and of hypophysectomised adult mice. Mitoses were counted after subsequent treatment with colchicine and showed greater mitotic activity in the germinal epithelium of the left ovary than in that of the right, which was used as a control. Bullough (1942a and c; 1946) has demonstrated that injection of oestrogens stimulates mitoses in the ovary of the mouse, both in the germinal epithelium and in the membrana granulosa, as well as in many other tissues of the body. He believes that in the normal animal it is the oestrogen in the follicular fluid which is the stimulating agent in the ovary, and that it acts directly on the cells in its immediate vicinity. This would account for the peaks in mitotic activity of the membrana granulosa in growing follicles, and of the germinal epithelium in the vicinity of ruptured follicles after ovulation. It may be concluded, in view of the unanimity of the results, that oestrogens stimulate mitosis in the ovaries, including the germinal epithelium, as well as in many other tissues of the body. It should be noted, however, that the discovery of cyclic proliferative activity in the germinal epithelium does not prove that the epithelial cells are transforming into oöcytes.

Experimental researches have thrown some light on the problem of whether oögenesis does, or does not, occur in adult mammals. Complete sterility was produced in mice by exposure to a standard dose of X-rays (Brambell, Parkes and Fielding, 1927a and b; Brambell and Parkes, 1927b; Brambell, Fielding and Parkes, 1928) during late embryonic life, before puberty or during maturity. All the small oöcytes degenerated and disappeared within a few hours after irradiation. The larger oöcytes in the older animals degenerated more slowly and a few appeared to mature in a normal manner and to be ovulated. Mature animals mated soon after irradiation could, and often did, become pregnant and produce and rear normal litters. When all the oöcytes had degenerated or had been ovulated, which took place within about forty days, the ovaries in the majority of animals became completely sterile. Some of the animals that had become pregnant after irradiation were killed upwards of forty days after X-ray treatment and were found to be completely devoid of oöcytes. Yet the oestrous cycle, as shown by the vaginal and uterine changes, continued in these animals, although the ovaries were devoid of follicles. Therefore the ovarian tissues were functional so far as the production of oestrin was concerned. The apparently normal character

of the germinal epithelium was more relevant. It proliferated two successive
generations of epithelial cords after irradiation in the immature animals. Nevertheless, although some of the animals were kept for as much as five months
after irradiation, the ovaries remained completely sterile and no reformation
of germ cells was observed. These experiments appear to admit of only two
explanations. Either the X-rays effected some permanent, but quite invisible,
change in the germinal epithelium which robbed it of all power of producing
germ-cells subsequently, although not destroying its power to proliferate, or else
germ-cells are not normally produced in the ovaries of mice after puberty. Clearly
the latter is the simpler explanation. Similar results have been obtained by
Geller (1930), Genther (1931) and Desaive (1940, 1941).

The phenomenon of ovarian regeneration following double ovariotomy, of
which several probable instances in man are recorded in the medical literature and
which has been clearly demonstrated in mice by Davenport (1925), Parkes,
Fielding and Brambell (1927), Hanson and Heys (1927), Haterius (1928) and
Pencharz (1929), also bears on the problem of germ-cell formation during maturity.
Double ovariotomy in mice is followed by cessation of the oestrous cycle. Ovarian
tissue regenerates after a variable period in some of the operated animals (about
9 per cent according to Parkes, Fielding and Brambell, 1927), as is shown both
by the reappearance of the oestrous cycle and by histological examination. The
regenerated tissue contains oöcytes, and large follicles or corpora lutea are not
infrequent, but the total number of oöcytes is invariably small in comparison to
that in normal ovaries. Such regeneration has been attributed usually to hypertrophy of small fragments of ovarian tissue left at operation but, at least in
some instances, this explanation appears inadmissible. Parkes, Fielding and
Brambell (1927) removed the ovaries together with the ovarian capsules and the
adjoining portions of the mesovaria, fat bodies and Fallopian tubes. Since the
ovarian capsule in the mouse forms a closed envelope around the ovary it is
difficult to see how fragments could be left *in situ* after this operation. Moreover,
in three cases in which ovarian tissue was regenerated and identified histologically,
it was shown by complete serial sections of the excised ovaries that they had been
removed intact. This appears to show conclusively that the regenerated
tissue does not arise necessarily from pre-existing ovarian fragments. It is possible
that the germ-cells contained in the regenerated tissue arise from extra-regional
primordial germ-cells, which failed to reach the genital ridges during their
formation and which remained dormant in the adjoining somatic tissues or
formed ectopic islands of ovarian tissue, which are not unknown (Krohn,
1951). The alternative conclusion is that they arise *de novo* from undifferentiated somatic elements. Yet if this were the case it would be difficult to
understand why regeneration only takes place in a small percentage of operated
animals and why the germ-cells are not more numerous in the ovarian tissue
when it does.

The work of Lipschütz (1925, 1928) and of Lipschütz and Voss (1925) on
partial ovariotomy in cats and rabbits, also provides evidence that oöcytes are not
formed during maturity. When one ovary and the greater part of the other
ovary were removed the remaining fragment underwent compensatory hypertrophy. The hypertrophied fragment continued to produce approximately the
same number of mature follicles at each oestrus as the two normal ovaries would

have done. After a time the number of small oöcytes in the ovarian fragment was found to be greatly reduced, obviously owing to the accelerated depletion caused by ovulation. Arai (1920b) found that unilateral ovariotomy hastened the reduction of the number of oöcytes in the surviving ovary. Edgar Allen (1923) admits that the number of new oöcytes, which he claims are formed in the remaining ovary after unilateral ovariotomy, is not increased, but he maintains that twice as many of these survive and are ovulated.

The regenerative capacity of the germinal epithelium in the rat was investigated by Butcher (1932). He claimed that occlusion of the ovarian vessels by ligatures brought about degeneration of the germ-cells in 6–8 days but that the epithelium survived and subsequently gave rise to new oöcytes. This experiment was repeated by Martinovitch (1934a and b) who found that some of the germ-cells often survived in the rat owing to the rapid revascularisation of the organ from the neighbouring tissues. Neither in the rat nor the rabbit was there any evidence of reformation of the germ-cells after their partial or total destruction. Latta and Pederson (1944) have attempted to stain intravitally the cells of the germinal epithelium of the rat by injecting dilute Indian ink into the ovarian capsule. They claim that the carbon particles could be identified subsequently in oöcytes and follicle cells and that this is evidence of their origin from the superficial cells of the germinal epithelium.

Evidence in favour of the formation of germ-cells during adult life is provided by examples of sex reversal in amphibians and birds. This falls into an entirely different category, for the new germ-cells pass through the characteristic phases of meiosis, unlike those that are alleged to be found in adult mammals. Thus Foote and Witschi (1939) state that female larvae of *Rana clamitans* can be transformed into males by injections of testosterone propionate. During the resulting transformation of the ovaries all the oöcytes degenerate but the oögonia survive, become included in the forming sex-cords, and become spermatogonia. The origin of the male germ-cells and of the spermatic tubules in ovaries transforming into testes has been investigated histologically by Fell (1923) in the fowl and by Brambell and Marrian (1929) in the pigeon. The germinal epithelium in the fowl proliferates sex-cords which differentiate into spermatic tubules containing germ-cells. The spermatic tubules and germ-cells in the pigeon, on the other hand, arise from the clear islet cells within the ovarian stroma. Since these islet cells are believed to arise from the elements of the medullary cords of the ovary, which degenerate during development (see p. 505) and which are homologous with the spermatic tubules in a normal testis, this origin is not so surprising. Thus the male germ-cells arise in the adult bird's ovary during sex reversal either from (*a*) a new proliferation of epithelial cords from the germinal epithelium, or (*b*) from the remnants of the medullary cords. Both in the fowl and the pigeon the spermatocytes formed in this way exhibit the characteristic prophase changes of the heterotypic division.

The origin of spermatogonia in sex-reversed birds conflicts with the Weismannian theory of the continuity of the germ-plasm. This theory demands that they should be derived entirely from the primordial germ-cells which migrated into the germinal ridges during embryonic life and which subsequently remained undifferentiated into somatic cells. It might be maintained in those cases where the spermatogonia arise directly from the germinal epithelium that they are

derived from primordial germ-cells which have remained in the ovary in an undifferentiated condition and are indistinguishable from the other epithelial elements.
The case of the pigeon described does not admit of this interpretation.   There is
no evidence in this case as to whether the clear islet cells, which gave rise to the
spermatogonia, originated from primordial germ-cells or from somatic cells contained in the medullary cords.   But the clear islet cells must be admitted to be
differentiated elements.   These cells, during their formation, undergo a process
of fatty degeneration (Fell, 1924).   Their transformation into spermatogonia is,
therefore, an amazing instance of redifferentiation.

II. Growth of the Follicle, Maturation of the Ovum, and Ovulation

The Growth of the Oöcyte

A comparative account of the cytology, nuclear and cytoplasmic, of the vertebrate oöcyte during the phases of growth and maturation is provided already in
standard works on cytology, such as that by Wilson (1928).   This description will
be confined, therefore, mainly to the marsupial and placental mammals.   Yet the
processes in the mammalian oöcyte, both nuclear and cytoplasmic, are essentially
similar to those in the lower vertebrates, although the mature ovum in the former
is only about $\frac{1}{10}$ mm. in diameter and contains little deutoplasm, whereas in the
latter it is large and yolk-laden.   It may exceed 25 mm. in diameter in the elasmobranchs, reptiles and birds.   The extensive literature is cited in the following
papers dealing with fishes (Maréchal, 1906 ; Jörgensen, 1913 ; Champy and Gley,
1923), amphibians (Stieve, 1921 ; Jägersten, 1935), reptiles (Loyez, 1906 ; D. R.
Bhattacharya, 1925 ; Mosella, 1926), birds (Loyez, 1906 ; van Durme, 1914 ;
Brambell, 1925 ; Ikeda, 1928 ; Marza and Marza, 1935 ; Marza, 1935 ; Olsen,
1942 ; Olsen and Fraps, 1944) and monotremes (Gatenby, 1922 ; Flynn and
Hill, 1939).

The nucleus of the full-grown oöcyte of monotremes (Flynn and Hill, 1939)
is saucer-shaped, with the concavity filled with vacuolated cytoplasm and directed
towards the periphery and the wide rim applied to the vitelline membrane (Fig. 5. 8).
In other mammals the nucleus of the oöcyte, throughout its growth, remains
vesicular and nearly spherical (Fig. 5. 21).   Although the nucleus does not undergo
any considerable change in structure during this growth phase, it increases in
volume and retains a constant size relation to the oöcyte as a whole (Brambell,
1928).   It is otherwise with the cytoplasm in which a complex series of changes
proceeds, involving in particular the mitochondria and Golgi bodies of the oöcyte.
These processes vary considerably in different species of mammals according to
the amount and character of the deutoplasm.   Since the deutoplasmic content of
the ova is invariably small, in comparison to that of the ova of other vertebrates,
the processes leading to its formation are correspondingly less intense.   Our
knowledge of the behaviour of the mitochondria in mammalian oögenesis is due
largely to the work of the Belgian school of cytologists led by O. van der Stricht, to
whose comparative summary of these researches reference should be made for the
earlier literature (O. van der Stricht, 1923).   The smallest oöcytes in the adult
ovary have a yolk body (*corps vitelline*) which apparently is the centrosphere, close
to the nucleus at one side of the cell, and a mitochondrial zone (*couche mitochondriale*

ou vitellogène) surrounding it and the nucleus. The peripheral cytoplasm contains few or no mitochondria. Thus the oöcyte has from the beginning a definite polarity, as in all other vertebrates. As soon as the oöcyte begins to grow this compact mitochondrial zone disperses and its constituent mitochondria become dispersed throughout the cytoplasm. The yolk body, which is thus deprived of its investing zone of mitochondria, tends to move away from the nucleus and may divide into two, three or four bodies. The mitochondria increase in number and tend to accumulate towards the periphery of the cytoplasm, forming a cortical zone (*couche corticale, mitochondriale*). Meanwhile, fatty yolk spheres appear in the cytoplasm and their accumulation pushes the nucleus to the periphery of the

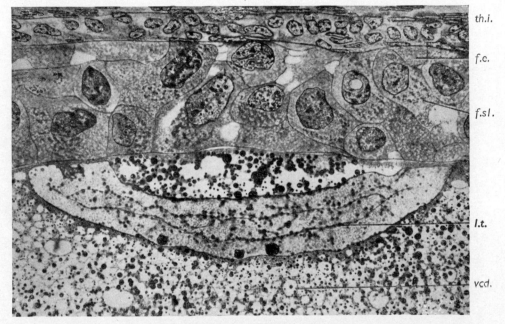

Fig. 5. 8—Section of the germinal disc of a fully grown oöcyte of Echidna showing the saucer-shaped nucleus (l.t.) with its rim applied to the vitelline membrane, the precursor of the follicular fluid (f.sl.) in the follicular cells (f.e.) and the theca interna (th.i.). The cytoplasm of the germinal disc is vacuolated (vcd.). × 550. (From Flynn and Hill, 1939.)

cell. The nucleus is surrounded by a zone of cytoplasm, free from yolk, which is connected with the cortical mitochondrial zone which envelopes the deutoplasm. The Golgi bodies of the oöcyte have been described for the guinea-pig, rabbit, bat, mouse and man (Sjövall, 1906; del Rio Hortega, 1913; Cattaneo, 1914; Kulesch, 1914; Henneguy, 1926; Nihoul, 1926; Gresson, 1933; Aykroyd, 1938; Beams and Sheehan, 1941). Those in the smallest oöcytes are clustered together at one side of the nucleus, evidently around the centrosphere. Later they break away from this position and become scattered throughout the cytoplasm, being associated often with the clumps of mitochondria. Infiltration into the cytoplasm of the oöcyte of Golgi bodies from the adjoining cells of the follicular epithelium, such as occurs in birds and reptiles, has been described in several Indian rodents by P. R. Bhattacharya (1931). This requires confirmation, especially as the Golgi bodies described in the epithelial cells by this author differ in appearance from those described by other workers (Henneguy, 1926 ; Gresson, 1933). Extrusion of nucleolar material from the nucleus into the cytoplasm of the growing oöcyte of the mouse has been described by Gresson (1933). Oögenesis in the rat and the mouse has been investigated also by Kremer (1924). It is apparent from this account that the cytoplasmic processes involved in the production of deutoplasm in the mammalian oöcyte are complicated and require further elucidation. Both the mitochondria and Golgi bodies play an important part in this process and nucleolar extrusion also may participate.

The amount of deutoplasm present in the full-grown oöcyte varies widely, both in quality and quantity, in different species of mammals. Fatty yolk-spheres, which blacken with osmium tetroxide, are present in considerable quantity in the ova of the dog (O. van der Stricht, 1923), ferret (Mainland, 1931a ; Hamilton, 1934), pig (Heuser and Streeter, 1929), cow (Hartman, Lewis, Miller and Swett, 1931), and *Dasyurus* (Hill, 1910) ; they are less abundant in the guinea-pig (Lams, 1913), bat (O. van der Stricht, 1909), cat (R. van der Stricht, 1911 ; Longley, 1911 ; Hill and Tribe, 1924), *Loris* (Rao, 1927 ; Hill, 1932), *Tarsius* and *Hapale* (Hill, 1932), and they are scarce in the rabbit (Gregory, 1930), mouse (Lams and Doorme, 1907), rat (Sobotta and Burckhard, 1910), and man (Loyez, 1911 ; O. van der Stricht, 1923). The amount of deutoplasm present in the oöcytes of the cat varies remarkably ; in those relatively rich in fat, the globules are mainly aggregated in the central region and towards one pole with smaller globules in the peripheral region beneath the mitochondrial zone ; in those relatively poor in fat, the larger globules are confined to a smaller central region. R. van der Stricht (1911) regarded these two types as distinct, and suggested that the first were female producing and the latter male producing, but Hill and Tribe (1924) regard them as the extremes of a variable series. The first type exhibits a clearly defined polarity, which is found also in the ferret (Mainland, 1931a ; Hamilton, 1934), guinea-pig, bat and several other species, but which is less obvious, or is absent, in the opossum, rat, rabbit, pig, cow, etc.

The Formation of the Zona Pellucida

The oöcyte in the mature follicle is surrounded by a thick transparent membrane, the zona pellucida or zona radiata. The term zona pellucida is preferable to zona radiata, as it does not admit of confusion with the surrounding cellular corona radiata. It may appear homogeneous or radially striated, owing to being traversed by very fine canals. The zona pellucida appears to be outside and distinct from, though closely applied to, the thin vitelline membrane, which is undoubtedly a true cell membrane and an integral part of the oöcyte to which it belongs. The zona pellucida becomes considerably attenuated, owing to stretching, during the growth of the oöcyte in vertebrates other than the marsupial and placental mammals. It is an extremely thin membrane, relative to the size of the cell, around the mature ova of Sauropsida and Monotremata, for example. It varies considerably in thickness in different species but is always well developed in marsupial and placental mammals, where it forms a relatively rigid envelope around the small ovum. The histochemical properties of the zona pellucida have been investigated by Braden (1952).

The origin of the zona pellucida is difficult to determine, some investigators

maintaining that it is formed by the oöcyte.   Van Beneden (1880) pointed out
that in some polyovular follicles in which the oöcytes were in contact a perfectly
normal zona pellucida was formed even over the area of contact where none of the
follicle cells could touch the oöcyte.   Similar evidence has been adduced by
O'Donoghue (1912) and Hartman (1926).   This provides the most convincing
argument in favour of the secretion of the zona pellucida by the oöcyte itself.
Waldeyer (1870) held that the zona pellucida is produced by the cells of the cumulus.
This view is upheld by the work of O. van der Stricht (1923) who regards it as a
fenestrated membrane, formed as a meshwork of terminal bars surrounding and
separating the inner ends of the cells of the corona radiata and arising from an
intercellular substance or cement produced by these cells.   He recognises an
inner denser zone, formed first, in which the radial canals are very fine, and an
outer later-formed region with larger cavities.   The fine inner ends of the cells
of the corona radiata are said to traverse the canals of the zona pellucida and to
provide protoplasmic connections between these cells and the oöcyte (Heape,
1886 ; O. van der Stricht, 1923 ; Mainland, 1932).   This occurs also in elasmobranchs and reptiles.   The zona pellucida arises in the reptiles (Thing, 1918 ;
Boyd, 1940) and birds (Brambell, 1925) in a similar manner to that described by
O. van der Stricht.   The intercellular substance or cement in the bird may be
formed by the breakdown and liquefaction of some of the cells of the follicular
epithelium.   Gatenby (1922) also affirms the follicular origin of the zona pellucida
in *Ornithorhynchus*, but believes that the substance of which it is formed is intracellular at first.   The zona pellucida is not a simple membrane but appears to
consist of inner and outer zones, of which the former is more homogeneous and
the latter more clearly radially striated.   Flynn and Hill (1939) agree that the
zona pellucida of Monotremes is a product of the follicular epithelium alone,
being secreted during the first phase of follicular growth when the oöcyte is less
than 1·0 mm. in diameter.   Thereafter it is not added to and it behaves as an
elastic membrane, becoming progressively thinner as it is stretched by the increase
in size of the oöcyte.   It is a perfectly homogeneous layer, without any perforations or fenestrations through which processes of the follicle cells could reach the
oöcyte.   They state that there is no evidence that terminal bars contribute to its
formation, as was suggested by O. van der Stricht (1923) and Thing (1918).
Champy and Gley (1923) state that in cyclostomes and teleosts the outer zone is
produced by the follicle but that the inner may be secreted by the oöcyte.   They
found that in *Acipenser* the zona pellucida encloses not only the oöcyte but also
an inner layer of follicular epithelial cells and that it is formed, in consequence,
between outer and inner layers of the follicular epithelium.   Therefore it must be
entirely of follicular origin in this instance at least.   The structure of the zona
pellucida in the oöcytes of several teleosts has been described by Becher (1928).
The peripheral cytoplasm of the oöcyte in the Anamnia, Sauropsida and Monotremata, has a radial fibrillar structure immediately beneath the zona pellucida
(Champy and Gley, 1923 ; Gatenby, 1922 ; Bhattacharya, Das and Dutta,
1929).

The follicle secretes structures on the outside of the zona pellucida in *Myxine*
(Lyngnes, 1930), *Petromyzon* and a few teleosts (Champy and Gley, 1923) for the
attachment of the egg when laid.   These exhibit a polarity corresponding with
that of the oöcyte itself.

The Maturation of the Ovum

It is not until ovulation is imminent, and the loosening of the cumulus and formation of the corona radiata have begun (see p. 445), that the final stages of maturation are entered upon in mammals.   Then the centrosome divides into two centrioles, around which asters appear.   These move apart and a spindle is formed between them.   Meanwhile the chromosomes have recondensed in the nucleus, the nuclear membrane disappears and the chromosomes, in diploid pairs, are set free in the cytoplasm and become arranged on the equator of the spindle. Each univalent chromosome, as a rule, clearly exhibits a constriction marking the future plane of cleavage during the homotypic division, so that the divalent chromosomes in the metaphase of the heterotypic division appear as tetrads.   The heterotypic spindle is always eccentric in position and situated close to the periphery at the animal pole of the oöcyte (Figs. 5. 19 and 5. 20).   It may be perpendicular, oblique or tangential to the surface, as in the mouse (Long and Mark, 1911).   The heterotypic division is rapidly completed and the first polar body separated.   The homotypic division is entered upon immediately, without the intervention of any resting phase, and the spindle is formed close to the site of the first polar body. The second polar spindle, like the first, may be perpendicular, oblique or tangential to the surface.   Sometimes, as in the guinea-pig, it is formed in a slightly projecting lobe of the cytoplasm of the oöcyte.   The first polar body may degenerate directly after formation, or it may enter upon a homotypic division simultaneously with that in the oöcyte.   Ovulation occurs as a rule after the separation of the first polar body and before the completion of the homotypic division, usually when the second polar spindle is in metaphase.   The homotypic division does not then proceed beyond metaphase until after fertilisation has occurred, normally in the upper part of the Fallopian tube, and the spermatozoon is in the cytoplasm of the secondary oöcyte.   This is the case in the rat (Long and Evans, 1922, Austin, 1951), mouse (Long and Mark, 1911 ; Togari, 1927 ; Snell, Fekete, Hummel and Law, 1940), bank vole (unpublished), pocket gopher (Mossman and Hisaw, 1940), guinea-pig (Lams, 1913), rabbit (Pincus and Enzmann, 1932), bat (O. van der Stricht, 1909 ; Wimsatt, 1944), shrew (unpublished), *Elephantulus* (van der Horst and Gillman, 1941), cat (R. van der Stricht, 1911), ferret (Robinson, 1918 ; Hamilton, 1934), pig (Corner, 1917), cow (Miller, Swett, Hartman and Lewis, 1931), rhesus monkey (Corner, 1923 ; Edgar Allen, 1927, 1928 ; Hartman and Corner, 1941) and other species.   So far as is known, the same rule holds for the marsupials also, certainly for *Dasyurus* (Hill, 1910) and *Didelphys* (Hartman, 1932b ; Martínez-Esteve, 1942).   The heterotypic spindle is formed before, but Cole and Miller (1935) state that the first polar body is not separated until immediately after, ovulation in the ewe.   Gresson (1941) believes that though ovulation in the mouse may take place during the homotypic division it sometimes occurs before the separation of the first polar body.   In man, Thomson (1919a) described the completion of both maturation divisions within the ovary, but subsequent investigation of more favourable materials (Stieve, 1926 ; Hinselmann, 1930 ; Allen, Pratt, Newell and Bland, 1930a and b ; Hamilton, 1944) leaves little room for doubt that man (Fig. 5. 19) does not differ from the majority of mammals in this respect.   The maturation phases in human ovarian oöcytes have been described also by Dixon (1927) and by Hoadley and Simons (1928).   Living human tubal ova have been described by Hamilton (1944). Thomson's results probably were due to mistaking early stages of atresia for normal maturation. The separation of both polar bodies before ovulation has been described, probably erroneously, in the mole also (Heape, 1886). The dog provides one well-established exception to the rule, for in it the first polar spindle is not formed until after ovulation (O. van der Stricht, 1908, 1923 ; Evans and Cole, 1931) and fertilisation may occur before the completion of the heterotypic division, for one oöcyte has been described with a heterotypic spindle and a spermatozoon in the cytoplasm. In the fox, also, the first polar spindle does not form until after ovulation and the spermatozoon enters the oöcyte when the second polar spindle is in metaphase (Pearson and Enders, 1943). Some of the Insectivora, however, provide the most remarkable exceptions. Convincing evidence has been provided that in *Ericulus* (Strauss, 1938), one of the Centetidae, the homotypic division is completed and fertilisation occurs normally within the ripe follicle, into which spermatozoa penetrate in large numbers. The fertilised ovum, at the time of ovulation, is already in the stage with two pronuclei. In the American shrew, *Blarina brevicauda*, the first polar body is separated before ovulation and fertilisation sometimes, perhaps, usually, occurs in the follicle (Pearson, 1944). In Monotremes (Flynn and Hill, 1939) the first polar spindle, when first formed, lies with its long axis tangential to the surface of the oöcyte. It rotates and becomes perpendicular to the surface of the oöcyte before the separation of the first polar body, which occurs in the follicle. The second polar spindle has been formed and a fluid-filled perivitelline space developed before ovulation. The second polar body is separated after ovulation, while the ovum is in the oviduct. Probably separation is independent of the occurrence of fertilisation. At fertilisation only a single spermatozoon penetrates the ovum, and polyspermy therefore does not occur.

Structure of the Follicle in Anamnia and Sauropsida

The follicles in all other vertebrates differ from those of the mammals in that the growing oöcytes fill them completely at all stages and no fluid-filled antra are developed. The follicles of cyclostomes, fishes, amphibians, reptiles and birds, although exhibiting considerable diversity of structure, especially in the development of the follicular epithelium, can be dealt with together. The follicles of the monotremes are intermediate in structure between those of the Sauropsida and of the higher mammals and will be considered separately.

The epithelium in the smallest follicles consists of a single layer of flattened cells. These become cubical and even columnar in form as growth proceeds and the epithelium thickens in consequence. Subsequently, during the final rapid growth of the oöcyte, the epithelium is stretched thin and consists of only a single layer of flattened epithelial cells around the mature oöcyte (Wallace, 1903 ; Loyez, 1906 ; van Durme, 1914 ; Hett, 1924). These changes in thickness of the epithelium are most marked in the elasmobranchs, reptiles and birds which have the largest and most heavily yolk-laden ova. Marza and Marza (1935) have recorded the thickness of the follicular epithelium in relation to the diameter of the contained oöcyte in the hen ; it reaches a maximum when the oöcyte is only $1 \cdot 5$ mm. in diameter and decreases continuously thereafter until the oöcyte attains its definitive size of $25 \cdot 0$ mm. in diameter. Some of the cells of the follicular epithelium in many elasmobranchs and reptiles differentiate into large " nutritive " elements. This differentiation of the epithelial cells in reptiles was noted by Gegenbaur (1861). Among the elasmobranchs Wallace (1903) did not find differentiation in *Spinax niger* in which the follicular epithelium remains single layered and more or less columnar in form at its maximum development. Giacomini (1896) found a similar condition in *Acanthias vulgaris*, *Scymnus lichia*, *Heptanchus cinereus* and *Mustelus laevis*. On the other hand, *Raia*, *Scyllium Torpedo*, *Myliobatis* and *Trygon* resemble *Chimaera monstrosa* (Wallace, 1903) in having a thick follicular epithelium composed of small indifferent cells and large specialised nutritive cells. The small cells give rise to the large cells and transitional stages can be found. The large cells lie next the oöcyte with the small cells on the outside, extending in wedge-shaped masses between the bases of the large cells. Differentiation into small, intermediate or transitional, and large cells

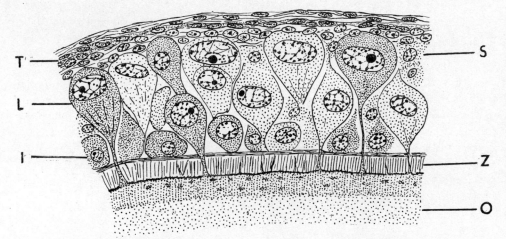

Fig. 5. 9—Part of the wall of a follicle of the lizard, *Lacerta muralis*, showing the theca (T), the small (S), intermediate (I) and large (L) cells of the follicular epithelium, and the radial striation of the zona pellucida (Z). Canalicular prolongations of the large cells can be seen to traverse the zona pellucida. O, cytoplasm of oöcyte. × 800. (After Loyez, 1906.)

has been described in the lizards and snakes (Fig. 5. 9) by Trinci (1905), Loyez (1906) and D. R. Bhattacharya (1925), to whom reference should be made for the earlier literature, but the last named finds no differentiation in the Chelonia. The large cells do not multiply, mitotically or otherwise, and disappear during the later growth of the oöcyte. Thus the follicular epithelium in the mature follicle of the lizard, as in other forms, consists of a single layer of small flattened epithelial cells (Hett, 1924). Holl (1893) described and figured in the follicular epithelium of the bird two kinds of cells, differing in chromophility rather than in size. He considered the elements with denser protoplasm to be supporting cells and those with clearer protoplasm nutritive cells. Mertens (1895) also found two kinds of epithelial cells in *Pica caudata* (Ray). A similar differentiation occurs in the follicular epithelium of the fowl (Brambell, 1925). The more chromophil elements, which arise from the others during the earlier growth of the oöcyte, stretch from the membrana propria to the surface of the oöcyte. They appear to transform into intercellular substance and ultimately to disappear from the epithelium. The other cells, which are in the majority, become arranged in several layers at the time of maximum development of the follicular epithelium. The more chromophil cells have been seen also by Marza and Marza (1935), but Loyez (1906) considers them to be artefacts. Loyez (1906) and Das (1931) both regard the follicular epithelium of the bird as pluristratified during its phase of maximum thickness, but Marza and Marza (1935) state that it consists of a single layer of long columnar cells and that the pluristratified appearance is deceptive and due to the majority of sections being slightly tangential. The follicular epithelium in cyclostomes (Champy and Gley, 1923), teleosts (Champy and Gley, 1923 ; Wallace, 1903) and amphibians (King, 1902 ; Smith, 1912 ; Hett, 1923b ; Rugh, 1935) is never pluristratified or differentiated into different kinds of cells. It does not attain any considerable thickness in amphibians (Rugh, 1935).

The large nutritive cells of elasmobranchs and reptiles (Fig. 5. 9) are prolonged into fine protoplasmic fibrils which traverse the zona pellucida and are connected with the cytoplasm of the oöcyte (Retzius, 1912 ; Wallace, 1903 ; Loyez, 1906 ; Thing, 1918). Fluid, semi-fluid or granular material from the large cells passes through these protoplasmic processes into the oöcyte in the reptiles (Loyez, 1906). The contents of the nucleus and even of the entire cell may pass in this way into the yolk, without having undergone previously any essential modification, or the cell may undergo first a sort of fatty degeneration and the resulting fine corpuscles pass into the oöcyte. The passage of Golgi bodies directly from the follicle cells to the oöcyte, prior to the formation of the zona pellucida, was described originally in the hen (Brambell, 1925). A similar infiltration of Golgi bodies was observed in the tortoise, where they pass through channels in the zona pellucida, by D. R. Bhattacharya (1925) and has since been observed in other reptiles, in fishes (D. R. Bhattacharya, Das and Dutta, 1929 ; P. R. Bhattacharya, 1929a and b), and again in birds (Das, 1931).

Mitoses are frequent in the cells of the follicular epithelium throughout the whole of the growth period (Hett, 1923a and b ; 1924 ; Brambell, 1925), although Schmidt (1898) and D. R. Bhattacharya (1925) failed to find any in the elasmo-branchs and tortoises respectively.

The follicular epithelium rests upon a basement membrane or membrana propria which separates it from the theca, in elasmobranchs, teleosts (Wallace, 1903), reptiles (Hett, 1924) and birds (Brambell, 1925 ; Hett, 1923a). Apparently a membrana propria is lacking in the Amphibia (Hett, 1923b ; Rugh, 1935).

The structure of the theca of the follicles of the vertebrates other than the mammals has received even less attention than that of the epithelium, and it is difficult to find any adequate account of it in the literature. Several authors have recognised a differentiation into theca externa and theca interna in reptiles and birds (Hett, 1923a ; 1924 ; Brambell, 1925 ; Cunningham and Smart, 1934), but it is doubtful if these are strictly comparable to those of mammals. Weekes (1934) only recognises the distinction between theca externa and theca interna in the follicles of lizards after they have ruptured. The theca interna then con-sists of fibroblasts, theca interna cells, which are probably a less differentiated form of the fibroblasts, connective-tissue fibres and capillaries. Collagen fibres are present according to Hett (1923a ; 1924) in both the theca interna and theca externa of reptiles and birds, but are more numerous in the latter, and occur in the theca of amphibians. Elastic fibres appear in the theca externa of reptiles and birds when the follicles have attained a certain size but do not occur in the theca interna, nor are they found in the theca in amphibians. Smooth muscle cells in the theca have been described by Rugh (1935) in the frog and by Phillips and Warren (1937) in the fowl. The theca in mature follicles of Amphibia and Sauropsida is much stretched and thin in consequence, especially so in Amphibia, where it forms a very thin investment around the follicle, on the side projecting into the central cavity of the ovary. The theca is richly supplied with blood and lymph vessels ; the larger vessels being most numerous in the outer part of the theca externa, which has a very loose texture. The follicles in fish, amphibians and reptiles, the ovaries of which have comparatively little stroma, project into the large sacs or cavities, lined with endothelium, which occupy the centre of the organ and which doubtless contain lymphoid transudation. Even in birds, in which the ovary is more compact and the stroma better developed, the medullary region is composed chiefly of numerous large lymph sinuses. Blood vessels are absent from the stigma or area where rupture will occur, both in the frog (Rugh, 1935) and the fowl (Phillips and Warren, 1937 ; Nalbandov and James, 1949). The stigma in the fowl is an oblong area extending nearly half-way round the circumference of the mature follicle.

Wallace (1903) records a definite orientation of the oöcyte within the follicle with reference to its polar axis in *Spinax* and *Chimaera*. He found that the animal pole is always directed inwards towards the centre of the ovary.

The Structure of the Follicle in Monotremata

The structure of the follicle in the monotremes is of particular interest because, although they give rise to well-developed corpora lutea, the oöcyte, on account of its large size, almost completely fills the follicle. The structure of the follicle has been described by Hill and Gatenby (1926), by Garde (1930), and by Flynn and Hill (1939). The follicular epithelium in small follicles consists of a single layer of small cubical or slightly flattened cells. It increases rapidly in thickness during the first phase of growth of the oöcyte up to a size of 1·0 mm. in diameter. During the second phase, while the oöcyte is doubling its diameter, it actually decreases slightly in thickness. During the third phase, while the oöcyte is growing from 2·0 mm. in diameter to its maximum size, the follicular epithelium again thickens rapidly, owing to enlargement of the cells, and attains its greatest development at the time of ovulation. The follicular epithelium in mature follicles, (Fig. 5. 10) measuring approximately 4·75 mm. in diameter with contained oöcytes 4·0 to 4·5 mm. in diameter, is 22 to 28μ in thickness. This is relatively much thicker than in the mature follicles of Sauropsida. It is significant that the epithelium attains its maximum development in reptiles and birds early in the growth of the follicle, becoming thinner thereafter, whereas it does so in the monotremes only when the follicle is mature. The epithelial cells of the mature follicle are large and plump with large oval nuclei. Caldwell (1887) described a layer of colloid-like fluid, which he called " pro-albumen," around the oöcyte, in the mature follicle of *Echidna*, secreted by the follicular epithelium on its inner face, next the zona pellucida. Flynn and Hill (1939) have observed this fluid completely surrounding the oöcyte in large follicles of *Ornithorhynchus* and *Echidna* (Fig. 5. 11). They have shown that it is secreted by the epithelial cells during the last phase of follicular growth, and they identify it with the follicular fluid of other mammals.

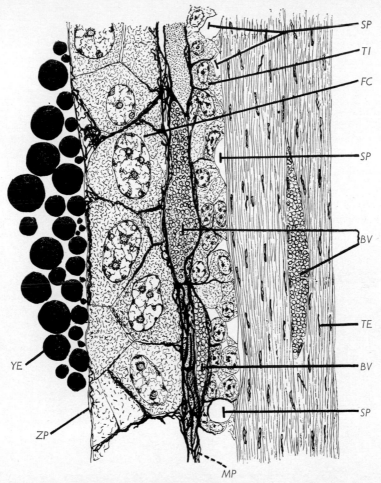

Fig. 5. 10—Part of the wall of the follicle of a full-grown oöcyte of *Ornithorhynchus*. BV, capillaries ; FC, follicular epithelium ; MP, membrana propria ; SP, spaces in theca interna ; TE, theca externa ; TI, theca interna ; YE, yolk spheres in cytoplasm of oöcyte ; ZP, zona pellucida. × 425. (From Hill and Gatenby, 1926.)

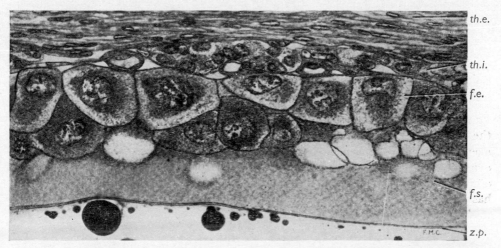

Fig. 5. 11.—Section through the follicular wall of a mature oöcyte about to ovulate of *Echidna*, showing the theca externa (th.e.), theca interna (th.i.), follicular epithelium (f.e.), follicular fluid (f.s.) and zona pellucida (z.p.). × 430. (From Flynn and Hill, 1939.)

Thus the follicles of monotremes are not solid structures, like those of reptiles and birds, but each contain a fluid-filled cavity, homologous with the antrum of the Graafian follicles of other mammals.

The theca of follicles containing oöcytes up to about 0·5 mm. in diameter is undifferentiated and consists of flattened concentrically arranged stromal cells. By the time the oöcyte has attained a diameter of 0·75 mm. the theca has thickened and differentiated into theca interna and theca externa. The theca interna consists of several layers of small cells with elongated nuclei, compactly arranged, with scattered fibroblasts among them. Both thecal layers are said to arise from the differentiated stroma cells of the primitive theca. The theca interna cells begin to enlarge by the time the oöcyte is 2·75 mm. in diameter, but they never attain a size approaching that of the epithelial cells. Their cytoplasm is frequently vacuolated. In the ripe follicle fibroblasts and fibres are absent from the theca interna. The thickness of the theca interna varies in different follicles and even in different parts of the same follicle. It is absent in places and at others it is nearly as thick as the epithelium (Fig. 5. 10). The theca externa consists of white fibrous connective tissue, with fibroblasts between the bundles of collagen fibres. Elastic fibres and smooth muscle appear to be absent, except from the walls of the arteries. The membrana propria, separating the theca interna from the epithelium, is a well-developed membrane containing fibroblasts. It arises as a fenestrated connective-tissue membrane. Capillaries are numerous in the theca interna and penetrate into the substance of the membrana propria.

The Structure of the Follicle in Marsupial and Placental Mammals

The smallest oöcytes in the adult ovary lie near the surfaces and are surrounded by primordial follicles, each consisting of a thin epithelial investment formed by a single layer of very flattened cells (Fig. 5. 5). No outer connective-tissue sheath or theca is differentiated from the surrounding stroma. The smallest follicles in the mouse measure only about 16·5μ in diameter, while the enclosed oöcyte is approximately 13μ in diameter (Brambell, 1928), but the size of the oöcyte, and consequently of the follicles, varies in different species. The primordial follicles are so numerous in some species that they may form a pronounced peripheral zone which is a conspicuous feature of the ovarian cortex, as in the dog, monkey and man, and still more marked in the rabbit, grey squirrel and cat (Deanesly and Parkes, 1933; Evans and Swezy, 1931). This is not the case in the mouse (Brambell, 1928), rat, guinea-pig (Evans and Swezy, 1931), shrew (Brambell, 1935), hedgehog (Deanesly, 1934), stoat (Deanesly, 1935) and other species. Frequently, primordial follicles are more numerous in the vicinity of the hilus of the ovary. This may be due to their formation continuing in this region up to or even after puberty (de Winiwarter, 1920). The remarkable occurrence in the ovaries of adult lemurs of nests of primordial follicles, in which the nuclei of the oöcytes are in the early stages of the heterotypic prophase (Gérard, 1920, 1932), has been referred to above.

The oöcyte and follicle, as they increase in size, sink gradually inwards into the deeper regions of the ovarian cortex. It is only when the follicle approaches maturity that it assumes again a peripheral position and protrudes from the surface of the ovary (Fig. 5. 15).

Membrana granulosa.

The flattened epithelial cells of the primordial follicle enter upon a phase of growth and proliferation at the same time as the contained oöcyte begins to enlarge. The changes in the follicle, then initiated, continue long after the oöcyte has attained its maximum size. The flattened epithelial cells increase in number and gradually become cubical, then columnar, in form. Their nuclei, which are elongated at first, become at the same time almost spherical. At this stage the limiting membranes of the epithelial cells are invisible or indistinct and the epithelium may be syncitial (Robinson, 1918). The single layer of columnar

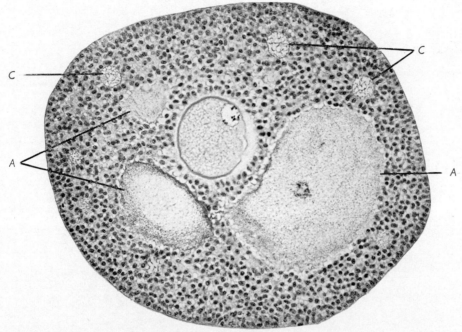

Fig. 5. 12—Photomicrograph of a small Graafian follicle of the rabbit showing the formation of the antrum from several separate cavities (A) and the bodies of Call and Exner (C).   × 240.

epithelium becomes transformed by cell-division into a double and then a triple layer of epithelium. The individual cells, as this transformation takes place, assume again a cubical or polygonal form and at this and all subsequent stages their limiting membranes are distinguishable. The follicle at this stage tends to be ovate rather than spherical in form. Soon the antrum appears as one or more small fluid-filled cavities among the epithelial cells (Fig. 5. 12) which, enlarging and coalescing, give rise to a single cavity at one side of the follicle. The antrum begins to develop very soon after the ovum has attained its maximum size but not before (Brambell, 1928 ; Parkes, 1931). The average size of follicle in which the antrum first appears varies somewhat in different species, being as little as 160μ in diameter in the common shrew (Brambell, 1935) and as much as 400μ in diameter in the pig (Parkes, 1931). The antrum, when formed, is bounded by the membrana granulosa or peripheral zone of epithelial cells which is several cells thick and is remarkably uniform (Fig. 5. 16).   Bluntschli and his collaborators have shown that in the Centetidae, *Hemicentetes* (Landau, 1938) and *Ericulus* (Strauss, 1938), the cells of the membrana granulosa swell and become loosened as the follicle enlarges, forming a spongy mass, but no definite cavity appears among them.   An antrum is not developed, even in the mature follicle, which thus lacks the characteristic feature of a true Graafian follicle.   The theca of the maturing follicle also shows loosening and increased blood effusion.

The discus proligerus or cumulus of epithelial cells surrounding the oöcyte is attached to the membrana granulosa at one side and projects into the antrum (Figs. 5. 13 and 5. 15).   The simple epithelium of the primordial follicle thus gives

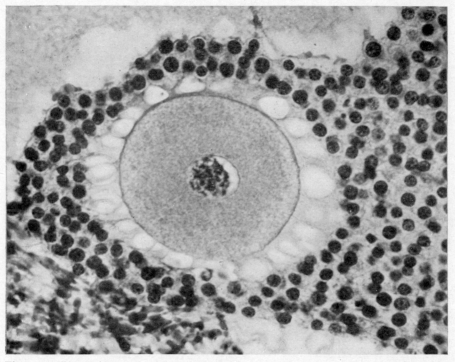

Fig. 5. 13—Photomicrograph of the oöcyte and discus proligerus of a small Graafian follicle of the baboon.   × 514.   (From Zuckerman and Parkes, 1932.)

rise directly by cell proliferation to the characteristic membrana granulosa and cumulus of the mammalian Graafian follicle.   The proliferation of the cells of the follicular epithelium is probably entirely mitotic, although it has been suggested (Robinson, 1918), without convincing evidence, that amitosis may occur in the very small follicles.   Mitosis has been observed frequently in the cells both of the membrana granulosa and cumulus in the larger follicles of many species (Robinson, 1918; Thomson, 1919b).   According to Walsh (1917) the rate of proliferation of the cells of the membrana granulosa of the guinea-pig is low in the small follicles and rises gradually until they have attained medium size ; thereafter it falls again almost to zero as maturity is reached.   The rate of mitosis in the cells of the membrana granulosa has been investigated also by Dogliotti (1926) and Bullough (1942c).   The latter author, using colchicine to arrest mitosis, found that the rate of growth is greatly accelerated at the time when the antrum appears. Mitoses are most frequent in the cells adjoining the oöcyte and the antrum, which constitute the high point of a mitotic gradient with the low point in the theca externa.   Lane and Davis (1939) give data of the changes in volume of the antrum, membrana granulosa and theca in the growing follicles of the rat and for the mitotic activity of the cells of the follicular wall during the oestrous cycle.   Many observers agree that mitosis does not occur in the membrana granulosa of the mature follicle about to rupture.

Although so much attention has been paid to the histology of the Graafian follicle, the cytology of its component cells has been relatively neglected.   Changes in the size of the nucleus in the cells of the membrana granulosa of *Ericulus* have been described by Niklaus (1950).   The mitochondria and the centrioles have been investigated by Chydenius (1929).   The mitochondria in the cells of the membrana granulosa are in the form of small granules and rods scattered throughout the cytoplasm (Robinson, 1918 ; Solomons and Gatenby, 1924 ; Gresson, 1933).   The Golgi apparatus of the membrana granulosa cells has been investigated in the guinea-pig (Henneguy, 1926), the mouse (Gresson, 1933), the rabbit and other mammals (Moricard, 1933, 1936 ; Moricard, Gothié and Tsatsaris, 1939), and in man (Solomons and Gatenby, 1924 ; Aykroyd, 1938).   It is small and compact and lies close to the nucleus.   According to Moricard, the epithelial cells of the follicle are definitely orientated, as shown by the position of the Golgi apparatus, in relation to the theca, oöcyte and antrum, and this orientation changes during the growth of the follicle.   The Golgi apparatus is on the side of the nucleus next to the oöcyte in very small follicles with a single layer of epithelial cells.   This orientation is maintained throughout the growth of the follicle in the outermost cells of the membrana granulosa, which rest upon the membrana propria. The Golgi apparatus is on the side of the nucleus away from the oöcyte in the cells adjoining the zona pellucida in follicles with two or more layers of epithelial cells and in which the oöcytes are full grown.   This polarity is reversed in the cells of the corona radiata in follicles about to ovulate.   The reversal occurs some time after copulation in the rabbit.   Most of the cells bordering the antrum have the Golgi apparatus on the side of the nucleus next to the liquor folliculi at first, but this polarity is reversed shortly before ovulation.   The polarity of the cells that do not adjoin the membrana propria, oöcyte or antrum is less regular.   Thus the polarity of the epithelial cells in very small follicles in which the oöcyte is growing rapidly, indicates that they are supplying materials to the oöcyte.   When the growth of the oöcyte is completed the orientation suggests the active secretion of the liquor folliculi and the physiological isolation of the oöcyte.   Finally, in follicles about to ovulate, the cells of the corona radiata become polarised towards the oöcyte again and appear to be actively secreting substances into it.   A similar polarity is shown beautifully by the corona radiata in the cat, figured by O, van der Stricht (1923), in the cells of which the centrosphere lies always between the nucleus and the oöcyte. Fat granules which blacken with osmium tetroxide and lipoid granules, staining with Scharlach R, are absent from the cells of the membrana granulosa of immature follicles, but appear in them near the time of ovulation (Robinson, 1918 ; Deanesly, 1930a).   They are small and uniform in size, and thus are distinguishable from the fat droplets which appear, in the form of larger and irregularly sized droplets, in the cells of degenerating follicles.   In mature follicles of the dog and cat fat droplets are found in the cells of the corona radiata (O. van der Stricht, 1923), as well as in those of the membrana granulosa.

It may be observed sometimes that some of the cells of the membrana granulosa stain differently to the majority, usually more densely. These are commonly regarded as pycnotic cells, but 'Espinasse (1934) regards them as healthy and a normal component of the membrana granulosa.

Structures known as the bodies of Call and Exner (1875) are present normally in the follicles of a few species, notably the rabbit (Figs. 5. 12 and 5. 14), prairie dog (Stockard, 1937), cat and man, although they do not occur in the follicles of many others. These bodies consist of a small cavity, containing a coagulum, around which the cells are radially arranged (Levi, 1903) and they may occur in the follicular epithelium before the appearance of the antrum or, after its appearance, either in the membrana granulosa or cumulus. The radial arrangement of the cells somewhat resembles that in the corona radiata, and it is possible that it is due to similar causes. Honoré (1900) regards these structures in the rabbit as due to the radial arrangement of groups of cells for the purpose of secreting a substance into the central cavity. He states that this secretion is at first homogeneous but becomes reticulate and increases in quantity. Finally, a very fine peripheral membrane is formed around it and the radial arrangement of the cells becomes less evident (Fig. 5. 14). Waldeyer (1870), Flemming (1885a), Nagel (1896) and Thomson (1919b) state that they are formed around vacuolated cells which are undergoing

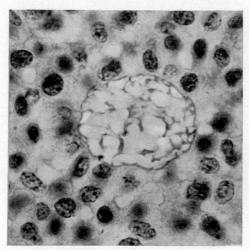

Fig. 5. 14—Photomicrograph of one of the bodies of Call and Exner shown in Fig. 5. 12. The definite limiting membrane and the coagulum within are shown. × 1,340.

liquefaction, and the latter author considers that the radial arrangement of the surrounding cells is purely mechanical and is not concerned with secretion. Whichever view is accepted, there can be no doubt that the contents of these bodies contributes to the formation of the liquor folliculi.

The membrana granulosa in mature follicles about to ovulate is remarkably uniform in thickness throughout except that it may be thinner or even perforated at the point where rupture will occur (Figs. 5. 15 and 5. 16). It becomes considerably folded, the folds projecting into the antrum (Fig. 5. 17) in the dog (Evans and Cole, 1931) and the fox (Pearson and Enders, 1943), but such folding is not known to occur, until after rupture, in the follicles of other species. The cells of the membrana granulosa of mature follicles do not differ much from those of smaller follicles as a rule, but in the hedgehog (Deanesly, 1934) they are said to be enlarged, presumably in preparation for their transformation into luteal cells.

A membrane, the membrana limitans interna, is formed on the inner surface of the membrana granulosa, next to the antrum, in the mature follicles, at least of some species. It was described first in the dog by Bouin and Ancel (1908) who

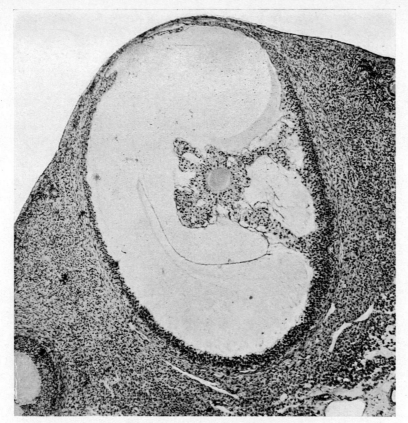

Fig. 5. 15—Photomicrograph of a mature Graafian follicle of the rabbit about to rupture. The wall of the follicle and the overlying tissues have become very thin at the point in the upper part of the picture where rupture will occur. Some extravasation of blood has taken place in this region. The discus proligerus and the corona radiata are forming. Both primary and secondary liquor folliculi can be distinguished in the antrum. × 53. (From Fee and Parkes, 1929.)

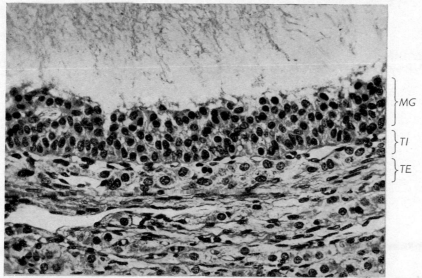

Fig. 5. 16—Photomicrograph of part of the wall of the follicle shown in Fig. 5. 15. MG, membrana granulosa ; TE, theca externa ; TI, theca interna. × 350. (From Brambell, 1930 ; Parkes's material.)

state that it arises from the inner cells of the membrana granulosa itself which become very flattened. A similar cellular membrane has been described in the

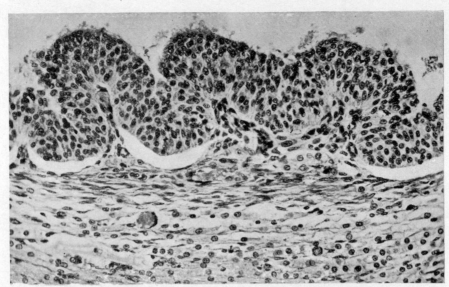

Fig. 5. 17—Photomicrograph of part of the wall of a mature Graafian follicle of a fox showing the folding of the membrana granulosa and the ingrowths of the theca interna containing blood vessels into the cores of the folds. × 290.

human follicle (Fig. 5. 18), by Thomson (1919b) and by Solomons and Gatenby (1924). A membrana limitans interna has also been described in follicles of the ferret by Robinson (1918), who regards it as arising from a condensation of the

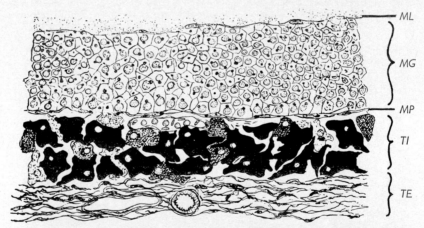

Fig. 5. 18—Part of the wall of a mature human Graafian follicle. The Golgi bodies can be seen in the cells of the membrana granulosa (MG). The stellate cells of the theca interna (TI) are large in comparison to the cells of the membrana granulosa. ML, membrana limitans interna ; MP, membrana propria ; TE, theca externa. × 480. (After Solomons and Gatenby, 1924.)

liquor folliculi in which are incorporated remnants of degenerating follicle cells. He states that it becomes detached from the membrana granulosa and extruded with the liquor folliculi at ovulation. A somewhat similar membrane has been observed by the author in the mature follicles of the bank-vole, and it appears to arise therein from cells of the theca interna which penetrate through the membrana granulosa and spread over its inner surface as a very thin cellular investing membrane.

The discus proligerus, or cumulus surrounding the oöcyte, is always more than one cell and is frequently many cells thick (Fig. 5. 13). It exhibits much individual and specific variation in shape and in the mode of its attachment to the follicular wall. Sometimes it is almost hemispherical and attached by a broad base to the membrana granulosa ; at other times it is nearly spherical and attached by a short neck or stalk. As the follicle approaches maturity the cells of the cumulus, except those adjoining the oöcyte, undergo loosening and dispersal (Figs. 5. 15 and 5. 19).

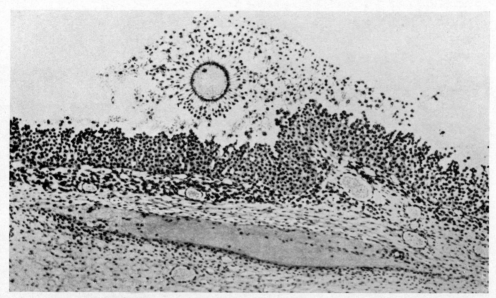

Fig. 5. 19—Part of the wall and the oöcyte of a mature human Graafian follicle 14 mm. in diam. The first polar spindle is formed within the oöcyte, which is surrounded by the corona radiata and is free in the antrum.   × 95.   (From Stieve, 1926.)

This results in the attachment of the cumulus to the wall of the follicle becoming less and finally disappearing at the time of ovulation. Robinson (1918) regards this loosening as due to the rapid secretion of liquor folliculi among the cells of the cumulus. He states that as the cells become dispersed their nuclei show signs of degeneration, the protoplasmic processes by which the cells were connected become destroyed and many of the cells break down and disappear. At the same time as these changes are taking place in the outer cells, the inner cells adjoining the oöcyte are transformed into a very beautiful corona radiata (Figs. 5. 19, 5. 20 and 5. 21). These cells become club-shaped and radially arranged around the oöcyte, to which their tapering ends are attached. Their nuclei migrate to the enlarged peripheral ends of the cells. The individual cells vary in length so that the nuclei become arranged not in one but in several rows. The corona radiata is formed in the mature follicles of the majority of other mammals, including the mouse (Long and Mark, 1911), dog (Evans and Cole, 1931), rabbit (Honoré, 1900), cow (Allen, Pratt, Newell and Bland, 1930a), cat (O. van der Stricht, 1923) and man (Stieve,

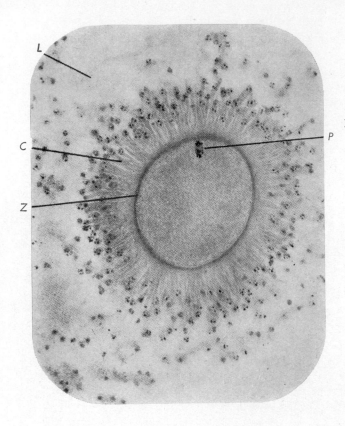

Fig. 5. 20—Photomicrograph of a section of the oöcyte and corona radiata within a Graafian follicle of a ferret about to ovulate. The animal was killed 30½ hrs. p.c. The oöcyte contains a first polar spindle (P) in late anaphase. The radial arrangement and the positions of the nuclei in the cells of the corona radiata (C) is shown. L, secondary liquor folliculi ; Z, zona pellucida. × 350. (From Robinson, 1918.)

Fig. 5. 21—Photomicrograph of part of a section of the oöcyte and corona radiata of a ferret 20 hrs. p.c. The radial arrangement and elongation of the cells (C) of the corona radiata is shown. The first polar spindle has not been formed within the oöcyte, the nucleus (N) of which is still in the dictyate stage. × 1,250. (From Robinson, 1918.)

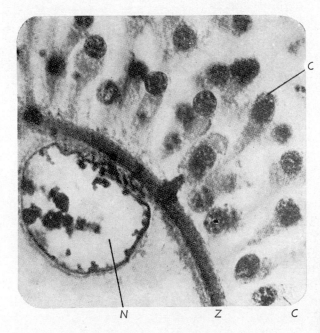

1926). The corona radiata remains for a time attached to the oöcyte in the Fallopian tube. Apparently, the spermatozoa cannot penetrate the corona and fertilisation cannot take place until it has dispersed, leaving the oöcyte naked. There is some evidence that it disperses more rapidly after copulation than in unmated females. McClean and Rowlands (1942) have shown that the enzyme, hyaluronidase, brings about the rapid dispersal of the cells of the corona radiata of the rat *in vitro*, and they suggest that the cells are embedded in a gel of hyaluronic acid, which is liquefied by the enzyme. The enzyme is present in semen, probably in the spermatozoa. This may explain why an accumulation of spermatozoa in the vicinity of the oöcyte is necessary to ensure the penetration of a single one, since the concentration of the enzyme would depend on the density of the suspension of spermatozoa. A corona radiata does not appear to be formed in the marsupials *Dasyurus* (Hill, 1910) and *Didelphys* (Hartman, 1932b). The mature oöcyte in the latter species lies in a convex cumulus, only projecting slightly into the antrum, and is covered by a layer of flattened cells one or two thick ; it is said to be extruded naked at ovulation (Martínez-Esteve, 1942). The oöcyte is extruded naked from the follicle in both *Ericulus* (Strauss, 1938) and *Elephantulus* (van der Horst, 1942). Indeed, in the latter species, no trace of even a zona pellucida could be found around the oöcyte once it had been ovulated, and it appeared to have been cast off with the corona radiata in the follicle. Fertilisation appears to take place while the oöcyte is still in the follicle in *Ericulus*, and this might account for the oöcyte being free from the corona when ovulated, but in *Elephantulus* fertilisation is said to take place in the Fallopian tube.

Much diversity of opinion has existed as to the position occupied in the follicle, in relation to the point of rupture, by the cumulus and its contained oöcyte. The earlier workers were divided ; many, including Nagel (1896), believing that it was situated on the deeper wall of the follicle opposite to the point of rupture, while others maintained that it was always superficial and near the rupture point. Sobotta (1895a), who had at his disposal sufficient material to give authority to his views, states that the position of the cumulus in the follicle of the mouse is entirely fortuitous. Thomson (1919b) in man, Hartman (1932b) in the opossum, to whom reference may be made for the earlier literature, Walton and Hammond (1928) in the rabbit, and the majority of modern workers also regard its position as depending on chance. Shaw (1927), however, came to the conclusion that in man the cumulus is at first on the deeper wall of the follicle and that owing to shifting or creep of the cells of the membrana granulosa, it finally assumes a superficial position. The problem can be solved finally only by careful study and reconstruction from serial sections of a large number of follicles, known to be mature by the presence of polar bodies or polar spindles in the oöcytes.

Liquor Folliculi

The antrum of the Graafian follicle is filled by a fluid, the liquor folliculi, and its appearance and distension is due to the secretion of this substance. Clearly this fluid must be derived ultimately from the blood either by simple lymphoid transudation or by active secretion on the part of the cells of the follicular wall. Two divergent views have been advanced as to the part played by the cells of the membrana granulosa and cumulus in this secretory process. Many authors, including Alexenko (1891), Janosik (1887), Lane-Claypon (1907), Schottlaender (1893), Sandes (1903), R. van der Stricht (1911) and Thomson (1919b), maintain that the liquor folliculi is a holocrine secretion which is contributed to largely by the products of disintegration and liquefaction of the cells. Nagel (1896) also regards it as produced partly by liquefaction of the cells and partly by transudation. On the other hand, Honoré (1900) maintains that in the rabbit it is secreted by the cells into the intercellular spaces in the same way that the urine is secreted by the epithelium of the renal tubules, and that destruction of the cells does not take place. He regards the bodies of Call and Exner as formed around such spaces, not around vacuolated and liquefying cells. Robinson (1918) entirely supports Honoré's contention. He states that in the ferret the liquor folliculi is formed as an intercellular secretion which forces apart the bodies of the cells and extends their substance into long inter-communicating filamentous processes. It is thus primarily a reticulum filled with fluid secreted by the cells. The secretion of the fluid and consequently the growth of the follicle, which is largely due to it, becomes increasingly rapid as the time of ovulation is approached, when the rate of proliferation of the cells (see p. 445) is waning. Nevertheless, the membrana granulosa maintains a uniform thickness in the maturing follicle. This fact is hard to reconcile with extensive cellular destruction and provides strong evidence in favour of the conclusions of Honoré and of Robinson.

The liquor folliculi does not present an entirely uniform appearance throughout the growth of the follicle. Robinson (1918) distinguishes histologically three kinds, the primary, secondary and tertiary liquor, secreted successively. The primary liquor folliculi, secreted during the earlier part of the growth of the antrum, has a well-developed reticulum and produces a dense coagulum under the action of certain fixatives. It is from this that Robinson believed the membrana limitans interna to be formed. The secondary liquor folliculi is formed in the vicinity of the cumulus during the rapid final growth of the follicle. This fluid is formed more rapidly, produces a less dense coagulum on fixation and is probably more fluid than the primary liquor folliculi. The tertiary liquor folliculi is formed immediately after the rupture of the follicle by the rapid exudation of fluid. It contains leucocytes and the debris of disintegrating cells which have become dislodged from the membrana granulosa at rupture. It forms a granular, adhesive and tenacious coagulum when fixed, filling the cavity of the discharged follicle and plugging the aperture of rupture, from which it may protrude.

It has long been known that the liquor folliculi of the mature follicle is very viscous in consistency (Hensen, 1876). Walton and Hammond (1928), who observed the actual process of ovulation in the living rabbit, state that it " does not squirt from the follicle but flows steadily and continuously for some little time. Gradually the liquor folliculi ceases to flow and appears to clot and forms, in the orifice, a plug which protrudes a little from the surface."

Theca

The growth of the follicle is accompanied by the gradual formation of the definite concentric sheath of dense stromal tissue around it which constitutes the theca. Probably the formation of this sheath, in the first instance, is due largely to the mechanical effects of the expanding follicle upon the surrounding tissues. The theca is well formed by the time the oöcyte within the follicle has attained its maximum size and, a little later, when the antrum has begun to form, it becomes differentiated into inner and outer layers (Figs. 5. 16, 5. 17, 5. 18), the theca interna and theca externa (Brambell, 1928).

The theca externa is relatively sharply demarcated from the theca interna within but it merges more gradually into the cortical stroma without, from which it can be distinguished by its denser nature and by the concentric arrangement of the fibrous tissue of which it is largely composed. It has a rich vascular supply, and numerous lymphatics traverse its substance. Fibrous connective tissue and smooth muscle are its chief components. The fibres in the former appear to be exclusively white or collagen fibres, for, as in *Ornithorhynchus* (Hill and Gatenby, 1926), elastic fibres were shown to be absent from the theca externa of the sow, except from the walls of the blood-vessels, by Corner (1919) and from that of man by Thomson (1919b).

Smooth muscle was described as entering into the theca externa of the mammalian follicle by Aeby in 1861. Since then it has been recognised in the theca externa of the pig by Grohe (1863), Corner (1919) and Guttmacher and Guttmacher (1921), of the cat by de Winiwarter and Sainmont (1909) and of man by Nagel (1896), de Winiwarter (1910) and Thomson (1919b). The last-mentioned author states that the smooth muscle invades the substance of the ovary along the line of the great vessels and follows them outwards as they reach the area of their distribution towards the cortex. Guttmacher and Guttmacher (1921) describe it as forming a coat around the follicle, in many places incomplete and interrupted by blood-vessels and connective tissue. They found quite large bundles of pure smooth muscle, in some cases next the theca interna. Smooth muscle cells were particularly numerous in the region of the blood-vessels. It must be concluded that smooth muscle is a regular and important component of the theca externa of the Graafian follicles of the higher mammals, although, as referred to above, it appears to be absent from the theca externa in the monotremes (Hill and Gatenby, 1926).

The theca interna consists of characteristic large vacuolated cells (Figs. 5. 16 and 5. 18) which may be termed the theca interna cells, with a loose reticulum of connective tissue, chiefly fibroblasts, between. Capillaries and small lymph channels are very numerous in it. As the follicle approaches maturity the capillary plexus becomes increasingly conspicuous and engorged with blood. The theca interna in placental mammals tends to increase in thickness as the follicle enlarges and reaches its greatest development at the time of ovulation (Brambell, 1928). However, in the marsupial *Dasyurus*, O'Donoghue (1914) found that the theca interna, though well developed in small follicles, was scarcely distinguishable in large ones. This was confirmed by Hill and Gatenby (1926) and is the converse of the condition found in placental mammals. It varies considerably in development in different species, being much more pronounced in some than in others. It does not display the same uniformity in thickness as the membrana granulosa, being scarcely recognisable as a distinct layer in some places and well developed elsewhere in the same follicle. It becomes very thin or disappears altogether in the vicinity of the rupture point in mature follicles, and is generally thicker than elsewhere beneath the cumulus ; Thomson (1919b) states that it is often more vascular in the latter region.   The author has observed very marked hypertrophy of the theca interna in the mature follicles of the bank vole (*Clethrionomys glareolus*, Schreber), especially in the vicinity of the cumulus, where it may form a thick pad covered by the membrana granulosa and projecting into the antrum.   The theca interna of large follicles in the pocket gopher, *Geomys bursarius* Shaw, according to Mossman (1937) is very thick and has all the structural features of a typical gland of internal secretion.   A similar development of the theca interna in the follicles of the goat during prooestrus is recorded by Harrison (1948a).   Hypertrophy of the theca interna of mature follicles during oestrus in the guinea-pig has been described by Stafford, Collins and Mossman (1942).   The theca interna in the mature follicles of the dog (Evans and Cole, 1931) and the fox is involved in the folding of the membrana granulosa (Fig. 5. 17); it extends in the fox into each fold, forming a core to it.

The theca interna cells can be observed frequently in mitosis.   These cells are characterised by the clear vacuolated cytoplasm and lightly staining oval nuclei in sections prepared by methods which do not preserve fat (Zuckerman and Parkes, 1932).   These cytoplasmic vacuoles contain blackened fat-spherules in osmicated material from the rat (Long and Evans, 1922) and the mouse (Deanesly, 1930a) ; distinguishable by their larger size and irregularity from the very fine regular fat granules of the membrana granulosa cells.   The theca interna cells in man (Fig. 5. 18) are particularly large, irregularly stellate in form, with a small eccentric nucleus and a compact juxta-nuclear Golgi apparatus ; in the pig they are much smaller in comparison to the cells of the membrana granulosa (Solomons and Gatenby, 1924).   The theca interna cells in man (Watrin, 1924) and the baboon (Zuckerman and Parkes, 1932) undergo enlargement immediately prior to ovulation.

Two views have been advanced as to the origin of the theca interna cells. Some authorities, including O. van der Stricht (1912) and Robinson (1918), regard them as derived from interstitial cells of the ovarian stroma which have become included in the theca as it was formed.   It should be mentioned in this connection, as will be shown later (p. 512), that there is considerable evidence that, on the contrary, the interstitial cells may be derived from the theca interna cells.   The majority of authors, including Sobotta (1896, 1897), B. M. Allen (1904), Drips (1919), Momogliano (1927), Deanesly (1930b) and Stockard (1937) regard them as derived from the connective-tissue elements of the undifferentiated theca, as appears to be the case in *Ornithorhynchus* (Hill and Gatenby, 1926.   See p. 438).

Membrana propria

A definite but very thin membrane separates the theca interna without from the membrana granulosa within.   This has been called the membrana propria or membrana limitans externa (Figs. 5. 16, 5. 17, 5. 18 and 5. 19).   Waldeyer (1870), Nagel (1896) and others regarded this as a thickened basement membrane produced by the membrana granulosa, but it is now generally recognised as a definite cellular connective-tissue membrane, formed from the theca interna, and containing fibroblasts (Thomson, 1919b ; Solomons and Gatenby, 1924).   Robinson (1918) regards it as consisting of two layers, the outer a connective-tissue structure which is firmly attached to the theca interna and the inner more firmly attached to the

cells of the membrana granulosa and possibly formed by them. The membrana
propria appears to be present invariably in mature Graafian follicles.

Vascular Supply of Follicle

The vascular supply of the follicles of the human ovary has been described in
detail by Clark (1900), that of the ovary of the pig by Andersen (1926), that in
man and a number of other mammals by Burruano (1934), that of the rat by

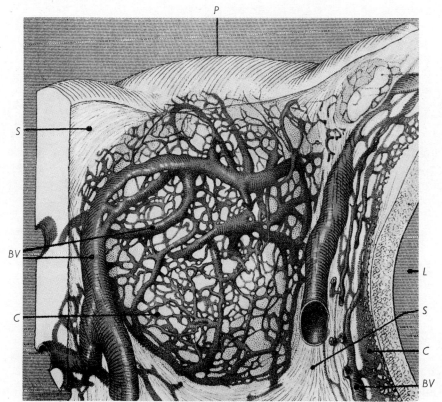

Fig. 5. 22—Blood vessels of the wall of a small follicle of the sow viewed from
the outer surface   The blood vessels were injected with indian ink and the
thick section was prepared by the Spalteholz method.   The larger arterioles
and venules (BV) are situated in the theca externa and the capillaries form
an inner wreath or subgranulosa plexus (C) on the inner surface of the theca
interna.   L, antrum of adjacent follicle; P, surface of ovary; S, stroma.
× 63.   (From Andersen, 1926.)

Bassett (1943) and that of the rabbit by Burr and Davies (1951).   Spiral arteries
have been shown to be present in the ovary of the rabbit by Reynolds (1947)
The smallest follicles have no special vascular supply of their own, lying simply
among the vessels of the stroma.   The follicle has acquired an individual supply
in the form of a vascular wreath surrounding it soon after the antrum has appeared.
By the time the theca interna is fully established this wreath is double, consisting
of two concentric networks of vessels (Fig. 5. 22).   The outer, situated in the theca
externa, arises from several small vessels which approach and spread over the
surface of the follicle to form a network of arterioles and venules.   The venules

anastomose freely but the arterioles do so only occasionally. Both the arterioles and venules of this outer network send tiny branches through the theca interna which connect with a dense single-layered capillary plexus. This plexus surrounds the whole follicle in the deeper layer of the theca interna immediately outside the membrana propria, and constitutes the inner network. The capillaries do not penetrate the membrana propria nor enter the membrana granulosa in the unruptured follicle, except perhaps in the region of the cumulus in mature follicles. Immediately before rupture a non-vascular area, the macula pellucida, appears at the apex of the protruding part of the follicle, where rupture will occur, in man (Clark, 1900), the pig (Corner and Amsbaugh, 1917) and the rabbit (Walton and Hammond, 1928 ; Markee and Hinsey, 1936). The last-named authors state that this macula pellucida is surrounded by a rosette of dilated vessels. Walton and Hammond (1928) suggest that the macula pellucida is formed by the increased internal pressure of the follicle cutting off the blood supply in this area.

Lymphatics of the follicle

The lymphatic supply of the follicle has been described in the human ovary by Poirier and Charpy (1923) and Polano (1903), and in the ovary of the pig by Andersen (1926). According to Andersen the lymphatics of the follicular wall develop slightly later than the blood-vessels. A complete network of many-valved lymph channels is formed first in the theca externa. These vessels accompany and surround most of the arterioles in this region, though there are many lymph vessels that are not peri-arterial. Branches from this outer network later penetrate the theca interna and form an inner network immediately outside the membrana propria, where the blood capillary network is situated. The meshes of this inner network and the individual vessels composing it are larger than those of the blood capillary net. The lymph vessels of the inner network are not valved, and it was shown conclusively that, as might have been expected, they do not communicate at any point directly with the antrum.

Innervation of the follicle

The wall of the Graafian follicle is innervated with sympathetic nerve fibres. Retzius (1893), Vos (1894) and Mandl (1895) stated that these fibres all belonged to the peri-vascular network and that no other sympathetic fibres penetrated the follicular wall. Kuntz (1919) apparently failed to distinguish nerves running to the follicles. Riese (1891) showed that the sympathetic nerves entering the ovary separate into those accompanying the blood-vessels and those running directly to the follicles. Guttmacher and Guttmacher (1921) confirmed this, showing that good-sized bundles of non-medullated fibres run to follicles, independently of the peri-vascular network. Riese (1891), von Herff (1892), von Gawronsky (1894), Winterhalter (1896) and Brill (1915) believe that the nerve fibres penetrate the theca interna and membrana granulosa as well as the theca externa. Abel and McIlroy (1912) state that they only penetrate the theca externa and theca interna. Guttmacher and Guttmacher (1921) describe them as forming a rich plexus in the theca externa with typical sympathetic motor-endings on the muscle cells ; therefore, by implication, they do not penetrate the theca interna or membrana granulosa. These authors claim to have shown experimentally that the autonomic innervation is double ; true sympathetic fibres acting as inhibitors and para-sympathetic fibres as excitatory nerves.   According to Pines and Schapiro (1930) fibres, in addition to those of the peri-vascular network, run to the follicles.   These fibres never penetrate the membrana granulosa, although they may reach its outer surface, and their end-organs are confined to the theca.   The growth of the follicle is accompanied by growth of the end-organs from tiny end-buds to big club-shaped terminal arborisations.

Polynuclear oöcytes, polyovular and anovular follicles

Abnormalities in follicular structure, that occur with varying frequency in different species and individuals, have attracted a great deal of attention, and a considerable literature on the subject has grown up.   These abnormalities fall

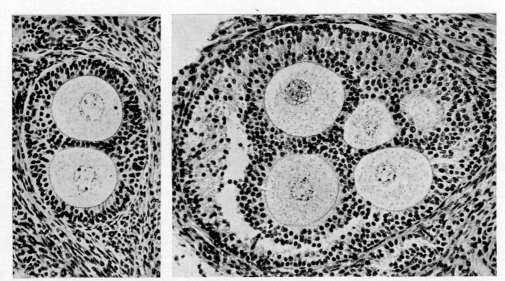

Fig. 5. 23—Photomicrographs of sections of biovular and polyovular follicles of a young dog. The cells of the membrana granulosa separate the oöcytes from each other within each follicle. The polyovular follicle contains at least five oöcytes and an incipient antrum is present.   × 305.

into one of three categories : polynuclear oöcytes, polyovular follicles and ano-vular follicles.   The earlier literature on polynuclear oöcytes and polyovular follicles has been admirably summarised by Hartman (1926).

Polynuclear oöcytes have been described in man, monkey, lemur, dog, cat, cow, pig, goat, rabbit, mouse, guinea-pig, armadillo and opossum (Hartman, 1926 ; Engle, 1927a ; Harrison, 1948a, 1949b).   They are of rare, or at most occasional, occurrence in most species but are found commonly, often in large numbers, in the ovaries of the opossum, *Didelphis virginiana*.   Binuclear oöcytes are more frequent than those with more nuclei, but examples have been described with numbers of nuclei varying up to sixteen.   Two theories have been advanced as to the origin of these ova ; that they arise by divisions of the nucleus unaccompanied by cell division or by fusion of two or more adjacent uninuclear germ-cells.   The evidence, although inconclusive, appears to favour the latter view.

Polyovular follicles have been found in man, monkey, lemur, dog (Fig. 5. 23), cat, ferret, pig, sheep, goat, rabbit, mouse, rat, guinea-pig, prairie dog, bat, armadillo, kangaroo, native cat and opossum (Hartman, 1926 ; Engle, 1927a ; Mainland, 1928 ; Evans and Swezy, 1931 ; Ota, 1934 ; Dederer, 1934 ; Stockard, 1937 ; Pankratz, 1938 ; Lane 1938 ; Waterman, 1943 ; Harrison, 1948a, 1949b ; Davis and Hall, 1950 ; Dawson, 1951). Although rare as a rule they appear to be of very common occurrence in the opossum among the marsupials and the dog among the placental mammals. They occur most frequently in embryonic or immature ovaries but are found also in adults. Primordial polyovular follicles are much more frequent than those exhibiting later stages of follicular growth ; indeed only one mature polyovular follicle has been recorded (O'Donoghue, 1912), although ones in which the antrum was present have been met with in several species. Biovular follicles (Fig. 5. 23) occur more frequently than those with larger numbers of ova. The record number of oöcytes in a single follicle is over 100, found in the opossum by Hartman (1926). The oöcytes in a single polyovular follicle may be all of one size or they may vary in size. Hartman distinguishes three types of these follicles ; those in which the oöcytes are separated by the cells of the membrana granulosa, those in which the oöcytes lie in direct contact with each other and those in which the oöcytes have a linear arrangement and the follicle consequently is elongated. Three theories have been advanced to account for the origin of polyovular follicles ; first, that they arise by the division of a single polynuclear oöcyte within its follicle ; secondly, that two or more adjacent uniovular follicles undergo concrescence ; thirdly, that they are due to the failure of a group of germ-cells and epithelial cells, proliferated from the germinal epithelium in the form of a cord, to become split up into uniovular follicles by the ingrowth of connective tissue between them. Both Hartman (1926) and Evans and Swezy (1931) support the last theory. The rarity of poly-ovular follicles approaching maturity in comparison to early stages shows that almost invariably these follicles either undergo atresia or, possibly, become uniovular by the degeneration of all but one of the contained oöcytes. However, in a large sample of 2,179 litters of wild rabbits, it was found (Allen, Brambell and Mills, 1947) that in 18 litters the number of implanted embryos exceeded the number of corpora lutea. Since no synchorionic twins were present, this could not be due to polyembryony and hence it was attributed to polyovular follicles ovulating two or more ova. It was calculated that 0·23 per cent of the follicles ovulating must have been polyovular, and that such follicles had ovulated in 1·32 per cent of litters. This appears to be the only record of functional polyovuly in mammals.

Anovular follicles have been described in the ovaries of bats (van Beneden, 1880), rabbits (Regaud and Lacassagne, 1913), rats (Davis and Hall, 1950), lemur (Gérard, 1920), opossum, armadillo, monkey, dog (League and Hartman, 1925), dingo and mouse (Tamura, 1927). They have also been mentioned occasionally in other animals and have been produced experimentally in large numbers in the ovaries of mice by means of X-rays (Brambell, Parkes and Fielding, 1927a and b ; Brambell and Parkes, 1927b). They vary from small structures corresponding in size to primordial follicles to relatively large bodies with many cells in each section. They never approach the size of a normal mature follicle nor develop a definite antrum, although in the larger ones irregular cavities may be present, apparently due to vacuolation of the cells. All the authors cited agree that they may arise from groups or nests of epithelial cells which have never contained oöcytes. It is clear also that they may arise from normal follicles, during the earlier stages of their development, by the disappearance of the oöcyte, either by degeneration *in situ* (Gérard, 1920 ; League and Hartman, 1925 ; Brambell and Parkes, 1927b), or by wandering out of the follicle (League and Hartman, 1925). They may occur both in immature and adult individuals. Recently Wilcox and Mossman (1945) have described epithelial cords which occur in some of the ovaries of adult shrews. In some instances these cords were attached to the germinal epithelium and appeared to be arising therefrom. In others they were in the medulla of the ovary. These more deeply situated cords had a limiting basement membrane and irregular cavities in the syncytial central cytoplasm. Some of them were connected to the rete tubules. Many of the cells in these cords were dividing actively but none resembled germ-cells. It is interesting that such structures have an obvious resemblance both to the medullary cords of the embryo, from which the spermatic tubules of the testis arise, and to anovular follicles of adult ovaries. Indeed, medullary cords and anovular follicles have much in common and differ from each other in structure principally in shape, the one being elongated and the other spherical. The elongated epithelial cords each containing several oöcytes that have been described (Brambell, 1929) as occurring in the cortex of the ovotestis of a pig, in the region intermediate between the predominantly ovarian and testicular parts, provides a link.

Growth of ovum and follicle

Analysis of the growth of the follicle relative to that of the contained oöcyte in the white mouse (Fig. 5. 24) has shown that it is divided into two phases (Brambell, 1928). During the first phase the growth of the oöcyte is rapid and is correlated with that of the follicle. At the end of this phase the oöcyte measures 70 μ in diameter and the follicle 125 μ in diameter. During the second phase the follicle

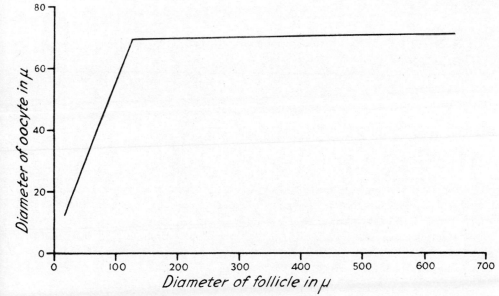

Fig. 5. 24—Graphical representation of the growth of the follicle and contained oöcyte of the white mouse. During the first phase the growth of the oöcyte and follicle is correlated. During the second phase the oöcyte does not grow significantly but the follicle increases from 125 to over 600 μ in diam. (From Brambell, 1928.)

grows from 125 μ to about 550 μ in diameter when ovulation takes place, but there is no significant correlated increase in the diameter of the oöcyte. Both the phases of growth approximate to linear regressions of diameter of oöcyte on diameter of follicle of the form : $y = a + bx$ where y = mean diameter of oöcyte and x = mean diameter of follicle, a and b being constants, as in Fig. 5. 24. The differentiation of the two most characteristic features of the Graafian follicle, the theca interna and antrum, does not take place until shortly after the beginning of the second phase, when the oöcyte has attained already its maximum size. Similar

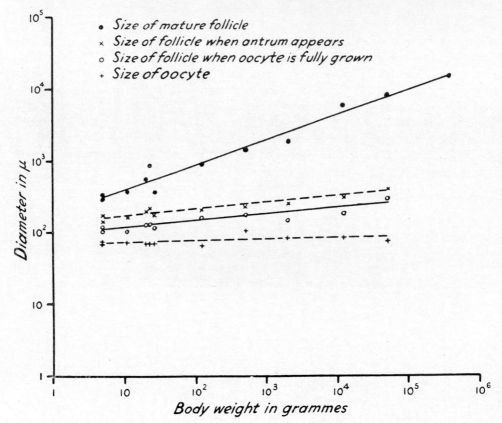

Fig. 5. 25—Graphical representation of diameter of the fully grown oöcyte and of the follicle when mature, when the antrum first appears and when the oöcyte has completed its growth, according to body-weight in a number of species of placental mammals (logarithmic scales are used). (Modified from Parkes, 1931.)

relations exist in the growth of the oöcyte and follicle in man (Green and Zuckerman, 1951), the rhesus monkey (Green and Zuckerman, 1947), baboon (Zuckerman and Parkes, 1932), rat (Parkes, 1931 ; Mandl and Zuckerman, 1952), ferret, rabbit, pig (Parkes, 1931), goat (Harrison, 1948a), shrews (Brambell, 1935 ; Brambell and Hall, 1937), bank vole (Brambell and Rowlands, 1936), spotted hyaena (Matthews, 1939), bats (Matthews, 1937a ; Wimsatt, 1944) and *Ericulus* (Strauss, 1938). Although in *Ericulus* (see p. 440) no antrum is developed, the membrana granulosa becomes loosened and spongy, probably owing to incipient secretion of liquor folliculi, during the second phase of growth. Matthews (1939), working on the hyaena, divides the first phase of growth of both oöcyte and follicle into two.

During the first, while the follicular epithelium is single-layered, the follicle does not grow as rapidly, relative to the oöcyte, as during the second.   Since the relationship of growth of oöcyte to growth of follicle is similar in so many species it is probable that it will be found to hold for all placental mammals.   No information is available regarding the relative growth of the oöcyte and follicle in any marsupial. Investigation of this relation in the opossum, for example, might yield results of considerable interest.

The size attained by the follicle at the end of the first phase shows only a slight tendency to increase with increasing body-size in the different species examined. This is associated with the relatively small size differences in the mature ovarian oöcytes of placental mammals.   They appear to vary, independently of the body-size of the species, according to the amount, always small, of reserve material within the cytoplasm.   The mature ovarian oöcytes of marsupials are, as a rule, larger than those of placental mammals but are nevertheless extremely small in relation to the size of the mature follicle.   The scattered references in the literature to the size of ova in the different species of mammals have been reviewed by Hartman (1929b).   The amount of increase in size of the follicle during the second phase of growth, unlike that of the first phase, shows a marked correlation with body-size, as does the size of the mature follicle at the time of ovulation (Parkes, 1931).   These facts are shown by the data in Table I, compiled from the literature referred to above, and from Fig. 5. 25.

TABLE I

Species.	Body weight of young mature females.	Diameter of follicle. End of 1st phase.	Diameter of follicle when antrum appears.	Diameter of follicle at maturity.	Increase in diameter of follicle during 2nd phase.
Lesser Horse-shoe Bat	5 gm.	115 μ	170 μ	300 μ	× 2·6
Lesser Shrew .	5 gm.	110 μ	140 μ	320 μ	× 2·9
Common Shrew .	11 gm.	105 μ	160 μ	350 μ	× 3·3
White Mouse . .	20 gm.	125 μ	200 μ	550 μ	× 4·4
Bank Vole . .	22 gm.	125 μ	220 μ	820 μ	× 6·6
Greater Horse-shoe Bat	25 gm.	116 μ	170 μ	350 μ	× 3·0
White Rat . .	120 gm.	160 μ	200 μ	900 μ	× 5·6
Ferret . . .	500 gm.	170 μ	230 μ	1400 μ	× 8·2
Rabbit . . .	2000 gm.	145 μ	250 μ	1800 μ	×12·4
Baboon . . .	12000 gm.	180 μ	310 μ	6000 μ	×33·3
Pig	50000 gm.	300 μ	400 μ	8000 μ	×26·6

It is apparent, therefore, that the major part of the growth of the Graafian follicle takes place after the growth of the oöcyte is completed and is due chiefly to the distension of the fluid-filled antrum.   Although the sizes of the ova of small, as compared to large, mammals do not differ significantly, the size of the mature follicle is directly related to body-size.   These conclusions bear directly on the problem of the morphological and physiological significance of the mammalian Graafian follicle.

Q*

The function of the Graafian follicle

The primitive function of the ovarian follicle is presumably the nutrition of the contained oöcyte. That this is the function of the follicle throughout its growth in the Sauropsida is shown by the cytological evidence of the passage of materials from the follicular cells into the cytoplasm of the oöcyte, both in reptiles and birds. Presumably it is also an important, if not the only, function of the follicle in the monotremes, which resemble the Sauropsida in that the mature oöcyte is large, almost filling the follicle. They differ from the Sauropsida in the differentiation of a well-developed theca interna, in the maximum development of the epithelium being attained only immediately before ovulation and in the secretion of some follicular fluid. The insignificantly small size of the oöcyte in comparison to the mature Graafian follicle in the higher mammals and the fact that its growth is virtually completed while the follicle is relatively small implies that in them the follicle has assumed other secondary functions, to the performance of which the major part of its growth and differentiation are directed. Moreover, Martinovitch (1938) has shown that the early growth of oöcytes up to 50–55 μ in diameter can take place *in vitro* in the absence of follicular epithelium in cultures of excised ovaries of embryonic and new-born rats and mice. Since the development of the characteristic fluid-filled antrum and the differentiation of the theca interna takes place after the oöcyte has completed its growth it is reasonable to assume that both structures are associated with these secondary functions. Many theories have been evolved as to the nature of these secondary functions of the Graafian follicle, some of which have become untenable in the light of present knowledge.

The rhythmic nature of follicular growth and ovulation and its synchronisation with the oestrous cycle led the older observers to conclude that follicular maturation was the direct cause of oestrus and accounted for its periodicity. Although Heape (1905) and Marshall (1911) dissented from this theory, it was greatly strengthened when Allen, Doisy and their co-workers (1923, 1924) succeeded in extracting the hormone now known as oestrin from liquor folliculi. This work appeared to demonstrate that the follicle elaborated this hormone and that it was liberated at ovulation by the rupture of the follicle, thus producing oestrus. Soon several workers, including Parkes and Bellerby (1926) demonstrated the presence of oestrin in considerable quantities in other tissues. The theory was finally rendered untenable by the demonstration that the oestrous cycle continues indefinitely in mice in which all the follicles, without exception, have been destroyed by means of X-rays (Parkes, 1926; Brambell, Parkes and Fielding, 1927a and b). A similar conclusion also follows from the fact that the final rapid growth of the follicle in the mouse does not take place until after the oestrus-producing stimulus, due to oestrin in the blood, has become operative (Brambell and Parkes, 1927a). It is therefore quite clear that the final growth and maturation of the Graafian follicle is not the direct cause of oestrus.

It has been suggested by Thomson (1919b) that the liquor folliculi may function as a protective, as well as a nutritive, medium surrounding the oöcyte. Since the zona pellucida provides a relatively stronger and more rigid protective envelope around the oöcyte of the higher mammals than it does in the Sauropsida, which have no liquor folliculi, it is difficult to understand why such a protective mechanism should be necessary. It has also been suggested that after ovulation the liquor folliculi may function by flushing the oöcyte into and down the Fallopian tube (Brambell, 1928). Since the liquor folliculi escaping from the living ruptured follicle is a very viscous fluid (see p. 448), it is more probable that by surrounding and forming a " bolus " around the minute oöcyte, thereby giving it greater mass, the whole may be more readily engulfed by the fimbria of the Fallopian tube. The oöcyte, on account of its very small size, might be very easily lost in the coelomic cavity if it were naked, especially in the larger animals which lack complete ovarian capsules.

Since the fluid-filled antrum is only found in the higher mammals and is not present in the Sauropsida, which have large yolky oöcytes, the necessity for its development may be correlated with the small size of the oöcyte. This suggests that the development of the fluid-filled antrum may be necessary to give the follicle sufficient bulk either (1) to afford sufficient area of follicular wall for the rapid formation of the corpus luteum after ovulation, or (2) to provide the mechanical conditions for ovulation. The first of these alternatives provides what is in many ways the most satisfying explanation of the relatively large size of the mature Graafian follicle in comparison to that of the contained oöcyte. The mammals alone develop true corpora lutea which are known to be functional endocrine organs. The close correlation of the size of the corpus luteum with body-size is understandable in the light of their endocrine function. The large size of the oöcyte in the monotremes insures that the internal surface area of the ruptured follicle is adequate for the rapid establishment of the corpus luteum without the development of an antrum. The development of the antrum in the marsupial and placental mammals results in the production of a follicle of comparable internal surface area in relation to body-size, despite the reduction in the size of the oöcyte, and this must facilitate the rapid development of a corpus luteum of comparable relative size.

The second alternative that the size of the Graafian follicle is conditioned by the mechanical requirements of ovulation includes several possibilities and raises the problem of the mechanism by which ovulation is effected.

The Mechanism of Follicular Rupture

The earliest record of the direct observation of the process of ovulation was provided by Brandt (1877) for *Rana temporaria*. He suggested that the expulsion of the oöcyte may be assisted by active contraction of the follicle, and noted that the margins of the opening in the follicular wall were always smooth in outline, not torn as they would be by violent rupture. Smith (1916) observed ovulation in the salamander, *Cryptobranchus allegheniensis*, in a single instance in which the oöcyte passed gradually through an opening considerably smaller than its greatest diameter, assuming as it did so a figure-of-eight shape. Recently ovulation in *Rana pipiens* has been described by Rugh (1935), who observed the process repeatedly. The stigma is preformed and clearly distinguishable from an early stage as the area where the follicular wall is continuous with the thin cortical wall of the ovary ; elsewhere the follicle projects freely into the central ovarian sac or cavity. The rupture is at first a mere pin-point which rapidly enlarges to the size of the stigma, being oval in shape and usually limited by large capillaries. The aperture rarely exceeds one-third or one-half the diameter of the oöcyte, which gradually passes through it in from 4 to 10 minutes. Contraction of the follicle closes up the aperture after ovulation. Rugh believes " that ovulation is a dual process, involving first the rupture of the follicle and subsequently the active contraction of follicular smooth muscle cells forcing the egg out through the area of rupture." Ryan and Grant (1940) claim that ovulation and maturation of the frog's oöcytes can be induced in excised ovaries *in vitro* by anterior pituitary substance. More recently Samartino and Rugh (1945) claim that the frog's ovary must have either its circulatory or its nervous connections or both intact if it is to respond by ovulating to the hormone of the anterior pituitary.

Ovulation was observed in the pigeon by Bartelmez (1912), who concluded from measurements of the unruptured follicle and ovulated ovum that rupture was due to increased intrafollicular pressure resulting from deposition of yolk. Phillips and Warren (1937) observed a number of ovulations in the fowl. During the laying of a clutch ovulation was found to occur between 7 and 74 minutes, the mean being 32 minutes, after laying of the previous egg. Thus the time of ovulation could be predicted with sufficient precision for experimental purposes. Follicles about to ovulate within an hour exhibited gradual obliteration of the small blood-vessels bordering the stigma, which appeared to become broader in consequence, and bulged areas appeared on the stigma. Since the obliterated blood-vessels reappeared after rupture and since no change was observed in the vascular supply of other large follicles not about to rupture, it was concluded that these changes were due to local pressure within the follicles, brought about by contraction of the smooth musculature producing prolonged tension in the follicular wall, not by yolk accumulation. They suggest that the oöcyte merely serves as a body upon which the muscles can contract to produce the necessary tension in the follicular wall. The rupture appeared at first as a tiny perforation near one end and extended as a slit-like tear through the centre of the oblong stigma, the oöcyte being rapidly expelled from the follicle. Follicles clamped off from the ovary, and even excised an hour before rupture was expected to occur, ovulated normally, hence neither the vascular supply nor the deposition of yolk during this period are essential for rupture.

The final growth of the follicle immediately preceding the oestrus at which ovulation occurs is very rapid in mammals (Myers, Young and Dempsey, 1936 ; Boling, Blandau, Soderwall and Young, 1941). Thus in the mouse the follicles grow on an average from 415 μ to 550 μ in diameter in the 48 hours preceding ovulation (Brambell and Parkes, 1927a). In the oestrous rabbit the follicles measure approximately 1·5 mm. in diameter at the time of copulation and when ovulation takes place about 10 hours later they average 1·8 mm. in diameter (Walton and Hammond, 1928). Thus ovulation is the climax of a final period of accelerated growth of the follicles. In the great majority of mammals ovulation occurs spontaneously at oestrus. It is dependent on copulation in a few, however, and occurs at a definite interval after copulation. Oestrus persists until copulation and ovulation have occurred in such animals. The rabbit and the ferret are examples in which ovulation follows 10 and 30 hours after copulation respectively. The thirteen-lined ground squirrel, *Spermophilus citellus tridecemlineatus* (Drips, 1919) the common shrew (Brambell, 1935), the lesser shrew (Brambell and Hall, 1937), and the American shrew, *Blarina* (Pearson, 1944) and the mink also belong to this group (*see* Asdell, 1946, for literature). The evidence available and the explanations that have been offered concerning the actual mechanism of ovulation may be summarised conveniently under three main headings : (1) enzyme action ; (2) internal pressure ; (3) growth processes.

Schochet (1916) demonstrated by dialysis and other means the presence of proteolytic enzymes in the liquor folliculi. He suggested that these enzymes may play a part in bringing about perforation of the follicle by autolysis of its wall. This view is supported by the regular oval outline of the rupture point, which does not resemble a tear produced by bursting, but it should be remembered that there is no evidence that the enzymes, shown by Schochet to be proteolytic *in vitro*, are in fact proteolytic *in vivo*.

The view to which most authorities subscribe is that the pressure within the Graafian follicles rises until its wall bursts at the weakest point, liberating the contents. The growth of the follicle and its spherical shape indicate that the pressure is probably greater within than without the follicle. Clearly such a rise in the internal pressure must be brought about either by increase in the content of the follicle or in the pressure exerted on it by the follicular wall. It is quite possible that the rise in internal pressure is brought about by the active secretion of liquor folliculi into the antrum either by the membrana granulosa, as is more generally supposed, or by the theca interna or by both. Such secretion against pressure is a known function of certain other tissues and there is no *a priori* reason why it should not occur within the follicle. It may be that the liquor folliculi is augmented also by lymphoid transudation, as has been suggested by Thomson (1919b) and by Burr and Davies (1951). It is also possible, although there is no evidence for it, that the increase in the amount of liquor folliculi is brought about osmotically, by the secretion of osmotically active substances into the antrum, resulting in endosmosis. Smith and Ketteringham (1938) suggested that in the rabbit ovulation is brought about by the liberation into the maturing follicle of an osmotically active substance, possibly a carbohydrate, probably from the bodies of Call and Exner. To test this hypothesis they reduced the blood-sugar content by means of insulin injections and claim to have prevented ovulation occurring after injection of urine of pregnancy. Of these alternative explanations, that of secretion against pressure involves the assumption of an impermeable limiting membrane in the follicular wall and that of endosmosis a semi-permeable limiting membrane. The pressure in either case will be exerted on this membrane and will produce in it a corresponding state of tension. The membrana granulosa, since its cells are not flattened but on the contrary tend to be columnar in the mature follicles of some species (Robinson, 1918), can scarcely be supposed to be the layer of the follicular wall which takes up this pressure, as has been pointed out by Thomson (1919b). The folding of the membrana granulosa in the mature follicles of the dog (Evans and Cole, 1931) and the fox points to a similar conclusion.

It was suggested by Waldeyer (1870) that increased intrafollicular pressure is brought about in the mature follicle by hypertrophy of the cells of the theca interna. Nagel (1896) also attributes rupture to this cause and describes richly vascularised ingrowths of theca interna cells as pushing the follicular contents towards the thinnest part. Many other authors also have favoured this view. It is well known that such hypertrophy of the theca interna immediately before ovulation does occur in many species. Indeed, the folding of the membrana granulosa in the mature follicles of the dog (Evans and Cole, 1931) and of the fox appears to be brought about by such hypertrophy, for ingrowths of theca interna cells form cores to each fold. The hypertrophy of the theca interna in the mature follicles of the bank vole has been noted also. An insuperable difficulty in the way of acceptance of this theory is that the amount of hypertrophy of the theca interna varies greatly from species to species. Thus Wester (1921) denies that any hypertrophy of the theca interna occurs in the cow and the goat and the same appears to be true of the opossum (Hartman, 1929a).

Both increased blood-pressure, with hyperaemia of the surrounding tissues, and contraction of the smooth musculature of the ovary have been invoked as exerting from without an increased pressure on the follicular contents. The rupture of a mature follicle was observed by Clark (1898) in an ovary that was being injected with a carmine-gelatine mass. He attributed ovulation in consequence to increased blood-pressure and the arrangement of the blood-vessels of the follicular wall. Guttmacher and Guttmacher (1921) tried to repeat Clark's observation by injecting ovaries of pigs containing mature follicles. Using great pressure for a short time the follicular vessels were seen to work out clearly, but rupture did not occur in a single instance. They obtained negative results also when using a constant pressure equivalent to over 300 mm. of mercury for several hours.

The erectile properties of the ovarian tissues, reported by Rouget (1858), have been invoked by Heape (1905) to account for ovulation. He suggests that vasodilation and distension of these erectile tissues results in increased pressure on the follicle, bringing about ovulation, and he prevented ovulation by ligaturing the ovarian vessels. De Winiwarter and Sainmont (1909) found that the ovary, together with all the internal genital tract, can undergo erection, and they believed that the increased tension of the ovarian stroma produced in this way caused ovulation. They attributed erection to the contraction of the smooth musculature of the mesovarium which, according to de Winiwarter (1910), acts partly by controlling the venous return from the organ. Thomson (1919b) suggested that ovulation may result in some instances from the increased vascular pressure in the capillary plexus of the theca interna, brought about either by increased flow or retarded venous return. Burr and Davies (1951) consider, from studies of the vasculature of the rabbit ovary, that lymphoid transudation into the follicle, causing it to swell rapidly, and into the medullary lymph channels, causing enlargement of the ovary, is responsible for ovulation. Hensen (1876) pointed out that turgescence of the ovarian tissues cannot be the cause of ovulation in species in which a number of follicles rupture at each oestrus because the discharge of the first follicle would tend to relieve the pressure on the remaining ones.

Contraction of the ovarian musculature may be the direct cause of ovulation. Völker (1905) suggested that the contraction of the muscle fibres of the ovarian cortex might be responsible. Thomson (1919b) also was of opinion that contraction, resulting from sympathetic nervous stimulation of the smooth muscle, by raising the intrafollicular pressure, may cause ovulation in some cases. The researches of Guttmacher and Guttmacher (1921) have shown conclusively that the musculature of the theca externa forms a sheath around the whole follicle. Apparently, contraction of this muscular sheath must inevitably result in compression of the follicle and a rise in intrafollicular pressure.

Any purely mechanical explanation of ovulation based on increased intra-follicular pressure does not appear to be in harmony with several well-established observations. In the first place, although the liquor folliculi will squirt from a large follicle in an excised ovary when it is artificially punctured it does not do so at ovulation in the living animals. Walton and Hammond (1928) were the first to observe ovulation taking place naturally *in vivo*. They describe the formation of a pimple at the surface of the follicle which gradually ruptures and allows the contents to stream down its side. The whole process strongly resembles the formation and rupture of a boil. During this process the follicle walls may gradually collapse, but in many cases there is not a very marked change in the volume of the follicle. These observations have been confirmed by Kelly (1931), J. T. Smith (1934) and Markee and Hinsey (1936). Hill, Allen and Kramer (1935) succeeded in taking cinematographic pictures of ovulation and describe the process as explosive. The rabbit was employed in all these researches be-cause, on account of ovulation being dependent on copulation and following about 10 hours thereafter, it provides material in which the approximate time of ovulation can be predicted and controlled. Ovulation in the living animal has not been observed in any other mammal so far. A second objection to the internal pres-sure theory of follicular rupture is provided, as mentioned above (p. 461), by the shape of the actual perforations in ruptured follicles. Moreover, in the bat, Wimsatt (1944) has noted a decrease in follicular tension, and hence in the size of the follicle, just before ovulation. This, together with a simultaneous enlargement of the cells of the discus proligerus, results in an almost complete disappearance of the antrum. Long and Mark (1911) state that in the mouse " the opening does not have the appearance one would expect to result from a rupture due to pressure from within." Markee and Hinsey (1936) examined by means of graphic reconstructions the rupture points in 90 follicles from 24 ovaries of rabbits. They found that they were oval in outline and uniformly without serration of the edges or other evidence of tearing. They state that their observa-tions " indicate that a portion of the ovarian wall bounding the stigma is actually removed at the time the rupture starts." A third difficulty in the way of a purely mechanical explanation of ovulation is the variation in the sizes of individual follicles at ovulation. Walton and Hammond (1928) point out that a small follicle may rupture simultaneously with or before a larger one in the rabbit, provided both are mature. Moreover, cystic follicles, although their walls are thinner than those of normal follicles, frequently attain abnormally large dimensions, yet do not rupture. Taken together, these three objections provide an insuperable difficulty in the way of an explanation of follicular rupture in terms of intrafollicular pressure alone. Ovulation in *Ericulus*, in which no antrum is found, is initiated by a slow shifting of the ovum towards the surface of the follicle, according to Strauss (1938). The ovum breaks through the surface, the theca having receded in this region, and slowly detaches itself from the granulosa, none of the cells of which remain attached to the ovum after ovulation. Ovulation therefore is not an abrupt process and is brought about by the swelling of the membrana granulosa, according to this author. Similar processes are described in two other insecti-vores. In *Elephantulus* (van der Horst and Gillman, 1940) an antrum is present in the follicle, which attains a maximum size of only 300–350 μ in diameter, but the follicular fluid is almost completely reabsorbed before ovulation. The cells of the membrana granulosa at the pole of the follicle furthest from the ovarian surface, become luteinised and form a mass of luteal cells which nearly fills the unruptured follicle. The adjoining region of the theca interna thickens also. When ovulation occurs the follicle opens widely and is partly evaginated. In *Blarina* (Pearson, 1944) the mature follicle measures 500–550 μ in diameter and contains a relatively small antrum. Growth of the membrana granulosa in the deeper hemisphere of the follicle precedes and accompanies ovulation and appears to be responsible for the expulsion of the oöcyte. Ovulation must be interpreted therefore as the outcome of more complex forces and as, in fact, the culmination of the growth process of the follicle as a whole. Strassmann (1923), probably rightly, regards ovulation as an " opening " rather than a " rupture " of the follicle. These growth processes result in an ordered series of changes in the tissues of the follicle, of which the secretion of the liquor folliculi, the loosening of the cumulus, the hypertrophy of the theca interna and the changes in the follicular wall leading up to perforation, are manifestations. Parkes (1931) has suggested that the ultimate size of the follicle may be associated with the mechanical problem of attaining a strategic peripheral position from which ovulation can take place and with bringing about a sufficient attenuation of the overlying ovarian tissues. Walton and Hammond (1928) describe the formation of an avascular macula pellucida at the apex of the follicle which gradually blows out as a pimple, and Markee and Hinsey (1936) have shown that this part of the wall of the follicle appears to be actually removed at ovulation. The former authors state that the theca ruptures first, with consequent slight extravasation of blood which can be seen beneath the surface around the base of the pimple before the actual surface opens.

Law of Follicular Constancy

The mean number of follicles which ovulate at each oestrus in mammals varies widely from species to species. Many species, including man, ovulate as a rule only one follicle at each oestrus. This may be assumed to be true of all those mammals which produce normally only a single young one at birth, including the bats, weighing only a few grams, and at the other extreme many of the larger ungulates, including the elephants and the whales. On the other hand, many species, including most of the smaller rodents and insectivores at one extreme and the pigs and large carnivores at the other, ovulate a number of follicles simultaneously. Few placental mammals produce more ova at each oestrus than the pig. Parkes (1923) found that, in 2020 litters of pigs born, 8 was the most frequent size of litter, and Wentworth (1914) records an extreme case of 23 young pigs in a litter. The mean number of follicles ovulated usually is slightly greater than the mean number of young born in any species, since some of the ova are not fertilised or die before birth. The armadillo, in which polyembryony occurs, is an exception to this rule. This animal normally ovulates one follicle at oestrus, the single ovum from which, by polyembryony, gives rise to four embryos (Patterson, 1913). Much larger numbers of follicles ovulate at each oestrus in the marsupials, *Didelphys* and *Dasyurus*, than in most placental mammals. Thus Hill (1910) records for *Dasyurus* several instances of 20 to 25 ova liberated simultaneously, two of 28, one of 30 and one of 35, while for *Didelphys*, Hartman (1926) states that the average number of ova shed at ovulation is 22, and he records a single instance of as many as 56. However, still greater numbers are recorded in some of the Insectivora, among the placental mammals. In Hemicentetes up to 20 ova have been found in each uterine horn (Bluntschli, 1937), although the litter size does not exceed 10, and in Centetes on one occasion 32, and on another 40 blastocysts were found (Bluntschli, 1938). However, the record is provided by Elephantulus in which about 60 ova are liberated from each ovary at a time (van der Horst and Gillman, 1941). Yet of these 120 ova only two can develop since their survival is limited by the presence of only one implantation site in each uterine horn. The remainder degenerate, some being unfertilised, at or before the 4-cell stage.

There is a tendency in any given species to ovulate a constant number of follicles at each oestrus, although variations from the mean are met with not only in different individuals but in the same individual during successive oestrous

TABLE II

DISTRIBUTION OF CORPORA LUTEA BETWEEN THE RIGHT AND LEFT OVARIES

Grouping according to difference between numbers in right and left ovaries.	Expected (m).	Observed.	Divergence (x).	x^2/m.
5 +	7·5	5	− 2·5	0·833
4	18·3	22	+ 3·7	0·748
3	39·7	25	− 14·7	5·443
2	69·6	70	+ 0·4	0·002
1	89·8	106	+ 16·2	2·922
0	52·1	49	− 3·1	0·184
Total . .	277·0	277	0·0	$\chi^2 = 10·132$

periods. This was demonstrated experimentally by the operative removal of one ovary or one ovary and part of the other ; the remaining ovary or fragment of ovary then underwent compensatory hypertrophy and continued to produce approximately the same number of mature follicles at each oestrus (Lipschütz, 1925 ; Lipschütz and Voss, 1925). This tendency of the ovaries to ovulate a constant number of follicles at oestrus is now generally recognised and is known to be under the hormonal control of the anterior lobe of the pituitary gland (see p. 467). In practice the number of follicles that ovulate at oestrus is determined conveniently by counts of the number of corpora lutea of the same age in the ovaries. Counts of 277 sets of corpora lutea in the ovaries of bank voles showed that the number varied from 1 to 12, the most frequent number being 4 and the mean 4·43 (Brambell and Rowlands, 1936).

The distribution of the follicles ovulating at a single oestrus between the two ovaries of a pair in polytocous species does not, as might be expected, tend to equality. Examples in which all the corpora lutea in a set are found to be in one of the ovaries are frequently met with and have been recorded in rabbits, mice, rats, pigs and other species. Danforth and de Aberle (1928) state that in the mouse the corpora lutea are distributed at random between the two ovaries. This is the case also in the common shrew (Brambell, 1935) lesser shrew (Brambell and Hall, 1937) and bank vole (Brambell and Rowlands, 1936). The distribution of 277 sets of corpora lutea of the last-named species, represented as the difference between the numbers in each ovary, are given in Table II, together with the expected distribution on the assumption that it is random. Testing by means of χ^2 (Fisher, 1930), the divergence of the observed from the expected values is found to be insignificant.

Despite the ancient myth that the right and left ovaries in man function alternately in producing the mature follicle in successive menstrual cycles, there is little evidence that either in man or in any other monotocous species the distribution is not random. Küpfer (1920a and b) states that although usually the right and then the left ovary functions in the cow, sometimes one ovary continues to function for several successive cycles. He thought that the right ovary tended to ovulate more frequently than the left. Hammond (1927) found that in 65 per cent the follicle ripened in the opposite ovary to that in which the previous ovulation occurred. Küpfer (1920a and b) found that of 17 twin pregnancies in cattle, eight resulted from an ovulation in both ovaries simultaneously and nine from an ovulation in one only. Similarly, in 16 sets of triplets, half came from ovulations in one ovary only. Quinlan and Mare (1931) found that in the Merino sheep the same ovary

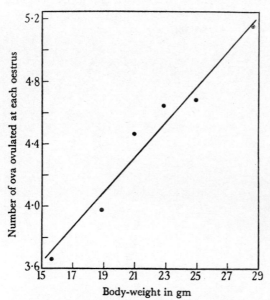

Fig. 5. 26—Graphical representation of the regression of the number of ova ovulated on body-weight in the bank vole. The points represent the mean values for each group. (From Brambell and Rowlands, 1936.)

may ovulate three times successively, both ovaries may ovulate at one oestrus or a double ovulation from one ovary may occur (*cf.* Marshall, 1903). In the monkey, Hartman (1932a) found alternation in some cases, in others as many as three successive ovulations from the same ovary. Enders, Pearson and Pearson (1946) state that in the fur seal a single follicle is ovulated each year and always from alternate ovaries, as is shown by the persistent remains of the corpus luteum of the previous ovulation.

The bats, among the placental mammals, are unique in this respect for in them only the right ovary is functional as a rule. Hartman (1932b) found only one exception to this rule in hundreds of specimens examined. According to Hill and Gatenby (1926) the left ovary alone is functional in *Ornithorhynchus*, while it is sometimes the left and sometimes the right in *Echidna*.

There is some evidence that within a given species the number of ova ovulated at each oestrus tends to be proportional to the body-weight of the individual. Thus MacDowell and Lord (1925) found that the number of corpora lutea rises in successive pregnancies in mice. This rise is more marked in the first three pregnancies than later, but there is no decline as late as the ninth to eleventh litters. Later, MacDowell, Allen and MacDowell (1929) showed that parity is more closely correlated with the number of corpora lutea formed at one oestrus than is age. Eliminating the influence of parity by using only first litters, weight at conception was found to be more closely correlated with the number of corpora lutea than is age. This relation has been examined statistically in the case of the bank vole (Brambell and Rowlands, 1936), where the number of corpora lutea in 264 complete sets from 194 animals of known body-weight were available. The linear regression of the form $y = 0.1144x + 1.92$ where $y =$ the number of corpora lutea in a set, and $x =$ the body-weight, was fitted to the data and found to be significant. This regression line and the means of each group are represented graphically in Fig. 5. 26. A similar relation has been found in the wild rabbit on more extensive data (Brambell, 1944). Since the pituitary controls the number of follicles ovulating, it may be significant that its weight is known to exhibit a positive heterogonic relation to body-size in the rabbit (Robb, 1928, 1929 ; Allanson, 1932). It follows that if the amount of follicle-stimulating hormone produced by the pituitary is proportional to its size, then positive heterogony of the pituitary would account for the number of ova ovulated being proportional to the body-size.

III. THE FORMATION OF THE CORPUS LUTEUM

Primitive Nature

The ruptured follicle, after the discharge of the oöcyte from the ovary, undergoes a series of changes which, primitively, lead directly to its resorption and disappearance. During this process the cells of the follicular wall give rise to a solid structure, transient in nature, the waste products of the gradual resorption of which doubtless find their way into the neighbouring blood-vessels or lymph channels and are conveyed away by the vascular stream. This solid structure, in the mammals at least, has become an endocrine organ, known as the corpus luteum, the internal secretion of which plays an important part in the control of the female reproductive processes. The first record of its observation appears to have been that of Volcherus Coiter in 1573. However, Harrison (1948b), in a recent review which contains an extensive bibliography of the literature on the corpus luteum, considers that Vesalius had observed it some years earlier. Associated with the assumption of this secondary function the mammalian corpus luteum passes through an initial phase of growth and development, becoming highly organised and as large as, or larger than, the follicle from which it was formed, before retrogression begins. The fully formed corpus luteum consists of large cells containing a yellow pigment, the luteal cells, separated from one another by an anastomosing framework of connective tissue containing numerous blood-vessels. Doubtless the complex and specialised mammalian corpus luteum has been evolved from the tissues of retrogressing ruptured follicles of primitive ancestral forms and it is possible, as has been suggested (Brambell, 1930), that the luteal hormone has been evolved from a katabolic product of the retrogression of these tissues present in the blood-stream after ovulation.

The Corpora Lutea of Vertebrates other than Mammals

The discharged follicles of vertebrates other than mammals give rise to structures to which the name corpus luteum has been applied frequently. These structures are not so well developed as the corpora lutea of mammals, to which they are obviously homologous, nor have they been shown yet to perform endocrine functions. Yet their structure and mode of origin, especially in the elasmobranchs and reptiles, in which they are better developed than in other fish, amphibians and birds, throws much light on the histogenesis of the mammalian corpus luteum. The possibility cannot be denied on morphological grounds that these corpora lutea, especially in viviparous forms, may function as organs of internal secretion.

Bühler (1902), who investigated the ovaries of cyclostomes and certain teleosts, was unable to find any hypertrophy of the wall of the ruptured follicle, and Cunningham (1897, 1921), also writing on teleosts, arrived at the same result. Champy and Gley (1923) found, likewise, that corpora lutea are not formed in teleosts, and deny that the epithelium persists at all in the ruptured follicles. The viviparous teleost, *Zoarces*, exhibits a remarkable specialisation (Wallace, 1903) of the ruptured follicles. These form clavate villi projecting into the central cavity of the single ovary, which functions as a uterus within which the young develop. On the other hand, in the elasmobranchs the discharged follicles give rise to distinct corpora lutea. The corpus luteum of *Myliobatis bovina* is described and figured by Giacomini (1896) as a glandular body in which the enlarged epithelium is penetrated by an extensive ingrowth of connective tissue and bloodvessels. Wallace (1903) has described the corpus luteum of *Spinax niger*. Contraction of the ruptured follicle results in thickening and folding of its wall. The follicular epithelium, single-layered in the unruptured follicle, becomes several cells thick, apparently in consequence of this contraction since mitoses were not found in it, and its individual cells hypertrophy. The membrana propria becomes deeply folded, but remains intact, thus clearly defining the limits of thecal and epithelial derivatives. Ingrowths of the connective tissue from the thickened theca grow into the folds of the membrana propria, forming a core to each. Later, blood-vessels grow along these radial trabeculae of connective tissue and vascularise the corpus luteum. A similar account of the formation of the corpus luteum, exclusively from the cells of the follicular epithelium, in *Torpedo marmorata* (Risso) is given by Champy and Gley (1923). The epithelial cells hypertrophy and become laden with fat globules, but do not develop pigment. These authors figure a well-developed framework of connective-tissue trabeculæ, containing blood-vessels, between the strands of epithelial cells in the fully developed solid corpus luteum. Corpora lutea are formed also in the basking shark (Matthews, 1950).

The ruptured follicles of Amphibia were described by Giacomini (1896) who showed that they soon atrophy and disappear. In *Triton vulgaris* (Hett, 1923b) the epithelium becomes several-layered, owing to the contraction of the follicular wall. Mitoses, though frequent in the ripe follicle, are absent after rupture.

Masses of yolk are secreted into the lumen of the discharged follicle but are extruded later. The epithelium disappears much sooner than in Sauropsida and nearly all the cells degenerate simultaneously. There is no ingrowth of connective tissue into the epithelium, such as occurs in elasmobranchs and amniotes. The connective tissue, which contains pigment, gradually degenerates, although mitoses occur in it. Hett distinguishes an inner dense zone of connective tissue, the theca compacta, corresponding to the theca interna and inner part of the theca externa of the unruptured follicle, and an outer looser zone rich in blood-vessels, the theca spongiosa. Cunningham and Smart (1934) also distinguish inner and outer regions in the theca of ruptured follicles of *Xenopus laevis*. Absorption of the empty follicle in this species begins immediately after rupture and proceeds rapidly, the follicular epithelium having disappeared by $6\frac{1}{2}$ days after ovulation.

Far better-developed corpora lutea are found among the reptiles than in amphibians. Lucien (1903) has described the corpora lutea in the viviparous lizards *Anguis* and *Seps* in which the cells of the follicular epithelium hypertrophy but do not undergo mitoses. Mingazzini (1893) also described reptilian corpora lutea, but a more complete account is provided by Hett (1924), using the lizard *Lacerta agilis*. The epithelium remains within the ruptured follicle and is recognisable as such at all stages of its development. The membrana propria persists for a time and separates the epithelium from the derivatives of the theca. A small amount of yolk is secreted into the lumen of the discharged follicle. Mitoses, although numerous before, do not occur in the epithelium after rupture. The theca is differentiated into an inner theca compacta, and an outer theca spongiosa, rich in blood-vessels. Buds of connective tissue containing capillaries grow into the epithelium in the later stages. During retrogression, the epithelial cells degenerate gradually one by one. Leucocytes are found among them after the ingrowth of the connective tissue and capillaries, but no pigment is found nor does any haemorrhage occur at any stage in the histogenesis of the corpus luteum. Cunningham and Smart (1934) found that the ruptured follicle retrogresses more rapidly in the oviparous *Lacerta viridis* than in the viviparous species *Anguis fragilis* and *Zootoca vivipara*, in which corpora lutea are present in the ovaries throughout the period of development of the embryos in the oviducts. Similar results were obtained independently by Weekes (1934) working on a number of species of lizards. In an oviparous species luteal regression began about 10 days after ovulation, before the eggs were laid. In several viviparous species, in which gestation lasts about three months, luteal regression began during the last month and was advanced at the time of parturition. Both in the oviparous and viviparous species the corpora lutea had disappeared completely within two weeks *post partum*. A peculiar coagulum appears among the cells in retrogressing corpora lutea, probably being produced by the degeneration of the luteal cells, and may be so copious that the corpus luteum superficially resembles mammary gland tissue. This author states that the luteal cells are derived exclusively from the follicular epithelial cells, which divide mitotically and amitotically, though mitotic figures are rare. The part played by thecal ingrowths varies in different species and is not related to whether they are oviparous or viviparous. In some species there are no thecal ingrowths; in others fibroblastic cells from the theca interna grow in in association with the blood-vessels, only connective-tissue fibres extending between the individual luteal cells in both cases. Finally, in other species fibroblasts not only grow in with the blood-vessels but penetrate between the individual luteal cells. Similar accounts of the structure and development of the corpora lutea have been given by Rahn (1939) for several species of viviparous snakes, and by Boyd (1940) for a viviparous gecko. The corpus luteum of a turtle has been described by Altland (1951). Both theca and granulosa are said to contribute to the luteal cells of the garter snake, in which the corpus luteum persists until parturition (Bragdon, 1952).

The discharged follicles in birds give rise to structures which are very transient. Giacomini (1896) recognised that the follicular epithelium persists after rupture and participates in the formation of these bodies. Their formation has been described in the hen by Sonnenbrodt (1908), Pearl and Boring (1918), Stieve (1918), Novak and Duschak (1923) and Hett (1922), in the jackdaw by Stieve (1919) and Hett (1923a), and in a number of other species by Davis (1942a) and by Romanoff (1943). The ruptured follicle, according to Stieve, has disappeared completely by 10 to 14 days after ovulation. It is at first a slack, empty bag, but in a few hours it has contracted to form a compact cup-shaped structure which is pedunculate, with the slit-like opening opposite the stalk. It is coloured by the accumulation of a yellow, fatty substance within it. According to Pearl and Boring, the corpus luteum of the hen is formed exclusively from the theca interna of the follicle, but this is not substantiated by recent researches. Hett (1923a) gives a detailed account of the changes in the discharged follicle of the jackdaw. The epithelium, one day after ovulation, is compacted and many cells thick. The cells become vacuolated, their boundaries become less distinct and, in places, syncytia may be formed. Mitoses are never found in the epithelium of the rup-tured follicle nor does pigment occur. A small amount of yolk (Hett, 1924) is secreted after rupture into the lumen, which otherwise contains only a few scattered blood corpuscles. The membrana propria, which appears to be very resistant, remains intact at first and becomes much folded. There is an ingrowth of con-nective tissue containing collagen fibres between the epithelial cells and into the epithelial syncytium in the latest stages. Some of the epithelial cells degenerate early and others persist for a much longer time. The theca is differentiated into compacta and spongiosa, as in the lizard. It becomes much thickened by contraction and the nuclei of many of the cells degenerate, undergoing extrusion, chromatolysis or clumping. Leucocytes appear in it. The collagen fibres disappear from the theca compacta. The bundles of fibres become homogeneous and the cells undergo vacuolar degeneration, both cells and fibres being sloughed off, in the theca spongiosa. Pigment, staining with fat dyes, is found in the inner region of the theca only. These degenerative changes result in the thick theca of the recently ruptured follicle becoming thin in later stages.

It is apparent that the follicles in vertebrates other than mammals begin to retrogress at the time of rupture and do so directly and continuously, except in elasmobranchs and reptiles. In these two groups alone retrogression is not direct, and the discharged follicles give rise to structures which are relatively persistent, especially in viviparous species. It is a matter of opinion whether the term corpus luteum can be applied properly to the discharged follicles in all these forms on grounds of homology with those of mammals ; whether it should be confined to those which are relatively persistent and in which the epithelial cells hypertrophy after ovulation, as in elasmobranchs and reptiles ; or whether it should be strictly limited to mammals, the endocrine functions of which alone are beyond dispute. However that may be, the changes in the ruptured follicles of these forms throw some light on the histogenesis of the mammalian corpus luteum. The evidence is convincing that the epithelium remains within the ruptured follicle and that in the elasmobranchs and reptiles the epithelial cells hypertrophy and form the chief elements of the so-called corpus luteum. The persistence in these two groups of the membrana propria renders it possible to determine with precision the fate of the epithelial derivates. It is noteworthy also that mitoses do not occur in the epithelial cells of the ruptured follicle and that in elasmobranchs, reptiles and birds, an ingrowth of connective tissue from the theca, containing capillaries, penetrates into and vascularises the epithelial mass in later stages. The continued secretion of yolk into the lumen of the discharged follicle, small in quantity in reptiles and birds, more plentiful in amphibians, described by Hett (1924), is of interest because it is suggestive of the secretion of liquor folliculi in the recently ruptured mammalian follicle as well as because of its bearing on the metabolism of yolk by the follicular cells. This observation is worthy of further investigation and requires confirmation.

The Corpora Lutea of Monotremata

Our knowledge of the structure and development of the corpus luteum of the Monotremata is due, almost entirely, to Hill and Gatenby (1926) and to Garde (1930), who quote the earlier literature. The extrusion of the large oöcyte results in collapse of the follicle with consequent reduction in size, folding of the wall and partial obliteration of the central cavity. The mature follicle of *Ornithorhynchus* measures about 4·75 mm. in diameter, as has been stated (p. 436), whilst the recently ruptured follicle measures only about 2·5 mm. in diameter. The corpus luteum, when fully developed, attains a maximum size of about 4·0 mm. in diameter. Thus, although it is evident that the ruptured follicle undergoes marked hypertrophy, the maximum size of the corpus luteum relative to that of the mature follicle before rupture compares unfavourably with that of placental mammals, in which the diameter of the fully developed corpus luteum equals or exceeds that of the mature follicle. In the monotremes the egg develops within the oviduct until the embryo has attained a stage comparable to that of the chick at 40 hours incubation and has about nineteen pairs of somites. After laying, the egg is incubated for a period before the young animal hatches. Thereafter a period of lactation follows. The corpus luteum develops remarkably rapidly, relative to the embryo, and attains its maximum by the time cleavage of the ovum is nearing completion. Regression sets in and proceeds some way before the egg is ready for laying. Unfortunately nothing is known regarding the history of the corpus luteum during the succeeding periods of incubation and lactation. The opening is still patent and the lumen, though cleft-like owing to collapse of the wall, is still distinct in developing corpora lutea with eggs varying from the stage of separation of the 2nd polar body to an early cleavage stage of about 20 blastomeres. A central clot of extravasated blood and detached epithelial cells fills the lumen and blocks the aperture. The epithelial cells, which are in process of transformation into luteal cells and have already hypertrophied, give rise to an epithelial plug projecting from, and blocking, the aperture. This plug is more conspicuous

(Fig. 5. 27) than that commonly encountered in the corpora lutea of placental mammals, doubtless because of the larger size of aperture required to allow the oöcyte to escape. No mitoses occur at any stage in the luteal cells. Osmiophil fat or lipoid, so characteristic of the luteal cells of placental mammals, is absent

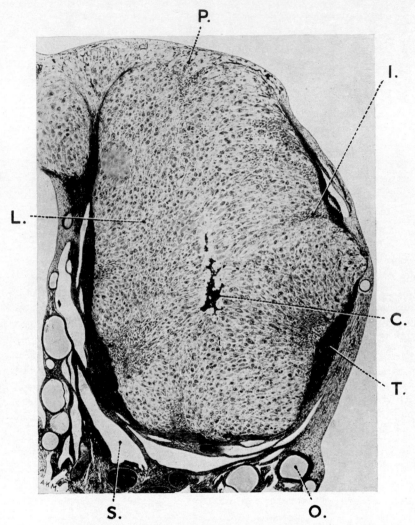

Fig. 5. 27—Section through the fully developed corpus luteum of *Orni-thorhynchus*. C, remains of blood-clot and connective-tissue core ; I, ingrowth of theca externa, along which are theca interna cells ; L, luteal cells ; O, oöcyte ; P, plug of luteal tissue occupying site of rupture of follicular wall ; S, lymph sinus ; T, theca externa. × 38. (From Hill and Gatenby, 1926.)

from those of *Ornithorhynchus*. The membrana propria disappears and the theca interna cells grow into the epithelium, especially in the region of the folds in the wall (Fig. 5. 28). Mitoses are present, though not abundant, in the theca interna cells. Hill and Gatenby state that the theca interna cells " appear to be par-ticularly active during the earlier stages of the formation of the corpus luteum, and in our view have a definite secretory function." The theca interna cells, unlike

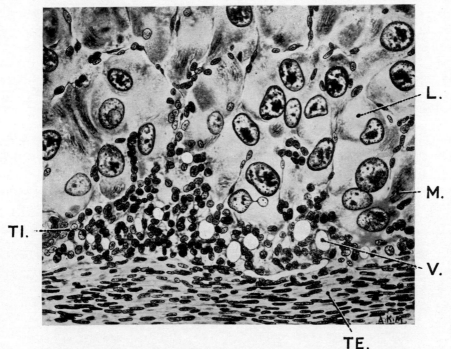

Fig. 5. 28—Part of the periphery of a well-developed corpus luteum of *Ornithorhynchus*. The theca interna (TI) forms a layer of irregular thickness, syncytial in character and containing large vacuoles (V). The luteal cells (L) contain filamentous mitochondria (chondriocontes) (M). TE, theca externa. × 350. (From Hill and Gatenby, 1926.)

the epithelial cells, do not hypertrophy at this or subsequent stages ; they tend to occur in masses (Fig. 5. 28), apparently syncytial since cell boundaries cannot be distinguished in them. Some areas of extravasated blood occur in the theca externa and capillaries invade the epithelium. Ingrowths of fibroblasts from the theca externa (Fig. 5. 29), especially at the folds, penetrate into the theca interna and, in places, even into the epithelium. It is stated that " these fibrous ingrowths of the theca externa may be said to determine the general architecture of the corpus luteum. They are not mere passive folds, but active ingrowths of the theca externa and, as they extend, the folding of the follicular lining becomes intensified and the follicular cavity becomes reduced to narrow clefts between the

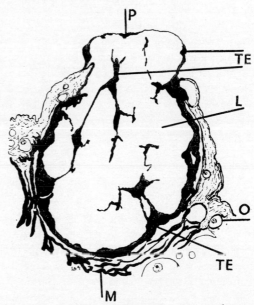

Fig. 5. 29—Section of a well-developed corpus luteum of *Ornithorhynchus* showing in black the theca externa and its trabecular ingrowths (TE). L, luteal tissue ; M, medulla of ovary ; O, oöcyte ; P, plug of luteal tissue. (From Hill and Gatenby, 1926.)

folds.   The ingrowths at the same time serve as a framework along which the theca interna cells spread and in which run many of the vessels supplying the luteal tissue. Finally, through the progressive enlargement of the luteal cells, the above-mentioned clefts between the folds become obliterated, and we have produced the solid corpus luteum as we have it in succeeding stages."   In the next stage, accompanied by eggs in which cleavage is nearing completion, the luteal cells have attained almost their maximum size. The connective-tissue trabeculae are joined to a central fibrous core, enclosing the remains of the central blood-clot, and to a delicate connective-tissue reticulum extending throughout the corpus luteum and investing, surrounding, and separating each luteal cell from its neighbours.   Regression is proceeding in all the subsequent stages and degenerating luteal cells become increasingly apparent.   Leucocytes invade the corpus luteum and become increasingly numerous, even occurring in the substance of luteal cells.   The theca interna cells do not begin to retrogress until after the luteal cells, about the time when the egg is laid.   There is no evidence that they ever assume fibroblastic activities.

A vesicular corpus luteum with a large central cavity containing colloid, in the form of a dense homogeneous coagulum, is described in *Echidna*. Vesicular corpora lutea occur in placental mammals, being notably common in the cow. They are attributed to the continued secretion of liquor folliculi by the ruptured follicle after the aperture has become closed, but no fluid-filled antrum is present in the unruptured follicle of *Echidna*.

The corpus luteum of the monotremes provides exceptionally favourable material for determining the part played by the follicular epithelium, theca interna and theca externa in its histogenesis. The cells derived from these three layers are readily distinguishable and unmistakable at all stages, owing to differences in size and cytological peculiarities, despite the disappearance of the membrana propria in the ruptured follicle. It is therefore indisputable that although the large luteal cells are derived exclusively from the hypertrophied epithelial cells, the theca interna also contributes much smaller and quite distinct elements.   It is clear also that the connective-tissue reticulum is derived from the theca externa. These conclusions have an important bearing on the much more difficult problem of the histogenesis of the corpus luteum in marsupial and placental mammals.

The Corpora Lutea of Marsupial and Placental Mammals

Histogenesis

The Graafian follicle of marsupial and placental mammals collapses and contracts after the expulsion of the oöcyte, with its corona radiata, and of the liquor folliculi.   In consequence, the recently ruptured follicle may measure no more than half the diameter of the fully grown follicle before ovulation, as is the case in the cow for example (Hammond, 1927). The collapse and contraction of the ruptured follicle result in folding of its wall, which is more marked in the large follicles of large species than in small ones, and in partial obliteration of the antrum. Some extravasation of blood in the tissues of the follicular wall and especially around the aperture occurs frequently after rupture. Although the occurrence of some blood, originating in this way, in the lumen of the recently ruptured follicle is normal, at least in the cow and several other species, the presence of any large quantity of blood in the antrum is always abnormal and leads invariably to the formation of cysts or aberrant corpora lutea. Paterson (1840) supposed that the corpus luteum is derived from the blood coagulum left in the cavity of the Graafian follicle after its discharge, but this theory has no modern adherents and is of historical interest only. On the other hand, there may be practically no haemorrhage in some species, such as the ferret (Robinson, 1918). Polymorph leucocytes are present in great abundance in the early stages of the formation of the corpus luteum in the sheep (Marshall, 1903). They disappear in later stages, some of them undergoing degeneration. Leucocytes have also been noted in the antrum of recently ruptured follicles of the ferret (Robinson, 1918). Their function may be assumed to be the destruction and removal of cell debris and red blood corpuscles from the lumen, preparatory to the formation of the luteal tissue.

The secretion of fluid by the follicular wall continues for an appreciable time after ovulation. This fluid, together with such cell debris, extravasated blood and leucocytes as are present, forms a tenacious coagulum or clot which fills the cavity of the follicle and plugs the aperture of rupture, from which it may project. The secretion of this tertiary liquor folliculi (see p. 448) may continue after the orifice in the wall of the follicle has closed, resulting in the partial or even total redistention of the discharged follicle. Thus according to Robinson (1918), in the ferret " the redistended follicle, which is the rudiment of the corpus luteum, contains a cavity as large as that which was present before rupture." In the cow, " the central cavity becomes filled with a glairy albuminous fluid similar to the liquor folliculi ; the blood clot being still visible at the point of rupture " (Hammond, 1927). A similar condition is met with in a variety of other animals, including the rabbit (Sobotta, 1897), rat (Long and Evans, 1922), mouse (Sobotta, 1896), dog (Evans and Cole, 1931), baboon (Zuckerman and Parkes, 1932), man (Falkiner, 1933), etc., and probably is the rule rather than the exception. Normally, as the luteal tissue becomes established, the central cavity is reduced and the fluid reabsorbed, leaving only a small central clot. Occasionally, in individual corpora lutea, in the cow (Hammond, 1927) and in other species, the fluid is not completely absorbed and the central cavity persists during the later stages of luteal development.

The corpora lutea of *Elephantulus* (van der Horst and Gillman, 1940) are formed in a unique manner, for the membrana granulosa is everted through the wide opening of the ruptured follicle. Consequently the corpus luteum is extroverted, the luteal cells being freely exposed on the surface of the ovary, being later covered by an overgrowth of the germinal epithelium from the sides.

The membrana propria does not persist in the discharged Graafian follicle but disappears immediately or very soon after ovulation. No doubt its disintegration, facilitated by its extreme delicacy, is due partly to the effects of contraction and collapse of the follicular wall and partly to the active ingrowth of thecal elements and blood capillaries into the membrana granulosa, which begins immediately after ovulation. The membrana propria does not serve, therefore, in the mammals, as it does in elasmobranchs and sauropsids, to define the limits of thecal and epithelial tissues in the ruptured follicle. It is exceedingly difficult to determine the extent to which each of the three cellular layers of the follicular wall participates in the development of the corpus luteum, which takes place with remarkable rapidity, and especially to elucidate the origin of the large, presumably glandular, luteal cells which are its most conspicuous and characteristic component.

This problem has attracted the attention of histologists for many years, and despite the most careful investigation by many competent observers, it is still far from solved. The literature of the subject is much too extensive to attempt a complete review, but bibliographies of the earlier works are provided by Sobotta (1899) and Marshall (1905) and references to the more recent are available in the papers referred to in the following pages. The views advanced by various authors can be summarised under three main headings : (1) that the luteal cells originate from the theca interna exclusively ; (2) that the luteal cells originate from the membrana granulosa exclusively ; and (3) that the membrana granulosa gives rise to luteal cells and the theca interna to cells which are either indistinguishable from, or resemble in their glandular appearance, the luteal cells and are distinct from the other connective-tissue cells of the corpus luteum.

The theory that the corpus luteum arises entirely from the connective tissue of the theca, and that the membrana granulosa does not contribute to it, was initiated by von Baer (1827). This involves the assumption that the membrana granulosa is either entirely discharged from the follicle at ovulation, with the oöcyte and liquor folliculi, or else is partly discharged and partly degenerates *in situ*. Among the principal supporters of the theory appear the names of Valentin (1835), Leuckart (1852), His (1865, 1899), Kölliker (1867, 1898), Slavjansky (1870), Gegenbaur (1861), Benckiser (1884), Paladino (1887, 1900), Bonnet (1891), Schottlaender (1893) and Minot (1892). Amongst others who have adopted this view are Nagel (1896, 1899), who investigated the human corpus luteum ; Clark (1898, 1899), who contributed an account of the formation of the corpus luteum in the sow and in man ; Doering (1899), who also worked upon the sow, and claimed to have confirmed Clark's account ; and Bühler (1900), Wendeler (1899), and Stoeckel (1902), who have examined and described developing human corpora lutea. Zschokke (1898) believed that the theca interna gives rise to the corpus luteum in the cow, mainly because of the thickness which it attains in the mature follicle ; a view which has been shared by Delestre (1910). Jankowski (1904) also held that the luteal cells are modified connective-tissue cells. The material employed in this research appears to have consisted of a miscellaneous collection of ovaries of pigs and guinea-pigs, the ages of the corpora lutea of which were unknown. He bases his opinion largely on the appearance of cells resembling luteal cells in the theca interna of the undischarged follicle. Williams (1903) takes up the same position, partly on the ground that the membrana granulosa presents extensive degenerative changes, and is usually cast off in great part at the time of rupture, and partly because certain cells of the theca interna come to resemble luteal cells prior to ovulation.

The second theory, which has been accepted much more widely, that the luteal cells are formed exclusively by the cells of the membrana granulosa of the undischarged Graafian follicle, was propounded by Bischoff (1842) as a result of his classical investigation of the embryology of the rabbit. It was supported by Pflüger (1863), Waldeyer (1870), Call and Exner (1875), Beigel (1878) and Schulin (1881) among the earlier investigators.

The credit belongs to Sobotta (1895b, 1896) of being the first to deal systematically with the problem and, with the publication of his papers on the corpus luteum in the mouse, the controversy entered upon a new phase. In Sobotta's investigation the material employed was collected upon a definite plan, the animals being killed at known intervals after copulation, in reference to the occurrence of which the time of ovulation had been determined previously. A large series of corpora lutea, representing successive stages in their development, was obtained, and confirmed the view that the luteal cells are the membrana granulosa cells much hypertrophied, the connective-tissue network being derived from the theca interna. Sobotta describes the theca externa as taking no share in the ingrowth, while the theca interna becomes entirely spent in the formation of the inter-epithelial reticulum. The hypertrophy of the membrana granulosa cells is in the nature of a simple enlargement, unaccompanied by division. Sobotta's con-clusions in regard to the development of the corpus luteum in the mouse were confirmed by him subsequently in further investigations carried out on similar lines on the corpora lutea of the rabbit (1897) and of the guinea-pig (1906). More-over, Stratz (1898) published descriptions of certain stages of luteal formation in *Tarsius*, *Tupaia* and *Sorex* which agree in essentials with those given by Sobotta.

The structure of the ovary and the cyclic changes which it undergoes in the marsupial-cat, *Dasyurus viverrinus*, have been investigated by Sandes (1903). He concluded that the cells of the membrana granulosa alone give rise to the luteal cells. These hypertrophy so as almost to fill the cavity of the discharged follicle before any ingrowth from the theca has taken place. The theca interna is so rudimentary that there is little difficulty in showing that it does not give rise to luteal elements but forms only the vascular connective tissue of the corpus luteum. O'Donoghue (1914) found much variation in the degree of development of the theca interna in different species of marsupials. Thus in Phascolomys it is com-posed of polygonal cells arranged in three or four rows. It is scarcely distin-guishable from the theca externa in the ripe follicle in Dasyurus, at the other extreme, but is better developed in small follicles. Both theca interna and externa participate in forming the connective-tissue ingrowths of the corpus luteum, in which the theca interna is largely used up.

The formation of the corpus luteum in the sheep was described by Marshall (1903). The animals were killed at successive intervals after copulation or, when copulation did not or was not known to occur, after oestrus was observed. It was concluded that the luteal cells arise exclusively from the membrana granulosa. The cells of the membrana granulosa continue to undergo mitotic division after the rupture of the follicle, but not with the same frequency as previously. The theca externa, as well as the theca interna, contributes to the formation of the connective-tissue network of the corpus luteum. The theca interna is entirely spent in producing this connective-tissue reticulum. Four days after oestrus the discharged follicle was found to have acquired all the characteristics of the fully developed corpus luteum, the luteal cells, as seen in section, being at least six times as large as the original epithelial cells. More recently, the development of the corpus luteum in the rabbit has been investigated by Marshall (1925), with similar results. No mitoses were observed, however, in the membrana granulosa cells of the ruptured follicle. Kurashige (1927), using accurately dated material, concluded that the theca interna gives rise to the connective-tissue reticulum of the corpus luteum in the rabbit. According to Robinson (1918) the luteal cells are formed from the membrana granulosa cells in the ferret.

Hammond (1927) states that in the cow the luteal cells are formed exclusively from the cells of the membrana granulosa and that the theca interna supplies the connective tissue and blood-vessels of the corpus luteum. The development of the corpus luteum of the mouse and the rabbit has been investigated by Deanesly (1930b), using modern histological methods to determine the part played by the theca interna. It was concluded that the luteal cells arise exclusively from the membrana granulosa. The theca interna at its maximum state of development includes numerous fat-containing cells of two kinds ; some of a fibroblastic type and others with larger and more oval nuclei. These cells do not become detached from the sheath but divide mitotically shortly after ovulation and give rise to fibro-blastic cells, containing fine fat granules, which penetrate inwards and constitute both the walls of the blood spaces and the supporting tissue of the corpus luteum. Thus the connective-tissue reticulum of the corpus luteum is formed of endothelial cells with small darkly staining nuclei. The theca interna is entirely used up in this way and, by 36 hours after ovulation, none of the large cells persist as such nor is there any evidence of their wholesale degeneration. The theca externa also participates in the vascularisation and forms the sheath of the corpus luteum, but the more active growth comes from the theca interna.

The formation of the corpus luteum in the baboon has been described by Zuckerman and Parkes (1932). The wall of the recently ruptured follicle is extensively folded, resulting in tongues of theca interna and externa projecting inwards. The cavity of the ruptured follicle is filled by a clot, probably formed of a mixture of blood and liquor folliculi, containing a few detached granulosa cells. The cells of the membrana granulosa hypertrophy, chiefly due to increase in cytoplasm, and give rise to the luteal cells. The luteal cells, as they enlarge, gradually encroach upon the central cavity, the corpus luteum becoming solid very slowly. The fibroblastic reticulum and blood-vessels grow in from the thecal cores in the folds of the wall. It is suggested that both the theca interna and externa are utilised to form the vascular reticular system of the corpus luteum and that there is no evidence that the theca interna produces secretory cells in the baboon. Van der Horst and Gillman (1942) provide convincing evidence of the origin of the luteal cells exclusively from the membrana granulosa in *Elephantulus*. In this little animal the conversion of the membrana granulosa cells into luteal cells begins before ovulation, when the membrana propria is still intact and there can be no doubt of the limits of the theca. Moreover, at ovulation the follicle is everted so that the inner surface of the membrana granulosa, transforming into luteal tissue, is freely exposed at the surface of the ovary and is not in contact with the theca interna.

A number of authors, although agreeing with those referred to above regarding the exclusive origin of the luteal cells from the membrana granulosa, deny that the theca interna is used up entirely in the production of the connective and vascular tissues and maintain that some of its cells persist unaltered, at least for a time, as a distinct component of the corpus luteum. This is the position adopted by Honoré (1900), working on the rabbit, who accepted the view that the membrana granulosa alone gives rise to the luteal cells. He concluded that the connective-tissue reticulum is derived in part from the theca externa and in part from the theca interna. The theca interna is not exhausted in the production of this in-growth, some part of it still remaining to form a layer within the outer theca in the fully formed corpus luteum. Volker (1904), likewise, finds that in the thirteen-lined ground squirrel the luteal cells arise from the membrana granulosa and the theca externa participates in the connective-tissue ingrowth, while the theca interna does not become exhausted in the process. Loeb (1906a and b) in the guinea-pig, Cohn in the rabbit (1903) and in man (1909) and Meyer (1911) in man also observed the theca interna cells persisting for a time in the developing corpus luteum.

The formation of the corpus luteum in the mouse was reinvestigated by Togari (1923). The luteal cells are formed by the enlargement, unaccompanied by cell division, of the cells of the membrana granulosa. The theca interna becomes irregular in thickness after ovulation but its cells remain at the periphery of the developing luteal tissue. Some of the theca interna cells show signs of degeneration several hours after ovulation, and by 60 hours all have disappeared, so that none are present in the fully grown corpus luteum. The polygonal cells of the theca interna reach their maximum differentiation before the rupture of the follicle when their cytoplasm " resembles a honeycomb with fat-like substance." Togari supports the view that these cells are nutritive in function but fails to find any evidence that they ever become transformed into connective-tissue fibroblasts, as was maintained by Sobotta (1896). The connective-tissue reticulum is formed from spindle-shaped cells of both the theca interna and theca externa.

A large series of human corpora lutea have been described by Watrin (1924, 1926). He noted that the theca interna cells are abundant and larger than those of the membrana granulosa at the time of ovulation. Elements of both theca interna and externa are said to participate in the vascularisation of the corpus luteum. The persistence for a time of some unaltered lipoid-containing theca interna cells at the periphery and along the connective-tissue trabeculae in a corpus luteum of ovulation was noted, but these cells had disappeared in later stages. Unaltered theca interna cells do not persist as such in the corpus luteum at the end of the first month of pregnancy.

According to Mossman (1937) the theca interna in the ruptured follicles of the pocket gopher, Geomys bursarius Shaw, a species in which it is very well developed, rapidly degenerates and takes no part in the formation of true luteal tissue ; although a ring of degenerating and metamorphosing theca interna cells may remain about the young corpus luteum until the embryos have begun to implant.

The view that, although the luteal cells are derived from the membrana granulosa, some at least of the cells of the theca interna persist unaltered as such, not participating in the formation of the connective and vascular tissues of the corpus luteum, leads to the third theory of the origin of the luteal tissue. According to this theory the membrana granulosa gives rise to luteal cells and the theca interna also gives rise to elements, presumably glandular, which are either indistinguishable from the other luteal cells or resemble them closely when ordinary histological methods are employed. These, in any event, are distinct from all other connective-tissue elements, in the corpus luteum. Schrön (1862) appears to have been the first to suggest that the luteal cells may have a dual origin, arising both from the cells of the membrana granulosa and of the theca interna. Rabl (1898) expressed a similar opinion.

An important account of the development of the corpora lutea in bats belonging to the genera Vesperugo, Vespertilio and Placotus was provided by O. van der Stricht (1901a and b). He found that the cells of the membrana granulosa hypertrophy and give rise to luteal cells.   Some mitotic division of the membrana granulosa cells was observed.   The majority of the luteal cells are formed in this way, but a minority arise from elements, which he identifies as interstitial cells, in the theca interna.   The luteal cells therefore have a dual origin.   The theca interna also gives rise to the vascular framework of the corpus luteum.   The same author says, in a later paper (1912), " en attendant de nouvelles recherches, surtout chez les grands mammifères, nous restons toujours convaincu de l'origine mixte."

The development of the corpora lutea in the pig has been described in detail in a series of papers by Corner (1915, 1919, 1921, 1948).   The membrana granulosa is retained intact, except for the loss of the cells of the discus proligerus, after rupture of the follicle.   Its cells do not divide mitotically but increase in size, the cytoplasm becoming laden with lipoid substances, and give rise to the luteal cells. During this process the membrana granulosa is invaded by blood capillaries from the theca interna which give rise to the vascular plexus of the corpus luteum, which when fully established is so complex that every luteal cell is in contact with a capillary.   The large lipoid-laden cells of the theca interna multiply mitotically.   They give rise to two types of elements.   The first occur in 8 to 10-day corpora lutea as a few distinct clumps of unaltered theca interna cells occupying their original position about the periphery and along the vascular trabeculae formed by the folds of the thecal wall of the collapsed follicle.   The second type pass into the luteal tissue, wandering among the luteal cells and becoming lodged throughout the whole structure.   These " theca lutein cells " could be distinguished from the true luteal cells by their smaller size, more deeply staining cytoplasm, often densely packed with minute regular vacuoles giving it a characteristic foamy appearance, and by the presence in osmium preparations of plentiful fat globules, which vary greatly in number and size.   These cells fit into the interstices between the swollen rounded surfaces of the larger " granulosa lutein cells " and, in consequence, they frequently have irregular outlines.   They persist in the regressing corpus luteum after the true luteal cells have disappeared.   There was no evidence that the cells of the theca interna are ever converted into fibroblasts or that they lay down the fibrils of the connective-tissue reticulum.   This reticulum of connective-tissue fibrils forms a dense network around all the luteal cells and, according to Corner, is formed by the endothelial cells of the capillary lining.   The development of the corpus luteum in the mare (Harrison, 1946), and the goat (Harrison, 1948a) is essentially similar.   Pederson (1951) maintains that both theca interna and granulosa cells transform into typical lutein cells in the rat.

Gatenby (1924) and Solomons and Gatenby (1924) investigated the structure of the corpora lutea of man and the pig, using modern cytological methods.   They showed that the true luteal cells originated exclusively from the membrana granulosa but they also found remarkable stellate cells scattered among them.   Silver impregnation, with or without subsequent staining in iron haematoxylin, blackened these cells intensely, showing them in sharp contrast with the surrounding luteal cells.   These stellate cells differed from the luteal cells not only in their shape and chromophility but also in the structure and arrangement of their cytoplasmic inclusions.   They were identified with those of the theca interna of the Graafian follicle, which they resembled both in cytological structure and in chromophility after silver impregnation, and with the " theca-lutein cells " of

Corner (1919). These theca interna cells persist as such in the corpus luteum until regression sets in, and there is no evidence that they give rise ever to connective-tissue fibres. The connective-tissue reticulum of the corpus luteum is said to arise from elements of the theca externa, not from endothelial cells as suggested by Corner. Cells resembling, but staining more darkly than, the luteal cells have been described in the human corpus luteum of menstruation by Ikeda (1928). Similar stellate cells, staining with Sudan black, have been described in the human corpus luteum of early pregnancy by White, Hertig, Rock and Adams (1951), who called these elements K cells, apparently being unaware of the work of Solomons and Gatenby and of Ikeda. Cells similar to the stellate cells of Solomons and Gatenby have been observed (Brambell, 1930) in the corpus luteum of the rabbit after fixation in Regaud's fluid and staining with iron haematoxylin. Recently, Corner (1948) has been able to demonstrate the persistence of the theca interna cells in the corpus luteum of the pig by means of their content of alkaline phosphatase. Some of these cells remain at the periphery of the corpus luteum whereas others become scattered amongst the granulosa luteal cells.

The formation of the corpus luteum of the rabbit has been reinvestigated by Togari (1926), who finds that it differs in several important respects from that of the mouse (1923). The luteal cells arise chiefly from cells of the membrana granulosa which undergo both hypertrophy and hyperplasia in the ruptured follicle, whereas in the mouse only hypertrophy occurs. The majority of the polygonal theca interna cells degenerate during the development of the corpus luteum but some give rise to " theca-lutein cells " ; in the mouse no luteal cells arise from the theca interna. The connective-tissue reticulum is formed, as in the mouse, from spindle-shaped cells of both the theca interna and externa.

Lamellar connective-tissue cells were observed by Kaltenegger (1915) in the corpus luteum of the cow after special staining methods. These cells were probably the same as the " theca-lutein cells " of Corner (1919) and the stellate theca interna cells of Gatenby (1924) and of Solomons and Gatenby (1924). Horrenberger (1928) maintained, on cytological grounds, that elements derived from the theca interna have a secretory function in the human corpus luteum.

It is difficult to synthesise the extraordinarily diverse views outlined above into a generalised account of existing knowledge of the histogenesis of the corpus luteum. Only the first theory can be dismissed with any confidence, for it has not received support during recent years, when modern histological methods and adequate series of developmental stages of known age have been employed. None of the supporters of this hypothesis appear to have examined a complete series of stages and in several instances atretic undischarged follicles (p. 501) appear to have been mistaken for true corpora lutea. Indeed, the opinion that the corpus luteum is entirely a connective-tissue structure appears to have been founded on the assumption, now generally acknowledged to be erroneous, that the changes exhibited by discharged follicles and atretic follicles are identical in character. Moreover, this hypothesis would be hard to co-ordinate with our knowledge of the changes in the ruptured follicles of other vertebrates, where the evidence for the persistence and participation of the epithelial elements is beyond question. The view expressed by Schafer (1929) that the corpus luteum may be developed in entirely different ways in different species of mammals will not be acceptable to many histologists.

It must therefore be admitted that the evidence in favour of the membrana granulosa giving rise to luteal cells is overwhelming. All the more important recent investigations have led to this conclusion. The transformation of the membrana granulosa cells into luteal cells in the ruptured follicle is brought about by

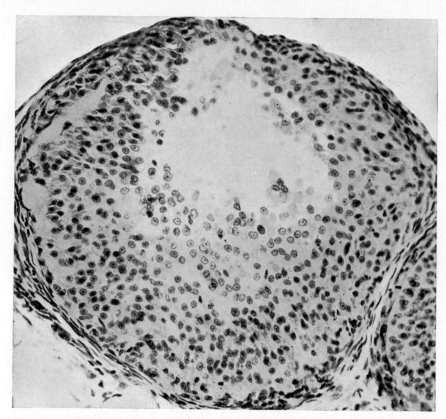

Fig. 5. 30—Photomicrograph of the developing corpus luteum of the common shrew showing the first indications of connective-tissue ingrowth from the theca. The cavity of the follicle is still apparent. Active ingrowth of the membrana granulosa is taking place ; the cells are enlarging and their nuclei are becoming rounded. × 300. (From Brambell, 1935.)

hypertrophy of the individual elements, especially of the cytoplasm (Figs. 5. 30 and 5. 31), accompanied by changes in the cytoplasmic organs and the accumulation of cytoplasmic inclusions, including granules of fats, lipoids and lutein pigment. Although mitotic figures are frequent in the membrana granulosa of the unruptured follicle they are either entirely absent or, at least, much less frequent (sheep, bats, etc.) in the developing corpus luteum. Indeed, it is possible that mitoses in enlarged theca interna cells, which had grown into the epithelium, were mistaken for dividing epithelial elements in those instances where these have been recorded. The solution of the problem of the part played by the theca interna presents far more difficulty. The theca interna of the mature follicle contains fibroblastic elements, blood capillaries and lymph channels, as well as the large theca interna cells, which undoubtedly contribute to the vascularisation and the formation of the connective-tissue reticulum. It is concerning the part played by the large cells, characteristic of the theca interna, that so much diversity of opinion exists. These cells only attain their maximum development in the unruptured Graafian follicles of placental mammals when ovulation is imminent. It is not unreasonable to assume therefore that the discharge of their functions is associated with the

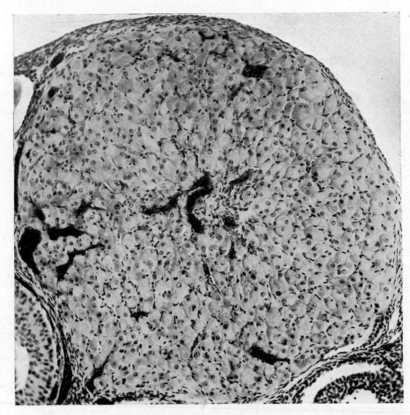

Fig. 5. 31—Photomicrograph of the corpus luteum of the common shrew at its maximum development shortly before implantation of the blastocysts. The luteal cells are very large and the connective-tissue reticulum is well developed. The corpus luteum is hyperaemic and its centre is occupied by a small clot. × 180. (From Brambell, 1935.)

changes initiated by ovulation ; to wit, the development of the corpus luteum. Whether these functions are the production of the vascular and connective tissues, of additional luteal cells or of special elements, distinct from both, has not been resolved finally. It would be arbitrary, in the light of existing knowledge, to favour any one of these hypotheses. Two significant facts, however, should be borne in mind in future investigations. It is well known that these cells commonly exhibit numerous mitoses in the recently ruptured follicle and that in atretic follicles (p. 501) they give rise unquestionably to cells which are frequently indistinguishable from the luteal cells of true corpora lutea. Since they produce luteal-like cells in the atretic follicle the possibility of their doing so also in the discharged follicle cannot be dismissed lightly. Some diversity of opinion exists also as to the part played by the theca externa in the ingrowth of connective tissue and vascularisation of the corpus luteum. It seems probable that it plays a larger part in these processes in the follicles of large animals, where the wall of the collapsed follicle is more folded and the connective-tissue framework of the corpus luteum is more highly developed, than it does in those of small animals. Whatever its origin, the connective tissue in the fully developed corpus luteum forms

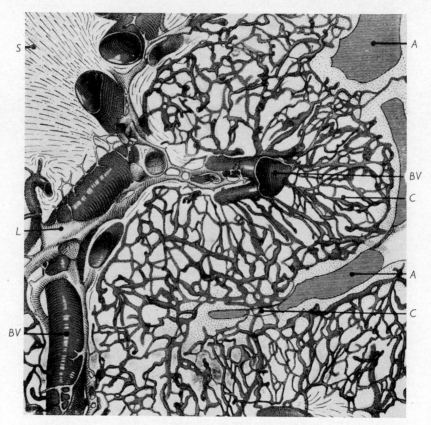

Fig. 5. 32—Blood vessels and lymphatics of the developing corpus luteum of the sow. The network of blood capillaries has extended throughout the granulosa and wherever the tongues of luteal tissue have touched anastomoses occur. The lymphatics, which form a network around the arterioles of the theca externa, have followed an arteriole along the core of the tongue of luteal tissue. A, antrum; BV, blood vessels of theca externa growing into the cores of the tongues of luteal tissue; C, blood capillaries in the luteal tissue; L, lymphatics; S, stroma. × 105. (From Andersen, 1926.)

a close-meshed reticulum surrounding every luteal cell, penetrating through the luteal tissue and forming a fibrous central plug, surrounding and gradually replacing the clot formed in the original cavity. Ikeda (1928) distinguishes two kinds of fibrils in the reticulum of the human corpus luteum. The larger trabeculae of connective tissue, in which the main blood-vessels run, arise from the apices of the folds of the follicular wall. Blood capillaries run throughout the tissues in the connective-tissue reticulum. The corpus luteum becomes, in this way, a solid, glandular and very vascular structure (Fig. 5. 31), somewhat exceeding in size the mature Graafian follicle from which it was formed.

Blood-vessels and lymphatics of the corpus luteum

The development and structure of the vascular supply of the corpus luteum of the pig (Fig. 5. 32) has been investigated by Andersen (1926) by means of injection technique. Capillaries begin to grow in from the capillary network in the theca interna and to penetrate into the membrana granulosa about the time of ovulation. Arterioles also grow inwards from the larger vessels in the theca externa. The wall of the follicle, when it collapses after rupture, becomes folded, each fold appearing in section as a tongue of membrana granulosa cells, with a central thecal core, which projects into the lumen. An arteriole, venules and lymphatics grow out along the thecal core of each such tongue. The arteriole runs out through the centre of the core and branches at the end, the branches returning towards the base of the tongue along the periphery of the core. Capillaries grow out from these arterioles into the membrana granulosa of the tongue, forming at first simple loops returning the blood by six or more venules, which may or may not fuse at the base of the tongue. Soon the capillaries anastomose to form a dense network in each tongue, and, as the central cavity is obliterated by the enlargement of the tissue, anastomoses between the capillaries of neighbouring tongues are established at the points of contact. Thus, in the fully developed corpus luteum, the larger vessels can be seen to enter from all sides, an arteriole and accompanying venules together, and to run a greater or less distance into the substance of the corpus luteum. The vessels give off capillaries at right angles to their course ; these capillaries form dense anastomoses, tending to run radially from the vessels, and join the networks which arise from neighbouring arterioles and venules.

The lymphatics lag behind the blood-vessels in their development. A single lymphatic vessel, arising from the network in the theca externa, grows in with each arteriole into the core of a tongue of tissue (Fig. 5. 32). It remains undivided at its base but branches within the tongue, forming a single-layered network of capillaries without valves which spreads over the surface of the thecal core of the tongue. After the corpus luteum has become solid another network of lymphatics is found, which Andersen calls the central system. This network occupies the position of the surfaces where neighbouring tongues of luteal tissue have come in contact. It consists, therefore, of a central sheet with radiating sheets running out from it between the luteal tongues. The lymphatics of this central system are connected with those of the peripheral system by capillaries traversing the luteal tissue. It is suggested that this central system arises by lymph-capillaries from the peripheral system penetrating through the membrana granulosa and spreading to form an anastomosing network over its inner surface. Thus the lymphatic system, when fully formed, is surprisingly well developed in the corpus luteum. During retrogression the lymphatic system disappears before the blood-vessels. The vascularisation of the corpus luteum of the rat has been described by Bassett (1943).

Innervation of the corpus luteum

Apart from the fibres of the perivascular network, which accompany the blood-vessels into the corpus luteum, Pines and Schapiro (1930) claim to have demonstrated other nerve fibres entering the luteal tissue, running between the luteal cells and forming bud-shaped end-organs which appear to be pericellular ; that is, arranged over the surfaces of the cells.

Cytology of the luteal cells

The transformation of a membrana granulosa cell into a luteal cell is accompanied by hypertrophy, as has been mentioned. Although some increase in the size of the nucleus occurs, this hypertrophy is due mainly to enlargement of the cytoplasm. The contribution of mitosis to the changes in volume and cellular density in the corpus luteum of the rat have been investigated by means of the colchicine technique by Bassett (1949). Every luteal cell in the functional corpus luteum is in intimate relation to the capillary system and exhibits the cytological characters of active glandular cells. Each luteal cell, according to Goormaghtigh (1927), is bipolar, with an arterial pole in close relation to a blood-capillary and a lymphatic pole adjoining a lymph-capillary. The nucleus is stated to be eccentric and nearer the lymphatic pole and the centrosome to be situated between the nucleus and the arterial pole. According to Chydenius (1926, 1929) as many as four centrioles may be present in a single luteal cell. The mitochondria are also oriented arterially. The mitochondria in the luteal cells of bats have been investigated by Levi (1913), who found that they were in the form of short, curved rods (chondriocontes) and exhibited little differentiation, and of man by Moulonguet (1927). On the other hand, in the luteal cells of the dog, Goormaghtigh (1927) found a variety of forms of mitochondria corresponding with the secretory state of the cell. He believed them to participate in the assimilation of the lipoidal droplets. Filamentous mitochondria were recorded in the luteal cells of the hedgehog by Regaud and Policard (1901) and in those of *Ornithorhynchus* by Hill and Gatenby (1926).

The Golgi apparatus of the luteal cells of the cow was described by Riquier (1910). It was found to occupy a circum-nuclear position in many of the cells. During regression it shrinks *pari passu* with the rest of the cell. It was concluded that it does not take a direct part in the formation of the fatty substances.

During the transformation of the membrana granulosa cells into luteal cells in the human ovary the Golgi apparatus undergoes great enlargement (Gatenby, 1924). It is sub-spherical in shape and juxta-nuclear in position and is made up of granular or rod-like dictyosomes arranged throughout all parts of the sphere, not confined to the cortex only. These dictyosomes are quite separate from each other and do not form a network. The Golgi apparatus in the fully formed luteal cell occupies nearly half the cell ; it is nearly always larger than the nucleus itself and it is about five times the diameter of the Golgi apparatus in a membrana granulosa cell of an unruptured follicle. In the later stages of the corpus luteum of pregnancy, and sometimes in that of menstruation, the Golgi apparatus loses its juxta-nuclear eccentric position and becomes scattered around the nucleus. The Golgi apparatus of the stellate chromophil cells, which this author identifies as originating from the theca interna, is less regular in shape and position and more coarsely granular in structure. These cells have characteristically a very eccentric nucleus with the Golgi apparatus in a juxta-nuclear position, sometimes extending into the branching processes of the cell. Both Corner (1915) and Goormaghtigh (1927) described what they believed to be the Golgi apparatus in the luteal cells of the pig and the dog respectively, but they identified it with a canalicular system, presumed to be the trophospongium of Holmgren.

The luteal cells contain, in addition to the cytoplasmic organs mentioned above, pigment, fatty or lipoidal spherules and secretory droplets, which usually appear as cytoplasmic vacuoles. The yellow pigment, known as lutein, gives its name and the characteristic colour to the corpus luteum. This pigment is particularly well-developed in the human corpus luteum and in that of the cow. According to Hammond (1927), the corpus luteum of the cow is at first pale, but soon becomes cream, then bright canary-yellow turning orange-red and, finally, bright scarlet or brown. The colour changes in the corpora lutea of cows have been described and figured also by Küpfer (1920a). In the pig (Corner, 1915) the corpus luteum is light grey tinged with pink, only turning yellow when old. During regression the pigment does not appear to be reabsorbed but remains in the regressing tissues. Lutein is not a derivative of haemoglobin but is, according to Escher (1913), a carotinoid, similar to those found in many other tissues and in the yolk of an egg. Hence it does not originate, as is often stated, from the transformation of the blood-clot which is sometimes, though not invariably (see p. 474–5) present in the recently ruptured follicle. The luteins are usually associated in their distribution with fats or lipoids and occur in the luteal cells in the fatty or lipoidal spherules which blacken with osmium tetroxide.

Gatenby (1924) has suggested that the lutein granules of the human corpus luteum may be modified mitochondria, swollen and loaded with lipochrome. He believes that they are lipoidal in nature and do not contain neutral fat. It is pointed out that they correspond in position with mitochondria, that they are extraordinarily regular in size, a fact noted by many observers, whereas fat-spherules are characteristically irregular in size. Mitochondria in many invertebrate ova become laden in a similar manner with lipochrome and impart to the egg its yellow or brown colour.

The changes in the fatty or lipoidal content of the corpus luteum have received a good deal of attention. Reference to the somewhat extensive literature can be found in the papers on the subject by Miller (1910, 1914), Watrin (1924, 1926), Steinforth (1928) and Horrenberger (1928) on the human corpus luteum, by Corner (1915, 1919, 1921) on the sow, by Cesa-Bianchi (1908) on the mare, cow and sow, by Long and Evans (1922) on the rat, by Mulon (1906) on the guinea-pig, by Skowron and Keller (1934) on the rabbit, by Drips (1919) on the spermophile, by Deanesly (1930a) on the mouse, by O. van der Stricht (1901a and b, 1912) and Levi (1913) on the bats and by Goormaghtigh (1927) on the bitch.

According to O. van der Stricht, the luteal cells of bats produce two distinct secretions, the first serous in nature and the second lipoidal. He distinguishes histologically three periods in the life of the corpus luteum of pregnancy : the first, extending from ovulation to the implantation of the embryo, is characterised by the abundance of the serous secretion ; the second, extending from implantation to mid-pregnancy, is marked by the presence of the lipoidal secretion in the form of droplets in the cells ; and the third, beginning towards the end of pregnancy, marks the onset of retrogression. Niskoubina (1909) also distinguishes three periods in the life of the corpus luteum of pregnancy in the rabbit. During the

third or retrogressive phase fatty degeneration of the luteal cells occurs. Levi
(1913) agrees with O. van der Stricht in distinguishing between the serous and
lipoidal secretions of the luteal cells of the bat, but insists that both are produced
concurrently, although the serous secretion is predominant at first. During the
second half of pregnancy he observed protein inclusions in the cytoplasm. Drips
(1919) also distinguished three phases in the luteal cells of the thirteen-lined
ground squirrel (*Spermophilus citellus tridecemlineatus*). The first, which extends
almost throughout gestation, is characterised by red granules, which are assumed
to be secretion, in the luteal cells. The second is characterised by lipoid droplets
in the luteal cells and lasts from before parturition to six weeks afterwards. The
third is the phase of retrogression. The cytology of the luteal cells of the ewe has
been investigated by Warbritton (1934), who failed to identify the secretory
products within the cells.

Corner (1915), like Cesa-Bianchi (1908), distinguishes exoplasmic and endoplasmic regions in the cytoplasm of the luteal cells of the sow. During early
stages of pregnancy the exoplasmic zone is extensive and includes numerous large
vacuolar spaces containing some stainable granules. Later these decrease in
number, and the endoplasmic region gradually extends outwards and finally forms
the whole of the cytoplasm. The fatty spherules increase in quantity during the
early stages of pregnancy, and, having reached a maximum, decrease thereafter.
Finally, shortly before parturition, fat reappears in the luteal cells in the form
of much fewer and larger globules of very variable size. By means of these
changes Corner claims to be able to distinguish cytologically seven phases in the
corpus luteum during pregnancy.

Goormaghtigh (1927) describes the occurrence of a substance in the luteal cells
of the dog, distinct from the lipoidal droplets, which has an affinity for iron-
haematoxylin after fixation with osmium tetroxide. This he calls " siderophil "
substance and regards as a complex mixture of fatty substances associated with
proteins. He concludes that the lipoidal droplets are transformed into siderophil
substance, which in its turn gives rise to the non-stainable secretion, and that
during this process protein materials are added to the lipoids. On this interpretation these various cytoplasmic substances represent stages in the production
of a single luteal secretion, not two distinct secretions as was concluded by O. van
der Stricht and by Levi. Working on this assumption, Goormaghtigh concludes
that the lipoids are assimilated from the blood at the arterial pole of the cell and
that the unstainable product is secreted into the lymph at the lymphatic pole.
Characteristically, the mitochondria, Golgi apparatus and centrosome are orientated
between the nucleus and the secretory pole in glandular cells. Consequently, the
arterial pole might be expected to be secretory and the lymphatic pole absorptive,
so that it is not improbable that Goormaghtigh is mistaken in his conclusion. It
would appear probable also that the siderophil substance of Goormaghtigh, which
occurs as irregular masses in peripheral vacuoles, is the same as the granules in
the exoplasmic vacuoles of Corner and possibly as the serous secretion of O. van
der Stricht and Levi. The content of fatty or lipoidal droplets in the luteal cells
of the pregnant bitch was observed to increase initially to a maximum about the
fifth day after oestrus and thereafter to decrease sharply. Very little was present
from the twelfth to fiftieth day of gestation, but fat rapidly accumulated again
during the twelve days preceding parturition.

Long and Evans (1922) in the rat and Deanesly (1930a) in the mouse both noted an increase in the content of lipoidal droplets in the luteal cells during the development and functional life of the corpus luteum. These droplets are remarkably uniform in size and in distribution in the cell during this period. Later, when retrogression begins, they are still further augmented but lose their uniformity in size and distribution. In the later stages of regression the lipoids are reabsorbed and the degenerating corpus luteum is left finally fat-free once more. The lipoidal droplets in the luteal cells of the rat were found to be similar in corpora lutea of ovulation (i.e. corpora lutea of dioestrus), of pseudo-pregnancy and of pregnancy, but in those of lactation they were markedly smaller in size.

It seems safe to conclude that the osmiophil droplets, whether or not they represent a secretory product or a stage in its formation, are found characteristically in functionally active luteal cells. They are in such cells strikingly uniform in size and evenly distributed. The presence of osmiophil substances unevenly distributed and unequal in size is, on the other hand, characteristic of regressing corpora lutea and is in the nature of fatty degeneration of the luteal cells. In some animals the phase of maximum development of the former type of uniform droplets is attained early in pregnancy and is separated by a period of decreased fat content from the phase of fatty degeneration characterised by the latter type of irregular and larger droplets. In other animals, such as the rat and the mouse, no such period of decreased fat content intervenes, and the onset of regression is marked by the augmentation in fatty content leading directly to increase and inequality in size of the previously uniform droplets.

It is extremely difficult to determine by histological methods the chemical nature of these droplets which blacken with osmium tetroxide, as has been emphasised by Gatenby (1924). They have been interpreted by various authors as fatty or lipoidal in nature. The majority of earlier workers regarded them as fat. As a result of microchemical investigation of the corpora lutea, Cesa-Bianchi (1908) concluded that they were lecithin. Corner (1915) and Goormaghtigh (1927) regard the droplets as mixtures of fats and lipoids. In reference to the morphological distinction between the osmiophil droplets of the functional and regressing corpora lutea, referred to above, it is interesting to note that Miller (1910, 1914) was unable to find neutral fat in the human corpus luteum of pregnancy, although it was present in regressing corpora lutea during the puerperium and in the corpus luteum of menstruation.

Growth and persistence of the corpus luteum

The history of the corpus luteum after it has become established varies according to whether the animal is non-pregnant, pregnant, or, if the corpora lutea were formed at the post-partum oestrus, lactating. These phenomena are correlated particularly with the length of time during which the corpus luteum persists in a functional condition, the rate at which it regresses and the maximum size it attains. Obviously, the resulting differences in growth and duration of the corpus luteum must be reflected also, to a greater or less extent, in histological differences. The initial development of the corpus luteum in any species is essentially similar whatever its subsequent history may be.

The nature of these changes in the corpora lutea have been investigated in a number of animals, of which the rat and the mouse have proved particularly instructive. Both these rodents are polyoestrous, with a short dioestrous cycle when unmated. Copulation which is sterile, either naturally or through experimental intervention, results in prolongation of the cycle, owing to the development of a pseudo-pregnant condition, to approximately double the length of the unmated cycle. Both have, also, an oestrous period accompanied by ovulation a few hours after parturition, the corpora lutea formed at which are present in the ovaries during lactation. They provide material, therefore, for the comparison of the corpora lutea during four different conditions; namely, dioestrus, pseudo-pregnancy, pregnancy and lactation. These may be called, conveniently, corpora

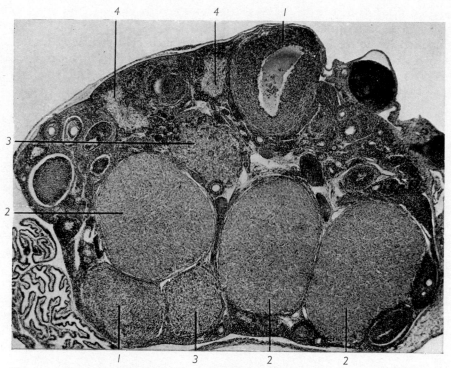

Fig. 5. 33—Photomicrograph of a section of the ovary of an adult bank vole showing four generations of corpora lutea. The newest are numbered 1 and the oldest 4.   × 40. (From Brambell and Rowlands, 1936.)

lutea of ovulation, pseudo-pregnancy, pregnancy or gestation and lactation respectively. According to Long and Evans (1922), the corpora lutea of ovulation in the rat formed during the unmated dioestrous cycle of approximately 5 days' duration, attain a size of 1·0 to 1·2 mm. in diameter. Changes became apparent in the lipoid content of the luteal cells, the quantity of lipoid increasing and the droplets becoming larger and irregular in size, about the time of the onset of the oestrous period succeeding that at which the corpora lutea originated. These lipoid changes are interpreted as a sign of the onset of luteal regression, although no diminution in the size of the corpus luteum could be detected until after another cycle had been completed; that is, until after the second oestrus succeeding that at which they were formed. Even when they begin to shrink in size they remain as comparatively substantial structures for one or two more cycles and are identifiable for an even longer period.   There are thus several successive generations of corpora lutea normally present in the ovaries of a mature unmated animal (Fig. 5.33), of which the most recent set, in process of development, are identifiable, the two preceding sets are almost indistinguishable from each other, both exhibiting the lipoid changes but showing no decrease in size, and the still older sets recognisable by the successive stages of reduction in size displayed by them.   The corpora lutea formed after sterile copulation are indistinguishable at first from those of ovulation, but the characteristic lipoid changes are not apparent until the end of pseudo-pregnancy and the onset of the next oestrus at about 13 days. Moreover, they attain a slightly greater maximum size of from 1·2 to 1·4 mm. in diameter.   The rate of regression exhibited by them is similar to that of the corpora lutea of ovulation.   They do not show, therefore, any signs of regression until several days after implantation of the embryos would have occurred if pregnancy had supervened.   The corpora lutea of pregnancy do not exceed in size those of ovulation until after the tenth day of gestation, when they attain a maximum of from 1·75 to 1·9 mm. in diameter.   They show no signs of regression until the onset of the post-partum oestrus some 12 hours after parturition.   Prior to regression the corpora lutea of ovulation, pseudo-pregnancy and gestation resemble each other closely in the size, regular arrangement and quantity of lipoid spherules in the luteal cells.   The corpora lutea of lactation, formed at the post-partum oestrus in a suckling animal, differ, according to Long and Evans, in having much smaller lipoid globules in the luteal cells, by which they can be distinguished from 24 to 30 hours after their formation.   They persist unchanged throughout lactation, attaining a maximum size of 1·4 mm. in diameter between the 14th and 20th day, but show signs of regression within 24 hours of the cessation of suckling. Long and Evans also observed the remarkable effect of gestation in accelerating the rate of regression of the corpora lutea of generations previous to those of pregnancy ; by the 20th day only the corpora lutea of gestation could be distinguished in the ovaries.   The variations in size of the corpora lutea of the rat have been investigated also by Weichert and Schurgast (1942) and by Boling (1942).

The changes in the corpora lutea of the mouse are essentially similar to those of the rat.   Deanesly (1930a) found that the corpora lutea, other than those of pregnancy, do not differ greatly in size ; those of ovulation being only slightly smaller than those of pseudo-pregnancy and lactation.   Unlike those of the rat, the corpora lutea of lactation of the mouse resemble those of pseudo-pregnancy, except in that they accumulate fat more slowly.   During gestation the corpora lutea enter upon a second period of growth at about 8 days after ovulation, which results in their attaining a size of about 1·0 mm. in diameter when fully developed, compared to the diameter of 0·7 mm. attained by those of pseudo pregnancy. This second growth phase of the corpora lutea of pregnancy thus begins after the embryos have become implanted at the end of the fifth day.   The occurrence of two separate phases of growth in the corpora lutea of pregnancy in the bank vole (*Clethrionomys glareolus britannicus*, Miller) has been observed also (Brambell and Rowlands, 1936 ; Brambell, 1937).   In this species the corpora lutea grow rapidly from the time of ovulation until the tubal ova are in the 8-cell stage.   Thereafter there is no growth and there is even an indication of a slight decrease in size, until implantation occurs, when a second but less rapid growth phase begins and continues without interruption until parturition (Fig. 5. 34). The corpora lutea of pregnancy in the thirteen-lined ground squirrel (*Spermophilus citellus tridecem-lineatus*) according to Drips (1919) do not regress before parturition, thus resembling those of the rat, mouse and bank vole. The mean diameter attained by the corpora lutea of ovulation, pseudo-pregnancy and pregnancy is respectively 700 μ, 820–860 μ and 900–1000 μ in the golden hamster (Deanesly, 1938).

According to Hammond (1917), the corpus luteum in the rabbit attains a larger size during the second half of pregnancy than it does in pseudo-pregnancy, but

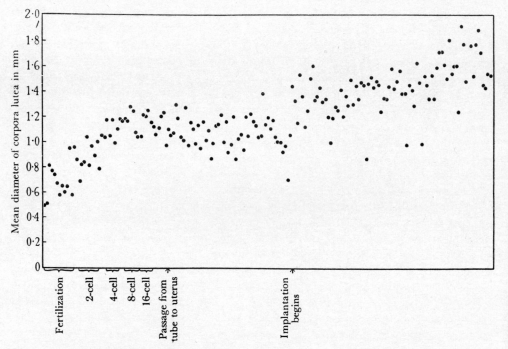

Fig. 5. 34—Graphical representation of the mean diameters of the corpora lutea of pregnancy present in the ovaries of each of 179 pregnant bank voles. The successive stages of pregnancy are arranged in order on the abscissa beginning with fertilisation at the origin and ending with approximately full-term on the right. It can be seen that there is an initial period of rapid growth ending, before the ova pass from the Fallopian tube into the uterus, and a second period of growth which begins when implantation occurs and continues until parturition. There is some evidence of a slight decrease in size between these two growth periods and there is reason to believe that implantation was delayed owing to lactation in many of the animals involved in this period. (From Brambell and Rowlands, 1936.)

Niskoubina (1909) claimed to have detected signs of regression histologically from mid-pregnancy onwards.

The corpus luteum of the non-pregnant sow is stated by Corner (1921) to attain its full size of 8 to 9 mm. in diameter at 7 days after ovulation. Regression, which can be detected both by changes in size and macroscopic appearance as well as histologically, begins at 15 days, although the next oestrus does not occur until 21 days. During gestation the corpus luteum grows until it reaches a diameter of 10–11 mm. after 2–3 weeks. It does not decrease in size until after parturition, but an accumulation of large irregular fat globules in the luteal cells can be detected 6–10 days before full term.   In the cow, according to Hammond (1927), who gives a full review of the earlier literature, the corpus luteum of ovulation attains its full size at or before the middle of the $19\frac{1}{2}$-day cycle.   It begins to diminish in size 3 days before the ensuing oestrus but the remains of the old corpus luteum, called a corpus rubrum on account of the colour imparted by the retained pigment, can be detected in the ovary for 3 or 4 cycles.   The corpus luteum of pregnancy is only slightly larger than that of ovulation ; it persists at its maximum size and its colour throughout gestation remains the same as that of the corpus luteum of ovulation at mid-cycle.

The cells of the membrana granulosa undergo enlargement before ovulation in the hedgehog (*Erinaceus europaeus*), as has been mentioned (p. 442).   Deanesly (1934) found that in the unmated animal they do not become luteinised nor do they undergo any further enlargement in the ruptured follicle, but on the contrary they become shrunken.   The corpus luteum of ovulation becomes normally vascularised but attains a size of only 0·7 to 1·0 mm. in diameter ; smaller than the unruptured follicle.   It decreases in size to about 0·5 mm. in diameter before the next ovulation, but persists at that size for a considerable time.   The corpora lutea of pregnancy and pseudo-pregnancy resemble each other both in size, 1·1 to 1·4 mm. in diameter, and histologically.   The cells of the membrana granulosa become luteinised, thus rendering them readily distinguishable from those of ovulation.   No shrinkage or other signs of regression were detectable either at parturition or at the end of the pseudo-pregnant cycle.

Ovulation only occurs after copulation, which it follows after an interval of 30 hours, in the ferret, and there is no post-partum oestrus so that the corpora lutea must be either of pseudo-pregnancy or pregnancy.   Moreover, in this species the duration of pseudo-pregnancy practically equals that of gestation.   It is consequently not surprising that Hammond and Marshall (1930) find no difference in size between the two kinds of corpora lutea.   Regression does not begin until about the time of parturition or at the end of pseudo-pregnancy, as the case may be.

The corpus luteum of pseudo-pregnancy undergoes development indistinguishable from that of pregnancy in the marsupial cat, *Dasyurus*, according to Sandes (1903).   He states that during pregnancy it attains its full development at the time when blastocysts 6·5 to 7 mm. in diameter are present in the uteri.   It remains in the same state for 7 to 8 weeks after parturition before retrogressing.   It was shown by Hill (1900) that the lips of the pouch young become free from the nipples, to which they were previously fused, at this time.   Such persistence, if it should be confirmed, on the part of the corpora lutea of gestation would be unique.   In the opossum, Hartman (1923) finds that the corpus luteum begins to degenerate before the end of the 12-day gestation period and that at parturition it " is already infiltrated with swarms of leucocytes and numerous connective-tissue cells."   Although Hartman's account differs in this respect from Sandes' (cf. *Dasyurus*), he agrees with the latter in describing the development and duration of the corpus luteum of pseudo-pregnancy as approximately equal to that of pregnancy (cf. Martínez-Esteve, 1942).

The corpus luteum of pregnancy in the common shrew (*Sorex araneus* Linnaeus) attains its maximum size of 500 μ in diameter at the time when the blastocysts pass from the Fallopian tube into the uterus (Brambell, 1935).   It remains at this size, without increasing perceptibly, throughout the greater part of pregnancy (Fig. 5.31), but it undergoes a rapid decline in size at the end and has shrunk to 200 µ in diameter by the time of parturition.   It disappears altogether early in lactation. A similar marked decrease in size before parturition of the corpora lutea of pregnancy occurs in the lesser shrew (*Sorex minutus* Linnaeus) (Brambell and Hall, 1937) and in the American shrew, *Blarina* (Pearson, 1944), in which they may have disappeared before parturition.   According to Deanesly and Parkes (1933) the corpus luteum of pregnancy in the grey squirrel (*Sciurus carolinensis*) begins to regress about half-way through pregnancy.   The corpora lutea of ovulation or pseudo-pregnancy in the stoat (*Mustela erminea*) undergo early regression and have disappeared by the time of the succeeding ovulation, while the corpora lutea of gestation begin to retrogress soon after mid-pregnancy (Deanesly, 1935). According to Mulon (1906) the corpora lutea of pregnancy in the guinea-pig become very fatty some time before parturition.   Goormaghtigh (1927) deduced on histological grounds a slowing down in functional activity of the corpus luteum in the dog half-way through gestation.

Among the Primates the corpus luteum of menstruation in the baboon begins to decrease in size shortly before menstruation and is very much reduced by the time of the next ovulation (Zuckerman and Parkes, 1932).   The corpus luteum, as well as the individual luteal cells, attains a greater size during pregnancy.   It appears to reach its maximum size early in gestation and to decline thereafter, disappearing rapidly after parturition.   The corpus luteum of the rhesus monkey has been very fully described and figured by Corner (1942, 1945).

The human corpus luteum of menstruation, according to Villemin (1908) develops for 8 to 10 days after ovulation, remains unchanged for 5 to 6 days and then begins to retrogress.   Miller (1914) also found that the beginning of menstruation coincided with the degeneration of the corpus luteum.   Watrin (1924, 1926) and Horrenberger (1928) both showed that the human corpus luteum of menstruation is histologically degenerate 10 to 12 days before the next ovulation is due.   Watrin notes also that it is inadequately vascularised, by comparison with the corpus luteum of pregnancy.   He found that the latter retrogresses before the end of gestation and is fibrous, shrunken and almost fat-free at term.   Ravano (1907) could find no essential difference between the human corpora lutea of pregnancy and of menstruation (that is, between the short-lived and persistent corpora lutea). Marcotty (1914) also found that the corpus luteum of pregnancy is essentially the same as that of menstruation, in the well-developed premenstrual state, and only equals it in size.

It will be observed that in many species, including the rat, mouse, bank vole, marmot, sow, cow, hedgehog, ferret, spotted hyaena (Matthews, 1939), fur seal (Enders, Pearson and Pearson, 1946 ; Pearson and Enders, 1951) and marsupial cat, the corpora lutea of pregnancy do not regress appreciably before parturition. Regression begins considerably before the end of gestation and the corpora lutea already exhibit marked shrinkage at parturition in a number of other species, including the shrews, grey squirrel, stoat, cat (Dawson, 1941 and 1946), horse, baboon and man.

The size of the corpus luteum is, of course, related to the size of the Graafian follicle from which it was formed, and hence to body-size.   The relation does not appear to be precise, since the fully developed corpora lutea of pregnancy may vary in different species from equality to slightly more than double the size of the mature follicles, as is shown by Table III, the date for which are derived from the papers cited in the text.

TABLE III

Species.	Diameter of follicle at ovulation.	Diameter of fully developed corpus luteum of pregnancy.
	mm.	mm.
Lesser Shrew	0·32	0·43
Common Shrew	0·35	0·43
Mouse	0·55	1·0
Bank Vole	0·82	1·6
Rat	0·90	1·9
Stoat	0·60 approx.	1·1
Grey Squirrel	1·01	1·1
Ferret	1·40	2·0
Hedgehog	1·25 approx.	1·3
Rabbit	1·8	2·2
Baboon	6·0	6·0
Pig	8·0	10·0
Cow	15·0	22·0

Interesting data regarding the size attained by the corpora lutea in whales are given by Matthews (1937b, 1938a, b and c), by Dempsey and Wislocki (1941), and by Harrison (1949a).

Regression

The histological phenomena of luteal regression have not received the same attention as have the developmental processes. Although they have been mentioned by the majority of authors who have dealt with the histology of the corpus luteum, detailed systematic accounts are not numerous. Such descriptions are available in the papers by Loeb (1910) on the guinea-pig, Corner (1921) on the pig and Long and Evans (1922) on the rat, among others. The information that is available points to the conclusion that the retrogressive processes are essentially similar, whether the corpora lutea are of ovulation, pseudo-pregnancy, pregnancy or lactation, in a variety of different species.

The first stage of retrogression is marked by fatty degeneration of the luteal cells. This is shown by the accumulation in the luteal cells of fat droplets of irregular size, which blacken with osmium tetroxide and are represented by conspicuous vacuoles in the cytoplasm after methods which do not preserve fats. This phase of fat accumulation is followed by one of reabsorption of the fat, accompanied by shrinkage and disappearance of the luteal cells. Numerous mitoses occur in the luteal cells in the retrogressing corpora lutea of the common shrew. Although the mitotic figures appear perfectly normal, this must be interpreted as a sign of retrogressive changes in the cells (Brambell, 1935). The disappearance of the luteal cells takes place gradually ; individual cells throughout the corpus luteum disappearing one by one, so that the number of luteal cells remaining is reduced continuously rather than that all vanish simultaneously. The removal of the debris of the disintegrating luteal cells is assisted by phagocytic invasion of the tissue. Polymorphonuclear leucocytes frequently are abundant in regressing corpora lutea. Long and Evans (1922) observed an abundance of macrophages in the regressing luteal tissues of the rat at the time when the lipoid content of the luteal cells is reduced notably. These macrophages were gorged with fatty substances, which, from their microchemical reactions, appeared to be fatty acids. According to Corner (1921) the " theca lutein cells " in the retrogressing corpus luteum of the pig persist and acquire " even denser stores of yellow-pigmented fat " long after the disappearance of the true luteal cells. The disappearance of the luteal cells is accompanied and followed by increase in the connective tissue and by reduction and ultimate atrophy of the vascular supply of the corpus luteum, apparently through collapse of the vessels. The increase in the connective tissue, doubtless, is more apparent than real, since the disappearance of the glandular elements and the resulting shrinkage of the tissues condenses the connective-tissue reticulum. Nevertheless, in later stages, and especially in the larger animals, there appears to be a real increase in the amount of connective tissue, which becomes collagenous and gives rise to the dense avascular corpus fibrosum. The corpus fibrosum gradually becomes merged with the surrounding tissues of the ovarian stroma but it may remain distinct for a very long time before finally disappearing. The pigment lutein appears to remain in the regressing corpus luteum after the luteal cells have disappeared. It is so concentrated in the corpus fibrosum of the cow as to give the deep red colour to which the name of corpus rubrum is due. In other species, such as the pig and man, it disappears ultimately ; the corpus fibrosum being characteristically white and known as a corpus albicans. The regression of the corpora lutea in the rhesus monkey has been studied by Corner (1942) by marking them, by means of laparotomy and tattooing. Two alternative methods of regression are described, one being the normal method and the other giving rise to relatively persistent and histologically distinctive corpora aberrantia. The cytological changes during regression of both these types are described by Rossman (1942).

IV. The Atretic Follicle

Follicular atresia is common and may be regarded as a process occurring regularly in the ovaries of vertebrates at all ages. However, atresia exhibits much variation not only in different species but also in follicles of different sizes. Several forms may be met with proceeding simultaneously in the same ovary. The regressing ovum may either be reabsorbed *in situ*, as in the atretic follicles of marsupial and placental mammals and the smaller follicles of other forms, or its contents may be discharged by rupture of the follicle, as in the larger follicles of monotremes, birds, reptiles, etc. Critical summaries of the literature are provided by Branca (1925) and by Garde (1930).

Atresia of Follicles in Vertebrates Other Than Mammals

Atresia of the follicles of fishes, amphibia, reptiles and birds has been described by Henneguy (1894), Bühler (1902, 1903), Pérez (1903), Dubuisson (1903, 1905a, b and c, 1906), Loyez (1906) and Pearl and Boring (1918).   All these authors agree that phagocytes play the principal part in the removal *in situ* of the degenerating oöcyte, but whereas Henneguy, Bühler, Pérez, Dubuisson and Loyez regard these phagocytes as derived from the follicular epithelium, Pearl and Boring describe them in the fowl as originating entirely from the theca interna.   Henneguy found marked proliferation of the epithelium in an atretic follicle of a bird, many of the cells containing yolk globules.   Henneguy, Bühler and Dubuisson noted that the phagocytes of epithelial origin were accompanied or followed by leucocytes.   Fusion of the yolk-spheres occurs characteristically in atretic oöcytes of amphibia.   Phagocytosis of the oöcyte is accompanied by ingrowth of the theca, and thecal blood-vessels, which finally obliterates the cavity of the follicle and gives rise to a fibrous nodule.   The crumpled zona pellucida is often a conspicuous feature of atretic follicles.   Sometimes atresia is accompanied by extravasation of blood in the follicular wall and into the cavity occupied by the disintegrating oöcyte, where the blood mingles with the yolk.   Matthews (1950) states that in the basking shark atretic follicles give rise to corpora lutea atretica.

The oöcyte, if large, may not be reabsorbed *in situ* but may be dispersed by rupture of the follicular wall.   Such atretic follicles have been observed by Dubuisson (1905a, 1906) in the fowl and the sparrow where rupture had taken place internally and the follicular contents had escaped into the neighbouring lacunae, presumably lymph spaces, in the ovary.   Phagocytes of epithelial origin together with remnants of the yolk were present in the follicular cavity and in the lacunae.   Atresia by follicular rupture in several other species of birds has been described by Davis (1942b).   Similar ruptured atretic follicles in the ovaries of viviparous lizards have been mentioned by Garde (1930).

Atresia of Follicles of Monotremes

Atresia in monotremes has been described by Hill and Gatenby (1926) and by Garde (1930).   The former authors state that " in small atretic follicles the degenerate contents are apparently reabsorbed *in situ*, but in the larger they would usually appear to be discharged directly through a break in the follicular wall, into an underlying lymph-sinus."   Owing to the discharge of the follicular contents, the medullary lymph sinuses of the ovary become engorged with yolk-spheres.   The membrana propria remains intact but shrinks away from the theca, the follicular epithelium appears to degenerate and the crumpled zona pellucida remains in the follicular cavity.   The theca undergoes marked hypertrophy and becomes very thick.   Ultimately the atretic follicle forms a spherical fibrous nodule in the cortical stroma of the ovary.   Garde (1930) observed atresia in follicles containing oöcytes o·3 mm. in diameter and upwards.   None of the follicles in the right non-functional ovary of *Ornithorhynchus* attained a size exceeding 1·3 mm. in diameter, and therefore all those that enter on the growth phase must undergo atresia.   Even in large follicles the oöcyte may be reabsorbed *in situ*.   When this occurs the cells of the follicular epithelium proliferate and migrate, giving rise to phagocytes which ingest the remains of the oöcyte. Otherwise atretic follicles may rupture either internally or externally. Internal rupture results in the discharge of the follicular contents into the medullary sinuses, as described by Hill and Gatenby. Phagocytes of epithelial origin dispose of the residue of the oöcyte remaining in the follicle, and of the zona pellucida, but phagocytes arising from the cells lining the sinuses take part in the removal of the yolk that has been discharged. External rupture leads to the dispersal of most of the follicular contents in the peritoneal cavity. The debris remaining in the follicle is disposed of by the phagocytes. Haemorrhage of the capillaries in the theca is not infrequent in all these forms of atresia.

Atresia of Follicles in Marsupial and Placental Mammals

Follicular atresia occurs so commonly in the ovaries of marsupials and placentals that it may be regarded as normal. Branca (1925) says " En un mot, l'atrésie, phénomène anormal, est la règle ; la ponte, processus physiologique, est l'exception." Although atretic follicles may be found as a rule in the ovaries at any time, both before puberty and during adult life, atresia occurs more commonly at certain periods than at others. One such wave of atresia overtakes all the follicles that have precociously entered upon the growth phase after birth, as was observed in the cat by de Winiwarter and Sainmont (1909). This period of extensive atresia occurs in the mouse about the time of weaning (Kingery, 1917 ; Brambell, 1927a). Many atretic follicles are present in the ovaries of new-born calves (Vatti, 1931). The incidence of atresia is greater at certain periods also in the ovaries of adult animals (Harman and Kirgis, 1938). The onset of anoestrus, in mammals with a restricted breeding season, is marked by atresia of the larger follicles in the ovaries. Similarly, follicular atresia increases as a rule during pregnancy and, more especially, during lactation anoestrus. Atresia of the larger follicles, resulting in the formation of corpora lutea atretica or false corpora lutea, is of common occurrence in many animals during mid-gestation. All the follicles which mature at oestrus in an unmated rabbit or ferret undergo atresia, since ovulation only occurs after copulation. Hill and White (1933) have shown, and it has been confirmed by Smelser, Walton and Whetham (1934), that in the un-mated rabbit several successive sets of follicles mature and become atretic during the period of continuous oestrus ; evidently the follicles, once mature, must either proceed to ovulate within 7 to 10 days or else become atretic. Although references to the incidence of atresia at these periods are frequent in the literature, very few investigators have attempted to obtain more precise information in the form of numerical estimates of the numbers of follicles affected. Arai (1920a) estimated the numbers of normal and atretic follicles in the ovaries of rats at different ages and similar data for the dog are provided by Schotterer (1928) (see p. 424). Asami (1920), from estimates based on one of each pair of ovaries of 3 immature and 26 adult rabbits killed at varying periods after copulation, found no noticeable difference in the proportion of normal and atretic follicles. Small, medium and large follicles undergo atresia at all stages of the oestrous cycle. Allen, Kountz and Francis (1925) showed that a rigorous process of selective elimination of the larger follicles takes place in adult swine. There are on an average 45 follicles, sufficiently large to be visible but under 3 mm. in diameter, in the ovaries 10 to 14 days before ovulation, of which 85 per cent are subsequently eliminated.   In the mouse, Engle (1927b) found variation in the number of atretic follicles corresponding with the oestrous cycle.   The maximum number corresponded with the first day and the minimum with the second day of dioestrus. During the first four days of pregnancy the number is lower but more constant. There were indications that this decrease in atresia was not characteristic of the whole of gestation but that an increase occurred later.

Degenerative changes may begin either in the oöcyte or in the follicle of the rabbit, according to Heape (1905).   Oöcytes which have entered upon, but not completed, the growth phase with the onset of atresia frequently grow prematurely to their full size.   The cytological changes in the oöcyte during atresia are complex, especially as regards the nuclear phenomena.   Atresia in immature follicles in the mouse is often accompanied by the appearance of a curious crystalloidal body in the cytoplasm which has been described by Mertens (1895), Chappellier (1909), Brambell (1927a) and Engle (1927b).   A similar body has been described in the oöcytes of *Macacus rhesus* by Pollak (1926), and in those of the opossum by Martínez-Esteve (1942).   The oöcyte in atretic follicles often exhibits mitotic divisions which simulate the maturation and cleavage divisions of the normal ovum.   The resemblance of these cleavages, occurring in the unfertilised oöcyte either in the atretic follicle or in the Fallopian tube, to those in the normal fertilised ovum have led to their being called " parthenogenetic."   The literature on the subject has been reviewed by Athias (1929).   Branca (1925) has given a detailed description of the changes in the degenerating oöcytes of the mouse and of the guinea-pig.   Sometimes degeneration is precocious and attacks the oöcyte during the growth phase.   The oöcyte may degenerate then without undergoing any divisions.   When mitosis occurs, the initial division, judged by its morphological characters, may correspond either to the first or second maturation division or to the first cleavage.   First maturation divisions, more or less aberrant, are frequent.   Second polar spindles may be formed, but Branca never observed a single instance of the completion of the second maturation division.   Sometimes the nucleus multiplies without any preliminary maturation or with an incomplete maturation, giving rise to a multi-nucleate mass.   Again, a more or less prolonged period of successive cell divisions may give rise to stages resembling the normal early ontogenetic stages.   Such parthenogenetic cleavages may give rise to morulae and, exceptionally, to blastulae.   Once a cellular mass consisting of a syncytium with large nuclei and a series of layers of cells was observed, which acted like the rudiment of an ovarian placenta.   The " placenta " in developing corroded the walls of the follicular vessels, causing haemorrhage (c.f. Loeb, 1930, 1932).   Sooner or later such atretic oöcytes stop developing and their degenerative tendencies become apparent ;   the parthenogenesis, beginning as segmentation, finishes as fragmentation.   Nuclear degeneration, by pycnosis, chromatolysis, etc., always precedes that of the cytoplasm.   Branca, in a single instance, also observed an example which he interpreted as fertilisation of an ovarian oöcyte.   The oöcyte was contained in a follicle approximately 225 μ in diameter in the ovary of a mouse eight days pregnant.   It was separated by tissue 150 μ in thickness from the ovarian surface.   The spermatozoon in the cytoplasm of the oöcyte seemed to be atypical, possessing two tails.   The first maturation spindle had not yet formed in the oöcyte.   Oöcytes activated in this way may account for ovarian pregnancies.

Maturation and cleavages in the ovarian oöcytes of the guinea-pig have been described by Harman (1935) and by Dempsey (1939b) also, and in the human ovary by Krafka (1939). Recently, degenerative changes in the ovarian oöcytes of the dog have been investigated by Kampmeier (1929) and in the immature ferret by Chang (1950).

Degeneration of the oöcyte always results in immediate atresia of the follicle, except in very small follicles in which the oöcyte may be reabsorbed *in situ* and an anovular follicle may be produced (see p. 454–5). The degenerating oöcyte and its zona pellucida may be invaded by cells which appear to be phagocytic and to participate in its removal. These phagocytes are regarded as modified epithelial cells by some authors, including Henneguy (1894), O. van der Stricht (1901c), Velloso de Pinho (1925) and Branca (1925). Stockard and Papanicolaou (1917) were of opinion that the chief invading cells were leucocytes, while Sandes (1903) and Newman (1913) considered that connective-tissue cells as well as leucocytes were involved. Asami (1920) stated that cells of the membrana granulosa may migrate even into the normal oöcyte, there becoming necrotic and disappearing, leaving behind faintly staining granules in the cytoplasm.

The degenerative changes in atretic follicles in various mammals have been investigated by many authors, including Schulin (1881), Flemming (1885b), Schottlaender (1891, 1893), Henneguy (1894), Janosik (1897), Kölliker (1898), Bouin (1899), O. van der Stricht (1901c), Sandes (1903), Marshall (1904), Heape (1905), Loeb (1905), Seitz (1905a and b, 1906), Ganfini (1907), Cohn (1909), Delestre (1910), Benthin (1911), Asami (1920), Salazar (1922a, b and c), de Winiwarter (1923), Velloso de Pinho (1923), Branca (1925), Hammond (1925), Brambell (1927a), Brambell, Parkes and Fielding (1927a and b), Garde (1930), Frommolt (1934), Deanesly (1934, 1935), Mossman (1937) and Matthews (1939). The form of atresia depends primarily on the stage of development which the follicle has attained when degeneration begins.

Small follicles frequently undergo direct degeneration, such as has been described in the mouse (Brambell, 1927a ; Brambell, Parkes and Fielding, 1927a and b). The degeneration and absorption of the oöcyte results in a cavity being formed in the follicle around the puckered and shrunken zona pellucida, the most persistent part of the oöcyte. The nuclei of the cells of the membrana granulosa became pycnotic, the cytoplasm vacuolated and the individual elements detached from the follicular wall and scattered in the cavity, where they degenerate completely. The zona pellucida persists for a time in the cavity, bounded by the theca, but finally it disappears. Schottlaender (1891, 1893) states that atresia can occur by fatty degeneration, as well as by chromatolysis, of the follicular cells. O. van der Stricht (1901c) also noted that atrophy and chromatolysis of the epithelial cells sometimes is accompanied by fatty degeneration.

Rupture of the blood-vessels of the theca and extravasation of blood into the antrum, forming a blood-follicle, frequently occurs in mature follicles, as was shown by Heape (1905). It is only follicles that were mature when atresia set in which give rise to such blood-follicles ; in others atresia is unaccompanied by any extravasation of blood. Individual mature follicles which, for some reason unknown, have failed to ovulate at oestrus give rise to blood-follicles in many species. Most of the maturing follicles which do not ovulate in an oestrous rabbit that is prevented from copulating, ultimately degenerate, sometimes forming blood-follicles (Heape, 1905 ; Hammond, 1925 ; Hill and White, 1933). Engorgement of the blood-vessels in the theca precedes their rupture. The membrana granulosa becomes detached from the theca interna and its degenerating remains, together with those of the oöcyte and the corona radiata, are mixed with the liquor folliculi and blood in the follicular cavity. The newly formed blood-follicles subsequently are suffused with a brilliant red colour. The cellular debris in the cavity disappears and the colour becomes brown and finally black in later stages. Such follicles persist for a long time but are, according to Hammond (1925), gradually absorbed in the same way as a blood blister in the skin. Brown and black pigment granules, probably derived from the blood pigment, are found in the connective-tissue cells of the theca of old blood-follicles. As the contents is reabsorbed the cavity is filled in gradually by the surrounding stroma.

Follicular degeneration may result also in the formation of cysts. The cavity in these, after the disappearance of the oöcyte and membrana granulosa, is filled with watery fluid and is lined by a single-layered squamous or cubical epithelium. Such cysts, which have been observed by Sandes (1903), Clark (1923) and Lipschütz and Voss (1925), may be very persistent and may attain a size greater than that of the normal follicle at the time of ovulation. Van der Horst and Gillman (1945) state that a great number of follicles undergo cystic degeneration during pregnancy in *Elephantulus*. During early pregnancy numerous small cystic follicles are formed. During mid-pregnancy their formation is suppressed and large cystic follicles are formed instead. During late pregnancy these disappear and small ones are again formed.

The atresia of medium and large Graafian follicles is accompanied frequently by ingrowth and hypertrophy of the cells of the follicular wall, leading to the formation in the follicular cavity of a nodule of tissue which closely resembles a normal corpus luteum in appearance but which is somewhat smaller in size. These nodules, on account of their histological characters, are called corpora lutea atretica, to distinguish them from true corpora lutea formed in ruptured follicles. They have been called also false corpora lutea, but this term, since it has been applied to the corpora lutea of menstruation in contradistinction to those of pregnancy, is ambiguous. The majority of authors are agreed that corpora lutea atretica result from the hypertrophy and hyperplasia of the cells of the theca interna after the degeneration of the membrana granulosa, and that the elements in them which resemble true luteal cells are thus of thecal, not epithelial, origin. Kölliker (1898) and Seitz (1906) observed the hypertrophy of the cells of the theca interna to form what the latter author called " theca lutein cells " in the corpus luteum atreticum. Seitz found that these luteal-like cells were formed only during pregnancy. Loeb (1917) described the enlargement of the theca interna cells of atretic follicles of the rabbit to form elements which were epithelioid and glandular in appearance. Bouin (1902) and Limon (1902), on account of the similarity in appearance and identity of origin of the cells of the theca interna of the Graafian follicle, of corpora lutea atretica and of the interstitial tissue, originated the idea of including all these tissues under the general term " glande interstitielle." Generally, disappearance of the oöcyte, swelling of the zona pellucida and degeneration of the follicular epithelium precedes the growth of the theca interna. Then the cells of the theca interna multiply and hypertrophy to give rise to the luteal-like cells. According to O. van der Stricht (1901c), atretic

follicles can give rise to corpora lutea atretica in the bats.   After the disappearance
of the oöcyte a central nodule of young connective-tissue cells, containing scattered
leucocytes and white globules, is found in the follicle.   Around this core is a thick
compact cortex of " interstitial cells," stuffed with fat ; these cells closely resemble
the luteal cells of the true corpus luteum.   Follicular atresia of this type is stated
by Deanesly (1935) to be very common in the stoat ; the theca interna cells enlarging
and multiplying and the membrana granulosa cells degenerating.   The theca
interna cells assume the appear-
ance of luteal cells and form a
nodule of tissue enclosing the
degenerating ovum.

The zona pellucida persists
for a long time in such atretic
follicles, and its crumpled remains
in the centre of the corpus luteum
atreticum is distinctive (Fig.
5. 36).   It should be mentioned,
however, that the presence of a
degenerate ovum cannot, by itself,
be regarded as an absolute indication of follicular atresia since a
number of examples are recorded
in the literature of its presence
in the centre of a true corpus
luteum, owing to the retention of
the oöcyte in the ruptured follicle.
Instances of this in the mouse
and the rabbit are recorded by
Sobotta (1896, 1897) and in
Vesperugo by O. van der Stricht
(1901d).

Fig. 5. 35—Photomicrograph of part of the wall of a
large Graafian follicle of the water shrew during
pregnancy.   Although the follicle is atretic the
membrana granulosa (MG) is distinct and is clearly
delimited by the membrana propria (MP) which is
intact.   The cells of the theca interna (TI) have
enlarged and closely resemble the luteal cells (LT)
which form most of the cortex.   The cells of the
membrana granulosa have not become lutealised
like those of the theca interna.   TE = theca externa.
× 600.

The formation of corpora
lutea atretica from the theca
interna of atretic follicles in the
ovaries of ferrets and of rats, that
had received pituitary injections,
have been described by Hill and
Parkes (1930) and by Engle and
Smith (1929) respectively.

The membrana granulosa does not degenerate always before the hypertrophy
of the theca interna and the transformation of its elements into luteal-like cells
occurs.   Many atretic follicles are found during pregnancy in the ovaries of the
water shrew, *Neomys fodiens*.   The membrana granulosa, in the earlier stages of
atresia of these follicles, shows little sign of degeneration and its cells resemble
those of the normal follicle, having undergone no enlargement.   The membrana
propria is intact, sharply defining the limits of the theca and membrana granulosa.
Yet the cells of the theca interna have hypertrophied and closely resemble the true
luteal cells in appearance (Fig. 5. 35).   The theca interna thus forms a broad halo

of luteal-like tissue surrounding the unaltered membrana granulosa and separated from it by the membrana propria. Here the origin of these luteal-like cells from the theca interna is unequivocal. Their resemblance to the true luteal cells of the corpora lutea of pregnancy, present in the same ovary, in material fixed in Bouin's fluid and stained with haematoxylin and eosin, is so close that when both were examined in the same field of the microscope no characteristic differences could be distinguished.

Several interesting forms of aberrant corpora lutea in the rhesus monkey, the majority formed from unruptured follicles, have been described by Corner,

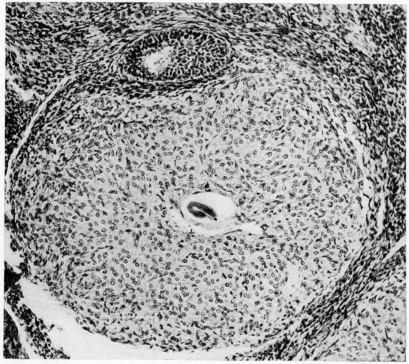

Fig. 5. 36—Photomicrograph of a small corpus luteum atreticum in the ovary of a baboon during early pregnancy. The crumpled remains of the zona pellucida of the oöcyte is conspicuous in the central cavity. × 150. (From Zuckerman and Parkes, 1932.)

Bartelmez and Hartman (1936). One of these types is composed chiefly of clear lipoid-filled cells, the disposition and structure of which indicated their origin from the theca interna. A distinct zone of darker cells, presenting all the characteristics of true luteal cells derived from the membrana granulosa, formed a wavy wreath at a short distance within the periphery. It was concluded that these corpora lutea represented a form of follicular atresia in which proliferation of the theca interna had occurred and had resulted in the thecal cells breaking through the membrana granulosa into the antrum and filling up that space. Luteinisation of the theca interna in atretic follicles in the ovaries of a number of primates has been described by Säglik (1938). Zuckerman and Parkes (1932) recorded the formation from small follicles in the ovaries of baboons during early pregnancy of large numbers of corpora lutea atretica. These corpora lutea atretica measured only 200–500 μ in diameter, as compared to 5·4–6·7 mm. in diameter for the corresponding corpora lutea of pregnancy. Each contained the remains of an oöcyte and most of the cells were smaller and possessed relatively less cytoplasm than true luteal cells (Fig. 5. 36). Some had a central core of cells indistinguishable from true luteal cells.

Although the majority of authors regard the corpora lutea atretica as originating exclusively from thecal hyperplasia, some maintain that elements of the membrana granulosa may persist and contribute to it (Pederson, 1951). Thus Sandes (1903) describes the hypertrophy of the membrana granulosa cells and the ingrowth of fibrous tissue among them, as in true corpora lutea, during atresia of the more mature follicles of *Dasyurus viverrinus*. Branca (1925) describes the formation in the mouse and the guinea-pig of atretic bodies from the epithelial cells of the membrana granulosa, among which capillaries penetrate early. Some of the epithelial cells become glandular but others transform into fibroblasts. The fibroblasts, so formed, extend, bundles of collagen fibres appear, and the whole structure is transformed into a nodule of connective tissue. Velloso de Pinho (1925) states that in *Eliomys quercinus* L. metaplasia of the membrana granulosa results in the formation of atretic bodies which join up with neighbouring ones to form larger nodules. Deanesly (1934) described the formation of similar bodies in the ovaries of parous hedgehogs. These arise through the coalescence of several small follicles in which the oöcytes have degenerated. The epithelial cells increase slightly in size, but are never as large as those of the ripe follicle or of the mature corpus luteum. Small vascular ingrowths arise from the theca but there is no active ingrowth such as that which occurs in the ruptured follicle. The fully formed epithelial mass is irregular in shape and contains vacuoles filled with fluid resembling liquor folliculi. Only one or, more rarely, two of these masses are present in the ovary, often situated near the hilus. Hall (1952) finds that accessory corpora lutea, formed from atretic follicles, are present in 64 per cent of wild Norway rats which have true corpora lutea in their ovaries. The atretic corpora lutea resembled the true corpora lutea histologically.

The formation of corpora lutea atretica, as mentioned above (Seitz, 1906 ; Brambell, in text ; Zuckerman and Parkes, 1932) is associated often with pregnancy. The formation of small corpora lutea atretica in the baboon is, according to the last-mentioned authors, peculiar to the early stages of pregnancy. The formation of corpora lutea atretica during pregnancy has been recorded also in a variety of other animals including the bank vole (Brambell and Rowlands, 1936), the mare (Cole, Howell and Hart, 1931), and the African elephant (Perry, 1953). In both the mare (Amoroso, Hancock and Rowlands, 1948) and the elephant ovulation occurs during pregnancy and corpora lutea are formed both from ruptured and from unruptured follicles. In the mare the original corpus luteum retrogresses early in pregnancy and is replaced during the second and third months by a number of accessory corpora lutea, formed from ruptured and unruptured follicles, which persist until mid-pregnancy. Thereafter, during the second half of pregnancy, there are no functional corpora lutea in the ovaries. In the elephant the original corpora lutea, formed about the time of conception, persist until mid-pregnancy, when they are replaced by a number, formed from both ruptured and unruptured follicles, which persist until term. Hence, functional corpora lutea are present in the ovaries throughout gestation.

In the ovaries of the Canadian porcupine (Mossman and Judas, 1949) many accessory corpora lutea are formed from atretic follicles at oestrus, but whereas those in the ovary containing the single true corpus luteum persist throughout pregnancy, those in the other ovary disappear early in pregnancy. A somewhat similar condition is found in the mountain viscacha (Pearson, 1949) in which, although both ovaries are potentially functional, it is the right ovary which ovulates the single follicle almost invariably. Accessory corpora lutea are formed during pregnancy in the right ovary only, which contains the true corpus luteum.

V. INTERSTITIAL TISSUE

Interstitial Cells of the Ovaries of Birds

The thecal walls of the ovarian follicles and the stroma of the ovaries of adult birds contain conspicuous cells, scattered singly or in small islets, which have a very clear cytoplasm, showing in sharp contrast to the surrounding tissue in preparations in which fats are not preserved. These clear islet cells, which are generally considered to correspond to the interstitial cells of mammalian ovaries, have been observed frequently. Their cytological characters in the ovary of the fowl have been described by Fell (1924). The nucleus, which is rather small for the size of the cell, is usually spherical or slightly crenated and often stains densely. The cytoplasm is honeycombed with spherical vacuoles, which, when the fats are not preserved, give it the characteristically clear appearance. These vacuoles are seen to be loaded with fat in osmicated material. The cytoplasm is crowded with rod-like and granular mitochondria. The small Golgi apparatus consists of three or more granules surrounding the juxta-nuclear archoplasm. Neither Nonidez (1922) nor Fell (1924) were able to find any evidence of mitoses in these cells.

Boring and Pearl (1917) regarded these as true, secretory interstitial cells strictly homologous, and indeed cytologically identical, with those of the cow. These authors (Pearl and Boring, 1918) described the multiplication and migration of these cells into the central cavities in discharged and atretic follicles, there to give rise to the luteal tissue. Therefore, they gave them the name of " luteal " cells, which term has been used by others subsequently. The name " luteal " cells is unfortunate since it assumes the identity of these cells with those occupying regressing ruptured follicles. Goodale (1919) claimed to find cells similar in size, shape and staining reactions in the thymus, blood and other organs. He concluded, therefore, that the " interstitial " or clear islet cells of the bird ovary are probably eosinophil leucocytes.

Firket (1914) described the origin of the clear islet cells in the embryo from the cells of the medullary cords, and his description has been confirmed by both Nonidez (1922) and by Fell (1924). According to Firket (1914) they arise in the adult from the connective-tissue elements of the stroma and not, as in the embryo, from epithelial elements. Both Nonidez (1922) and Fell (1924) recognise the formation of islet cells in the adult ovary but maintain that they arise from epithelial elements, derived originally from the medullary cords, which have become included in the thecae of follicles and in the stroma. The formation of these cells proceeds much more actively in the thecae of atretic follicles than in normal ones, according to Fell. Benoit (1926) also concludes that they arise exclusively from epithelial elements. There seems little room for doubt, in view of these researches, that the clear islet cells in the ovary of the bird do arise, at least in the embryo, from epithelial elements. This raises the problem of their homology or otherwise with the interstitial cells of the mammalian ovary. It will be shown (p. 510) that the evidence, though conflicting, favours the connective tissue rather than the epithelial origin of the latter. It would appear, therefore, to be premature to consider the homology of the islet cells of the bird with the interstitial cells of the mammal as definitely established, as has been assumed. We therefore prefer the retention of the purely descriptive term " clear islet cells " for these elements in the avian ovary rather than the application of the term " interstitial cells " to them.

It is interesting to note that, in a case of sex-reversal in a female pigeon, the origin of the new sex-cords and their transformation into spermatic tubules could be traced with exceptional clearness, and that these arose from the clear islet cells of the ovarian tissues (Brambell and Marrian, 1929) (see p. 427).

Interstitial Cells of the Mammals

Schrön (1862) and Pflüger (1863) appear to have been the first to draw attention to the interstitial cells of the mammalian ovary. However, Tourneux (1879) was the first to point out their similarity to the interstitial cells of the testis and to give them in consequence the name of ovarian interstitial cells.

The interstitial cells of the mammalian ovary are large polyhedral or globular elements which possess the cytological characters of glandular elements. The cytoplasm contains lipoidal droplets, first noted by Bouin (1899), which blacken with osmic acid and are represented by numerous small vacuoles in preparations which do not preserve lipoids. These inclusions have been regarded by Athias (1920) as secretory products. According to Cesa-Bianchi (1907) these lipoidal substances can be demonstrated outside the cells, and O. van der Stricht (1912) described the expulsion of fatty products accumulated in the peripheral cytoplasm of the cells, followed by accumulation of these products in the intercellular spaces. Athias (1920), on the contrary, failed to find any substances showing lipoidal reactions in the intercellular spaces or lymphatics adjoining the interstitial cells and concluded that lipoidal substances undergo chemical changes before they are secreted. Jonckheere (1930) also failed to find the lipoids outside the cells and arrived at the same conclusions as Athias. Mitochondria are abundant in the interstitial cells. Their structure and behaviour in these cells in the ovaries of bats have been described in detail by Athias (1920), who reviewed the earlier literature. The mitochondria are in the form of rods (chondriocontes) and granules. The rod-like forms multiply and give rise to the granules. The latter appear to become transformed into droplets of fat and to decrease in number as these increase. The centrosome or attraction sphere of the interstitial cells in the rabbit was observed first by Child (1897). Since then, Limon (1902), Aimé (1906), Regaud and Dubreuil (1906) and Athias (1920) have demonstrated it in the cells of bats, the horse, guinea-pig, etc. The Golgi apparatus has been described in the interstitial cells of the rabbit and the bat by Rio Hortega (1913) and by Cattaneo (1914). The nuclei of these cells, like those of many other glandular elements, are polychromatic. Some of the cells have densely stained nuclei while others are almost transparent, taking the stain very weakly. The polychromatism, first noted by Regaud and Policard (1901) with the rabbit and guinea-pig, is largely independent of the methods of fixation and staining employed and is very clearly shown. The variation in chromaphility is due, according to Regaud and Dubreuil (1906), to the presence or absence of a strongly stainable diffuse substance in the nuclear sap. Athias (1920) observed and figured this condition in the interstitial cells of bats. Regaud and Dubreuil (1906) claimed to have observed frequent amitosis in the interstitial cells of the rabbit and Athias (1920) described numerous mitoses in those of bats, but Jonckheere (1930) failed to find any evidence of either direct or indirect division of the interstitial cells of the dog's ovary.

Opinions differ as to the changes undergone by the interstitial cells and as to whether they degenerate at the end of a secretory cycle. Limon (1902) regarded them as persisting indefinitely without undergoing any marked change. O'Donoghue (1916) concluded that in the marsupials the interstitial tissue, after its formation at an early stage of development, persists indefinitely without degenerating and only undergoes slight hypertrophy during the periods of ovarian activity. Other authors believe that the cells undergo a definite cycle of changes leading to degeneration. Sainmont (1906) distinguished young, transitional, mature, degenerate and hypertrophied stages. The hypertrophied cells, characterised by large fat spherules, he believed, could transform again into connective-tissue cells after resorption of the fat and decrease in size. Regaud and Dubreuil (1906) distinguished young, mature, ageing and decrepit stages in the interstitial cells of the rabbit. The latter degenerate and are replaced by newly formed elements. Aimé (1906) distinguished in the ovaries of the foetal horse xanthochrome cells containing yellow pigment which, he believed, were stages in the fatty degeneration of the interstitial cells. De Winiwarter (1908) described young, transitional and mature stages of the human interstitial cells. Athias (1920) found no evidence that the interstitial cells in bats ever dedifferentiate into connective-tissue cells, but believed that degeneration was common. Jonckheere (1930) suggested that the interstitial cells of the dog's ovary pass through a regular cycle which is repeated. After differentiating from the connective-tissue cells, the interstitial cells increase in size and become laden with lipoidal inclusions. They dedifferentiate again into connective-tissue cells when the secretion has been discharged. It follows that the secretion is not holocrine and does not involve degeneration of the cells. Dedifferentiation of the interstitial cells in the human ovary has been described also by Tropea (1929) and in the opossum ovary by Martínez Esteve (1942).

Specific Variation in Interstitial Tissue

The degree of development of the interstitial tissue in the ovaries of different species of mammals varies widely. It is, for example, particularly well developed and forms a conspicuous component of the ovaries in the rabbit, ferret, stoat, mole and the bats. It is poorly developed and its presence even has been denied in other animals, such as the cow, mare and woman. Many authors, including de Winiwarter (1908), believe that interstitial tissue is invariably present in the ovaries of mammals, although recognising its variability in different species; a view which recent investigations have tended to confirm. Nevertheless, several authors have attempted to divide the mammals into two groups according to whether this tissue was present or absent. Fraenkel (1905), Aimé (1907) and Schaeffer (1911) examined the ovaries of a large number of species and concluded that even in those belonging to the same genus there was frequently much variability, interstitial tissue being present in the ovary of one and absent from the ovary of another.   These three authors all considered interstitial tissue to be absent from the human ovary, yet its presence has been demonstrated clearly by Pinto (1905), Seitz (1906), Cesa-Bianchi (1907), Wallart (1907, 1908), de Winiwarter (1908) and Cohn (1909).   Careful investigation has revealed its presence in the

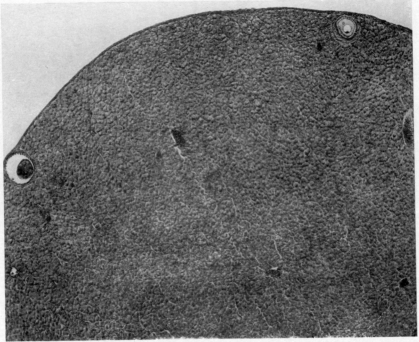

Fig. 5. 37—Photomicrograph of part of the ovary of the water shrew during late pregnancy.   The ovary is composed of a continuous mass of " luteal " tissue in which the outlines of individual corpora lutea cannot be distinguished.   Only small follicles are present in the peripheral regions.   Apparently atresia of all the larger follicles and lutealisation of the interstitial tissue has occurred.   × 92.

ovaries of other species also in which it was alleged to be absent. O'Donoghue (1916) found that the amount of interstitial tissue present in the ovaries of different species of marsupials was just as variable as in placentals. He found that it was present in varying degrees in the ovaries of ten species of Diprotodontia, but he could not find it in the six species of Polyprotodontia examined. The period of development at which the interstitial tissue differentiates in the ovaries also varies widely in different species of mammals.

Changes Correlated with Reproduction in the Interstitial Tissue

The interstitial tissue in the ovaries of adult animals undergoes changes, both in quantity and character, associated with the other reproductive processes. Increase in number and hypertrophy of the individual cells during the latter part of pregnancy has been described frequently. The increase is associated with the increased follicular atresia which commonly occurs during the second half of gestation. Increased development of the interstitial tissue in the human ovary during pregnancy was noted by Wallart (1907) and has been confirmed by other authors. According to Seitz (1906) all the larger follicles in the human ovaries undergo atresia during pregnancy with a consequent considerable increase, which becomes intensified as gestation proceeds, in the number of interstitial cells. These cells increase in size, become laden with fat and lutein and assume the appearance of the luteal cells. Similar changes take place in the interstitial cells of the rabbit's ovary during gestation. Goodall (1920) noted that in a rabbit just after parturition " Every interstitial cell seems to be converted into cells resembling, in every particular but one, the true luteal cells of the corpora lutea. That one and only distinction consists in a slightly smaller size of the extra corpus cells." The interstitial tissue in the ovaries of bats attains its maximum development during pregnancy and lactation, as has been observed by Cesa-Bianchi (1907) and by Athias (1920). The most remarkable instance of these changes in the interstitial tissue during pregnancy known to the author is provided by the water shrew, *Neomys fodiens*. The interstitial tissue in this species becomes greatly hypertrophied during pregnancy and the individual cells become virtually indistin-

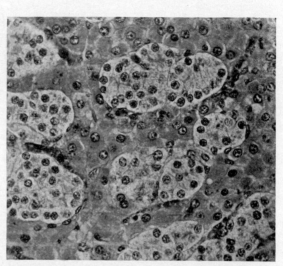

Fig. 5. 38—Photomicrograph of the medullary region of the ovary of a parous mole during winter anoestrus. The greater part of the ovary is composed of the cords of epithelial cells, surrounded by hypertrophied interstitial cells, that are shown. Only small follicles are present in the periphery of the ovary. × 540. (Parkes' material.)

guishable from the luteal cells in the accompanying corpora lutea of pregnancy, both in size and characteristic staining affinities, and from the theca interna cells of atretic follicles. All the larger follicles simultaneously undergo atresia (see p. 502–3). These changes result in marked hypertrophy of the whole ovary, which becomes globular and smooth in contour, presenting a macroscopic appearance in marked contrast to that of the non-pregnant animal. In sections the whole ovary appears at first sight to consist of a single mass of luteal tissue containing small normal follicles in the peripheral regions (Fig. 5. 37) and a few larger follicles in various stages of atresia. The outlines of the true corpora lutea are invisible or can only be distinguished with difficulty by carefully tracing the position of the thin enveloping theca externa. This condition is reflected in the ovaries of parous animals, after the regression of the luteal tissue, by the presence of considerable quantities of pigment throughout the whole of the ovarian stroma.[1]

[1] A detailed description of the changes in the reproductive organs of the water shrew has been published since this was written (Price, 1953).

A similar complete luteinisation of all the interstitial cells in the ovaries of the new world monkeys during pregnancy, resulting in loss of identity of the true corpus luteum, has been described and figured by Dempsey (1939a). Similar changes have been described in the marmoset (Wislocki, 1939).

The ovaries of adult moles (*Talpa europaea*) during anoestrus present an appearance which, macroscopically, closely resembles that of pregnant water shrews. They are much hypertrophied as compared to the ovaries of adult animals, pregnant or non-pregnant, during the breeding season, and, like those of the pregnant water shrew, are globular in shape and smooth in contour. Sections

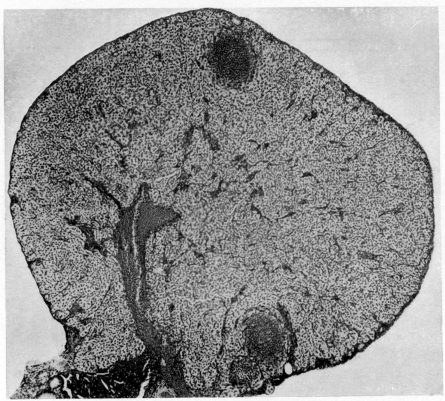

Fig. 5. 39—Photomicrograph of the ovary of a Noctule bat at the beginning of anoestrus. This animal had mated and spermatozoa were present in the tract. No large follicles are present and the ovary consists mainly of hypertrophied interstitial tissue. × 78.

of such ovaries show that they are composed chiefly of cords of epithelial cells and interstitial cells (Fig. 5. 38), as has been described by Matthews (1935). The interstitial tissue in the ovaries of the mole has been described also by Limon (1902), Popoff (1911) and Altmann (1927). Similar changes occur in the ovaries of some bats also (Fig. 5. 39).

Origin of the Interstitial Tissue

The problem of the origin of the interstitial cells of the mammalian ovary has attracted as much attention as that of the luteal cells and even more divergent views have been expressed as to the precise elements from which they are derived.

Almost every cellular component of the ovary has been invoked.   The literature, which is extensive, has been well reviewed by Athias (1920), Jonckheere (1930), and Kingsbury (1939), amongst others, in recent years.   The various views that have been expressed can be reduced to two comprehensive theses, namely, the epithelial origin and the connective-tissue origin of the interstitial cells.

The theory of the epithelial origin of the ovarian interstitial cells has been supported, amongst others, by Schrön (1862), Nussbaum (1880), Schulin (1881), Rouget (1882), Harz (1883), Chiarugi (1885), Janosik (1887), Paladino (1887), Lane-Claypon (1905, 1907), Ganfini (1906, 1907, 1909), Popoff (1911), Rasmussen (1918), Gérard (1920), Ochoterena and Ramirez (1920), Goormaghtigh (1921), Kitahara (1923), Velloso de Pinho (1925), Kohn (1926), and Tsukaguchi and Okamoto (1928).   These authors have assigned the origin of the interstitial cells to a variety of epithelial elements within the ovary, including epithelial cells of mesonephric origin, the germinal epithelium, medullary cords, epithelial elements in the stroma, the membrana granulosa of atretic follicles and the luteal cells of retrogressing corpora lutea.   Harz (1883) and Chiarugi (1885) both suggested that the interstitial cells arise from epithelial elements of mesonephric origin, but this theory has received no support in recent years.   Lane-Claypon (1905) put forward the remarkable view that cells derived from the germinal epithelium, and which were potential oöcytes with deutobroque nuclei, gave rise in the rabbit to both the membrana granulosa and interstitial cells as well as the definitive germ-cells.   These cells, having arrived at the deutobroque stage, " remain quiescent for a while, until finally they regress, and pass into a condition of subserviency to the needs of those which have become ova.   Both follicle-cells and interstitial cells are, however, still potential ova.   They have passed through the initial stages, and only need enlargement and nuclear transformations in order to become ova should the appropriate stimulus be given."   This author actually described the origin of oöcytes from interstitial cells in the ovary of the adult rabbit.   McIlroy (1910) has supported the view that the interstitial cells are derived from the germ-cells.   Rasmussen (1918) attributed to them an origin from the germinal epithelium in the woodchuck, *Marmota monax*.

Several authors have described the origin of interstitial cells from the medullary cords of the ovary.   Popoff (1911) believed that they arose in this way in the ovary of the mole.   Gérard (1920) described the migration of anovular follicles from the cortex into the medulla of the ovary of the adult *Galago mossambicus*.   There they give rise to secondary medullary cords from the cells of which the interstitial cells arise.   The ovarian stroma in the dog is full of inactive epithelial elements which arise both from the germinal epithelium and from the medullary cords, according to Tsukaguchi and Okamoto (1928).   These cells, assuming a glandular structure and secretory function, become interstitial cells.   The cells of the membrana granulosa in atretic follicles of *Eliomys quercinus*, L. undergo metaplasia and give rise to nodules of interstitial tissue, according to Velloso de Pinho (1925).   The interstitial cells in the cat are derived, according to Schrön (1862), from the luteal cells of regressing corpora lutea.

The theory of the connective-tissue origin of the interstitial cells has received even wider support and more general acceptance in recent years.   Among the supporters of this view may be mentioned Pflüger (1863), van Beneden (1880), Plato (1897), Coert (1898), Kölliker (1898), Rabl (1898), Bouin (1899), Regaud and Policard (1901), Limon (1902), Cohn (1903), B. M. Allen (1904), Sainmont (1906), Seitz (1906), Aimé (1907), de Winiwarter and Sainmont (1909), Bouin and Ancel (1909), Giannelli (1909), Comes (1909), Fraenkel (1905, 1911), Popoff (1911), Benthin (1911), O. van der Stricht (1912), Kingsbury (1914), O'Donoghue (1916), Athias (1920), Goodall (1920), Long and Evans (1922), Bascom (1923), Shaw (1926), de Winiwarter (1929), Jonckheere (1930), Bernardo-Comel (1930a and b, 1931), Deanesly (1935) and Mossman (1937). These authors have regarded either the undifferentiated connective-tissue cells of the ovarian stroma or the cells of the theca interna of normal or atretic follicles, or else both, as the source of the interstitial cells. The origin from undifferentiated stromal elements has been maintained by Sainmont (1906) and de Winiwarter and Sainmont (1909) in the cat, by de Winiwarter (1929), Jonckheere (1930) and by Popoff (1911) in the dog. Thus Popoff ascribes entirely different origins to these cells in the ovaries of the mole and the dog respectively. The interstitial tissue in the marsupials, according to O'Donoghue (1916), is to be regarded as a tissue *sui generis*, since it is present in the ovaries of pouch-young before it could have been derived from follicular elements. He admits, however, that it may originate from modified stromal cells at a very early stage.

Many authors, including Limon (1902), Seitz (1906), Benthin (1911), Long and Evans (1922), Bascom (1923), Shaw (1926), Deanesly (1935), Mossman (1937), Guthrie and Jeffers (1938) and Martínez-Esteve (1942), maintain that the theca interna cells of retrogressing follicles give rise to the interstitial cells, either directly or else indirectly through the formation of corpora lutea atretica. Stafford and Mossman (1945) consider that most of the interstitial cells in the guinea-pig ovary are formed from the theca interna of degenerating follicles and that they can, and do, revert to fibroblasts. According to Mossman (1937) the theca interna cells of both normal ruptured and atretic follicles give rise to interstitial cells in the ovaries of adult pocket gophers, *Geomys bursarius*, Shaw. In this species the theca interna exhibits an extraordinary development, being thicker relative to the whole follicle than in any other mammal in which it has been described. Both in atretic and ruptured follicles the theca interna degenerates but some of the cells persist and, becoming detached, give rise to interstitial cells. This appears to be the only source of interstitial cells in the adult. It is possible that interstitial cells may arise from theca interna elements which have persisted after the degeneration of the true luteal cells in retrogressing corpora lutea. It is noteworthy, in this connection, that Corner (1921) states that the " theca lutein cells " in the corpus luteum of the pig " survive the blow which destroys the granulosa lutein cells ; for among the débris and the collapsed capillaries, and also in occasional clumps at the periphery, are found numerous cells which, by reason of their usually angular or elongated shape, foamy cytoplasm, and wealth of osmium-staining fatty material, can hardly be deemed other than the theca lutein cells." " When after a few days the nuclear fragments and the vacuolar spaces left by the degenerated granulosa derivatives have disappeared, the lipoid-laden cells are more clearly seen, enmeshed in the scar-tissue, where they persist for weeks, acquiring even denser stores of yellow-pigmented fat."

The occurrence of interstitial cells in the ovaries of embryos or very young animals, before follicular atresia has begun, has led several observers to ascribe a dual origin to them ; from undifferentiated stromal cells during embryonic and early life and from the theca interna elements of atretic follicles in more mature animals. This view has received support from O. van der Stricht (1912), Kingsbury (1914) and Athias (1920) amongst others. Moreover, many of those authors who have attributed the origin of the interstitial cells to the theca interna cells alone have been concerned only with the ovaries of adult animals. Athias (1920) made a very thorough investigation of the interstitial cells in the ovaries of several species of bats, of ages ranging from embryos to parous adults and including specimens killed at all seasons of the year. He concluded that in the young animal the interstitial cells are derived entirely from connective-tissue elements of the stroma, but that in the older animal they are derived principally from the theca interna cells of atretic follicles, although some are derived directly from stromal elements. The origin of the interstitial tissue has been investigated also by Wolz (1912), Brugnatelli (1919) and Tassovatz (1927). Recently Rennels (1951) has claimed, on the basis of histochemical characters, that the interstitial cells of the rat's ovary have a dual origin. The primary interstitial cells of the juvenile ovary are formed from epithelial cells of cortical ingrowths or of the granulosa of follicles. The secondary interstitial cells, formed later in development, are derived from the theca interna cells of atretic follicles. Dawson and McCabe (1951) arrive at a similar conclusion and believe that the primary interstitial tissue is replaced by the secondary.

Dempsey (1939a) finds that in new world monkeys, during the reproductive cycle and pregnancy, large quantities of interstitial tissue are formed in the ovaries as a result of luteal transformation of atretic follicles. This interstitial tissue is claimed to be of two cell-types ; a large-celled kind apparently derived from the membrana granulosa and indistinguishable from the luteal cells of the corpus luteum, and a small-celled kind which appears to be derived from the theca interna.

Bibliography

ABEL, W., & McILROY, A. L. (1912). The arrangement and distribution of nerves in certain mammalian ovaries. *Proc. Roy. Soc. Med., Obstet. Gynaec.*, **6**, 240.

ABRAMOWICZ, H. (1913). Die Entwicklung der Gonadenanlage und Entstehung der Gonocyten bei *Triton taeniatus Schneid. Morph. Jb.*, **47**, 593.

AEBY, C. (1861). Die glatten Muskelfasern in den Eierstöcken der Wirbelthiere. *Arch. Anat. Physiol., Lpz.*, 1861, 635.

AGDUHR, E. (1927). Studies on the structure and development of the bursa ovarica and the tuba uterina in the mouse. *Acta Zool., Stockh.*, **8**, 1.

AIMÉ, P. (1906). Les cellules interstitielles de l'ovaire chez le cheval. *C. R. Soc. Biol., Paris*, **61**, 250.

—— (1907). Recherches sur les cellules intcrotitielles de l'ovaire chez quelques mammifères. *Arch. Zool. Exp. Gén.*, **7**, 95.

ALEXENKO, N. (1891). Contribution à l'histologie normale et pathologique des ovaries de la femme. *Ann. Gynéc. Obstet.*, **35**, 417.

ALLANSON, M. (1932). The growth of the pituitary body in the female rabbit. *J. exp. Biol.*, **9**, 117.

ALLEN, B. M. (1904). The embryonic development of the ovary and testis of the mammals *Amer. J. Anat.*, **3**, 89.

—— (1905). The embryonic development of the rete-cords and sex-cords of *Chrysemys. Amer. J. Anat.*, **5**, 79.

—— (1906). The origin of the sex-cells of *Chrysemys. Anat. Anz.*, **29**, 217.

ALLEN, B. M. (1907a). A statistical study of the sex-cells of *Chrysemys marginata*. *Anat. Rec.*, **1**, 64.

—— (1907b). An important period in the history of the sex-cells of *Rana pipiens*. *Anat. Anz.*, **31**, 339.

—— (1910). The origin of the sex-cells of Amia and Lepidosteus. *J. Morph.*, **22**, 1.

—— (1911a). The origin of the sex-cells in *Chrysemys* (a reply to Dustin). *Anat. Anz.*, **39**, 603.

—— (1911b). The origin of the sex-cells in *Necturus*. *Science*, **33**, 268.

ALLEN, EDGAR (1923). Ovogenesis during sexual maturity. *Amer. J. Anat.*, **31**, 439.

—— (1927). The menstrual cycle of the monkey, *Macacus rhesus* : Observations on normal animals, the effects of removal of the ovaries and the effects of injections of ovarian and placental extracts into the spayed animals. *Contr. Embryol. Carneg. Instn.*, **19**, 1.

—— (1928). An unfertilized tubal ovum from *Macacus rhesus*. *Anat. Rec.*, **37**, 351.

—— & CREADICK, R. N. (1937). Ovogenesis during sexual maturity. The first stage, mitosis in the germinal epithelium, as shown by the colchicine technique. *Anat. Rec.*, **69**, 191.

—— & DOISY, E. A. (1923). An ovarian hormone : preliminary report of its localization, extraction and partial purification, and action in test animals. *J. Amer. Med. Ass.*, **81**, 819.

—— KOUNTZ, W. B., & FRANCIS, B. F. (1925). Selective elimination of ova in the adult ovary. *Amer. J. Anat.*, **34**, 445.

—— & OTHERS (1924). The hormone of the ovarian follicle ; its localization and action in test animals, and additional points bearing upon the internal secretion of the ovary. *Amer. J. Anat.*, **34**, 133.

—— PRATT, J. P., NEWELL, Q. U., & BLAND, L. J. (1930a). Human tubal ova ; related early corpora lutea and uterine tubes. *Contr. Embryol. Carneg. Instn.*, **22**, 45.

—— —— —— —— (1930b). Human ova from large follicles ; including a search for maturation divisions and observations on atresia. *Amer. J. Anat.*, **46**, 1.

—— THOMAS, T. B., WILSON, J. G., & HESSION, D. A. (1943). Differential growth in the ovaries and genital tract near the time of ovulation in rats treated with colchicine. *Amer. J. Anat.*, **72**, 291.

ALLEN, P., BRAMBELL, F. W. R., & MILLS, I. H. (1947). Studies on sterility and prenatal mortality in wild rabbits. I. The reliability of estimates of prenatal mortality based on counts of corpora lutea, implantation sites and embryos. *J. exp. Biol.*, **23**, 312

ALTLAND, P. D. (1951). Observations on the structure of the reproductive organs of the box turtle. *J. Morph.*, **89**, 599.

ALTMANN, F. (1927). Untersuchungen über das Ovarium von *Talpa europaea* mit besonderer Berücksichtigung seiner cyclischen Veränderungen. *Z. ges. Anat.* 1. *Z. Anat. EntwGesch.*, **82**, 482.

AMOROSO, E. C., HANCOCK, J. L., & ROWLANDS, I. W. (1948). Ovarian activity in the pregnant mare. *Nature, Lond.*, **161**, 355.

ANDERSEN, D. H. (1926). Lymphatics and blood-vessels of the ovary of the sow. *Contr Embryol. Carneg. Instn.*, **17**, 107.

ARAI, H. (1920a). On the postnatal development of the ovary (albino rat), with especial reference to the number of ova. *Amer. J. Anat.*, **27**, 405.

—— (1920b). On the cause of the hypertrophy of the surviving ovary after semispaying (albino rat) and on the number of ova in it. *Amer. J. Anat.*, **28**, 59.

ASAMI, G. (1920). Observations on the follicular atresia in the rabbit ovary. *Anat. Rec.*, **18**, 323.

ASDELL, S. A. (1946). *Patterns of mammalian reproduction*. Ithaca, New York.

ATHIAS, M. (1920). Recherches sur les cellules interstitielles de l'ovaire des cheiroptères. *Arch. Biol., Paris*, **30**, 89.

—— (1929). Les phénomènes de division de l'oocyte au cours de l'atrésie folliculaire chez les mammifères. *Arch. Anat. Micr.*, **25**, 405.

AUNAP, E. (1913). Über die Chondriosomen der Gonocyten bei Knochenfischen. *Anat. Anz.*, **44**, 449.

AUSTIN, C. R. (1951). Activation and the correlation between male and female elements in fertilisation. *Nature, Lond.,* **168,** 558.

AYKROYD, O. E. (1938). The cytoplasmic inclusions in the oogenesis of man. *Z. Zellforsch.,* **27,** 691.

BAER, C. E. VON (1827). *De Ovi mammalium et hominis genesi Epistolam ad Academiam imperialem scientiarum petropolitanam.* Lipsiae.

BARTELMEZ, G. W. (1912). The bilaterality of the pigeon's egg. A study in eggs organzation from the first growth period of the oocyte to the beginning of cleavage. *J. Morph.,* **23,** 269.

BASCOM, K. F. (1923). The interstitial cells of the gonads of cattle with especial reference to their embryonic development and significance. *Amer. J. Anat.,* **31,** 223.

BASSETT, D. L. (1943). The changes in the vascular pattern of the ovary of the albino rat during the estrous cycle. *Amer. J. Anat.,* **73,** 251.

—— (1949). The lutein cell population and mitotic activity in the corpus luteum of pregnancy in the albino rat. *Anat. Rec.,* **103,** 597.

BEAMS, H. W., & SHEEHAN, J. F. (1941). The yolk-nucleus complex of the human ovum. *Anat. Rec.,* **81,** 545.

BEARD, J. (1900). The morphological continuity of the germ-cells in *Raja batis.* *Anat. Anz.,* **18,** 465.

—— (1902a). The germ-cells of *Pristiurus.* *Anat. Anz.,* **21,** 50.

—— (1902b). The germ-cells. 1. *Raja batis.* *Zool. Jb. Anat. Ont.,* **16,** 615.

—— (1904). The germ-cells. 1. *Raja batis.* *J. Anat., Lond.,* **38,** 82, 205, 341.

BECCARI, N. (1921). Studi sulla prima origine delle cellule genitali nei vertebrati. 2. Ricerche nella *Salamandrina perspicillata.* *Arch. ital. Anat. Embriol.,* **18** (Suppl.), 29.

—— (1924). Studi sulla prima origine delle cellule genitali nei vertebrati. 3. Ricerche nel *Bufo viridis.* *Arch. ital. Anat. Embriol.,* **21,** 332.

—— (1925). Studi sulla prima origine delle cellule genitali nei vertebrati. 4. Ovogenesi larvale, organo del Bidder e differenziamento die sessi nel *Bufo viridis.* *Arch. ital. Anat. Embriol.,* **22,** 483.

—— (1929). Dati e considerazioni sulla natura dell' organo del Bidder dei Bufonidi. *Arch. ital. Anat. Embriol.,* **26,** 273.

BECHER, H. (1928). Beitrag zur feineren Struktur der Zona radiata des Knochenfischeies und über ein durch die Struktur der Eihülle bedingtes optisches Phänomen. *Z. mikr.-anat. Forsch.,* **13,** 591.

VAN BEEK, W. F. (1924). Die Entwicklung des Eierstockes beim Rinde. *Z. ges. Anat.* 1. *Z. Anat. EntwGesch.,* **71,** 458.

BEIGEL, H. (1878). Zur Naturgeschichte des corpus luteum. *Arch. Gynaek.,* **13,** 109.

BENCKISER, A. (1884). Zur Entwickelungsgeschichte des corpus luteum. *Arch. Gynaek.,* **23,** 350.

VAN BENEDEN, E. (1880). Contribution à la connaissance de l'ovaire des mammifères. *Arch. Biol. Paris,* **1,** 475.

BENOIT, J. (1926). Sur l'origine des cellules interstitielles de l'ovaire de la poule. *C. R. Soc. Biol., Paris,* **94,** 873.

—— (1930). Contribution à l'étude de la lignée germinale chez le poulet. Destruction précoce des gonocytes primâires par les rayons ultra-violets. *C. R. Soc. Biol., Paris,* **104,** 1329.

—— (1931). Destruction des gonocytes primaires dans le blastoderme du poulet par les rayons ultra-violets, aux premiers stades du développement embryonnaire. *Int. Congr. Sex Res.,* **2nd.,** 162.

BENTHIN, W. (1911). Ueber Follikelatresie in Säugetierovarien. *Arch. Gynaek.,* **94,** 599.

BERENBERG GOSSLER, H. (1913). Die Urgeschlechtszellen des Hühnerembryos am 3. und 4. Bebrütungstage, mit besonderer Berücksichtigung der Kern- und Plasmastrukturen. *Arch. mikr. Anat.,* **81,** 24.

BERGER, L. (1923). La glande sympathicotrope du hile de l'ovaire ; ses homologies avec la glande interstitielle du testicule. *Arch. Anat., Strasbourg,* **2,** 255.

—— (1928). Sympathicotrope Zellen im Eierstock und ihre neurokrine Funktion. *Virchow's Arch.,* **267,** 433.

BERNARDO-COMEL, M. C. (1930a). Per la migliore conoscenza dell' istogenesi dell' ovaia della donna. *Boll. Soc. ital. Biol. sper.*, **5**, 45.

—— (1930b). Ulteriori ricerche sull' istogenesi dell' ovaia della donna. *Boll. Soc. ital. Biol. sper.*, **5**, 929.

—— (1931). Intorno alle cellule interstiziale dell' ovaia di donna nel periodo fetale. *Arch. ital. Anat. Embriol.*, **29**, 78.

BHATTACHARYA, D. R. (1925). Les inclusions cytoplasmiques dans l'oogénèse de certains reptiles. Thèse. *Faculté des Sciences, Paris, A*, 1037.

—— DAS, R. S., & DUTTA, S. K. (1929). On the infiltration of Golgi bodies from the follicular epithelium to the egg. *Z. Zellforsch.*, **8**, 566.

BHATTACHARYA, P. R. (1929a). Notes on cell organs in the oogenesis of the house gecko. *Allahabad Univ. Stud.*, **6**, 21.

—— (1929b). The infiltration of Golgi bodies from the follicular epithelium to the egg in fishes. *Allahabad Univ. Stud.*, **6**, 53.

—— (1931). The infiltration of Golgi bodies from follicular epithelium to the egg in mammals. *Allahabad Univ. Stud.*, **7**, 1.

BISCHOFF, T. L. W. (1842). *Entwicklungsgeschichte des Kanincheneies.* Braunschweig.

BLOCKER, H. W. (1933). Embryonic history of the germ cells in *Passer domesticus* (L.). *Acta Zool. Stockh.*, **14**, 111.

BLUNTSCHLI, H. (1937). Die Fruhentwicklung eines Centetinen (*Hemicentetes semispinosus* Cuv.). *Rev. Suisse Zool.*, **44**, 271.

—— (1938). Le développement primaire et l'implantation chez un centetiné (Hemicentetes). *C. R. Ass. Anat. Bale*, **1**.

BÖHI, U. (1904). Beiträge zur Entwicklungsgeschichte der Leibeshöhle und der Genital-anlage bei den Salmoniden. *Morph. Jb.*, **32**, 505.

BOLING, J. L. (1942). Growth and regression of corpora lutea during the normal estrous cycle of the rat. *Anat. Rec.*, **82**, 131.

—— BLANDAU, R. J., SODERWALL, A. L., & YOUNG, W. C. (1941). Growth of the Graafian follicle and the time of ovulation in the albino rat. *Anat. Rec.*, **79**, 313.

BONNET, R. (1891). *Grundriss der Entwickelungsgeschichte der Haussäugethiere.* Berlin.

BORCEA, J. (1906). Recherches sur le système uro-génital des elasmobranches. *Arch. Zool. Exp. Gen.*, **4**, 199.

BORING, A. M., & PEARL, R. (1917). Sex studies. 9. Interstitial cells in the reproductive organs of the chicken. *Anat. Rec.*, **13**, 253.

BOUIN, M. (1900). Histogenèse de la glande génitale femelle chez *Rana temporaria* (L.). *Arch. Biol., Paris*, **17**, 201.

BOUIN, P. (1899). Atrésie des follicules de de Graaf et formation de faux corps jaunes. *Bibliogr. Anat.*, **7**, 296.

—— (1902). Les deux glandes à sécrétion interne de l'ovaire ; la glande interstitielle et le corps jaune. *Rev. Méd. Est.*, **34**, 465.

—— & ANCEL, P. (1908). Sur la différenciation d'une membrane propre d'origine épithéliale pendant le développement du corps jaune chez le chienne. *C. R. Soc. Biol., Paris*, **65**, 201.

—— —— (1909). Sur les homologies et la signification des glandes à sécrétion interne de l'ovaire. *C. R. Soc. Biol., Paris*, **67**, 464.

BOUNOURE, L. (1925). L'origine des gonocytes et l'évolution de la première ébauche génitale chez les batraciens. *Ann. Sci. Nat.*, **8**, 201.

—— (1934). Recherches sur la lignée germinale chez la grenouille rousse aux premiers stades du développement. *Ann. Sci. Nat.*, **17**, 67.

—— (1935a). Une preuve expérimentale du rôle du déterminant germinal chez la gre-nouille rousse. *C. R. Acad. Sci., Paris*, **201**, 1223.

—— (1935b). Sur la possibilité de réaliser une castration dans l'œuf de la grenouille rousse ; résultats anatomiques. *C. R. Soc. Biol., Paris*, **120**, 1316.

—— (1937a). Le déterminant germinal est-il bien en cause dans l'atrophie des gonades consécutive à l'action des rayons ultra-violets sur le pôle inférieur de l'œuf de grenouille ? *C. R. Soc. Biol., Paris*, **125**, 895.

BOUNOURE, L. (1937b). Les suites de l'irradiation du déterminant germinal, chez la grenouille rousse. Par les rayons ultra-violets : résultats histologiques. *C. R. Soc. Biol., Paris*, **125**, 898.

—— (1937c). Le sort de la lignée germinale chez la grenouille rousse après l'action des rayons ultraviolets sur le pôle inférieur de l'œuf. *C. R. Acad. Sci., Paris*, **204**, 1837.

—— (1937d). La constitution des glandes génitales chez la grenouille rousse après destruction étendue de la lignée germinale par l'action des rayons ultraviolets sur l'œuf. *C. R. Acad. Sci., Paris*, **204**, 1957.

BOVY, J. (1928). Recherches sur le corps de Wolff et l'origine des connexions urogénitales chez la souris. *Arch. Biol., Paris*, **39**, 139.

BOYD, M. M. M. (1940). The structure of the ovary and the formation of the corpus luteum in *Hoplodactylus maculatus*, Gray. *Quart. J. micr. Sci.*, **82**, 337.

BRACHET, A. (1935). *Traité d'embryologie des vertébrés*. Paris.

BRADEN, A. W. H. (1952). Properties of the membranes of rat and rabbit eggs. *Aust. J. sci. Res., B.*, **5**, 460.

BRAGDON, D. E. (1952). Corpus luteum formation and follicular atresia in the common garter snake, *Thamnophis sirtalis*. *J. Morph.*, **91**, 413.

BRAMBELL, F. W. ROGERS (1925). The oogenesis of the fowl (*Gallus bankiva*). *Philos. Trans.* B, **214**, 113.

—— (1927a). The development and morphology of the gonads of the mouse. 1. The morphogenesis of the indifferent gonad and of the ovary. *Proc. Roy. Soc.* B, **101**, 391.

—— (1927b). The development and morphology of the gonads of the mouse. 2. The development of the Wolffian body and ducts. *Proc. Roy. Soc.* B, **102**, 206.

—— (1928). The development and morphology of the gonads of the mouse. 3. The growth of the follicles. *Proc. Roy. Soc.* B, **103**, 258.

—— (1929). The histology of an hermaphrodite pig and its developmental significance. *J. Anat., Lond.*, **63**, 397.

—— (1930). *The Development of sex in vertebrates*. London.

—— (1935). Reproduction in the common shrew (*Sorex araneus* Linnaeus). I. The oestrous cycle of the female. *Philos. Trans.* B, **225**, 1.

—— (1937). The influence of lactation on the implantation of the mammalian embryo. *Amer. J. Obstet. Gynaec.*, **33**, 942.

—— (1944). The reproduction of the wild rabbit, *Oryctolagus cuniculus* (L). *Proc. zool. Soc. Lond.*, **114**, 1.

—— FIELDING, U., & PARKES, A. S. (1928). Changes in the ovary of the mouse following exposure to X-rays. 4. The corpus luteum in the sterilized ovary, and some concluding experiments. *Proc. Roy. Soc.* B, **102**, 385.

—— & HALL, K. (1937). Reproduction of the lesser shrew (*Sorex minutus* Linnaeus). *Proc. zool. Soc. Lond.* 1937, 957.

—— & MARRIAN, G. F. (1929). Sex-reversal in a pigeon (*Columba livia*). *Proc. Roy. Soc.* B, **104**, 459.

—— & PARKES, A. S. (1927a). The normal ovarian cycle in relation to oestrus production. *Quart. J. exp. Physiol*, **18**, 185.

—— —— (1927b). Changes in the ovary of the mouse following exposure to X-rays. 3. Irradiation of the non-parous adult. *Proc. Roy. Soc.* B, **101**, 316.

—— —— & FIELDING, U. (1927a). Changes in the ovary of the mouse following exposure to X-rays. 1. Irradiation at three weeks old. *Proc. Roy. Soc.* B, **101**, 29.

—— —— —— (1927b). Changes in the ovary of the mouse following exposure to X-rays. 2. Irradiation at or before birth. *Proc. Roy. Soc.* B, **101**, 95.

—— & ROWLANDS, I. W. (1936). Reproduction of the bank vole (*Evotomys glareolus* Schreber). 1. The oestrous cycle of the female. *Philos. Trans.* B, **226**, 71.

BRANCA, A. (1925). L'ovocyte atrésique et son involution. *Arch. Biol., Paris*, **35**, 325.

BRANDT, A. (1877). Fragmentarische bemerkungen über das ovarium des frosches. *Z. wiss. Zool.*, **28**, 575.

BRANNAN, D. (1927). The sympathicotropic cells of the ovary and testis. *Amer. J. Path.*, **3**, 343.

BRILL, W. (1915). Untersuchungen über die Nerven des Ovariums. *Arch. mikr. Anat.*, **86**, 338.

BRODE, M. D. (1928). The significance of the asymmetry of the ovaries of the fowl. *J. Morph.*, **46**, 1.

BRUGNATELLI, E. (1919). Sulla natura della cellula luteinica e della cellula interstiziale dell' ovaio. *Folia Gynaec. Pavia*, **13**, 111.

BÜHLER, A. (1900). Entwickelungsstadien menschlicher corpora lutea. *Anat. Anz.*, **18**, *Verh. Anat. Ges. Jena*, 150.

—— (1902). Rückbildung der Eifollikel bei Wirbelthieren. 1. Fische. *Morph. Jb.*, **30**, 377.

—— (1903). Rückbildung der Eifollikel bei Wirbelthieren. 2. Amphibien. *Morph. Jb.*, **31**, 85.

BULLOUGH, W. S. (1942a). Effect of oestrin injections on the mouse ovary. *Nature, Lond.*, **149**, 271.

—— (1942b). Oogenesis and its relation to the oestrous cycle in the adult mouse. *J. Endocrinol.*, **3**, 141.

—— (1942c). The method of growth of the follicle and corpus luteum in the mouse ovary. *J. Endocrinol.*, **3**, 150.

—— (1946). Mitotic activity in the adult mouse, *Mus musculus L.* A study of its relation to the oestrous cycle in normal and abnormal conditions. *Philos. Trans.* B, **231**, 453.

BURGER, J. W. (1937). The continuity of the germ cells in the urodele, *Plethodon cinereus* (Green). *J. Morph.*, **60**, 489.

DE BURLET, H. M., & DE RUITER, H. J. (1920). Zur Entwickelung und Morphologie des Säugerhodens. 1. Der Hoden von *Mus musculus*. *Anat. Hefte*, **59**, 325.

BURNS, R. K. (1930). The process of sex transformation in parabiotic Amblystoma. 1. Transformation from female to male. *J. exp. Zool.*, **55**, 123.

—— (1931). The process of sex transformation in parabiotic Amblystoma. 2. Transformation from male to female. *J. exp. Zool.*, **60**, 339.

—— (1935). The process of sex transformation in parabiotic Amblystoma. 3. Conversion of testis to ovary in heteroplastic pairs of *A. tigrinum* and *A. punctatum*. *Anat. Rec.*, **63**, 101.

—— (1938). The effects of crystalline sex hormones on sex differentiation in Amblystoma. I. Estrone. *Anat. Rec.*, **71**, 447.

—— (1939). The effects of crystalline sex hormones on sex differentiation in Amblystoma. II. Testosterone propionate. *Anat. Rec.*, **73**, 73.

BURR, J. H., & DAVIES, J. I. (1951). The vascular system of the rabbit ovary and its relationship to ovulation. *Anat. Rec.*, **111**, 273.

BURRUANO, C. (1934). Contributo allo studio della vascolarizzazione dell' ovaio. *Scr. Biol. L. Castaldi*, **9**, 269.

BUTCHER, E. O. (1927). The origin of the definitive ova in the white rat (*Mus norvegicus albinus*). *Anat. Rec.*, **37**, 13.

—— (1929). The origin of the germ cells in the lake lamprey (*Petromyzon marinus unicolor*). *Biol. Bull.*, *Wood's Hole*, **56**, 87.

—— (1932). Regeneration in ligated ovaries and transplanted ovarian fragments of the white rat (*Mus norvegicus albinus*). *Anat. Rec.*, **54**, 87.

CALDWELL, W. H. (1887). The embryology of the Monotremata and Marsupialia. *Philos. Trans.* B, **178**, 463.

CALL, E. L., & EXNER, S. (1875). Zur Kenntniss des Graafschen Follikels und des Corpus luteum beim Kaninchen. *S.B. Akad. Wiss. Wien.*, **71**, Abt. 3, 321.

CATTANEO, D. (1914). Ricerche sulla struttura dell' ovario dei mammiferi. *Arch. ital. Anat. Embriol.*, **12**, 1.

CELESTINO DA COSTA, A. (1932a). Les gonocytes primaires chez les mammifères. *C. R. Ass. Anat. Nancy*, **27**, 198.

—— (1932b). L'état actuel du problème de l'origine des cellules sexuelles. *Bull. Ass. Anat.*, **27**, 1.

CESA-BIANCHI, D. (1907). Osservazioni sulla struttura e sulla funzione della cosidetta " ghiandola interstiziale dell' ovaia." *Arch. Fisiol.*, **4**, 523.

—— (1908). Di alcune particolarità di struttura e dei fenomeni di secrezione del corpo luteo. *Int. Mschr. Anat. Physiol.*, **25**, 1.

CHAMPY, C., & GLEY, P. (1923). Observations cytologiques sur les ovocytes des poissons et de quelques autres vertébrés. *Arch. Anat. Micr.*, **19**, 241.

CHANG, M. C. (1950). Cleavage of unfertilised ova in immature ferrets. *Anat. Rec.*, **108**, 31.

CHAPPELLIER, A. (1909). Follicules pluriovulaires et dégénérescence ovulaire chez la souris blanche. *C. R. Soc. Biol., Paris*, **66**, 543.

CHENG, T. H. (1932). The germ cell history of *Rana cantabrigensis* Baird. 1. Germ cell origin and gonad formation. 2. Sex differentiation and development. *Z. Zellforsch.*, **16**, 497.

CHIARUGI, G. (1885). Ricerche sulla struttura dell' ovaia della lepre (*Lepus timidus* Linn.). *Atti Accad. Fisiocr. Siena.*, **4**, 19.

CHILD, C. M. (1897). Centrosome and sphere in cells of the ovarian stroma of mammals. *Zool. Bull.*, **1**, 87.

CHYDENIUS, J. J. (1926). Über die Struktur in den Corpus Luteum-Zellen des Menschen und ihre Veränderungen während des Menstruationszyklus und bei Gravidität. *Arb. Path. Inst. Univ. Helsingf.*, **4**, 319.

—— (1929). Über die Struktur und die Strukturveränderungen in den Zellen des Follikel-apparates der menschlichen Ovarien. *Arb. Path. Inst. Univ. Helsingf.*, **6**, 1.

CIERI, G. M. (1932). Sulle cosidette cellule cromaffini dell' ovario. *Morgagni*, **74**, 1235.

CLARK, E. B. (1923). Observations on the ova and ovaries of the guinea-pig, *Cavia cobaya*. *Anat. Rec.*, **25**, 313.

CLARK, J. G. (1898). Ursprung, Wachsthum und Ende des Corpus luteum nach Beobach-tungen am Ovarium des Schweines und des Menschen. *Arch. Anat. Physiol.*, *Lpz., Anat. Abt.*, 1898, 95.

—— (1899). The origin, growth and fate of the corpus luteum as observed in the ovary of the pig and man. *Johns Hopk. Hosp. Rep.*, **7**, 181.

—— (1900). The origin, development and degeneration of the blood-vessels of the human ovary. *Johns Hopk. Hosp. Rep.*, **9**, 593.

COERT, II. J. (1898). Over de ontwikkeling en den bouw van de geslachtsklier bij de zoogdieren meer in het bijzonder van den cierstok. *Academisch Proefschrift, Rijks-Universiteit, Leiden*.

COHN, F. (1903). Zur Histologie und Histogenese des Corpus luteum und des interstitiellen Ovarialgewebes. *Arch. mikr. Anat.*, **62**, 745.

—— (1909). Ueber das Corpus luteum und den atretischen Follikel des Menschen und deren cystische Derivate. *Arch. Gynaek.*, **87**, 367.

COLE, F. J. (1905). Notes on Myxine. *Anat. Anz.*, **27**, 323.

COLE, H. H., HOWELL, C. E., & HART, G. H. (1931). The changes occurring in the ovary of the mare. *Anat. Rec.* **49**, 199.

—— & MILLER, R. F. (1935). Changes in the reproductive organs of the ewe with some data bearing on their control. *Amer. J. Anat.*, **57**, 39.

COMES, S. (1909). Alcuni particolari istologici sugli elementi donde proviene il materiale nutritivo dell' ovocite dei mammiferi. *Arch. ital. Anat. Embriol.*, **7**, 501.

CONEL, J. LeR. (1917). The urogenital system of Myxinoids. *J. Morph.*, **29**, 75.

CORNER, G. W. (1915). The corpus luteum of pregnancy, as it is in swine. *Contr. Embryol. Carneg. Instn.*, **2**, 69.

—— (1917). Maturation of the ovum in swine. *Anat. Rec.*, **13**, 109.

—— (1919). On the origin of the corpus luteum of the sow from both granulosa and theca interna. *Amer. J. Anat.*, **26**, 117.

—— (1921). Cyclic changes in the ovaries and uterus of the sow, and their relation to the mechanism of implantation. *Contr. Embryol. Carneg. Instn.*, **13**, 117.

—— (1923). Ovulation and menstruation in *Macacus rhesus*. *Contr. Embryol. Carneg. Instn.*, **15**, 73.

Corner, G. W. (1942). The fate of the corpora lutea and the nature of the corpora aberrantia in the rhesus monkey. *Contr. Embryol. Carneg. Instn.*, **30**, 85.

—— (1948). Alkaline phosphatase in the ovarian follicle and in the corpus luteum. *Contr. Embryol. Carneg. Instn.*, **32**, 1.

—— & Amsbaugh, A. E. (1917). Oestrus and ovulation in swine. *Anat. Rec.*, **12**, 287.

—— Bartelmez, G. W., & Hartman, C. G. (1936). On normal and aberrant corpora lutea of the rhesus monkey. *Amer. J. Anat.*, **59**, 433.

—— with Hartman, C. G., & Bartelmez, G. W. (1945). Development, organisation, and breakdown of the corpus luteum in the rhesus monkey. *Contr. Embryol. Carneg. Instn.*, **31**, 117.

Cowperthwaite, M. H. (1925). Observations on pre- and post-pubertal oogenesis in the white rat, *Mus norvegicus albinus*. *Amer. J. Anat.*, **36**, 69.

Cunningham, J. T. (1897). On the histology of the ovary and of the ovarian ova in certain marine fishes. *Quart. J. micr. Sci.*, **40**, 101.

—— (1921). *Hormones and heredity*. London.

—— & Smart, W. A. M. (1934). The structure and origin of corpora lutea in some of the lower vertebrata. *Proc. Roy. Soc. B*, **116**, 258.

Danforth, C. H., & deAberle, S. B. (1928). The functional interrelation of the ovaries as indicated by the distribution of foetuses in mouse uteri. *Amer. J. Anat.* **41**, 65.

Dantschakoff, W. (1908). Untersuchungen über die Entwickelung des Blutes und Bindegewebes bei den Vögeln. 1. Die erste Entstehung der Blutzellen beim Hühnerembryo und der Dottersack als blutbildendes Organ. *Arb. Anat. Inst., Wiesbaden*, **37**, 471.

—— (1931a). Keimzelle und Gonade. 1a. Von der entodermalen Wanderzelle bis zur Urkeimzelle in der Gonade. *Z. Zellforsch.*, **13**, 448.

—— (1931b). Keimzelle und Gonade. Die entodermale Wanderzelle als Stammzelle in der Keimbahn. Experimentelle Beweise. Vorläufige Mitteilung. *Z. Zellforsch.*, **14**, 376.

—— (1932a). Keimzelle und Gonade. 2b. Ganzheit des Gewebekomplexes als Faktor in der Entwicklung der Gonade. *Z. Zellforsch.*, **15**, 581.

—— (1932b). Les cellules génitales et leur continuité. *Rev. Gén. Sci. Pur. Appl.*, **43**, 295.

—— (1933). Keimzelle und Gonade. 5. Sterilisierung der Gonaden im Embryo mittels Röntgenstrahlen. *Z. Zellforsch.*, **18**, 56.

—— Dantschakoff, W., Jr., & Bereskina, L. (1931). Keimzelle und Gonade. 1a'. Identität der Urkeimzellen und der entodermalen Wanderzellen. *Z. Zellforsch.*, **14**, 323.

Das, R. S. (1931). On the cytoplasmic inclusions in the oogenesis of birds. *Russk. Arkh. Anat.*, **10**, 309.

Davenport, C. B. (1925). Regeneration of ovaries in mice. *J. exp. Zool.*, **42**, 1.

Davis, D. E. (1942a). The regression of the avian post-ovulatory follicle. *Anat. Rec.*, **82**, 297.

—— (1942b). The bursting of the avian follicles at the beginning of atresia. *Anat. Rec.*, **82**, 153.

—— & Hall, O. (1950). Polyovuly and anovular follicles in the wild Norway rat. *Anat. Rec.*, **107**, 187.

Dawson, A. B. (1941). The development and morphology of the corpus luteum of the cat. *Anat. Rec.*, **79**, 155.

—— (1946). The postpartum history of the corpus luteum of the cat. *Anat. Rec.*, **95**, 29.

—— (1951). Histogenetic interrelationships of oöcytes and follicle cells. A possible explanation of the mode of origin of certain polyovular follicles in the immature rat. *Anat. Rec.*, **110**, 181.

—— & McCabe, M. (1951). The interstitial tissue of the ovary in infantile and juvenile rats. *J. Morph.*, **88**, 543.

Deal, R. E. (1931). The development of sex characters in the tree frog. *Anat. Rec.*, **48**, 27.

DEANESLY, R. (1930a). The corpora lutea of the mouse, with special reference to fat accumulation during the oestrous cycle. *Proc. Roy. Soc.* B, **106**, 578.

—— (1930b). The development and vascularisation of the corpus luteum in the mouse and rabbit. *Proc. Roy. Soc.* B, **107**, 60.

—— (1934). The reproductive processes of certain mammals. VI. The reproductive cycle of the female hedgehog. *Philos. Trans.* B, **223**, 239.

—— (1935) The reproductive processes of certain mammals. IX. Growth and reproduction in the stoat (*Mustela erminea*). *Philos. Trans.* B, **225**, 459.

—— (1938). The reproductive cycle of the golden hamster (*Cricetus auratus*). *Proc. zool. Soc. Lond.* A, **108**, 31.

—— & PARKES, A. S. (1933). The reproductive processes of certain mammals. IV. The oestrous cycle of the grey squirrel (*Sciurus carolinensis*). *Philos. Trans.* B, **222**, 47.

DEBEYRE, A. (1933). Sur la présence de gonocytes chez un embryon humain au stade de la ligne primitive. *C. R. Ass. Anat., Lisbonne*, **28**, 240.

DEDERER, P. H. (1934). Polyovular follicles in the cat. *Anat. Rec.*, **60**, 391.

DEFRETIN, R. (1924). Origine et migration des gonocytes chez le poulet. *C. R. Soc. Biol., Paris*, **91**, 1082.

DELESTRE, M. (1910). Recherches sur le follicule de de Graaf et le corps jaune de la vache. *J. Anat., Paris*, **46**, 286.

DEMPSEY, E. W. (1939a). The reproductive cycle of New World monkeys. *Amer. J. Anat.*, **64**, 381.

—— (1939b). Maturation and cleavage figures in ovarian ova. *Anat. Rec.*, **75**, 223.

—— & WISLOCKI, G. B. (1941). The structure of the ovary of the humpback whale (*Megaptera nodosa*). *Anat. Rec.*, **80**, 243.

DESAIVE, P. (1940). Contribution radio-biologique à l'étude de l'ovaire. *Arch. Biol., Paris*, **51**, 5.

—— (1941). Contribution radio-biologique à la démonstration de la fixité, dans l'ovaire de lapine adulte, des sources du développement folliculaire. *Acta neerl. morph.*, **4**, 10.

DIXON, A. F. (1927). Human oocyte showing first polar body and metaphase stage in formation of second polar body. *Irish J. Med. Sci.*, 1927, 149.

DODDS, G. S. (1910). Segregation of the germ-cells of the teleost *Lophius*. *J. Morph.*, **21**, 563.

DOERING, H. (1899). Beitrag zur Streitfrage über die Bildung des Corpus luteum. *Anat. Anz.*, **16**, 299.

DOGLIOTTI, G. C. (1926). Sulla velocità d'accrescimento degli elementi della granulosa ovarica nei mammiferi. *Monit. Zool. Ital.*, **37**, 115.

DRIPS, D. (1919). Studies on the ovary of the spermophile (*Spermophilus citellus tredecemlineatus*) with special reference to the corpus luteum. *Amer. J. Anat.*, **25**, 117.

DUBUISSON, H. (1903). Dégénérescence normale des ovules non pondus. *C. R. Acad. Sci., Paris*, **136**, 1690.

—— (1905a). Dégénérescence des ovules chez le moineau, la poule et le pigeon. *C. R. Soc. Biol., Paris*, **59**, 472.

—— (1905b). Dégénérescence des ovules chez les reptiles. *C. R. Soc. Biol., Paris*, **59**, 473.

—— (1905c). Sur les débuts de la dégénérescence dans les ovules de batraciens. *C. R. Soc. Biol., Paris*, **59**, 531.

—— (1906). Contribution à l'étude du vitellus. *Arch. Zool. Exp. Gén.*, **5**, 153.

DUKE, K. L. (1941). The germ cells of the rabbit ovary from sex differentiation to maturity. *J. Morph.*, **69**, 51.

—— (1944). Activity of the germinal epithelium in the ovary of a pregnant harvest mouse. *Anat. Rec.*, **89**, 135.

VAN DURME, M. (1914). Nouvelles recherches sur la vitellogenèse des œufs d'oiseaux aux stades d'accroissement, de maturation, de fécondation et du début de la segmentation. *Arch. Biol., Paris*, **29**, 71.

DUSTIN, A. P. (1907). Recherches sur l'origine des gonocytes chez les amphibiens. *Arch. Biol., Paris*, **23**, 411.

DUSTIN A. P., (1910). L'origine et l'evolution des gonocytes chez les reptiles (*Chrysemys marginata*). *Arch. Biol., Paris*, **25**, 495.

—— (1911). A propos de l'origine des sex-cells. *Anat. Anz.*, **40**, 250.

EIGENMANN, C. H. (1891). On the precocious segregation of the sex-cells in *Micrometrus aggregatus* Gibbons. *J. Morph.*, **5**, 481.

ENDERS, R. K., PEARSON, O. P., & PEARSON, A. K. (1946). Certain aspects of reproduction in the fur seal. *Anat. Rec.*, **94**, 213.

ENGLE, E. T. (1927a). Polyovular follicles and polynuclear ova in the mouse. *Anat. Rec.*, **35**, 341.

—— (1927b). A quantitative study of follicular atresia in the mouse. *Amer. J Anat.*, **39**, 187.

—— (1931). Prepubertal growth of the ovarian follicle in the albino mouse. *Anat. Rec.*, **48**, 341.

—— & SMITH, P. E. (1929). The origin of the corpus luteum in the rat as indicated by studies upon the luteinization of the cystic follicle. *Anat. Rec.*, **43**, 239.

ESCHER, H. H. (1913). Über den Farbstoff des Corpus luteum. *Hoppe-Seyl. Z.*, **83**, 198.

'ESPINASSE, P. G. (1934). The membrana granulosa of the mouse. *Nature, Lond.*, **134**, 182.

ESSENBERG, J. M. (1923). Sex-differentiation in the viviparous teleost *Xiphophorus helleri* Heckel. *Biol. Bull., Wood's Hole*, **45**, 46.

EVANS, H. M., & COLE, H. H. (1931). An introduction to the study of the oestrous cycle in the dog. *Mem. Univ. Calif.*, **9**, 65.

—— & SWEZY, O. (1931). Ovogenesis and the normal follicular cycle in adult mammalia. *Mem. Univ. Calif.*, **9**, 119.

EVERETT, N. B. (1942). The origin of ova in the adult opossum. *Anat. Rec.*, **82**, 77.

—— (1943). Observational and experimental evidences relating to the origin and differentiation of the definitive germ-cells in mice. *J. exp. Zool.*, **92**, 49.

FALKINER, N. McI. (1933). A study of the structure and vascular conditions of the human corpus luteum in the menstrual cycle and in pregnancy. *Irish J. Med. Sci.*, 1933, 1.

FEDOROW, V. (1907). Ueber die Wanderung der Genitalzellen bei *Salmo fario*. *Anat. Anz.*, **31**, 219.

FEE, A. R., & PARKES, A. S. (1929). Studies on ovulation. 1. The relation of the anterior pituitary body to ovulation in the rabbit. *J. Physiol.*, **67**, 383.

FELIX, W. (1912). In *Manual of human embryology*. By F. Keibel and F. P. Mall, **2**, 752. Philadelphia.

FELL, H. B. (1923). Histological studies on the gonads of the fowl. 1. The histological basis of sex reversal. *J. exp. Biol.*, **1**, 97.

—— (1924). Histological studies on the gonads of the fowl. 2. The histogenesis of the so-called " Luteal " cells in the ovary. *J. exp. Biol.*, **1**, 293.

FERRONI, C., & FERRI, E. (1939). Alterazioni delle arterie delle ovarie in rapporto con l'età. *Arch. ital. Anat. Embriol.*, **41**, 411.

FIRKET, J. (1913). Recherches sur les gonocytes primaires (Urgeschlechtszellen) pendant la période d'indifférence sexuelle et le développement de l'ovaire chez le poulet. *Anat. Anz.*, **44**, 166.

—— (1914). Recherches sur l'organogenèse des glandes sexuelles chez les oiseaux. *Arch. Biol., Paris*, **29**, 201.

—— (1920a). On the origin of germ cells in higher vertebrates. *Anat. Rec.*, **18**, 309.

—— (1920b). Recherches sur l'organogénèse des glandes sexuelles chez les oiseaux. *Arch. Biol., Paris*, **30**, 393.

FISCHEL, A. (1930). Über die Entwicklung der Keimdrüsen des Menschen. *Z. Ges. Anat.* 1. *Z. Anat. EntwGesch.*, **92**, 34.

FISCHER, I. (1935). Zur Keimbahnfrage bei den urodelen Amphibien. *Z. mikr.-anat. Forsch.*, **37**, 219.

FISHER, R. A. (1930). *Statistical methods for research workers*. Edinburgh.

FLEMMING, W. (1885a). Studien über Regeneration der Gewebe. 9. Ueber die Regeneration verschiedener Epithelien durch mitotische Zelltheilung. *Arch. mikr. Anat.*, **24**, 371.

FLEMMING, W. (1885b). Ueber die Bildung von Richtungsfiguren in Säugethiereiern beim Untergang Graaf'scher Follikel. *Arch. Anat. Physiol.*, Leipzig, 1885, 221.

FLORIAN, J. (1931). " Urkeimzellen " bei einem 625μ langen menschlichen Embryo. *Anat. Anz.*, **72**, *Verh. Anat. Ges. Jena*, 286.

FLYNN, T. T. (1930). On the unsegmented ovum of Echidna (*Tachyglossus*). *Quart. J. micr. Sci.*, **74**, 119.

—— & HILL, J. P. (1939). The development of the Monotremata. 4. Growth of the ovarian ovum, maturation, fertilisation, and early cleavage. *Trans. Zool. Soc. Lond.*, **24**, 445.

FOOTE, C. L., & WITSCHI, E. (1939). Effect of sex hormones on the gonads of frog larvae (*Rana clamitans*). Sex inversion in females ; stability in males. *Anat. Rec.*, **75**, 75.

FORBES, T. R. (1940). Studies on the reproductive system of the alligator. IV. Observations of the development of the gonad, the adrenal cortex, and the Müllerian duct. *Contr. Embryol. Carneg. Instn.*, **28**, 129.

FRAENKEL, L. (1905). Vergleichend histologische Untersuchungen über das Vorkommen drüsiger Formationen im interstitiellen Eierstocksgewebe (glande interstitielle de l'ovaire). *Arch. Gynaek.*, **75**, 443.

—— (1911). Die interstitielle Eierstocksdrüse. *Berl. Klin. Wschr.*, **48**, 60.

FRASER, E. A. (1919). The development of the urogenital system in the Marsupialia, with special reference to *Trichosurus vulpecula*. *J. Anat., Lond.*, **53**, 97.

FROMMOLT, G. (1934). Studien an Makakusovarien. *Z. Geburtsh. Gynäk.*, **107**, 165.

FUSS, A. (1911). Ueber extraregionäre Geschlechtszellen bei einem menschlichen Embryo von 4 Wochen. *Anat. Anz.*, **39**, 407.

—— (1913). Über die Geschlechtszellen des Menschen und der Säugetiere. *Arch. mikr. Anat.*, **81**, 1.

GANFINI, C. (1906). Sulla struttura e sviluppo delle cellule interstiziale dell' ovaia. *Boll. Accad. Med. Genova*, **21**, 41.

—— (1907). Sul probabile significato fisiologico dell' atresia follicolare nell' ovaio di alcuni mammiferi. *Arch. ital. Anat. Embriol.*, **6**, 346.

—— (1909). Sulla struttura e sviluppo delle cellule interstiziali dell' ovajo. *Arch. ital. Anat. Embriol.*, **7**, 373.

GARDE, M. L. (1930). The ovary of *Ornithorhynchus*, with special reference to follicular atresia. *J. Anat., Lond.*, **64**, 422.

GASPARRO, E. (1908). Osservazioni sull' origine dell cellule sessuali nel *Gongylus ocellatus*. *Monit. Zool. Ital.*, **19**, 105.

GATENBY, J. BRONTË (1922). Some notes on the gametogenesis of *Ornithorhynchus paradoxus*. *Quart. J. micr. Sci.*, **66**, 475.

—— (1924). Notes on the human ovary, with special reference to a corpus luteum of ovulation. *Proc. R. Irish Acad.* B, **36**, 65.

VON GAWRONSKY, N. (1894). Ueber Verbreitung und Endigung der Nerven in den weiblichen Genitalien. *Arch. Gynaek.*, **47**, 271.

GEGENBAUR, C. (1861). Ueber den Bau und die Entwickelung der Wirbelthiereier mit partieller Dottertheilung. *Arch. Anat. Physiol., Lpz.*, 1861, 491.

GELLER, F. C. (1930). Zellveränderungen im Eierstock der geschlechtsreifen weissen Maus nach Röntgenbestrahlung. *Arch. Gynaek.*, **141**, 61.

GENTHER, I. T. (1931). Irradiation of the ovaries of guinea-pigs and its effect on the oestrous cycle. *Amer. J. Anat.*, **48**, 99.

GÉRARD, P. (1920). Contribution à l'étude de l'ovaire des mammifères. L'ovaire de *Galago mossambicus* (Young). *Arch. Biol.*, Paris, **30**, 357.

—— (1932). Études sur l'ovogenèse et l'ontogenèse chez les lémuriens du genre *Galago*. *Arch. Biol.*, Paris, **43**, 93.

GIACOMINI, E. (1896). Contributo all' istologia dell' ovario dei Selaci con speciale riguardo sopra ad alcune particolarità di struttura riscontrate nell' ovario di *Myliobatis boviva*. Geoff. St. Hil. *Ric. Lab. Anat. Norm. Univ. Roma*, **5**, 221.

GIANNELLI, L. (1909). Ricerche sullo sviluppo delle cellule interstiziali dell' ovario e del testicolo in *Lepus cuniculus*. *Atti Accad. Sci. Med. Nat. Ferrara.*, **83**, 1.

GILLMAN, J. (1948). The development of the gonads in man, with a consideration of the rôle of fetal endocrines and the histogenesis of ovarian tumors. *Contr. Embryol. Carneg. Instn.*, **32**, 81.

GOETTE, A. (1875). *Die Entwickelungsgeschichte der Unke.* Leipzig.

GOLDSMITH, J. B. (1928). The history of the germ cells in the domestic fowl. *J. Morph.*, **46**, 275.

—— (1932). The history of the germ cells in the albino rat (*Mus norvegicus albinus*). *Trans. Amer. Micr. Soc.*, **51**, 161.

—— (1935). The primordial germ cells of the chick. 1. The effect on the gonad of complete and partial removal of the " germinal crescent " and of removal of other parts of the blastodisc. *J. Morph.*, **58**, 537.

GOODALE, H. D. (1919). Interstitial cells in the gonads of domestic fowl. *Anat. Rec.*, **16**, 247.

GOODALL, J. R. (1920). The origin of epithelial tumours of the ovary. *Proc. Roy. Soc. Med., Obstet. Gynaec.*, **13**, 63.

GOODRICH, E. S. (1930). *Studies on the structure and development of vertebrates.* London.

GOODRICH, H. B., DEE, J. E., FLYNN, C. M., & MERCER, R. N. (1934). Germ cells and sex differentiation in *Lebistes reticulatus*. *Biol. Bull., Wood's Hole*, **67**, 83.

GOORMAGHTIGH, N. (1921). Organogénèse et histogénèse de la capsule surrénale et du plexus coeliaque. *Arch. Biol., Paris*, **31**, 83.

—— (1927). Le corps jaune de la chienne gravide. Contribution à l'étude du métabolisme des lipoïdes. *Arch. Biol., Paris*, **37**, 46.

GREEN, S. H., & ZUCKERMAN, S. (1947). A comparison of the growth of the ovum and follicle in normal rhesus monkeys, and in monkeys treated with oestrogens and androgens. *J. Endocrinol.*, **5**, 207.

—— —— (1951). Quantitative aspects of the growth of the human ovum and follicle *J. Anat., Lond.*, **85**, 373.

GREGORY, P. W. (1930). The early embryology of the rabbit. *Contr. Embryol. Carneg. Instn.*, **21**, 141.

GRESSON, R. A. R. (1933). A study of the cytoplasmic inclusions and nucleolar phenomena during the oogenesis of the mouse. *Quart. J. micr. Sci.*, **75**, 697.

—— (1941). A study of the cytoplasmic inclusions during maturation, fertilization and the first cleavage division of the egg of the mouse. *Quart. J. micr. Sci.*, **82**, 35.

GROHE, F. (1863). Ueber den Bau und das Wachsthum des menschlichen Eierstocks, und über einige krankhafte Störungen desselben. *Virchow's Arch.*, **26**, 271.

GRUENWALD, P. (1942). The development of the sex cords in the gonads of man and mammals. *Amer. J. Anat.*, **70**, 359.

GUTHRIE, M. J., & JEFFERS, K. R. (1938). A cytological study of the ovaries of the bats *Myotis lucifugus lucifugus* and *Myotis grisescens*. *J. Morph.*, **62**, 523.

GUTTMACHER, M. S., & GUTTMACHER, A. F. (1921). Morphological and physiological studies on the musculature of the mature Graafian follicle of the sow. *Johns Hopk. Hosp. Bull.*, **32**, 394.

HAMLETT, G. W. D. (1935a). Primordial germ cells in a 4·5 mm. human embryo. *Anat. Rec.*, **61**, 273.

—— (1935b). Extra-ovarial sex cords on an armadillo ovary. *Anat. Rec.*, **62**, 195.

HALL, O. (1952). Accessory corpora lutea in the wild Norway rat. *Texas Rep. Biol. Med.*, **10**, 32.

HALL, R. W. (1904). The development of the mesonephros and the Müllerian duct in Amphibia. *Bull. Mus. Comp. Zool. Harv.*, **45**, 31.

HAMILTON, W. J. (1934). The early stages in the development of the ferret : fertilisation to the formation of the prochordal plate. *Trans. Roy. Soc. Edin.*, **58**, 251.

—— (1944). Phases of maturation and fertilisation in human ova. *J. Anat., Lond.*, **78**, 1.

HAMMOND, J. (1917). On the causes responsible for the developmental progress of the mammary glands in the rabbit during the latter part of pregnancy. *Proc. Roy. Soc.* B, **89**, 534.

—— (1925). *Reproduction in the rabbit.* Edinburgh.

HAMMOND, J. (1927). *The physiology of reproduction in the cow.* Cambridge.

—— & MARSHALL, F. H. A. (1930). Oestrus and pseudo-pregnancy in the ferret. *Proc. Roy. Soc.* B, **105**, 607.

HANN, H. W. (1927). The history of the germ cells of *Cottus bairdii* Girard. *J. Morph.*, **43**, 427.

HANSON, F. B., & HEYS, F. (1927). On ovarian regeneration in the albino rat. *Proc. Soc. exp. Biol., N.Y.*, **25**, 183.

HARGITT, G. T. (1924). Germ-cell origin in the adult salamander, *Diemyctylus viridescens* *J. Morph.*, **39**, 63.

—— (1925). The formation of the sex glands and germ cells of mammals. 1. The origin of the germ cells in the albino rat. *J. Morph.*, **40**, 517.

—— (1930a). The formation of the sex glands and germ cells of mammals. 3. The history of the female germ cells in the albino rat to the time of sexual maturity. *J. Morph.*, **49**, 277.

—— (1930b). The formation of the sex glands and germ cells of mammals. 4. Continuous origin and degeneration of germ cells in the female albino rat. *J. Morph.*, **49**, 333.

—— (1930c). The formation of the sex glands and germ cells of mammals. 5. Germ cells in the ovaries of adult, pregnant, and senile albino rats. *J. Morph.*, **50**, 453.

HARMAN, M. T. (1935). Parthenogenesis in the ovaries of guinea pigs. *Trans. Kans. Acad. Sci.*, **38**, 319.

—— & KIRGIS, H. D. (1938). The development and atresia of the Graafian follicle and the division of intra-ovarian ova in the guinea pig. *Amer. J. Anat.*, **63**, 79.

HARRISON, R. J. (1946). The early development of the corpus luteum in the mare. *J. Anat., Lond.*, **80**, 160.

—— (1948a). The changes occurring in the ovary of the goat during the oestrous cycle and in early pregnancy. *J. Anat., Lond.*, **82**, 21.

—— (1948b). The development and fate of the corpus luteum in the vertebrate series. *Biol. Rev.*, **23**, 296.

—— (1949a). Observations on the female reproductive organs of the Ca'aing whale *Globiocephala melaena* Traill. *J. Anat., Lond.*, **83**, 238.

—— (1949b). Multiovular follicles in the ovaries of lower primates. *Nature, Lond.*, **164**, 409.

—— & MATTHEWS, L. H. (1951). Sub-surface crypts in the cortex of the mammalian ovary. *Proc. zool. Soc. Lond.*, **120**, 699.

HARTMAN, C. (1923). The oestrous cycle in the opposum. *Amer. J. Anat.*, **32**, 353.

HARTMAN, C. G. (1926). Polynuclear ova and polyovular follicles in the opossum and other mammals, with special reference to the problem of fecundity. *Amer. J. Anat.* **37**, 1.

—— (1929a). Some excessively large litters of eggs liberated at a single ovulation in mammals. *J. Mammal*, **10**, 197.

—— (1929b). How large is the mammalian egg ? *Quart. Rev. Biol.*, **4**, 373.

—— (1932a). Studies in the reproduction of the monkey *Macacus (Pithecus) rhesus*, with special reference to menstruation and pregnancy. *Contr. Embryol. Carneg. Instn.*, **23**, 1.

—— (1932b). *Sex and internal secretions.* Chap. 14. New York.

—— & CORNER, G. W. (1941). The first maturation division of the macaque ovum. *Contr. Embryol. Carneg. Instn.*, **29**, 1.

—— LEWIS, W. H., MILLER, F. W., & SWETT, W. W. (1931). First findings of tubal ova in the cow, together with notes on oestrus. *Anat. Rec.*, **48**, 267.

HARZ, W. (1883). Beiträge zur Histiologie des Ovariums der Säugethiere. *Arch. mikr. Anat.*, **22**, 374.

HATERIUS, H. O. (1928). An experimental study of ovarian regeneration in mice. *Physiol. Zoöl.*, **1**, 45.

HEAPE, W. (1886). The development of the mole (*Talpa europea*), the ovarian ovum, and segmentation of the ovum. *Quart. J. micr. Sci.*, **26**, 157.

—— (1905). Ovulation and degeneration of ova in the rabbit. *Proc. Roy. Soc.* B, **76**, 260.

HENNEGUY, L. F. (1894). Recherches sur l'atrésie des follicules de Graaf. *J. Anat., Paris*, **30**, 1.

―― (1926). Sur la situation de l'appareil de Golgi dans les cellules folliculaires de l'ovaire de cobaye. *C. R. Soc. Biol., Paris*, **94**, 764.

HENSEN, V. (1876). Beobachtungen über die Befruchtung und Entwicklung des Kaninchens und Meerschweinchens. *Z. Anat. EntwGesch.*, **1**, 213 and 353.

VON HERFF, O. (1892). Ueber den feineren Verlauf der Nerven im Eierstocke des Menschen. *Z. Geburtsh. Gynäk.*, **24**, 289.

HETT, J. (1922). Das Corpus luteum der Vögel. *Anat. Anz.*, **55**, *Verh. Anat. Ges. Jena*, **31**, 153.

―― (1923a). Das Corpus luteum der Dohle (*Colaeus monedula*). *Arch. mikr. Anat.*, **97**, 718.

―― (1923b). Das Corpus luteum des Molches (*Triton vulgaris*). *Z. Ges. Anat.* 1. *Z. Anat. EntwGesch.*, **68**, 243.

―― (1924). Das Corpus luteum der Zauneidechse (*Lacerta agilis*). *Z. mikr.-anat. Forsch.*, **1**, 41.

―― (1931). Über das Bindegewebe des Vogeleierstockes nach der Eiablage nebst Bemerkungen über den Sprung atretischer Follikel. *Z. mikr.-anat. Forsch.*, **25**, 428.

HEUSER, C. H., & STREETER, G. L. (1929). Early stages in the development of pig embryos, from the period of initial cleavage to the time of the appearance of limb-buds. *Contr. Embryol. Carneg. Instn.*, **20**, 1.

HEYS, F. (1931). The problem of the origin of germ cells. *Quart. Rev. Biol.*, **6**, 1.

HIGUCHI, K. (1932). Über die erste Anlage der menschlichen Keimdrüs und ihre geschlechtliche Differenzierung. *Arch. Gynaek.*, **149**, 144.

HILL, J. P. (1900). On the foetal membranes, placentation and parturition of the native cat (*Dasyurus viverrinus*). *Anat. Anz.*, **18**, 364.

―― (1910). The early development of the Marsupialia, with special reference to the native cat (*Dasyurus viverrinus*). *Quart. J. micr. Sci.*, **56**, 1.

―― (1932). The developmental history of the Primates. *Philos. Trans.* B, **221**, 45.

―― & GATENBY, J. BRONTË (1926). The corpus luteum of the Monotremata. *Proc. zool. Soc. Lond.*, **47**, 715.

―― & TRIBE, M. (1924). The early development of the cat (*Felis domestica*). *Quart. J. micr. Sci.*, **68**, 513.

HILL, M., & PARKES, A. S. (1930). The relation between the anterior pituitary body and the gonads. 2. The induction of ovulation in the anoestrous ferret. *Proc. Roy. Soc.* B, **107**, 30.

―― & WHITE, W. E. (1933). The growth and regression of follicles in the oestrous rabbit. *J. Physiol.*, **80**, 174.

HILL, R. T., ALLEN, EDGAR, & KRAMER, T. C. (1935). Cinemicrographic studies of rabbit ovulation. *Anat. Rec.*, **63**, 239.

HINSELMANN, H. (1930). Weiteres über den Reifegrad der menschlichen Eizelle im Eierstock. *Z. mikr.-anat. Forsch.*, **19**, 163.

HIS, W. (1865). Beobachtungen über den Bau des Säugethiereierstockes. *Arch. mikr. Anat.*, **1**, 151.

―― (1899). (Discussion.) *Anat. Anz.*, **16**, *Verh. Anat. Ges. Jena*, 37.

HOADLEY, L., & SIMONS, D. (1928). Maturation phases in human oöcytes. *Amer. J. Anat.*, **41**, 497.

HOFFMANN, C. K. (1889). Zur Entwicklungsgeschichte der Urogenitalorgane bei den Reptilien. *Z. Wiss. Zool.*, **48**, 260.

―― (1892). Étude sur le développement de l'appareil uro-génital des oiseaux. *Verh. Akad. Wet. Amst.*, **1**, 1.

HOLL, M. (1893). Über die reifung der Eizelle bei den Säugethieren. *S.B. Akad. Wiss. Wien.*, Abt. 3., **102**, 249.

D'HOLLANDER, F. (1904). Recherches sur l'oogenèse et sur la structure et la signification du noyau vitellin de Balbiani chez les oiseaux. *Arch. Anat. Micr.*, **7**, 117.

HONORE, C. (1900). Recherches sur l'ovaire du lapin. 1. Note sur les corps de Call & Exner et la formation du liquor folliculi. 2. Recherches sur la formation du corps jaune. *Arch. Biol., Paris*, **16**, 537.

HORRENBERGER, R. (1928). Contribution à l'étude du follicule ovarique et du corps jaune chez la femme. *Arch. Anat., Strasbourg,* **8,** 129.

VAN DER HORST, C. J. (1942). Early stages in the embryonic development of *Elephantulus.* *S. Afr. J. med. Sci.,* **7** (Biol. Suppl.), 55.

—— & GILLMAN, J. (1940). Ovulation and corpus luteum formation in *Elephantulus.* *S. Afr. J. med. Sci.,* **5,** 73.

—— —— (1941). The number of eggs and surviving embryos in *Elephantulus.* *Anat. Rec.,* **80,** 443.

—— —— (1942). The life history of the corpus luteum of menstruation in *Elephantulus.* *S. Afr. J. med. Sci.,* **7,** 21.

—— —— (1945). The behaviour of the Graafian follicle of *Elephantulus* during pregnancy, with special reference to the hormonal regulation of ovarian activity. *S. Afr. J. med. Sci.,* **10** (Biol. Suppl.), 1.

HULPIEU, H. (1925). Observations of the definitive sex-cells of the chick. *Proc. Okla Acad. Sci.,* **5,** 70.

HUMPHREY, R. R. (1925). The primordial germ cells of *Hemidactylium* and other Amphibia. *J. Morph.,* **41,** 1.

—— (1927a). Extirpation of the primordial germ cells of *Amblystoma* : its effect upon the development of the gonad. *J. exp. Zool.,* **49,** 363.

—— (1927b). Modification or suppression of the so-called migration of primordial germ cells in anuran embryos. *Anat. Rec.* (abstract), **35,** 41.

—— (1928). The developmental potencies of the intermediate mesoderm of *Amblystoma* when transplanted into ventrolateral sites in other embryos : the primordial germ cells of such grafts and their rôle in the development of a gonad. *Anat. Rec.,* **40,** 67.

—— (1929a). The early position of the primordial germ cells in urodeles : evidence from experimental studies. *Anat. Rec.,* **42,** 301.

—— (1929b). Studies on sex reversal in *Amblystoma.* 1. Bisexuality and sex reversal in larval males uninfluenced by ovarian hormones. *Anat. Rec.,* **42,** 119.

—— (1929c). Studies on sex reversal in *Amblystoma.* 2. Sex differentiation and modification following orthotopic implantation of a gonadic preprimordium. *J. exp. Zool.,* **53,** 171.

—— (1931a). Studies on sex reversal in *Amblystoma.* 3. Transformation of the ovary of *A. tigrinum* into a functional testis through the influence of a testis resident in the same animal. *J. exp. Zool.,* **58,** 333.

—— (1931b). Studies on sex reversal in *Amblystoma.* 4. The developmental potencies exhibited by the modified (" freemartin ") ovary of *Amblystoma tigrinum* following removal of the testis which had induced its modification. *J. exp. Zool.,* **58,** 367.

—— (1931c). Studies on sex reversal in *Amblystoma.* 5. The structure of ovaries of *A. tigrinum* subjected for long periods to the influence of a testis resident in the same animal. *Anat. Rec.,* **51,** 135.

—— (1933). Studies on sex reversal in *Amblystoma.* 6. Interactions of ovary and testis in Arkansas strain of *Amblystoma punctatum.* *Proc. Soc. exp. Biol., N.Y.,* **30,** 1078.

—— (1935a). Studies on sex reversal in *Amblystoma.* 7. Reversal of sex type in gonadic preprimordia of *A. punctatum* males implanted in females of more rapidly growing species. *Anat. Rec.,* **62,** 223.

—— (1935b). Studies on sex reversal in *Amblystoma.* 8. Sex type of gonads developed from gonadic preprimordia of *A. punctatum* implanted in axolotl females. *Proc. Soc. exp. Biol., N.Y.,* **33,** 102.

—— (1936a). Studies on sex reversal in *Amblystoma.* 9. Reversal of ovaries to testes in parabiotic *A. tigrinum.* *J. exp. Zool.,* **73,** 1.

—— (1936b). Studies on sex reversal in *Amblystoma.* 10. Sex reversal in parabiotic *A. punctatum* of various local races. *Amer. J. Anat.,* **59,** 347.

ICHIKAWA, A. (1937). Masculinization by testicular transplantation in spayed female *Triturus pyrrhogaster* with remarks on testis-ova and the modification of lateral-line organs. *J. Fac. Sci. Hokkaido Univ., Zool.,* **6,** 71.

IKEDA, T. (1928). Über die genetische Veränderung der Zellorganellen, besonders der Golgischen Apparate in Vogeleizellen. *Folia Anat., Japon.*, **6**, 389.

JÄGERSTEN, G. (1935). Untersuchungen über den strukturellen Aufbau der Eizelle. *Zool. Bidr. Uppsala*, **16**, 1.

JANKOWSKI, J. (1904). Beitrag zur Entstehung des Corpus luteum der Säugetiere. *Arch. mikr. Anat.*, **64**, 361.

JANOSIK, J. (1885). Histologisch-embryologische Untersuchungen über das Urogenitalsystem. *S.B. Akad. Wiss. Wien.*, **91**, Abt. 3, 97.

—— (1887). Zur histologie des Ovariums. *S.B. Akad. Wiss. Wien.*, **96**, Abt. 3, 172.

—— (1890). Bemerkungen über die Entwicklung des Genitalsystems. *S.B. Akad. Wiss. Wien*, **99**, Abt. 3, 260.

—— (1897). Die Atrophie der Follikel und ein seltsames Verhalten der Eizelle. *Arch. mikr. Anat.*, **48**, 169.

JARVIS, M. M. (1908). The segregation of the germ-cells of *Phrynosoma cornutum*. *Biol. Bull., Wood's Hole*, **15**, 119.

JENKINSON, J. W. (1913). *Vertebrate embryology*. Oxford.

JKEDA, K. (1928). Beitrag zur Histologie des Corpus luteum. Eigenfibrillen der Luteinzellen. Dunkle Luteinzellen. Rückbildung der Luteinzellen nach Abort und Schwangerschaft. *Z. Geburtsh. Gynäk.*, **93**, 229.

JOHNSTON, P. M. (1951). The embryonic history of the germ cells of the largemouth black bass, *Micropterus salmoides salmoides*. (Lacépède). *J. Morph.*, **88**, 471.

JONCKHEERE, F. (1930). Contribution à l'histogénèse de l'ovaire des mammifères. L'ovaire de *Canis familiaris*. *Arch. Biol., Paris*, **40**, 357.

JORDAN, H. E. (1917). Embryonic history of the germ-cells of the loggerhead turtle (*Caretta caretta*). *Pap. Tortugas Lab.*, **11**, 313.

JÖRGENSEN, M. (1913). Zellenstudien. 1. Morphologische Beiträge zum Problem des Eiwachstums. *Arch. Zellforsch.*, **10**, 1.

KALTENEGGER, A. (1915). Beiträge zur Sterilität des Rindes mit besonderer Berucksichtigung des histologischen Ursprunges und Ausbaues des Corpus luteum. *Wien. Tierärztl. Mschr.*, **2**, 12.

KAMPMEIER, O. F. (1929). On the problem of " parthenogenesis " in the mammalian ovary. *Amer. J. Anat.*, **43**, 45.

KELLY, G. L. (1931). Direct observation of rupture of the Graafian follicle in a mammal. *J. Fla. Med. Ass.*, **17**, 422.

KING, H. D. (1902). The follicle sacs of the amphibian ovary. *Biol. Bull., Wood's Hole*, **3**, 245.

—— (1908). The oögenesis of *Bufo lentiginosus*. *J. Morph.*, **19**, 369.

KINGERY, H. M. (1917). Oogenesis in the white mouse. *J. Morph.*, **30**, 261.

KINGSBURY, B. F. (1913). The morphogenesis of the mammalian ovary : *Felis domestica*. *Amer. J. Anat.*, **15**, 345.

—— (1914). The interstitial cells of the mammalian ovary : *Felis domestica*. *Amer. J. Anat.*, **16**, 59.

—— (1939). Atresia and the interstitial cells of the ovary. *Amer. J. Anat.*, **65**, 309.

KIRKHAM, W. B. (1916). The germ cell cycle in the mouse. *Anat. Rec.*, **10**, 217.

KITAHARA, Y. (1923). Über die Entstehung der Zwischenzellen der Keimdrüsen des Menschen und der Säugetiere und über deren physiologische Bedeutung. *Arch. EntwMech. Org.*, **52**, 550.

KOCH, W. (1926). Untersuchungen über die Entwicklung des Eierstockes der Vögel. 1. Die postembryonale Entwicklung der Form und des Aufbaues des Eierstockes beim Haushuhn (*Gallus domesticus* L.). *Z. Mikr.-Anat. Forsch.*, **7**, 1.

KOHN, A. (1926). Über den Bau des embryonalen Pferdeeierstockes. *Z. Ges. Anat.* 1. *Z. Anat. EntwGesch.*, **79**, 366.

—— (1928). Über " Leydigsche Zwischenzellen " im Hilus des menschlichen Eierstockes. *Endokrinologie*, **1**, 3.

KOHNO, S. (1925). Zur Kenntnis der Keimbahn des Menschen. *Arch. Gynaek.*, **126**, 310.

KÖLLIKER, A. (1867). *Handbuch der Gewebelehre des Menschen*. Leipzig.

—— (1898). Ueber Corpora lutea atretica bei Säugetieren. *Anat. Anz.*, **14**, *Verh. Anat. Ges. Jena*, 149.

KRAFKA, J. (1939). Parthenogenic cleavage in the human ovary. *Anat. Rec.*, **75**, 19.

KREMER, J. (1924). Studien zur oogenese der Säugetiere nach Untersuchungen bei der Ratte und Maus. *Arch. mikr. Anat.*, **102**, 337.

KROHN, P. L. (1951). Endometriosis and supernumerary ectopic ovarian tissue in a rhesus monkey. *J. Obstet. Gynaec.*, **58**, 430.

KULESCH, L. (1914). Der Netzapparat von Golgi in den Zellen des Eierstockes. *Arch. mikr. Anat.*, **84**, 142.

KUMMERLÖWE, H. (1930a). Vergleichende Untersuchungen über das Gonadensystem weiblicher Vögel. 1. *Columba livia domestica. Z. mikr.-anat. Forsch.*, **21**, 1.

—— (1930b). Vergleichende Untersuchungen über das Gonadensystem weiblicher Vögel. 2. *Passer domesticus* (L). *Z. mikr.-anat. Forsch.*, **22**, 259.

—— (1931a). Vergleichende Untersuchungen über das Gonadensystem weiblicher Vögel. 3. Ausgewählte Beispiele aus verschiedenen Vogelordnungen. *Z. mikr.-anat. Forsch.*, **24**, 455.

—— (1931b). Vergleichende Untersuchungen über das Gonadensystem weiblicher Vögel. 4. Über zwei singende Kanarienvogelweibchen und über ein Amselweibchen mit ungewöhnlich intensiver Schnabelfärbung. *Z. mikr.-anat. Forsch.*, **25**, 311.

KUNTZ, A. (1919). The innervation of the gonads of the dog. *Anat. Rec.*, **17**, 203.

KÜPFER, M. (1920a). Beiträge zur Morphologie der weiblichen Geschlechtsorgane bei den Säugetieren. *N. Denkschr. Schweiz. Naturf. Ges.*, **56**, 1.

—— (1920b). Beiträge zur Morphologie der weiblichen Geschlechtsorgane bei den Säugetieren. Über das Auftreten gelber Körper am Ovarium des domestizierten Rindes und Schweines. *Vjschr. Naturf. Ges. Zürich*, **65**, 377.

KURASHIGE, S. (1927). Über die Entstehung des Corpus luteum beim Kaninchen. *J. Coll. Agric. Sapporo.*, **20**, 1.

KUSCHAKEWITSCH, S. (1910). Die Entwicklungsgeschichte der Keimdrüsen von *Rana esculenta*. Ein Beitrag zum Sexualitätsproblem. *Festsch. R. Hertwig. Jena*, **2**, 61.

LAMS, H. (1913). Étude de l'œuf de cobaye aux premiers stades de l'embryogenèse. *Arch. Biol., Paris*, **28**, 229.

—— & DOORME, J. (1907). Nouvelles recherches sur la maturation et la fécondation de l'œuf des mammifères. *Arch. Biol., Paris*, **23**, 259.

LANDAU, R. (1938). Der ovariale und tubale Abschnitt des Genitaltraktus beim nichtgraviden und beim früh-graviden *Hemicentetes*-Weibchen. *Bio-morphosis*, **1**, 228.

LANE, C. E. (1938). Aberrant ovarian follicles in the immature rat. *Anat. Rec.*, **71**, 243.

—— & DAVIS, F. R. (1939). The ovary of the adult rat. I. Changes in growth of the follicle and in volume and mitotic activity of the granulosa and theca during the estrous cycle. *Anat. Rec.*, **73**, 429.

LANE-CLAYPON, J. E. (1905). On the origin and life history of the interstitial cells of the ovary in the rabbit. *Proc. Roy. Soc.* B, **77**, 32.

—— (1907). On ovogenesis and the formation of the interstitial cells of the ovary. *J. Obstet. Gynaec.*, **11**, 205.

LATTA, J. S., & PEDERSON, E. S. (1944). The origin of ova and follicle cells from the germinal epithelium of the ovary of the albino rat as demonstrated by selective intra-vital staining with India ink. *Anat. Rec.*, **90**, 23.

LEAGUE, B., & HARTMAN, C. G. (1925). Anovular Graafian follicles in mammalian ovaries. *Anat. Rec.*, **30**, 1.

LEUCKART, R. (1852). Das Weber'sche Organ und seine Metamorphosen. *Illustr. Med. Ztg.*, **1**, 69.

LEVI, G. (1903). Dei corpi di Call ed Exner dell' ovajo. *Monit. Zool. Ital.*, **13**, 298.

—— (1913). Note citologiche sulle cellule somatiche dell' ovaio dei mammiferi. *Arch. Zellforsch.*, **11**, 515.

LIMON, M. (1902). Étude histologique et histogénique de la glande interstitielle de l'ovaire. *Arch. Anat. Micr.*, **5**, 155.

LIPSCHÜTZ, A. (1925). Dynamics of ovarian hypertrophy under experimental conditions. *Brit. J. exp. Biol.*, **2**, 331.

—— (1928). New developments in ovarian dynamics and the law of follicular constancy. *J. exp. Biol.*, **5**, 283.

LIPSCHÜTZ, A. & VOSS, H. E. V. (1925).   Further developments on the dynamics of ovarian hypertrophy.   *Brit. J. exp. Biol.*, **3**, 35.

LOEB, L. (1905).   Über hypertrophische Vorgänge bei der Follikelatresie nebst Bemerkungen über die Oocyten in den Marksträngen und über Teilungserscheinungen am Ei im Ovarium des Meerschweinchens.   *Arch. mikr. Anat.*, **65**, 728.

—— (1906a).   Ueber die Entwickelung des Corpus luteum beim Meerschweinchen.   *Anat. Anz.*, **28**, 102.

—— (1906b).   The formation of the corpus luteum in the guinea-pig.   *J. Amer. med. Ass.*, **46**, 416.

—— (1910).   The cyclic changes in the ovary of the guinea-pig.   *J. Morph.*, **22**, 37.

—— (1917).   The relation of the ovary to the uterus and mammary gland from the experimental aspect.   *Trans. Amer. Gynec. Soc.*, **42**, 172.

—— (1930).   Parthenogenetic development of eggs in the ovary of the guinea-pig.   *Proc. Soc. exp. Biol., N.Y.*, **27**, 413.

—— (1932).   The parthenogenetic development of eggs in the ovary of the guinea-pig.   *Anat. Rec.*, **51**, 373.

LONG, J. A., & EVANS, H. M. (1922).   The oestrous cycle in the rat and its associated phenomena.   *Mem. Univ. Calif.*, **6**, 1.

—— & MARK, E. L. (1911).   The maturation of the egg of the mouse.   *Contr. Embryol. Carneg. Instn.*, **142**, 1.

LONGLEY, W. H. (1911).   The maturation of the egg and ovulation in the domestic cat.   *Amer. J. Anat.*, **12**, 139.

LOYEZ, M. (1906).   Recherches sur le développement ovarien des œufs méroblastiques à vitellus nutritif abondant.   *Arch. Anat. Micr.*, **8**, 69.

—— (1911).   Sur la structure de l'oocyte de la femme à la période d'accroissement.   *C. R. Ass. Anat., Paris*, **13**, 49.

LUCIEN, M. (1903).   Note préliminaire sur les premières phases de la formation des corps jaunes chez certains reptiles.   *C. R. Soc. Biol., Paris*, **55**, 1116.

LYNGNES, R. (1930).   Beiträge zur Kenntnis von *Myxine glutinosa* L.   1. Über die Entwicklung der Eihülle bei *Myxine glutinosa*.   *Z. Morph. Ökol. Tiere*, **19**, 591.

McCLEAN, D., & ROWLANDS, I. W. (1942).   Role of hyaluronidase in fertilization.   *Nature, Lond.*, **150**, 627.

McCOSH, G. K. (1930).   The origin of the germ cells in *Amblystoma maculatum*.   *J. Morph.*, **50**, 569.

MACDOWELL, E. C., ALLEN, E., & MACDOWELL, C. G. (1929).   The relation of parity, age and body weight to the number of corpora lutea in mice.   *Anat. Rec.*, **41**, 267

—— & LORD, E. M. (1925).   The number of corpora lutea in successive mouse pregnancies.   *Anat. Rec.*, **31**, 131.

McILROY, A. L. (1910).   The development of the germ cells in the mammalian ovary, with special reference to the early phases of maturation.   *Proc. Roy. Soc. Edinb.*, **31**, 151.

MAINLAND, D. (1928).   The pluriovular follicle, with reference to its occurrence in the ferret.   *J. Anat., Lond.*, **62**, 139.

—— (1931a).   The early development of the ferret : The cytoplasm.   *J. Anat., Lond.*, **65**, 411.

—— (1931b).   The connective-tissue nuclear density of human ovaries.   *Anat. Rec.*, **51**, 107.

—— (1932).   The early development of the ferret : The zona granulosa, zona pellucida and associated structures.   *J. Anat., Lond.*, **66**, 586.

MANDL, L. (1895).   Ueber Anordnung und Endigungsweise der Nerven im Ovarium.   *Arch. Gynaek.*, **48**, 376.

MANDL, A. M., & ZUCKERMAN, S. (1952).   The growth of the oöcyte and follicle in the adult rat.   *J. Endocrinol.*, **8**, 126.

MARCOTTY, A. (1914).   Ueber das Corpus luteum menstruationis und das Corpus luteum graviditatis.   *Arch. Gynaek.*, **103**, 63.

MARÉCHAL, J. (1906).   Sur l'ovogénèse des sélaciens et de quelques autres chordates.   *Cellule*, **24**, 5.

MARKEE, J. E., & HINSEY, J. C. (1936). Observations on ovulation in the rabbit. *Anat. Rec.*, **64**, 309.

MARSHALL, F. H. A. (1903). The oestrous cycle and the formation of the corpus luteum in the sheep. *Philos. Trans.* B, **196**, 47.

—— (1904). The oestrous cycle in the common ferret. *Quart. J. micr. Sci.*, **48**, 323.

—— (1905). The development of the corpus luteum : a review. *Quart. J. micr. Sci.*, **49**, 189.

—— (1911). On the ovarian factor concerned in the recurrence of oestrus. *J. Physiol.*, **43**, *Proc. Physiol. Soc.*, 21.

—— (1925). Hammond's *Reproduction in the rabbit*. Edinburgh.

MARTÍNEZ-ESTEVE, P. (1942). Observations on the histology of the opossum ovary. *Contr. Embryol. Carneg. Instn.*, **30**, 17.

MARTINOVITCH, P. N. (1934a). La ligature temporaire des ovaires de la lapin et le problème de l'ovogenèse postnatale chez cet animal. *C. R. Soc. Biol., Paris*, **116**, 1294.

—— (1934b). La ligature permanente des ovaires de rats blancs et le problème de la formation postnatale de cellules germinatives chez cet animal. Expériences effectuées sur des ovaires décapsulés. *C. R. Soc. Biol., Paris*, **118**, 349.

—— (1938). The development *in vitro* of the mammalian gonad. Ovary and ovogenesis. *Proc. Roy. Soc.* B, **125**, 232.

MARX, L. (1941). Replacement of ovocytes in the ovary of normal and hormone-injected young rats. *Anat. Rec.*, **79**, 115.

MARZA, V. D. (1935). The formation of the hen's egg. 5. Histochemistry of yolk-formation. *Quart. J. micr. Sci.*, **78**, 191.

—— & MARZA, E. V. (1935). The formation of the hen's egg. 2. The follicular epithelium during growth. *Quart. J. micr. Sci.*, **78**, 160.

MASCHKOWZEFF, A. (1934). Zur Phylogenie der Geschlechtsdrüsen und der Geschlechtsausfuhrgänge bei den Vertebrata. *Zool. Jb.*, **59**, 1.

MATSUMOTO, T. (1932). On the early localization and history of the so-called primordial germ cells in the chick embryo. *Sci. Rep. Tôhoku Univ., Biol.*, **7**, 89.

MATTHEWS, L. H. (1935). The oestrous cycle and intersexuality in the female mole (*Talpa europaea* Linn.). *Proc. zool. Soc. Lond.*, 1935, 347.

—— (1937a). The female sexual cycle in the British horse-shoe bats, *Rhinolophus ferrumequinum insulanus* Barrett-Hamilton and *R. hipposideros minutus* Montagu. *Trans. zool. Soc. Lond.*, **23**, 224.

—— (1937b). The Humpback whale, *Megaptera nodosa*. " *Discovery* " *Rep.*, **17**, 7.

—— (1938a). The Sperm whale, *Physeter catodon*. " *Discovery* " *Rep.*, **17**, 93.

—— (1938b). Notes on the Southern Right whale, *Eubalaena australis*. " *Discovery* " *Rep.*, **17**, 169.

—— (1938c). The Sei whale, *Balaenoptera borealis*. " *Discovery* " *Rep.*, **17**, 183.

—— (1939). Reproduction in the spotted hyaena *Crocuta crocuta* (Erxleben). *Philos. Trans.*, **230**, 1.

—— (1950). Reproduction in the basking shark, *Cetorhinus maximus* (Gunner). *Philos. Trans.* B. **234**, 247.

MERTENS, H. (1895). Recherches sur la signification du corps vitellin de Balbiani dans l'ovule des mammifères et des oiseaux. *Arch. Biol., Paris*, **13**, 389.

MEYER, R. (1911). Ueber Corpus luteum-Bildung beim Menschen. *Arch. Gynaek.*, **93**, 354.

MIHÁLKOVICS, G. VON (1885). Untersuchungen über die Entwickelung des Harn- und Geschlechtsapparates der Amnioten. *Int. Mschr. Anat. Histol.*, **2**, 41, 65, 284, 348, 387, 435.

MILLER, F. W., SWETT, W. W., HARTMAN, C. G., & LEWIS, W. H. (1931). A study of ova from the fallopian tubes of dairy cows, with a genital history of the cows. *J. agric. Res.*, **43**, 627.

MILLER, J. W. (1910). Die Rückbildung des Corpus luteum. *Arch. Gynaek.*, **91**, 263.

—— (1914). Corpus luteum, Menstruation und Gravidität. *Arch. Gynaek.*, **101**, 568.

MINGAZZINI, P. (1893). Corpi lutei veri et falsi de rettili. *Ric. Lab. Anat. Norm. Univ. Roma.*, **3**, 105.

Minot, C. S. (1892). *Human embryology.* New York.

Momogliano, E. (1927). L'evoluzione dell' apparato follicolare dell' ovaio nella vita fetale. *Ric. Morfol.*, **7**, 55.

Monroy, A. (1939). Sulla localizzazione delle cellule genitali primordiali in fasi precoci di sviluppo. Ricerche sperimentali in Anfibi Anuri. *Arch. ital. Anat. Embriol.*, **41**, 368.

Moricard, R. (1933). Zone de Golgi du follicule ovarien. *Ann. Anat. Path. Méd.-Chir.*, **10**, 1.

—— (1936). Déclenchement de la métaphase de la première mitose de maturation de l'ovocyte par injection de mitosine. *Ann. Physiol. Physicochim. Biol.*, **12**, 763.

—— Gothié, S., & Tsatsaris, B. (1939). Mécanismes cytoplasmiques du déclenchement de la métaphase de la première mitose de maturation de l'ovocyte des mammifères (in vivo, in vitro et cinématographie). *Arch. Exp. Zell.*, **22**, 291.

Mosella, R. G. (1926). Über einige Veränderungen der Nucleolarsubstanz während des Wachstums des Ovocyt und des Eifollikels bei *Lacerta muralis.* *Anat. Anz.*, **62**, 76.

Mossman, H. W. (1937). The thecal gland and its relation to the reproductive cycle : A study of the cyclic changes in the ovary of the pocket gopher, *Geomys bursarius* (Shaw). *Amer. J. Anat.*, **61**, 289.

—— (1938). The homology of the vesicular ovarian follicles of the mammalian ovary with the coelom. *Anat. Rec.*, **70**, 643.

—— & Hisaw, F. L. (1940). The fetal membranes of the pocket gopher illustrating an intermediate type of rodent membrane formation. 1. From the unfertilized tubal egg to the beginning of the allantois. *Amer. J. Anat.*, **66**, 367.

—— & Judas, I. (1949). Accessory corpora lutea, lutein cell origin, and the ovarian cycle in the Canadian porcupine. *Amer. J. Anat.*, **85**, 1.

Moulonguet, P. (1927). Le chondriome des cellules du corps jaune humain. *C. R. Soc. Biol., Paris*, **97**, 1652.

Mulon, P. (1906). Évolution des " corps osmophiles " inclus dans les cellules à lutéine du cobaye. *C. R. Soc. Biol., Paris*, **61**, 272.

Muratori, G. (1937). Embryonal germ-cells of the chick in hanging-drop cultures. *Contr. Embryol. Carneg. Instn.*, **26**, 59.

Myers, H. I., Young, W. C., & Dempsey, E. W. (1936). Graafian follicle development throughout the reproductive cycle in the guinea-pig, with especial reference to changes during oestrus (sexual receptivity). *Anat. Rec.*, **65**, 381.

Nagel, W. (1896). Die weiblichen Geschlechtsorgane. *Handbuch der Anatomie des Menschen.* Jena.

—— (1899). Über neuere Arbeiten auf dem Gebiete der Anatomie der weiblichen Geschlechtsorgane. *Ergebn. Anat. EntwGesch.*, **8**, 210.

Nalbandov, A. V., & James, M. F. (1949). The blood-vascular system of the chicken ovary. *Amer. J. Anat.*, **85**, 347.

Nelsen, O. E., & Swain, E. (1942). The prepubertal origin of germ-cells in the ovary of the opossum (*Didelphys virginiana*). *J. Morph.*, **71**, 335.

Neumann, H. O. (1927). Fremdartige Zellen im Eierstock. *Virchows Arch.*, **263**, 274.

—— (1928). Die Hiluszellen des Ovariums. *Zbl. Gynäk.*, **52**, 2625.

—— (1929). Histologische Studien zur Frage der sympathicotropen Zellen (L. Berger) bzw. der Hiluszellen des Ovariums. *Arch. Gynaek.*, **136**, 550.

Newman, H. H. (1913). Parthenogenetic cleavage of the armadillo ovum. *Biol. Bull., Wood's Hole*, **25**, 54.

Nihoul, J. (1926). Recherches sur l'appareil endocellulaire de Golgi dans les premiers stades du développement des mammifères. *Cellule*, **37**, 21.

Niklaus, S. (1950). Die Kerngrösse des Follikelepithels wäkrend des Sexualzyklus beim Borstenigel. *Z. Zellforsch.*, **35**, 240.

Niskoubina, N. (1909). Recherches sur la morphologie et la fonction du corps jaune de la grossesse. *Thèse, No. 12, Faculté de Médecine, l'Université de Nancy.*

Nonidez, J. F. (1922). Estudios sobre las gónadas de la gallina. 2. El tejido intersticial del ovario. *Libro en honor de D. S. Ramón y Cajal, Madrid*, **2**, 137.

Novak, J., & Duschak, F. (1923). Die Veränderungen der Follikelhüllen beim Haushuhn nach dem Follikelsprung. *Z. Ges. Anat.* 1. *Z. Anat. EntwGesch.*, **69**, 483.

Nussbaum, M. (1880). Zur Differenzierung des Geschlechts im Thierreich. *Arch. mikr. Anat.*, **18**, 1.

Ochoterena, I., & Ramirez, E. (1920). The origin and evolution of the interstitial cells and of the ovary, and the significance of the different internal secretions of the ovary. *Endocrinology*, **4**, 541.

O'Donoghue, C. H. (1912). The corpus luteum in the non-pregnant *Dasyurus* and poly-ovular follicles in *Dasyurus*. *Anat. Anz.*, **41**, 353.

—— (1914). Über die Corpora lutea bei einigen Beuteltieren. *Arch. mikr. Anat.*, **84**, 1.

—— (1916). On the corpora lutea and interstitial tissue of the ovary in the Marsupialia. *Quart. J. micr. Sci.*, **61**, 433.

Okamoto, T. (1928). Über den Ursprung des Follikelepithels des Eierstockes beim Hunde. *Folia Anat. Japon.*, **6**, 689.

Okkelberg, P. (1921). The early history of the germ cells in the brook lamprey, *Entosphenus wilderi* (Gage), up to and including the period of sex differentiation. *J. Morph.*, **35**, 1.

Olsen, M. W. (1942). Maturation, fertilization, and early cleavage in the hen's egg. *J. Morph.*, **70**, 513.

—— & Fraps, R. M. (1944). Maturation, fertilization, and early cleavage of the egg of the domestic turkey. *J. Morph.*, **74**, 297.

Ota, T. (1934). Polyovular follicles of dogs. *Jap. J. Obstet. Gynec.*, **17**, 207.

Paladino, G. (1887). Ulteriori ricerche sulla distruzione e rinnovamento continuo del parenchima ovarico nei mammiferi. *Anat. Anz.*, **2**, 835.

—— (1900). Per la dibattuta questione sulla essenza del corpo luteo. *Anat. Anz.*, **17**, 451.

Pankratz, D. S. (1938). Some observations on the Graafian follicles in an adult human ovary. *Anat. Rec.*, **71**, 211.

Parkes, A. S. (1923). Studies on the sex-ratio and related phenomena. IV. The frequencies of sex combinations in pig litters. *Biometrika*, **15**, 373.

—— (1926). On the occurrence of the oestrous cycle after X-ray sterilisation. 1. Irradiation of mice at three weeks old. *Proc. Roy. Soc.* B, **100**, 172.

—— (1931). The reproductive processes of certain mammals. II. The size of the Graafian follicle at ovulation. *Proc. Roy. Soc.* B, **109**, 185.

—— & Bellerby, C. W. (1926). Studies on the internal secretions of the ovary. 1. The distribution in the ovary of the oestrus-producing hormone. *J. Physiol.*, **61**, 562.

—— Fielding, U., & Brambell, F. W. R., (1927). Ovarian regeneration in the mouse after complete double ovariotomy. *Proc. Roy. Soc.* B, **101**, 328.

Pasteels, J. (1953). Contribution à l'étude du développement des Reptiles. 1. Origine et migration des gonocytes chez deux Lacertiliens (*Mabuia megalura* et *Chamaeles bitaeniatus*). *Arch. Biol.*, Paris, **64**, 227.

Paterson, R. (1840). Observations on corpora lutea. *Edinb. Med. Surg. J.*, **53**, 49.

Patterson, J. T. (1913). Polyembryonic development in *Tatusia novemcincta*. *J. Morph.*, **24**, 559.

Pawlowski, E. (1929). Über die sogenannten Hiluszellen des Ovariums. *Endokrinologie*, **3**, 321.

Pearl, R., & Boring, A. M. (1918). Sex studies. 10. The corpus luteum in the ovary of the domestic fowl. *Amer. J. Anat.*, **23**, 1.

Pearson, A. K., & Enders, R. K. (1951). Further observations on the reproduction of the Alaskan fur seal. *Anat. Rec.*, **111**, 695.

Pearson, O. P. (1944). Reproduction in the shrew (*Blarina brevicauda* Say). *Amer. J. Anat.*, **75**, 39.

—— (1949). Reproduction of a South American rodent, the mountain viscacha. *Amer. J. Anat.*, **84**, 143.

—— & Enders, R. K. (1943). Ovulation, maturation and fertilization in the fox. *Anat. Rec.*, **85**, 69.

Pederson, E. S. (1951). Histogenesis of lutein tissue of the albino rat. *Amer. J. Anat.*, **88**, 397.

Pencharz, R. I. (1929).   Experiments concerning ovarian regeneration in the white rat and white mouse.   *J. exp. Zool.*, **54**, 319.

Pérez, C. (1903).   Sur la résorption phagocytaire des ovules chez les tritons.   *Ann. Inst. Pasteur*, **17**, 617.

Perle, S. (1927).   Origine de la première ébauche génitale chez *Bufo vulgaris*.   *C. R. Acad. Sci., Paris*, **184**, 303.

Perry, J. S. (1953).   The reproduction of the African elephant, *Loxodonta africana*.   *Philos. Trans.* B, **237**, 93.

Peter, A. (1929).   Die Arterienversorgung von Eierstock und Eileiter.   Untersuchungen bei Hund und Katze an Spalteholz-Injektionspräparaten.   *Z. Ges. Anat.* 1. *Z. Anat. EntwGesch.*, **89**, 763.

Peter, K. (1904).   Normentafel zur Entwicklungsgeschichte der Zauneidechse (*Lacerta agilis*).   *Normentaf. Wirbelt.*, **4**, 1.

Pflüger, E. F. W. (1863).   *Ueber die Eierstöcke der Säugethiere und des Menschen.*   Leipzig.

Phillips, R. E., & Warren, D. C. (1937).   Observations concerning the mechanics of ovulation in the fowl.   *J. exp. Zool.*, **76**, 117.

Pincus, G., & Enzmann, E. V. (1932).   Fertilisation in the rabbit.   *J. exp. Biol.*, **9**, 403.

—— —— (1937).   The growth, maturation and atresia of ovarian eggs in the rabbit.   *J. Morph.*, **61**, 351.

Pines, L., & Schapiro, B. (1930).   Über die Innervation des Eierstockes.   *Z. mikr.-anat. Forsch.*, **20**, 327.

Pinto, C. (1905).   Note istologiche sulle modificazioni delle ovaia in gravidanza.   *Ann. Ostet. Ginec.*, **27**, 476.

Plato, J. (1897).   Zur Kenntniss der Anatomie und Physiologie der Geschlechtsorgane.   *Arch. mikr. Anat.*, **50**, 640.

Poirier, P., & Charpy, A. (1923).   *Traité d'anatomie humaine.*   Paris.

Polano, O. (1903).   Beiträge zur Anatomie der Lymphbahnen im menschlichen Eierstock.   *Mschr. Geburtsh. Gynak.*, **17**, 281 and 466.

Politzer, G. (1933).   Die Keimbahn des Menschen.   *Z. Ges. Anat.* 1. *Z. Anat. EntwGesch.*, **100**, 331.

Pollak, W. (1926).   Über Kristalloide in Eizellen von *Macacus rhesus*.   *Anat. Anz.*, **61**, 202.

Ponse, K. (1924).   L'organe de Bidder et le déterminisme des caractères sexuels secondaires du crapaud (*Bufo vulgaris* L.)   *Rev. suisse Zool.*, **31**, 177.

—— (1927).   Les hypothèses concernant la signification de l'organe de Bidder du crapaud.   *C. R. Soc. Biol., Paris*, **96**, 777.

Popoff, N. (1911).   Le tissu interstitiel et les corps jaunes de l'ovaire.   *Arch. Biol., Paris*, **26**, 483.

Prenant, A. (1890).   Remarque à propos de la constitution de la glande génitale indifférente et de l'histogenèse du tube séminifère.   *C. R. Soc. Biol., Paris*, **2**, 192.

Price, M. (1953).   The reproductive cycle of the water shrew, *Neomys sodiens bicolor* Shaw.   *Proc. zool. Soc. Lond.*, **123**, 599.

Quinlan, J., & Mare, G. S. (1931).   The physiological changes in the ovary of the Merino sheep in South Africa, and their practical application in breeding.   *Rep. Vet. Res. S. Afr.*, **17**, 661.

Rabl, H. (1898).   Beitrag zur Histologie des Eierstockes des Menschen und der Säugetiere nebst Bemerkungen über die Bildung von Hyalin und Pigment.   *Arb. Anat. Inst. Wiesbaden*, **11**, 109.

Rahn, H. (1939).   Structure and function of placenta and corpus luteum in viviparous snakes.   *Proc. Soc. Exp. Biol., N.Y.*, **40**, 381.

Rao, C. R. N. (1927).   On the structure of the ovary and the ovarian ovum of *Loris lydekkerianus* Cabr.   *Quart. J. micr. Sci.*, **71**, 57.

Rasmussen, A. T. (1918).   Cyclic changes in the interstitial cells of the ovary and testis in the woodchuck (*Marmota monax*).   *Endocrinology*, **2**, 353.

Rauh, W. (1926).   Ursprung der weiblichen Keimzellen und die chromatischen Vorgänge bis zur Entwicklung des Synapsisstadiums.   Beobachtet an der ratte (*Mus decumanus albinus*).   *Z. Ges. Anat.* 1. *Z. Anat. EntwGesch.*, **78**, 637.

—— (1929).   Das Chondriom in den ersten Keimzellen der ratte.   Eine Keimbahnuntersuchung.   *Z. Ges. Anat.* 1. *Z. Anat. EntwGesch.*, **89**, 271.

RAVANO, A. (1907). Ueber die Frage nach der Thätigkeit des Eierstocks in der Schwanger-schaft. *Arch. Gynaek.*, **83**, 587.

REAGAN, F. P. (1916). Some results and possibilities of early embryonic castration. *Anat. Rec.*, **11**, 251.

REGAUD, C., & DUBREUIL, G. (1906). Recherches sur les cellules interstitielles de l'ovaire chez la lapin. *Bibliogr. Anat.*, **15**, 169.

—— & LACASSAGNE, A. (1913). Les follicules anovulaires de l'ovaire chez la lapine adulte. *C. R. Ass. Anat.*, *Lausanne*, **15**, 15.

—— & POLICARD, A. (1901). Notes histologiques sur l'ovaire des mammifères. *C. R. Ass. Anat.*, *Lyon*, **3**, 45.

REINHARD, L. (1924). Die Entwicklung des Parablasts und seine Bedeutung bei teleostiern nebst der Frage über die Entstehung der Urgeschlechtszellen. *Arch. mikr. Anat.*, **103**, 339.

RENNELS, E. G. (1951). Influence of hormones on the histochemistry of ovarian interstitial tissue in the immature rat. *Amer. J. Anat.*, **88**, 63.

RETZIUS, G. (1893). Ueber die Nerven der Ovarien und Hoden. *Biol. Untersuch.*, **5**, 31.

—— (1912). Zur Kenntnis der Hüllen und besonders des Follikelepithels an den Eiern der Wirbeltiere. *Biol. Untersuch.*, **17**, 1.

REYNOLDS, S. R. M. (1947). Adaptation of the spiral artery in the rabbit ovary to changes in organ-size after stimulation by gonadotrophins ; effect of ovulation and luteinisation. *Endocrinology*, **40**, 381.

RICHARDS, A., & THOMPSON, J. T. (1921). The migration of the primary sex-cells of *Fundulus heteroclitus*. *Biol. Bull.*, *Wood's Hole*, **40**, 325.

RIESE, H. (1891). Die feinsten Nervenfasern und ihre Endigungen im Ovarium der Säuge-tiere und des Menschen. *Anat. Anz.*, **6**, 401.

DEL RIO HORTEGA, P. (1913). Détails nouveaux sur la structure de l'ovaire. *Trab. Lab. Invest. Biol. Univ. Madr.*, **11**, 163.

RIQUIER, J. K. (1910). Der innere Netzapparat in den Zellen des Corpus luteum. *Arch. mikr. Anat.*, **75**, 772.

RISLEY, P. L. (1933). Contributions on the development of the reproductive system in *Sternotherus odoratus* (Latreille). 1. The embryonic origin and migration of the primordial germ cells. 2. Gonadogenesis and sex differentiation. *Z. Zellforsch.*, **18**, 459.

ROBB, R. C. (1928). Is pituitary secretion concerned in the inheritance of body size ? *Proc. nat. Acad. Sci.*, *Wash.*, **14**, 394.

—— (1929). On the nature of hereditary size limitation. II. The growth of parts in relation to the whole. *J. exp. Biol.*, **6**, 311.

ROBINSON, A. (1918). The formation, rupture, and closure of ovarian follicles in ferrets and ferret-polecat hybrids, and some associated phenomena. *Trans. Roy. Soc. Edinb.*, **52**, 303.

ROMANOFF, A. L. (1943). Growth of avian ovum. *Anat. Rec.*, **85**, 261.

ROSSMAN, J. (1942). On the lipin and pigment in the corpus luteum of the rhesus monkey. *Contr. Embryol. Carneg. Instn.*, **30**, 97.

ROUGET, C. (1858). Recherches sur les organes érectiles de la femme, et sur l'appareil musculaire tubo-ovarien, dans leur rapports avec l'ovulation et la menstruation. *J. de la Physiol.*, **1**, 320.

—— (1882). " Ovaire " in " *Dictionnaire encyclopédique des Sciences médicales.*" Paris.

RUBASCHKIN, W. (1907). Über das erste Auftreten und Migration der Keimzellen bei Vögelembryonen. *Arb. Anat. Inst. Wiesbaden*, **35**, 241.

—— (1909). Über die Urgeschlechtszellen bei Säugetieren. *Arb. Anat. Inst. Wiesbaden*, **39**, 603.

—— (1910). Chondriosomen und Differenzierungsprozesse bei Säugetierembryonen. *Arb. Anat. Inst. Wiesbaden*, **41**, 399.

—— (1912). Zur Lehre von der Keimbahn bei Säugetieren. Über die Entwickelung der Keimdrüsen. *Arb. Anat. Inst. Wiesbaden*, **46**, 343.

RUGH, R. (1935). Ovulation in the frog. 2. Follicular rupture to fertilization. *J. exp. Zool.*, **71**, 163.

Ryan, F. J., & Grant, R. (1940). The stimulus for maturation and for ovulation of the frog's egg. *Physiol. Zool.*, **13**, 383.

Sâglik, S. (1938). Ovaries of Gorilla, Chimpanzee, Orang-Utan and Gibbon. *Contr. Embryol. Carneg. Instn.*, **27**, 179.

Sainmont, G. (1906). Recherches relatives à l'organogenèse du testicule et de l'ovaire chez le chat. *Arch. Biol., Paris*, **22**, 71.

Salazar, A. L. (1922a). Sur l'existence de faux corps jaunes autonomes dans la glande interstitielle de la lapine. *Anat. Rec.*, **23**, 189.

—— (1922b). Sur la forme de dégénérescence des follicules anovulaires de Regaud et d'autres reliquats provenant des cordons ovigènes de l'ovaire de la lapine. *Anat. Rec.*,**24**,79.

—— (1922c). Sur une forme particulière d'atrésie des follicules de de Graaf (lapin), révélée par la méthode tannoferrique. *Amer. J. Anat.*, **30**, 503.

Samartino, G. T., & Rugh, R. (1945). Frog ovulation *in vitro*. *J. exp. Zool.*, **98**, 153.

Sandes, F. P. (1903). The corpus luteum of *Dasyurus viverrinus*, with observations on the growth and atrophy of the Graafian follicle. *Proc. Linn. Soc., N.S.W.*, **28**, 364.

Schaeffer, A. (1911). Vergleichend histologische Untersuchungen über die interstitielle Eierstockdrüse. *Arch. Gynaek.*, **94**, 491.

Schafer, E. Sharpey (1929). *The essentials of histology*. London.

Schapitz, R. (1912). Die Urgeschlechtszellen von *Amblystoma*. Ein Beitrag zur Kenntnis der Keimbahn der urodelen Amphibien. *Arch. mikr. Anat.*, **79**, 41.

Schmidt, A. H. (1898). Untersuchungen ueber das Ovarium der Selachier. *Tijdschr Ned. Dierk. Ver.*, **6**, 1.

Schmidt, I. G. (1942). Mitotic proliferation in the ovary of the normal mature guinea pig treated with colchicine. *Amer. J. Anat.*, **71**, 245.

—— & Hoffman, F. G. (1941). Proliferation and ovogenesis in the germinal epithelium of the normal mature guinea pig ovary, as shown by the colchicine technique. *Amer. J. Anat.*, **68**, 263.

Schochet, S. S. (1916). A suggestion as to the process of ovulation and ovarian cyst formation. *Anat. Rec.*, **10**, 447.

Schotterer, A. (1928). Beitrag zur Feststellung der Eianzahl in verschiedenen Altersperioden bei der Hündin. *Anat. Anz.*, **65**, 177.

Schottlaender, J. (1891). Beitrag zur Kenntniss der Follikelatresie nebst einigen Bemerkungen über die unveränderten Follikel in den Eierstöcken der Säugethiere. *Arch. mikr. Anat.*, **37**, 192.

—— (1893). Ueber den Graaf'schen Follikel, seine Entstehung beim Menschen und seine Schicksale bei Menschen und Säugethieren. *Arch. mikr. Anat.*, **41**, 219.

Schreiner, K. E. (1904). Über das Generationsorgan von *Myxine glutinosa* (L). *Biol. Zbl.*, **24**, 91, 121, 162.

Schrön, O. (1862). Beitrag zur Kenntniss der Anatomie und Physiologie des Eierstocks der Säugethiere. *Z. Wiss. Zool.*, **12**, 409.

Schulin, K. (1881). Zur Morphologie des Ovariums. *Arch. mikr. Anat.*, **19**, 442.

Seitz, L. (1905a). Die Luteinzellenwucherung in atretischen Follikeln, eine physiologische Erscheinung während der Schwangerschaft. *Zbl. Gynäk.*, **29**, 257.

—— (1905b). Zur Frage der Luteinzellenwucherung in atretischen Follikeln während der Schwangerschaft. *Zbl. Gynäk.*, **29**, 578.

—— (1906). Die Follikelatresie während der Schwangerschaft, insbesondere die Hypertrophie und Hyperplasie der Theca interna-Zellen (Thecaluteïnzellen) und ihre Beziehungen zur Corpus luteum-Bildung. *Arch. Gynaek.*, **77**, 203.

Shaw, W. (1926). The interstitial cells of the human ovary. *J. Obstet. Gynaec.*, **33**, 183.

—— (1927), Ovulation in the human ovary : its mechanism and anomalies. *J. Obstet. Gynaec.*, **34**, 469.

Simkins, C. S. (1923). On the origin and migration of the so-called primordial germ cells in the mouse and the rat. *Acta zool., Stockh.*, **4**, 241.

—— (1925). Origin of the germ cells in *Trionyx*. *Amer. J. Anat.*, **36**, 185.

—— (1928). Origin of the sex cells in man. *Amer. J. Anat.*, **41**, 249.

—— & Asana, J. J. (1930). Development of the sex glands of *Calotes*. 1. Cytology and growth of the gonads prior to hatching. *Quart. J. micr. Sci.*, **74**, 133.

SJÖVALL, E. (1906).   Ein Versuch, das Binnennetz von Golgi-Kopsch bei der Spermato-
und Ovogenese zu homologisieren.   *Anat. Anz.*, **28**, 561.

SKOWRON, S., & KELLER, T. (1934).   Die histologischen Veränderungen der Fettsubstanzen
des gelben Körpers beim Kaninchen während und nach der Schwangerschaft,
nebst allgemeinen Bemerkungen über die Fettverteilung im Eierstock.   *Z. Zellforsch.*, **21**, 425.

SLATER, D. W., & DORNFELD, E. J. (1945).   Quantitative aspects of growth and oöcyte
production in the early prepubertal rat ovary.   *Amer. J. Anat.*, **76**, 253.

SLAVJANSKY, K. (1870).   Zur normalen und pathologischen Histologie des Graaf'schen
Bläschen des Menschen.   *Virchow's Arch.*, **51**, 470.

SMELSER, G. K., WALTON, A., & WHETHAM, E. O. (1934).   The effect of light on ovarian
activity in the rabbit.   *J. exp. Biol.*, **11**, 352.

SMITH, B. G. (1912).   The embryology of *Cryptobranchus allegheniensis*, including com-
parisons with some other vertebrates.   *J. Morph.*, **23**, 61.

—— (1916).   The process of ovulation in the Amphibia.   *Rep. Mich. Acad. Sci.*, **18**,
102.

SMITH, J. T. (1934).   Some observations on the rupture of the Graafian follicles in rabbits.
Amer. J. Obstet. Gynaec., **27**, 728.

—— & KETTERINGHAM, R. C. (1938).   Rupture of the Graafian follicles.   *Amer. J. Obstet.
Gynaec.*, **36**, 453.

SNEIDER, M. E. (1937).   Cytological abnormalities in the oocytes of the 3-week kitten's
ovary.   *Anat. Rec.*, **70**, 13.

SNELL, G. D., FEKETE, E., HUMMEL, K. P., & LAW, L. W. (1940).   The relation of mating,
ovulation and the estrous smear in the house mouse to time of day.   *Anat. Rec.*,
76, 39.

SOBOTTA, J. (1895a).   Die Befruchtung und Furchung des Eies der Maus.   *Arch. mikr.
Anat.*, **45**, 15.

—— (1895b).   Ueber die Bildung des Corpus luteum bei der Maus.   *Anat. Anz.*, **10**, 482.

—— (1896).   Ueber die Bildung des Corpus luteum bei der Maus.   *Arch. mikr. Anat.*,
47, 261.

—— (1897).   Über die Bildung des Corpus luteum beim Kaninchen.   *Anat. Hefte*, **8**,
469.

—— (1899).   Über die Entstehung des Corpus luteum der Säugetiere.   *Ergebn. Anat.
EntwGesch.*, **8**, 923.

—— (1906).   Über die Bildung des Corpus luteum beim Meerschweinchen.   *Arb. Anat.
Inst. Wiesbaden*, **32**, 89.

—— & BURCKHARD, G. (1910).   Reifung und Befruchtung des Eies der weissen Ratte.
Arb. Anat. Inst. Wiesbaden, **42**, 433.

SOLOMONS, B., & GATENBY, J. BRONTË (1924).   Notes on the formation, structure and
physiology of the corpus luteum of man, the pig, and the duck-billed platypus.
J. Obstet. Gynaec., **31**, 1.

SONNENBRODT (1908).   Die Wachstumsperiode der Oöcyte des Huhnes.   *Arch. mikr.
Anat.*, **72**, 415.

SPEHL, G., & POLUS, J. (1912).   Les premiers stades du développement des glandes
génitales chez l'axolotl.   *Arch. Biol., Paris*, **27**, 68.

STAFFORD, W. T., COLLINS, R. F., & MOSSMAN, H. W. (1942).   The thecal gland in the
guinea pig ovary.   *Anat. Rec.*, **83**, 193.

—— & MOSSMAN, H. W. (1945).   The ovarian interstitial gland tissue and its relation to
the pregnancy cycle in the guinea pig.   *Anat. Rec.*, **93**, 97.

STANLEY, A. J. (1937).   Sexual dimorphism in North American hawks.   1. Sex organs.
J. Morph., **61**, 321.

STEIN, K. F., & ALLEN, E. (1942).   Attempts to stimulate proliferation of the germinal
epithelium of the ovary.   *Anat. Rec.*, **82**, 1.

STEINFORTH, T. (1928).   Fettbefunde im Corpus luteum bei Extrauteringravidität im
Vergleiche mit denen bei normaler intrauteriner Gravidität.   Zur Frage der Rück-
bildung des Corpus luteum in früher Zeit der Schwangerschaft.   *Z. Geburtsh.
Gynäk.*, **92**, 71.

Stieve, H. (1918). Über experimentell, durch veränderte äussere Bedingungen hervorgerufene Rückbildungsvorgänge am Eierstock des Haushuhnes (*Gallus domesticus*). *Arch. EntwMech. Org.*, **44**, 531.

——— (1919). Die entwicklung des Eierstockseies der Dohle (*Colaeus monedula*). *Arch. mikr. Anat.*, **92**, 137.

——— (1921). Die entwicklung der Keimzellen des Grottenolmes (*Proteus anguineus*). 2. Die Wachstumsperiode der Oözyte. *Arch. mikr. Anat.*, **95**, 1.

——— (1926). Die regelmässigen Veränderungen der Muskulatur und des Bindegewebes in der menschlichen Gebärmutter in ihrer Abhängigkeit von der Follikelreife und der Ausbildung eines gelben Körpers, nebst Beschreibung eines menschlichen Eies im Zustand der ersten Reifeteilung. *Z. mikr.-anat. Forsch.*, **6**, 351.

——— (1927). Die Entwicklung der Keimzellen und der Zwischenzellen in der Hodenanlage des Menschen. *Z. mikr.-anat. Forsch.*, **10**, 225.

Stockard, A. H. (1937). Studies on the female reproductive system of the prairie dog, *Cynomys leucurus*. 2. Normal cyclic phenomena of the ovarian follicles. *Pap. Mich. Acad. Sci.*, **22**, 671.

Stockard, C. R., & Papanicolaou, G. N. (1917). The existence of a typical oestrous cycle in the guinea pig, with a study of its histological and physiological changes. *Amer. J. Anat.*, **22**, 225.

Stoeckel, W. (1902). Über die cystische Degeneration der Ovarien bei Blasenmole, zugleich ein Beitrag zur Histogenese der Luteïnzellen. *Beiträge zur Geburtshilfe und Gynäkologie, Festschrift H. Fritsch, Leipzig*, p. 136.

Strassmann, E. (1923). Warum platzt der follikel ? *Arch. Gynaek.*, **119**, 168.

Stratz, C. H. (1898). *Der geschlechtsreife Saeugethiereierstock*. Haag.

Strauss, F. (1938). Die Befruchtung und der Vorgang der Ovulation bei *Ericulus* aus der Familie der Centetiden. *Bio-Morphosis*, **1**, 281.

van der Stricht, O. (1901a). La rupture du follicule ovarique et l'histogénèse du corps jaune. *C. R. Ass. Anat., Lyon*, **3**, 33.

——— (1901b). La ponte ovarique et l'histogenèse du corps jaune. *Bull. Acad. Méd. Belg.*, **15**, 216.

——— (1901c). L'atrésie ovulaire et l'atrésie folliculaire du follicule de de Graaf, dans l'ovaire de chauve-souris. *Anat. Anz.*, **19**, *Verh. Anat. Ges. Jena*, 108.

——— (1901d). Une anomalie intéressante de formation de corps jaune. *Ann. Soc. Méd. Gand.*, **80**, 151.

——— (1908). La structure de l'œuf de chienne et la genèse du corps jaune. *C. R. Ass. Anat., Marseille*, **10**, 1.

——— (1909). La structure de l'œuf des mammifères. III. L'oocyte à la fin du stade d'accroissement, au stade de la maturation, au stade de la fécondation et au début de la segmentation. *Mém. Acad. R. Belg.*, **2**, 1.

——— (1912). Sur la processus de l'excrétion des glandes endocrines : le corps jaune et la glande interstitielle de l'ovaire. *Arch. Biol., Paris*, **27**, 585.

——— (1923). Étude comparée des ovules des mammifères aux différentes périodes de l'ovogenèse, d'après les travaux du Laboratoire d'Histologie et d'Embryologie de l'Université de Gand. *Arch. Biol., Paris*, **33**, 229.

van der Stricht, R. (1911). Vitellogenèse dans l'ovule de chatte. *Arch. Biol., Paris*, **26**, 365.

Stromsten, F. A. (1929). History of the germ cells in the goldfish. *Anat. Rec.*, **44**, 254. Abstracts.

Sun, Y. C. (1923). Post-pubertal ovogenesis in the guinea pig. *Anat. Rec.*, **25**, 114. Abstracts.

Swezy, O. (1929). The ovarian chromosome cycle in a mixed rat strain. *J. Morph.*, **48**, 445.

——— (1933). *Ovogenesis and its relation to the hypophysis : the effects of pregnancy, hypophysectomy, thyroidectomy, and administration on the ovary of the rat.* Private publication.

Swift, C. H. (1914). Origin and early history of the primordial germ-cells in the chick. *Amer. J. Anat.*, **15**, 483.

SWIFT, C. H. (1915).   Origin of the definitive sex-cells in the female chick and their relation
    to the primordial germ-cells.   *Amer. J. Anat.*, **18**, 441.
—— (1916).   Origin of the sex-cords and definitive spermatogonia in the male chick.
    Amer. J. Anat., **20**, 375.
SWINGLE, W. W. (1921).   The germ cells of anurans.   1. The male sexual cycle of *Rana
    catesbeiana* larvae.   *J. exp. Zool.*, **32**, 235.
—— (1926).   The germ cells of anurans.   2. An embryological study of sex differentiation
    in *Rana catesbeiana*.   *J. Morph.*, **41**, 441.
TAMURA, Y. (1927).   On anovular follicles in the ovaries of the sterile dingo and the aged
    mouse.   *J. Anat., Lond.*, **61**, 325.
TASSOVATZ, S. (1927).   Étude de glande thécale chez la femme.   *Thèse de Strasbourg*.
THING, A. (1918).   The formation and structure of the zona pellucida in the ovarian eggs
    of turtles.   *Amer. J. Anat.*, **23**, 237.
THOMSON, A. (1919a).   The maturation of the human ovum.   *J. Anat., Lond.*, **53**, 172.
—— (1919b).   The ripe human Graafian follicle, together with some suggestions as to its
    mode of rupture.   *J. Anat., Lond.*, **54**, 1.
TOGARI, C. (1923).   On the origin of the corpus luteum of the mouse.   *Aichi J. exp. Med.
    Nagoya*, **1**, 1.
—— (1926).   On the corpus luteum of the rabbit.   *Folia Anat. Japon.*, **4**, 337.
—— (1927).   On the ovulation of the mouse.   *Nagoya J. Med. Sci.*, **2**, 17.
TORREY, T. W. (1945).   The development of the urinogenital system of the albino rat.
    II. The gonads.   *Amer. J. Anat.*, **76**, 375.
TOURNEUX, F. (1879).   Des cellules interstitielles du testicule.   *J. Anat., Paris*, **15**, 305.
TRIBE, M., & BRAMBELL, F. W. ROGERS (1932).   The origin and migration of the primordial
    germ-cells of *Sphenodon punctatus*.   *Quart. J. micr. Sci.*, **75**, 251.
TRINCI, G. (1905).   Osservazioni sur follicoli ovarici dei rettili e di altri vertebrati, con
    speciale riguardo alla struttura e funzione della granulosa.   *Arch. ital. Anat.
    Embriol.*, **4**, 1.
TROPEA, U. (1929).   Cellule interstiziali ed altri elementi a contenuto lipoideo nelle ovaie
    della donna.   *Ann. Ostet. Ginec.*, **51**, 1347.
TSCHASCHIN, S. (1910).   Ueber die Chondriosomen der Urgeschlechtszellen bei Vögel-
    embryonen.   *Anat. Anz.*, **37**, 597 and 621.
TSUKAGUCHI, R., & OKAMOTO, T. (1928).   Der Ursprung der interstitiellen Zellen des
    Ovariums beim Hunde.   *Folia Anat. Japon.*, **6**, 663.
UCHIDA, T. (1937).   Studies on the sexuality of Amphibia.   3. Sex-transformation in
    Hynobius retardatus by the function of high temperature.   *J. Fac. Sci. Hokkaido
    Univ., Zool.*, **6**, 59.
VALENTIN, G. (1835).   *Handbuch der Entwickelungsgeschichte des Menschen.*   Berlin.
VANNEMAN, A. S. (1917).   The early history of the germ cells in the armadillo, *Tatusia
    novemcincta*.   *Amer. J. Anat.*, **22**, 341.
VATTI, G. (1931).   Contributo all' istologia dell' ovaio fetale nei bovini.   *Boll. Soc. Eustach.*,
    29, 125.
VELLOSO DE PINHO, A. (1923).   Atrésie de l'épithélium folliculaire ovarique chez les
    mammifères.   *C. R. Soc. Biol., Paris*, **88**, 830.
—— (1925).   Sur une forme particulière de transformation folliculaire caractéristique de
    l'ovaire du lérot (*Eliomys quercinus* L.) : faux corps jaunes métaplastiques.   *Anat.
    Rec.*, **30**, 211.
VILLEMIN, F. (1908).   *Le corps jaune considéré comme glande à sécrétion interne de l'ovaire.*
    Paris.
VÖLKER, O. (1904).   Über die Histogenese Corporis lutei bei den Ziesel (*Spermophilus
    citillus*).   *Bull. Int. Acad. Prague (Médicine)*, **8**, 17.
—— (1905).   Ueber die Histogenese des Corpus luteum beim Ziesel (*Spermophilus cit.*).
    Arch. Anat. Physiol., Lpz., Anat. Abt., 1905, 301.
VOS, J. DE (1894).   Étude sur l'innervation de l'ovaire.   *Bull. Acad. Méd. Belg.*, **8**, 552.
WALDEYER, W. (1870).   *Eierstock und Ei.*   Leipzig.
WALLACE, W. (1903).   Observations on ovarian ova and follicles in certain teleostean and
    elasmobranch fishes.   *Quart. J. micr. Sci.*, **47**, 161.

WALLART, J. (1907). Untersuchungen über die interstitielle Eierstocksdrüse beim Men-
    schen. *Arch. Gynaek.*, **81**, 271.

—— (1908). Untersuchungen über das Corpus luteum und die interstitielle Eierstocks-
    drüse während der Schwangerschaft. *Z. Geburtsh. Gynäk.*, **63**, 520.

—— (1927). Sur le tissu paraganglionnaire de l'ovaire humain. *Arch. Anat.*, *Strasbourg*,
    7, 3.

—— (1930a). Contribution à l'étude du rete ovarii. *Arch. Biol.*, *Paris*, **40**, 1.

—— (1930b). Entfaltung und Rückbildung der paraganglionären Zellen im menschlichen
    Eierstocke. *Arch. Gynaek.*, **143**, 176.

WALSH, L. S. N. (1917). The growth of the ovarian follicle of the guinea pig under normal
    and pathological conditions. *J. exp. Med.*, **26**, 245.

WALTON, A., & HAMMOND, J. (1928). Observations on ovulation in the rabbit. *Brit. J.
    exp. Biol.* **6**, 190.

WARBRITTON, V. (1934). The cytology of the corpora lutea of the ewe. *J. Morph.*, **56**,
    181.

WATERMAN, A. J. (1943). Studies of normal development of the New Zealand White
    strain of rabbit. I. Ovogenesis. II. External morphology of the embryo.
    Amer. J. Anat., **72**, 473.

WATRIN, M. (1924). Étude histochimique et biologique du corps jaune de la femme.
    Arch. int. Méd. Exp., **1**, 97.

—— (1926). Le corps jaune de la femme. *Arch. int. Méd. Exp.*, **2**, 203.

WATZKA, M., & ESCHLER, J. (1933). Extraglanduläre Zwischenzellen im Eierstockhilus
    des Schweines. *Z. mikr.-anat. Forsch.*, **34**, 238.

WEEKES, H. C. (1934). The corpus luteum in certain oviparous and viviparous reptiles.
    Proc. Linn. Soc., N.S.W., **59**, 380.

WEICHERT, C. K., & SCHURGAST, A. W. (1942). Variations in size of corpora lutea in the
    albino rat under normal and experimental conditions. *Anat. Rec.*, **83**, 321.

WEISMANN, A. (1885). *Die Continuität des Keimplasma's als Grundlage einer Theorie der
    Vererbung.* Jena.

WENDELER, P. (1899). Entwicklungsgeschichte und Physiologie des Eierstockes. In
    A. Martin's *Handbuch der Krankheiten der weiblichen Adnexorgane.* 2. *Die
    Krankheiten der Eierstöcke und Nebeneierstöcke.* Leipzig.

WENTWORTH, E. N. (1914). Sex in multiple births. *Science*, **39**, 611.

WEST, C. M. (1937). A human embryo of twenty-five somites. *J. Anat., Lond.*, **71**, 169.

WESTER, J. (1921) *Eierstock und Ei, Befruchtung und Unfruchtbarkeit bei den Haustieren.*
    Berlin.

WHEELER, W. M. (1900). The development of the urinogenital organs of the lamprey.
    Zool. Jb. Anat. Ont., **13**, 1.

WHITE, M. J. D. (1945). *Animal cytology and evolution.* Cambridge.

WHITE, R. F., HERTIG, A. T., ROCK, J., & ADAMS, E. (1951). Histological and histo-
    chemical observations on the corpus luteum of human pregnancy with special
    reference to corpora lutea associated with early normal and abnormal ova.
    Contr. Embryol. Carneg. Instn., **34**, 55.

WICHMANN, S. E. (1912). Über die Entstehung der Urogenitalverbindung und die Bedeu-
    tung der Müllerschen Genitalgänge bei den Säugetieren. *Arb. Anat. Inst. Wies-
    baden*, **45**, 629.

WILCOX, D. E., & MOSSMAN, H. W. (1945). The common occurrence of " testis " cords
    in the ovaries of a shrew (*Sorex vagrans* Baird). *Anat. Rec.*, **92**, 183.

WILLIAMS, J. W. (1903). *Obstetrics.* New York.

WILLIER, B. H. (1932). *Sex and internal secretions.* Chap. 4. New York.

—— (1937). Experimentally produced sterile gonads and the problem of the origin of
    germ cells in the chick embryo. *Anat. Rec.*, **70**, 89.

WILSON, E. B. (1928). *The cell in development and heredity.* New York.

WILSON, K. M. (1926). Origin and development of the rete ovarii and the rete testis in
    the human embryo. *Contr. Embryol. Carneg. Instn.*, **17**, 69.

WIMSATT, W. A. (1944). Growth of the ovarian follicle and ovulation in *Myotis lucifugus
    lucifugus. Amer. J. Anat.*, **74**, 129.

DE WINIWARTER, H. (1901).   Recherches sur l'ovogenèse et l'organogenèse de l'ovaire des
    mammifères (lapin et homme).   *Arch. Biol., Paris*, **17**, 33.
—— (1908).   Das interstitielle Gewebe der menschlichen Ovarien.   *Anat. Anz.*, **33**, 1
—— (1910).   Contribution à l'étude de l'ovaire humain.   *Arch. Biol., Paris*, **25**, 683.
—— (1920).   Couche corticale définitive au hile de l'ovaire et pseudo-néoformation ovu-
    laire.   *C. R. Soc. Biol., Paris*, **83**, 1406.
—— (1923).   Les débuts de l'atrésia folliculaire.   *C. R. Soc. Biol. Paris*, **89**, 960.
—— (1924).   L'appareil phéochrome de l'ovaire humain.   *Bull. Histol. Tech. Micr.*, **1**, 145.
—— (1929).   Origine du tissu interstitiel.   *Arch. Anat. Micr.*, **25**, 75.
—— (1942).   Y a-t-il néoformation d'ovules dans l'ovaire des mammifères adultes?
    Arch. Biol., Paris, **53**, 259.
—— & SAINMONT, G. (1909).   Nouvelles recherches sur l'ovogenèse et l'organogenèse de
    l'ovaire des mammifères (chat).   *Arch. Biol., Paris*, **24**, 1.
WINTERHALTER, E. H. (1896).   Ein sympathisches Ganglion im menschlichen Ovarium,
    nebst Bemerkungen zur Lehre von dem Zustandekommen der Ovulation und
    Menstruation.   *Arch. Gynaek.*, **51**, 49.
WISLOCKI, G. B. (1939).   Observations on twinning in marmosets.   *Amer. J. Anat.*, **64**,
    445.
WITSCHI, E. (1915).   Experimentelle Untersuchungen über die Entwicklungsgeschichte der
    Keimdrüsen von *Rana temporaria*.   *Arch. mikr. Anat.*, **85**, 9.
—— (1921).   Development of gonads and transformation of sex in the frog.   *Amer. Nat.*,
    55, 529.
—— (1929a).   Studies on sex differentiation and sex determination in amphibians.
    1. Development and sexual differentiation of the gonads of *Rana sylvatica*.   *J.
    exp. Zool.*, **52**, 235.
—— (1929b).   Studies on sex differentiation and sex determination in amphibians.
    2. Sex reversal in female tadpoles of *Rana sylvatica* following the application of
    high temperature.   *J. exp. Zool.*, **52**, 267.
—— (1929c).   Studies on sex differentiation and sex determination in amphibians.
    3. Rudimentary hermaphroditism and Y chromosome in *Rana temporaria.*
    J. exp. Zool., **54**, 157.
—— (1930).   Studies on sex differentiation and sex determination in amphibians.   4. The
    geographical distribution of the sex races of the European grass frog (*Rana
    temporaria* L.).   A contribution to the problem of the evolution of sex.   *J. exp.
    Zool.*, **56**, 149.
—— (1931).   Studies on sex differentiation and sex determination in amphibians. 5. Range
    of the cortex-medulla antagonism in parabiotic twins of Ranidae and Hylidae.
    J. exp. Zool., **58**, 113.
—— (1933a).   Studies on sex differentiation and sex determination in amphibians. 6. The
    nature of Bidder's organ in the toad.   *Amer. J. Anat.*, **52**, 461.
—— (1933b).   Studies on sex differentiation and sex determination in amphibians.
    7. Sex in two local races of the spotted salamander, *Amblystoma maculatum* Shaw.
    J. exp. Zool., **65**, 215.
—— (1935).   Die Amphisexualität der embryonalen Keimdrüsen des Haussperlings, *Passer
    domesticus* (Linnaeus).   *Biol. Zbl.*, **55**, 168.
—— (1936).   Studies on sex differentiation and sex determination in amphibians.
    8. Experiments on inductive inhibition of sex differentiation in parabiotic twins
    of salamanders.   *Anat. Rec.*, **66**, 483.
—— (1937).   Studies on sex differentiation and sex determination in amphibians.
    9. Quantitative relationships in the induction of sex differentiation, and the
    problem of sex reversal in parabiotic salamanders.   *J. exp. Zool.*, **75**, 313.
—— (1948).   Migration of the germ cells of human embryos from the yolk sac to the
    primitive gonadal folds.   *Contr. Embryol. Carneg. Instn.*, **32**, 67.
WOLF, L. E. (1931).   The history of the germ cells in the viviparous teleost *Platypoecilus
    maculatus*.   *J. Morph.*, **52**, 115.
WOLFF, E., & HAFFEN, K. (1952).   Sur le developpement et la differenciation sexuelle des
    gonades embryonnaires d'oiseau en culture in vitro.   *J. exp. Zool.*, **119**, 381.

WOLZ, E. (1912).   Untersuchungen zur Morphologie der interstitiellen Eierstocksdrüse des Menschen.   *Arch. Gynaek.*, **97**, 131.

WOODGER, J. H. (1925).   Observations on the origin of the germ cells of the fowl (*Gallus domesticus*), studied by means of their Golgi bodies.   *Quart. J. micr. Sci.*, **69**, 445.

WOODS, F. A. (1902).   Origin and migration of the germ-cells in *Acanthias*.   *Amer. J. Anat.*, **1**, 307.

ZSCHOKKE, E. (1898).   Ueber die Ursachen der Unfruchtbarkeit des Rindes.   *Landw. Jb. Schweiz.*, **12**, 252.

ZUCKERMAN, S. (1951).   The number of oöcytes in the mature ovary.   *Recent Prog. Hormone Res.*, **6**, 63.

—— & PARKES, A. S. (1932).   The menstrual cycle of the Primates.   V. The cycle of the baboon.   *Proc. zool. Soc. Lond.*, 1932, 139.

CHAPTER 6

CHANGES IN THE ACCESSORY REPRODUCTIVE ORGANS OF THE NON-PREGNANT FEMALE

By P. Eckstein and S. Zuckerman

I—Introduction

The four phases of the oestrous cycle—prooestrus, oestrus, metoestrus and dioestrus—are associated with cyclic changes in the ovaries, vagina, uterus, uterine tubes and, in some species, the mammary glands, the external genitalia and the circumgenital skin. The ovarian cycle, which is considered in detail in Chapter 10, consists essentially in the maturation of the Graafian follicle, the discharge of the ovum, and the consequent formation of a corpus luteum. Prooestrus and oestrus occur in the follicular phase of the cycle, ovulation usually taking place towards the end of oestrus. Metoestrus and dioestrus or pseudopregnancy constitute the luteal phase of the cycle. There are no sharp qualitative differences between the morphological changes which characterise dioestrus and those of pseudopregnancy, which can be regarded as representing an extended dioestrus.

The uterine changes which occur during the oestrous cycle vary from species to species, but in general comprise a phase of glandular proliferation during prooestrus and oestrus, when the Graafian follicles are maturing, and a phase of secretory differentiation during dioestrus (or pseudopregnancy), when corpora lutea are present. Cyclic vaginal changes are very pronounced in many species, and it was the discovery of their occurrence in the guinea-pig (Stockard and Papanicolaou, 1917) that opened the way to the detailed investigation of the oestrous cycle in living animals (*see* Chapter 4). The vaginal cycle consists basically of (*a*) a phase of epithelial growth during prooestrus and early oestrus, (*b*) a phase of cornification and epithelial desquamation at full oestrus, and (*c*) a phase of recuperation during metoestrus and dioestrus, when the epithelium is invaded by leucocytes. In many species these various phases can be followed by microscopic study of a specimen of the vaginal " mucus," which is secured either by " smearing " the vagina with a blunt probe, or by " lavage " with a pipette.

The following account is concerned only with changes in the vagina, uterus and uterine (Fallopian) tubes of mammals. Changes in the mammary glands are dealt with in Chapter 20.

As a rule, description is limited to the condition of the accessory organs in the oestrous cycle and pseudopregnancy. Occasionally, where it seemed pertinent to do so, the changes of pregnancy are briefly referred to.

543

II—PROTOTHERIA

MONOTREMATA (= Ornithodelphia)[1]

Tachyglossus ; Echidna (Spiny anteater ; Echidna)
Ornithorhynchus (Duckbill ; Platypus)

The histological changes which occur in the monotreme oviduct during the reproductive cycle have been studied by Hill (1933, 1941).

In both *Ornithorhynchus* and *Echidna* the oviduct is a lengthy and convoluted structure, the thinner cranial part of which represents the uterine tube and the thicker caudal part the uterus. The free end of the uterine tube is expanded into a periovarial funnel or infundibulum, and with the next or upper segment comprises two-thirds of the total length of the oviduct. The remainder is formed by a middle glandular and a terminal or junctional segment.

The mucous membrane of the tube is raised into numerous well-developed folds. Its lining consists of a single-layered columnar epithelium, the height and histological character of which vary in the different tubal segments. The oviduct as a whole exhibits waves of cytological and secretory activity which can be correlated with the ovarian cycle and with the passage of the ovum.

In the region of the infundibulum the epithelium is composed of ciliated and non-ciliated cells. Only the non-ciliated cells are secretory, and during the period of follicular maturation they produce a large amount of clear fluid. This is shed into the periovarial space just before ovulation, and is thought by Hill to ensure the direct passage of the oöcyte into the lumen of the tube. The secretion ceases after ovulation, and the cells revert to their inactive form.

The non-ciliated cells in the adjoining upper segment of the tube are believed to be responsible for the thin layer of albumen which the fertilised ovum acquires during its rapid passage into the uterus. The cells are most active, and the bulk of their secretion is shed immediately after ovulation, as the egg enters the infundibulum.

In addition to an epithelium similar to that of the upper segment, the middle or glandular part of the oviduct contains a large number of convoluted tubal glands. These glands are lined by high columnar cells and produce a secretion which helps to form the basal layer of the shell of the ovum. In the junctional region of the oviduct uterine glands begin to replace those of the tubal variety. The uterine glands become active shortly after the tubal glands, and their secretions form the intermediate or " rodlet " layer of the shell.

The uterus has a much thicker wall than the uterine tube, and its folded mucosa undergoes well-defined changes during the reproductive cycle. Thus during early pregnancy the endometrium is thicker, more vascular and oedematous than in the non-pregnant state, and the lumina of its glands, which are lined by large non-ciliated cells, show a marked increase in diameter. In one specimen of platypus killed at oestrus the glands were filled with masses of sperm (Hill, 1933). It is thought that the glands secrete in successive phases, and that they elaborate at least two distinct secretions. During the first phase of activity they produce the nutritive fluid absorbed by the oöcyte during its intra-uterine stage of development.

[1] The classification follows that adopted in Chapters 2 and 4.

During the second, they form the outer protective (or third) layer of the shell, which is laid down after the egg has reached full size. As Hill (1941) points out, the formation of two or more secretions by one type of glandular cells is a rare but not unique phenomenon.

III—METATHERIA

MARSUPIALIA (= Didelphia)

Fam. *Didelphidae*
> *Didelphis* (Common opossum)

Fam. *Dasyuridae*
> *Dasyurus* (Native cat)

Fam. *Macropodidae*
> *Bettongia* (Brush-tailed " rat " kangaroo).

As described on p. 231, most marsupials are polyoestrous and breed throughout the greater part of the year. Gestation is generally short, and delivery of the young occurs either through a temporary or a permanent median vaginal passage.

Family *Didelphidae*

Didelphis

Vaginal changes

The opossum has a well-marked vaginal cycle, lasting about 28 days (Hartman, 1923), which is characterised by both macro- and microscopic changes.

During the breeding season the walls of the lateral vaginal canals, urogenital sinus and median vaginal cul-de-sac (p. 65) hypertrophy and their lumina widen.

At oestrus the lateral canals are very vascular and distended with a slightly viscous fluid. After ovulation they quickly involute.

These gross changes are accompanied by cyclic alterations in the vaginal epithelium and in the composition of the vaginal smear. The epithelium covering the median cul-de-sac consists of high columnar mucin-secreting cells, and is stated to be higher during the luteal stage than during the follicular part of the cycle (Morgan, 1946a).

The epithelium of the urogenital sinus and lateral vaginae during anoestrus is about 5 to 6 cells deep, but grows to 15 layers of cells in prooestrus. No leucocytes are present, and the stratum corneum is differentiated from the deeper epithelial layers only by the more vacuolated character of its cells. At oestrus, the stratum corneum loses its nuclei and undergoes massive desquamation, a process which is completed in three to four days. After ovulation the vaginal wall is invaded by leucocytes, which then begin to appear in the vaginal contents.

The vaginal smear characteristic of dioestrus consists of a few nucleated epithelial cells, some leucocytes, and, very rarely, a few cornified cells. During prooestrus the composition of the smear changes to large flat nucleated cells, and at oestrus to fully cornified cells (Hartman, 1923 ; Risman, 1947). Desquamation of cornified cells from the lateral vaginal canals is continuous throughout the breeding season ; in the urogenital sinus the process is rhythmic.

The histological response of the different parts of the vaginal apparatus to oestrogenic and luteal stimulation has been studied in detail by Risman (1947).

Uterine changes

During anoestrus the uteri return to their virgin size, the involution affecting both the mucosa and muscularis. The glands are straight or only slightly coiled, and are lined by a low columnar epithelium containing relatively large nuclei. Large silver-reducing ("argentaffine") cells are frequent in the connective tissue of the endometrium, especially near the cavum uteri (Morgan, 1946a, b).

Considerable growth takes place during prooestrus, the change in the gross size of the uterus being due partly to an increase in the number of its tissue elements, and partly to increased vascularity of the stroma. At oestrus the glands become greatly coiled, especially in their basal regions, and cell division is very active. Cilia, which cannot be recognised during the anoestrous period, are readily seen at this stage, and the superficial epithelium tends to become pseudo-stratified.

When fertilisation does not occur, ovulation is followed by a phase of pseudo-pregnancy. The size and turgidity of the uterus increase further—largely because of the accumulation of fluid in the stroma. Mitotic activity is then at its maximum, and in section the mucosa appears as a mass of long, lace-like folds. The epithelial cells lining the uterine lumen are very broad, non-ciliated and have basally disposed nuclei, but the glands contain large numbers of ciliated cells (Morgan, 1946a). These changes are almost indistinguishable from those which occur during true pregnancy.

In the non-gravid female involution of the uterus sets in approximately two weeks after ovulation. It begins with the resorption of interstitial fluid and cellular exudate, and proceeds to the degeneration of the glandular and surface epithelium, until the resting stage is reached about the 20th day. The lumen of the dioestrous uterus is filled with both degenerating and normal cells.

Changes in the uterine tubes

During the breeding season the tubes become hypertrophied, but the epithelium lining them does not appear to undergo any marked cyclic change (Morgan, 1946a).

Family *Dasyuridae*

Dasyurus

The uterine cycle in the marsupial cat, *Dasyurus viverrinus*, seems to be similar in kind to that of the opossum (Hill & O'Donoghue, 1913).

Prooestrus lasts from 4 to 12 days, and during this time the uterine mucosa increases in thickness and becomes more vascular, while its glands become longer and convoluted, and the epithelium tends to thicken. These changes continue during oestrus, which lasts one or two days, and for a further post-oestrous period of variable length, at the end of which ovulation occurs spontaneously. According to Hill and O'Donoghue (1913), this period of post-oestrous delay may last for 5 to 6 days, but Hartman (1923) questions the reliability of this estimate, and believes that ovulation takes place shortly after the end of heat. Pregnancy or

" pseudopregnancy " then ensues, the latter term having been coined by Hill and O'Donoghue to indicate the excessive and essentially pregnancy-like development of the uterus and mammary apparatus which occurs in *Dasyurus* during the luteal stage of the infertile cycle. During pseudopregnancy the uteri enlarge considerably and become still more vascular. The epithelial lining is high columnar, and the uterine glands are markedly coiled. Later, there is extensive degeneration and desquamation of the surface and glandular epithelium, occasionally accompanied by extravasation of blood. Regeneration sets in at the end of pseudopregnancy, which is believed to last about two weeks. The changes in the pseudopregnant uterus of *Dasyurus* are by no means unique, and find their parallel in eutherian mammals (e.g. in the normal bitch and in the rabbit, either after sterile copulation or certain experimental procedures).

Remarkable proliferation occurs also in the pouch during the reproductive cycle (O'Donoghue, 1911 ; Hill and O'Donoghue, 1913). At the end of pseudo-pregnancy the female may " clear out " the hypertrophied pouch in the same way as does the pregnant animal, as though preparing it for the reception of young (*see* p. 233).

Family Macropodidae

Bettongia

The uterine changes of pregnancy and pseudopregnancy in the Tasmanian rat-kangaroo, *Bettongia cuniculus*, have been studied by Flynn (1930). This species differs from the two discussed above in so far as only one ovum is liberated at ovulation. Consequently, if fertilisation ensues, one uterine horn is in a pregnant, and the other in a pseudopregnant condition, implantation occurring in alternate horns in successive pregnancies. If the mating proves to be sterile, both horns become pseudopregnant, and the changes they then undergo are the same as in the corresponding phase of *Dasyurus viverrinus*, i.e. " the pseudo-pregnant uterus returns more or less gradually to the condition of anoestrum or dioestrum." When one uterine horn is pregnant, the pseudopregnant horn cannot be distinguished from it until after the middle of pregnancy, which lasts about 6 weeks. Throughout the second half of pregnancy this horn is in a " well stimulated condition, exhibiting a turgid mucosa, with a well-developed lymph and blood supply."

During mid-pregnancy the uterine glands of the sterile horn are subdivided into superficial non-secretory and basal secretory parts, and there is marked oedema and widespread degeneration and loss of the epithelium. Near the end of gestation the lumen of the non-pregnant horn is compressed and grooved, owing to the resorption of oedema fluid through the glands, some of which become distended with what Flynn describes as resorbed " lymphatic " material. Just before parturition occurs in the contralateral uterus, there is a " convulsive expulsion of the contained lymph from the connective tissue of the mucosa of the pseudo-pregnant uterus." Immediately after delivery this horn undergoes prooestrous changes.

In *Bettongia*, as opposed to the opossum, ciliation of the uterine glands is strongly developed during anoestrus, as well as during the cycle. The endometrial changes during prooestrus and oestrus appear to be the same as in the opossum.

IV—EUTHERIA

(Placentalia ; Monodelphia)

EDENTATA (= *Xenarthra*)

Dasypus (Armadillo)

According to Hamlett (1932), the uterine mucosa of the nine-banded armadillo (*Dasypus novemcinctus*) becomes slightly bloodshot about the time of ovulation, a change which is sufficiently well-marked and specific to allow of a diagnosis of ovulation.   Hamlett points out that this change, which may be related to the release of oestrogenic hormone, occurs before the single corpus luteum starts functioning. At the same time the uterine tube of the side containing the active ovary becomes much swollen and hyperaemic.   During the ensuing " free vesicle " stage of about 4 months (*see* p. 237), the uterus is hypertrophied and vascular, but the blastocyst remains only slightly adherent to the uterine wall. At the end of this quiescent phase the corpus luteum becomes active and the uterus again swollen and congested, and implantation takes place.

Following parturition the uterus involutes and gradually returns to the non-pregnant condition.

PERISSODACTYLA

Equus (Domestic horse)

Cyclic alterations in the vagina of the mare are slight, and consist of proliferation and cornification of the epithelium during oestrus (Hammond and Wodzicki, 1941). At the end of heat the superficial layers are cast off, and the epithelium becomes infiltrated by leucocytes.   These changes are more marked in the upper vagina than in the vestibule.   Regeneration of the epithelium takes place during metoestrus.

As might be expected, vaginal smears are very inconstant and of little help in the identification of the different phases of the cycle (*see* Aitken, 1927 ; Asdell, 1946).   According to Day and Miller (1940), the vaginal mucosa is moist and glistening at the time of oestrus, but this passes off quickly after ovulation, which is believed to occur during the last few days of heat (*see* p. 239).

Only slight and indefinite changes occur in the uterine mucosa during the cycle.   Mitotic figures are said to be most numerous during prooestrus, and this phase is followed by "degeneration " of the epithelial cells during oestrus, with a subsequent gradual return to normal (Seaborn, 1925).   According to Hammond and Wodzicki (1941), however, the epithelium is highest two days after the end of heat (Fig. 6. 1).   The structure of the uterine glands does not undergo any striking modifications during the oestrous cycle.

Slightly more marked changes take place in the cervix uteri, which contains no tubular glands but numerous mucous cells.   Most of their secretion is produced during the second half of oestrus.   At that time the epithelial cells are columnar, greatly swollen and filled with mucus, which is also present as a wide layer in the lumen of the cervix. According to Hammond and Wodzicki, the mucus tends to be more profuse as well as more liquid at oestrus than during other phases

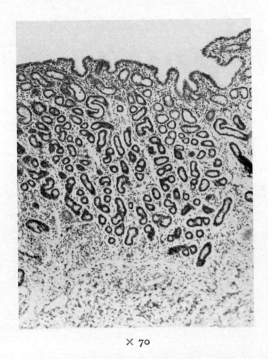

× 70

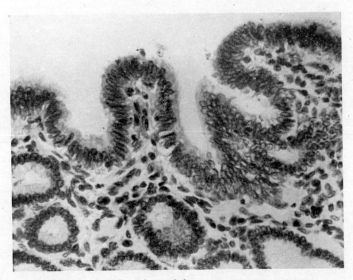

Fig. 6. 1—Endometrium of the mare at oestrus, × 350.

of the cycle, and this may facilitate the ascent of spermatozoa which, in the mare, are not deposited in the vagina but ejaculated directly through the relaxed external os.

There are no significant cyclic changes in the uterine tube.

ARTIODACTYLA

Fam. *Bovidae*
    Bos (Domestic cattle)
    Ovis (Sheep)
    Capra (Goat)

Fam. *Suidae*
    Sus (Pig)

Family *Bovidae*

Genera : *Bos ; Ovis ; Capra*

Bos

Many descriptions have been published of the histological changes in the accessory reproductive organs of the cow (for reviews *see* Hammond, 1927 ; Asdell, 1946). The following outline is based mainly on the accounts of Cole (1930) ; Asdell (1946, 1947) ; and of Weber, Morgan and McNutt (1948).

The vaginal cycle

The vagina of the cow consists of two separate regions which are structurally distinct, and which differ in their histological reactions during the cycle. The lower part or vestibule possesses an atypical stratified squamous epithelium, while the upper, the vagina proper, is lined by a lower type of epithelium, with a superficial layer of mucus-producing cells.

In the vestibular region prooestrus and oestrus are characterised by hyperaemia, oedema and subepithelial leucocytic infiltration. Shortly after oestrus the thickness of the epithelium increases markedly, and the epithelial cells of the middle layer become swollen and polyhedral, while the superficial squamous cells undergo progressive keratinisation and, occasionally, true cornification (Cole, 1930). According to Murphey (1924), desquamation may also occur.

The posterior region of the true vagina has an epithelial lining of polyhedral to columnar cells. During heat both the epithelium and supporting stroma become markedly infiltrated with leucocytes. Blood is also extravasated into the vaginal wall at oestrus and during the succeeding 8 to 11 days (Hammond, 1927 ; Cole, 1930). External bleeding, however, is generally restricted to the first or second days of metoestrus, the only time when, according to Cole, enough mucus is secreted to carry the extravasated red cells away. On the other hand, there is good evidence (Krupski, 1917 ; Asdell, 1946 ; Weber *et al.*, 1948) that the macroscopic haemorrhage shortly after oestrus is, partly if not wholly, of uterine origin, especially in young cows and heifers (*see* below).

The changes in the vaginal mucous membrane near the cervix are more definite and striking than in any other part of the vagina. During prooestrus the superficial layer of the mucosa, 1 or 2 cm. from the cervix, consists of large goblet cells supported by about four layers of polyhedral cells. At oestrus these are reduced to one or two, and the superficial epithelium consists of extremely tall, narrow columnar and actively mucus-secreting cells (Fig. 6. 2). There is also some oedema and congestion of the stroma. Two days after oestrus the epithelium is lower and again several layers deep, while the congestion and oedema have disappeared.

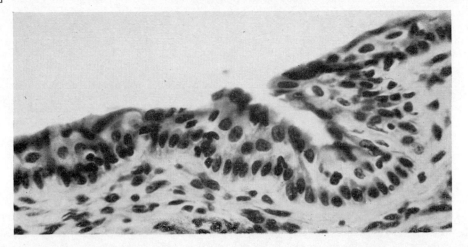

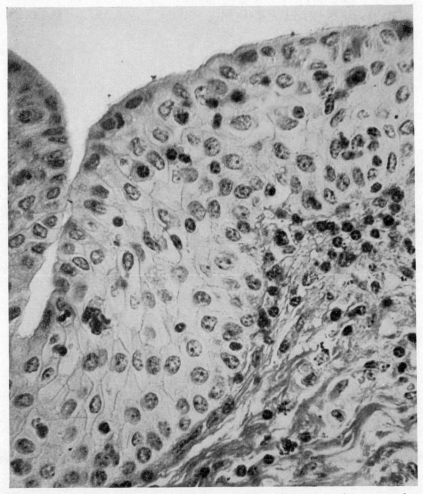

Fig. 6. 2—Vagina of the cow during oestrus.   × 650.   *Above*, 5 cm. from external os ;
below, at level of external os.

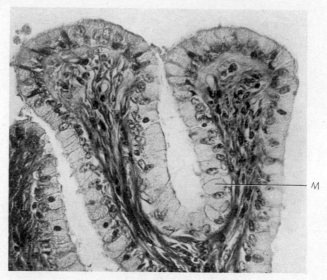

— M

× 350

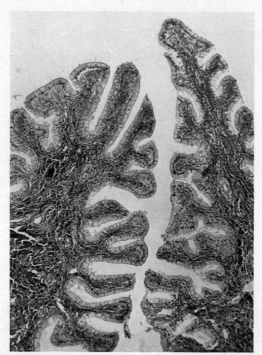

Fig. 6. 3—Cervix of the cow at oestrus, showing extensive
mucification (M) of the epithelium.   × 70.

Eight to 11 days after oestrus the epithelium is " vacuolar and somewhat degenerate in character," and becomes infiltrated by lymphocytes (Cole, 1930).

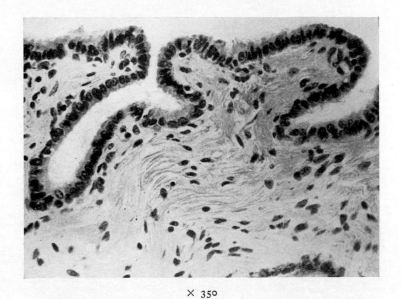

× 350

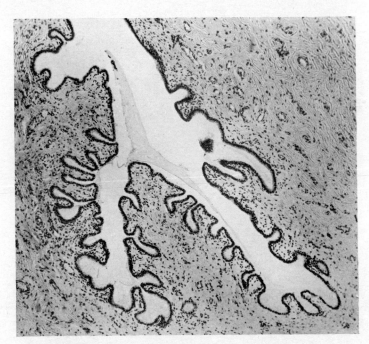

Fig. 6. 4—Cervix of the cow during dioestrus.   × 70.

The changes observed in the cervix uteri are very similar to those in the upper vagina (Figs. 6. 3 and 6. 4).   At oestrus the cervix secretes a great deal of mucus,

T*

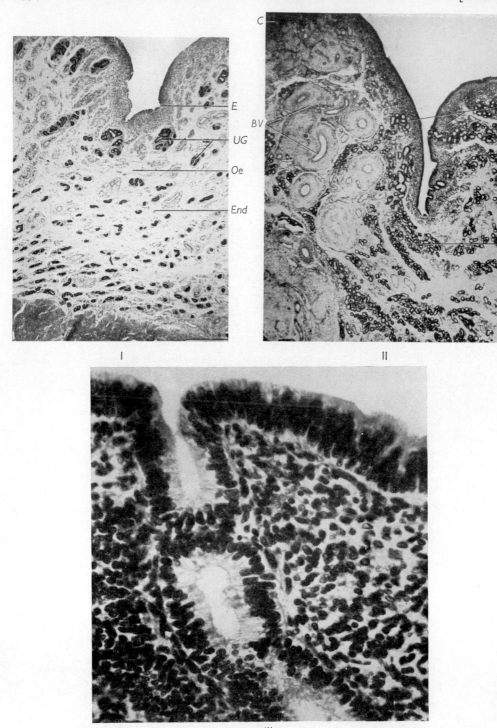

Fig. 6. 5—Uterus of the cow during (I) oestrus (× 11) and (II and III) dioestrus (× 20 and × 335). I, showing marked oedema (Oe) of the endometrium (End), simple uterine glands (UG) and columnar epithelium (E) lining the cavum uteri, and II, showing marked development of the uterine glands and large, thick-walled vessels (BV). C, cotyledonary area ; IC, inter-cotyledonary area.

which together with the vaginal secretions proper account for the large amount of stringy mucus present in the vulva at that stage (*see* Asdell, 1946, and p. 244).

There is some disagreement about the nature of such cyclic changes as occur in the vaginal smear of the cow ; the method is clearly not a reliable one for identifying the various phases of the reproductive cycle.

Uterine changes

The changes in the uterus are fairly clear-cut (Cole, 1930).   During prooestrus the epithelium is tall columnar and pseudostratified, with basal nuclei ; rarely it may be ciliated (Weber *et al.*, 1948).   The glandular epithelium is not as tall as that lining the cavum uteri (Fig. 6. 5, III).   The basal glands are spiral, and the stroma very vascular, although no extravasation of blood occurs.   The epithelial cells lining the uterine cavity may, however, contain blood pigment (Weber *et al.*).   At oestrus the glandular epithelium is taller and the stroma more oedematous.   Scattered through the stroma are many cells, including erythrocytes.   Two days after oestrus the basal glands are more coiled and are filled with secretion, while the stroma is less oedematous.   Glandular hypertrophy and vascularity of the stroma are most marked 8 days after oestrus, and signs of regression appear about the 15th day.   Cole did not observe any extravasation of blood into the uterine cavity at oestrus.   Such a change is, however, stated to occur both by Hammond (1927) and by Zietzschmann (1921), as well as by other writers (*see* Hammond).

The origin of the uterine haemorrhage which occurs in the cow has been studied in detail by Weber *et al.* (1948).   These authors used normal virgin heifers, 14 to 20 months old, and established a series of changes from the formation of subserous and subepithelial haematomata and the escape of plasma through an apparently intact surface epithelium, to the occurrence of massive haemorrhage associated with extensive epithelial erosion.   Most of these events begin immediately after the end of oestrus, and culminate on the second to third day of metoestrus.   Degeneration is less pronounced in the caruncles (cotyledons) than in the inter-cotyledonary areas, where many sites of epithelial disruption and direct capillary haemorrhage into the uterine lumen can be observed (Fig. 6. 6).   The resulting mixture of serous fluid, blood corpuscles, and epithelial cells, passes through the cervix into the vagina.

It would appear from the account of Weber *et al.* that the occurrence of uterine haemorrhage is definitely established, and that it is probably the main source of the vaginal bleeding which is not uncommonly observed in young cows and heifers during the second and third days after the end of heat.   It should be added that this does not necessarily apply to older cows, which are stated to bleed less frequently (*see* Asdell, 1946), possibly because of the greater thickness of their uterine epithelium.

Regenerative changes set in *pari passu* with the process of degeneration.   According to Weber *et al.*, mitoses can be seen on the first day after oestrus, and proliferation of the surface and glandular epithelium continue " through and beyond the bleeding period."

Changes in the uterine tube

According to Asdell (1946), the lumen of the tube contains more mucus and leucocytes on the second day of metoestrus than at other times.   The epithelium is

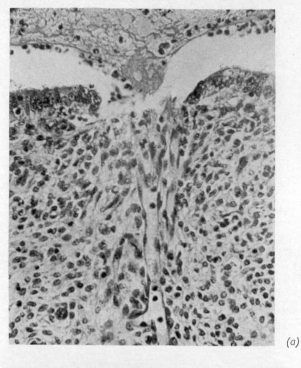

(a)

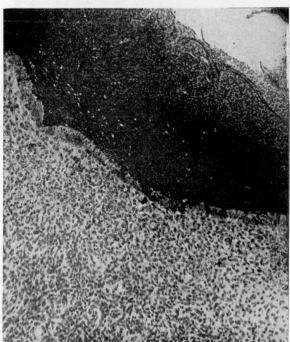

(b)

Fig. 6. 6—Uterine haemorrhage in the heifer, (*a*) showing disruption of the epithelium and capillary haemorrhage directly into the lumen of the uterus ; (*b*) showing bleeding by diapedesis through the intact epithelium covering a cotyledon. There is a massive accumulation of erythrocytes and fibrin strands in the uterine cavity. (Photomicrographs lent by Dr. A. F. Weber.)

tallest and possesses many ciliated elements at oestrus.   It becomes reduced in height at about the 8th day of the cycle.

Ovis

Changes in the vagina

The cyclical changes that occur in the vagina of the ewe during the oestrous cycle have been studied by Casida and McKenzie (1932), Darlow and Hawkins (1932), Grant (1934), Cole and Miller (1935) and McKenzie and Terrill (1937). While stressing individual variability of different ewes, and regional variation within the vagina, most reports agree about the occurrence of a definite, if not very striking, series of changes.

The stratified epithelium of the vagina reaches its greatest height during oestrus and immediately after.   It is lowest at the end of dioestrus and in early prooestrus.   According to McKenzie and Terrill (1937), the growth in height of the epithelium is brought about by increases in both the number of cell layers and the thickness of each cell layer.   Keratinisation and desquamation of the superficial cells of the epithelium can be observed at all stages of the cycle except early in oestrus, but it is always regional and never generalised (Grant, 1934).   Most intense cornification and desquamation take place at the close of heat and during metoestrus.   Oedema and congestion are greatest during prooestrus and oestrus, while leucocytes are most abundant during the luteal phase (dioestrus), when mitoses are also numerous.   Extravasation of blood does not occur.   During pregnancy mucous changes take place in the vaginal epithelium.

The vaginal smear

There is some difference of opinion about the value of the vaginal smear as a means of following the phases of the cycle in the ewe.   According to Cole and Miller (1935), the method is of great help.   Early oestrus can be recognised " by a profuse flow of transparent watery mucus ; metoestrum by a copious, dry, cheesy smear consisting chiefly of large squamous epithelial cells ; dioestrum usually by a scant smear consisting of epithelial cells and a variable number of leucocytes."   From this it appears that cornification is much more marked in the ewe than in the cow, and that it is most intense during metoestrus, i.e. at a later stage of the cycle than in other mammals.   The observations of McKenzie and Terrill (1937) are in agreement with these findings.   On the other hand, Polovtzeva and Fomenko (1933) report that only 22 per cent of 1,346 ewes which took the ram were in oestrus, as determined by the vaginal smear technique (*see* also Asdell, 1946).   According to Cole and Miller, vaginal smears indicating a condition of oestrus are commonly obtained in the lactating ewe.

Changes in the uterus

The cyclic changes undergone by the endometrium of the ewe have been closely studied (Marshall, 1903 ; Casida and McKenzie, 1932 ; Grant, 1934 ; Cole and Miller, 1935 ; McKenzie and Terrill, 1937).

The cervical stroma becomes congested and oedematous during oestrus, but extravasation of blood does not take place.   Mucus is produced throughout the cycle and, according to Grant, the amount secreted does not vary with the phase of the cycle, although at oestrus it is much less tenacious and more profuse.   Cole and Miller (1935), on the other hand, report the occurrence of cytological changes which they relate to the increased flow of mucus at oestrus.   The histological structure of the active cervix during the sexual season differs conspicuously from that of the cervix during anoestrus.

Cyclic changes in the body of the uterus, while slight, appear to be more distinct than those in the cervix.   During anoestrus the organ is in a state of quiescence.   Dark-brown or black pigment is present in many ewes, especially in the region beneath the epithelium, both in the cotyledonary areas and between them.   According to Grant (1934) and Cole and Miller (1935), this pigment occurs at all times—before sexual maturity, during anoestrus and in pregnancy.   It is believed to be derived from melanoblasts and not from blood pigment (Grant, 1934).   During the period of growth (prooestrus and oestrus), the stromal cells show mitotic activity, but the epithelium remains unaffected.   There is also marked oedema and vascular congestion of the mucosa.

According to Marshall (1903), the congestion leads to the breaking down of some of the vessels during prooestrus.   Frequently, the first extravasation takes place from vessels situated immediately beneath certain parts of the stroma, where the nuclei are most thickly distributed.   The blood collects immediately beneath the epithelium and may pass into the uterine cavity, but this does not occur invariably.   A few epithelial cells may be torn off, but this is not constant and is never severe enough to cause denudation of the stroma.   As the breeding season progresses, there is a tendency for these changes to become less marked, and eventually most of the congested vessels subside without rupturing.

Kazzander (1890) appears to have been the first to detect extravasated blood in the sheep's endometrium.   It was not, however, observed by Cole and Miller (1935), nor is it reported by McKenzie and Terrill (1937), or by Asdell (1946).

Increased growth and coiling of the endometrial glands, with an increase in the height of the epithelium in the fundus of the glands, occurs during the luteal part of the cycle.   During this phase, the epithelium lining the cavum uteri is deeply folded.   The cells of the cotyledons show the most pronounced growth, and increase in size from 11–17 μ to about 40–50 μ during the week following the end of heat.   At the height of this stage they tend to be pseudostratified, but regress shortly afterwards (Casida and McKenzie, 1932).

Changes in the uterine tubes

Changes in the uterine tubes are reported by Casida and McKenzie, who regard them as being more definite than those which occur in the vagina and uterus.   The ciliated columnar epithelium is highest during oestrus and metoestrus, and during the luteal phase of the cycle the cells exhibit conspicuous cytoplasmic projections.

Capra

The histological changes in the reproductive organs of the goat have been described by Hamilton and Harrison (1951).

The vagina undergoes slightly more pronounced changes than other parts of the genital tract.   These changes consist in the sudden appearance, at oestrus, of cornification and desquamation of the most superficial layers of the stratified squamous epithelium. As a result, the thickness of the epithelium becomes much reduced, and non-nucleated cornified cells staining brightly with picric acid or orange G., as well as densely-staining nucleated cells, appear in the lumen of the vagina. These changes are confined to the first two days of the cycle, for the rest of which the vaginal epithelium is relatively inactive, apart from a brief period, between the 9th and 12th day, when it has the appearance of a transitional epithelium. According to Hamilton and Harrison, this change can be related to the activity of the corpus luteum, which reaches its greatest diameter by the 12th day, and subsequently declines (*see* p. 250).

The cyclic changes in the uterus are slight and resemble those which occur in the cow and sow.

Family *Suidae*

Sus

Changes in the vagina

The vaginal cycle in the sow has been described by McKenzie (1926) and Wilson (1926).

During dioestrus the smear consists of varying numbers of leucocytes and nucleated epithelial cells and a few cornified elements. The leucocyte count is highest during the two to four days following the end of heat, when a whitish discharge, consisting of mucus and many white and other cells, may collect at the vulva (*see* Zupp, 1924). Marked cornification does not occur, but large numbers of nucleated epithelial cells are shed during the latter half of oestrus. Parallel histological changes occur in the vaginal wall. Proliferation begins shortly before, and reaches its maximum during oestrus. True cornification does not occur, and the post-oestrous degeneration consists mainly in the appearance of large vacuoles and leucocytic infiltration of the mucosa (*see* Asdell, 1946).

Changes in the uterus

The cyclic changes in the endometrium of the sow have been described by Corner (1921) and McKenzie (1926). They involve variations in the degree of surface folding and stromal oedema of the mucosa, and in the rate of proliferation of the epithelium.

The mucosa is divided into a superficial zone containing few glands, and a basal zone with numerous very tortuous glands. The lumina of the straight superficial segments are wider than those of the deeper glands which they drain. During oestrus the uterine epithelium is tall columnar and pseudostratified, while stromal oedema is conspicuous. Mitotic figures are very numerous, and signs of vacuolar degeneration and nuclear chromatolysis are also evident. This degeneration begins immediately before the onset of oestrus. The signs of epithelial degeneration disappear after ovulation, and the individual cells increase in size. Mitosis continues throughout the first week after ovulation, during which the stromal oedema diminishes considerably. The simple tall columnar cells of the surface epithelium then become arranged in a wavy manner, after which, between the 10th and 15th days from ovulation, they are reduced in size and frayed, due apparently to the liberation of glycogen.

Changes in the uterine tube

The tubal epithelium is ciliated and reaches a height of 25 μ during and just after heat. It declines to 10 μ in dioestrus, and is then gradually restored to its previous maximum (Snyder, 1923). The histological changes undergone by the tubal musculature during the cycle of the sow have been studied by Anapolsky (1928). The muscle fibres are longest during oestrus, and smallest during the implantation (i.e. luteal) phase. These changes appear to be correlated with cyclic variations in tubal motility, the longest muscle fibres being present at the time when contractility is greatest.

TUBULIDENTATA

Orycteropus (Aardvark or ant-deer)

A few observations on the histological appearance of the sterile and previously parous uterine horn of a pregnant aardvark have been published by Van der Horst (1949–50).

This species is closely related to the *Xenarthra*, but is now recognised as belonging to an independent order (Simpson, 1945). It possesses a uterus duplex, and is stated to carry only a single young (Van der Horst).

The endometrium of the non-pregnant horn consists of three zones. The superficial one is very cellular and congested, and is traversed by almost straight glands. The middle layer of coarse connective tissue is rendered conspicuous by many blood vessels with thick hyaline walls, while the deepest or glandular layer is characterised by the presence of mucous glands and their ducts. There is no difference between the mesometrial and antimesometrial border of the uterus.

Van der Horst points out that a similar stratification of the endometrium is present in certain other mammals such as *Manis*, the scaly anteater, belonging to the Pholidota, and in *Talpa* and *Sorex* among the Insectivora.

LAGOMORPHA

Oryctolagus (Rabbit)

The vagina

The rabbit does not exhibit an obvious vaginal cycle (Courrier, 1926 ; Snyder, 1926; Kunde and Proud, 1929). In mature and sexually receptive animals the lower end of the vagina tends to show a purplish discoloration, but this is not observed in all does (Friedman, 1938). The vaginal epithelium is simple and columnar, except in the lowest segment where it is stratified squamous. The high columnar cells of the upper region are mucus-secreting (Fig. 6. 7), and normally undergo neither proliferation nor desquamation (Courrier, 1926). The vagina enlarges markedly during pregnancy, and involutes slowly after parturition (Hammond, 1940).

The vaginal smear

It is generally believed that vaginal smears are of no help in diagnosing the reproductive state of the animal. Thus Kunde and Proud (1929) point out that mating and fertilisation occur in the presence of a cellular picture which may correspond to any of the phases of the vaginal cycle in the rat (see p. 566).

A more recent study, how- ever, indicates that the vagina of normal rabbits undergoes cyclic changes which are re- flected in the cytology of the vaginal contents (Hamilton, 1951). This author examined smears taken directly from the vaginal wall with a special loop, and found periodic fluc- tuations in the numbers of two types of cell, large cornified non-nucleated elements stain- ing consistently orange-red with Shorr's stain, and small nucleated epithelial cells with more variable staining pro-

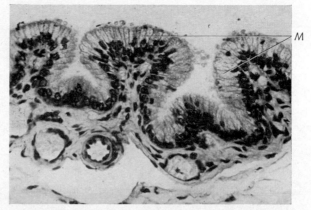

Fig. 6. 7—Vagina of the rabbit during pseudopregnancy, showing the columnar, mucus-secreting cells (M) of the epithelial lining. × 400.

perties.   There were times when the cornified cells constituted 80–100 per cent of the total smear picture, and in unmated does such peaks recurred at regular four- to six-day intervals.

The uterus

The uterus of the rabbit has six endometrial folds.   The two that are meso- metrial form the placenta and are usually larger, more vascular and less glandular than both the obplacental folds, situated on the antimesometrial border, and the periplacental folds which are intermediate in position.   In pseudopregnancy these structures are generally equal in size, but during pregnancy the four non-placental folds are almost obliterated.   In view of the lack of a true oestrous cycle in the rabbit (oestrus persisting for long periods, see p. 258), only the pre- and post- ovulatory phases need to be considered in the non-pregnant animal.

At oestrus the surface layer of epithelial cells is straight and almost continuous, being rarely broken by short glandular invaginations.   The cells are of two types, large cubical and frequently ciliated cells, and high columnar ones with fusiform nuclei (Klein, 1933).   According to Parker (1931), ciliated cells are more frequent in the cervical segment and do not undergo cyclic changes in size or number. The uterine stroma is hyperaemic and not markedly glandular (Fig. 6. 8, II).

The endometrium of the luteal phase is characterised by pronounced glandular development (Ancel and Bouin, 1911 ; Hammond and Marshall, 1914).   Early in pseudopregnancy the glands do not extend far into the stroma, but later they increase in number and proliferate rapidly until they penetrate almost as far as the myometrium, which is also greatly hypertrophied (Fig. 6. 9).   This relative lateness of glandular development is typical of the rabbit, and contrasts with a corresponding precocity in the cat (see p. 601).

The histological changes in the uterine mucosa during pseudopregnancy and unilateral pregnancy become noticeable after the 32nd hour post-coitum (Knaus, 1930).   They have been studied in detail by Bouin and Ancel (1910), des Cilleuls

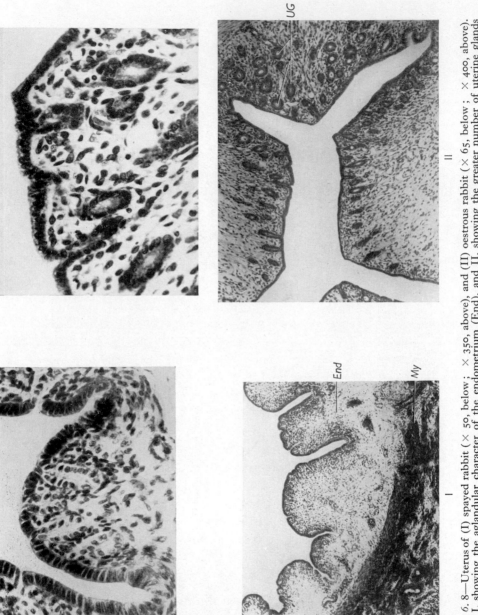

Fig. 6. 8—Uterus of (I) spayed rabbit (× 50, below; × 350, above), and (II) oestrous rabbit (× 65, below; × 400, above). I, showing the aglandular character of the endometrium (End), and II, showing the greater number of uterine glands (UG) and increased cellularity of the stroma. My, myometrium.

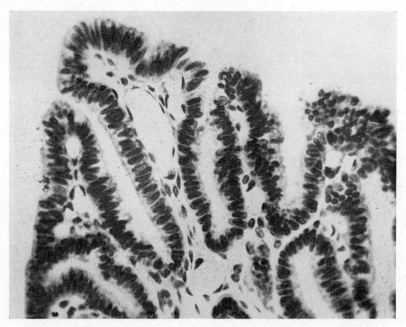

× 530

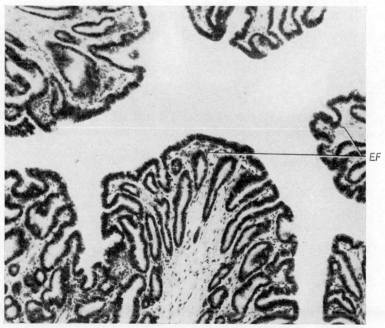

EF

Fig. 6. 9—Uterus of the rabbit on the 5th day of pseudopregnancy.
Showing the endometrial folds (EF) which form the " dentelle " of
Bouin and Ancel (1910).　× 85.

(1914), Knaus (1930), Deanesly and Parkes (1931) and Klein (1933). Up to the 8th day the surface and glandular epithelium proliferate, as a result of which a spongy lace-work of endometrical folds is formed, and the uterine lumen assumes a deeply serrated outline (the " dentelle " of Bouin and Ancel, 1910 ; see Fig. 6. 9). After the 10th day the surface epithelium becomes transformed into a syncytium not unlike that present in the ferret (see p. 595). At that stage the glands are distended, and the stroma is represented mainly by the connective-tissue cores of the endometrial folds. After the 14th day the syncytium begins to involute and eventually sloughs off, thus leading to the appearance of free cell masses and giant cells in the lumen of the uterus.

At the end of pseudopregnancy, the active phase of which lasts about 16 days in the rabbit (Knaus, 1950), the endometrium becomes congested, and blood may be extravasated into the stroma (Hammond and Marshall, 1914 ; Hammond, 1925). This has not been observed during the breakdown of the sterile horn up to the 24th day of unilateral pregnancy (Deanesly and Parkes, 1931).

During approximately the first two weeks after ovulation, the changes outlined above are identical whether fertilisation takes place or not. As Knaus has shown, they, as well as the altered uterine contractility, are intimately related to the development and secretion of the corpora lutea (see Knaus, 1950). The changes can be reproduced with progesterone in castrate does, and in this way four or five stages in the development of the pseudopregnant endometrium have been arbitrarily and qualitatively selected by various workers as a basis for estimating the progestational effects of luteal hormone (Allen, 1930 ; Clauberg, 1933 ; McPhail, 1934 ; Robson, 1935). The close parallelism between the condition of the uterine mucosa and the state of the ovaries is also shown by the fact that deciduomata can be induced in the non-pregnant horn up to, but not after, the 12th day of gestation (Courrier and Kehl, 1930). When produced, however, they persist until the 16th day, which coincides approximately with the end of the active life of the corpora lutea.

The only obvious change which occurs in the cervix uteri of the rabbit during the various reproductive phases is an increase in the number of clear goblet-like cells in the later stages of pseudopregnancy and pregnancy (Hammond, 1925). According to Hamilton (1951), the staining properties of the cervical epithelium also show slight cyclic variations in the oestrous animal.

Considerable involution of the uterus occurs during lactation. The organ becomes thin and of a papery consistency, and the mucosal folds almost disappear, those on the mesometrial side being least affected. Involution occurs even when pregnancy supervenes after post-partum mating, and as a result the blastocysts are resorbed either before or after attachment.

The uterine tube

Changes in the uterine tube of the rabbit have been described by Moreaux (1913), Cohnen (1927), Westman (1930) and Westman, Jorpes and Widström (1931). It appears that during sexually quiescent phases the mucosa is composed of ciliated columnar cells, between which are scattered non-ciliated secretory cells. No secretion is present in the lumen. After ovulation and in early pregnancy, the mucosa consists of secretory cells similar to ordinary mucous cells, and there are few ciliated cells. During these phases the tube is congested, and secretion is present in the lumen. Experiments performed by Westman *et al.* (1931), suggest that these changes are controlled by the secretion of the corpora lutea. Westman (1900) has also shown that the thick membrane by which the ova are normally surrounded in the tubes, is provided by the secretory cells, and that the ova degenerate if deprived of this protective cover.

RODENTIA

Fam. *Muridae*
        Rattus (Common rat)
        Mus (Common mouse)
        Mastomys (Multimammate mouse)

Fam. *Sciuridae*
        Sciurus (Squirrel)
        Citellus (Ground squirrel ; chipmunk)

Fam. *Cricetidae*
    Subfam. *Cricetinae*
            Cricetus (Golden hamster)
            Cricetulus (Chinese hamster)
    Subfam. *Microtinae*
            Clethrionomys (Bank vole)

Fam. *Caviidae*
        Cavia (Guinea-pig)

As explained on p. 264, rodents vary greatly in their patterns of reproductive behaviour. Some, such as certain types of squirrel, have a very restricted breeding season, during which the female may undergo only a few sexual cycles. Others, such as field-mice and voles, are seasonally polyoestrous, and in the unmated state, experience a succession of oestrous cycles over a considerable part of the year. Common laboratory species like rats, mice, hamsters and guinea-pigs, are continually polyoestrous, reproducing at all times of the year. Correspondingly marked differences occur in the duration of the cycle, and in the functional behaviour of the corpus luteum in this order of mammals.

In view of the outstanding importance of rats and mice as experimental animals, the cycle in the reproductive tract of the Muridae will be considered first.

Family Muridae

Genera : Rattus ; Mus ; Mastomys

Rattus and Mus

Vaginal changes

Very clear-cut cyclic changes occur in the vaginal mucosa and vaginal contents of the rat and mouse. The following description is taken mainly from Long and Evans (1922), Allen (1922), Parkes (1926, 1928) and Clauberg (1931).

Changes in the vagina during the oestrous cycle. In dioestrus the vaginal epithelium consists of a Malpighian layer of 3 to 7 rows of cells, and is heavily infiltrated with leucocytes (Allen, 1922 ; Snell, 1941). Towards the end of this phase the epithelium begins to proliferate, and the number of layers of cells approximately doubles, while leucocytosis ceases. During prooestrus a stratum granulosum develops and, as oestrus approaches, it becomes converted into a stratum corneum (Fig. 6. 10, II). The superficial cornified cells are shed, and desquamation continues throughout the second half of oestrus and early metoestrus. In this way the height of the epithelium is steadily reduced (Fig. 6. 10, III). Later in metoestrus, as well as in dioestrus, even the uppermost parts of the Malpighian layer are lost (as shown by the composition of the vaginal smear, *see* below), and with the return of leucocytosis the cycle of changes in the vaginal wall is repeated.

Changes in the vagina during pseudopregnancy, pregnancy and lactation. As described on p. 276, pseudopregnancy can be induced by sterile mating and by a variety of experimental procedures. In the mouse this condition lasts approximately 11 days (Parkes, 1926) and in the rat about 14 days (Slonaker, 1929).

The most superficial cells of the vaginal epithelium of the pseudopregnant rat are cuboidal or cylindrical, and the intermediate cell layers show vacuolisation (Long and Evans, 1922).

In the latter half of pregnancy the epithelium of the vagina undergoes mucification (Long and Evans, 1922). After the second week of lactation the number of layers of cells in the vaginal mucosa is reduced to two, the superficial layer being cubical or low columnar.

The vaginal smear during the normal cycle. The basic constituents of the vaginal smear are nucleated epithelial cells, cornified cells and leucocytes (Allen, 1922 ; Long and Evans, 1922 ; Snell, 1941). By the use of special staining methods such as that of Shorr (1941), various subgroups of these three cell types, based on the chemical reactions of the cytoplasm, can be recognised (*see* Hartman, 1944). The relative proportions of each type of cell found in the vaginal contents vary characteristically during the different phases of the oestrous cycle (Allen, 1922 ; Long and Evans, 1922 ; Voss, 1930), but there are marked individual and strain differences, and variations depending on the number of smears taken each day (Snell, 1941 ; Hartman, 1944).

During dioestrus the vagina usually contains a little mucus in which are entangled leucocytes and nucleated basophilic, and sometimes vacuolated cells. At prooestrus leucocytes disappear, and the smear consists either of sheets of or isolated, lightly-staining hexagonal epithelial cells, which become progressively acidophilic. At oestrus the vaginal smear is "cheesy," and consists exclusively of non-nucleated cornified cells which stain a brilliant orange-red with Shorr's stain. Long and Evans divide this phase into two stages, during the second of which cornified cells are more abundant, although the female no longer accepts the male.

In late oestrus cornified elements begin to diminish, and leucocytes appear in the vaginal smear. At the same time, large basophilic epithelial cells with vesicular nuclei (so-called " Shorr " cells ; Hartman, 1944) appear. During metoestrus and early dioestrus the smear is thick and consists almost entirely of leucocytes, and a few cornified cells, Shorr cells, and basophilic epithelial cells (Mandl, 1951a).

Although, according to Young, Boling and Blandau (1941), sexual receptivity usually begins when the smear contains 75 per cent nucleated epithelial and 25 per cent non-nucleated cornified cells, it is now generally agreed that the prevalence of a certain type of cell in the vagina is not a completely reliable index

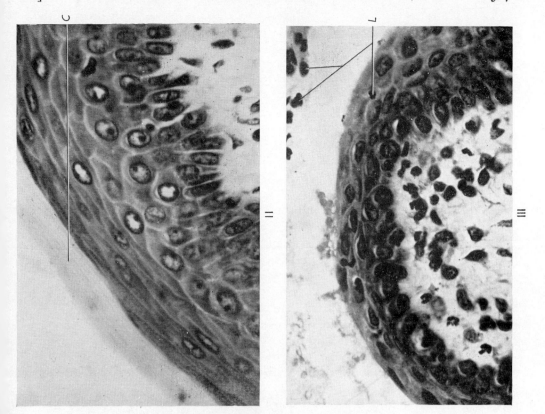

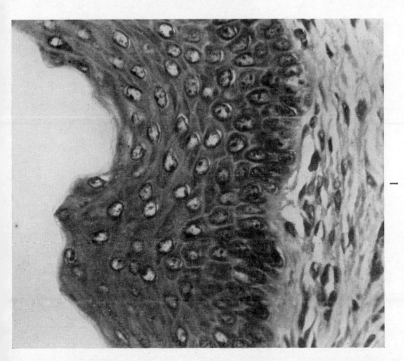

Fig. 6. IC—Vagina of the rat during prooestrus (I) ; oestrus (II) ; and dioestrus (III), × 530.   Showing in II, a well-marked zone of cornification (C) ; in III, the greatly reduced width of the epithelium, and the presence of numerous leucocytes (L), both in the wall and lumen of the vagina.

of the physiological state of the animal. Thus heat in the rat may occur in the absence of a cornified smear, and vice versa (*see* Young, 1941). According to Blandau, Boling and Young (1941), the " copulatory response " is a better test of sexual receptivity, and by means of this method they have established a mean duration of heat of $13 \cdot 7 \pm 4 \cdot 55$ hours (range of 1–28) in the mature female. This compares with averages of 3 to 12 hours, given by Long and Evans, and with 3 to 21 hours, as established by Ball (1937).

Cornification of the vaginal epithelium, unassociated with a physiological state of heat, has also been observed in intact and spayed animals either as a result of mechanical irritation of the vagina or of vitamin A deficiency (Evans and Bishop, 1922; Wade and Doisy, 1935; Emery and Schwabe, 1936; Krichesky and Glass, 1947; *see* also Reynolds, 1949). The most satisfactory methods for obtaining vaginal smears in rats and mice are discussed by Snell (1941) and Nicholas (1949).

Cyclic vaginal changes, similar in general character and duration, though not in intensity, to those present in normal animals, occur in ovariectomised rats (Kostitch and Télébakovitch, 1929; Mandl, 1951b).

The vaginal smear during pseudopregnancy, pregnancy and lactation. During pseudopregnancy the vaginal smear is of the dioestrous type and contains much mucus. Red blood cells are often observed about three days before the onset of the next oestrous period (Parkes, 1929a).

In the pregnant rat the vaginal smear consists of a great deal of mucus, a few leucocytes and nucleated epithelial cells. Red blood cells appear between the 12th and 16th days, and constitute the " placental sign." Long and Evans regarded this blood as being of placental origin, but according to Stafford (1930) and Venable (1939), it is derived from decidual vessels and blood sinuses, and escapes from the lowest implantation site into the vagina. Irregular and slight bleeding also occurs during pregnancy in the mouse (Parkes, 1926) and, apparently, in other rodents such as the cotton rat, *Sigmodon hispidus* (Meyer and Meyer, 1944), and the Asiatic vole, *Microtus guentheri* (Lasch, 1949).

During lactation the smear is of the dioestrous type. An oestrous smear usually occurs in the mouse during the fourth week post partum (Atkinson and Leathem, 1946).

Uterine changes during the cycle

During dioestrus the uterus of the rat or mouse is small, avascular and has a slit-like lumen. It is lined by a simple columnar epithelium (Fig. 6. 11, III). Mitoses are most frequent in the endometrial glands of the mouse during late dioestrus and early prooestrus, becoming fewer as " functional activity increases " (Allen, 1922). In the rat, mitoses do not occur in the glands and are only rarely observed in the surface epithelium (Allen, 1931).

During prooestrus the uterine horns fill with a watery and non-coagulable fluid (Long and Evans), and the columnar epithelial cells lining them become cuboidal (Fig. 6. 11, I). The accumulation of free fluid in the lumen is preceded by a marked rise in the weight, water and glycogen content of the uterus (Astwood, 1939; Boettiger, 1946). Astwood found that in the rat uterine size and hydration reach a maximum during prooestrus, that is to say, before the establishment of an oestrous condition in the vagina. With the first appearance of cornified cells in the smear, the water content of the uterine wall falls abruptly, and its total weight more gradually.

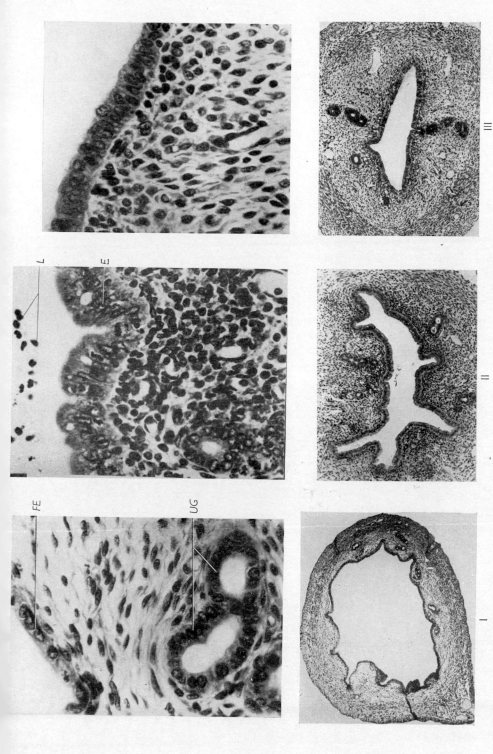

Fig. 6. II—Uterus of the rat during (I) prooestrus (× 30, below ; × 350, above), (II) oestrus and (III) dioestrus (× 55, below ; × 400, above).
I, showing the great dilatation of the uterus accompanied by flattening of the epithelium (FE) lining the cavum uteri ; II, showing the great height of the columnar epithelium (E), and a few leucocytes (L) in the lumen ; III, showing the reduced size and inactive appearance of the uterus and its epithelial lining.   UG, uterine glands.

the other hand, the distension of the lumen persists until late oestrus, when the retained fluid is rapidly discharged through the cervical canals.

Oestrus is marked by signs of degeneration in the epithelium of the cavum uteri. These comprise loss of the basement membrane, vacuolar degeneration and leucocytic invasion. Denudation of the uterus does not occur, and the degeneration is at first unassociated with signs of repair ; few or no mitoses are ever seen. There are no degenerative changes either in the glands, which are small, or in the stroma (Fig. 6. 11, II).

During metoestrus degeneration and regeneration proceed together, and the uterus rapidly returns to the condition typical of dioestrus.

Cyclic changes in the vascular architecture of the uterus of the rat have been described by Williams (1948). The outstanding feature is endometrial hyperaemia along the antimesometrial border during late dioestrus, followed by a stage of relative ischaemia of this area during oestrus. This finding can be contrasted with observations in the ferret (Hamilton and Gould, 1940) and guinea-pig (Bacsich and Wyburn, 1940, 1941), in both of which a similar type of hyperaemia develops, but is confined to the oestrous phase.

Uterine changes during pseudopregnancy

In the rat the endometrial changes of pseudopregnancy are clearly defined, although not immediately apparent on low-power microscopic examination. They begin with the disappearance of leucocytes, and with an increase in the size and number of the stromal nuclei, mitoses occasionally being seen. On the 7th and 8th days rapid epithelial proliferation takes place, the epithelium also becoming lower (Allen, 1931). From the 10th day until almost the beginning of the next prooestrous period 4 days later, the surface epithelium becomes folded or " hillocky." Clauberg (1931) describes a movement of the epithelial nuclei from the basement membrane during this phase. The most superficial layer of the epithelium is stated to undergo temporary mucification, and to disintegrate towards the end of pseudopregnancy (Schick, 1943).

Early in pseudopregnancy the uterus is capable of responding to appropriate stimuli (such as the insertion of a thread through the uterine wall : Long and Evans, 1922) by local growth of the endometrium. As a result of such mechanical irritation, blocks of decidual cells similar to those observed during early pregnancy develop, and produce conspicuous and externally visible nodules, the so-called deciduomata or placentomata (Fig. 6. 12). This capacity continues only for a short period, and disappears before the 5th or 6th day after ovulation in the rat, and even earlier in the mouse. It is associated with sensitisation of the endometrium by progesterone secreted by the corpora lutea. The fact that no deciduomata can be produced during the oestrous cycle of the mouse and rat indicates that in these species the corpora lutea of the normal cycle secrete relatively little progesterone. None the less it can be shown, e.g. in the rat, that there is an active, though varying, rate of secretion of progesterone throughout the cycle (Constantinides, 1947).

Changes in the cervix

Cyclic changes in the cervix uteri have been described by Hamilton (1947).

In the rat the two uterine horns open into the vagina through two separate cervical canals. Histologically, two segments can be identified in the cervix, a

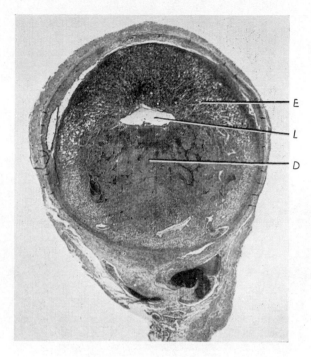

× 15

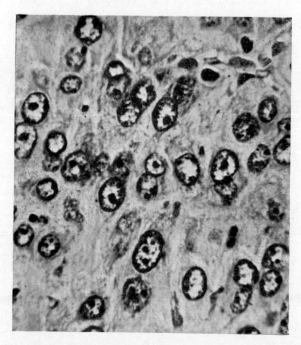

Fig. 6. 12—Transverse section through the deciduoma-bearing uterus of a rat. D, deciduoma ; E, unchanged endometrium ; L, lumen of uterus.   × 350.   From Selye and McKeown (1935).

wer one which is similar to the vagina, and an upper which is transitional between the lower cervix and the uterus. The structure of each segment, and the nature and amount of its contribution to the vaginal discharge, vary during the cycle.

During prooestrus the distinction between the upper and lower cervical segments begins to become manifest. The epithelium consists of a deeper cornifying layer and a superficial one of mucoid epithelial cells, which desquamate in late prooestrus. At oestrus the two segments are clearly differentiated, the lower one exhibiting the staining properties of the vagina (i.e. bright orange with Shorr's stain), and the upper those of the uterus (blue-green with Shorr's stain). The epithelium lining the uterus is of the columnar type, whereas the lower cervix is covered with cornified cells which are discharged during late oestrus and become part of the vaginal contents. The process of epithelial desquamation is continued into metoestrus, and both during this stage and the next (dioestrus), the cervix is inactive, contributing mainly leucocytes to the vaginal smear, and there is no sharp histological differentiation between the upper and lower cervical segments.

In the mouse the structure of the cervix does not appear to undergo any striking variations during the cycle (see Allen, 1922).

Changes in the uterine tube

Long and Evans state that the distal folds of the uterine tube of the rat are distended with fluid for a period of at least 12 hours after the estimated time of ovulation. These folds always contain the eggs, but as the ova move towards the uterus, the more proximal loops of the tube do not become distended.

According to Allen (1922), the uterine tubes of the mouse are not affected by the periodic leucocytosis which involves the rest of the reproductive tract. They do, however, show degenerative changes in the epithelium during metoestrus and early dioestrus. These changes have been reinvestigated by 'Espinasse (1935), who doubts whether they are related to the oestrous cycle.

Mastomys

The oestrous cycle of the multimammate mouse (*Mastomys erythroleucus*, Temm.) resembles that of the common mouse and rat in its general features, but differs by the " extraordinary intensity " of the histological changes in the reproductive tract (Brambell and Davis, 1941).

The vaginal cycle is remarkable for the extensive mucification of the superficial parts of the epithelium which takes place not merely before parturition, as in the rat and mouse, but also at prooestrus. At oestrus the layer beneath these mucified cells cornifies. Following copulation both the superficial mucified and deeper cornified layers slough off, leaving behind a thick nucleated epithelium which subsequently, in dioestrus, becomes infiltrated with leucocytes.

As in the rat and mouse, the uterus fills with fluid during heat, and the distension becomes so intense that each horn has a diameter of 0·5 cm., while its stretched wall may be only 0·1 mm. thick in parts. This distension begins before ovulation, and continues for some time after copulation and fertilisation of the ova.

Family *Sciuridae*
Genera : *Sciurus* ; *Citellus*

Sciurus

The vaginal cycle in the grey squirrel, *S. carolinensis*, appears to follow the typical rodent pattern (*see* above). Before puberty and during anoestrus the vagina is lined by a thin layer of flattened epithelium. " As oestrus approaches the vagina enlarges and the epithelium thickens and becomes cornified. . . . In late pregnancy the vaginal epithelium becomes columnar ; during lactation it returns to the resting condition " (Deanesly and Parkes, 1933).

The usual prooestrous development takes place in the uterus, and at oestrus the cavum uteri is distended with fluid, as in the rat and mouse. The greatest development of the uterine tubes also occurs at oestrus.

Citellus

During anoestrus the vulva of the ground squirrel is small, and the vagina is occluded (Johnson, Foster and Coco, 1933). Its folded epithelium is low cuboidal (Foster, 1934). During prooestrus the vulva reddens, and the vaginal epithelium proliferates rapidly, until at the end of this phase, when the epithelium is still cuboidal, canalisation occurs. During oestrus the vagina contains much fluid, and becomes cornified. If mating takes place, a vaginal plug is formed, which is essentially similar to that of the guinea-pig (*see* p. 581). If copulation does not occur, the animal remains in a " semi-oestrous condition," during which the vaginal smear is " cheese-like " and consists of nucleated and cornified epithelial cells. Isolated females remain in this condition for a month or longer. They will not mate, and eventually pass into a state in which the vagina remains open, but smears show small cuboidal epithelial cells similar to those of prooestrus. This phase generally passes into anoestrus (Foster, 1934).

During pregnancy the vagina remains open, and shortly before parturition the epithelium becomes slightly mucified.

A detailed account of the uterine changes in this species is given by Foster. During anoestrus glands are usually absent in non-parous animals, and the cells lining the cavum uteri are low, containing small nuclei and scanty cytoplasm. During prooestrus all tissue elements proliferate, and glands appear in the stroma. At oestrus these changes are maximal, and the epithelium is very high. Ovulation is dependent on copulation (Foster, 1934 ; *see* p. 268) When it has occurred, the surface epithelium becomes vacuolated, and an extensive leucocytic invasion of all the uterine layers takes place. By the third day after ovulation, changes indicative of pregnancy and luteal action (folding of surface epithelium and coiling of glands) are obvious.

The epithelium of the uterine tube undergoes regression at ovulation (Foster). The change is temporary, and the cells resume their original height 36 hours post coitum, but regress again on the 5th day of pregnancy.

Family *Cricetidae*

Subfamily *Cricetinae*

Genera : *Cricetus* ; *Cricetulus*

Cricetus

The structural changes during the oestrous cycle of the golden hamster, *Cricetus auratus*, are somewhat different from those of the mouse and rat (Deanesly, 1938).

Vaginal changes

At oestrus the wall of the upper vagina consists of epithelial villi, lined by masses of irregular mucus-secreting cells set upon 3 to 8 layers of cornified epithelium. About 1 cm. above the vulva this type of epithelial lining changes into ordinary stratified squamous epithelium. At the line of junction are two lateral vaginal pouches, whose cornified epithelium is continuously proliferating and sloughing. The mucous cells of the upper vagina are shed in large numbers after each oestrus, as shown by vaginal smears and histological sections. Externally, this phase is characterised by the appearance of an opaque, sticky discharge from the vagina on every 4th day of the cycle. Post-oestrous proliferation and desquamation of the epithelium of the upper vagina coincides with leucocytic infiltration. During pregnancy and pseudopregnancy the vagina is covered by short villi lined by mucified epithelium (*see* Klein, 1937). During lactation the villi of the upper vagina are short, and their epithelium consists of two or three rows of cells, the most superficial of which is cuboidal.

The vaginal smear

Earlier workers (Deanesly, 1938) believed that it is impossible to differentiate the stages of the cycle in the golden hamster by means of vaginal smears Subsequent studies, however (Peczenik, 1942 ; Kent and Smith, 1945 ; Ward, 1946), have shown that this can be achieved, provided smears are carefully taken from the upper vagina. In this way three main phases can be distinguished : a short prooestrus lasting for a few hours ; oestrus itself ; and a longer met- and dioestrus. There is some difference of opinion about the precise cell picture and duration of each stage, but oestrus appears to be characterised by numerous nucleated epithelial cells of varying shape, a few cornified cells, and the complete absence of leucocytes. This phase lasts for approximately one day (15 hours, Ward ; 27·4 hours, Kent and Smith), and is followed by met- and dioestrus, during which leucocytes and oval epithelial cells predominate. Leucocytes begin to disappear during the subsequent prooestrus. Thus the character of the vaginal cycle of the hamster differs from that of the more common laboratory rodents. The type of vaginal smear of normal females at the height of oestrus resembles that of prooestrus in rats and mice, and of early oestrus in the ferret.

The vaginal response of the golden hamster to oestrogen and gonadotrophin has been investigated by Peczenik (1942).

The cyclic changes in the uterus of the golden hamster resemble, but are less distinct than those of the rat and mouse.

Cricetulus

The vaginal and uterine cycle of the Chinese hamster, *Cricetulus griseus*, is very similar to that of the rat and mouse (Parkes, 1931).

The total (average) length of the cycle is $4\frac{1}{2}$ days. The longest phase (met- and dioestrus) is characterised by large numbers of leucocytes and some nucleated epithelial cells in the vaginal smear. During prooestrus the vaginal contents are made up solely of epithelial cells, which are gradually replaced by cornified cells as oestrus approaches. The oestrous phase, during which the vaginal smear consists entirely of cornified cells, is " remarkably prominent " in the Chinese hamster, and more " definite " than in ordinary laboratory rodents. Towards its close nucleated cells may appear, as they do in the European type of hamster.

The cycle of events in the endometrium resembles that in the mouse and rat, but there is less oestrous distension of the endometrium.

In some females collected in the field, though not in others maintained in the laboratory, Parkes found a number of nodules on the mesometrial side of the uterine horns. From their close resemblance to luteal tissue he considered them homologous to the myometrial glands which develop in the rabbit during late pregnancy.

Subfamily *Microtinae*

Clethrionomys

The histological changes in the reproductive organs of the bank vole, *Clethrionomys (Evotomys) glareolus*, during the breeding season are practically identical with those in the rat and mouse (Brambell and Rowlands, 1936).

Family *Caviidae*

Cavia

The vaginal cycle

Stockard and Papanicolaou's original observations (1917) on the vaginal cycle of the guinea-pig were made in order to decide, by microscopic methods, whether or not an oestrous or prooestrous flow from the vagina occurs in this species. The vaginae of a number of virgin females were examined daily over a long period, and smears were made " from the substances that happened to be present in the lumen." This " simple method," which was destined to revolutionise the study of reproductive phenomena, and to have repercussions throughout the field of endocrinology, showed that " a definite sexual period occurs lasting for about 24 hours and returning with a striking regularity every 15 or 16 days." During this 24-hour period the vagina contains " an abundant fluid which is for about the first half of the time of a mucous consistency. The vaginal fluid then changes into a thick and cheese-like substance which finally becomes slowly liquefied and serous. This thin fluid exists for a few hours and then disappears. Occasionally towards the end of the process a slight trace of blood may be present giving the fluid a bloody-red appearance, otherwise it is milk-white or cream-color." During this period of sexual receptivity (oestrus) the genital tract is congested, and the uterine horns are slightly swollen.

The vaginal smear. Further observation showed that " the relative numbers of various cell types in the fluid at different stages are so definite that one . . . may diagnose the exact sexual stage of the animal concerned solely by an examination of the smear." The oestrous changes in the vaginal smear, which are summarised in Table I, are directly correlated with phases of proliferation and degeneration in the vaginal epithelium, and with the ovarian cycle.

TABLE I

Vaginal Changes during Oestrus in the Guinea-pig (after Stockard and Papanicolaou, 1917, from Parkes, 1929b)

Stage.	Contents of vagina.	Duration (hours).	Condition of ovaries.	Condition of vagina.
I	Mucous secretion. Cornified epithelial cells	6–12	Mature follicles	Vaginal epithelium being shed. Infiltration of leucocytes beginning
II	Cheesy. Great numbers of nucleated epithelial cells	2–4	Ovulation	Leucocytes increasing. Desquamation of epithelium continuing
III	Fluid thinner. Leucocytes beginning to appear	4–6		Congestion. Leucocytes entering lumen
IV	Large numbers of leucocytes and often red blood cells	1–2	Corpora lutea forming	Rupture of a few capillaries, followed by regeneration

Leucocytes are never absent from the vagina, except during stages I and II of oestrus ; they are constantly present during dioestrus. According to Young (1937), stage I of oestrus can be subdivided into two phases. During the first (Ia), some 25 per cent of females are sexually receptive, and the vaginal smear contains only squamous epithelial cells. During the early and middle parts of the second phase (Ib), cornified cells make up about half of the elements in the smear picture, and approximately 60 per cent of the animals are in heat. The remaining 15–20 per cent of does experience oestrus during the last part of this phase, when the smear consists almost entirely of cornified cells. Young regards Stockard and Papanicolaou's stage IV, in which erythrocytes appear in the vaginal smear, as being due partly, if not entirely, to the trauma resulting from the taking of smears.

Histological changes in the vagina. More detailed accounts of the histological changes in the vaginal wall have been given by Selle (1922), Kelly (1929), Courrier (1930), Schmidt (1943), and Tribby (1943). In the foetus and for a few weeks after birth, the vaginal epithelium of the guinea-pig is of a simple columnar type. From the 4th week until the first oestrus it becomes transformed into a high columnar epithelium which is also characteristic of pregnancy. Squamous epithelium develops deep to the mucous cells, which are shed at puberty, the process of desquamation sometimes lasting for as many as four cycles.

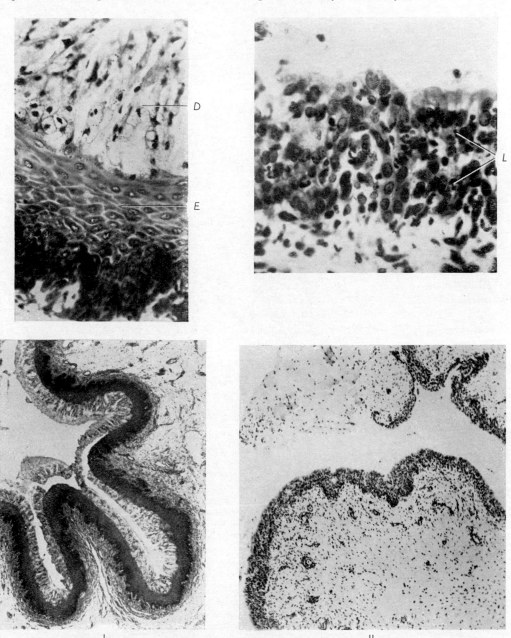

Fig. 6. 13—Vagina of the guinea-pig. I, between prooestrus and oestrus (× 26, below ; × 225, above) ; II, during dioestrus (× 63, below ; × 420, above). Showing in I, highly stratified epithelium (E) with cornification and desquamation (D) of the superficial layers, and in II, low atrophic epithelium containing many leucocytes (L) after the end of desquamation.

During dioestrus the vaginal epithelium of the mature guinea-pig is very thin (10–15 μ), and during the first 8 to 10 days after oestrus it consists of low stratified squamous cells arranged in a ragged line.   From then until the onset of prooestrus the epithelium increases to a height of 50–70 µ, and a basal layer of columnar or cuboidal elements, as well as an intermediate prickle-cell zone, can be recognised, in addition to the most superficial layer of squamous or mucoid cells (Tribby, 1943).   Prooestrus is characterised by intense proliferation, indicated by mitotic activity (Schmidt, 1943).   The epithelium reaches its greatest depth (175–200 µ), and is composed of some 17 layers of cells (Tribby).   Most of this hypertrophy is due to an increase in the width of the prickle-cell zone but, in addition, a transitional layer of flattened (and later " cornified ") cells develops between the prickle cells and the surface layer.   As heat approaches, large numbers of superficial ("mucoid") cells desquamate and are shed in clusters into the vagina (Fig. 6. 13, I). Consequently, smears taken at that time consist predominantly of nucleated epithelial cells and few or no leucocytes.   The thickness of the vaginal epithelium at oestrus is reduced to about 120 µ, and it decreases further when the transitional zone of cornified cells disintegrates and desquamates into the vagina, sometimes as a perfect cast of the lumen.   Towards the end of heat the vaginal wall, which has become highly congested and oedematous, is invaded by leucocytes, which eventually infiltrate the epithelium and enter the vagina.   Desquamation continues during metoestrus, until the epithelium is reduced to its original dioestrous dimensions (Fig. 6. 13, II).   At the same time oedema, hyperaemia and leucocytosis subside, and the smear consists of small nucleated epithelial cells.   Occasionally, erythrocytes may be present during metoestrus (see Young, 1937 ; Asdell, 1946). Later still, the number of leucocytes increases again.

During pregnancy the vaginal epithelium usually consists of high columnar mucous cells (Fig. 6. 14).   Nicol (1933) has, however, observed typical oestrous smears in two of four pregnant does, and Young (1941) has reported the occurrence of heat in one female on the 43rd day of gestation.

When the ovaries are removed, the vaginal epithelium regresses to the simple columnar type characteristic of foetal and neonatal life.   This epithelium does not secrete mucus as does that of late pregnancy.

The anatomical significance of the cyclic vaginal changes outlined above, which are under the control of oestrogen (Allen, Hisaw and Gardner, 1939), has been discussed by Kelly (1929).   Kelly points out that the cyclic character of these changes was noted by Lataste as early as 1877, and that the mucoid transformation of pregnancy was studied intensively by Lataste's pupil Morau in 1889.   It was Retterer (1891, 1892), however, who showed that the Müllerian ducts in the guinea-pig (" future proximal segment of the vagina ") have a stratified polyhedral epithelium as far as their junction with the urogenital sinus (" future distal segment "), which has stratified squamous epithelium.   The columnar and mucous transformations affect only the Müllerian section of the vagina, the germinal layer of the epithelium being multipotent.   With this interpretation Lataste disagreed (1892). According to him, the primitive vaginal cell is columnar in form, and Kelly, like Courrier (1923, 1926), accepts this view, pointing out that the columnar epithelium is the normal and the squamous epithelium the exception, being dependent on stimulation by oestrogen.   It is clear that any decision about the primitive character of the multipotent vaginal epithelium must depend ultimately on embryological evidence.

The vagina of the guinea-pig is normally occluded by a " vaginal closure membrane " at all times except oestrus and parturition.   It may, however, also

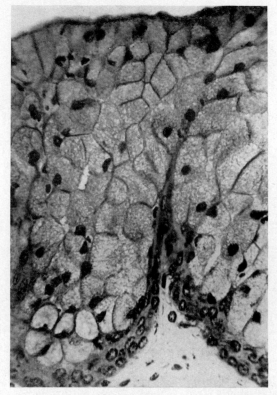

× 350

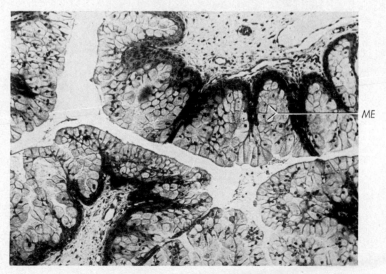

Fig. 6. 14—Vagina of the guinea-pig during late pregnancy.   Extensive
mucification of the epithelium (ME).   × 100.

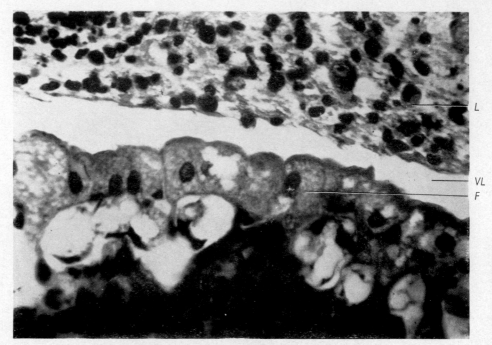

× 533

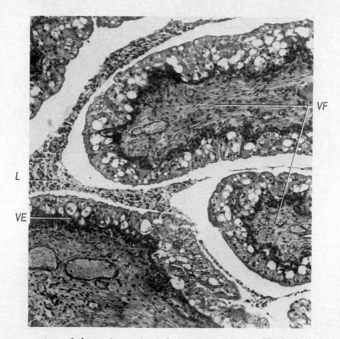

Fig. 6. 15—The vagina of the guinea-pig 6 days post-partum.   Vaginal folds (VF) lined by
degenerating epithelium (VE) containing foamy cells (F).   Numerous leucocytes (L) in the
lumen (VL).   × 100.

open at certain times during pregnancy (Ford, Webster and Young, 1951 ; *see* also p. 281). The vaginal membrane is described by Stockard and Papanicolaou (1919) as follows : " The external orifice of the vagina is crescentic in shape and the urethral opening lies in front of it in the midline. The anterior and posterior lips of the crescent-shaped opening come together, and a delicate epithelial membrane grows over the opening and unites the lips. This occurs shortly after the heat period in females that have not copulated, and in those that have copulated the closure follows the expulsion of the vaginal plug." Mating, according to these workers, occurs during stage I of the oestrous period—as diagnosed by vaginal smears. On the other hand, Young (1937), who has reinvestigated the problem in great detail, points out that the time of heat " varies with respect to a given vaginal condition," and that " ovulation tends to remain associated with heat rather than with the vaginal condition " (*see* p. 280). Young (1937, 1941) also discusses the relationship of natural oestrus to the experimental conditions under which oestrus can be induced.

Leuckart in 1847 was the first to report on the formation of a " vaginal plug " in the guinea-pig after coitus. The plug has been studied and described by several workers, and Stockard and Papanicolaou (1919) give the following description of its formation : " Immediately after copulation the coagulated seminal fluid forms a mass within the lumen of the vagina and partly extending into the uterus. Around this mass the mucosa forms a close fitting envelope, thus preventing its early dislocation. The envelope serves to retain the plug in the vagina until the fourth stage of the oestrous cycle at which time the enveloping epithelium becomes completely separated from the vaginal wall by the dissolving effects of the leucocytes." When mating does not occur, the epithelium is shed in smaller pieces during the last stage of oestrus (stage IV), but occasionally it may be cast off " *en masse* without copulation." The latter occurrence is also reported by Selle (1922), who points out that only the cornified layers are shed.

Uterine changes

The changes which occur in the uterus of the guinea-pig during the oestrous cycle have been described by Loeb (1914), whose observations are confirmed by Stockard and Papanicolaou (1917). During dioestrus both the cavum uteri and the glands are lined by a single layer of ciliated cuboidal to low columnar epithelial cells (Fig. 6. 16, II). Mitosis and secretory activity are absent or at a minimum, and the stroma contains some leucocytes. Prooestrus is marked by proliferation of both epithelium and stroma. The epithelium becomes tall columnar, and that of the cavum uteri assumes a pseudostratified appearance (Fig. 6. 16, I). As the second stage of oestrus begins (Table I), leucocytes gather in large numbers beneath the surface epithelium, and the stroma becomes markedly congested, especially along the antimesometrial aspect of the uterine horns (Bacsich and Wyburn, 1940). This localised hyperaemia is not present during other stages of the oestrous cycle, but occurs in pregnancy as well as after oestrogen treatment of intact animals, and must be regarded as a preparation for implantation (Bacsich and Wyburn, 1941). In the third stage of oestrus leucocytes pass into and between the lining cells of the cavum uteri, beneath which haematomata may develop. Regeneration begins at the end of the third phase of oestrus, epithelial replacement taking place from the necks of the glands. There is a rapid increase in the number of

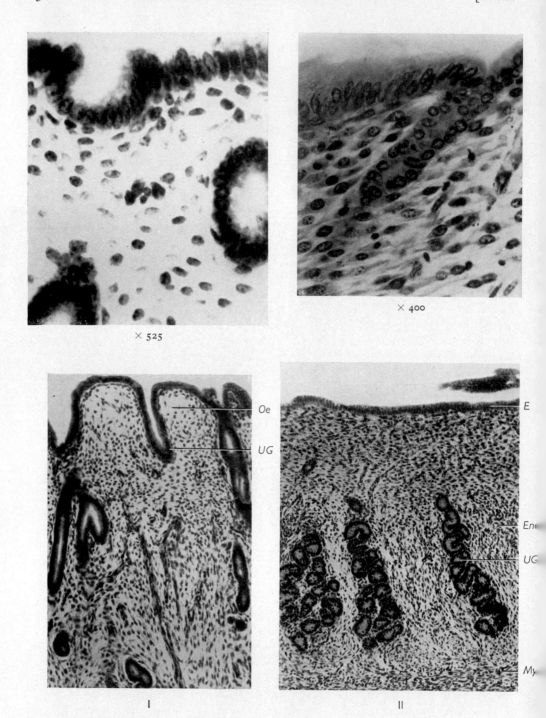

Fig. 6. 16—Uterus of the guinea-pig. I, between prooestrus and oestrus ($\times$ 100); II, during dioestrus ($\times$ 100). Showing superficial oedema (Oe) of the endometrium (End) and straight uterine glands (UG) in I, and high columnar epithelium (E), dense stroma and coiled uterine glands in II.   My, myometrium.

mitoses in the epithelium lining both the surface and the uterine glands, which reaches a maximum on about the third post-oestrous day (Schmidt, 1943). Cell division then slows down, stopping after the fourth day. The new epithelium, growing out from the glands, pushes the old degenerated epithelium, often still connected to pieces of stroma, into the cavum uteri. These cast-off uterine cells are commonly found in the vaginal fluid, which may also contain red blood cells from the uterine haematomata. Red corpuscles appear to occur irregularly during metoestrus, but in one instance, referred to by Asdell (1946), the haemorrhage produced was severe enough to kill the animal. Erythrocytes may occasionally be found within the bodies of white cells.

The process of regeneration is very rapid, lasting, according to Stockard and Papanicolaou, no more than 6 to 10 hours. These authors describe the same process of oestrous disintegration to which Loeb draws attention, but from their account it would seem to be a more distinctive feature than Loeb supposed. Loeb, moreover, does not refer to the occurrence of haematomata.

Hamilton (1933) and Nicol (1933) have studied the involution and repair of the uterus after parturition, and conclude that the process is quicker when ovulation occurs during the post-partum oestrus, and quicker still when the latter is accompanied by fertilisation.

Nicol (1932, 1935) has also described in detail the reactions of the guinea-pig uterus to intravitam staining with Trypan blue. He states that there is a " cyclic and topographical distribution of vitally stained rounded cells." During dioestrus there is little staining, and the cells are scattered throughout the endometrium. During prooestrus staining is maximal and concentrated in the stratum compactum. From then until oestrus the staining reaction diminishes. According to Fluhmann (1928, 1932), there is no cyclic variation in the number of vitally staining cells in the rabbit uterus.

The cellular changes in the sterile horn of a pregnant uterus are very slight. In four specimens removed between the 21st and 45th days of pregnancy, the glands were less highly developed than at various stages of the normal cycle. This may be significant in view of the fact that the uterine glands of the guinea-pig, unlike those of the rabbit and other mammals, take no part in the formation of the placenta (Deanesly and Parkes, 1931).

Cervical changes

The detailed studies of Sjövall (1938), Jurow (1943) and Schmidt (1943) have revealed periodic changes in the histological structure and mitotic activity of the cervical epithelium, as in the rest of the reproductive tract.

The cervix of the guinea-pig consists of two parts, an upper or transitional one, and a lower portion in which the previously divided canals fuse and form a single external os (*see* p. 98).

The changes summarised below are most marked in the lower cervical segment.

The mucosa of the cervix is covered by a two-layered epithelium, a deeper or basal zone which is made up of squamous cells, and a more superficial layer which consists of cuboidal or columnar, mucus-secreting cells. During dioestrus the mucous membrane presents few and relatively simple folds ; mitoses are scarce, and there is little or no secretion. During prooestrus the mucosal folds increase in number and complexity, and many mitoses are present in the epithelium. The basal cells are enlarged and arranged in several layers, while the superficial cells are distended with mucus and have centrally-disposed nuclei. During early oestrus the cervical glands continue to develop and secrete. At this stage they show no signs of desquamation, and no leucocytes are present in the mucosa. During late oestrus the mucus-secreting cells increase in number and begin to desquamate. This is most noticeable in the lower cervix, where the superficial (mucous) zone separates from the basal (squamous) part, along a cleavage line of cornified cells. According to Schmidt, the mucous cells show many mitoses during this phase, which coincides with the early development of the corpus luteum. Degenerative changes appear at a later stage in the basal cells. The mucosa becomes thin and " punched-out " through focal necrosis, and leucocytic invasion becomes marked and generalised.

Changes in the uterine tube

As in other parts of the reproductive tract, secretory activity and proliferation of the epithelial cells of the uterine tubes occur mainly after ovulation. At that time the cells lining the ampulla are of the mucus-secreting type with clear cyto-plasm and basal nuclei. During other stages of the cycle the epithelium of the entire uterine tube consists of low cells with a granular cytoplasm (Schmidt).

CETACEA

The only detailed studies of the cyclic changes in the female reproductive organs of whales appear to be those of Matthews (1948) and Harrison (1949).

In the balaenopterid whales examined by Matthews, the epithelial lining of the endometrium was either completely absent or grossly deficient, due presumably to post-mortem changes. Harrison met with the same condition in an immature *Globicephala*, but established that in an adult female, shortly after ovulation, the epithelium was of the high columnar, pseudostratified type. In both types of whale the mucosa of the uterus is differentiated into two layers, a thin superficial stratum compactum, which contains the ducts of the uterine glands as well as a plexus of capillaries, and a thicker deep stratum spongiosum, in which are found the con-voluted parts of the glands.

In anoestrous blue and fin whales the average width of the entire endometrium is 2·4 mm. (range 1·5–4·0), of which the compact layer accounts for about 0·2 mm., and the spongy layer for the rest. The uterine glands are greatly coiled and branched, but few extend into the stratum spongiosum, and the surface of the mucosa is smooth or raised into low ridges. The glands are lined with columnar epithelium, and have small or no visible lumina.

The onset of oestrus is marked by endometrial growth, and in one female, shortly after ovulation, the mucosa was about 8–9 mm. and the stratum com-pactum over 0·3 mm. deep (Matthews). During the progestational part of the cycle the uterine glands become wider and more closely packed. Large tortuous vessels are present throughout the stratum spongiosum, and there is a dense subepithelial network of capillaries, some of which are so superficially placed that they bulge into the lumen of the uterus. Red blood corpuscles have been noticed occasionally in the uterine cavity and in the vaginal contents (Mackintosh and

Wheeler, 1929), but in Matthews' opinion this may have been due to post-mortem degeneration of the mucosa, and should not be considered a physiological occurrence.

The endometrium regresses gradually during pregnancy and more rapidly after parturition, and during lactation its dimensions are those characteristic of anoestrus. It is of interest that in whales corpora lutea persist for very long periods, and possibly throughout the life of the female (*see* Harrison, 1949).

CARNIVORA

> Fam.   *Canidae*
> > *Canis* (Domestic dog)
> > *Vulpes* (Fox)
>
> Fam.   *Mustelidae*
> > *Mustela* (Ferret ; stoat ; weasel ; mink)
>
> Fam.   *Hyaenidae*
> > *Crocuta* (Spotted hyaena)
>
> Fam.   *Felidae*
> > *Felis* (Cat ; lion)

Family Canidae

Canis

The cyclic changes which occur in the accessory reproductive organs of the female dog were first described by Friedländer in 1870, and have since been studied in great detail by Marshall and Jolly (1906) ; Keller (1909) ; Marshall and Halnan (1917) ; Gerlinger (1923, 1925) ; Evans and Cole (1931) ; Arenas and Sammartino (1939) ; Griffiths and Amoroso (1939) ; and Mulligan (1942). The time relations of the various events in the reproductive cycle of the dog are discussed on p. 289. For the purposes of the present account it is necessary to bear in mind that the bitch has two or sometimes three heat periods in a year. Prooestrus, which may last some ten days, is associated with bleeding from the vulva. This bleeding may continue into oestrus, which lasts about a week. Ovulation is spontaneous, and occurs on the first or second day of oestrus, which is the time of acceptance of the male. If conception takes place, pregnancy lasts from 58 to 63 days. If it does not occur, a phase of pseudopregnancy follows ovulation and lasts for approximately two months. This is succeeded by anoestrus.

Vaginal changes

The bitch shows a well-marked vaginal cycle. During anoestrus the epithelium of the vagina proper consists of two or three layers of low columnar or cuboidal cells. Rapid proliferation occurs during prooestrus, and the epithelium is transformed into a high stratified squamous lining in which a well-marked Malpighian layer, a stratum granulosum, and a superficial stratum corneum, can be recognised. Proliferation continues, and at the time the bitch first accepts the male, the vagina is lined by 12–20 layers of low stratified squamous cells. The occurrence of true cornification has been claimed by Evans and Cole (1931), but this is denied by

Arenas and Sammartino (1939). Desquamation of the superficial layers occurs throughout prooestrus and oestrus, and eventually results in a marked thinning of the mucosa. During metoestrus the vaginal epithelium is columnar, the change from the squamous type usually occurring about the 8th to 10th day after the end of oestrus.

Twenty-four hours after the last acceptance of the male, the vaginal epithelium becomes rapidly infiltrated with leucocytes. Their migration into the lumen of the organ, and presence in the vaginal smear continues throughout metoestrus and pseudopregnancy.

The vaginal vestibule in the bitch is lined with a low stratified epithelium which grows in height in prooestrus, but which does not undergo any of the other cyclic changes that take place in the epithelium of the true vagina. On the other hand, the cervical mucosa represents an extension of that of the vagina, and undergoes identical histological modifications during the cycle (Arenas and Sammartino, 1939).

The vaginal smear

There are characteristic changes in the vaginal smear (Evans and Cole, 1931 ; Griffiths and Amoroso, 1939). During anoestrus the vaginal fluid is abundant, and smears contain many nucleated epithelial cells and a variable proportion of leucocytes. According to Griffiths and Amoroso, red blood cells make their appearance at the beginning of prooestrus, and hence before external bleeding is recognisable. They become abundant during late prooestrus and oestrus, when the smear consists almost exclusively of erythrocytes and cornified cells, poly- morphs and nucleated epithelial cells being completely absent. The sudden reappearance of nucleated epithelial cells marks the end of oestrus, and numerous leucocytes are present during the first few days of metoestrus. Later the typical resting condition is re-established.

Uterine changes

During anoestrus the uterus is small and somewhat flattened, and the mucosa shallow and deficient in glands and vessels. The surface and glandular epithelium consists of low columnar or cuboidal cells with basal nuclei. The muscular wall is also poorly developed (Fig. 6. 17, I).

During prooestrus the uterus grows rapidly, the mucosa thickening and be- coming more vascular and oedematous. The hyperaemia is well marked just below the surface epithelium (Fig. 6. 17, II), and extends also into the subepithelial connective tissue (Evans and Cole, 1931). Focal bleeding from ruptured sub- epithelial capillaries occurs in minute areas, but no true blood lacunae are formed, as e.g. in primates during menstruation. Although Marshall and Jolly (1906) have occasionally observed epithelial cells lying free in the uterine cavity, the consensus of opinion (Gerlinger, 1925 ; Evans and Cole, 1931 ; Meyer and Saiki, 1931 ; Arenas and Sammartino, 1939), is that neither stromal nor epithelial degeneration take place during prooestrus in the bitch. The blood, which undoubtedly appears in the vaginal smear during that phase, is believed to find its way into the cavity of the uterus by a process of diapedesis through the intact epithelial lining. Evans and Cole, however, have never observed erythrocytes passing through the epithelium in areas of marked subepithelial haemorrhage.

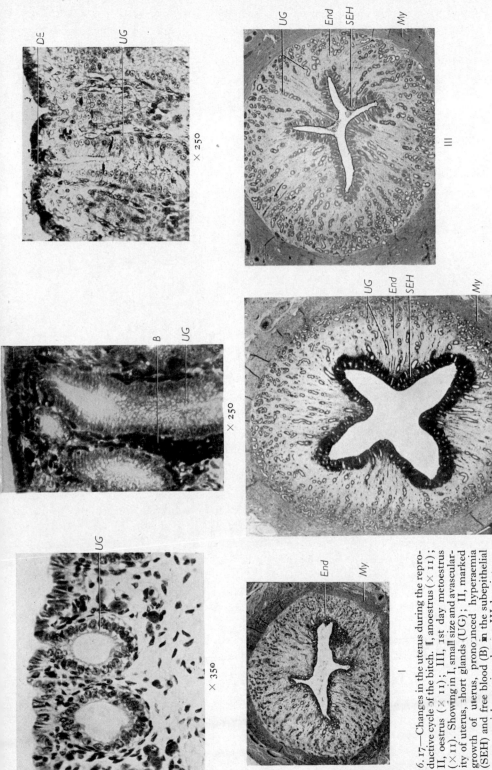

(Sections lent by Dr. I. W. Rowlands.)

Fig. 6.17.—Changes in the uterus during the reproductive cycle of the bitch. I, anoestrus (× 11); II, oestrus (× 11); III, 1st day metoestrus (× 11). Showing in I, small size and avascularity of uterus, short glands (UG); II, marked growth of uterus, pronounced hyperaemia (SEH) and free blood (B) in the subepithelial zone; straight uterine glands; III, less intense congestion of the subepithelial zone; degenerative changes in the superficial epithelium (DE); coiled uterine glands. End, endometrium; My, myometrium.

Congestion of the endometrium is associated with glandular proliferation. The glands are of two kinds : shallow crypt-like invaginations with narrow necks, and long glands which penetrate the whole thickness of the stroma and become slightly coiled as they approach the myometrium. The glandular epithelium is tall and cylindrical and, except during mitosis, the nuclei are relatively small and basally disposed.

During early oestrus the appearance of the uterus differs little from that of prooestrus. The oedema persists but vascular congestion is less, and bleeding ceases. The extravasated red and white cells gradually disappear, and the glands seem less active. According to Evans and Cole, growth of the glandular epithelium, in particular that of the crypts and deeper glands, occurs during the second half of oestrus, when leucocytes are abundant. Throughout prooestrus and oestrus macrophages containing brown pigment, possibly representing haemosiderin, can be seen in the endometrium (Mulligan, 1942). In the bitch this phase is followed either by pregnancy or pseudopregnancy, depending on the occurrence of fertilisation.

Pseudopregnancy

According to Evans and Cole, the endometrium of animals killed a day after the last acceptance of the male is differentiated into three zones : a superficial one containing the smaller crypt-like glands referred to above ; a middle, clear zone consisting mainly of connective tissue and the neck portions of the true uterine glands ; and an outer zone, close to the myometrium, occupied by the coiled basal parts of the glands.

The pseudopregnant changes are characterised by continued proliferation of the uterine glands and surface epithelium, and by progressive folding of the mucosa. As the corpora lutea develop, two well-defined zones can be distinguished in the endometrium, an inner compact one containing large numbers of superficial crypts with a good deal of stroma, and a deeper spongy zone which consists of a network of dilated uterine glands set in a scanty tunica propria. As the luteal phase becomes fully established, the compact zone is transformed into a mass of epithelial villi which project into the cavum uteri and almost occlude its lumen (Fig. 6. 18). The epithelium of this villous mass consists of large cells which have vacuolated cytoplasm, and contain various intracellular deposits (*see* Amoroso, 1952). At the same time, the glands of the spongy zone diminish in number and become dilated, their basal segments close to the myometrium remaining unaltered. These endometrial changes precede implantation and placentation, and in the fortnight that follows ovulation the pseudopregnant endometrium cannot be differentiated from endometrium found between implantation sites in pregnant animals.

Endometrial regression begins in the second half of pseudopregnancy and pregnancy. Descriptions of the process vary. According to Marshall and Halnan (1917), the endometrial capillaries suddenly begin to break down between the 7th and 9th week after ovulation, and blood is once again extravasated into the stroma. Such a change was not observed by Evans and Cole, according to whom the process of regression is slow and gradual, and extends from the 20th to the 88th day of metoestrus. Gerlinger, on the other hand, describes the epithelium of the compact zone as a desquamating mass, which becomes liquefied by autolysis. This massive disintegration of the endometrium is not associated, according to

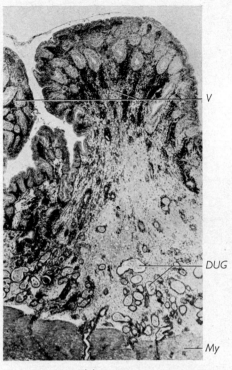

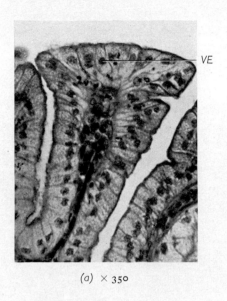

(a) × 350

(a) × 11

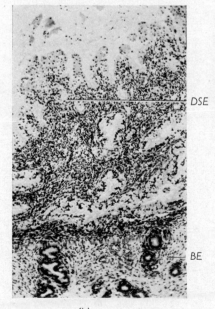

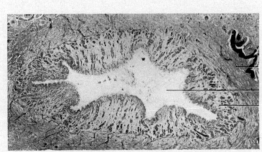

(c) × 11

(b) × 70

Fig. 6. 18—Uterus of the bitch during pseudopregnancy (three stages in the same female ; (a)
50–58th day ; (b) 64th–72nd day ; (c) 78–86th
day). Showing in (a) extensive folding of the
mucosa and formation of villi (V) covered by
high columnar, vacuolated epithelium (VE),
dilated lower parts of uterine glands (DUG) ;
(b) degeneration of hypertrophied superficial
endometrium (DSE) with preservation of basal
endometrium (BE) ; (c) return to anoestrous
state. End, endometrium ; My, myometrium ;
L, lumen.

(Sections lent by Dr. I. W. Rowlands.)

Gerlinger, with capillary rupture or extravasation of blood, and is therefore described by him as " white menstruation " (Fig. 6, 18). This stage is also characterised by the presence of sudanophilic material in the superficial layers of the mucosa (Arenas and Sammartino, 1939).

When the process of regeneration is complete, the surface epithelium is reformed from the remaining epithelial elements, and the glands begin to regenerate. The uterus then returns to its anoestrous condition.

Changes in the uterine tubes

During anoestrus the mucosal folds in the uterine tubes of the bitch are well developed close to the ovary, but inconspicuous near the tubo-uterine junction. The epithelium consists of a single layer of small, non-ciliated columnar cells with relatively large nuclei and a cytoplasm which gives no evidence of secretion (Fig. 6. 19, I). During prooestrus the tube increases greatly in volume, its mucosal folds become attenuated, and its glandular epithelium becomes differentiated into ciliated and non-ciliated cylindrical cells, containing fine fuchsinophilic granules (Fig. 6. 19, II).

The tubes maintain this appearance throughout oestrus, but after ovulation signs of secretory activity disappear, and when the luteal phase is fully established none of the cells are ciliated (Fig. 6. 19, III). The tube thus gradually returns to its anoestrous state.

Vulpes

There have been few detailed studies of the changes which occur in the uterus and vagina of the fox. The most important are those of Rowlands and Parkes (1935) on the red fox, and of Kakushkina (1937) on the silver fox.

The vagina

In the immature silver fox the vaginal epithelium consists of two to three layers of cuboidal cells. At the onset of the sexual season the epithelium becomes highly stratified. Cornification occurs during oestrus (Kakushkina, 1937 ; Bassett and Leekley, 1942), which is marked by swelling of the vulva. The vaginal smear generally contains some epithelial cells, while cornified cells appear during prooestrus, and increase to a maximum on the first day of oestrus (Bassett and Leekley). After the end of heat, which in the vixen lasts about two to three days, leucocytes appear in the smear and subsequently increase in number.

If conception does not occur, oestrus is followed by pseudopregnancy. The vagina of a pseudopregnant red fox studied by Rowlands and Parkes was remarkable in so far as it was occluded between the level of the cervix and the opening of the urethra into the urogenital sinus. The vaginal fornices were distended to form a sac lined by flattened epithelium and containing a mass of coagulated secretion. Whether this is a regular feature remains to be established.

During anoestrus the vagina resumes the appearance which it has in the immature animal.

The uterus

The uterus grows gradually during the first year of life, the increase being roughly proportional to that in body weight. Up to September the myometrium

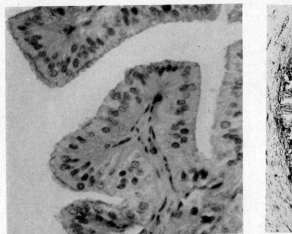

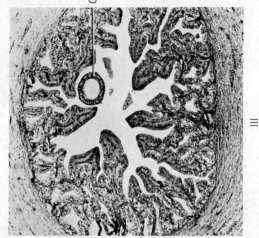

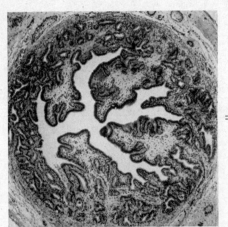

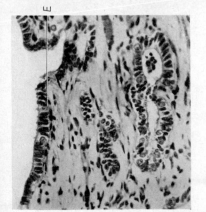

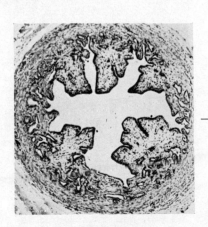

Fig. 6. 19—Changes in the uterine tube of the bitch. I, anoestrus ; II, oestrus ; III, 1st day metoestrus. × 40, below ; × 290, above. Showing in I, small size of tube and low columnar epithelium (E) ; II, more extensive folding of the mucosa and high columnar ciliated epithelium (CE) ; III, complex folding of mucosa, free oöcyte (O).

is poorly developed, and the endometrium is narrow and possesses few glands. Towards the end of the year growth is rapid, and numerous glands develop. During prooestrus (January or February), the uterus becomes large and its stroma dense and vascular. At oestrus the glands are slightly convoluted, and there is marked congestion of the mucosa. Blood is extravasated into the stroma, and makes its way into the lumen of the uterus. According to Kakushkina, this coincides with maturation of the ovarian follicles, and hence appears to be comparable to the oestrous bleeding of the bitch. Pseudopregnancy is associated with considerable further growth of the endometrium. The numerous uterine glands become very coiled, and there is marked oedema of the stroma. The glands are lined by tall columnar epithelium, which frequently appears to occlude their lumen, and that of the uterus itself. Towards the end of pseudopregnancy degeneration and desquamation of the epithelium of the cavum uteri occurs. Extravasation of blood was not observed by Rowlands and Parkes during this phase. The uterus then passes into its atrophic anoestrous condition.

Family *Mustelidae*

Mustela

The Ferret

Vaginal changes

Marshall (1933) and Hamilton and Gould (1940) have given full descriptions of the changes which take place in the vagina of the ferret (*Mustela furo*). During anoestrus the vaginal epithelium consists of 2 to 5 layers of rather shallow or low columnar cells, arranged somewhat irregularly (Fig. 6. 20, I). Leucocytic infiltration of the wall of the vagina is usual. Considerable proliferation occurs between prooestrus and oestrus, and the epithelium becomes many-layered and oedematous, the superficial cells beginning to cornify and desquamate (Fig. 6. 20, II). There are marked variations in the thickness of the oestrous epithelium in different animals (e.g. from 6 to 18 layers of cells). According to Hamilton and Gould, cornification is at first more marked in the upper than in the lower part of the vagina.

In the event of pregnancy, cornification continues until about the end of the second week, after which the vaginal epithelium is composed of tall and non-cornified columnar cells. During pseudopregnancy the epithelium is narrow, consisting of a layer of small irregularly-arranged cells above a single row of columnar cells. During lactation the epithelium appears to become even shallower.

The vaginal smear

During anoestrus the vaginal smear, which may be difficult to obtain, contains a small number of nucleated epithelial cells and leucocytes (Parkes, 1930 ; Hamilton and Gould, 1940). Three variations of epithelial cell can be distinguished in the smear : nucleated squamous ; large round ; and small, round cells (Hamilton and Gould). The first two are derived from the vaginal wall, and the third from the cervix and fused part of the uterine horns. As heat approaches and the vulva begins to swell, leucocytes disappear, and only cornified squamous cells remain. There is no perfect correspondence between the degree of swelling of the vulva and the state of the vaginal smear, some females with moderately swollen vulvae manifesting a full oestrous smear and vice versa. Leucocytes and epithelial cells reappear after ovulation, and by the 5th day no cornified cells are present, the

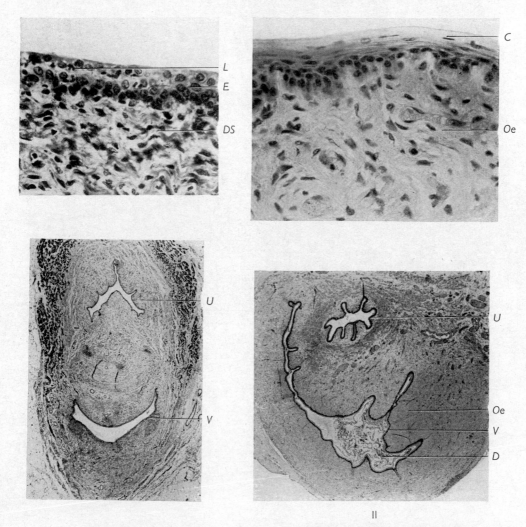

Fig 6. 20—Vagina and vaginal epithelium of the ferret during anoestrus (I) and oestrus (II) (× 11, below; × 350, above). Showing in (I) small vagina (V) and shallow vaginal epithelium (E) containing leucocytes (L); dense stroma (DS); in II, enlarged vagina and oedema (Oe) of perivaginal tissues, cornification (C) and desquamation (D) of hypertrophied vaginal epithelium. U, urethra.

smear remaining the same during the 6 weeks of pregnancy. If coitus does not result in ovulation, an oestrous smear persists.

Uterine changes

The following account of uterine changes in the ferret is taken from Marshall (1904), Hammond and Marshall (1930), Marshall (1933) and Hamilton and Gould (1940).

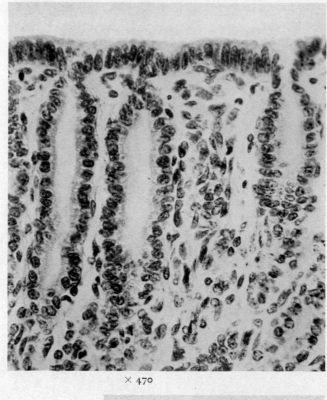

× 470

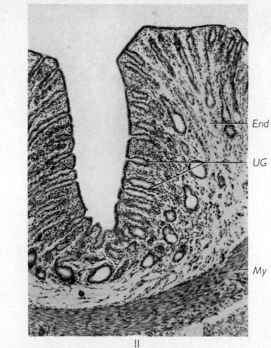

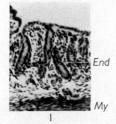

Fig. 6. 21—Uterus of the ferret during I, anoestrus (× 140), and II, oestrus (× 70).   Showing
in I, diminutive size of uterus and shallow endometrium (End) with few glands ; in II,
great proliferation of endometrium with numerous tubular glands (UG).   My, myometrium.

During anoestrus the uterus is small, the mucosa thin and the glands are compact and undeveloped (Fig. 6. 21, I).   The surface and glandular epithelium is of a low cuboidal type.   The cavum uteri is widely open, and shows poorly developed endometrial folds.

The onset of vulval swelling is associated with marked growth of the uterus (Fig. 6. 21, II).   The mucosa develops more rapidly than the myometrium, and is thrown up into a number of folds which encroach on the uterine cavity.   There is glandular proliferation, each gland having a large lumen lined by a tall epithelium, and being filled with secretion.   The uterus as a whole becomes hyperaemic, and in some cases there is extravasation of blood into the dense stroma.   The histological changes in the fused part of the uterus and cervix are essentially similar to those in the horns, except for an intense leucocytic infiltration at oestrus (Hamilton and Gould).

Pseudopregnancy

The endometrium continues in its oestrous condition until ovulation has occurred and corpora lutea begin to form.   The endometrial changes during pseudopregnancy appear to be similar to those which have been described in the rabbit, cat, and especially in the dog (*see* p. 588).   The uterine horns become larger, and the endometrial folds much more prominent and branched than at oestrus. During this phase there is gradual thinning of the basal mucosa from which the endometrial folds arise, and the folds (four main ones and several subsidiary ones) become more separated from each other.   They appear to be supported by a central stroma with radiating secondary limbs, and consist mainly of proliferated epithelial cells which form a "plasmodium" containing large spherical nuclei.

At the end of the second week after ovulation, the mucosa is still compact, although the deeper glands are somewhat distended.   When the more superficial plasmodium develops, this epithelium changes from columnar to cuboidal.   Full development of the pseudopregnant endometrium does not occur until about the 4th week (Fig. 6. 22).

Signs of degeneration begin to appear during the 5th week of pseudopregnancy, when the uterine horns decrease in size.   The superficial cells become smaller and disintegrate, and giant nuclei appear in the basal zone of the endometrium.   By the end of the 6th week most of the superficial plasmodium has disappeared, and at the end of the 7th re-formation of the surface epithelium and of the endometrium generally is well advanced.   About 8 weeks after the preceding ovulation the animal begins to come on heat again.

The process of destruction of the pseudopregnant uterine mucosa is very similar to that described in the bitch by Gerlinger (1925) ; (*see* p. 588). Vascularity of the regressing endometrium is slight, and there is no extravasation of blood into the stroma.   The differences between pseudopregnant development in the rabbit, on the one hand, and in the bitch and ferret, on the other, are related by Hammond and Marshall to differences in the modes of placentation in these various species.

During the first 5 weeks of gestation, the appearance of the pregnant uterus in the regions between blastocysts is identical with that of the pseudopregnant uterus.   At about $5\frac{1}{2}$ weeks (i.e. 3 to 4 days before parturition), the implantation sites become continuous, and the endometrial folds begin to disappear.   In all other respects the similarity of the uterine changes in the two conditions is striking.

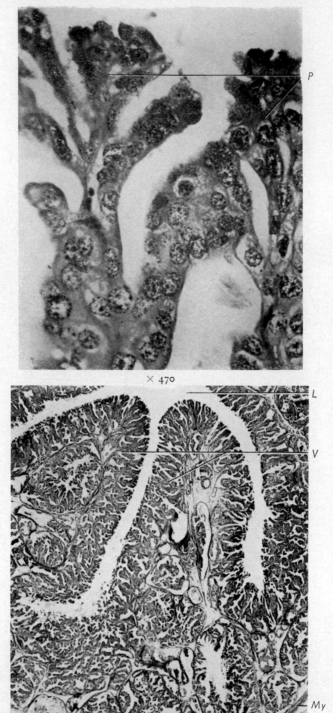

× 470

Fig. 6. 22—The uterus of the ferret on the 29th day of pseudopregnancy. Showing the marked transformation of the mucosa (cf. Fig. 6. 21, II) resulting in the formation of large endometrial villi (V) covered by a " plasmodium " of proliferated epithelial cells (P). My, myometrium ; L, lumen of uterus.   × 70.

In one experiment Hammond and Marshall divided the uterine tube on one side and ligatured the uterine horn of the same side close to its junction with the body of the uterus. The experimental animal was autopsied at the 5th week of gestation, and it was found that the " sterile horn of pregnancy," though identical in histological structure, was much larger than a uterine horn in the corresponding stage of pseudopregnancy. Similar observations have been made on the rabbit by Knaus (1928).

The stoat

The structure of the accessory reproductive organs of the stoat (*Mustela erminea*) and the cyclic changes to which they are subject, are similar to those of the female ferret, in spite of striking differences in the reproductive behaviour of the two animals (*see* p. 293).

The vagina

The vaginal epithelium of the stoat undergoes a definite cycle of changes, proliferating and cornifying before oestrus, and desquamating after ovulation. During the later phases of pregnancy the vaginal epithelium consists of a single, even row of tall columnar cells with basal nuclei. The epithelium of the vulva increases in height at oestrus, and is subsequently shed (Deanesly, 1935).

The uterus

As in the cat and ferret, the projection of 4 to 6 prominent endometrial folds gives the uterine lumen of the stoat a stellate outline in cross-section. At oestrus the epithelial lining of the endometrium is 10 to 12 μ in height, and the stroma is highly cellular and oedematous. During the luteal stage of the cycle, which develops slowly, the lining epithelium increases to a depth of 30 to 40 μ, and the stromal oedema subsides, while the glands develop rapidly. The cells lining the cavum uteri tend to invade the underlying stroma, but there is no obvious breakdown of the epithelium at the end of this phase.

In the earlier stages of pregnancy the endometrium is no different from that of metoestrus, but as gestation proceeds the superficial glands disappear from the non-placental endometrium, which develops a number of finely branching villi covered with a syncytial epithelium. These proliferative changes reach a maximum towards the end of pregnancy, when the appearance of the uterus is very similar to that of the ferret in the corresponding reproductive phase (*see* p. 595).

The uterine tubes

During oestrus the uterine tubes undergo changes similar to those which occur in the cat (*see* p. 604). The whole tube swells, the stroma becomes oedematous, and the epithelium proliferates.

The cyclic changes undergone by the reproductive tract of the weasel (*Mustela nivalis*) resemble in all essentials those described for the stoat (Deanesly, 1944).

The mink

As noted on p. 296, the mink (*Mustela vison*) has a single annual breeding season, in March. Ovulation is induced by copulation, and there is a variable delay in the implantation of the blastocysts (Hansson, 1947).

Vaginal changes

During anoestrus the vaginal smear contains only leucocytes and cellular debris. At the end of this phase the secretion becomes less scanty and consists predominantly of large, irregular and incompletely cornified epithelial cells. As prooestrus slowly changes into oestrus these cells become larger, more cornified, and tend to have rolled-up corners, while at the same time the amount of mucus increases. After ovulation there is a transitory increase in cornified elements, but this soon stops, and the smear returns to the oestrous condition. After a variable interval of some two to three weeks, the vaginal epithelium begins to desquamate again, and large numbers of cornified squamous cells reappear in the smear. This in turn is followed by leucocytic infiltration of the vaginal wall and by the presence of leucocytes in the smear. The second bout of cornification and desquamation appears to coincide with the recurrence of activity in the corpora lutea, and with implantation of the previously unattached blastocysts.

Uterine changes

During anoestrus the surface epithelium consists of an even layer of cuboidal or low columnar cells, and the stromal glands are inactive. From prooestrus until oestrus the uterus grows considerably, and becomes congested. The glands become more open, at the same time as the cells lining them and the surface increase in size. There is little change after ovulation and before implantation. Once attachment of the blastocysts has taken place, the mucosa becomes very folded and covered by tall columnar cells with apically disposed nuclei and fringed luminal surfaces. Similar changes occur during the greater part of pseudopregnancy, which in the mink lasts for at least 40 days.

Changes in the uterine tube

During anoestrus the tubal epithelium consists mainly of low cuboidal cells; ciliated cells are rare, and there is little secretion. During the transition from prooestrus to oestrus the stroma swells and becomes greatly congested, while the tube as a whole is more " solid," and fills with secretion. The epithelium gains in height, and most cells become ciliated. As a rule, the epithelium remains in this condition after ovulation and during the tubal passage of the ova. Occasionally, however, the epithelium of the tube " degenerates," and the number of ciliated elements in it decreases. According to Hansson, the latter condition is associated with functionally active, and the former with inactive corpora lutea. Since epithelial " degeneration " also occurs in pseudopregnancy and late pregnancy, Hansson concludes that in the normal female reactivation of the corpora lutea occurs at an intermediate stage.

Family *Hyaenidae*

Crocuta

The following summary of the histological changes in the reproductive tract of the spotted hyaena (*C. crocuta*) is based on Matthews' comprehensive account (1941a).

Changes in the vagina

In the prepubertal animal the vagina is small, and its epithelium, which is some 20–30 μ deep, consists of low stratified cells supported by a basal layer of columnar cells. The vagina of anoestrous parous females is similar, but the epithelium measures about 30–40 μ, and the corium is highly vascular.

At prooestrus the epithelium increases in depth to 100–200 μ and comprises 8 to 10 layers of cells. Most of these are polyhedral, except the basal layer which remains cubical or columnar. The most superficial cells become mucified and contain large vacuoles. The corium is engorged with blood.

During oestrus the corium is about three times as deep as it is in anoestrus, while the epithelium is 300–400 μ thick and differentiated into two distinct zones. The deeper stratum, about 150 μ in thickness, consists mainly of large clear polyhedral cells. The superficial layer measures between 150 and 300 μ in depth, and consists of cornified cells, which are shed into the lumen of the vagina. By the end of oestrus this layer and the adjacent cells of the basal zone are lost.

During pregnancy the epithelium measures only 50 μ in thickness, and consists of some 3 to 4 layers of cells. During lactation the vagina involutes to the anoestrous condition.

Matthews also describes marked changes in the histological structure of the greater vestibular (Bartholin's) glands, correlated with the reproductive cycle.

Changes in the uterus

During anoestrus (or lactational involution) the internal surface of the uterus is smooth. The mucosa varies from 150–500 μ in thickness, and possesses only a few small glands. During prooestrus the endometrium increases to a thickness of 600–800 μ, and numerous glands develop. The glands then increase in length, and the lumen of each horn becomes filled with secretion. The uterus as a whole is highly vascular, but extravasation of blood does not occur. The epithelium remains intact, and becomes reduced to a single layer of cells 8–10 μ in height.

Growth is intensified during oestrus. The mucosa of the uterine horns increases to a depth of about 1·2 mm., and contains numerous straight glands which almost penetrate into the myometrium. On the other hand, the earlier congestion of the endometrium entirely disappears, and only few and small blood vessels remain.

Typical progestational proliferation occurs during the early part of pregnancy, and the mucosa grows in depth to 1·5–2·0 mm. The changes are less marked in the body of the uterus than in the horns, in which the glands are separated only by narrow strips of stromal tissue.

After further growth during the later stages of pregnancy, the endometrium begins to degenerate, and eventually the " whole of the glandular part of the mucosa," including stroma, glandular secretions and blood, is shed into the lumen of the uterus. Only the flattened bases of the uterine glands are preserved, and from the epithelium of these glands the endometrium is eventually restored.

The uterine tubes do not appear to undergo any important changes during the reproductive cycle.

Family *Felidae*

Felis

The following account of the changes which occur in the accessory reproductive organs of the cat during the oestrous cycle is based mainly on the descriptions of Gros (1933, 1936); Bourg (1935); Liche and Wodzicki (1939); and Dawson and Kosters (1944).

The vaginal cycle

Changes in the vagina. The vaginal epithelium of the anoestrous cat consists of 3 to 4 layers of small, nucleated non-cornified cells. These proliferate rapidly during prooestrus, and at oestrus the epithelium is made up of some 24 layers, of which the superficial 10 contain cornified, non-nucleated and actively desquamating cells. They are shed into the vaginal lumen separately or in flakes (Gros, 1936; Liche, 1939). At the same time, glandular offshoots of the vaginal wall (Bourg, 1935; Gros, 1936) hypertrophy, and secrete mucus. In unmated cats oestrus and the associated vaginal changes continue for about 8 days, gradually becoming less intense. By the 8th day the vaginal epithelium varies in thickness from 8 to 15 layers of cells, and is invaded by leucocytes.

If coitus takes place, desquamation and leucocytic infiltration occur much sooner (within 24 hours after ovulation), and at the end of two weeks the vagina has completely resumed its resting condition, which is maintained throughout pregnancy (or pseudopregnancy). In the latter third of gestation, a further change occurs, and the cells of the most superficial layer become more columnar, and their cytoplasm clearer. This is the only specific change of pregnancy, but according to Gros (1936), it cannot be compared with the intense vaginal mucification which occurs in the pregnant guinea-pig. Bourg (1935), however, affirms that the superficial layer of vaginal cells undergoes a definite mucous metaplasia, and states that the lumen of the vagina becomes filled with a mucous secretion. Towards the end of pregnancy leucocytes infiltrate the epithelium, the most superficial cells of which become larger and more polygonal.

If abortion occurs, or if the young are removed after birth, a new phase of oestrus, characterised by a thick and superficially cornified epithelium, sets in.

The vaginal smear. According to Liche and Wodzicki (1939), four different stages in the composition of the vaginal smear can be recognised. Prooestrus is characterised by large numbers of nucleated epithelial cells of fairly uniform shape. During oestrus the smear picture is inconstant. The essential elements are both nucleated and non-nucleated cornified cells, whose relative proportions vary between individuals and, apparently, according to the time of the year. In addition, there may be smaller round and intensely staining epithelial cells, leucocytes, and even free deformed nuclei. During metoestrus the smear consists exclusively of leucocytes, and during anoestrus of a variety of nucleated cells differing in shape, size and staining reactions.

Changes in the greater vestibular glands of female cats have been studied by Barrington (1913), who found that the epithelium of these glands becomes rich in mucin shortly before oestrus and in the latter half of pregnancy; during lactation the amount of mucin in Bartholin's glands is small.

Changes in the uterus

Several longitudinal folds of endometrium project into the cavum uteri, which is thus stellate on cross-section. During anoestrus the diameter of the uterine horn is about 5 mm., but it increases somewhat just before prooestrus (Bourg, 1935; Dawson and Kosters, 1944). The endometrial glands are short, straight and narrow. They and the lumen of the uterus are lined by a single layer of flat or low cuboidal epithelial cells about 6 to 12 μ thick (Foster and Hisaw, 1935).

During prooestrus the diameter of the uterine horns increases to about 6 to 7 mm. The glands elongate but remain essentially straight, while their lining cells increase in height. At oestrus both the endo- and myometrium are hypertrophied, and the glands, which now tend to be slightly coiled, are actively proliferating (Fig. 6. 23b). The surface epithelium is tall columnar, about 20 to 29 μ in height, and of the " pseudostratified " type, owing to crowding of the nuclei (Foster and Hisaw, 1935 ; Dawson and Kosters, 1944).

If coitus does not occur these changes continue, but gradually become less marked, and after about 10 days the endometrium resumes its anoestrous condition. Bourg (1935) states that if ovulation does not occur the Graafian follicles become atretic, and the hypertrophied endometrium undergoes rapid regression. He also refers specifically to the congestion of the endometrial vessels during oestrus, a fact which is not mentioned in Gros' descriptions.

The changes which occur in the endometrium during pregnancy and pseudopregnancy have been studied by Gros (1933, 1935, 1936), Foster and Hisaw (1935), and Dawson and Kosters (1944). Two successive stages, the second developing about one week after the first, can be recognised (Courrier and Gros, 1933 ; Gros, 1933, 1936). Early in the first stage, the uterine glands become much larger, and extend everywhere from the surface epithelium to the myometrium, being separated from each other only by narrow bridges of stromal tissue. At first, the epithelium of the cavum uteri is not much altered, but within two days of mating the cells lining the glands, both in their straighter proximal and more tortuous distal parts, become greatly swollen and secretory in type. They increase in height to about 40 μ ; their cytoplasm becomes clearer, and the nuclei, which are basally disposed, are small and stain deeply. Glycogen then accumulates, and the nuclei become displaced apically and compressed longitudinally. Sperm may be found in the lumina of the glands a few hours after copulation (Dawson and Kosters, 1944).

Towards the end of the first week after ovulation the surface epithelium becomes transformed into an intricate lace-work which invests the lumen of the uterus, and gives it a characteristic fringed appearance (Fig. 6. 23c). During the course of the following week the endometrium becomes differentiated into a superficial region formed by crypts and the distended necks of glands (the " dentelle épithéliale "), and a deeper, more spongy zone made up of mucous glands with no obvious lumina (Fig. 6. 23d). Numerous mitoses are to be seen in the epithelium at this stage, during which implantation of the ova takes place.

Gros points out that the course of development of the endometrium of the cat during the luteal phase differs materially from that of the rabbit. In the first instance, in the rabbit, there is practically no early glandular activity, which is a characteristic feature in the cat. Secondly, the superficial epithelial lace-work develops immediately in the rabbit and is well formed by the end of the first week, whereas it has not begun to demonstrate itself at that time in the cat. Gros relates these differences to the fact that in the rabbit the fertilised ova enter the uterine horns on the 3rd day, and are implanted by the 7th, whereas in the cat they reach the uterus on the 6th day after coitus, and are not implanted until the 13th or

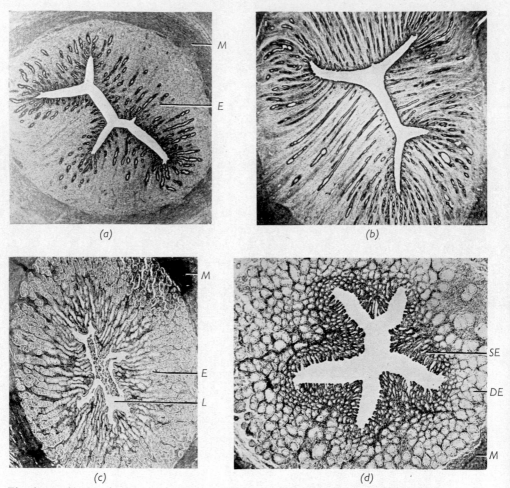

(a)   (b)

(c)   (d)

Fig. 6. 23—Changes in the uterus of the cat during the reproductive cycle. (a) anoestrus (× 30); (b) 5¼ hours after successful mating on the 3rd day of oestrus (× 20); (c) 7th day of pseudo-pregnancy induced by cervical stimulation (× 23); (d) 10 days after successful mating (× 30).

Note in: (a) the relatively thin endometrium with short, straight and narrow glands; (b) the thickened endometrium and the greater length, but otherwise unchanged character, of the uterine glands; (c) the fringed outline of the mucosa and the greatly dilated and tortuous uterine glands which open freely into the lumen (L); (d) the marked transformation of the endometrium, which is now subdivided into an inner, complexly-folded zone (SE) and an outer, more spongy part (DE). E, endometrium; M, myometrium.

Photomicrographs by Dr. Allen B. Dawson.

14th day (Courrier and Gros, 1933). The excessive secretion of the uterine glands in the first week of the luteal phase of the cat provides nourishment (" embryo-trophe ") for the free blastocysts.

During pregnancy the endometrium decreases in thickness, and the cells lining the glands decrease in height. During the last weeks of pregnancy the uterus becomes progressively infiltrated by leucocytes. This process is accentuated just before and after parturition, and leads to rapid desquamation of the superficial epithelial lace-work, and to a breaking-up of the entire mucosa within about a week of delivery (Gros, 1936 ; Dawson, 1946). Bourg (1935) has studied the involution of an experimentally induced luteal phase in the uterus of the cat, and emphasises its resemblance to the " white menstruation " of the bitch (Gerlinger, 1925 ; *see* also p. 588).

It may be noted that decidual cells do not appear in the endometrium of the pregnant cat, and that, as Gros found, a decidual reaction cannot be provoked by passing a thread through the uterine horn during the period of life of the corpus luteum.

Changes in the non-gravid uterine horn

The changes which occur in the non-gravid horn of a unilaterally pregnant uterus have been described by Gros (1935, 1936). On the 39th day of pregnancy (about 25 days before term), the superficial fringes of the endometrium still persist, but the deeper glandular zone is less prominent. Shortly afterwards (43rd day), the endometrial fringes undergo leucocytic infiltration, and their epithelium begins to desquamate, complete regression being delayed until after parturition.

The long persistence of the superficial endometrial lace-work in the sterile horn of the cat is another feature which distinguishes this species from the rabbit. Gros has suggested that in the cat the placenta provides the stimulus for the maintenance of the lace-work during late pregnancy. He bases this view on the observation that ovariectomy up to the 47th day of pregnancy is followed by abortion and regression of the differentiated endometrium, a change which does not occur when the operation is performed after the 49th day.

Changes during pseudopregnancy

The histological features of the uterus during natural or artificially induced pseudopregnancy in the cat have been studied by Gros (1935, 1936), Foster and Hisaw (1935), and other workers (*see* Dawson and Kosters, 1944). Opinions differ about the duration of pseudopregnancy. According to Gros, it is very variable but lasts approximately a month and a half, while the results of Foster and Hisaw and van Dyke and Li (1938) indicate that it is nearer 30 than 40 days in length. All authors agree, however, that the histological changes in the pseudopregnant uterus parallel, except for some delay, those of normal gestation up to about the 3rd week. After the 30th day regression sets in. Involution of the elaborate endometrial lace-work is brought about by degeneration of the epithelium, and by intense leucocytic infiltration (with pus formation) accompanied by haemorrhage, as in the menstruation of primates (Gros, 1935).

Mention was made on p. 303 of a cat which gave birth to two kittens and, after an interval of 13 days, to two more (Markeee and Hinsey, 1935a). The right uterine horn, which delivered first, had involuted during the period in which the left remained in a pregnant state. Markee and Hinsey (1935b) hold that the amount of growth in a uterine horn depends, among other factors, not only upon the number of foetuses, but upon their weights, a finding which indicates that there may be a local factor which also influences the growth of the uterus in pregnancy.

Changes in the uterine tube

During anoestrus and after ovariectomy the epithelium of the tube is flat, and consists of small cuboidal cells of about 12 to 15 µ height (Foster and Hisaw, 1935; Bourg, 1935; Gros, 1936). During prooestrus and oestrus the epithelium becomes in greater part columnar (about 20 to 40 µ) and ciliated. Interspersed among these cells are many non-ciliated cells with dark pyriform nuclei. During the luteal phase the tubal epithelium returns to its resting condition. According to Bourg, considerable degeneration takes place in the tubes at the beginning of gestation.

Most of the various histological changes which occur in the vagina, uterus and tubes of the normal cat have been reproduced by the injection of gonadotrophic and gonadal hormones by Bourg (1935), Foster and Hisaw (1935), Rowlands and McPhail (1936), Windle (1939), and others (*see* Dawson and Kosters, 1944).

According to Matthews (1941b), the cyclic changes in the genital tract of the wild cat (*Felis sylvestris grampia*) closely resemble those in the domestic cat.

In the lioness (*Felis leo*) the vaginal smear contains a variety of nucleated epithelial cells during anoestrus, similar to those found at that time in the cat. At oestrus the smear consists predominantly of large, non-nucleated cornified cells, while the remainder is made up of smaller cells with pyknotic nuclei (Liche and Wodzicki, 1939).

CHIROPTERA

I. The insectivorous bats

        Fam.   *Rhinolophidae*
                Rhinolophus (Horse-shoe bat)

        Fam.   *Vespertilionidae*
                Pipistrellus (Pipistrelle)
                Nyctalus (Noctule bat)
                Miniopterus (Long-winged bat)
                Vespertilio (Serotine bat)

        Fam.   *Hipposideridae*
                Triaenops (Tropical Old World bat)

        Fam.   *Nycteridae*
                Nycteris (Hispid bat)

        Fam.   *Phyllostomatidae*
                Glossophaga (Long-tongued " vampire ")

II. The fruit-eating bats

        Fam.   *Pteropidae*
                Pteropus (Fruit bat)

Rhinolophid and vespertilionid bats differ in the manner in which the spermatozoa are stored in the reproductive tract of the hibernating female. As noted on p. 310, in the Vespertilionidae the sperm are retained within the distended uterus or in the uterine glands. In the Rhinolophidae the main mass of sperm forms the core of the vaginal plug which is deposited in a ventral pocket of the vagina, although a small number may also be found in the uterine glands and in the uterine tubes (Matthews, 1937).

Changes in the vagina

In the Rhinolophidae (Courrier, 1924b ; Matthews, 1937) the vagina of the new-born animal has a stratified squamous epithelium with a basal layer of cylindrical cells. The mucosa of the lower part of the vagina is thicker than that of the upper, and occasionally the organ is not completely canalised.

In the prepubertal female the muscle wall of the vagina forms longitudinal thickenings which project into the lumen of the vagina. Later, these ridges become flattened by epithelial proliferation which almost occludes the upper part of the vagina (Matthews, 1937).

At the onset of oestrus in the autumn, the vagina of both virgin and parous females shows prominent folds lined by deeply stratified cornified epithelium. After the formation of the vaginal plug during copulation, the upper part of the vagina is markedly distended and the epithelial ridges are obliterated. In its centre the plug consists of " structureless " (Matthews, 1937) or " mucous " (Courrier, 1924b) material and of spermatozoa ; more peripherally, various layers of vaginal epithelium can be recognised. Fertilisation occurs in the following spring, and the plug disappears after the blastocyst has reached the uterus. The observation by Rollinat and Trouessart (1897), noted on p. 311, that the vaginal plug is expelled en masse, so that the vulva is lacerated and bleeding ensues, was not confirmed by Matthews (1937).

Matthews (1941c) also describes the presence of a hard hyaline plug in the vagina of the pregnant Triaenops afer Peters, an African species belonging to the Hipposideridae. The epithelium in contact with the obstruction is in process of rapid proliferation, and its surface layers are rapidly shed.

During pregnancy the cavity of the vagina is large and irregularly folded, but the epithelium of its shallow mucosa remains stratified. The lumen diminishes greatly in size during lactation anoestrus, when the mucosa becomes even shallower.

In certain African species of insectivorous bats the folded epithelium consists of a deep zone of polyhedral cells, and a superficial layer of columnar and frequently mucified cells (Matthews, 1941c). Occasionally, the most superficial layer is cornified and desquamating (e.g. in Nycteris luteola).

In the vespertilionid pipistrelle (P. pipistrellus), in which sperms are not stored in the vagina, and in which there is no vaginal pouch as in the horse-shoe bats, post-coital proliferation of the epithelium completely obliterates the vaginal lumen (Courrier, 1924b). A similar process takes place in Nyctalus noctula (Grosser, 1903), but in this species the epithelial layers become separated from the underlying connective tissue (see p. 311). In the pipistrelle and other vespertilionid bats the deeper part of the vaginal epithelium (or plug) consists of about 12 layers of Malpighian cells with a superficial band of cornified cells, and there are no leucocytes. The mucosa remains in this condition from immediately after the autumnal copulation until fertilisation in the spring.

The prolonged phase of epithelial proliferation in the vagina of vespertilionid and other bats is indicative of sustained oestrogenic stimulation (see below).

Changes in the uterus

The changes which occur in the uterus of rhinolophid bats have been systematically studied by Matthews (1937), who also provides information about a variety of non-European types of insectivorous bat (Matthews, 1941c).

In immature horse-shoe bats the endometrium is lined by columnar epithelium, and there are no glands. The cavum uteri is somewhat irregular, owing to the presence of thick endometrial folds. The uterus remains in this condition throughout the first year of life, but at the beginning of the next, i.e. in the second spring, a few glands without lumina develop, usually at the tubal end of the right (or functional) uterine horn (Matthews, 1937).

By the time of the first oestrus, the endometrium has proliferated until it is more than five times as deep as in the immature animal. It contains numerous glands with large lumina, and its surface epithelium is stratified. There is no further change until the spring (that is to say, after copulation and during hibernation), when renewed growth and glandular development take place. The uterus involutes during lactation.

In the Vespertilionidae, the uterus becomes distended with sperm after the autumn copulation, and reaches a size several times that of the bladder. Courrier (1924b) studied one of this group of bats (*Pipistrellus pipistrellus*), and found that in this species the endometrium is very glandular throughout hibernation. Most of the cells are high columnar, and their apical regions are full of fine granules. The sperms are grouped in bundles with their heads towards the epithelium of the glands.

In *Myotis lucifugus*, a vespertilionid bat studied both by Reeder (1939) and Wimsatt (1944), the uterine epithelium during hibernation consists of a single row of columnar cells. Ciliated cells are absent in the uterine horns, but are frequent in the lower half of the body of the uterus and upper end of the cervix. The uterine glands are narrow and tubular, and open mainly on or near the mesometrial aspect of the horns. A large Graafian follicle persists in one of the ovaries from the time of the autumn copulation, and hence some degree of oestrogenic stimulation is maintained throughout hibernation. The glandular epithelium proliferates somewhat more during hibernation than it does in the preceding, resting stage. Small and large leucocytes are invariably present in the uterus of the hibernating *Myotis* (Guthrie, 1933). Spermatozoa are ingested by the larger leucocytes, and Guthrie believes that this is the principal method of elimination of sperm in this species (*see* also p. 312).

At the time of ovulation (in the spring), the epithelium starts proliferating rapidly, and the stroma becomes oedematous and hyperaemic. The uterine glands grow larger, and their epithelium becomes taller, changes which Wimsatt relates to the onset of secretion of luteal hormone. Complete progestational transformation of the endometrium occurs later, when an ovum is present in the oviduct. The glands, which contain much secretion, increase considerably in length and tortuosity, and their cells become highly columnar. The epithelium lining the uterus becomes pseudostratified, and during the passage of the fertilised ovum through the tube oedema and congestion of the stroma increase.

In an African type of vespertilionid bat (*Miniopterus dasythrix* Temm.) the mucosa of the uterine horns during early pregnancy measures 300–700 μ in width, and consists entirely of coiled glands. These are lined by a single layer of polyhedral cells continuous with the cuboidal or columnar cells of the surface epithelium (Matthews, 1941c). In the prepubertal animal the mucosa is only 80 μ thick.

The Nycteridae appear to be seasonally polyoestrous and may have two pregnancies in quick succession, in contrast to the single litter produced each year by almost all other insectivorous bats (*see* p. 310). Matthews (1941c) was able to study several stages of the sexual cycle in *Nycteris luteola*. In the anoestrous female the mucosa of the uterine horns is ridged by folds covered by a single layer of cubical cells and containing few glands. There is no common uterine cavity, and the two cervical canals, which are lined by low columnar cells, open into the vagina by two distinct external orifices. At prooestrus and oestrus the endometrium is more extensively folded and vascularised, but otherwise differs little from the anoestrous condition just described. This applies also to the sterile horn and cervical canal during unilateral pregnancy.

Unusual uterine changes have been described by Hamlett (1934) in a South American type of bat, *Glossophaga soricina*, belonging to the family Phyllostomatidae. This species is monoestrous, and copulates and ovulates late in the spring. The endometrium before ovulation is shallow, and its glandular development is poor. After ovulation the mucosa thickens, and the glands become longer and coiled, the greatest amount of proliferation occurring in the fundus of the uterus. If fertilisation does not occur, the proliferated endometrium sloughs off at the end of the oestrous cycle, a process which Hamlett regards as uterine bleeding. The specimens figured by Hamlett do not, however, show a very close resemblance to the premenstrual endometrium of primates, and rather suggest the " interval " type of bleeding (associated with a mucosa in the proliferative phase of the cycle), which is sometimes seen in Old World monkeys and in women. Uterine bleeding has also been claimed to occur in certain frugivorous bats (*see* Wiltshire, 1883 ; Kohlbrugge, 1904, 1913).

The curious glandular modification undergone by the endometrium of the pregnant horn in the giant fruit bat (*Pteropus giganteus*) has already been referred to (Marshall, 1949 ; *see* p. 309). The localised reaction, which is observed only in the presence of an active corpus luteum, is a prerequisite for successful implantation of the blastocyst. In spite of its asymmetric development, the change appears to be principally due to the action of progesterone, associated with some other specifically local factor. A similar condition has been described in the uterus of the non-pregnant elephant shrew by van der Horst and Gillman (1941 ; and p. 326).

Changes in the uterine tubes

The changes which occur in the uterine tubes have been described for the Rhinolophidae by Matthews (1937), and for the Vespertilionidae by Courrier (1924b). In mature English horse-shoe bats, as studied by Matthews, the ovarian and uterine parts of the tubes are fully differentiated. The mucosa of the ovarian segment is much folded and is lined by ciliated epithelial cells possessing particularly large nuclei. That of the uterine part is thrown into four or five low ridges, lined by non-ciliated cubical to low columnar cells. The only change which occurs at the onset of the autumnal oestrus is an increase in the complexity of the mucosal folds, and in the size of the whole tube. It remains in this condition until the spring, when, on the approach of ovulation, the folding of the mucosa becomes more exaggerated, and the lining cells grow, their nuclei becoming relatively smaller. Both parts of the tube involute towards the end of lactation.

In the pipistrelle (*Pipistrellus pipistrellus*) and the serotine bats (*Vespertilio serotinus*) the cycle of changes appears to be more pronounced than in the horse-shoe bats. During hibernation the epithelium of the juxta-uterine segment is tall columnar and mostly non-ciliated. In the lateral part of the tube the cells are generally ciliated and less secretory. The tube remains in this condition through-out the hibernating period, but during gestation the lining epithelium becomes very low, signs of secretion disappear, and many of the cells desquamate.

As in the case of the uterine secretions, Courrier believes that the secretion in the uterine tube nourishes the sperms which enter that part of the reproductive tract. He points out that numerous leucocytes are to be seen at the ovarian end of the tube and in the ovarian bursa, neither of which is glandular, and he explains their presence as phagocytes whose activity is stimulated by the presence of sperms that have died owing to the lack of a nutritive medium. Guthrie (1933), however, records the presence of leucocytes in all parts of the tubes of the hibernating *Myotis lucifugus*, as well as in the uterine horns. In the same species the epi-thelium of the proximal part of the tube undergoes extreme vacuolation and sloughs off during early pregnancy (Wimsatt, 1944). It regenerates during later gestational stages, and is eventually restored to the normal resting condition.

INSECTIVORA

Fam.   *Erinaceidae*
         Erinaceus (Hedgehog)

Fam.   *Talpidae*
         Talpa (Old World mole)

Fam.   *Soricidae*
         Sorex (Common and lesser shrew)
         Blarina (Short-tailed shrew)

Fam.   *Macroscelididae*
         Elephantulus (Elephant shrew)

Family *Erinaceidae*

Erinaceus

Changes in the vagina

The cyclic changes undergone by the vagina of the hedgehog are very pro-nounced (*see* Courrier, 1924a, b ; Deanesly, 1934), and are, to some extent, externally discernible, for the vagina enlarges at the beginning of the breeding season and becomes greatly dilated at oestrus. The distension is only present during the oestrous cycle, and subsides during pregnancy, pseudopregnancy and lactation.

Structural changes are most evident in the upper part of the vagina. During hibernation the epithelium is low (30 to 100 μ), and consists of 4 or 5 layers of cells. At the beginning of the season these begin to proliferate, and by April the vagina and the vaginal epithelium grow rapidly, both in parous and non-parous animals.   The epithelium becomes deeply stratified and cornified, but begins to desquamate before it reaches its greatest thickness.   In cycles in which mating does not take place, intermittent growth and sloughing continue, and the epithelium varies between 120 and 180 μ in thickness, the most superficial cornified layer accounting for 60 to 120 μ.   More intensive sloughing occurs after copulation, and the whole of the upper vagina becomes filled with fluid containing cornified debris.   Desquamation continues during pregnancy, until the vaginal mucosa is once again shallow.

The greater vestibular glands (*see* p. 118) become much enlarged and secrete actively during the breeding season.   Changes in the other vaginal glands are less conspicuous.

Changes in the uterus

During the cycle.   Although young female hedgehogs do not breed in their first season, a considerable amount of uterine development can take place before the beginning of the winter anoestrus.   First-season specimens may, in fact, be obtained in September, in which the endometrium is of the adult type, with a wide lumen, oedematous stroma, and numerous and well-developed glands.

In the mature animal the weight of the uterus fluctuates according to the reproductive phase, being lowest in the anoestrous or non-pregnant female, and highest during pseudopregnancy.   As the first oestrus of the breeding season approaches, the endometrial stroma becomes less dense, and new glands develop from the surface epithelium, to replace the glands of the preceding season, many of which may still be present in a degenerated form.

During pseudopregnancy.   If mating does not occur, the endometrium remains practically unaltered after ovulation.   If sterile copulation occurs, the surface epithelium is thrown into folds, and the supporting stroma becomes oedematous. Deanesly (1934) believes that this change, which gives the surface epithelium a " notched appearance," is due not to epithelial proliferation, but to the collapse of the previously oedematous endometrium.   In addition, some degree of progestational proliferation, as indicated by growth and secretion in the epithelium of the uterus and cervix, can take place ; occasionally, the uterine stroma may appear disorganised, as it also does in early pregnancy.

During pregnancy.   Uteri containing young blastocysts show congestion of the subepithelial stroma, with some destruction of the epithelial lining and extravasation of blood into the uterine cavity and cervix.   Subsequently, when free blastulae are present, the epithelium undergoes progestational changes, and grows into a fringe of irregular folds and crypts.   Late in pregnancy, the epithelium between implantation sites forms an irregular multicellular network with small projections and shallow crypts of secreting cells.

Oedema and disorganisation of the placental sites appear to persist even after the first post-partum ovulation has occurred, but involution takes place when lactation is established, and the endometrium becomes extremely dense and almost non-glandular.   The transformation of the involuted uterus of lactation into the uterus of oestrus follows roughly the same course as the transition from the anoestrous to the oestrous state.

As noted on p. 317, spermatozoa persist for a very long time in the uterus of the hedgehog, and may be found even late in pregnancy.   The fact that they can penetrate into the deeper recesses of the uterus and cervix (Deanesly, 1934) may partly account for this morphological " survival." This does not, of course, imply any prolonged fertilising power on the part of the sperm.

Family *Talpidae*

Talpa

The microscopical changes which occur in the reproductive organs of the female mole are of unusual interest, largely because of the formation and obliteration of the vaginal lumen at the beginning and end of each breeding season (*see* p. 319).

Changes in the vagina

During winter the skin of the perineum is formed by a thin stratum corneum overlying a Malpighian layer of some 5 tiers of cells, deep to which is the dermis (Matthews, 1935). The cells of the Malpighian layer are connected by an epithelial strand to the blind end of the utero-vaginal canal. Early in March, at the beginning of the breeding season, this strand becomes 15 to 20 cells thick, those in the centre becoming cornified. Canalisation occurs as they are shed. An external opening is established when the closure membrane, in the perineum, breaks down. Closure of the vaginal orifice begins immediately after parturition, usually in early May. The surrounding muscle fibres shorten, and the lateral margins of the opening start " healing " (Matthews, 1935). The distal end of the utero-vaginal canal then begins to close, and the epithelial fusion proceeds distally towards the perineum, resulting in the formation of a smooth or only slightly puckered closure membrane. The healing is frequently associated with the deposition of black pigment in the perineum, especially along the line marking the site of the original orifice.

The clitoridal (preputial) sheath (" repli balano-préputial ") of the adult female mole also undergoes well-marked annual changes (Godet, 1947).

Changes in the utero-vaginal canal

The mole lacks a cervix uteri, and the two uterine horns open directly into a single and markedly kinked utero-vaginal canal. During prooestrus this grows in length and breadth, its S-shaped bend becoming greatly exaggerated. As oestrus approaches growth accelerates, and by the third week in March the previously thin canal is transformed into a conspicuous abdominal organ, over half the length of the entire body. Simultaneously, the uterine horns enlarge, but they do not reach their maximum size until the first part of April. Regression of the utero-vaginal canal sets in immediately pregnancy occurs, in the first days of April, and by the third week of that month the canal has shrunk to about 30 per cent of the body length. It resumes its anoestrous size (about 20 per cent) at the end of lactation early in June.

The lining of the utero-vaginal canal consists of a thin stratified and somewhat-folded epithelium, deep to which is a prominent submucous layer of fibrous tissue. In the anoestrous animal the epithelium measures about 7 μ, and the submucous layer 50 μ in thickness, while the entire canal has a diameter of about 1 to 1·5 mm. During prooestrus the epithelium increases to a depth of some 10 to 20 layers of cells, and the superficial zone becomes cornified. At oestrus epithelial proliferation and desquamation are at their height, the epithelial and submucous layers measure about 100 μ and 500 μ respectively, and the entire canal about 3·5 mm. in transverse diameter. These dimensions are maintained during the earlier part of pregnancy, but later there is a gradual regression which continues until after parturition and the closure of the vaginal orifice.

Changes in the uterine horns

During the breeding season the uterine horns increase greatly in length, development beginning at prooestrus and reaching its maximum early in April, during the first stages of pregnancy. The length of the horns decreases slightly after parturition, and the process of involution is complete by the end of June (Matthews, 1935).

The anoestrous endometrium is lined by a single row of columnar cells, and is thrown into several folds. There are only scattered glands. During prooestrus the mucosa increases from 70 μ to 200 μ in thickness, and becomes very hyperaemic, especially at the mesometrial side. Growth continues into oestrus, when the horns increase in diameter, mainly as a result of endometrial and myometrial proliferation. The mucosa at this time is about 600 μ deep. Shortly after fertilisation there is further "enormous" proliferation of the mucosa along the antimesometrial aspects of the uterine horns, and the glands become very conspicuous. On the opposite side the mucosa remains thin, and the surface epithelium and that lining the glands becomes tall columnar.

Family *Soricidae*
Genera : *Sorex ; Blarina*
Sorex

The cyclic changes in the reproductive organs of the common and lesser shrews (*Sorex araneus* Linn. and *Sorex minutus* Linn.) have been described by Brambell (1935) and Brambell and Hall (1936).

Vaginal changes

The vagina of the prepubertal shrew is closed from its upper end to the urethral orifice, the epithelium consisting of a solid band 15 to 20 μ thick. The lower, patent region of the vagina is lined by stratified epithelium 20 to 40 μ thick, thrown into deep folds, and contains desquamated epithelial cells and leucocytes. Canalisation of the upper vagina is completed during the first prooestrus of the breeding season, largely through progressive cornification and desquamation of the superficial layers of the epithelial lining. Thus in the shrew, cornification of the vaginal epithelium precedes the onset of the first period of heat. Epithelial proliferation, accompanied by cornification, becomes intense during oestrus. The epithelium reaches a height of 50 to 110 μ, but then sloughs off in late oestrus, and is reduced to about 50 μ. At the same time the subepithelial stroma becomes very hyperaemic and infiltrated by leucocytes.

During pregnancy the epithelium is reformed, entirely by nucleated cells, but desquamation of its superficial layers continues. The upper vagina gradually decreases in diameter, until it becomes almost occluded. In this extreme condition, the epithelium is " in the form of a central nearly solid core approximately 100 μ in diameter, from which a number of solid epithelial lamellae 7–25 μ in thickness radiate " (Fig. 6. 24). The vaginal lumen is re-established towards the end of pregnancy. The epithelium is nucleated and deeply stratified, but does not become completely cornified during the post-partum oestrus. Vaginal occlusion, corresponding to that described in the common shrew, has also been observed in the pseudopregnant fox (p. 590) and in certain bats (p. 605) ; it contrasts with the formation of a special, previously non-existing canal in many marsupials, in whom it permits delivery of the young through a median (pseudovaginal) passage, instead of through the lateral vaginae (*see* p. 62).

Fig. 6. 24—Transverse section of the upper vagina of the common shrew during mid-pregnancy, showing the complete occlusion of the lumen brought about by fusion of the epithelial folds (× 65). From Brambell (1935).

Changes in the uterus

The uterus of the immature shrew is circular in transverse section and simple in structure. The surface epithelium comprises a single layer of cylindrical cells with basally disposed nuclei. The glands, as noted on p. 123, are situated on the antimesometrial side, and are very poorly developed. In the non-parous common shrew there is a characteristic zone of clear fibrous tissue between the mucosa and the myometrium (Brambell, 1935). This layer is also present in the uterus of the oestrous mole, but is lacking in the lesser shrew (Brambell and Hall, 1936), and in the short-tailed shrew (Pearson, 1944).

At the time of the first oestrus the endometrium is deep, the stroma having become denser, and the glands more numerous and better developed. Since ovulation appears to be invariably followed by conception, no phase of pseudopregnant endometrial development is known.

In early pregnancy the growth of both the endometrium and the muscular wall obliterates the submucosal layer of fibrous tissue mentioned above. The endometrium becomes more vascular, and the glands proliferate greatly, their lumina being convoluted and distended with secretion. The surface epithelium then appears to be pseudostratified, and no leucocytes can be seen either within the stroma or in the cavum uteri.

The epithelium of the cervix exhibits similar, but less well-marked changes during oestrus and early pregnancy.

When the fertilised ova reach the uterine cornua, the part of the cavum uteri opposite the mesometrium becomes distended and forms a spherical chamber around each blastocyst. This change causes a reorganisation in the disposition of the glands, and presumably as a result of the stretching of the antimesometrial uterine wall, the epithelium becomes drawn out into a single thin layer of cubical cells.

The shrew experiences a post-partum oestrus, during which the uterus is thin and folded, and its lumen is crowded with cell debris, through which the spermatozoa ascend.

Changes in the uterine tube

Such cyclic changes as occur in the uterine tube of the shrew are very slight. The epithelial cells of the part of the tube adjacent to the ovary are ciliated, and during oestrus cytoplasm appears to be extruded from them, as in the mouse ('Espinasse, 1935). This form of secretion is at its height in early pregnancy, but decreases towards its end.

Blarina

Certain details of the structural changes in the accessory reproductive organs of the short-tailed shrew have been published by Pearson (1944) and by Wimsatt and Wislocki (1947).

In general the histological appearance of the vagina during anoestrus and oestrus is the same as in the common and lesser shrews (*see* p. 611). During pregnancy, however, the lumen does not become occluded, and the epithelium remains thin throughout. After parturition proliferation again occurs, and the superficial layers of cells are cornified during lactation.

The cavity of the resting and prooestrous uterus is narrow and lined by simple columnar epithelium, measuring about 5 to 7 μ in height. The few tubular or slightly coiled glands present are concentrated on the antimesometrial border, and are lined by a low columnar epithelium. In contrast to *Sorex araneus*, there is no true submucous ring of fibrous tissue, but the endometrial stroma can be divided into an inner compact and an outer oedematous " spongy " zone. During oestrus, and especially after ovulation, the uterine cavity enlarges rapidly. The epithelium of the mucosa increases to a height of 30 to 40 μ, and becomes arranged in a number of prominent folds. The nuclei of the surface cells are irregularly disposed, and thus appear " pseudostratified." The glands also enlarge and become dilated. Leucocytes are present within the epithelium and lumen of the uterus (Wimsatt and Wislocki, 1947). The changes associated with implantation of the blastocysts are similar to those described by Brambell for the common shrew, as are also the changes undergone by the epithelium of the uterine tubes (*see* Pearson, 1944).

Family *Macroscelididae*

Elephantulus

The essential facts of the reproductive cycle in the elephant shrew have been summarised in Chapter 4.   The following account of the histological changes in the uterus is based on the comprehensive descriptions of van der Horst and Gillman (1941, 1942a, b, c, d).

In the immature and anoestrous mature female the uterus is very small, and is lined by a single layer of low columnar cells.   The uterine glands are shallow and extend into a narrow zone of cellular stroma (Fig. 6. 25a).   During anoestrus they may be cystic.

Generalised oedema in the deepest zone of the endometrium, and involving its entire circumference, marks the beginning of the proliferative (" oestrogenic ") phase.   At the same time the epithelial and connective-tissue elements rapidly increase in size and number, and the uterus as a whole becomes much larger. The oedema spreads, and eventually involves the whole thickness of the endometrium.   The stromal cells become widely separated, and on cross-section the uterus appears " sodden " (Fig. 6. 25b).   At this stage the uterine glands are straight and moderately dilated, and resemble " small test tubes."   At ovulation, the surface epithelium consists of tall columnar cells, and the stroma is deeply infiltrated with leucocytes.   The subepithelial capillaries are congested, and red cells may pass into the stroma or through the epithelium into the uterine cavity.

Shortly after ovulation, the generalised oedema subsides, first in the superficial and then in the deep parts of the endometrium.   During this brief phase the stroma is, as in early oestrus, subdivided into a superficial compact and a deeper oedematous zone, and leucocytic infiltration disappears.

Dehydration of the stroma continues, and the remaining peripheral zone of oedema becomes steadily reduced in width.   During this, the early luteal stage of the cycle, the stroma separating the glands, which are now slightly coiled, is extremely dense.   In the region in which the so-called endometrial " polyp " develops, the cavity of the uterus is lined by very thick epithelium.

The polyp forms during the later part of the luteal phase and passes through various stages.   It begins as an area of localised oedema on the mesometrial border of the uterus, accompanied by cystic dilatation of the middle sections of the glands, and by an increase in the size of the stromal cells.   As a result of this circumscribed growth of the endometrium, which occurs some 2 to 3 mm. above the junction of the horns with the median uterus, the previously elongated uterine cavity becomes triangular (Fig. 6. 25c).

The ripening polyp consists of greatly hypertrophied and superficially congested endometrium, about four to six times deeper than the endometrium characteristic of the succeeding phase of the cycle. It is made up of elongated and curved glands dilated in their middle portions, and of masses of modified elements which resemble decidual cells. When fully developed, the polyp forms a pendulous mass which protrudes into the uterine cavity (Fig. 6. 25d).   The average size of the polyp is 0·5 mm. at its base, but there is great variation, and an exceptionally large polyp may be 2·5 mm. long and extend as far as the junction of the horns with the median part of the uterus.   At this stage the uterine horn has the external

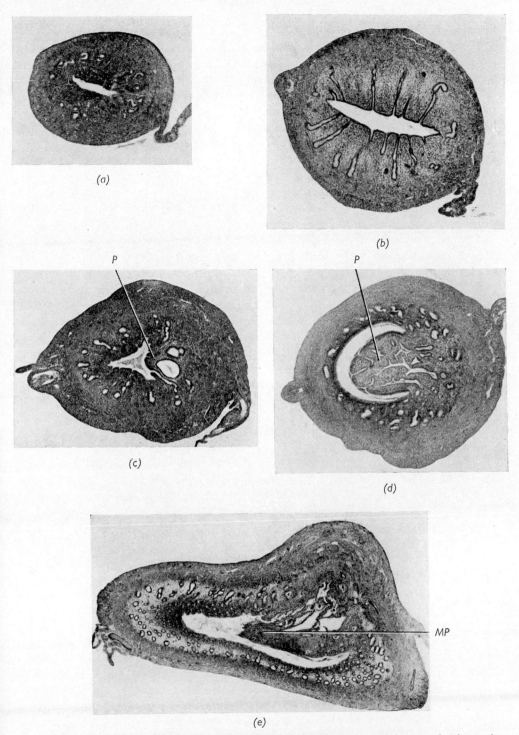

Fig. 6. 25—Uterus of the elephant shrew (*Elephantulus*) at various stages of the reproductive cycle. (*a*) virgin animal during anoestrus ; (*b*) at the time of ovulation ; (*c*) beginning polyp formation (P), early progestational stage ; (*d*) almost mature polyp (P), late progestational stage ; (*e*) oblique section of a " menstruating " large polyp (MP), showing localised nature of the endometrial changes. Photomicrographs lent by Dr. J. Gillman.

appearance of an elongated swelling similar to, but less circumscribed than an early pregnancy.

Van der Horst and Gillman consider the polyp to be a cyclic premenstrual phenomenon, which is absent when fertilisation and implantation occur. The polyp ultimately breaks down, and its contents spill into the lumen of the uterus (Fig. 6. 25e). During this process the glands become compressed, subepithelial haemorrhages occur, and blood cells extravasate into the stroma, until the epithelial lining finally ruptures and the polyp sloughs off from its site of attachment. Van der Horst and Gillman believe the process of degeneration to be essentially comparable to menstruation in higher primates, even though it occurs only in a very restricted part of each uterine horn.

Regeneration is swift and starts almost immediately after the beginning of " menstruation." It proceeds fastest in areas least affected by the degenerative process. There is no time-lag between the process of repair and the next oestrus, and hence desquamation, degeneration and proliferation of the endometrium may occur simultaneously in the same uterus.

Implantation of the blastocyst in *Elephantulus* is on the mesometrial border of each horn, close to its junction with the median uterus. Van der Horst and Gillman suspect, but were unable to prove, that the sites of implantation and menstruation are identical (1942a). They emphasise, however, that the appearance of the uterus during the stage of polyp formation and in early pregnancy are dissimilar, and consequently that " the processes leading up to one or the other condition are fundamentally different and are determined by the presence or absence of a fertilised ovum." They argue that a similar distinction also exists in the case of *Macaca* and the human female (1942b).

The same authors (1942c) have described the rare occurrence of spontaneous deciduomata in elephant shrews. In this condition the uterine lumen is filled by an endometrial tumour which presents all the histological features of early pregnancy. The development of the tumour depends on the presence of active corpora lutea in the ovaries. The deciduoma is believed to arise as a result of the natural stimulus provided by an early, and subsequently dying, embryo. The occasional occurrence of pre-implantation abortion has been established in *Elephantulus* (van der Horst and Gillman, 1942d).

TUPAIIDAE

A phase of uterine bleeding appears to occur during the oestrous cycle of the tree shrew, *Tupaia javanica*, and it is also likely that the bleeding occurs about the time of ovulation (Stratz, 1898 ; van Herwerden, 1905). Thus, Stratz describes a uterus with swollen horns containing a coagulum of blood and desquamated epithelial tissue, associated with a very large ripe follicle and two smaller ones in the ovaries. In another specimen with a similar uterus, a fertilised ovum was present in one of the uterine tubes. These and other observations led Stratz to the view that there is a constant association in *Tupaia* between the process of " menstruation " and the maturation of the ovum, and that fertilisation takes place at the end of the phase of bleeding.

PRIMATES

Suborder LEMUROIDEA
   Fam. *Lorisidae*
     Loris (Slender loris)

Suborder TARSIOIDEA
     Tarsius (Spectral tarsier)

Suborder PITHECOIDEA

   The Platyrrhine (New World) Monkeys
   Fam. *Cebidae*
     Ateles (" Spider " monkey)
     Alouatta (Howling-monkey)
     Cebus (Capuchin)
   Fam. *Hapalidae*
     Hapale ; Callithrix (Marmoset)

   The Catarrhine (Old World) Monkeys
   Fam. *Cercopithecidae*
    Subfam. *Cercopithecinae*
      Macaca (Macaques)
      Papio (Baboons)
    Subfam. *Colobinae*
      Semnopithecus (Langur)

   The Anthropoid Apes and Man
   Fam. *Hylobatidae*
     Hylobates (Gibbon)
   Fam. *Pongidae*
     Pan (Chimpanzee)
     Gorilla (Gorilla)
   Fam. *Hominidae*
     Homo (Man)

Suborder LEMUROIDEA

Family *Lorisidae*

Loris

The only studies of the cyclic changes that occur in the reproductive organs of *Lorisidae* appear to be those of Narayan Rao (1927, 1932). They relate to the slender loris (*Loris lydekkerianus*), which probably breeds twice a year, and which is said to experience at most two oestrous cycles in a given season (p. 330).

During anoestrus the epithelium lining the cavum uteri consists of low cuboidal cells, and the uterine glands are closely packed. In the " growth " stage (? pro-oestrus) there is " hypertrophy " of the superficial parts of the epithelium, a feature which is stated to be confined to the upper end of the uterus. During the " degenerative " (? late luteal) stage the glands increase in size and number, and there

x*

is generalised congestion of the stroma. The uterine glands are dilated, and their accumulated secretions, as well as extravasations of red cells from the congested superficial capillaries, contribute to the formation of subepithelial " lacunae " and to a patchy desquamation of the mucous membrane which Narayan Rao believes to be menstrual in character. The total amount of blood which is lost into the uterine cavity in this way is, however, small and escapes " in smears."

According to Hill (1933) and most other authorities, the *Lemuroidea* do not undergo menstrual cycles (*see* p. 331).

Suborder TARSIOIDEA

Tarsius

The changes which occur in the ovaries and uterus of *Tarsius spectrum* were first described in 1898 by Stratz, and later in greater detail by van Herwerden in 1905. Both of these investigators based their conclusions upon a study of anatomical material collected in the field.

Van Herwerden describes a phase of endometrial proliferation and progressive glandular development. The mucosa gradually becomes hyperaemic, and red cells collect in the superficial parts of the stroma. A little of the extravasated blood finds its way into the lumen of the uterus, both by diapedesis and through rupture of the surface epithelium.

There appears to be no constant relationship between menstruation and ovulation. A menstrual endometrium was found in specimens whose ovaries contained large follicles or both recent and degenerating corpora lutea. In other specimens an endometrium in the intermenstrual phase was associated with recent corpora lutea.

More recent studies of living captive tarsiers by Catchpole and Fulton (1939, 1943) and Hill, Porter and Southwick (1952) have not clarified this problem. Both groups of workers found occasional erythrocytes in the vagina and, in a few cycles, observed by Hill *et al.*, " definite external bleeding " occurred. Neither they nor Catchpole and Fulton were able to establish the relation of bleeding to the stages of the cycle. On the other hand, Catchpole and Fulton observed a definite vaginal cycle of an average length of about 23 days (p. 331). There is a short stage of full cornification lasting for only 24 hours, which is followed by leucocytic invasion.

Suborder PITHECOIDEA

The Platyrrhine (New World) Monkeys

Families *Cebidae, Hapalidae*

Genera : *Ateles ; Alouatta ; Cebus ; Hapale* (= *Callithrix*)

The vaginal cycle

The spider monkey (*Ateles*) is of unusual interest in the history of primate reproductive physiology, for it was the first New World or platyrrhine species in which the occurrence of slight, but unmistakably menstrual bleeding was clearly established (Goodman and Wislocki, 1935). These authors found that vaginal washings taken from an adult female became tinged with blood at intervals of about 24 to 27 days. The bleeding, which could be traced to the cervix uteri, lasted for three to four days at a time, and was never externally visible. The amount and composition of the sediment obtained from the lavages varied cyclically, as in *Cebus* (*see* below). It may be added that Goodman and Wislocki were unable to produce oestrogen-withdrawal bleeding in the spayed animal previously studied by them in the intact state. A similar failure in experiments on two *Cebus* monkeys was reported by Zuckerman (1935).

In a subsequent study, Dempsey (1939) demonstrated a clear cycle of changes in the vagina of *Ateles*. During the follicular stage there is progressive keratinisation of the outer layer of the vaginal epithelium, resulting in the formation of numerous projecting denticles. These are partially sloughed off in the middle of the cycle, but even during the luteal phase the lumen of the vagina is lined by a distinct layer of cornified cells.

In *Alouatta*, the howler monkey, the vaginal epithelium is lower and less cornified than in *Ateles*, and shows no marked or regular changes. In *Cebus*, the capuchin monkey, there is a well-defined vaginal cycle which averages about 18 days in length (Hamlett, 1939 ; p. 333). At the end of menstruation (when it occurs), the vaginal lavage is clear and, apart from a few squamous cells and leucocytes, consists mainly of small nucleated epithelial cells. During the pre-ovulatory part of the cycle there is an increasing desquamation of cornified cells. Ovulation coincides with a peak in cornification, and is followed by the sudden appearance of leucocytes. This stage only lasts for two to three days, after which the lavage, while sometimes clear, frequently becomes tinged with blood.

The uterine cycle

The microscopic changes in the uterine mucosa of platyrrhine monkeys during the reproductive cycle are basically similar to, but less pronounced than those in the rhesus monkey (p. 622). Progestational changes as a rule are slight, except possibly in marmosets (*see* Wislocki, 1939).

The first histological demonstration of menstruation in platyrrhines was reported by Howard (1930). She noted extensive extravasation and epithelial desquamation in the endometrium, and visible blood in the lumen of the uterus in two *Cebus* monkeys, but did not observe any external (that is, vaginal) bleeding. Howard's findings were confirmed by Dempsey (1939), and extended by Kaiser (1947b). Both workers observed leucocytic infiltration of the stroma and areas of degeneration and desquamation, not only in the surface epithelium but also in that lining the superficial portions of the uterine glands of spider, howler and capuchin monkeys. Erythrocytes were seen both in the mouths of the glands and in the stroma near them, as well as in the lumen of the uterus itself, thus accounting for the microscopic vaginal bleeding referred to above. A striking feature of the menstrual phase in these three species, according to Kaiser, is the remarkably good preservation of the desquamating tissues, which contrasts markedly with their necrotic and disorganised appearance in the macaque.

Kaiser's failure to identify any coiled endometrial arterioles in the three species studied by him is of particular significance, since it indicates that true menstrual disintegration of the uterine mucosa can occur in the absence of these vessels. This point is discussed more fully below (p. 629).

Some observations on the appearance of the endometrium during pregnancy in various platyrrhine monkeys have been published by Wislocki (1929, 1930).

The Catarrhine (Old World) Monkeys

Family *Cercopithecidae*

Subfam. *Cercopithecinae*

Genera : *Macaca ; Papio*

Macaca

The Rhesus Monkey

Changes in the vagina

A definite cycle in the vaginal epithelium of the rhesus monkey (*M. mulatta*) has been described by Westman (1932) and Davis and Hartman (1935). According to Westman, the epithelium at the end of menstruation is low, and consists of a

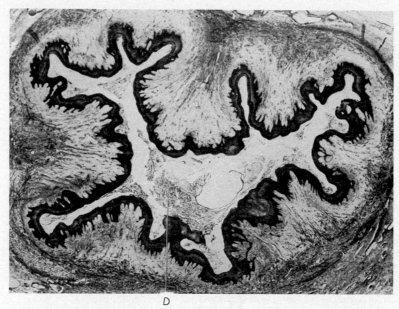

D

Fig. 6. 26—Vagina of the rhesus monkey during the follicular phase of the cycle, showing intense cornification and desquamation (D) of the superficial layers of the epithelium ($\times$ 11).

narrow zone of flattened polyhedral, non-cornified cells, supported by a few basal layers. During the follicular phase these layers proliferate, as a result of which the thickness of the mucosa increases (Fig. 6. 26). At the time of ovulation the epithelium shows : a well-developed basalis displaying numerous mitoses ; an intermediate layer and intra-epithelial band of cornification (the so-called Dierks' layer) ; and a highly cornified superficial zone, the cells of which contain isolated pyknotic nuclei (Davis and Hartman).

Progressive desquamation of the stratum corneum and vacuolisation of its cells occur during the luteal stage ; occasionally, it and the entire functional layer may be lost during this phase (Davis and Hartman). By the first day of menstruation the cornified zone has almost completely disappeared, and the surface of the exposed deeper epithelium presents a ragged appearance, while the subepithelial tissues show marked infiltration by polymorphonuclear leucocytes. These invade the epithelium during the menstrual flow, but disappear gradually after its end, and are almost absent at mid-cycle. In one specimen obtained during an anovulatory cycle, the vagina was very thin, showed only a trace of cornification, and was heavily infiltrated with leucocytes (Westman, 1932). A very similar picture is presented by the vagina during the second half of pregnancy. Following parturition, the mucosa is restored to its previous height (Davis and Hartman, 1935).

According to Van Dyke and Ch'en (1936, 1940), the vaginal mucosa contains a smaller concentration of water, lipids, glycogen and cholesterol during the follicular phase than during the luteal part of the cycle. In the case of lipids, the difference is largely accounted for by a marked increase in phosphatide.

The vaginal smear

The vaginal smear in the rhesus monkey conforms roughly to the general mammalian pattern, in so far as cornified cells predominate, and leucocytes almost disappear at the time of ovulation (Allen, 1927 ; Westman, 1932). De Allende, Shorr and Hartman (1945), using Shorr's modified Masson stain, have made a detailed study of the smear picture and its variations in ovulatory and anovulatory cycles. They recognise a variety of principal cell types, and some 7 different phases in a complete ovulatory cycle. During the stage of macroscopic haemorrhage, the smear consists of erythro- and leucocytes, mucus and cellular debris, as well as basophilic polygonal cells with small to pyknotic nuclei. The number of cornified epithelial cells increases gradually during the post-menstrual and preovulatory phases of the cycle. Just before ovulation there is a sudden rise in the proportion of cornified cells with a striated acidophilic cytoplasm and eccentric darkly-staining nuclei. Ovulation itself is characterised by a peak in the number of fully cornified cells, which may constitute 75–95 per cent of the total cell content of the smear, and by an almost complete disappearance of leucocytes and coagulated mucus. Unfortunately, not all animals behave in this typical fashion, and hence the vaginal smear, while helpful, " does not afford an absolute diagnosis of ovulation."

After ovulation there is a noticeable increase in leucocytes and mucus ; a decrease in the proportion of cornified cells ; and some clumping and folding of the epithelial elements. About 7 or 8 days before the beginning of menstruation, the number of cornified cells rises again, but not as much as in the preovulatory period. It then falls to its lowest relative value (20–25 per cent). This secondary peak appears to be characteristic of the monkey, and does not occur in women.

In cycles unaccompanied by ovulation, the ovulatory and pre- and post-ovulatory phases are missing, and cornification is as a rule not very pronounced. In addition, there is a greater proportion of leucocytes and degenerating cells from the deeper layers of the epithelium than occurs in ovulatory cycles.

The sexual skin

The cyclic histological changes which occur in the sexual skin of the macaque do not appear to have been systematically studied, although the macroscopic features of this area in normal and experimental animals have been investigated extensively (Collings, 1926 ; Allen, 1927 ; Zuckerman, 1930 ; Hartman, 1932 ; Bachman, Collip and Seyle, 1935, 1936 ; Zuckerman, van Wagenen and Gardiner, 1938 ; Eckstein, 1948).

The most striking changes, both in external configuration and microscopic structure, take place between puberty and adolescence, when the sexual skin undergoes its so-called " maturation," an account of which has already been given (p. 139). The histology of the skin in adolescent females has been described by Aykroyd and Zuckerman (1938). In the immature monkey it differs little from that of skin in other parts of the body. The connective-tissue cells of the dermis consist mainly of small and crowded fibroblasts and some mast cells, and mitoses in the dermis and epidermis are rare. During the first (pubertal) phase of maturation mitoses are numerous, and the dermis becomes much thicker. The cellular elements become widely dispersed in the fibrous matrix, so much so that the cross-sectional area occupied by a given number of fibroblasts increases four to six times, compared with normal unswollen skin. Most of this increase is due to an accumulation of intercellular fluid. The fibroblasts themselves also increase in size. In fully-grown animals the connective-tissue cells are less widely dispersed and less swollen than during puberty, and the sexual skin as a whole undergoes no obvious changes other than in colour (*see* p. 336).

The uterus

In normal rhesus monkeys the structure of the endometrium is the same throughout the uterus, but the mucosa is thickest in the midline of the body (where implantation takes place), and decreases towards the sides (Bartelmez, Corner and Hartman, 1951). The appearance of the endometrial glands may vary slightly in different areas of one specimen, or in different uteri representing the same phase of the cycle, but they are rarely cystic and show no branching, except in their basal parts (Fig. 6. 27). The epithelium lining both the glands and the surface consists predominantly of secretory cells, which produce glycogen and mucus. In addition, small groups of ciliated cells can be found during the premenstrual stage, while single narrow elements (so-called " rod " cells ; Bartelmez *et al.*, 1951) may occur at any time. The stroma is made up of a reticular tissue with many connective-tissue cells and abundant ground substance. Macrophages are rare, and decidual cells do not appear except in pregnancy.

According to Daron (1936), the endometrial vessels are of two kinds : small and straight branches which supply the basal third of the mucosa (the " basal arteries "), and large, closely coiled vessels (the " spiral arteries "), which are surrounded by dense stroma, and in histological sections appear as circumscribed " vascular fields." The spiral vessels are continuations of the radial arteries, and extend from the myometrium towards the epithelial surface, before they break up into leashes of precapillary arterioles. They supply most of the middle and the entire superficial zone of the endometrium and, unlike the basal arteries, are distinguished by an abundance of elastic tissue in their walls (Okkels and Engle, 1938 ; *see* also Ramsey, 1949).

The epithelial and stromal elements, and the spiral arteries of the endometrium all undergo periodic changes during the menstrual cycle.

(a) *Histological changes.* The most recent as well as the most comprehensive study of histological changes in the endometrium is that of Bartelmez, Corner and Hartman (1951). It confirms and extends earlier accounts by Sutton (1886), Heape (1896, 1897), Corner (1923), Hartman (1932), Westman (1932) and Bartelmez (1937, 1940).

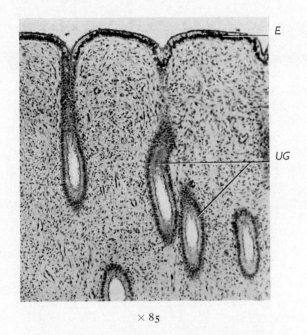

×85

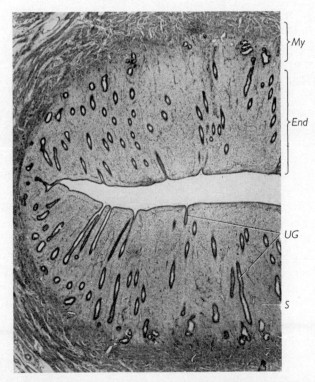

Fig. 6. 27—Endometrium of the rhesus monkey during the follicular phase. ×10. End, endometrium;
My, myometrium; E, epithelium; S, stroma; UG, uterine glands. (From Zuckerman, 1937a.)

The material investigated by Bartelmez, Corner and Hartman consisted of 129 well-preserved and fully documented reproductive tracts. The material was grouped according to the condition of the ovaries, a more reliable method than that based on uterine histology alone, or on menstrual history. Five different stages of the normal cycle (follicular, progravid, regressive, menstrual and repair) are recognised and discussed in detail.

During the early follicular stage (when the ovaries contain no large follicles), the maximum thickness of the endometrium is about 2 mm. The surface epithelium is unbroken, and the glands show frequent mitoses. The stroma is " loose," and extravascular erythrocytes are absent or rare. When large Graafian follicles are present in the ovaries, the endometrium ranges from 3 to 4 mm. in depth, and the incidence of mitoses in the cells of the superficial epithelium is about 6 to 7 per cent, and over 10 per cent in those of the deeper glands (Bensley, 1951). The surface epithelium is smooth, and its nuclei are frequently arranged in two tiers (Fig. 6. 27). There is secretion in the glands and in the uterine lumen ; in the view of Bartelmez and his co-workers, this may be a prerequisite for successful fertilisation. During this phase the endometrium contains over 86 per cent of water, and 2·2 per cent of glycogen (van Dyke and Ch'en, 1936).

In an appreciable number of specimens relating to this early follicular stage, the glands were dilated and tortuous, and resembled the progravid condition more than some uteri that were actually associated with young corpora lutea. It is also of interest that during the late follicular stage extravasated red cells can be frequently seen in the superficial stroma and uterine lumen. Their presence provides an explanation for the mid-cycle or ovulatory bleeding, which is a common occurrence in macaques (see Hartman, 1932, and p. 335).

At the time of ovulation the mucosa becomes a little thinner and less oedematous. The superficial cells of the stroma are enlarged, and there are fewer mitoses in the epithelium of the cavum uteri.

Early in the luteal phase all specimens show sinuous, " saw-toothed " and dilated glands, which contain abundant secretion rich in glycogen (Fig. 6. 28). In the view of Bartelmez et al., this suggests a " change from a secretion adapted to the needs of the spermatozoa to one favorable for the survival of the blastocyst free in the uterine cavity." The epithelium lining the surface and glands is tall and pseudostratified, and appreciable numbers of cells in mitosis persist only in the basal parts of the endometrium. The stroma is generally oedematous, and contains increasing amounts of metachromatic ground substance, while its cellular elements are smaller than during the preceding stage. In a few uteri the stroma is dense, probably because of a delay in the development of the oedema, which invariably occurs in more advanced progravid stages. There is no important difference between non-pregnant and pregnant uteri belonging to this early luteal group.

During the later progravid phase (associated with mature corpora lutea), the endometrium averages about 4 to 5 mm. in thickness. The surface epithelium is relatively low, but the glands have dilated further, and are sacculated (Fig. 6. 28). Their cells vary in size, and are loaded with glycogen, while the total concentration of glycogen in the endometrium during this phase reaches 3·4 per cent (van Dyke and Ch'en, 1936). The stroma is highly oedematous, but there are no decidual cells. On the other hand, uteri traumatised during this stage of the cycle, or while

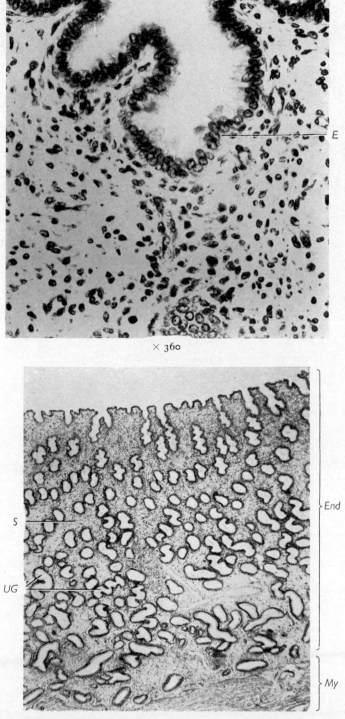

× 360

Fig. 6. 28—Endometrium of the rhesus monkey on the 27th day of the cycle. × 30. The nuclei
of the epithelial cells lining the cavum uteri (E) vary in position (cf. Fig. 6. 27). End,
endometrium ; My, myometrium ; S, stroma ; UG, uterine glands.

under the influence of progesterone, will develop deciduomata (Hisaw, 1935 ; Hisaw, Greep and Fevold, 1937 ; Rossman, 1940).

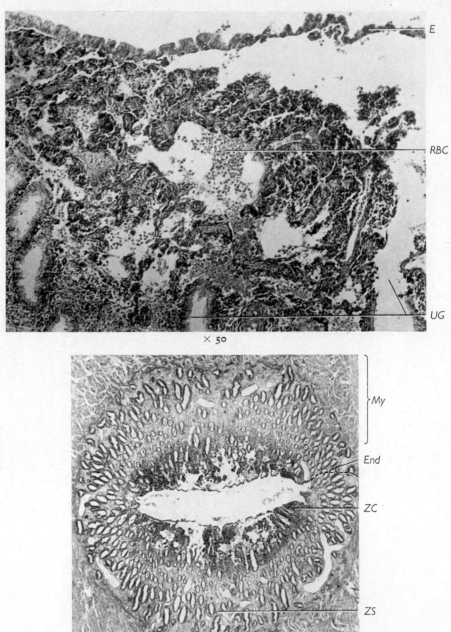

Fig. 6. 29—Menstrual disruption of progestational endometrium of the rhesus monkey.   × 13. End, endometrium ; My, myometrium ; ZC, zona compacta ; ZS, zona spongiosa ; UG, uterine glands ; E, epithelium breaking away from stroma ;   RBC, collection of erythrocytes. (From Zuckerman, 1937b.)

Before menstruation begins, and coinciding with the degeneration of the corpus luteum, the progravid endometrium undergoes involution. The process is characterised by loss of oedema, collapse of capillaries and glands, and by involu-tionary changes in the glandular epithelium.   The endometrial arteries are highly contorted, owing to shrinkage of the mucosa, and some specimens contain arterial emboli (plasma clots) with minute extravasations of erythrocytes. Almost identical changes are shown by pregnant uteri at the time of the implantation bleeding (or " placental-sign ").   A similar phase of premenstrual ischaemia occurs also in endometrial transplants grafted into the anterior chamber of the eye (Markee, 1940), and Bartelmez *et al.* believe that all three conditions are strictly comparable.

Menstruation itself is an extension and exaggeration of this stage of regression. Its gross morphological and histological characters are influenced by the duration and intensity of the preceding progravid (progestational) development.   In men-struation which occurs after ovulation, a variety of different stages, depending on the extent of premenstrual involution, can be observed.   In cases in which this regression is relatively slight, the mucosa on the first day of the flow is about 2 to 3 mm. thick, and possesses a partly-intact to fully-denuded surface epithelium (Fig. 6. 29).   As a rule, extravasation and sloughing involve only the superficial third of the endometrium, contrary to the common belief that the greater part of the uterine mucosa is lost at menstruation.   Thus Westman (1932) found that in a specimen removed on the second day of menstruation, only the compacta had been shed, the spongy layer showing no signs of necrosis and extravasation. However, involution of the stromal cells and loss of intercellular fluid during the menstrual flow (van Dyke and Ch'en, 1936) are pronounced, and account for the subsequent regression of the mucosa, which may eventually be reduced to a total thickness of less than 1 mm. (Bartelmez *et al.*, 1951).   In later stages, too, the lumen of the uterus is distended with the menstrual discharge, and the uterine glands appear as simple tubes (Fig. 6. 29).   The haemorrhagic mass may contain large numbers of leucocytes (Bartelmez, 1933).

After the third day of bleeding mitoses may reappear in the superficial parts of the glands, and rehydration of cells and ground substance in the intermediate zone of the endometrium contribute towards the restoration of the mucosa.   Where menstruation is not preceded by ovulation, the bleeding occurs from an endo-metrium which measures about 1 to 1·5 mm. in thickness, and which in structure resembles the " interval " type described by Corner (1923, 1927).   The glands are well spaced, simple and almost straight, but may occasionally be secreting (Fig. 6. 30).   The stroma is involuted, and variably infiltrated with leucocytes.

The stage of repair begins before the end of external haemorrhage, and may start in one area, while another is still bleeding.   On the third to fourth day of menstruation the depth of the mucous membrane varies between 1 and 3 mm. Resurfacing, which is brought about by the growth of cells from the mouths of glands, is almost complete by that time, as is also the restoration of the superficial capillary network.   The new lining epithelium may be squamous or low columnar, and loose granulation tissue spreads over the arterioles, which are in the process of dedifferentiation (*see* (b), below).   As mitotic activity increases, and with the development of oedema in the zone immediately beneath the epithelium, the uterus resumes the appearance characteristic of the follicular phase.

(b) *Vascular changes.*   A variety of studies have been made to establish the morphological characteristics and cyclic changes of the endometrial arteries. Daron's views (1936) about the nature and arrangement of the vessels have already

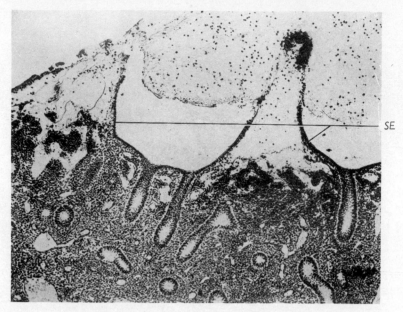

Fig. 6. 30—Menstruation from a follicular (" interval ") type of endometrium (Talapoin monkey).
× 65.   SE, surface epithelium disrupted by haemorrhage.   (From Zuckerman, 1937a.)

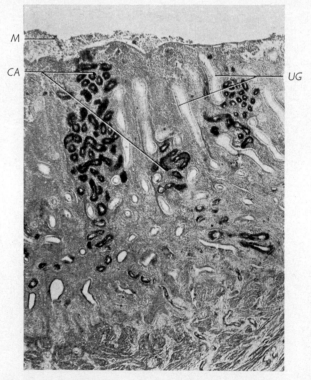

Fig. 6. 31—Coiled arteries forming vascular fields in the endometrium of the menstruating rhesus
monkey.   (Section stained for elastic tissue by Weigert's method ;   × 40.)   CA, coiled artery
immediately beneath superficial epithelial lining ; M, menstrual clot in lumen of uterus ;
UG, uterine glands.   Section lent by Prof. P. L. Krohn.

been summarised above (p. 622). This author points out that during the luteal stage the spiral arteries grow towards the uterine lumen, and that in doing so they become more coiled and acquire thicker and specially differentiated walls (Fig. 6. 31). Just before menstruation their tips can be seen immediately beneath the epithelium, and while bleeding is in progress, their terminal branches and the more peripheral parts of the coiled arteries are destroyed. At the end of the degenerative process only the basal, straight vessels and the deeper parts of the coiled arteries, together with the corresponding zones of the endometrium, remain. During the repair phase the vessels grow into the regenerating mucosa, and become redifferentiated as the spiral arteries of the new endometrium. In anovulatory cycles no such growth occurs, and the arterial pattern remains similar to that in the proliferative phase of the cycle.

This picture of the cyclic growth and differentiation of the endometrial arteries has been used by Markee, in combination with his own observations on endometrial fragments grafted into the eyeball of rhesus monkeys, to evolve an hypothesis of the menstrual mechanism. In his earlier investigations, Markee (1932) had reported rhythmic fluctuations in the vascularity of the uterine mucosa of the macaque, similar to the " blush and blanch " phenomenon previously described by him in the guinea-pig. Markee's subsequent observations (1940, 1947) show that, a few days before the beginning of menstruation, the grafted endometrium decreases rapidly in thickness, a change which can be attributed to the reabsorption of tissue fluid from the stratum spongiosum. This in turn leads to increased coiling of the spiral arteries, vascular stasis and vasoconstriction. In Markee's opinion, vasoconstriction is the outstanding feature in this sequence of events. It is exhibited only by the coiled vessels, in marked contrast to the straight arteries, which maintain a normal circulation in the basal parts of the endometrium throughout menstruation. In the more superficial zones of the endometrium the pronounced vascular " crisis " leads to the formation of multiple minute haematomata, and eventually to the desquamation and disintegration of the endometrium.

This particular concept of menstrual bleeding hinges on the presence of coiled arteries in the endometrium. These occur in catarrhine genera like *Macaca* and *Papio*, as well as in the chimpanzee, but not in at least three types of platyrrhine monkey which, nevertheless, experience periodic microscopic bleeding from a desquamating endometrium; in this respect, the position of the gibbon is somewhat intermediate (Kaiser, 1947a, b ; *see* also p. 633). A further difficulty is introduced by the fact that even in the rhesus monkey, during anovulatory menstruation, the coiled segments of the spiral arteries are smaller and structurally less well differentiated than in ovulatory menstruation, as well as being restricted to the basal zone of the endometrium, and hence to the levels least affected by the menstrual process (Kaiser, 1947a ; 1948).

This complex and controversial subject has been fully discussed in several recent reviews (Reynolds, 1947 ; Ramsey, 1949 ; Zuckerman, 1949, 1951 ; Corner, 1951 ; Bartelmez *et al.*, 1951).

The cervix uteri

The changes undergone by the cervical mucosa during the menstrual cycle and pregnancy have been investigated by Hamilton (1949). According to this author,

the height of the cells of the endocervix varies regularly in ovulatory cycles.   The
most marked increase occurs at about the time of ovulation, and subsidiary peaks
on days 3 and 22 respectively.   At other times the glandular epithelium is much
lower (Fig. 6. 32).   Corresponding variations in the secretory activity and branching
of the cervical glands are noticeable.   According to Westman (1932), most of the
cervical mucus is secreted during the luteal phase.   In anovulatory cycles epithelial
height and secretion are reduced until about the 18th day, but increase markedly
during the premenstrual phase.

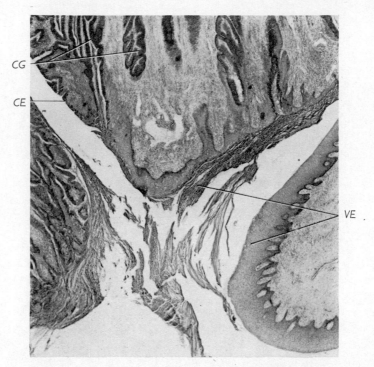

Fig. 6. 32—The external os uteri in the rhesus monkey (× 26).
Transition between desquamating vaginal epithelium (VE)
and columnar epithelium (CE) at the lower end of the cervical
canal. CG, cervical glands. (From Sandys and Zuckerman,
1938.)

The uterine tube

At the middle of the cycle the epithelium of the tube is uniformly tall and even,
and shows marked mitotic activity (Allen, 1938 ; Hartman, 1939).   At that time
secretory cells are abundant, ciliated (non-secretory) cells predominating both at
the beginning and end of the cycle (Westman, 1932).

The Common Macaque

Observations on the character of the vaginal mucosa and smear during the
cycle of the common macaque (*M. irus*) have been made by Joachimovits (1928),
Spiegel (1930, 1950), and Corner (1932).   These authors agree that periodic
changes are generally slight and frequently inconstant, and that they are of little
use in predicting the phase of the menstrual cycle.

Joachimovits (1928) has published an extensive study of the histological changes in the uterus of the common macaque. Apart from minor details, the overall picture and sequence of events appear to be very similar to that in the rhesus monkey and man. Joachimovits stresses the fact that in the common macaque (as in *M. mulatta, see* p. 627) only the superficial zone of the uterine mucosa disintegrates and is eliminated during menstruation. In this respect the catarrhine monkeys, with the possible exception of the baboon (*see* p. 632), appear to differ from man, in whom approximately the inner half of the menstruating endometrium (the so-called functionalis) is cast off (*see* below).

The Bonnet Monkey

Satisfactory vaginal smears are difficult to obtain in both toque and bonnet monkeys (*M. sinica* and *M. radiata*), owing to the presence of a plug of viscid mucus which usually obstructs the vagina and dilutes the sample (*see* p. 341, above). For that reason it is doubtful how much significance can be attached to Hill's observations (1939) of a single and irregularly cyclic toque monkey. In this animal the smear consisted of isolated squamous cells entangled in a mass of mucus. Hill observed a gradual rise in the number of these cells, lasting over a period of 16 days, followed by a sudden drop, after which there was a new increase in squamous cells, accompanied by the appearance of numerous leucocytes. This phase preceded the onset of menstruation by a short interval. In the bonnet macaque (*M. radiata*), too, vaginal desquamation is inconspicuous, cornified cells never constituting more than 10 per cent of the entire cell content of the vagina, compared with a maximum of over 80 per cent in the rhesus monkey (Hartman, 1932, 1938).

According to Hill (1939), the endometrium of *M. sinica* undergoes cyclic changes similar to those which occur in other types of macaque.

Papio

The vaginal cycle

The outstanding features of the vaginal cycle in the baboon are pronounced cornification during the follicular phase, and progressive desquamation of the superficial layers during the luteal part of the cycle (Zuckerman and Parkes, 1932). Proliferation starts during menstruation, and at its end growth and cornification of the vaginal epithelium are well advanced. Growth continues during the follicular phase, and at ovulation the greatly thickened epithelium is completely keratinised and begins to slough off into the vaginal lumen. Desquamation is at its height at the end of the luteal stage, when the epithelium consists only of a basal layer of small and compact cells covered by stratified epithelial cells, and is heavily infiltrated by leucocytes.

The vaginal epithelium is completely inactive during the early part of gestation and lactation. Signs of reactivation are apparent in later stages of pregnancy, and there may be mucification (Zuckerman and Parkes, 1932).

The vaginal smear

The vaginal smear of the baboon has been studied repeatedly (Zuckerman, 1930 ; Gillman, 1935, 1937). Zuckerman reported on a few cycles in an Anubis baboon (*P. anubis*), and a yellow baboon (*P. cynocephalus*), and found that epithelial cornification and desquamation were most intense about the middle of the cycle, when leucocytes were absent.   These reappeared during the phase of subsidence of the sexual skin, and persisted throughout menstruation and the early part of the follicular phase.   Gillman, who studied chacma baboons (*P. porcarius*), divided the vaginal cycle into various phases which can be related to the state of the sexual skin.   During the postmenstrual stage (when the perineum is at rest), mucus, leucocytes and deep epithelial cells predominate.   In the next phase, characterised by pronounced swelling of the sexual skin, leucocytes disappear, and practically all cells are flat and cornified.   As the swelling begins to abate, the squamous cells become wrinkled and aggregated into large masses, externally manifest as a copious, thick, white vaginal discharge.   During the 4th or premenstrual phase the perineum returns to its resting stage, cornified elements are less numerous than deep epithelial cells, and leucocytes reappear.   This is followed by menstruation itself.

The sexual skin cycle

Zuckerman and Parkes (1932) have briefly described the histological changes which occur in the sexual skin of the baboon during the menstrual cycle.   At the time of maximum turgescence the tissue making up the swelling consists of an opalescent white, jelly-like material.   After regression it appears less homogeneous and fibrous.   During the period of swelling the connective-tissue cells are widely dispersed, a change which can be ascribed to an accumulation of intercellular fluid. At that time the density of the subcutaneous tissues, as indicated by the number of nuclei per unit area of skin, is about one-quarter that during the phase of sexual skin subsidence.

The uterine cycle

The cycle of changes in the uterus and cervix of the baboon resembles that of the macaque and man (Zuckerman and Parkes, 1932).   Menstruation, however, appears to be more extensive than in other catarrhines, and involves the inner two-thirds of the endometrium.   The process is of very sudden onset, and affects different endometrial regions to different degrees.   Well-formed and numerous coiled arterioles are present in the uterine mucosa at the time of menstruation (Kaiser 1947a).

The changes in the uterine tube

The uterine tube of the baboon appears to be vascular and active immediately after ovulation.   At menstruation it contains large masses of debris, and what were interpreted as degenerated red cells (Zuckerman and Parkes, 1932).   During lactation the tube shows marked regression, as does the rest of the reproductive tract.

Subfamily *Colobinae*

Semnopithecus

The only detailed histological study of cyclic changes in the uterus of the langur (*S. entellus*) appears to be that of Heape, published in 1894.   Heape's material consisted of some 48 specimens, which he classified on the basis of the state of the endometrium into a number of different stages. The details he furnishes about the condition of the ovaries found in each of these stages suggest, in the light of present knowledge, that many of his observations and some of his interpretations need qualification (*see* Zuckerman, 1931). Thus his finding (1894, 1897) that not one of 42 females had ovulated, is difficult to reconcile with his statement that in 10 of them signs of premenstrual growth of the uterus were present. But, whatever the exact correlations between the ovarian and endometrial cycles, it is clear from Heape's description that the histological sequence of events within the uterus of the langur resembles in all essentials that in other catarrhine species such as the rhesus monkey.

The Anthropoid Apes and Man

Family *Hylobatidae*

Hylobates

The vagina

The vaginal epithelium of the gibbon (*H. lar*) consists of a superficial cornified region supported by a stratified basal zone (Dempsey, 1940). During the follicular phase the outer layer is thick and thrown into numerous folds and hard denticles, similar to those present in certain platyrrhine monkeys (*see* p. 134). This layer becomes considerably reduced in thickness at the time of ovulation, but is still present during the luteal part of the cycle. In spite of these changes in the structure of the surface epithelium, Matthews (1946) states that the vaginal cell content of the gibbon shows very inconstant fluctuations during the menstrual cycle. He studied a young mature female hoolock (*H. hoolock* Harlan) for a number of years, and found that both the number and types of cells present in vaginal lavages varied greatly, but quite irregularly, and could not be correlated with the phase of the menstrual cycle.

The uterus

A few observations on cyclic changes in the uterus of the gibbon have been published by Dempsey (1940). During the follicular phase the surface epithelium consists of a single layer of columnar cells, while the glands arising from it are shallow. During the luteal part of the cycle these glands are conspicuously coiled and extend deeply into the mucosa, which is also markedly thicker than before ovulation. In one uterus Dempsey obtained evidence of a menstruation-like process. This was confirmed by Kaiser (1947a) who, however, found necrotic changes to be slight and the desquamating endometrium to be remarkably well preserved. In this and all other endometria examined by Kaiser, except one, coiled arterioles were present, but appeared " far simpler in all respects " than those of the rhesus monkey during ovulatory menstruation. In the single atypical uterus the surface epithelium was in immediate contact with the myometrium, and there was " no endometrium proper in which a coiled arteriole could occur." Kaiser (1947b) discusses the significance of these findings in relation to views about the mechanism of menstruation (*see* p. 629).

Family *Pongidae*

Genera : *Pan ; Gorilla*

Pan

The cyclic variations in the cytology of the chimpanzee's vagina have been investigated by Tinklepaugh and van Campenhout (1931). According to these authors, the total epithelial cell count is very low at the beginning of the follicular stage, gradually builds up to a maximum a few days before the onset of menstruation, and then falls abruptly, so that by the beginning of the menstrual flow practically no cellular elements other than erythocytes may be present. At the end of menstruation the smear consists of a mixture of epithelial cells. Later, during the follicular phase, completely cornified cells appear, but only persist for a short while, and at the beginning of menstrual haemorrhage the smear consists mainly of clear epithelial cells.

The number of leucocytes varies similarly, but shows no definite relation to the phases of the cycle. Small numbers of red cells are also frequently seen, and are considered by Tinklepaugh and van Campenhout to be traumatic in origin. During the first three months of pregnancy Tinklepaugh (1933) observed a gradual increase in the number of leucocytes, and marked variability in epithelial cells, in spite of the persistence of recurring phases of genital swelling and of sexual receptivity in the female concerned.

There appear to be no detailed studies of histological changes in the uterus during the menstrual cycle, but the process of menstruation is reported to resemble that in the macaque, including the presence of numerous well-developed coiled arteries (Kaiser, 1947a).

Gorilla

There is little information about the microscopic changes undergone by the reproductive tract of the gorilla.

Cyclic changes in the vaginal smear are not very pronounced (Noback, 1939). During the menstrual phase nucleated epithelial cells are scanty. They increase to a maximum during the proliferative stage, and at the time of ovulation there are, in addition, masses of cornified cells. The total epithelial cell count and that of squamous elements drops again during the premenstrual period. Leucocytes are present at all times, and show no regular changes in relation to the phases of the cycle.

The histological appearance of the uterus of a non-gravid gorilla has been briefly described by Wislocki (1932). The endometrium is " active and hypertrophied," and contains numerous branched and slightly serrated glands which secrete freely. The epithelium lining the glands as well as the surface of the mucosa is columnar. The stroma is filled with large fusiform and small round cells, and neither leucocytes nor extravasated red cells are present.

The stage of the cycle at which the specimen was secured is unknown, but the appearance of a section of the endometrium is suggestive of the " interval " or early luteal phase.

Family *Hominidae*

Homo

Changes in the vaginal epithelium

The epithelium of the human vagina, like that of the rhesus monkey (p. 620), is made up of a basal, intermediate and superficial zone. The cyclic changes it undergoes are not as clear-cut as in rats and mice, and consist of quantitative rather than qualitative variations in the character of the cells that are shed into the vaginal lumen. Proliferation of the basal layer and cornification and desquamation of the superficial zone occur at all stages of the cycle, cornification being most marked and the epithelium as a whole best developed at about the time of ovulation. Subsequently, regression sets in, and is most pronounced during the late luteal phase (Papanicolaou, Traut and Marchetti, 1948 ; De Allende and Orías, 1950). Earlier claims (e.g. Dierks, 1927) that the most superficial layers of the epithelium (the so-called " functionalis " and intra-epithelial cornified zone) disintegrate during each menstrual period and subsequently regenerate have not been substantiated (*see* Papanicolaou, 1933 ; Traut, Bloch and Kuder, 1936). The glycogen content of the more superficial epithelial cells appears to be highest during the progestational part of the cycle, and falls just before menstruation (Rakoff, Feo and Goldstein, 1944).

The vaginal smear

The cytological characters of the human vaginal fluid and vaginal smear have been studied in great detail, and appear to be fundamentally similar to those of the rhesus monkey (p. 621), similar cell types occurring under corresponding conditions, and in corresponding stages of the cycle (Papanicolaou, 1933 ; Rubenstein, 1940 ; De Allende, Shorr and Hartman, 1945 ; Papanicolaou *et al.*, 1948 ; De Allende and Orías, 1950 ; Ayre, 1951). A few differences, such as a secondary peak of cornification during the luteal phase of the monkey, which is absent in women, are probably of a minor character.

De Allende and Orías divide the normal vaginal cycle in women into four main stages : a menstrual phase, marked by the presence of erythrocytes ; a post-menstrual stage with a predominance of epithelial cells derived from the intermediate layer of the vaginal epithelium and, on average, some 30 per cent of cornified cells ; the ovulatory phase, characterised by a high proportion (45 per cent to 90 per cent) of cornified cells and by the " clean " appearance of the smear ; and the luteal phase, in which the proportion of cornified elements decreases, while epithelial cells of the intermediate type and leucocytes increase. De Allende and Orías have established an average " curve of cornification " and emphasise that it is impossible to determine the day of the cycle from a single smear, correct appraisal being dependent on the examination of continuous series of daily specimens during a whole cycle.

The smear picture in anovulatory cycles is very variable, but in general conforms to that described for the macaque (p. 621). A study of the cytology of the vaginal smear during the second half of pregnancy has been reported by Pannemans (1951).

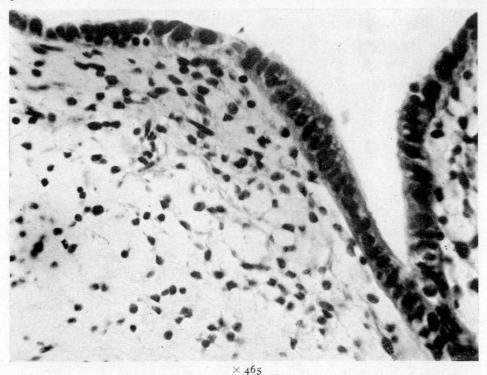

× 465

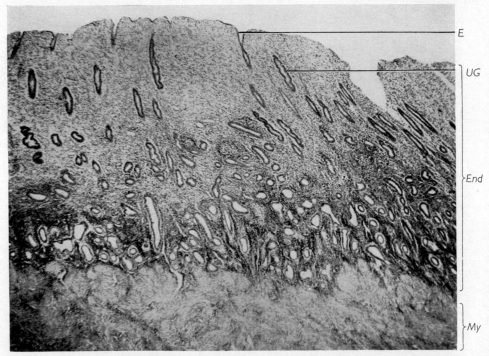

E

UG

End

My

Fig. 6. 33—Human endometrium during the postmenstrual (early proliferative) phase, showing a relatively thin mucosa, loose stroma and straight uterine glands (UG). Beginning epithelialisation (E) of the surface by the outgrowth of cuboidal cells from the basal parts of the glands. × 35. End, endometrium ; My, myometrium. Section lent by Dr. Kathleen Hall.

The uterus

Histological changes in the endometrium.   The physiological nature of the structural changes which take place in the human endometrium during the menstrual
cycle was first recognised by Hitschmann and Adler (1908).   Schröder (1915,
1930) correlated them with the phases of the ovarian cycle and suggested a subdivision into four phases which is still accepted to-day.   Detailed accounts of
these changes can be found in most textbooks of histology (Cowdry, 1932 ; Maximow and Bloom, 1948 ; Stöhr, Jr., 1951) and gynaecology (Williams, 1950 ;
Shaw, 1952), and in many specialised articles or monographs (Joachimovits, 1928 ;
Bartelmez and Bensley, 1932 ; Bartelmez, 1933 ; Papanicolaou, Traut and
Marchetti, 1948).

In general the human endometrial cycle resembles that of the macaque (p. 622).
Active changes are confined to the more superficial parts of the mucosa, and do not
involve the deeper or basal zone.   During menstruation the disrupted surface
begins to be repaired by outgrowths of epithelial cells from the torn glands, and
from such surface epithelium as may not have been destroyed (Fig. 6. 33).   This
process is immediately succeeded by the follicular or " proliferative " phase, in
which the endometrium grows in thickness, the glands lengthening but remaining
straight and relatively narrow, and the stroma becoming increasingly oedematous
(Fig. 6. 33).   Towards the end of this phase the epithelial cells lining the uterine
glands are elongated and have central nuclei.   In ovulatory cycles this stage is
gradually followed by the luteal or " secretory " phase, during which the endometrium reaches its greatest thickness.   The uterine glands dilate and assume a
tortuous or corkscrew-shaped outline (O'Leary, 1929), becoming distended with
secretion.   The epithelial cells lining them become more compact, and their
nuclei take up basal positions.   Globules of secretion containing glycogen collect
near the apices of the cells, and eventually break away from them (Papanicolaou,
Traut and Marchetti, 1948).   Glycogen is also present in the lumina of the glands.
The stroma remains oedematous, and its constituent cells swell and begin to
resemble the decidual cells of early pregnancy.   Many of them collect near the
mouths of the uterine glands beneath the epithelium lining the cavum uteri, and
in this way the functional layer of the endometrium becomes subdivided into a
more superficial compact zone (" stratum compactum ") containing the necks of
the uterine glands, and a deeper or spongy zone (" stratum spongiosum ") made
up largely of the dilated lower segments of the glands (Fig. 6. 34).   The deepest
part of the mucosa, the so-called " basalis," is in intimate contact with the myometrium and contains the blind ends of the uterine glands surrounded by dense stroma.

During the immediate premenstrual or regressive stage of the cycle, vascular
changes predominate (*see* below), and culminate in localised extravasations of
blood and subsequent degeneration of the more superficial parts of the endometrium (Fig. 6. 35b).   This is accompanied by pronounced leucocytic infiltration
of the entire mucosa and disappearance of oedema, as a result of which the endometrium as a whole becomes much thinner.   The superficial parts then break
down and are cast off when menstruation itself begins.   The extent of tissue loss
varies considerably (Bohnen, 1927 ; Joachimovits, 1928 ; Bartelmez, 1931, 1933 ;
see also Bartelmez, Corner and Hartman, 1951), but it seems agreed that the whole
of the compact zone and at least part of the stratum spongiosum are shed in ovulatory menstruation, only the basalis invariably remaining intact.

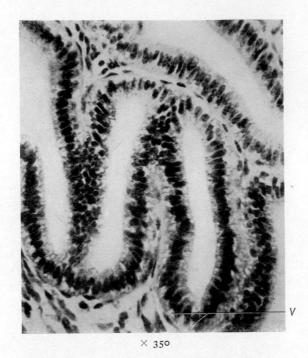

× 350

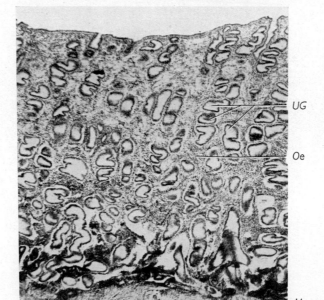

Fig. 6. 34—Human endometrium during the early progestational phase, showing beginning differentiation into a superficial compact and a deeper spongy zone.   Stromal oedema (Oe) and tortuous uterine glands (UG) lined by high columnar epithelial cells with frequent subnuclear (secretion) vacuoles (V) (× 30).   My, myometrium.

In cycles not preceded by ovulation bleeding usually occurs from a proliferative type of endometrium, and much less tissue is lost (Bartelmez, 1933).

Regeneration of the denuded mucosa begins even before the end of macroscopical haemorrhage, and is stated to be practically complete within two to three days after the end of the flow (Shaw, 1952).

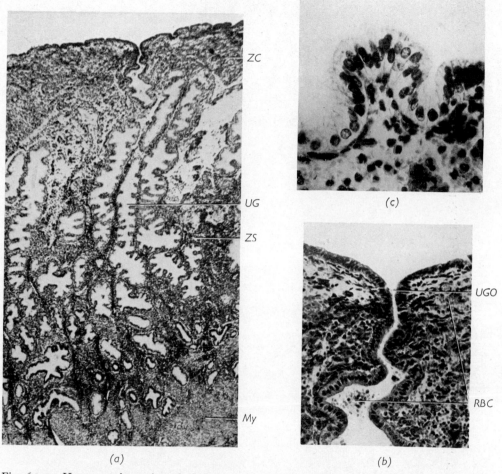

Fig. 6. 35—Human endometrium during the early menstrual phase, showing typical corkscrew appearance of the uterine glands (UG) and extravasation of red blood cells (RBC) into the superficial parts of the endometrium (*a* and *b*). The high columnar tufted epithelium lining the cavum uteri (*c*) is very similar to that found at a comparable stage of the cycle in the uterus of the rhesus monkey (cf. Fig. 6. 28). (*a*) × 40 ; (*b*) × 160 ; (*c*) × 400. UGO, opening of uterine gland ; ZC, zona compacta ; ZS, zona spongiosa ; My, myometrium.

These basic facts have been known for a long time, but the frequency and extent of deviations from the course of events outlined above have only been more recently recognised. Individual variability and non-occurrence of ovulation, particularly evident at the beginning and end of reproductive life, irregularity in the length of the follicular phase (Rossman and Bartelmez, 1946 ; Papanicolaou et al., 1948), or delay in the shedding of the menstrual mucosa (Brewer and Jones, 1947, 1948), all obscure the underlying normal pattern, and may make it difficult to interpret correctly histological specimens obtained at different stages of the human cycle.   Moreover, inadequate methods of fixation often lead to artefacts in the histological appearance of the endometrium (Bartelmez, 1940).

Recent advances in endometrial cytology and histochemistry have been summarised by Vesterdahl-Jørgensen (1950).   Glycogen and muco-polysaccharides occur at all stages of the cycle, but are most conspicuous during the luteal phase. Fat accumulates in the glandular epithelium during the second part of the cycle and disappears before menstruation (Gillman, 1941).   Alkaline phosphatase activity is highest in the first, and becomes progressively reduced during the remainder of the cycle (Atkinson and Engle, 1947; Atkinson, 1950).   Metachromatic staining material appears both in the lumina of the uterine glands (Bartelmez and Bensley, 1932) and in the stroma during the proliferative part of the cycle (Wislocki, Bunting and Dempsey, 1950), and has also been described within the decidual cells (Sylvén, 1945).   According to von Numers (1942), both the ground substance and the reticulum of the stroma undergo cyclic alterations.   In addition, the histological changes accompanying implantation of the ovum and the histochemical properties of the placenta and decidua have received much recent attention (Hertig and Rock, 1944, 1945 ; Hertig, 1946 ; Rock and Hertig, 1948 ; Wislocki and Dempsey, 1945, 1948).

Vascular changes.   Although changes in the blood supply of the human endometrium have been studied intensively, no generally accepted conclusions have emerged, partly because most investigations have necessarily been limited to surgical or post-mortem material.   It is commonly thought, however, that the arrangement of the vessels and the modifications they undergo during the menstrual cycle follow the pattern described by Daron (1936) and Markee (1940) in the rhesus monkey (p. 629).

Numerous arterio-venous anatomoses occur in the human endometrium, and it has been claimed by a Scandinavian school of workers (see Okkels, 1950) that these undergo cyclic changes.

The cervix

The occurrence of well-marked cyclic changes in the epithelium of the human cervix has been asserted by some workers (e.g. Wollner, 1938), and denied by others (e.g. Sjövall, 1938; Bradburn and Webb, 1951).   The consensus of opinion appears to be that such changes, if they exist at all, are slight and more closely correlated with variations in the epithelium of the vagina and ectocervix (the " portio vaginalis ") than with those in the endometrium (*see* Papanicolaou *et al.*, 1948).   On the other hand, there is a definite cycle in the amount, composition and sperm penetrability of the cervical mucus (see p. 356).

During pregnancy the cervix uteri of women and monkeys (p. 340) grows considerably and becomes thin-walled.   The cervical glands develop enormously and secrete large masses of mucus which form a plug to seal the external os (Stieve, 1927 ; Hamilton, 1949; Nesbitt and Hellman, 1952).   Both the cervical mucus and stroma stain metachromatically (Wislocki *et al.*, 1950).

The uterine tube

Cyclic changes in the epithelium of the human uterine tube appear to be slight (Snyder, 1924 ; Novak and Everett, 1928).   During the follicular part of the cycle the epithelium grows rapidly and forms an even border of tall columnar cells of both the ciliated and non-ciliated variety, averaging 30 μ in height. During the luteal phase the epithelium is irregular and averages about 20 μ. The ciliated elements remain unchanged, while the nuclei of the non-ciliated cells vary greatly in shape and size, protruding frequently beyond the limits of the ciliated cells, and may even be extruded into the lumen of the tube (Joël, 1939 ; Papanicolaou *et al.*, 1948). During menstruation the tubal epithelium is at its lowest. The ciliated cells are cuboidal, while the non-ciliated ones are greatly compressed and appear as " peg " cells.

Glycogen is present in both the epithelium and stroma of the tube. According to Joël and Papanicolaou *et al.*, it increases gradually during the follicular phase and reaches a maximum early during the luteal part of the cycle.

Bibliography

AITKEN, W. A. (1927). Some observations on the oestrous cycle and reproductive phenomena of the mare. *J. Amer. vet. med. Ass.*, **70**, 481.

ALLEN, E. (1922). The oestrous cycle in the mouse. *Amer. J. Anat.*, **30**, 297.

—— (1927). The menstrual cycle in the monkey, *Macacus rhesus* : observations on normal animals, the effects of removal of the ovaries and the effects of injections of ovarian and placental extracts into the spayed animals. *Contr. Embryol. Carneg. Instn.*, **19**, 1.

—— (1938). Hyperplasia in the epithelium of the uterine tubes. *Amer. J. Obstet. Gynec.*, **35**, 873.

—— HISAW, F. L., & GARDNER, W. U. (1939). Chap. 8 (The endocrine functions of the ovaries) in *Sex and internal secretions*. Ed. E. Allen. London.

ALLEN, W. M. (1930). Physiology of the corpus luteum. VI. The production of progestational proliferation of the endometrium of the immature rabbit by progestin (an extract of the corpus luteum) after preliminary treatment with oestrin. *Amer. J. Physiol.*, **92**, 612.

—— (1931). I. Cyclical alterations of the endometrium of the rat during the normal cycle, pseudo-pregnancy and pregnancy. II. Production of deciduomata during pregnancy. *Anat. Rec.*, **48**, 65.

ALLENDE, I. L. C. DE, & ORÍAS, O. (1950). *Cytology of the human vagina.* New York.

—— SHORR, E., & HARTMANN, C. G. (1945). A comparative study of the vaginal smear cycle of the rhesus monkey and the human. *Contr. Embryol. Carneg. Instn.*, **31**, 1.

AMOROSO, E. C. (1952). Chap. 15 (" Placentation ") in *Marshall's physiology of reproduction.* 3rd ed., Vol. II. London.

ANAPOLSKY, D. (1928). Cyclic changes in the size of muscle fibers of the Fallopian tube of the sow. *Amer. J. Anat.*, **40**, 459.

ANCEL, P., & BOUIN, P. (1911). Recherches sur les fonctions du corps jaune gestatif. II. Sur le déterminisme du développement de la glande mammaire au cours de la gestation. *J. Physiol. Path. gén.*, **13**, 31.

ARENAS, N., & SAMMARTINO, R. (1939). Le cycle sexuel de la chienne. Etude histologique. *Bull. d'histol. (appliqué à la physiol. et la pathol.)*, **16**, 229.

ASDELL, S. A. (1946). *Patterns of mammalian reproduction.* London.

—— (1947). In *The physiology of domestic animals.* Ed. H. H. Dukes. 6th ed. New York.

ASTWOOD, E. B. (1939). Changes in the weight and water content of the uterus of the normal adult rat. *Amer. J. Physiol.*, **126**, 162.

ATKINSON, W. B. (1950). Studies on the effects of steroid sex hormones on alkaline phosphatase in the endometrium. In *Menstruation and its disorders.* Ed. E. T. Engle. Springfield, Ill.

ATKINSON, W. B., & ENGLE, E. T. (1947). Studies on endometrial alkaline phosphatase during the human menstrual cycle and in the hormone-treated monkey. *Endocrinology*, **40,** 327.

—— & LEATHEM, J. H. (1946). The day to day level of estrogen and progestin during lactation in the mouse. *Anat. Rec.*, **95,** 147.

AYKROYD, O. E., & ZUCKERMAN, S. (1938). Factors in sexual-skin oedema. *J. Physiol.*, **94,** 13.

AYRE, J. E. (1951). *Cancer cytology of the uterus.* New York.

BACHMAN, C., COLLIP, J. B., & SELYE, H. (1935). The effects of prolonged oestriol administration upon the sex skin of *Macaca mulatta*. *Proc. Roy. Soc.* B, **117,** 16.

—— —— —— (1936). Further studies of sex skin reactions in *Macaca mulatta*. *Proc. Soc. exp. Biol., N.Y.*, **33,** 549.

BACSICH, P., & WYBURN, G. M. (1940). Cyclic variations in the vascular architecture of the uterus of the guinea pig. *Trans. Roy. Soc. Edinb.*, **60,** 79.

—— —— (1941). Hormonal analysis of the cyclic variations in the vascular architecture of the uterus of the guinea pig. *Trans. Roy. Soc. Edinb.*, **60,** 465.

BALL, J. (1937). A test for measuring sexual excitability in the female rat. *Comp. Psychol. Monog.*, **14** (No. 1).

BARRINGTON (1913). The variations in the mucin content of the bulbo-urethral glands. *Int. Mschr. Anat. Physiol.*, **30.** (Quoted by Marshall, F. H. A., 1922.)

BARTELMEZ, G. W. (1931). The human uterine mucous membrane during menstruation. *Amer. J. Obstet. Gynec.*, **21,** 623.

—— (1933). Histological studies on the menstruating mucous membrane of the human uterus. *Contr. Embryol. Carneg. Instn.*, **24,** 141.

—— (1937). Menstruation. *Physiol. Rev.*, **17,** 28.

—— (1940). Some effects of fixation and other insults on uterine epithelial cells in primates. *Anat. Rec.*, **77,** 509.

—— & BENSLEY, C. M. (1932). Human uterine gland cells. In *Cowdry's Special Cytology.* 2nd ed., **3,** 1523. New York.

—— CORNER, G. W., & HARTMAN, C. G. (1951). Cyclic changes in the endometrium of the rhesus monkey (*Macaca mulatta*). *Contr. Embryol. Carneg. Instn.*, **34,** 99.

BASSETT, C. F., & LEEKLEY, J. R. (1942). *North Amer. Vet.*, **43,** 454. (Quoted by S. A. Asdell, 1946.)

BENSLEY, C. M. (1951). Cyclic fluctuations in the rate of epithelial mitoses in the endometrium of the rhesus monkey. *Contr. Embryol. Carneg. Instn.*, **34,** 87.

BLANDAU, R. J., BOLING, J. L., & YOUNG, W. C. (1941). The length of heat in the albino rat as determined by the copulatory response. *Anat. Rec.*, **79,** 453.

BOETTIGER, E. G. (1946). Changes in the glycogen and water content of the rat uterus. *J. cell. comp. Physiol.*, **27,** 9.

BOHNEN, P. (1927). Wie weit wird das Endometrium bei der Menstruation abgestossen? *Arch. Gynaek.*, **129,** 459.

BOUIN, P., & ANCEL, P. (1910). Recherches sur les fonctions du corps jaune gestatif. I. Sur le déterminisme de la préparation de l'utérus à la fixation de l'œuf. *J. Physiol. Path. gén.*, **12,** 1.

BOURG, R. (1935). Etudes des modifications provoquées par la gravidine au niveau de l'ovaire et du tractus génital chez la chatte. I. Modifications chez la chatte impubère. *Arch. Biol., Paris*, **46,** 47.

BRADBURN, G. B., & WEBB, C. F. (1951). Cyclic variations in the endocervix. *Amer. J. Obstet. Gynec.*, **62,** 997.

BRAMBELL, F. W. R. (1935). Reproduction in the common shrew (*Sorex araneus* Linnaeus). I. The oestrous cycle of the female. *Philos. Trans.* B, **225,** 1.

—— & DAVIS, D. H. S. (1941). Reproduction of the multimammate mouse (*Mastomys erythroleucus* Temm.) of Sierra Leone. *Proc. zool. Soc. Lond.* B, **111,** 1.

—— & HALL, K. (1936). Reproduction in the lesser shrew (*Sorex minutus* Linnaeus). *Proc. zool. Soc. Lond.*, **1936,** 957.

—— & ROWLANDS, I. W. (1936). Reproduction of the bank vole (*Evotomys glareolus* Schreber). *Philos. Trans.* B, **226,** 71

BREWER, J. I., & JONES, H. O. (1947). Studies on human corpus luteum. Histologic variation in corpora lutea and in corpus luteum. Endometrial relationships at the onset of normal menstruation. *Amer. J. Obstet. Gynec.*, **54**, 561.

—— —— (1948). Studies of the human corpus luteum. Corpus luteum-endometrial relationships in functional uterine bleeding. *Amer. J. Obstet. Gynec.*, **55**, 18.

CASIDA, L. E., & McKENZIE, F. F. (1932). The oestrous cycle of the ewe ; histology of the genital tract. *Univ. Mo. Agric. Exp. Sta. Res. Bull.*, 170. (Quoted by Hamilton, W. J., & Harrison, R. J., 1951.)

CATCHPOLE, H. R., & FULTON, J. F. (1939). Tarsiers in captivity. *Nature, Lond.*, **144**, 514.

—— —— (1943). The oestrous cycle in *Tarsius* : observations on a captive pair. *J. Mammal.*, **24**, 90.

CILLEULS, DES (1914). Recherches sur la signification physiologique de l'amitose. *Arch. Anat. micr.*, **16**, 132. (Quoted by Courrier, R., 1945.)

CLAUBERG, C. (1931). Genitalzyklus und Schwangerschaft bei der weissen Maus (Anatomische Studien an Ovarium, Uterus and Scheide). Dauer des Genitalzyklus. *Arch. Gynaek.*, **147**, 549.

—— (1933). *Die weiblichen Sexualhormone.* Berlin.

COHNEN, K. (1927). Über den Mechanismus der Eiwanderung durch den Eileiter mit besonderer Berücksichtigung der zyklischen Veränderungen am Eileiterepithel des Kaninchens. *Z. mikr.-anat. Forsch.*, **2**, 472. (Quoted by Hansson, A., 1947.)

COLE, H. H. (1930). A study of the mucosa of the genital tract of the cow, with special reference to the cyclic changes. *Amer. J. Anat.*, **46**, 261.

—— & MILLER, R. F. (1935). Changes in the reproductive organs of the ewe with some data bearing on their control. *Amer. J. Anat.*, **57**, 39.

COLLINGS, M. R. (1926). A study of the cutaneous reddening and swelling about the genitalia of the monkey, *Macacus rhesus. Anat. Rec.*, **33**, 271.

CONSTANTINIDES, P. (1947). Progesterone secretion during the oestrous cycle of the unmated rat. *J. Endocrinol.*, **5**, lxiv.

CORNER, G. W. (1921). Cyclic changes in the ovaries and uterus of the sow and their relation to the mechanism of implantation. *Contr. Embryol. Carneg. Instn.*, **13**, 119.

—— (1923). Ovulation and menstruation in *Macacus rhesus. Contr. Embryol. Carneg. Instn.*, **15**, 73.

—— (1927). The relation between menstruation and ovulation in the monkey. *J. Amer. med. Ass.*, **89**, 1838.

—— (1932). The menstrual cycle of the Malayan monkey, *Macaca irus. Anat. Rec.*, **52**, 401.

—— (1951). Our knowledge of the menstrual cycle. *Lancet*, **1**, 919.

COURRIER, R. (1923). La structure de l'épithélium du vagin chez le cobaye et ses modifications. *C. R. Ass. Anat.*, 123. (Quoted by Courrier, R., 1945.)

—— (1924a). Le rythme vaginal du hérisson ; action de l'injection de liquide folliculaire. *C. R. Soc. Biol., Paris*, **90**, 808.

—— (1924b). Le cycle sexuelle chez la femelle des mammifères. Etude de la phase folliculaire. *Arch. Biol., Paris*, **34**, 369.

—— (1926). Modifications vaginales chez la lapine au cours de la vie génitale. *C. R. Soc. Biol., Paris*, **94**, 280.

—— (1930). Structure et histologie de l'appareil génital femelle. *Encyclopédie medicochirurgicale*, 2e éd. Paris.

—— (1945). *Endocrinologie de la gestation.* Paris.

—— & GERLINGER, H. (1922). Le cycle glandulaire de l'epithélium de l'oviducte chez la chienne. *C. R. Soc. Biol., Paris*, **87**, 1363.

—— & GROS, G. (1932). Contribution à l'étude du cycle génital de la chatte. *C. R. Soc. Biol., Paris*, **110**, 275.

—— —— (1933). Données complémentaires sur le cycle génital de la chatte. *C. R. Soc. Biol., Paris*, **114**, 275.

—— & KEHL, R. (1930). Le déciduome expérimental chez la lapine gestante. *C. R. Soc. Biol., Paris*, **104**, 1180.

COWDRY, E. V. (1932). *Special cytology.* 2nd ed. New York.

DARLOW, A. E., & HAWKINS, L. E. (1932). The oestrous cycle in the sheep. *Proc. Amer. Soc. Anim. Prod.*, 205.

DARON, G. H. (1936). The arterial pattern of the tunica mucosa of the uterus in *Macacus rhesus*. *Amer. J. Anat.*, **58**, 349.

DAVIS, M. E., & HARTMAN, C. G. (1935). Changes in vaginal epithelium during pregnancy in relation to the vaginal cycle. *J. Amer. med. Ass.*, **104**, 279.

DAWSON, A. B. (1946). The effects of lactation on the post-partum involution of the uterus of the cat. *Amer. J. Anat.*, **79**, 241.

—— & KOSTERS, B. A. (1944). Preimplantation changes in the uterine mucosa of the cat. *Amer. J. Anat.*, **75**, 1.

DAY, F. T., & MILLER, W. C. (1940). A comparison of the efficiency of methods of diagnosing equine pregnancy, with special reference to the mucin test. *Vet. Rec.*, **52**, 711.

DEANESLY, R. (1934). The reproductive processes of certain mammals. Part VI. The reproductive cycle of the female hedgehog. *Philos. Trans.* B, **223**, 239.

—— (1935). The reproductive processes of certain mammals. Part IX. Growth and reproduction in the stoat (*Mustela erminea*). *Philos. Trans.* B, **225**, 459.

—— (1938). The reproductive cycle of the golden hamster (*Cricetus auratus*). *Proc. zool. Soc. Lond.* A, **108**, 31.

—— (1944). The reproductive cycle of the female weasel (*Mustela nivalis*). *Proc. zool. Soc. Lond.*, **114**, 339.

—— & PARKES, A. S. (1931). The functions of the corpus luteum. V. Changes in the sterile horn during pregnancy, and their relation to changes in the corpus luteum. *Proc. Roy. Soc.* B, **109**, 196.

—— —— (1933). The reproductive processes of certain mammals. IV. The oestrous cycle of the grey squirrel (*Sciurus carolinensis*). *Philos. Trans.* B, **222**, 47.

DEMPSEY, E. W. (1939). The reproductive cycle of New World monkeys. *Amer. J. Anat.*, **64**, 381.

—— (1940). The structure of the reproductive tract in the female gibbon. *Amer. J. Anat.*, **67**, 229.

DIERKS, K. (1927). Der normale mensuelle Zyklus der menschlichen Vaginalschleimhaut. *Arch. Gynaek.*, **130**, 46.

DYKE, H. B. VAN, & CH'EN, G. (1936). Observations on the biochemistry of the genital tract of the female macaque particularly during the menstrual cycle. *Amer. J. Anat.*, **58**, 473.

—— —— (1940). The distribution of lipoids in the genital tract of the monkey at different stages of the menstrual cycle. *Amer. J. Anat.*, **66**, 411.

—— & LI, R. C. (1938). The secretion of progesterone by the cat's ovary following the formation of corpora lutea due to the injection of anterior pituitary extract or prolan. *Chin. J. Physiol.*, **13**, 213. (Quoted by Dawson, A. B., & Kosters, B. A., 1944.)

ECKSTEIN, P. (1948). The growth and development of the rhesus monkey. M.D. thesis. University of Cambridge.

EMERY, F. E., & SCHWABE, E. L. (1936). The vaginal smears of rats as influenced by frequent examinations. *Anat. Rec.*, **64**, 147.

ENGLE, E. T., & SMITH, P. E. (1938). The endometrium of the monkey and estrone-progesterone balance. *Amer. J. Anat.*, **63**, 349.

'ESPINASSE, P. G. (1935). The oviducal epithelium of the mouse. *J. Anat., Lond.*, **69**, 363.

EVANS, H. M., & BISHOP, K. S. (1922). On the relations between fertility and nutrition. II. The ovulation rhythm in the rat on inadequate nutritional regimes. *J. metab. Res.*, **1**, 335.

—— & COLE, H. C. (1931). An introduction to the study of the oestrous cycle in the dog. *Mem. Univ. Calif.*, Vol. 9.

FLUHMANN, C. F. (1928). The reticulo-endothelial cells of the uterus : an experimental study. *Amer. J. Obstet. Gynec.*, **15**, 783.

—— (1932). The influence of sex hormones on the reticulo-endothelial cells of the uterus and a possible application to the treatment of pelvic inflammatory conditions. *Amer. J. Obstet. Gynec.*, **24**, 654.

FLYNN, T. T. (1930).   The uterine cycle of pregnancy and pseudo-pregnancy as it is in the diprodont marsupial *Bettongia cuniculus*.   *Proc. Linn. Soc.*, *N.S.W.*, **55**, 506.

FORD, D. H., WEBSTER, R. L., & YOUNG, W. C. (1951).   Rupture of the vaginal closure membrane during pregnancy in the guinea pig.   *Anat. Rec.*, **109**, 707.

FOSTER, M. A. (1934).   The reproductive cycle in the female ground squirrel *Citellus tridecemlineatus* (Mitchill).   *Amer. J. Anat.*, **54**, 487.

—— & HISAW, F. L. (1935).   Experimental ovulation and the resulting pseudopregnancy in anoestrous cats.   *Anat. Rec.*, **62**, 75.

FRIEDLÄNDER, C. (1870).   *Physiologisch-anatomische Untersuchungen über den Uterus.* Leipzig.

FRIEDMAN, M. H. (1938).   Criteria for the selection of oestrous rabbits.   The significance of occasional factors.   *Endocrinology*, **22**, 354.

GERLINGER, H. (1923).   Le cycle oestrien de l'utérus chez la chienne et ses rapports chronologiques avec le cycle oestrien de l'ovaire.   *C. R. Soc. Biol.*, *Paris*, **89**, 193.

—— (1925).   *Le cycle sexuel chez la femelle des Mammifères.*   Recherches sur la chienne. Thèse en medicine.   Strasbourg.

GILLMAN, J. (1935).   The cyclical changes in the external genital organs of the baboon (*P. porcarius*).   *S. Afr. J. Sci.*, **32**, 342.

—— (1937).   The cyclical changes in the vaginal smear in the baboon and its relationship to the perineal swelling.   *S. Afr. J. med. Sci.*, **2**, 44.

—— (1941).   The lipines in the human endometrium during the menstrual cycle and pregnancy and their relationship to the metabolism of oestrogen and progesterone. *S. Afr. J. med. Sci.*, **6**, 59.

GODET, R. (1947).   Variations périodiques de la structure du repli balano-préputial chez la taupe de sexe femelle.   *C. R. Soc. Biol.*, *Paris*, **225**, 145.

GOODMAN, L., & WISLOCKI, G. B. (1935).   Cyclical uterine bleeding in a New World monkey (*Ateles geoffroyi*).   *Anat. Rec.*, **61**, 379.

GRANT, F. (1934).   Studies on the physiology of reproduction in the ewe.   Part II. Changes in the vagina and cervix.   *Trans. Roy. Soc. Edinb.*, **58**, 16.

GRIFFITHS, W. F. B., & AMOROSO, E. C. (1939).   Prooestrus, oestrus, ovulation and mating in the greyhound bitch.   *Vet. Rec.*, **51**, 1279.

GROS, G. (1933).   Recherches préliminaires sur le cycle génital chez la chatte.   *Bull. Histol. Tech. micr.*, **10**, 5.

—— (1935).   Evolution de la muqueuse utérine chez la chatte.   *C. R. Soc. Biol.*, *Paris*, **118**, 1575.

—— (1936).   Contribution à l'endocrinologie sexuelle.   Le cycle génital de la chatte. *Thèse, Université d'Alger.*, No. 21.

GROSSER, O. (1903).   Die physiologische bindegewebige Atresie des Genitalkanals von *Vesperugo noctula* nach erfolgter Kohabitation.   *Anat. Anz.*, **23**, 129.   (Quoted by Hartman, C. G., 1933.)

GUTHRIE, M. J. (1933).   The reproductive cycles of some cave bats.   *J. Mammal.*, **14**, 199.

HAMILTON, C. E. (1947).   The cervix uteri of the rat.   *Anat. Rec.*, **97**, 47.

—— (1949).   Observations on the cervical mucosa of the rhesus monkey.   *Contr. Embryol. Carneg. Instn.*, **33**, 81.

—— (1951).   Evidences of cyclic reproductive phenomena in the rabbit.   *Anat. Rec.*, **110**, 557.

HAMILTON, W. J. (1933).   The restoration and regeneration of the epithelium and endometrium of the uterus of *Cavia* post partum in non-pregnant animals.   *Trans. Roy. Soc. Edinb.*, **57**, 593.

—— & GOULD, J. H. (1940).   The normal oestrous cycle of the ferret : the correlation of the vaginal smear and the histology of the genital tract, with notes on the distribution of glycogen, the incidence of growth and the reaction to intravitam staining by trypan blue.   *Trans. Roy. Soc. Edinb.*, **60**, 87.

—— & HARRISON, R. J. (1951).   Cyclical changes in the uterine mucosa and vagina of the goat.   *J. Anat.*, *Lond.*, **85**, 316.

HAMLETT, G. W. D. (1932).   The reproductive cycle in the armadillo.   *Z. wiss. Zool.*, **141**, 143.

HAMLETT, G. W. D. (1934). Uterine bleeding in a bat, *Glossophaga soricina*. *Anat. Rec.*, **60**, 9.

—— (1939). Reproduction in American monkeys. I. Estrous cycle, ovulation and menstruation in *Cebus*. *Anat. Rec.*, **73**, 171.

HAMMOND, J. (1925). *Reproduction in the rabbit*. Edinburgh ; London.

—— (1927). *The physiology of reproduction in the cow*. Cambridge.

—— (1940). *Farm animals*. London.

—— & MARSHALL, F. H. A. (1914). The functional correlation between the ovaries, uterus, and mammary glands in the rabbit, with observations on the oestrous cycle. *Proc. Roy. Soc.* B, **87**, 422.

—— —— (1930). Oestrus and pseudopregnancy in the ferret. *Proc. Roy. Soc.* B, **105**, 607.

—— & WODZICKI, K. (1941). Anatomical and histological changes during the oestrous cycle of the mare. *Proc. Roy. Soc.* B, **130**, 1.

HANSSON, A. (1947). The physiology of reproduction in mink (*Mustela vison*, Schreb.), with special reference to delayed implantation. *Acta zool.*, *Stockh.*, **28**, 1.

HARRISON, R. J. (1949). Observations on the female reproductive organs of the Ca'aing whale *Globiocephala melaena* Traill. *J. Anat.*, *Lond.*, **83**, 238.

HARTMAN, C. G. (1923). The oestrous cycle in the opossum. *Amer. J. Anat.*, **32**, 353.

—— (1932). Studies in the reproduction of the monkey, *Macacus (Pithecus) rhesus*, with special reference to menstruation and pregnancy. *Contr. Embryol. Carneg. Instn.*, **23**, 1.

—— (1938). Some observations on the bonnet macaque. *J. Mammal.*, **19**, 468.

—— (1939). In *Sex and internal secretion*. Ed. E. Allen. London.

—— (1944). Some new observations on the vaginal smear of the rat. *Yale J. Biol. Med.*, **17**, 99.

HEAPE, W. (1894). The menstruation of *Semnopithecus entellus*. *Philos. Trans.* B, **185**, 411.

—— (1896). The menstruation and ovulation of Macacus rhesus. *Proc. Roy. Soc.* B, **60**, 202.

—— (1897). The menstruation and ovulation of *Macacus rhesus*, with observations on the changes undergone by the discharged follicle. Part II. *Philos. Trans.* B, **188**, 135.

HERTIG, A. T. (1946). Diagnosing the endometrial biopsy. In *Proceedings of the conference on diagnosis in sterility*. Ed. E. T. Engle. Springfield, Ill.

—— & ROCK, J. (1944). On the development of the early human ovum, with special reference to the trophoblast of the previllous stage : a description of 7 normal and 5 pathologic human ova. *Amer. J. Obstet. Gynec.*, **47**, 149.

—— —— (1945). Two human ova of the pre-villous stage, having a developmental age of about seven and nine days respectively. *Contr. Embryol. Carneg. Instn.*, **31**, 65.

HERWERDEN, M. A. VAN (1905). *Bijdrage tot de Kennis van den menstrueelen Cyclus*. Leiden.

HILL, C. J. (1933). The development of Monotremata. Part I. The histology of the oviduct during gestation. *Trans. zool. Soc. Lond.*, **21**, 413.

—— (1941). The development of the Monotremata. Part V. Further observations on the histology and the secretory activities of the oviduct prior to and during gestation. *Trans. zool. Soc. Lond.*, **25**, 1.

HILL, J. P., & O'DONOGHUE, C. H. (1913). The reproductive cycle in the marsupial *Dasyurus viverrinus*. *Quart. J. micr. Sci.*, **59**, 133.

HILL, W. C. O. (1933). A monograph on the genus *Loris*. With an account of the external, cranial and dental characters of the genus : a revision of the known forms ; and the description of a new form from Northern Ceylon. *Ceylon J. Sci.* B, **18**, 89.

—— (1939). The menstrual cycle of the toque macaque (*Macaca sinica* Linn.), with observations on its uterine structure, compared with that of other macaques. *Ceylon J. Sci.* D, **5**, 21.

—— PORTER, A., & SOUTHWICK, M. D. (1952). The natural history, endoparasites and pseudoparasites of the tarsiers (*Tarsius carbonarius*) recently living in the Society's gardens. *Proc. zool. Soc. Lond.*, **122**, 79.

Hisaw, F. L. (1935). The physiology of menstruation in macacus rhesus monkeys. I. Influence of the follicular and corpus luteum hormones. II. Effects of anterior pituitary extracts. *Amer. J. Obstet. Gynec.*, **29**, 638.

—— (1944). The placental gonadotrophin and luteal function in monkeys (*Macaca mulatta*). *Yale J. Biol. Med.*, **17**, 119.

—— Greep, R. O., & Fevold, H. L. (1937). The effects of oestrin-progestin combinations on the endometrium, vagina and sexual skin of monkeys. *Amer. J. Anat.*, **61**, 483.

Hitschmann, F., & Adler, L. (1908). Der Bau der Uterusschleimhaut des geschlechtsreifen Weibes mit besonderer Berücksichtigung der Menstruation. *Mschr. Geburtsh. Gynäk.*, **27**, 1.

Horst, C. J. van der (1949–1950). An early stage of placentation in the aardvark, *Orycteropus*. *Proc. zool. Soc. Lond.*, **119**, 1.

—— & Gillman, J. (1941). The menstrual cycle in *Elephantulus*. *S. Afr. J. med. Sci.*, **6**, 27.

—— —— (1942a). Pre-implantation phenomena in the uterus of *Elephantulus*. *S. Afr. J. med. Sci.*, **7**, 47.

—— —— (1942b). A critical analysis of the early gravid and post-menstrual phenomena in the uterus of *Elephantulus*, *Macaca* and the human female. *S. Afr. J. med. Sci.*, **7**, 134.

—— —— (1942c). The spontaneous development of deciduomata in *Elephantulus*. *S. Afr. J. med. Sci.*, **7**, 127.

—— —— (1942d). Pre-implantation abortion in *Elephantulus*. *S. Afr. J. med. Sci.*, **7**, 120.

Howard, E. (1930). The X-zone of the suprarenal cortex in relation to gonadal maturation in monkeys and mice and to epiphyseal unions in monkeys. *Anat. Rec.*, **46**, 93.

Joachimovits, R. (1928). Studien zu Menstruation, Ovulation, Aufbau und Pathologie des weiblichen Genitales bei Mensch und Affe (*Pithecus fascicularis mordax*). *Biol. Gen.*, **4**, 447.

Joël, K. (1939). The glycogen content of the Fallopian tube during the menstrual cycle and during pregnancy. *J. Obstet. Gynaec., Brit. Emp.*, **46**, 731.

Johnson, G. E., Foster, M. A., & Coco, R. M. (1933). The sexual cycle of the thirteen-lined ground squirrel in the laboratory. *Trans. Kans. Acad. Sci.*, **36**, 250.

Jurow, H. N. (1943). Cyclic variations in the cervix of the guinea pig. *Amer. J. Obstet. Gynec.*, **45**, 762.

Kaiser, I. H. (1947a). Histological appearance of coiled arterioles in the endometrium of rhesus monkey, baboon, chimpanzee and gibbon. *Anat. Rec.*, **99**, 199.

—— (1947b). Absence of coiled arterioles in the endometrium of menstruating new world monkeys. *Anat. Rec.*, **99**, 353.

—— (1948). Failure of massive doses of estrogen to promote growth of endometrial coiled arterioles. *Endocrinology*, **43**, 127.

Kakushkina, E. A. (1937). The normal reproductive cycle of silver foxes. *Bull. Biol. Med. Exp., U.S.S.R.*, **4**, 26.

Kazzander, J. (1890). Über die Pigmentation der Uterinschleimhaut des Schafes. *Arch. mikr. Anat.*, **36**, 507. (Quoted by Cole, H. H., & Miller, R. F., 1935.)

Keller, K. (1909). Über den Bau des Endometriums beim Hunde mit besonderer Berücksichtigung der cyklischen Veränderungen an den Uterindrüsen. *Anat. Hefte (Wiesb.)*, **39**, 307.

Kelly, G. L. (1929). The histological transformations in the vaginal epithelium of the guinea pig. *Amer. J. Anat.*, **43**, 247.

Kent, Jr., G. C., & Smith, R. A. (1945). A study of the estrous cycle in the golden hamster (*Cricetus* (*Mesocricetus*) *auratus* Waterhouse). *Anat. Rec.*, **92**, 263.

Klein, M. (1933). La muqueuse utérine de la lapine. Contribution à l'histophysiologie des muqueuses. *Bull. Histol. Tech. micr.*, **10**, 227.

—— (1937). The mucification of the vaginal epithelium in rodents. *Proc. Roy. Soc. B*, **124**, 23.

KNAUS, H. (1928). Experimentelle Untersuchungen zur Physiologie und Pharmakologie der Uterusmuskulatur im Puerperium. *Arch. exp. Path. Pharmak.*, **134**, 225.

—— (1930). Über die Funktion des Corpus luteum. *Klin. Wschr.*, **9**, 961.

—— (1950). *Die Physiologie der Zeugung des Menschen.* Wien.

KOHLBRUGGE, J. H. F. (1904). Das bei der Menstruation ausgestossene Ei. *Z. Morph. Anthr.*, **12**, 579. (Quoted by Hamlett, G. W. D., 1934.)

—— (1913). Befruchtung und Keimbildung bei der Fledermaus *Xantharpya amplexicaudata*. *Verh. Akad. Wet.*, *Amst.*, Sect. 2, Deel 17, 1.

KOSTITCH, A., & TÉLÉBAKOVITCH, A. (1929). Sur un rythme vaginal chez les animaux ovariectomisés. *C. R. Soc. Biol.*, *Paris*, **100**, 51.

KRICHESKY, P., & GLASS, S. J. (1947). Vaginal cornification in spayed rats by intravaginal application of non-estrogenic substances. *Endocrinology*, **41**, 196.

KRUPSKI, A. (1917). Beiträge zur Physiologie der weiblichen Sexualorgane des Rindes. *Schweiz. Arch. Tierheilk.*, **59**, 1.

KUNDE, M. M., & PROUD, T. (1929). The ineffectiveness of vaginal smears in predicting the oestrous cycle in the rabbit. *Amer. J. Physiol.*, **88**, 446.

LASCH, W. (1949). Zur Kenntnis der Formelemente des Vaginalabstrichs bei *Microtus guentheri D. et A.* vom Beginn der Paarung bis zur Geburt. *Ann. paediatr.*, **172**, 352.

LATASTE, F. (1892). Transformation périodique de l'épithélium du vagin des rongeurs (Rythme vaginal). *C. R. Soc. Biol.*, *Paris*, **44**, 765.

—— (1893). Rythme vaginal des mammifères. *C. R. Soc. Biol.*, *Paris*, **45**, 135.

LEUCKART, R. (1847). *Zur Morphologie und Anatomie der Geschlechtsorgane.* Göttingen. (Quoted by Stockard, C. R., & Papanicolaou, G. N., 1919.)

LICHE, H. (1939). Oestrous cycle in the cat. *Nature, Lond.*, **143**, 900.

—— & WODZICKI, K. (1939). Vaginal smears and the oestrous cycle of the cat and lioness. *Nature, Lond.*, **144**, 245.

LOEB, L. (1914). The correlation between the cyclic changes in the uterus and the ovaries in the guinea-pig. *Biol. Bull.*, *Wood's Hole*, **27**, 1.

LONG, J. A., & EVANS, H. M. (1922). The oestrous cycle in the rat and its associated phenomena. *Mem. Univ. Calif.*, Vol. 6.

MACKINTOSH, N. A., & WHEELER, J. F. G. (1929). Southern blue and fin whales. "*Discovery*" *Rep.*, **1**, 257.

MANDL, A. M. (1951a). The phases of the oestrous cycle in the adult white rat. *J exp. Biol.*, **28**, 576.

—— (1951b). Cyclical changes in the vaginal smear of adult ovariectomized rats. *J exp. Biol.*, **28**, 585.

MARKEE, J. E. (1932). Rhythmic vascular uterine changes. *Amer. J. Physiol.*, **100**, 32.

—— (1940). Menstruation in intraocular endometrial transplants in the rhesus monkey. *Contr. Embryol. Carneg. Instn.*, **28**, 219.

—— (1947). In *Progress in Gynaecology*. Ed. T. V. Meigs, & S. H. Sturgis. London.

—— & HINSEY, J. C. (1935a). A case of probable superfetation in the cat. *Anat. Rec.*, **61**, 241.

—— —— (1935b). Studies on uterine growth. II. A local factor in the pregnant uterus of the cat. *Anat. Rec.*, **61**, 311.

MARSHALL, A. J. (1949). Pre-gestational changes in the giant fruit bat (*Pteropus giganteus*) with special reference to asymmetric endometrial reaction. *Proc. Linn. Soc.*, *Lond.*, **161**, 26.

MARSHALL, F. H. A. (1903). The oestrous cycle and the formation of the corpus luteum in the sheep. *Philos. Trans.* B, **196**, 47.

—— (1904). The oestrous cycle in the common ferret. *Quart. J. micr. Sci.*, **48**, 323.

—— (1922). *The physiology of reproduction.* 2nd ed. London.

—— (1933). Cyclical changes in the vagina and vulva of the ferret. *Quart. J. exp. Physiol.*, **23**, 131.

—— & HALNAN, E. T. (1917). On the post-oestrous changes occuring in the generative organs and mammary glands of the non-pregnant dog. *Proc. Roy. Soc.* B, **89**, 546.

MARSHALL, F. H. A., & JOLLY, W. A. (1906).   Contributions to the physiology of mammalian
    reproduction.   Part I.   The oestrous cycle in the dog.   *Philos. Trans.* B, **198**, 99.
MATTHEWS, L. H. (1935).   The oestrous cycle and intersexuality in the female mole (*Talpa
    europaea* Linn.).   *Proc. zool. Soc. Lond.*, **1935**, 347.
—— (1937).   The female sexual cycle in the British horse-shoe bats, *Rhinolophus ferrum-
    equinum insulanus* Barrett-Hamilton and *R hippodiseros minutus* Montagu.   *Trans.
    zool. Soc. Lond.*, **23**, 213.
—— (1941a).   Reproduction in the spotted hyaena, *Crocuta crocuta* (Erxleben).   *Philos.
    Trans.* B, **230**, 1.
—— (1941b).   Reproduction in the Scottish wild cat, *Felis sylvestris grampia* Miller.   *Proc.
    zool. Soc. Lond.* B, **111**, 59.
—— (1941c).   Notes on the genitalia and reproduction of some African bats.   *Proc. zool.
    Soc. Lond.* B, **111**, 289.
—— (1946).   Notes on the genital anatomy and physiology of the gibbon (*Hylobates*).
    Proc. zool. Soc. Lond., **116**, 339.
—— (1948).   Cyclic changes in the uterine mucosa of balaenopterid whales.   *J. Anat.,
    Lond.*, **82**, 207.
MAXIMOW, A. A., & BLOOM, W. (1948).   *A textbook of histology.*   5th ed.   Philadelphia,
    London.
McKENZIE, F. F. (1926).   The normal oestrous cycle in the sow.   *Univ. Missouri Coll.
    Agric. Res. Bull.*, No. 86.
—— & PHILLIPS, R. W. (1931).   Some observations on the estrual cycle in the sheep.
    Proc. Amer. Soc. Anim. Prod., 138.
—— & TERRILL, C. E. (1937).   Estrus, ovulation and related phenomena in the ewe.
    Univ. Missouri Coll. Agr. Res. Bull., No. 264.
McPHAIL, M. K. (1934).   The assay of progestin.   *J. Physiol.*, **83**, 145.
MEYER, B. J., & MEYER, R. K. (1944).   Growth and reproduction of the cotton rat, *Sig-
    modon hispidus hispidus*, under laboratory conditions.   *J. Mammal.*, **25**, 107.
MEYER, R. K., & SAIKI, S. (1931).   Homology of prooestrous bleeding in the dog.   *Proc
    Soc. exp. Biol., N.Y.*, **29**, 301.
MORAU, H. (1889).   Des transformations épithéliales, physiologiques et pathologiques.
    Thèse de Paris.   (Quoted by Lataste, F., 1892.)
MOREAUX, R. (1913).   Recherches sur la morphologie et la fonction glandulaire de
    l'épithélium de la trompe utérine chez les mammifères.   *Arch. Anat. micr.*,
    14, 515.
MORGAN, C. F. (1946a).   Sexual rhythms in the reproductive tract of the adult female
    opossum and effects of hormonal treatments.   *Amer. J. Anat.*, **78**, 411.
—— (1946b).   The occurrence of argentaffine cells in the uterus of the opossum.   *Anat.
    Rec. (Proc.)*, **94**, 390.
MULLIGAN, R. M. (1942).   Histological studies on the canine female genital tract.   *J
    Morph.*, **71**, 431.
MURPHEY, H. S. (1924).   Studies of the oestrous or genital cycle of the ox.   *J. Amer. vet.
    med. Ass.*, **65**, 598.
NARAYAN RAO, C. R. (1927).   Observations on the habits of *Loris lydekkerianus*.   *J. Mysore
    Univ.*, **1**, 57.
—— (1932).   On the occurrence of glycogen and fat in liquor folliculi and uterine secretion
    in *Loris lydekkerianus*.   *J. Mysore Univ.*, **6**, 140.
NESBITT, R. E. L., & HELLMAN, I. M. (1952).   The histopathology and cytology of the
    cervix in pregnancy.   *Surg. Gynec. Obstet.*, **94**, 10.
NICHOLAS, J. S. (1949).   Chapter 4 (Experimental methods and rat embryos) in *The rat in
    laboratory investigation.*   Ed. E. J. Farris, & J. Q. Griffith, Jr.   2nd ed.   Phila-
    delphia, London, Montreal.
NICOL, T. (1932).   The uterus of *Cavia* after intravitam staining with Trypan blue.   Pre-
    liminary note.   *J. Anat., Lond.*, **66**, 181.
—— (1933).   Studies on the reproductive system in the guinea-pig ; variations in the
    oestrous cycle of the virgin animal, after parturition, and during pregnancy.   *Proc.
    Roy. Soc. Edinb.*, **53**, 220.

NICOL, T. (1935). The female reproductive system in the guinea-pig—intravitam stain-ing; fat production; influence of hormones. *Trans. Roy. Soc. Edinb.*, **58**, 449.

NOBACK, C. R. (1939). The changes in the vaginal smears and associated cyclic pheno-mena in the lowland gorilla (*Gorilla gorilla*). *Anat. Rec.*, **73**, 209.

NOVAK, E., & EVERETT, H. S. (1928). Cyclical and other variations in the tubal epithelium. *Amer. J. Obstet. Gynec.*, **16**, 449.

NUMERS, C. VON (1942). Über die Zellformen des Stromagewebes der menschlichen Gebärmutterschleimhaut. *Acta obstet. gynec. scand.*, **22** (Suppl. III).

O'DONOGHUE, C. H. (1911). The growth changes in the mammary apparatus of *Dasyurus* and the relation of the corpora lutea thereto. *Quart. J. micr. Sci.*, **57**, 187.

OKEY, R., BLOOR, W. R., & CORNER, G. W. (1930). The variations in the lipids of the uterine mucosa in the pig. *J. biol. Chem.*, **86**, 307.

OKKELS, H. (1950). Chap. 2 (The vascular anatomy of the adult human uterus). In *Modern trends in obstetrics and gynaecology*. Ed. K. Bowes. London.

—— & ENGLE, E. T. (1938). Studies on the finer structure of the uterine blood vessels of the *Macacus* monkey. *Acta path. microbiol. scand.*, **15**, 150.

O'LEARY, J. L. (1929). Form changes in the human uterine gland during the menstrual cycle and in early pregnancy. *Amer. J. Anat.*, **43**, 289.

PANNEMANS, K. (1951). Etude du frottis vaginal entre le sixieme et le huitième mois de la grossesse. *Bruxelles-med.* **31**, 2303. (Cited in Quart. Rev. Obst. Gyn., 195.)

PAPANICOLAOU, G. N. (1933). The sexual cycle in the human female as revealed by vaginal smears. *Amer. J. Anat.*, **52**, 519.

—— TRAUT, H. F., & MARCHETTI, A. A. (1948). *The epithelia of woman's reproductive organs.* New York.

PARKER, G. H. (1931). The passage of sperms and of eggs through the oviducts in terres-trial vertebrates. *Philos. Trans.* B, **219**, 381.

PARKES, A. S. (1926). Observations on the oestrous cycle of the albino mouse. *Proc. Roy. Soc.* B, **100**, 151.

—— (1928). The length of the oestrous cycle in the unmated normal mouse : records of one thousand cycles. *Brit. J. exp. Biol.*, **5**, 371.

—— (1929a). The functions of the corpus luteum. II. The experimental production of placentomata in the mouse. *Proc. Roy. Soc.* B, **104**, 183.

—— (1929b). *The internal secretions of the ovary.* London, New York, Toronto.

—— (1930). The functions of the corpus luteum. IV. The relation of oestrin to the luteal phase of the oestrous cycle. *Proc. Roy. Soc.* B, **107**, 188.

—— (1931). The reproductive processes of certain mammals. Part I. The oestrous cycle of the Chinese hamster (*Cricetulus griseus*). *Proc. Roy. Soc.* B, **108**, 138.

PEARSON, O. P. (1944). Reproduction in the shrew (*Blarina brevicauda* Say). *Amer. J. Anat.*, **75**, 39.

PECZENIK, O. (1942). Actions of sex hormones on oestrous cycle and reproduction of the golden hamster. *J. Endocrinol.*, **3**, 157.

POLOVTZEVA, V., & FOMENKO, M. (1933). The determination of the time of ovulation in the sheep by vaginal smears. *Probl. Zlintn.*, No. **5**, 95.

POMMERENKE, W. T., & VIERGIVER, E. (1947). Relationship between cervical mucus and basal temperature cycles. *Amer. J. Obstet. Gynec.*, **54**, 676.

QUINLAN, J., & MARÉ, G. S. (1931). The physiological changes in the ovary of the merino sheep in South Africa, and their practical application in breeding. *17th Rep. Vet. Res.*, *S.A.*, 663.

RAKOFF, A. E., FEO, L. G., & GOLDSTEIN, L. (1944). The biologic characteristics of the normal vagina. *Amer. J. Obstet. Gynec.*, **47**, 467.

RAMSEY, E. M. (1949). The vascular pattern of the endometrium of the pregnant rhesus monkey (*Macaca mulatta*). *Contr. Embryol. Carneg. Instn.*, **33**, 113.

REEDER, E. (1939). Cytology of the reproductive tract of the female bat *Myotis lucifugus lucifugus*. *J. Morph.*, **64**, 431.

RETTERER, E. (1891). Sur la morphologie et l'évolution de l'épithélium du vagin des mammifères. *C. R. Soc. Biol., Paris*, **44**, 101.

—— (1892). Évolution de l'épithélium du vagin. *C. R. Soc. Biol., Paris*, **44**, 566.

REYNOLDS, S. R. M. (1947). The physiologic basis of menstruation : a summary of current concepts. *J. Amer. med. Ass.*, **135**, 552.

—— (1949). *Physiology of the uterus.* 2nd ed. New York.

RISMAN, G. C. (1947). The effects of estradiol and progesterone on the reproductive tract of the opossum, and their possible relation to parturition. *J. Morph.*, **81**, 343.

ROBSON, J. M. (1932). Pregnancy changes in the rabbit's uterus and their relation to endocrine activity.—II. The action of gonadotropic preparations of the pituitary and of pregnancy urine. *Quart. J. exp. Physiol.*, **22**, 7.

—— (1935). The response of the uterus of hypophysectomized rabbits to extracts of the corpus luteum. *J. Physiol.*, **84**, 296.

ROCK, J., & HERTIG, A. T. (1948). The human conceptus during the first two weeks of gestation. *Amer. J. Obstet. Gynec.*, **55**, 6.

ROLLINAT, R., & TROUESSART, E. (1897). Sur la reproduction des chauve-souris. Les Rhinolophes. *Mém. Soc. zool. Fr.*, **10**, 114.

ROSSMAN, I. (1940). The deciduomal reaction in the rhesus monkey (*Macaca mulatta*). I. The epithelial proliferation. *Amer. J. Anat.*, **66**, 277.

—— (1941). Cyclic changes in the endometrial lipins of the rhesus monkey. *Amer. J. Anat.*, **69**, 187.

—— & BARTELMEZ, G. W. (1946). Delayed ovulation, a significant factor in the variability of the menstrual cycle. *Amer. J. Obstet. Gynec.*, **52**, 28.

ROWLANDS, I. W., & McPHAIL, M. K. (1936). The action of progestin on the uterus of the cat. *Quart. J. exp. Physiol.*, **26**, 109.

—— & PARKES, A. S. (1935). The reproductive processes of certain mammals. VIII. Reproduction in foxes (*Vulpes* spp.). *Proc. zool. Soc. Lond.*, **1935**, 823.

RUBENSTEIN, B. B. (1940). The vaginal smear—basal body temperature and its application to the study of functional sterility in women. *Endocrinology*, **27**, 843.

SANDYS, O. C., & ZUCKERMAN, S. (1938). Observations on the cervix uteri and the urethra of monkeys. *J. Anat., Lond.*, **72**, 352.

SCHICK, R. J. (1943). Changes in the whole vagina of the mouse during estrus and pregnancy. *J. Morph.*, **72**, 305.

SCHMIDT, I. G. (1943). Proliferation in the genital tract of the normal mature guinea pig treated with colchicine. *Amer. J. Anat.*, **73**, 59.

SCHRÖDER, R. (1915). Anatomische Studien zur normalen und pathologischen Physiologie des Menstruationszyklus. *Arch. Gynaek.*, **104**, 27.

—— (1930). Die weiblichen Genitalorgane. In *Handb. d. mikr. Anat. d. Menschen.* Ed. W. v. Möllendorff. Bd. 7. Berlin.

SEABORN, E. (1925). The oestrous cycle in the mare and some associated phenomena. *Anat. Rec.*, **30**, 277.

SELLE, R. M. (1922). Changes in the vaginal epithelium of the guinea-pig during the oestrous cycle. *Amer. J. Anat.*, **30**, 429.

SELYE, H., COLLIP, J. B., & THOMSON, D. L. (1935). Endocrine interrelations during pregnancy. *Endocrinology*, **19**, 151.

—— & McKEOWN, T. (1935). Studies on the physiology of the maternal placenta in the rat. *Proc. Roy. Soc.* B, **119**, 1.

SHAW, W. (1952). *Textbook of Gynaecology.* 6th ed. London.

SHORR, E. (1941). A new technic for staining vaginal smears. III. A single differential stain. *Science*, **94**, 545.

SIMPSON, G. G. (1945). The principles of classification and a classification of mammals. *Bull. Amer. Mus. Nat. Hist.*, Vol. 85.

SJÖVALL, A. (1938). Untersuchungen über die Schleimhaut der Cervix uteri. *Acta obstet. gynec. scand.*, **18**, Suppl. 4.

SLONAKER, J. R. (1929). Pseudopregnancy in the albino rat. *Amer. J. Physiol.*, **89**, 406.

Snell, G. D. (1941). Chap. 2 (Reproduction) in *Biology of the laboratory mouse*. Ed. G. D. Snell. Philadelphia.

Snyder, F. F. (1923). Changes in the Fallopian tube during the ovulation cycle and early pregnancy. *Johns Hopk. Hosp. Bull.*, **34**, 121.

—— (1924). Changes in the human oviduct during the menstrual cycle and pregnancy. *Johns Hopk. Hosp. Bull.*, **35**, 141.

—— (1926). Ovulation in the rabbit. *Anat. Rec. (Proc.)*, **32**, 242.

Spiegel, A. (1930). Beobachtungen über den Sexualzyklus, die Gravidität und die Geburt bei Javamakaken (*Macaca irus mordax* Thomas & Wroughton [*cynomolgos* L.]). *Arch. Gynaek.*, **142**, 561.

—— (1950). Weitere Beobachtungen und Untersuchungen über die Fortpflanzung bei Javamakaken (*Macaca irus mordax* Th. und Wr. (*cynomolgos* L.)). *Arch. Gynaek.*, **177**, 530.

Stafford, E. S. (1930). The origin of the blood of the " placental sign." *Anat. Rec.*, **47**, 43.

Stieve, H. (1927). *Der Halsteil der menschlichen Gebärmutter, sein Bau und seine Aufgaben während der Schwangerschaft, der Geburt und des Wochenbettes.* Leipzig.

Stockard, C. R., & Papanicolaou, G. N. (1917). The existence of a typical oestrous cycle in the guinea-pig—with a study of its histological and physiological changes. *Amer. J. Anat.*, **22**, 225.

—— —— (1919). The vaginal closure membrane, copulation and the vaginal plug in the guinea-pig, with further considerations of the oestrous rhythm. *Biol. Bull., Wood's Hole*, **37**, 222.

Stöhr, Jr., P. (1951). *Lehrbuch der Histologie und der mikroskopischen Anatomie des Menschen.* Berlin, Göttingen, Heidelberg.

Stratz, K. H. (1898). *Der geschlechtsreife Säugethiereierstock.* Den Haag.

Sutton, J. B. (1886). Menstruation in monkeys. *Brit. Gynaec. J.*, **2**, 285 ; 303.

Sylven, B. (1945). The occurrence of ester sulphuric acid of high molecular weight and of mast cells in the stroma of the normal uterine corpus mucosa. *Acta obstet. gynec. scand.*, **25**, 189.

Tinklepaugh, O. L. (1933). Sex cycles and other cyclic phenomena in a chimpanzee during adolescence, maturity, and pregnancy. *J. Morph.*, **54**, 521.

—— & Campenhout, E. van (1931). The vaginal cell content of the mature and immature chimpanzee. *Anat. Rec.*, **48**, 309.

Traut, H. F., Bloch, P. W., & Kuder, A. (1936). Cyclical changes in the human vaginal mucosa. *Surg. Gynec. Obstet.*, **63**, 7.

Tribby, C. L. (1943). The intracellular lipin, mucoid, and glycogen of the vaginal epithelium of the guinea pig. *Anat. Rec.*, **86**, 425.

Venable, J. H. (1939). Intra-uterine bleeding in the pregnant albino rat. The " placental sign." *Anat. Rec.*, **74**, 273.

Vesterdahl-Jørgensen, J. (1950). The cytology of the uterine epithelia. In *Modern trends in obstetrics and gynaecology*. Ed. K. Bowes. London.

Voss, H. E. (1930). Der Postpartum-Östrus der Nagetiere. *Biol. Gen.*, **6**, 433. (Quoted by Snell, G. D., 1941.)

Wade, N. J., & Doisy, E. A. (1935). Cornification of vaginal epithelium of ovariectomized rat produced by smearing. *Proc. Soc. exp. Biol., N.Y.*, **32**, 707.

Ward, M. C. (1946). A study of the oestrous cycle and the breeding of the golden hamster, *Cricetus auratus*. *Anat. Rec.*, **94**, 139.

Weber, A. F., Morgan, B. B., & McNutt, S. H. (1948). A histological study of metrorrhagia in the virgin heifer. *Amer. J. Anat.*, **83**, 309.

Westman, A. (1926). A contribution to the question of the transit of the ovum from ovary to uterus in rabbits. *Acta obstet. gynec. scand.*, **5**, 1.

—— (1930). Studies of the function of the mucous membrane of the uterine tube. *Acta obstet. gynec. scand.*, **10**, 288.

—— (1932). Studien über den Sexualzyklus bei Makakus-rhesus-Affen, nebst einigen Bemerkungen über den menstruellen Blutungsmechanismus. *Acta obstet. gynec. scand.*, **12**, 282.

WESTMAN, A., JORPES, E., & WIDSTRÖM, G. (1931). Untersuchungen über den Schleimhautzyklus in der Tuba uterina, seine hormonale Regulierung und die Bedeutung des Tubensekrets für die Vitalität der befruchteten Eier. *Acta obstet. gynec. scand.*, **11**, 279.

WILLIAMS, M. F. (1948). The vascular architecture of the rat uterus as influenced by estrogen and progesterone. *Amer. J. Anat.*, **83**, 247.

Williams Obstetrics (1950). 10th ed. By N. J. Eastman. New York.

WILSON, K. M. (1926). Histological changes in the vaginal mucosa of the sow in relation to the oestrous cycle. *Amer. J. Anat.*, **37**, 417.

WILTSHIRE, A. (1883). Lectures on the comparative physiology of menstruation. *Brit. med. J.*, **1**, 395 ; 446 ; 500.

WIMSATT, W. A. (1944). An analysis of implantation in the bat, *Myotis lucifugus lucifugus*. *Amer. J. Anat.*, **74**, 355.

—— & WISLOCKI, G. B. (1947). The placentation of the American shrews, *Blarina brevicauda* and *Sorex fumeus*. *Amer. J. Anat.*, **80**, 361.

WINDLE, W. F. (1939). Induction of mating and ovulation in the cat with pregnancy urine and serum extracts. *Endocrinology*, **25**, 365.

WISLOCKI, G. B. (1929). On the placentation of primates, with a consideration of the phylogeny of the placenta. *Contr. Embryol. Carneg. Instn.*, **20**, 51.

—— (1930). On a series of placental stages of a platyrrhine monkey (*Ateles geoffroyi*) with some remarks upon age, sex and breeding period in platyrrhines. *Contr. Embryol. Carneg. Instn.*, **22**, 173.

—— (1932). On the female reproductive tract of the gorilla with a comparison of that of other primates. *Contr. Embryol. Carneg. Instn.*, **23**, 163.

—— (1939). Observations on twinning in marmosets. *Amer. J. Anat.*, **64**, 445.

—— BUNTING, H., & DEMPSEY, E. W. (1950). The chemical histology of the human uterine cervix with supplementary notes on the endometrium. In *Menstruation and its disorders*. Ed. E. T. Engle. Springfield, Ill.

—— & DEMPSEY, E. W. (1939). Remarks on the lymphatics of the reproductive tract of the female rhesus monkey (*Macaca mulatta*). *Anat. Rec.*, **75**, 341.

—— —— (1945). Histochemical reactions of the endometrium in pregnancy. *Amer. J. Anat.*, **77**, 365.

—— —— (1948). The chemical histology of the human placenta and decidua with reference to mucopolysaccharides, glycogen, lipids and acid phosphatase. *Amer. J. Anat.*, **83**, 1.

—— FAWCETT, D. W., & DEMPSEY, E. W. (1951). Staining of stratified squamous epithelium of mucous membranes and skin of man and monkey by the periodic acid-Schiff method. *Anat. Rec.*, **110**, 359.

WOLLNER, A. (1938). The histologic correlationship of endometrial and cervical biopsies, with comments on the etiology of endocervicitis. *Amer. J. Obstet. Gynec.*, **36**, 10.

YOUNG, W. C. (1937). The vaginal smear picture, sexual receptivity and the time of ovulation in the guinea-pig. *Anat. Rec.*, **67**, 305.

—— (1941). Observations and experiments on mating behaviour in female mammals. *Quart. Rev. Biol.*, **16**, 135, 311.

—— BOLING, J. L., & BLANDAU, R. J. (1941). The vaginal smear picture, sexual receptivity and time of ovulation in the albino rat. *Anat. Rec.*, **80**, 37.

ZIETZSCHMANN, O. (1921). Über Funktionen der weiblichen Genitale bei Säugetier und Mensch. *Arch. Gynaek.*, **115**, 201.

ZUCKERMAN, S. (1930). The menstrual cycle of the primates. Part I. General nature and homology. *Proc. zool. Soc. Lond.*, **1930**, 691.

—— (1931). The menstrual cycle of the primates. Part III. The alleged breeding season of Primates, with special reference to the Chacma baboon (*Papio porcarius*). *Proc. zool. Soc. Lond.*, **1931**, 325.

—— (1935). Variation in the sensitivity of different species of monkeys to oestrin. *J. Physiol.*, **84**, 191.

—— (1937a). The menstrual cycle of the primates. XI—The part played by oestrogenic hormone in the menstrual cycle. *Proc. Roy. Soc. B*, **123**, 457.

Zuckerman, S. (1937b). The menstrual cycle of the primates. XII—The interaction of ovarian hormones in the cycle. *Proc. Roy. Soc.* B, **124,** 150.

—— (1949). The menstrual cycle. *Lancet,* **1,** 1031.

—— (1951). The hormonal basis of uterine bleeding. *Acta endocr., Copenhagen,* **7,** 378.

—— & Parkes, A. S. (1932). The menstrual cycle of the primates. Part V. The cycle of the baboon. *Proc. zool. Soc. Lond.,* **1932,** 139.

—— Wagenen, G. van, & Gardiner, R. H. (1938). The sexual skin of the rhesus monkey. *Proc. zool. Soc. Lond.* A, **108,** 385.

Zupp, B. A. (1924). Studies on the oestral flow of the pig. *Anat. Rec.,* **27,** 244.

INDEX OF AUTHORS

A

C

E

F

G

H

L

M

N

O

P

Q

R

S

T

U

Uchida, 416, 539

V

Valentin, 476, 539
Valle, 202, 224
Vanneman, 400, 539
Vatti, 498, 539
Vazquez-Lopez, 259, 392
van de Velde, 354, 392
Velloso de Pinho, 500, 504, 511, 539
Venable, 277, 392, 568, 652

Venning, 353, 355, 356, 358, 359, 392
Verney, 259, 381
Vesalius, 467
Vesterdahl-Jørgensen, 640, 652
Vevers, 255, 392
Viergiver, 353, 356, 386, 393, 650
Villemin, 494, 539
Vimeux, 353, 356, 389

Vivien, 171, 176, 225
Vogt, C., 310, 393
Vogt, M., 259, 277, 381, 393
Voitellier, 29, 41
Völker, 462, 478, 539
Volsøe, 198, 199, 225
Vos, 452, 539
Voss, 426, 465, 501, 530, 566, 652
Vosseler, 63, 154, 235, 393

W

Wade, N. J., 568, 652
Wade, O., 266, 268, 393
van Wagenen, 131, 137, 138, 139, 141, 154, 155, 335, 337, 338, 339, 340, 367, 368, 393, 396, 654
Waldeyer, 397, 431, 442, 450, 461, 476, 539
Waldo, 88, 154, 253, 394
Walker, 87, 90, 96, 154, 276, 393
Wallace, A. R., 30, 41
Wallace, R., 240, 246, 393
Wallace, W., 16, 41, 433, 434, 435, 436, 468, 539
Wallart, 418, 508, 509, 540
Walsh, 440, 540
Walton, A., 258, 261, 262, 297, 298, 373, 390, 393, 447, 448, 452, 460, 463, 464, 498, 537, 540
Walton, C. L., 3, 4, 5, 7, 8, 9, 13, 35, 38
Warbritton, 383, 488, 540
Ward, 270, 393, 574, 652
Warren, D. C., 29, 41, 215, 216, 225, 436, 460, 534
Warren, E. P., 243, 393
Warren, E. R., 273, 393
Warwick, E. J., 248, 261, 364
Warwick, T., 311, 313, 314, 367
Waterman, 454, 540
Watkin, 9, 41
Watrin, 450, 479, 487, 494, 540
Watson, A., 26, 41, 204, 225
Watson, J. S., 275, 380
de Watteville, 355, 393
Watzka, 418, 540
Weatherford, 253, 395
Webb, 640, 642
Weber, A. F., 244, 393, 550, 555, 556, 652
Weber, M., 49, 51, 52, 56, 63, 81, 154
Webster, 281, 370, 581, 645
Weekes, 23, 24, 41, 196, 197, 198, 225, 435, 469, 540

Weichert, 181, 225, 278, 393, 491, 540
Weinstein, 258, 259, 381
Weismann, 10, 41, 397, 540
Wells, 49, 95, 154, 266, 267, 384, 393, 394
Wendeler, 476, 540
Wentworth, 464, 540
Wesenberg-Lund, 7, 41
West, C. M., 398, 540
West, E., 240, 394
Wester, 462, 540
Westermarck, 34, 41
van der Westhuysen, 83, 154, 257, 395
Westman, 259, 394, 564, 565, 620, 621, 622, 627, 630, 652, 653
Wheeler, J. F. G., 9, 41, 98, 100, 151, 176, 177, 225, 283, 284, 287, 381, 394, 398, 401, 585, 648
Wheeler, W. M., 540
Whetham, 24, 41, 258, 390, 498, 537
White, M. J. D., 421, 540
White, R. F., 481, 540
White, W. E., 258, 259, 376, 383, 394, 498, 501, 526
Whitney, 4, 41
Wichmann, 410, 540
Wickens, 303, 381
Widström, 564, 653
Wiedersheim, 45, 154
Wiesner, 275, 354, 356, 362, 384
Wigglesworth, 12, 42
Wight, 269, 300, 394
Wilcox, 123, 154, 455, 540
Wilder, 183, 225
Wilkinson, 394
Willey, 9, 15, 42
Williams, C. B., 10, 12, 41, 42
Williams, J. H., 256, 394
Williams, J. W., 476, 540, 637, 653
Williams, M. F., 570, 653
Williams, P. C., 275, 388

Willier, 406, 415, 540
Wilson, D. C., 356, 394
Wilson, E. B., 421, 428, 540
Wilson, J. G., 281, 363
Wilson, K. M., 410, 540, 559, 653
Wilson, R. B., 355, 394
Wilson, S. G., 243, 394
Wilson, W. K., 262, 394
Wiltshire, 19, 27, 42, 255, 394, 607, 653
Wimsatt, 88, 154, 310, 312, 313, 314, 315, 394, 432, 456, 463, 540, 606, 608, 613, 653
Windle, 604, 653
de Winiwarter, 403, 407, 408, 411, 413, 414, 418, 421, 438, 449, 462, 498, 500, 507, 508, 512, 541
Winterhalter, 452, 541
Wishart, 260, 394
Wislocki, 43, 49, 51, 57, 66, 68, 83, 100, 130, 132, 133, 134, 135, 137, 138, 142, 143, 144, 145, 146, 149, 154, 238, 253, 257, 259, 332, 333, 339, 346, 371, 394, 395, 495, 510, 521, 541, 613, 618, 619, 634, 640, 645, 653
Witherby, 28, 42
Witschi, 46, 154, 188, 206, 213, 224, 225, 240, 395, 400, 404, 408, 409, 410, 412, 415, 416, 427, 523, 541
Wodzicki, 70, 71, 150, 239, 240, 373, 380, 548, 549, 600, 604, 646, 648
Wolf, 397, 541
Wolfe, 278, 395
Wolff, 420, 541
Wollner, 640, 653
Wolz, 513, 542
Wood, F. D., 273, 395
Wood, T. R., 355, 372
Woodger, 401, 542
Wood Jones, 154, 155, 233, 234, 237, 238, 290, 310, 319

SUBJECT INDEX

AARDVARK, changes in uterus of, 560
Acanthodactylus, breeding season in, 23
Acanthodactylus pardalis deserti, sexual cycle in, 194
Accessory reproductive organs of non-pregnant mammal, changes in, 543 *seq.*
Accipiter gentilis, ovulation in, 213
Acipenser ruthenus, cyclical changes in reproductive organs of, 160
Actinia mesembryanthemum, breeding habits of, 5
Adochianectes glaucus, breeding habits of, 287
Adolescent sterility, 357
Adrenal function during human pregnancy, 359
Agelaius phoeniceus, sexual cycle in, 206
Agouti : golden, breeding habits of, 282 ; hairy-rumped, breeding habits of, 282
Ailuropoda melanoleuca, breeding habits of, 293
Albatross, mating habits of, 30
Alces gigas, breeding habits of, 252
Alcyonium digitatum, breeding habits of, 5
Alouatta : labia in, 134 ; testis of, 132
Alouatta palliata, breeding habits of, 332
Alouatta seniculus, gestation in, 333
Alternation of generations in *Chermes*, 10
Amblystoma, paedogenesis in, 183
Amia, breeding season in, 16
Amphibia : breeding season in, 19 *seq.* ; cyclical changes in reproductive organs of, 178–88
Amphibolurus muricatus : breeding season in, 23 ; sexual cycle in, 196
Amphioxus, gonadal tissue in, 45
Amphioxus lanceolatus, breeding season in, 15
Amphitre ornata, breeding season in, 8
Ampulla, 44 : of elephant, 80 ; of mouse, 86 ; of stallion, 68
Ampullary gland, 51
Anableps, cyclical changes in reproductive organs of, 164
Anal glands, 51, 54 : of hyaena, 105 ; of rabbit, 86 ; of tree shrews, 126
Anal pouch of hyaena, 105
Anal scent-glands of snakes, 33
Anchistioides antiquensis, breeding season in, 9
Anguis fragalis : breeding season in, 23 ; sexual cycle in, 193
Annelida, breeding habits of, 7, 8
Anniella, ovaries of, 47
Anoestrous period, 227
Anoestrum, 227
Anoestrus, 228
Anolis caroliensis, sexual cycle in, 195
Anopheles, egg-formation in, 11
Anovular follicles, 453, 454
Ant-deer, changes in uterus of, 560
Anteater, spiny. *See Echidna aculeata*
Anthropoid apes : ischial callosities in, 147 ; oestrous cycle in, 347–52 ; reproductive tract in, 142–7 ; sexual skin in, 147
Antilocapra americana : breeding season in, 250 ; phenomena associated with breeding in, 31

Antilope cervicapra, breeding season in, 250
Antlers, seasonal changes in, 30, 31, 252, 253
Antrum of Graafian follicle, 439, 440, 447
Anura, cyclical changes in reproductive organs of, 183–8
Aotes zonalis : cervix of, 133 ; testis of, 132
Apeltes quadracus, cyclical changes in reproductive organs of, 172–5
Apes, anthropoid. *See* Anthropoid apes
Aphis : breeding season in, 10 ; parthenogenesis in, 10
Apodemus sylvaticus, breeding habits of, 264
Arcella vulgaris, life cycle of, 3
Archidoris tuberculata, breeding season in, 15
Arenicola, breeding season in, 8
Argobuccinum australasiae, breeding season in, 13
Armadillo : changes in accessory reproductive organs of, 548 ; reproduction in, 237, 238. *See also Dasypus*
Arthropoda, breeding season in, 8 *seq.*
Artiodactyla, reproductive tract in, 72 *seq.*
Arvicola amphibius, reproductive habits of, 271
Asterias rubens, breeding season in, 14
Asymmetry of reproductive organs in lower vertebrates, 46
Ateles : clitoris in, 134 ; labia majora in, 134 ; ovary of, 133 ; processus vaginalis in, 132 ; uterus of, 133 ; vagina of, 133, 134
Ateles geoffroyi, breeding habits of, 332, 333
Aves. *See* Birds
Axis axis, breeding habits of, 251
Axolotl, breeding season in, 21
Aye aye, reproductive organs of, 127

BABOON : changes in accessory reproductive organs of, 631, 632 ; menstrual cycle in, 343, 344 ; oestrous cycle in, 343–6 ; ovulation in, 345 ; pregnancy in, 345, 346 ; puberty in, 345 ; reproductive physiology of, 343–6 ; sexual skin cycle in, 344 ; vaginal smear in, 631, 632
Baculum, 56 ; of clitoris, in capuchin monkey, 134 ; of clitoris, in *Lorisiformes*, 128 ; of *Lemuroidea*, 128 ; of mouse, 87 ; of rhesus monkey, 137
Badger, breeding habits of, 299, 300
Balaena mysticetus, breeding habits of, 287
Balaenidae, reproductive tract of, 98
Balaenoptera acutorostrata, breeding habits of, 287
Balaenoptera borealis, breeding habits of, 286
Balaenoptera musculus, breeding habits of, 284
Balaenoptera physalus : breeding habits of, 284 ; testes of, 99
Balaenopteridae, reproductive tract of, 98
Bandicoot. *See Perameles*
Bank vole, breeding season of, 264